CALCULUS AND ANALYTIC GEOMETRY

SECOND EDITION

CALCULUS

AND ANALYTIC

Robert C. Fisher, THE OHIO STATE UNIVERSITY

Allen D. Ziebur, STATE UNIVERSITY OF NEW YORK AT BINGHAMTON

GEOMETRY

PRENTICE-HALL, INC., *Englewood Cliffs, New Jersey*

Prentice-Hall Mathematics Series

CALCULUS AND ANALYTIC GEOMETRY SECOND EDITION

Robert C. Fisher and Allen D. Ziebur

Current printing (last digit):

12   11   10   9   8   7   6   5   4   3

Designed by Harry Rinehart

Illustrations by Felix Cooper

C-11221

PRENTICE-HALL INTERNATIONAL, INC., *London*
PRENTICE-HALL OF AUSTRALIA, PTY. LTD., *Sydney*
PRENTICE-HALL OF CANADA, LTD., *Toronto*
PRENTICE-HALL OF INDIA, PVT, LTD., *New Delhi*
PRENTICE-HALL OF JAPAN, INC., *Tokyo*

PREFACE

Since the first edition of this book appeared, the mathematical preparation of students entering American colleges and universities has improved markedly, and we have designed the second edition to take that improvement into account. In particular, this edition is much more "rigorous" than its predecessor; the word "proof" appears more frequently, and the words "it is true that" are seen less often. Furthermore, the widespread use of set notation and language in school mathematics makes it possible for us to use them here.

Because students come to us with varying degrees of preparation, a good deal of the material in the early chapters will be familiar to some students and not to others. We have therefore made a special effort in this new edition, particularly in the problems, to provide at least something that is new to everybody. Students meeting calculus and analytic geometry for the first time should confine their attention to the basic text material; students with a better background might try their hand at some of the harder problems.

Our primary goal, however, is unchanged. We still feel that a student reads his textbook in his room, without an instructor on hand to translate it for him. So our major objective was to provide him with a book from which he could—by himself—gain a true picture of what calculus is all about. There are many parts of the text which retain their original content but which have been rewritten as our classroom experience suggested changes that would improve the clarity of exposition. Geometric motivation is still the basis for any explanation of calculus, and we have used it as fully as we know how.

The general plan is unaltered. In the first chapter we discuss such ideas as functions, graphs, slopes of lines, and limits as a background to calculus proper. Chapter 2 contains definitions and techniques of differentiation, and Chapter 3 consists of applications of the derivative. In Chapter 4 we study the conic sections. Chapters 5, 6, and 7 are devoted to integration, and thus by the end of Chapter 7 we have covered the basic theory and techniques of the calculus of functions on the real line. In Chapters 8 and 9 we interweave geometry and calculus. Here we place strong emphasis on the use of vectors and vector notation, both in the plane and in space. Chapter 10 is a chapter on linear algebra. Strictly speaking, some of the sections on systems of linear equations may look out of place in a calculus book, but many students will have no other place to learn this important material. Diagonalizing matrices is not traditional fare for a textbook at this level, but it certainly has important applications, both in geometry, as we have indicated, and in other fields. Chapters 11 and 12 are devoted to the differential and integral calculus of functions on R^n when $n > 1$. Chapter 13 presents tools, such as l'Hospital's Rule and improper integrals, that are both important in themselves and useful for the final chapter, Chapter 14, on infinite series. The subject of differential equations is not accorded any special treatment, but in the course of the book the student learns how to solve differential equations of the first order of the types that go by the names of "variables separable," "linear," and "exact."

Our thanks are again due to our editor and third author W. E. Mangas. His blue pencil has done much to bring order out of our sometimes random prose. Harry Rinehart is responsible for the two-color illustrations and over-all text design. We think this use of color will be a real help to the student.

R. C. F.

A. D. Z.

TO THE STUDENT

Mathematics is a deductive science; that is, mathematical results are deduced by reasoning from first principles. Theoretically, therefore, we should develop our subject by first setting down a few axioms and then constructing, in a sequence of logical steps, the entire structure of calculus.

Practically, of course, we don't proceed this way. Calculus didn't spring up just to fill a vacuum; it grew as it was needed to solve problems in geometry, physics, and other "practical" fields. The basic ideas of calculus are best expressed in geometric language, and you will be well along in your understanding of the subject when it is clear in your mind what this language says. Once you have mastered the geometry of the situation, you are ready to tackle the deductive proofs of our theorems. Naturally, you should do your best to understand these proofs, but don't be discouraged if you find some of them difficult. You can't expect to learn calculus all at once—it is a broad and a deep subject which has taken about 300 years to develop.

What we hope you get out of this course is a clear geometric picture of what calculus is all about. You should also get an idea of the proofs of some of the basic theorems. Finally, and this is an important point, you should develop a fluency in the language of calculus. Learn to use the technical terms, signs, and symbols of calculus correctly. Of course, it's the ideas of calculus, and not the notation in which they are expressed, that are important. But you can never hope to understand a concept that you can't even write down. If you gain this geometric insight and technical fluency, you will be ready to go on to a deeper study of calculus or to apply it to other subjects.

CONTENTS

ix

EXPONENTIAL, LOGARITHMIC,
INVERSE TRIGONOMETRIC,
AND HYPERBOLIC FUNCTIONS, 269

TECHNIQUES
OF INTEGRATION, 326

POLAR COORDINATES.
VECTORS IN THE PLANE, 372

l'HOSPITAL'S RULE.

IMPROPER INTEGRALS.

TAYLOR'S FORMULA, 652

SEQUENCES

AND INFINITE SERIES, 683

APPENDIX, 743

BASIC CONCEPTS

AND THE LIMIT

O N E

Scientists and engineers study relationships. An engineer, for example, would be interested in the relationship between the thrust of a rocket engine and its rate of fuel consumption. If he can express this relationship in a quantitative way—the number of pounds of thrust that corresponds to the number of pounds of fuel burned per second, for example—so much the better. Calculus and analytic geometry are two of the most important mathematical tools used to study quantitative relationships. In this first chapter we will begin by considering some basic concepts such as numbers, sets, functions, graphs, and so on, that are prerequisite for our study of calculus. Our presentation of these topics is somewhat brief, since in many instances it will be a review for you. Nevertheless, experience shows that many students who take calculus have as much trouble with such things as absolute values, inequalities, factoring, and so on, as they do with calculus itself. So it will pay you to master this material (if you have not done so already). In the last two sections of the first chapter we introduce

1

the central idea of calculus—the concept of a limit. Although a thorough understanding of the limit concept will come only after you have studied it and used it many times, you should make an effort to understand the basic ideas in Sections 10 and 11, even if you cannot remember all the proofs that we give there.

I   THE REAL NUMBERS

It should not surprise you if a mathematics book starts with a discussion of numbers—a great deal of mathematics is based on numbers. In this section we summarize some of the facts about the real number system that we will need as we study calculus. You are probably familiar with most of this material; it is found in every elementary algebra text.

Each **real number** can be written as an unending decimal expression. Thus the real numbers π, 2, and $\frac{1}{3}$ can be written as $\pi = 3.14159 \ldots , 2 = 2.000 \ldots ,$ and $\frac{1}{3} = .333 \ldots .$ Among the real numbers are the **integers,** $\ldots , -2, -1, 0, 1, 2, \ldots ,$ and the **rational numbers,** such as $-\frac{3}{2}, \frac{22}{7}, \frac{0}{3}.$ A rational number can be written as a *ratio* of two integers. The decimal expression of a rational number is "repeating"; that is, certain digits keep recurring in successive blocks, as in the number $23.46731731731 \ldots ,$ where we suppose that the block 731 is repeated indefinitely. We will assume that you are familiar with the rules of arithmetic of real numbers.

The **number scale** provides a convenient geometric representation of the real number system. To construct the number scale, we choose two points of a horizontal line and label the left-hand point 0 and the right-hand point 1. The point labeled 0 is called the **origin** and the point labeled 1 is the **unit point.** The distance between these two points is the unit of distance. You can readily see (Fig. 1-1)

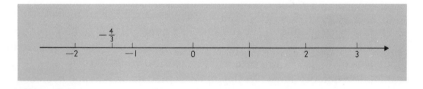

Figure 1-1

how points representing integers and rational numbers are located, once the origin and the unit point are chosen. For example, since $-\frac{4}{3} = -1 - \frac{1}{3},$ the point $-\frac{4}{3}$ is one-third of the way from -1 to $-2.$

It is not difficult to see how each point of the number scale determines an unending decimal. For an example of the correspondence between points of a line and unending decimals, let us look at Fig. 1-2. The point P lies between 2 and 3. If the segment between 2 and 3 is divided into 10 equal parts, then the points of division represent the numbers 2.1, 2.2, ..., 2.9, and we see that P lies between 2.7 and 2.8. Now the segment between 2.7 and 2.8 is divided into 10 equal subdivisions, one of which contains P. Suppose that P lies between 2.72 and 2.73. Then to the first two decimal places, the decimal expression associated with P is 2.72. Theoretically, we could continue this process indefinitely, if we agree than any segment of the number scale, no matter how small, can be divided

Figure 1-2

into 10 equal parts. In this way we generate an unending decimal expression. (If P should be one of our points of division, we can regard all further digits in the expression as 0.) The converse also is true; every unending decimal expression determines a point of the number scale. Hence, *each point of the number scale is the graphical representation of a real number, and to each real number there corresponds a point of the number scale.*

Logically, a number and its corresponding point of the number scale should be distinguished as two different things. The number associated with a point is called the **coordinate** of the point. In practice, however, we often refer to the "point" 5, and so on.

When the number scale is displayed with the usual left-to-right orientation, as in Figs. 1-1 and 1-2, one number is smaller than another if it lies to the left of the other. A formal definition of this order relation is based on the fact that every real number is either positive, or zero, or negative.

Definition 1-1. *We say that **a is less than b** ($a < b$) and **b is greater than a** ($b > a$) if $b - a$ is a positive number. The symbols $<$ and $>$ are called **inequality signs.***

Thus we see, for example, that according to this definition the statements "a is positive" and "$a > 0$" say exactly the same thing. Notice how this formal definition is related to our geometric idea that smaller numbers lie to the left of larger ones. The number scale shows the point -5 to be to the left of -3, and $-3 - (-5)$ is the positive number 2, which means, according to Definition 1-1, that -5 is less than -3. The notation $a < b < c$ means that $a < b$ and $b < c$. For obvious geometric reasons, we say that b is **between** a and c. Thus the number 4 is between 2 and 7, since $2 < 4 < 7$.

The following rules for operating with inequality symbols are consequences of the fact that sums and products of positive numbers are positive:

(1-1)   If $a < b$ and $b < c$, then $a < c$.

(1-2)   If $a < b$, then $a + c < b + c$ for any number c.

(1-3)   If $c > 0$ and $a < b$, then $ac < bc$.

(1-4)   If $c < 0$ and $a < b$, then $ac > bc$.

Let us show why Rule 1-3 is valid, and leave the verification of the other rules to you in the problems. In Rule 1-3 we assume that c is positive and $a < b$; hence $b - a$ is positive. The product of the positive numbers $(b - a)$ and c is the positive number $(b - a)c = bc - ac$. But to say that this difference is positive is to say that $ac < bc$, which is exactly the conclusion of Rule 1-3.

The notation $a \leq b$ or $b \geq a$ means that a is a number that is either less than b or equal to b; that is, a is *not greater* than b. For example, $4 \leq 6$ and $6 \leq 6$, since neither 4 nor 6 is greater than 6. The basic rules that govern the use of the symbol $\leq$ are just like the rules we use with the symbol $<$.

Another result of the graphical representation of the system of real numbers as points of the number scale is the introduction of the geometric concept of *distance* into our number system. Let x be a number that is represented by a point of the number scale. Then the number of units between this point and the origin is called the **absolute value** of x and is denoted by the symbol $|x|$. Thus $|2| = 2$, $|-3| = 3$, $|\pi| = \pi$, and so on. The absolute value of a number gives only its distance from the origin, not its direction. If $|x| = 5$, for example, we know that x is either the number 5 or the number -5, since both these numbers, and no others, are 5 units from the origin.

We can also formulate a definition of absolute value that does not rely on geometric notions. This definition yields the same result as the geometric definition.

Definition 1-2.   *For any real number a,*

$$|a| = a \text{ if } a \geq 0, \text{ and } |a| = -a \text{ if } a < 0.$$

From this definition we see that $|2| = 2$, since $2 > 0$, while $|-3| = -(-3) = 3$, since $-3 < 0$. These examples illustrate the fact that *the absolute value of a number is never negative.*

A glance at the number scale will show you that for any two points a and b, the number $|b - a|$ is the distance between them. Notice that $|b - a| = |a - b|$, so the distance between two points of the number scale is obtained by subtracting their coordinates in either order and taking the absolute value of the difference. If we want to find the distance without using absolute values, we should subtract the coordinate of the left point (smaller number) from the coordinate of the right point (larger number).

Example 1-1. Verify that the distance between the points $a = -3$ and $b = 2$ is given by the number $|b - a|$ (or $|a - b|$).

Solution. The points -3 and 2 are shown on the number scale in Fig. 1-3. It is obvious that they are 5 units apart, and $5 = |2 - (-3)| = |-3 - 2|$. Notice

Figure 1-3

that we can also determine the distance, 5, by subtracting the left number, -3, from the number on the right, 2.

P R O B L E M S   I

1. What is the number that is represented by the point of the number scale that is:
   (a) $\frac{1}{3}$ of the way from 2 to 3?   (b) $\frac{3}{4}$ of the way from -6 to -5?
   (c) $\frac{1}{5}$ of the way from -5 to 10?   (d) midway between -3 and 4?

2. List all the integers between -2 and 3. Can you list all the real numbers between -2 and 3? All the rational numbers?

3. Suppose you know that a and b are numbers such that $a < b$. Which of the following inequalities do you then know to be true?
   (a) $\dfrac{a}{3} < \dfrac{b}{3}$ (b) $a + 5 \leq b + 4$

   (c) $a < \dfrac{a + b}{2} < b$ (d) $a^2 < b^2$

   (e) $\sqrt{|a|} < \sqrt{|b|}$ (f) $a^{-1} > b^{-1}$

4. What can you say about the number x if:
   (a) $|x| = 4$?   (b) $|x - 1| = 3$?
   (c) $|2x| = 2x$?   (d) $|x - 1| = 1 - x$?

5. What can you say about the number x if:

(a) $|x| \leq 4$?
(b) $|x - 1| > 3$?
(c) $|2x| \geq 2x$?
(d) $|x - 1| \leq 1 - x$?

6. If you know that $a^2 < b^2$, what can you conclude about the relation between a and b?

7. Express the following statements about points of a number scale (with its usual orientation) in terms of inequality signs and absolute values:

(a) The point x is more than 3 units to the right of the point y.
(b) The point x is closer to the origin than is the point y.
(c) The distance between the point x and the point 3 is less than $\frac{1}{2}$.
(d) The points x and y are more than 5 units apart.

8. Explain why the following statements are true:

(a) $|x| = \sqrt{x^2}$
(b) $|x|$ is the larger of the numbers x and $-x$

9. Find two rational numbers x and y such that:

(a) $x < \pi < y$ and $y - x < .01$
(b) $x < \sqrt{3} < y$ and $y - x < .1$

10. Prove that the following rules of inequality are valid:

(a) Rule 1-1 (b) Rule 1-2 (c) Rule 1-4

11. If $a = .141414\ldots$, then $100a = 14.141414\ldots$, and $100a - a = 14.141414\ldots$ $-.141414\ldots$, or $99a = 14$. Thus $a = \frac{14}{99}$. Use a similar argument to write $b = .142142142\ldots$ and $c = 2.999\ldots$ as fractions.

12. Suppose that $p \geq 0$ and that x is a real number. Explain why the two statements $-p \leq x \leq p$ and $|x| \leq p$ say exactly the same thing.

13. Show that $\frac{1}{2}(a + b + |a - b|)$ is the larger of the numbers a and b, and $\frac{1}{2}(a + b - |a - b|)$ is the smaller.

14. What can you say about the number x if:

(a) $\left| \frac{1}{x} - 2 \right| < 2$
(b) $\left| \frac{1}{x} - 2 \right| < 3$

(c) $\left| \frac{1}{x} - 2 \right| < 1$
(d) $|x^2 - 7| < 2$

(e) $(x^2 - 7) < 2$
(f) $|x(x - 7)| \leq x$

15. Let a and b be a pair of real numbers. Explain why $-|a| \leq a \leq |a|$ and $-|b| \leq b \leq |b|$. From these inequalities, conclude that $-(|a| + |b|) \leq a + b \leq (|a| + |b|)$, and then use the result of Number 12 to obtain the **triangle inequality**, $|a + b| \leq |a| + |b|$. Substitute various numbers for a and b to get a better idea of what this important inequality says.

16. In the inequality you obtained in the preceding problem, replace a with $a - c$ and b with $c - b$ to show that, for any three numbers a, b, and c, $|a - b| \leq |a - c| + |b - c|$.

17. Replace a with $a - b$ in the triangle inequality to obtain the inequality $|a| - |b| \leq |a - b|$. Explain why it is true that $||a| - |b|| \leq |a - b|$ for any two numbers a and b.

2 SETS AND INTERVALS

We will often have occasion to discuss *sets* of mathematical objects, such as the set of positive integers, or the set of points that make up some curve in the plane, so now let us introduce some of the terminology and notation of set theory. The most straightforward way to specify a set is to list its **elements, or members.** Thus $\{2, 4, 6, 8\}$ is the set whose members are the four numbers 2, 4, 6, and 8. We enclosed the members of this set in braces $\{\ \}$ to indicate that we think of the set as an entity in itself. In line with this idea of a set as a mathematical entity, sets are often named by letters; for example, we might say "let Q be the set of rational numbers." Of course, many times we specify a set without listing its members, perhaps because there are too many or because we don't know them. For instance, we can't list all the members of the set of rational numbers, and we don't want to list all the integers between 1 and 1 billion; there are too many. We denote this latter set by the symbols $\{n \mid 1 < n < 10^9, n$ an integer$\}$. On the left of the vertical line appears a "typical" element of the set; on the right is the condition that this element be a member of the set. Thus the set $\{x \mid x^{12} - 17x^5 = 1492, x$ a complex number$\}$ is the set of (complex) solutions of the equation $x^{12} - 17x^5 = 1492$. We can't list the members of this set because we don't know how to solve the given equation. The "Fundamental Theorem of Algebra," however, tells us that there are solutions, and so there are some members (complex numbers) of our set. Observe that the letter x plays no essential role in this notation; we could equally well write our set as $\{z \mid z^{12} - 17z^5 = 1492, z$ a complex number$\}$. You will become familiar with this notation in its various forms as you see it used over and over again in the pages ahead.

When we specify a set by describing some property of its members, we have to be alert to the possibility that our set may be the **empty set** $\varnothing$, the set that has no members. Thus $\{x \mid x^2 + 1 = 0, x$ a real number$\} = \varnothing$. We can also describe $\varnothing$ as the set of all circles of radius -3.

To indicate that an element a **is a member of a set** A, we write $a \in A$. We also say that a **belongs to** A or that a **is contained in** A. For example, $\frac{1}{2} \in Q$ (where Q denotes the set of rational numbers). To denote the fact that π is not a member of the set of rational numbers, we write $\pi \notin Q$. We will consistently use R^1 to denote the set of real numbers. Thus $x \in R^1$ means that x is a real number. Here R is to suggest the word "real," and the superscript 1 distinguishes R^1 from the sets R^2 and R^3, consisting of pairs and triples of real numbers, which we will introduce later.

There is a well-developed and quite extensive algebra of sets, of which we will need only the simplest ideas. If every member of a set A is also a member of a set B, then we say that A **is a subset of** B or A **is contained in** B**,** and we write $A \subseteq B$. Notice that it is possible to have $A \subseteq B$ and $B \subseteq A$; these statements are both true if, and only if, the sets A and B contain the same elements, in which case we say that $A = B$. The **union** of two sets A and B is the set $A \cup B$ that we obtain by lumping together the elements of the sets A and B into a single set. Symbolically,

$$A \cup B = \{x \mid x \in A \quad or \quad x \in B\}.$$

(The "or" used here includes the possibility that x belongs to both A and B.) For example, we can think of R^1 as the union of the set of rational numbers and the set of irrational numbers. The **intersection** of two sets A and B is the set $A \cap B$ whose members are the elements that the sets A and B have in common; that is,

$$A \cap B = \{x \mid x \in A \quad and \quad x \in B\}.$$

Thus, for example, $\{n \mid n$ an integer divisible by 2$\} \cap \{n \mid n$ an integer divisible by 3$\}$ is the set of integers divisible by 6. Notice that for any two sets A and B, we have $A \cap B \subseteq A \subseteq A \cup B$ (we will agree that the empty set is a subset of every set).

> **Example 2-1** Let $a(x) = x^{13} - 3x^5 + 1$, and $b(x) = 3x^{56} - 6x^3 + x$, and suppose that $A = \{x \mid a(x) = 0, x \in R^1\}$, and $B = \{x \mid b(x) = 0, x \in R^1\}$. Show that $A \cup B$ is the set of real solutions of the equation $a(x) \cdot b(x) = 0$.
>
> *Solution.* If we denote the set of real solutions of the equation $a(x) \cdot b(x) = 0$ by S, we are to show that $S = A \cup B$. We are *not* going to find all the elements of these sets and then compare them. Rather, we are going to show that $A \cup B \subseteq S$ and $S \subseteq A \cup B$. If $r \in A \cup B$, then $r \in A$ or $r \in B$ (or both), and thus r is a number that satisfies one (or both) of the equations $a(x) = 0$ and $b(x) = 0$. Hence r satisfies the equation $a(x) \cdot b(x) = 0$, and so $r \in S$. Thus each point of $A \cup B$ is also a point of S; that is, $A \cup B \subseteq S$. Conversely, suppose $r \in S$; that is, suppose $a(r) \cdot b(r) = 0$. This equation implies that either $a(r) = 0$ or $b(r) = 0$ (or both). Thus $r \in A \cup B$, and so we have shown that each point of S is also a point of $A \cup B$; in other words, $S \subseteq A \cup B$. We have now verified that $A \cup B \subseteq S \subseteq A \cup B$, which is equivalent to the equation $A \cup B = S$.

In calculus, when we speak of a set of numbers, we mean a set of real numbers; that is, a subset of R^1, and the sets of numbers we use most often are the *intervals*. Suppose a and b are numbers, with $a < b$. Then the **open interval** (a, b) is the set of all numbers between a and b, in symbols,

$$(a, b) = \{x \mid a < x < b\}.$$

For example, $\pi \in (1, 5)$ and $2 \in (1, 5)$, but $0 \notin (1, 5)$ and $1 \notin (1, 5)$. The open interval (a, b) does not contain its **endpoints** a and b. The **closed interval** $[a, b]$ is the set of all points between a and b and the points a and b also, in symbols,

$$[a, b] = \{x \mid a \leq x \leq b\}.$$

Notice that we use *parentheses to denote an open interval and brackets to denote a closed interval.* In particular, a set consisting of a single point is a closed interval. Thus, for example, $[5, 5] = \{x \mid 5 \leq x \leq 5\} = \{5\}$. We sometimes speak of "half-open" or "half-closed" intervals, which are defined as follows:

$$(a, b] = \{x \mid a < x \leq b\},$$

$$[a, b) = \{x \mid a \leq x < b\}.$$

Example 2-2.   Find $(-1, 3) \cup [2, 5)$ and $(-1, 3) \cap [2, 5)$.

Solution.   From a sketch (Fig. 2-1) we can easily determine that when we lump together the points of the intervals $(-1, 3)$ and $[2, 5)$, we obtain the interval $(-1, 5)$.

Figure 2-1

Similarly, the intervals $(-1, 3)$ and $[2, 5)$ have the points of $[2, 3)$ in common. Therefore, $(-1, 3) \cup [2, 5) = (-1, 5)$ and $(-1, 3) \cap [2, 5) = [2, 3)$.

We will consider the set $\{x \mid c < x\}$, where c is a given number, as an interval whose left endpoint is c but which *does not have a right endpoint.* We use the usual interval notation, but with the symbol ∞ in place of the nonexistent right endpoint. Since we are talking about numbers greater than c, the left endpoint c is not contained in the interval, and the parenthesis symbol rather than the bracket is appropriate. Our interval has no right endpoint, so it makes no sense to ask whether or not the right endpoint belongs to the interval. We will simply adopt the convention that with the symbol ∞ we can use either the bracket or the parenthesis, and either the word "closed" or the word "open". Thus

$$(c, \infty) = (c, \infty] = \{x \mid c < x\}.$$

The symbol $-\infty$ is used in place of a nonexistent left endpoint. Thus, for example, $[-\infty, 7] = \{x \mid x \leq 7\}$. These conventions allow us to write $R^1 = (-\infty, \infty) = [-\infty, \infty] = (\infty, \infty] = [-\infty, \infty)$. Notice that *the symbol ∞ does not stand for a number.* When we speak of an interval (a, b), you will have to infer from the context whether it is possible that a might be $-\infty$ or b might be ∞. If we specifically refer to the **finite interval** (a, b), we will mean that a and b stand for numbers, and the symbols $-\infty$ and ∞ are not allowed.

Example 2-3. Write the set $\{x \mid x^2 - x - 2 > 0\}$ as an interval or a union of intervals.

Solution. Since $x^2 - x - 2 = (x - 2)(x + 1)$, our given inequality may be written as $(x - 2)(x + 1) > 0$. A product is positive if, and only if, both factors have the same sign, so both numbers $(x - 2)$ and $(x + 1)$ are positive or both are negative. In the first case, we must have $x > 2$, and in the second case, we must have $x < -1$. Thus x must belong to the interval $(2, \infty)$ or to the interval $(-\infty, -1)$. In symbols,

$$\{x \mid x^2 - x - 2 > 0\} = (-\infty, -1) \cup (2, \infty).$$

Every set of real numbers is contained in the closed interval $[-\infty, \infty]$, and it is easy to see that many sets are contained in smaller closed intervals. For example, the set of all rational numbers with numerator 1 is contained in the closed interval $[-1, 1]$. This set is also contained in the closed intervals $[-7, 10]$ and $[-3, 2]$, and many others, but the *smallest closed interval* that contains the set of rational numbers with numerator 1 is the interval $[-1, 1]$. As another example, consider the set of all positive rational numbers whose squares are less than 2. This set is contained in the intervals $[-1, 5]$, $[0, 2]$, and so on. The *smallest* closed interval that contains this set is the interval $[0, \sqrt{2}]$. You might notice that neither 0 nor $\sqrt{2}$ belongs to the set of positive rational numbers with squares less than 2. But even though the endpoints of the interval $[0, \sqrt{2}]$ are not members of our given set, you cannot find a smaller closed interval that contains the set.

In the two examples we have just discussed, it was fairly easy to select the smallest closed interval that contains the given set. We are not always so fortunate. For example, it is not an easy matter to find the smallest closed interval that contains the set $\left\{ \left(\frac{n+1}{n} \right)^n \Big| n \text{ a positive integer} \right\}$. Nevertheless, it is one of the fundamental properties of the system of real numbers that this set—and every other set of real numbers (except the empty set)—is contained in a smallest closed interval. Technically speaking, *the smallest closed interval that contains a set A is the closed interval that contains A and is contained in every closed interval that contains A.*

Property 2-1. (*The **completeness** of the real numbers.*) *Every non-empty set of real numbers is contained in a smallest closed interval.*

The table at the top of the next page exhibits some examples that illustrate the completeness property of the real numbers. You should use a number scale to picture these examples, and others.

We have defined the union of two given sets, and we can easily extend this definition to cases in which there are more than two sets. Thus, the union of any

The set A	The smallest closed interval containing A
$\{3\}$	$[3, 3]$
$(-1, 5)$	$[-1, 5]$
$(-1, 2] \cup [5, 10]$	$[-1, 10]$
The set of positive integers	$[1, \infty]$
The set of rational numbers	$[-\infty, \infty]$
$\left\{\dfrac{1}{n} \,\middle|\, n \text{ a positive integer}\right\}$	$[0, 1]$

collection of sets is the set that we obtain by lumping together all the members of all the sets in the collection to form one set. More precisely, *an element belongs to the union of a collection of sets if it belongs to at least one of the sets of the collection.* Similarly, the intersection of a collection of sets is the set of elements that the sets in the collection have in common. More precisely, *an element belongs to the intersection of a collection of sets if it belongs to every set in the collection.* This extension of the ideas of union and intersection from collections of only two sets to collections of larger numbers of sets is perfectly obvious when our collections consist of a finite number of sets. Our definitions, however, do not restrict us to finite collections.

Example 2-4. Let S be a non-empty set of real numbers. Show that the intersection of all the closed intervals that contain S is the smallest closed interval that contains S.

Solution. Let $[a, b]$ be the smallest closed interval that contains S, and let I be the intersection of all the closed intervals that contain S. We are to show that $I \subseteq [a, b]$ and $[a, b] \subseteq I$. By definition, each member of the intersection I must be a member of *every* closed interval that contains S, and since $[a, b]$ is such a closed interval, we see that $I \subseteq [a, b]$. On the other hand, if $[c, d]$ is *any* closed interval that contains S, it must contain the *smallest* such interval, which is $[a, b]$. Thus each point of $[a, b]$ is a member of *every* closed interval that contains S, and so $[a, b] \subseteq I$.

P R O B L E M S   2

1. On a number scale, make sketches of $A \cup B$ and $A \cap B$ for the following choices of A and B.
(a) $A = (-2, 3),\ B = (1, 4]$
(b) $A = [-2, 2],\ B = (1, 4)$
(c) $A = (2, 3),\ B = (3, 4)$
(d) $A = (2, 3],\ B = [3, 4)$
(e) $A = (0, \frac{22}{7}),\ B = (\pi, \infty)$
(f) $A = (0, 1),\ B = \varnothing$

2. What can you conclude about a and b if you are told that $[a, b] \subseteq (a, b)$?

3. Does the everyday usage of the word "interval" agree with our definition in this text?

4. Express the sets of points that satisfy the following inequalities as intervals or unions of intervals.

(a) $|x| > 3$ (b) $|x + 1| \geq 2$ (c) $|x + 3| \leq 2$

(d) $|2x - 4| > 8$ (e) $|5 - 4x| < 3$ (f) $|3 - 4x| > 5$

(g) $x^3 - 3x^2 + 2x > 0$ (h) $\dfrac{x + 1}{x - 1} \leq 0$ (i) $|x - 1| \leq |x + 1|$

5. Let $[a, b]$ be a finite interval. Show that $x \in [a, b]$ if, and only if, $|x - \frac{1}{2}(a + b)| \leq \frac{1}{2}(b - a)$.

6. If $A \subseteq B$, show that $A \cup B = B$ and $A \cap B = A$.

7. Suppose $A = \{x \,|\, a(x) = 0\}$ and $B = \{x \,|\, b(x) = 0\}$, where $a(x) = \cos(\pi x^5 - x^3 + x)$ and $b(x) = \sin(2\pi x^5 - 2x^3 + 2x)$.

(a) Show that $A \cup B = \{x \,|\, a(x) \cdot b(x) = 0\}$.

(b) Show that $A \cap B = \{x \,|\, |a(x)| + |b(x)| = 0\}$.

(c) Show that $A \subseteq B$.

(d) Is $A = B$?

(e) Which of the following statements are true: $0 \in B$, $1 \in B$, $2 \in B$?

(f) Show that $r \in B$ if, and only if, $-r \in B$.

(g) What is the smallest closed interval that contains B?

(h) Let I be the set of integers. What is $I \cap B$? $I \cap A$?

8. Suppose that a, b, c, and d are real numbers such that $[a, b] \cap [c, d] \neq \varnothing$.

(a) Show that $[a, b] \cup [c, d] = \left[\dfrac{a + c - |a - c|}{2}, \dfrac{b + d + |b - d|}{2} \right]$.

(b) Show that

$$[a, b] \cap [c, d] = \left[\frac{a + c + |a - c|}{2}, \frac{b + d - |b - d|}{2} \right].$$

9. If $A \subseteq R^1$ and $B \subseteq R^1$, define $A + B = \{x + y \,|\, x \in A, y \in B\}$.

(a) Find $[1, 2] + [3, 4]$.

(b) Find $(a - p, a + p) + (b - q, b + q)$.

(c) Find $(-\infty, 3) + (12, \infty)$.

(d) Show that $[-1, 0] + [0, 1] = [-1, 0] \cup [0, 1]$.

(e) Is it always true that $A + B = A \cup B$?

(f) Is it always true that $(a, b) + (c, d) = (a + c, b + d)$?

10. If a is the smallest element of a set A of real numbers and b is the largest element of A, show that the smallest closed interval that contains A is the interval $[a, b]$. Does every set of real numbers contain a smallest element and a largest element?

11. In each case, find the smallest closed interval containing the set specified:

(a) $\{-1, 0, 1, 2\}$.

(b) The set of prime numbers less than 100.

(c) The set of common logarithms of all positive numbers.

(d) $\{\log |\sin x| \,|\, x \text{ a real number}\}$.

(e) $\left\{ \sin \dfrac{1}{n} \,\middle|\, n \text{ a positive integer} \right\}$.

(f) $\{.1, .11, .111, .1111, \ldots\}$.

(g) The set of radii of circles, each of which contains a square of sidelength 1 in its interior.

12. Find the intersection and the union of each of the following collections of sets:
   (a) The collection of intervals $\{[3 - r, 3 + r] \mid r \in (0, \infty)\}$.
   (b) The collection of intervals $\{[-\sin r, \sin r] \mid r \in (0, \pi/2)\}$.

13. Let $r \in (0, 1)$. Show that the intersection of the collection of all closed intervals of the form $\left[\dfrac{1}{1 + r}, \dfrac{1}{1 - r}\right]$ is the interval $[1, 1]$.

14. Let $r \in [2, \infty]$. Show that the union of the collection of closed intervals of the form $\left[\dfrac{1}{r}, \dfrac{r - 1}{r}\right]$ is the open interval $(0, 1)$.

3 CARTESIAN COORDINATES AND THE DISTANCE FORMULA

In Section 1, we discussed the manner in which real numbers are associated with points of a line. In this section, we will consider the corresponding procedure in two dimensions.

Let us begin by drawing two number lines meeting at right angles at their origins, with the positive direction upward on one line and to the right on the other (see Fig. 3-1). These number lines are called **coordinate axes.** The horizontal line is the **X-axis,** and the vertical line is the **Y-axis.** Let P be any point of the plane and construct through P lines that are perpendicular to the axes. If x is the number represented by the foot of the perpendicular to the X-axis and y is the corresponding number of the Y-axis, then the pair of numbers (x, y) is associated with P. Conversely, let (x, y) be any pair of numbers. Then construct a line perpendicular to

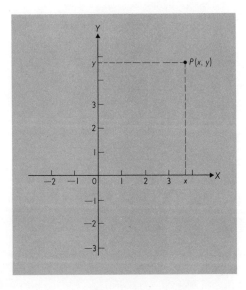

Figure 3-1

the X-axis at the point x, and construct a line perpendicular to the Y-axis at the point y. The intersection of these two lines will determine exactly one point, P, to be associated with the pair of numbers (x, y). In summary, with each point of the plane there is associated a pair of numbers (x, y), and with each pair of numbers there is associated a point P of the plane. The numbers x and y are the **coordinates** of P.

We have just described a **cartesian coordinate system** (named after the seventeenth century French philosopher and mathematician René Descartes). We have established a correspondence between a geometric system (points) and an algebraic system (pairs of numbers). We will consistently use the symbol R^2 to denote the set of ordered pairs of real numbers. In symbols,

$$R^2 = \{(x, y) \mid x \text{ and } y \text{ are real numbers}\}.$$

Thus our coordinate system gives us a one-to-one correspondence between the points of the plane and the elements of R^2. We sometimes ignore the logical distinction between a geometric point of a coordinate plane and its coordinates, and no confusion will arise if we speak of the "point" (x, y) instead of the "point whose coordinates are (x, y)."

The points $(3, 1)$, $(-2, 3)$, $(-2, -1)$, and $(4, -2)$ are shown in Fig. 3-2. Notice that the first number of a coordinate pair is the X-coordinate, and the second is the Y-coordinate. The two axes divide the coordinate plane into four regions, or **quadrants.** We will agree that the axes do not belong to any quadrant. These quadrants are numbered I, II, III, and IV, as shown in Fig. 3-2.

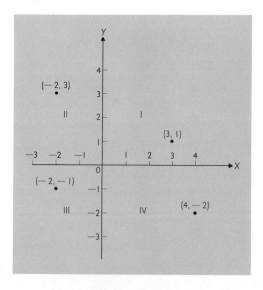

Figure 3-2

The distance between points a and b of a number scale is $|a - b|$. We can also calculate the distance between two points of the coordinate plane.

Example 3-1. The point P_1 has coordinates $(-2, -1)$, and the point P_2 has coordinates $(2, 2)$. Find the distance $\overline{P_1 P_2}$ between these points.

Solution. The points P_1 and P_2 are plotted in Fig. 3-3. Let P_3 be the point $(2, -1)$. It is apparent that the points P_1, P_2, and P_3 are the vertices of a right triangle, with

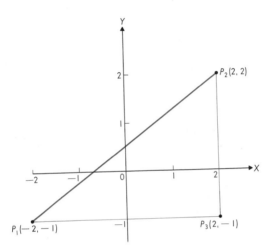

Figure 3-3

the right angle at P_3. Since the points P_2 and P_3 lie in the same vertical line, you can easily see that the distance between them is 3 units. Similarly, the distance $\overline{P_1 P_3} = 4$. Now according to the Pythagorean Theorem,

$$\overline{P_1 P_2^2} = \overline{P_1 P_3^2} + \overline{P_3 P_2^2} = 16 + 9 = 25.$$

It follows that $\overline{P_1 P_2} = 5$.

The concept of the distance between two points is so important that we shall develop a formula for it. The arguments we use are the same as the ones we used in Example 3-1.

Theorem 3-1. *Let P_1 and P_2 with coordinates (x_1, y_1) and (x_2, y_2) be any two points of the plane. Then the distance $\overline{P_1 P_2}$ is given by the formula*

(3-1)
$$\overline{P_1 P_2} = \sqrt{(x_2 - x_1)^2 + (y_2 - y_1)^2}.$$

Proof. As in Example 3-1, the auxiliary point P_3 with coordinates (x_2, y_1) is introduced (see Fig. 3-4) in such a way that the points P_1, P_2, and P_3 form a right triangle with the right angle at P_3. The legs of this triangle are $\overline{P_1P_3}$ and $\overline{P_2P_3}$ units long, and the length of the hypotenuse, $\overline{P_1P_2}$, is the distance we wish to find. Again, according to the Pythagorean Theorem,

$$(3\text{-}2) \qquad \overline{P_1P_2^2} = \overline{P_1P_3^2} + \overline{P_2P_3^2}.$$

Since the points P_1 and P_3 have the same Y-coordinate, you can easily

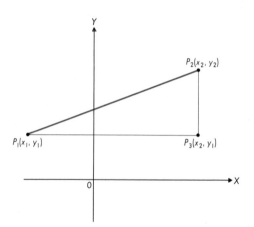

Figure 3-4

convince yourself that $\overline{P_1P_3} = |x_2 - x_1|$. Hence

$$\overline{P_1P_3^2} = |x_2 - x_1|^2 = (x_2 - x_1)^2.$$

Similarly,

$$\overline{P_2P_3^2} = |y_2 - y_1|^2 = (y_2 - y_1)^2.$$

We can therefore write Equation 3-2 as

$$\overline{P_1P_2^2} = (x_2 - x_1)^2 + (y_2 - y_1)^2,$$

which is equivalent to Equation 3-1.

You will use the distance formula so often that you should memorize it.

Example 3-2.   Find the distance between the points $(-3, 2)$ and $(2, -3)$.

Solution.   You should realize that it makes no difference which point is designated P_1. If the first point is labeled P_2 and the second P_1, the distance formula yields

$$\overline{P_1P_2} = \sqrt{(-3 - 2)^2 + (2 + 3)^2} = 5\sqrt{2}.$$

Example 3-3.   Find the distance between the point (x, y) and the origin.

Solution.   Let P_1 be the point $(0, 0)$ and P_2 be the point (x, y), and apply the distance formula. The distance turns out to be

$$\sqrt{(x - 0)^2 + (y - 0)^2} = \sqrt{x^2 + y^2}.$$

If P_1, P_2, and P_3 are any three points, then

(3-3) $$\overline{P_1P_3} \leq \overline{P_1P_2} + \overline{P_2P_3},$$

and the equality sign holds if, and only if, the point P_2 belongs to the line segment joining P_1 and P_3. This important property of distance is called the **triangle inequality,** for reasons that will be obvious to you from a glance at Fig. 3-5. The

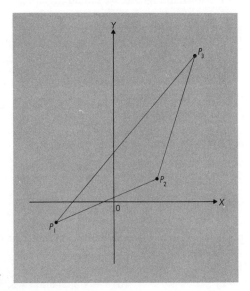

Figure 3-5

truth of this inequality is apparent from the geometry of the situation, but we can check it by using Formula 3-1 and considerable algebra.

Example 3-4.   Find the point Q that is $\frac{3}{4}$ of the way from the point P $(-4, -1)$ to the point R $(12, 11)$ along the segment PR.

Solution.   Figure 3-6 illustrates the situation; we are to find the numbers x and y, the coordinates of Q. To find these two numbers, we might write the two equations $\overline{PQ} = \frac{3}{4}\overline{PR}$ and $\overline{QR} = \frac{1}{4}\overline{PR}$ in terms of x and y and solve. Although this method

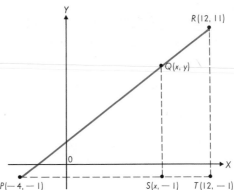

Figure 3-6 $P(-4, -1)$ $S(x, -1)$ $T(12, -1)$

will work, it is easier to use a little geometry. If we introduce the auxiliary points $S(x, -1)$ and $T(12, -1)$ shown in Fig. 3-6, we obtain the similar triangles PSQ and PTR. Therefore,

$$\frac{\overline{PS}}{\overline{PT}} = \frac{\overline{PQ}}{\overline{PR}} \quad \text{and} \quad \frac{\overline{QS}}{\overline{RT}} = \frac{\overline{PQ}}{\overline{PR}}.$$

From our figure, we see that $\overline{PS} = x + 4$, $\overline{PT} = 16$, $\overline{QS} = y + 1$, and $\overline{RT} = 12$, and it is a condition of the problem that $\dfrac{\overline{PQ}}{\overline{PR}} = \dfrac{3}{4}$. Hence $\dfrac{x + 4}{16} = \dfrac{3}{4}$ and $\dfrac{y + 1}{12} = \dfrac{3}{4}$, from which it follows that $x = 8$ and $y = 8$.

P R O B L E M S   3

1. Plot the following points of R^2 in a coordinate plane and find the distance between them:
   (a) $(1, 2)$ and $(3, 7)$ (b) $(2, -1)$ and $(-2, 1)$
   (c) $(1, 1)$ and $(-3, -2)$ (d) $(-\sqrt{2}, 2)$ and $(\sqrt{5}, 5)$

   (e) $(\cos 3, 0)$ and $(0, \sin 3)$ (f) $(1, \pi)$ and $\left(-1, \dfrac{1}{\pi}\right)$

   (g) $(\log 6, \log 4)$ and $(\log 3, \log 8)$

2. How far apart are the points
   (a) $(t, |t|)$ and $(-|t|, t)$?   (b) $(\cos u, \sin u)$ and $(\cos v, \sin v)$?
   (c) $(5, \tan t)$ and $(4, 0)$?   (d) $(1 + t^2, -t^3)$ and $(1 - t^2, t)$?
   (e) $(\log |\sin t|, \log |\cos t|)$ and $(\log |\cos t|, \log |\sin t|)$?

3. In what quadrant does the point $(-y, x)$ lie if the point (x, y) lies
   (a) in Quadrant I?   (b) in Quadrant II?
   (c) in Quadrant III?   (d) in Quadrant IV?

4. Plot every point (x, y) such that $x \in \{-1, 0, 1\}$ and $y \in \{2, 3, 4\}$. What is the radius of the smallest circular disk that contains this set?

5. Use the distance formula to determine if the triangle with vertices $(1, 1)$, $(3, 2)$, and $(2, 12)$ is a right triangle.

6. Find the area of the region bounded by the triangle whose vertices are the points $(-1, 2)$, $(3, 2)$, and $(-4, 6)$.

7. Two vertices of a square are $(-3, 2)$ and $(-3, 6)$. Find three pairs of other possible vertices.

8. Use similar triangles, rather than the distance formula, to find:
   (a) The point that is $\frac{2}{3}$ of the way from $(-2, 1)$ to $(4, 10)$.
   (b) A point that divides the segment with endpoints $(-3, -1)$ and $(7, 14)$ in the ratio $3/2$.
   (c) The midpoint of the segment with endpoints (x_1, y_1) and (x_2, y_2).

9. One of the points of a certain circle is the point $(-1, \sqrt{5})$, and its center is the origin. Show that the point $(\sqrt{2}, 2)$ is also a point of the circle. Can you find other points of this circle?

10. Find the point of the X-axis that is equidistant from the points $(0, -2)$ and $(6, 4)$.

11. Find the relation between the numbers x and y if the point (x, y) is equidistant from the origin and the point $(1, 1)$.

12. Use Inequality 3-3 to determine whether or not the following points are colinear:
   (a) $(4, -3)$, $(-5, 4)$, and $(0, 0)$ (b) $(3, 2)$, $(-\frac{4}{3}, \frac{5}{9})$, and $(6, 3)$

13. What points of the X-axis are more than 5 units from the point $(2, 3)$?

14. Three vertices of a parallelogram are $(-1, -1)$, $(1, 4)$, and $(2, 1)$. Find all possibilities for the fourth vertex.

15. For two non-empty sets A and B of points of the plane, we think of all the possible distances between pairs of points, one of the points being a member of A and the other a member of B. This set of nonnegative numbers is contained in a smallest closed interval $[r, s]$, where $r \geq 0$, and we take the number r to be the distance between the sets A and B. Find the distance between the following pairs of sets:
   (a) $\{(0, y) \mid y \geq 1\}$ and the X-axis
   (b) Quadrant I and Quadrant III
   (c) The set of points which are less than 2 units from the point $(-4, 6)$ and the set of points that lie below the X-axis

4   SUBSETS OF THE PLANE

Plane geometric figures, such as circles, lines, and so on, are simply sets of points, subsets of the plane. To specify a figure in geometry, therefore, we describe a collection of points. For example, we think of a circle of radius 5 as the set of points that are 5 units from a given point, the center of the circle. When we introduce a coordinate system into the plane, we can consider subsets of the plane to be subsets of R^2. Now we can use numerical relations to specify plane point sets. For example, the subset $\{(x, y) \mid y < 0 < x\}$ of R^2 is defined to be the set of pairs of numbers that satisfy the numerical relation $y < 0 < x$, and this set is geometrically described as Quadrant IV of the coordinate plane. The term *analytic geometry* refers to this numerical description of point sets, and as we go along you will see how the introduction of numbers into geometry enables us to use analytic techniques of algebra, calculus, and so on, to solve geometric problems. Conversely, we will often find it helpful to apply geometric arguments to analytic problems.

Example 4-1. Find a relation between the numbers x and y that specifies that a point (x, y) belongs to the union of Quadrants I and III.

Solution. The points of Quadrants I and III are completely characterized as those points whose coordinates have the same sign. Thus,

$$(\text{Quadrant I}) \cup (\text{Quadrant III}) = \{(x, y) \mid xy > 0\}.$$

In the above example we gave a numerical description of a set and a geometric description of a set, and we asserted that the sets were equal. A formal proof that these geometric and numerical descriptions define the same set would require us to show two things: (i) if the point (x, y) belongs to the set (Quadrant I) $\cup$ (Quadrant III), then $xy > 0$; and (ii) if $xy > 0$, then $(x, y) \in$ (Quadrant I) $\cup$ (Quadrant III). In our solution of Example 4-1 we accepted these statements as obviously true; indeed, they are. Nevertheless, the principle is important, and you must keep it in mind.

The set of points in a coordinate plane whose coordinates satisfy a numerical relation is called the **graph** of the relation. Thus the union of the first and third quadrants is the graph of the inequality $xy > 0$. Most of the relations whose graphs we will study will be *equations* in x and y. Two relations (in particular, two equations) are said to be **equivalent** if they have the same graph in a coordinate plane.

Example 4-2. Give a geometric description of and sketch the graph of the equation $(x - 2)^2 + (y - 6)^2 = 25$. In other words, geometrically describe the following subset of R^2: $\{(x, y) \mid (x - 2)^2 + (y - 6)^2 = 25\}$.

Solution. We can find any number of points of the graph of this equation simply by replacing x with a "suitable" number and solving the resulting equation for y. Thus, if we replace x with 2, we obtain the equation $(y - 6)^2 = 25$, whose solutions are $y = 1$ and $y = 11$. The points $(2, 1)$ and $(2, 11)$ are then points of our graph. Similarly, we find the points $(-1, 2)$ and $(-1, 10)$ by letting $x = -1$ and solving for y, and so on. We could continue to calculate points indefinitely and plot them, as we plotted our known points in Fig. 4-1. The more points we plot, the more our figure will "take shape," but this method will never yield the complete picture of the graph of our equation. Let us therefore turn to the equivalent equation

$$\sqrt{(x - 2)^2 + (y - 6)^2} = 5$$

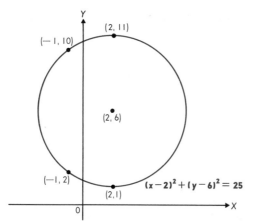

Figure 4-1

for a geometric description of our graph. We recognize the left-hand side of this equation as the expression for the distance between the points (x, y) and $(2, 6)$. Thus, in words, the equation says, "The distance between the points (x, y) and $(2, 6)$ is 5." Therefore, a point (x, y) belongs to the graph of the equation $(x - 2)^2 + (y - 6)^2 = 25$ if, and only if, it is a point of the circle of radius 5 whose center is the point $(2, 6)$. We have sketched this circle in Fig. 4-1.

In Example 4-2 we started with an equation and found a geometric description of its graph. Now let us look at an example in which we proceed in the opposite direction. We will start with a point set, described geometrically, in a coordinate plane and find an equation of which the set is the graph. We speak of such an equation as an *equation of the set*. To find an equation of a given set, we must translate into a numerical relation between x and y the geometric language that tells us that a point (x, y) belongs to the set.

Example 4-3.   Find an equation of the perpendicular bisector of the segment that joins the points $(-5, 4)$ and $(1, -2)$.

Solution.   From the geometric description of our set, it is easy to make the sketch shown in Fig. 4-2. The given conditions tell us that a point (x, y) of our set is equidistant from the points $(-5, 4)$ and $(1, -2)$. We use the distance formula to express this statement as the equation

$$\sqrt{(x + 5)^2 + (y - 4)^2} = \sqrt{(x - 1)^2 + (y + 2)^2}.$$

Conversely, each point whose coordinates satisfy this equation is equidistant from the points $(-5, 4)$ and $(1, -2)$, and therefore is a point of the perpendicular bisector of the segment that joins these points. This equation is perfectly correct, but we can write it in a simpler form. If we square both sides of our equation, multiply out the expressions in the parentheses, and collect terms, we obtain the equation $x - y + 3 = 0$, which is also an equation of the perpendicular bisector.

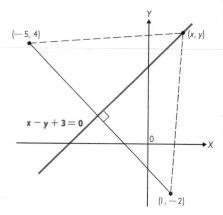

In the preceding example, we found two equations of the same set of points in a coordinate plane. Instead of speaking of such equations as equivalent equations, we will often speak of them as *two forms of the same equation*. Furthermore, in the same way that we identify a pair of coordinates (x, y) with the point it represents, we will talk about the equation of a point set in a coordinate plane as if the equation *were* the set. Thus, in the preceding example we might speak of the perpendicular bisector $x - y + 3 = 0$.

Figure 4-2

In Example 4-2 we could look at the given equation and quickly deduce that its graph is a circle. It is important to be able to find equations of other simple figures, and soon you will know that certain equations have lines as their graphs, and so on. There are times, however, when we can't immediately tell what the graph of a given equation looks like. Then we plot as many points as is practical, use various devices that we will pick up as we go along (including some techniques of calculus), and fill in what we hope is the rest of the graph "by eye."

Example 4-4.   Sketch the graph of the equation $x^2 = y^3$.

Solution.   We make the table that appears in Fig. 4-3 by making several replacements of x and solving for y in each case. The points of this table are then plotted and joined as shown in the figure. At this time it is not possible for us to be absolutely sure that the graph has a "cusp" at the origin. Later you will see how calculus helps us make such decisions. The symmetry of the graph about the Y-axis tells us

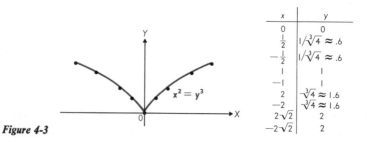

x	y
0	0
$\frac{1}{2}$	$1/\sqrt[3]{4} \approx .6$
$-\frac{1}{2}$	$1/\sqrt[3]{4} \approx .6$
1	1
-1	1
2	$\sqrt[3]{4} \approx 1.6$
-2	$\sqrt[3]{4} \approx 1.6$
$2\sqrt{2}$	2
$-2\sqrt{2}$	2

Figure 4-3

that the points of the graph can be paired, points of each pair having the same Y-coordinate and X-coordinates that differ only in sign, such as the pair $(1, 1)$ and $(-1, 1)$, and so on.

The intersection of the graphs of two relations is the intersection of two subsets of R^2 and consists of those points whose coordinates satisfy both relations.

Example 4-5. Find the intersection of the circle that we plotted in Example 4-2 and the line that we plotted in Example 4-3.

Solution. We are to find the points of the following subset of R^2:

$$\{(x, y) \mid (x - 2)^2 + (y - 6)^2 = 25\} \cap \{(x, y) \mid x - y + 3 = 0\}.$$

Thus we must find all pairs of numbers that satisfy the two equations $(x - 2)^2 + (y - 6)^2 = 25$ and $x - y + 3 = 0$. From the second of these equations we find $y = x + 3$, and when we replace y with $x + 3$ in the first equation we have

$$(x - 2)^2 + (x - 3)^2 = 25,$$

$$x^2 - 5x - 6 = 0,$$

$$(x + 1)(x - 6) = 0.$$

Therefore, $x = -1$, or $x = 6$, and since $y = x + 3$, we see that the intersection is the set $\{(-1, 2), (6, 9)\}$.

Most of our graphs of equations will be "one-dimensional" figures, such as those shown in Figs. 4-1, 4-2, and 4-3. In these cases we will say that the graph is a *curve*. Not all simple looking equations in x and y, however, have graphs that are simple curves.

Example 4-6. Sketch the graph of the equation $y + |y| = x + |x|$.

Solution. An easy way to find the points of this graph is to check each quadrant separately. If $x \geq 0$ and $y \geq 0$, we have $|x| = x$ and $|y| = y$, and our equation becomes $2y = 2x$; that is, $y = x$. As you can see, those points with equal coordinates (such as $(1, 1)$, $(7, 7)$, and so on) lie in a line that bisects the first quadrant, as shown in Fig. 4-4. Each point of Quadrant II has the form $(-a, b)$, where a and b are positive, and for such a point the left-hand side of our equation becomes $b + b = 2b > 0$, while the right-hand side becomes $-a + a = 0$. Thus there are no points of our graph in Quadrant II. Similarly, there are no points of the graph in Quadrant IV. Every point of the form $(-a, -b)$, where $a \geq 0$ and $b \geq 0$, however, satisfies the equation; for in this case we have $-b + b = -a + a$. Thus, as shown in Fig. 4-4, the graph of the equation $y + |y| = x + |x|$ is the union of Quadrant III, the negative X-axis, the negative Y-axis, and the half line that contains the origin and bisects Quadrant I.

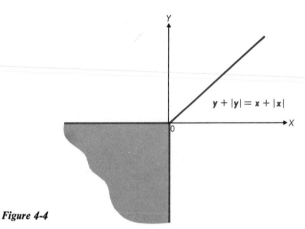

$$y + |y| = x + |x|$$

Figure 4-4

P R O B L E M S   4

1. Give a geometric description of the following subsets of R^2:
   (a) $\{(x, y) \mid x > 0\}$
   (b) $\{(x, y) \mid |y| < 1\}$
   (c) $\{(x, y) \mid xy = 0\}$
   (d) $\{(x, y) \mid 0 \le x \le 1 \text{ and } 0 \le y \le 1\}$
   (e) $\{(x, y) \mid x^2 + y^2 < 4\}$
   (f) $\{(x, y) \mid 0 < x < y\}$

2. Find relations between x and y that specify that a point (x, y) belongs to the following sets:
   (a) The set of points that are more than 3 units from the point $(1, -2)$.
   (b) The set of points that are more than 4 units below the X-axis.
   (c) (Quadrant II) $\cup$ (Quadrant IV)
   (d) The Y-axis
   (e) The set of points that are between 2 and 3 units from the origin.
   (f) (The X-axis) $\cap$ (The Y-axis)

3. Sketch the graphs of the following equations
   (a) $2y = |x| + x$
   (b) $|x| + |y| = 0$
   (c) $\log x \log y = 0$
   (d) $y = |x|$
   (e) $|y| = |x|$
   (f) $(x + 3)^2 + (y - 2)^2 = 9$

4. By plotting points and using your judgment, sketch as best you can the graphs of the following equations:
   (a) $y = x |x|$
   (b) $y = \log |x|$
   (c) $y = |\log x|$
   (d) $y = |x + 2|$
   (e) $x^2 + 4y^2 = 4$
   (f) $x^2 - 4y^2 = 4$

5. Find equations of the following sets of points:
   (a) The circle of radius 2 whose center is the point $(-1, -3)$.
   (b) The perpendicular bisector of the segment that joins the points $(-1, 3)$ and $(3, 9)$.
   (c) The points that are twice as far from the point $(2, -1)$ as they are from the point $(1, -2)$.

(d) The points that are equidistant from the X- and Y-axes.

(e) The line that is parallel to the Y-axis and contains the point (π, π).

(f) The points whose Y-coordinates are 3 units greater than their X-coordinates.

6. Find the intersection of the graphs of the given pairs of equations.

(a) $y = x^2$ and $x = y^2$ (b) $y - 3x = 1$ and $x + 3y = 1$

(c) $y = \sin x$ and $y = \tan x$ (d) $(x - 2)^2 + (y + 1)^2 = 4$ and $y = x - 5$

(e) $y = x^2$ and $2y - x = 1$ (f) $x^2 - y^2 = 3$ and $x^2 + y^2 = 5$

7. Sketch the point sets that are defined by the following relations:

(a) $(|x| + x)y = 0$ (b) $|x| + x < 2y$

(c) $(|x| + x)(|y| + y) = 0$ (d) $|x| - x + |x - y| = 0$

(e) $(x^2 + y^2 - 4)(x^2 + y^2 - 9) = 0$ (f) $|y| < |x|$

8. Suppose that $a(x, y)$ and $b(x, y)$ are expressions in x and y. Explain why the graph of the equation $a(x, y) b(x, y) = 0$ is the union and the graph of the equation $|a(x, y)| + |b(x, y)| = 0$ is the intersection of the graphs of the equations $a(x, y) = 0$ and $b(x, y) = 0$.

9. Show that the union of the graphs of the equations

$$y = \tfrac{3}{4}|x| + \sqrt{1 - x^2} \quad \text{and} \quad y = \tfrac{3}{4}|x| - \sqrt{1 - x^2}$$

is the graph of the equation $25x^2 - 24|x|y + 16y^2 = 1$. On what day in February might you expect to see this point set?

5 FUNCTIONS

Let us begin our discussion of functions by looking at a simple physical example that illustrates the practical origins of the abstract mathematical idea of a function. In elementary physics we learn that if we apply E volts across a 5-ohm resistance, then a current of $\dfrac{E}{5}$ amperes flows through the resistance (Ohm's Law). Thus with each number (of volts) there is paired a number (of amperes), and the collection of these number pairs is a *function*. Since one of the chief goals of any science is the development of such laws or rules that pair with a given quantity some other quantity, we see that functions play a central role in scientific investigations. Calculus was developed to give us a better understanding of these quantitative relationships. It is correct to say that calculus is a study of functions, and therefore it is necessary for us to gain a thorough understanding of the function concept before we can begin to talk about calculus itself.

The notion of a function involves three things: (1) a set D, called the *domain* of the function, (2) a set R, called the *range* of the function, and (3) a rule that assigns to each element $x \in D$ an element $y \in R$. The set of pairs $\{(x, y) \mid x \in D, y$ the corresponding element of $R\}$ is the function. We usually use letters, such as $f, g, F, G,$ and ϕ to name functions. Thus, in a particular context, f might be the name of the function whose domain is the set $\{1, 2, 3, 4\}$, whose range is the set $\{4, 5, 6\}$, and whose rule of correspondence that pairs elements of the range with elements of the domain is given by the following table:

Element of the domain of f	1	2	3	4
Corresponding element of the range of f	5	4	4	6

If x is an element of the domain of a function f, then the corresponding element of the range is denoted by $f(x)$. Thus, in the present example, $f(1) = 5, f(2) = 4$, $f(3) = 5$, and $f(4) = 6$. The symbol $f(x)$ is read "f of x," and it is called the **value** of f at x. You can think of the equation $f(1) = 5$ as a symbolic abbreviation for the sentence, "In our function f, the element that corresponds to 1 is 5." Notice that f and $f(x)$ are two quite different things; f is the name of the function, whereas $f(x)$ is an element of its range. The function f is a set of pairs; in symbols $f = \{(x, f(x)) \mid x \in D\}$. For instance, in the example of this paragraph, f is the set $\{(1, 5), (2, 4), (3, 4), (4, 6)\}$.

Although the general definition of a function imposes no restriction on the kinds of objects that make up the sets D and R (points, angles, numbers, and so on, are perfectly acceptable), it is a fact that in most of the functions we meet in our early study of calculus, the sets D and R are sets of real numbers. It will make our discussion of functions more direct and more concrete if for the present we restrict our attention to such functions. You will find it easy to make any adjustments in terminology that may be required when we deal with other types of functions later. For the moment, then, we will consider that a function is a collection of pairs of real numbers; that is, a function is a subset of R^2. Not every subset of R^2 is a function. To each number x in the domain of a function there corresponds just one number y; that is, the first member of each number pair determines the second. Thus a function cannot contain two number pairs with the same first member, and we have the following formal definition.

Definition 5-1.   *A subset of R^2 is called a **function** if it does not contain two pairs with the same first member. The set of all the first members of the pairs that constitute a function is the **domain** of the function, and the set of second members is the **range**.*

Example 5-1.   Which of the following sets are functions:
$A = \{(5, 1), (4, 2), (4, 3), (6, 4)\}$,
$B = \{(x, y) \mid y = |x|, x \in (-\infty, \infty), y \in [0, \infty)\}$, and
$C = \{(x, y) \mid x = |y|, x \in [0, \infty), y \in (-\infty, \infty)\}$?

Solution.   Neither one of the sets *A* and *C* is a function, for *A* contains the pairs (4, 2) and (4, 3), while *C* contains, for example, the pairs (1, 1) and (1, − 1). The set *B*, on the other hand, is a function. For if $(x, y) \in B$, then $y = |x|$; that is, the entire pair (x, y) is determined by its first member. Notice that a function may contain two pairs with the same *second* member; for example, our function *B* contains the pairs (1, 1) and (−1, 1).

Example 5-2.   Let *f* be the function whose domain is the interval $[-5, 5]$, whose range is the interval $[0, 5]$, and in which the equation $y = \sqrt{25 - x^2}$ is the rule that assigns to a number $x \in [-5, 5]$ a corresponding number $y \in [0, 5]$. In other words, our function *f* is the set

$$f = \{(x, y) \mid y = \sqrt{25 - x^2}, x \in [-5, 5], y \in [0, 5]\}.$$

Find $6f(0) + f(-3) \cdot f(4)$.

Solution.   The symbols $f(0)$, $f(3)$, and $f(4)$ represent numbers. We must find these numbers, multiply the first by 6, and add the result to the product of the other two. By definition, $f(0)$ is the number that corresponds to 0, so we have $f(0) = \sqrt{25 - 0^2} = 5$. Similarly, $f(-3) = \sqrt{25 - (-3)^2} = 4$, and $f(4) = \sqrt{25 - 4^2} = 3$. Therefore $6f(0) + f(-3) \cdot f(4) = 6 \cdot 5 + 4 \cdot 3 = 42$.

The rule of correspondence of the function in our preceding example is expressed by the equation $f(x) = \sqrt{25 - x^2}$. To find the number that this rule assigns to a given number in the domain of *f*, we merely replace the letter *x* wherever it appears in the equation with the given number. We followed this procedure in Example 5-2. If *a*, $|a|$, and $(2 + h)$ represent numbers in the interval $[-5, 5]$, then the corresponding numbers in the range of *f* are $f(a) = \sqrt{25 - a^2}$, $f(|a|) = \sqrt{25 - |a|^2} = \sqrt{25 - a^2}$, and $f(2 + h) = \sqrt{25 - (2 + h)^2} = \sqrt{21 - 4h - h^2}$. It is helpful to think of the correspondence in this case as being defined by the equation $f(\ ) = \sqrt{25 - (\ )^2}$, where any symbol representing a number in the domain of *f* may be inserted in both parentheses.

The first sentence of Example 5-2, which defines our function *f*, is correct— both mathematically and grammatically. But it is certainly a complicated collection of words, and the set notation that follows is simpler. We can convey the same idea even more briefly. In the first place, there is no need to specify the range of this function. If in the formula $\sqrt{25 - x^2}$ we substitute each number of the domain of *f*, we obtain the interval $[0, 5]$; thus the range is determined when we assign the domain and the rule of correspondence. Actually, when the domain of a function consists of all the real numbers for which the rule of correspondence yields real numbers, we usually don't explicitly specify the domain either. Thus we might define our function *f* as the set $f = \{(x, y) \mid y = \sqrt{25 - x^2}\}$, or simply say that *f* is defined by the equation $y = \sqrt{25 - x^2}$ or by the equation $f(x) = \sqrt{25 - x^2}$.

Then the domain of f is understood to be the interval $[-5, 5]$, since $\sqrt{25 - x^2}$ is a real number if, and only if, $x \in [-5, 5]$.

Example 5-3. Let f be defined by the equation $f(x) = \dfrac{x}{|x|}$. What is the "understood" domain D, and what is the range R of f?

Solution. We can replace x in the formula $\dfrac{x}{|x|}$ with any number except 0, so D is the set of non-zero real numbers; that is, $D = (-\infty, 0) \cup (0, \infty)$. If x is negative, $f(x) = -1$, and if x is positive, $f(x) = 1$. Thus there are only the two numbers -1 and 1 in the range of f; $R = \{-1, 1\}$.

The functions we have been talking about in this section are subsets of R^2, and so we can picture them as sets of points in a coordinate plane. The point set that represents a function f is called the **graph** of f. Since $f = \{(x, y) \mid y = f(x)\}$, we see that the graph of the *function f* is the same set of points as the graph of the *equation $y = f(x)$*. A sketch of the graph of a function can give you a feel for the function; whenever possible you should have a picture of a function in your mind as you work with it.

Example 5-4. Sketch the graph of the function of Example 5-3.

Solution. This function consists of the points of the set

$$\{(x, -1) \mid x \in (-\infty, 0)\} \cup \{(x, 1) \mid x \in (0, \infty)\}.$$

When we plot these points in a coordinate plane, we obtain the graph shown in Fig. 5-1

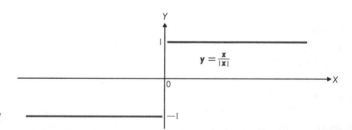

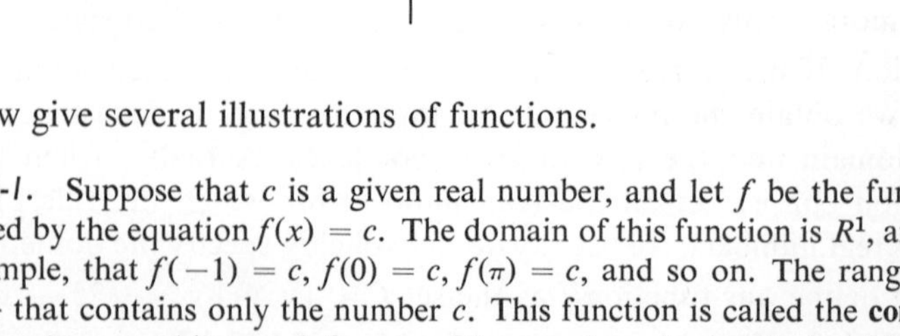

Figure 5-1

We will now give several illustrations of functions.

Illustration 5-1. Suppose that c is a given real number, and let f be the function that is defined by the equation $f(x) = c$. The domain of this function is R^1, and we see, for example, that $f(-1) = c$, $f(0) = c$, $f(\pi) = c$, and so on. The range of f is the set $\{c\}$ that contains only the number c. This function is called the **constant function with value** c, and its graph for a positive number c is sketched in Fig. 5-2.

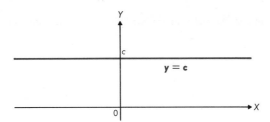

Figure 5-2

Illustration 5-2. Another common function is the **identity function** *j* that is defined by the equation $j(x) = x$. Both the domain and range of *j* are R^1. We have $j(7) = 7$, $j(\sqrt{2}) = \sqrt{2}$, and so on. Thus $j = \{(x, x) \mid x \in R^1\}$, and its graph is shown in Fig. 5-3.

Illustration 5-3. The symbol $[\![x]\!]$ denotes the **greatest integer** *n* such that $n \leq x$. To find $[\![x]\!]$, therefore, we "round off" the decimal representation of *x* to the next lowest whole number. Thus, $[\![\pi]\!] = 3$, $[\![\sqrt{2}]\!] = 1$, $[\![3]\!] = 3$, $[\![-3]\!] = -3$, $[\![-\frac{1}{2}]\!] = -1$, and $[\![-\pi]\!] = -4$. If we define a function *G* by the equation $G(x) = [\![x]\!]$, then we see that the domain of *G* is R^1, and the range of *G* is the set of all integers. Almost every time you state your age you are using this function. You say you are 18, for example, when you are actually $18\frac{1}{4}$, and $18 = [\![18\frac{1}{4}]\!]$. When a dealer prices a certain item at \$4.95, he hopes you will read the tag as $[\![4.95]\!] = 4$ dollars. We have sketched the graph of the equation $y = [\![x]\!]$ in the Fig. 5-4.

Illustration 5-4. Let us assume that the materials used in making a cylindrical tin can cost .012¢ per square inch for the curved surface and 0.21¢ per square inch for the top or bottom. Suppose we want to make a can with a capacity of 54π cubic inches. But the volume alone does not completely determine the dimensions of the can; it may be tall and thin, or short and squat. We may select any positive number *r* and make the radius of the base of the can *r* inches. Since the volume is already fixed, the choice of *r* determines the height of the can, and hence the dimensions of the can are then completely determined. The cost of the can depends

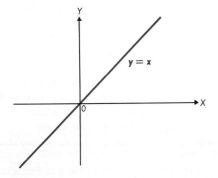

Figure 5-3

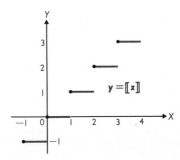

Figure 5-4

on its dimensions, so we see that the cost of the can depends on our choice of the base radius *r*. Let us suppose that a can of base radius *r* inches costs *c* cents, and find a formula that expresses *c* in terms of *r*.

Clearly, *c* = (area of curved surface) × .012 + (area of ends) × .021. If the can is *h* inches high and has a base radius of *r* inches, the area of the curved surface is $2\pi rh$ square inches and the area of the top (or bottom) is πr^2 square inches. Therefore

(5-1) $$c = (2\pi rh)(.012) + (2\pi r^2)(.021).$$

We have now expressed the cost of the can in terms of the dimensions *r* and *h*, but we wanted to express *c* in terms of *r* alone. We therefore write a formula for *h* in terms of *r*. Since the volume of the can is 54π cubic inches, $\pi r^2 h = 54\pi$, and hence $h = \dfrac{54}{r^2}$. Now we replace *h* in Equation 5-1 by $\dfrac{54}{r^2}$ and get the equation

(5-2) $$c = \frac{108\pi}{r}(.012) + (2\pi r^2)(.021).$$

This equation defines a function. As far as the equation is concerned, the domain of the function could be the set of all non-zero numbers, but in terms of the original problem, we see that we must take $r > 0$. Thus the domain in which we are interested is the interval $(0, \infty)$. It is not so easy to find the range of this function; we will discuss that question in Section 23. A sketch of its graph appears in Fig. 23-1.

Illustration 5-5.   Let *f* be the function whose domain is the interval $(0, 1)$ and whose rule of correspondence is expressed as follows:

(i) If we can write a decimal expression for *x* in which, after some point, all the digits are 0 (for example, $x = .135000\ldots$), then $f(x) = 0$.
(ii) Otherwise, $f(x) = 1$.

Thus we have $f(\tfrac{1}{4}) = 0$, $f(\tfrac{1}{3}) = 1$, $f(\tfrac{1}{2}) = 0$, and so on. Notice that if *x* is an irrational number, then $f(x) = 1$. Try to sketch the graph of this function.

P R O B L E M S   5

1. Each of the following statements determines a function. In each case, give the function a letter as a name, determine its domain and range, find a formula that gives its rule of correspondence if you can, and find 3 points of its graph.
   (a) To each positive integer let there correspond the next largest integer.
   (b) To each non-negative number let there correspond the sum of its square and its non-negative square root.
   (c) To each positive number let there correspond the sum of the number and its reciprocal.

(d) To each positive integer let there correspond the sum of its first and last digits.

(e) To each prime number let there correspond the number of times it appears when 1,000,000 is factored into a product of primes.

2. Determine the "understood" domains of the functions that are defined by the following equations:

(a) $f(x) = \sqrt{x-1}$

(b) $g(x) = \log(1-x)^2$

(c) $H(x) = 2\log(1-x)$

(d) $u(t) = \sqrt[3]{\dfrac{|t+1|}{t+1}}$

(e) $F(x) = \log\dfrac{x+1}{x-1}$

(f) $G(z) = \sqrt{\dfrac{z+1}{z-1}}$

(g) $p(x) = \dfrac{1}{[\![x]\!]}$

(h) $q(x) = \dfrac{[\![x]\!]}{x+|x|}$

3. What is the difference between the function p that is defined by the equation $p(q) = \dfrac{q}{6} + \dfrac{6}{q}$ and the function q that is defined by the equation $q(p) = \dfrac{p}{6} + \dfrac{6}{p}$?

4. If $f(x) = x^2 + 1$, find

(a) $f(3-2)$

(b) $f(3) - f(2)$

(c) $f(3 \cdot 2)$

(d) $f(3) \cdot f(2)$

(e) $f(\frac{1}{4})$

(f) $\dfrac{1}{f(4)}$

(g) $f(\sqrt{3})$

(h) $\sqrt{f(3)}$

(i) $f(\log 2)$

(j) $\log f(2)$

(k) $f(\tan 1)$

(l) $\tan f(1)$

5. Find examples of constant functions for which the following statements are *not* true:

(a) $f(x^2) = f(x)^2$

(b) $f(|x|) = |f(x)|$

(c) $f(x+y) = f(x) + f(y)$

(d) $f(-x) = -f(x)$

(e) $f(-x) = f(x)$

(f) $f\left(\dfrac{1}{x}\right) = \dfrac{1}{f(x)}$

(g) $f([\![x]\!]) = [\![f(x)]\!]$

6. Find examples of constant functions for which the statements in Number 5 *are* true.

7. Let $f(k)$ denote the number of "n's" that occur in the kth word of the sentence in the preceding question. What is the domain of f? What is its range? Find $f(1) + f(4) - f(5)$.

8. Is the set $\{(x, y) \mid |y| = |x|\}$ a function?

9. Is the set $\{(x, y) \mid y = \sqrt{x-1}\} \cup \{(x, y) \mid y = \sqrt{1-x}\}$ a function?

10. The graph of a certain function g is the line segment that joins the points $(-3, 0)$ and $(0, 6)$. What is the domain of g? What is the range of g? Find $2g(-2) - 3g(-1)$.

11. In the theory of common logarithms, what is the number $[\![\log N]\!]$ called?

12. Sketch the graph of the function f if:

(a) $f(x) = -[\![x]\!]$

(b) $f(x) = [\![-x]\!]$

(c) $f(x) = -[\![-x]\!]$

(d) $f(x) = [\![2x]\!]$

(e) $f(x) = 2[\![x]\!]$

(f) $f(x) = [\![|x|]\!]$

(g) $f(x) = |[\![x]\!]|$

(h) $f(x) = [\![x]\!]^{-1}$

13. The postage on first class mail is 5¢ per ounce or any fraction thereof. If it costs $p(x)$ cents to mail a letter that weighs x ounces, what is the formula that expresses $p(x)$ in terms of x? (Hint: See the preceding problem.)

14. A box with a square base x inches by x inches has a volume of 25 cubic inches. Express the area of the surface of the box in terms of x.

15. A cubical box is constructed with wooden sides that cost 5¢ per square foot and with a cardboard top and bottom that cost 1¢ per square foot. Express the cost of the box in terms of the length of a side of the box.

16. A conical cup is to be made of paper costing .01¢ per square inch and is to be fitted with a circular cardboard lid costing .1¢ per square inch. The volume of the container is to be 3π cubic inches. If the radius of the base of the cone is r inches and the cost is c cents, express c in terms of r. (The volume and lateral surface area of a cone are given by the formulas $V = \pi r^2 h/3$, $S = \pi r \sqrt{r^2 + h^2}$.)

6 THE TRIGONOMETRIC FUNCTIONS

We assume that you have studied trigonometry and are familiar with the trigonometric functions—sine, cosine, tangent, and so on. However, when you studied elementary trigonometry you probably were primarily concerned with angles and triangles. In calculus we need to adopt a numerical as well as a geometric view of the trigonometric functions; we must consider them as subsets of R^2. In order to orient ourselves to this numerical point of view, we present a brief review of the numerical aspects of trigonometry.

First, we will discuss the sine and cosine functions. When we define a trigonometric function, as with any function that is a subset of R^2, we must specify a set of numbers as its domain and a rule that assigns a number to each number of the domain set. The set of all real numbers is the domain of both the sine and cosine functions. The number assigned to a real number t by the sine function is denoted by **sin** t. Similarly, **cos** t is the number associated with the number t by the cosine function. The numbers $\cos t$ and $\sin t$ are determined in the following way. We draw the circle whose center is the origin and whose radius is 1 (Fig. 6-1). Starting at the point $(1, 0)$, we proceed $|t|$ units along the circumference of this **unit circle**—counterclockwise if t is positive, and clockwise if t is negative. In this way we reach a point P. *The X-coordinate of P is the number cos t, and the Y-coordinate of P is the number sin t*. Notice that in this definition we simply assume that we know how to measure arclength along a circle; a long theoretical discussion of this concept here would take us too far afield (see Section 71).

Example 6-1. Find the numbers cos π, sin (−π/2) and sin 3π/4.

Solution. The circumference of our unit circle is 2π. Thus if we proceed π units along the circle in the counterclockwise direction from the point (1, 0), we will arrive at the point (−1, 0). Since cos π is the X-coordinate of this point, cos π = −1. Similarly, if we proceed π/2 units in the clockwise direction, we arrive at the point (0, −1). It follows that sin (−π/2) = −1. If we proceed 3π/4 units along the circle in the counterclockwise direction from (1, 0), we will arrive at a point P midway along that portion of the circle that lies in the second

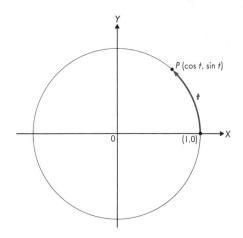

Figure 6-1

quadrant (see Fig. 6-2). Let us denote the coordinates of P by (x, y). Then, according to the definition of the sine function, we have sin 3π/4 = y, so we must find the number y. It is apparent that for our point P, x = −y. Furthermore, since P is

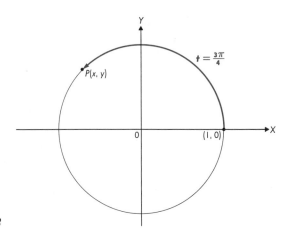

Figure 6-2

one unit from the origin, $x^2 + y^2 = 1$. Thus $(-y)^2 + (y)^2 = 1$, or $y^2 = \frac{1}{2}$. Since y is positive in Quadrant II, we obtain $y = \dfrac{1}{\sqrt{2}}$. Finally, then,

$$\sin \frac{3\pi}{4} = \frac{1}{\sqrt{2}} = \frac{\sqrt{2}}{2}.$$

The other trigonometric functions—tangent, cotangent, cosecant, and secant—are defined by the equations

(6-1)

$$\tan t = \frac{\sin t}{\cos t}$$

$$\cot t = \frac{\cos t}{\sin t}$$

$$\csc t = \frac{1}{\sin t}$$

$$\sec t = \frac{1}{\cos t}.$$

The sine and cosine functions as defined in this section can be related to the same functions defined in terms of angles in the following way. With an angle POQ in standard position (vertex the origin and initial side along the X-axis as in Fig. 6-3), we can associate a number t, the directed distance along the unit circle from the initial side to the terminal side of the angle. This number t is then the **radian measure** of $\angle POQ$. The definitions of the trigonometric functions are such that if T is any trigonometric function, $T(\angle POQ) = T(t)$. Thus, for example, the sine of the *angle POQ* is the same as the sine of the *number t* that is the radian measure of $\angle POQ$. If $P(x, y)$ is a point of the terminal side of an angle of t radians, and if $r = \sqrt{x^2 + y^2}$, we can use similar triangles (see Fig. 6-3) to derive the fundamental equations

(6-2)

$$\sin t = \frac{y}{r}$$

$$\cos t = \frac{x}{r}$$

$$\tan t = \frac{y}{x}$$

$$\cot t = \frac{x}{y}$$

$$\csc t = \frac{r}{y}$$

$$\sec t = \frac{r}{x}.$$

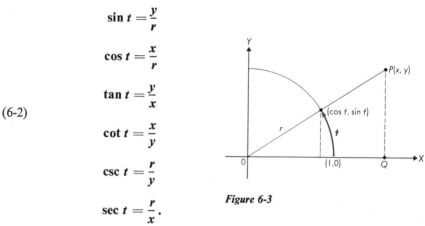

Figure 6-3

We shall assume that you are familiar with a number of standard trigonometric identities and formulas, several of which are listed in the Appendix.

Example 6-2.   Find the distance between the points (cos t, sin t) and (1, 0) shown in Fig. 6-1.

Solution.   If we use d to denote the desired distance, the distance formula (Equation 3-1) gives us

$$d^2 = (\cos t - 1)^2 + \sin^2 t$$
$$= \cos^2 t - 2 \cos t + 1 + \sin^2 t$$
$$= 2 - 2 \cos t$$
$$= 2(1 - \cos t)$$
$$= 4 \sin^2 \tfrac{1}{2} t.$$

Therefore,

$$d = \sqrt{4 \sin^2 \tfrac{1}{2} t}$$
$$= 2 \, |\sin \tfrac{1}{2} t|.$$

Figures 6-4, 6-5, and 6-6 show the graphs of the sine, cosine, and tangent functions.

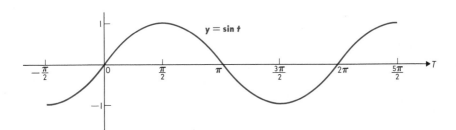

Figure 6-4

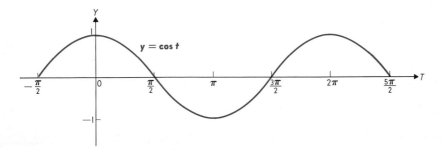

Figure 6-5

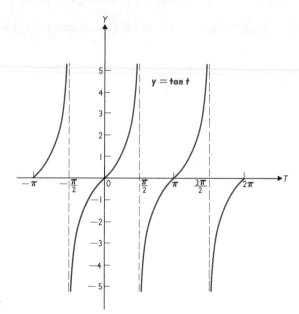

Figure 6-6

P R O B L E M S   6

1. Use a sketch of the unit circle to estimate each of the following numbers.
  (a) sin 1   (b) cos 1   (c) cot 1.5   (d) sin ½

2. Use a sketch of the unit circle to determine which of the following inequalities are true.
  (a) sin 2 < sin 3   (b) cos 2 < cos 3
  (c) cos 3 < sin 3   (d) cos 3 < sin 2
  (e) sin 3 < cos 2   (f) |cos 3| < |cos 2|

3. Use a sketch of the unit circle to find the following numbers.
  (a) sin π/4   (b) cos π/4
  (c) tan π/4   (d) sin π/3
  (e) cos π/3   (f) sin π/6

4. The symbol sin 2° stands for the sine of an angle that measures 2°. Use a sketch of the unit circle to determine which of the following inequalities are true.
  (a) sin 2 < sin 2°   (b) cos 2 < cos 2°
  (c) tan 2 < tan 2°   (d) cos 3 < cos 3°

5. Which of the following numbers are positive?
  (a) sin 2   (b) tan 3
  (c) cos 1.5   (d) csc 4
  (e) cot 5   (f) sec 6
  (g) cos 820°   (h) sin (−460°)

6. Describe the following subsets of the coordinate plane:
   (a) $\{(\cos t, \sin t) \mid 0 \leq t \leq \pi\}$
   (b) $\{(\sin t, \cos t) \mid 0 \leq t \leq \pi\}$
   (c) $\{(x, \sin 2x) \mid 0 \leq x \leq \pi\}$
   (d) $\{(x, 2\cos x) \mid 0 \leq x \leq \pi\}$
   (e) $\{(x, \frac{1}{2}\tan 2x) \mid 0 \leq x \leq \pi\}$
   (f) $\{(|\cos t|, |\sin t|) \mid 0 \leq t \leq 2\pi\}$

7. Describe the following subsets of R^1:
   (a) $\{x \mid [\![\sin x]\!] = 1\}$
   (b) $\{x \mid [\![\tan x]\!] = 1\}$
   (c) $\{x \mid \sin x \cos x = 0\}$
   (d) $\{x \mid \tan x \cot x = 0\}$

8. Which of the following sets are functions?
   (a) $\{(\sin x, x) \mid x \in R^1\}$
   (b) $\{(\sin x, x) \mid x \in [0, \pi]\}$
   (c) $\{(\sin x, x) \mid x \in [-\pi/2, \pi/2]\}$
   (d) $\{(|\sin x|, x) \mid x \in [-\pi/2, \pi/2]\}$
   (e) The four sets obtained by replacing sin x with cos x in (a), (b), (c), and (d)

9. Conclude from geometric considerations that $|\sin t| \leq |t|$. Hence conclude that $1 - t^2 \leq \cos^2 t \leq 1$.

10. Find the following numbers.
   (a) $\sec(-31\pi/4)$
   (b) $\cos 31\pi/6$
   (c) $\csc(-31\pi/4)$
   (d) $\sin 19\pi/3$
   (e) $\cot(-31\pi/4)$
   (f) $\tan 22\pi/3$

11. Show that $\sqrt{1 + \sin 2x} = |\sin x + \cos x|$.

12. Simplify:

   (a) $(\sin x + \cos x)^2 - \sin 2x$

   (b) $\dfrac{\sin^2 2t}{(1 + \cos 2t)^2} + 1$

   (c) $\sin^2 2t - \cos^2 2t$

   (d) $(\sin 2t)(\cos 2t)$

   (e) $\dfrac{2\sin^2 t - 1}{\sin t \cos t} + \cot 2t$

   (f) $\dfrac{\sec t + \tan t}{\cos t - \tan t - \sec t}$

   (g) $\dfrac{\sin t \cot t (\sec t - 1)}{1 - \cos t}$

   (h) $\dfrac{\sin x}{\sec x + 1} + \dfrac{\sin x}{\sec x - 1}$

13. If a central angle in a circle of radius r measures t radians, then $s = rt$, where s is the directed length of the intercepted arc. A circle with a radius of 2 contains a central angle that intercepts an arc 5 units long. What is the measure of the angle in radians? In degrees?

14. The radius of the front wheel of a child's tricycle is 10 inches and the rear wheels each have a radius of 6 inches. The pedals are fastened to the front wheel by arms that are 7 inches long. How far does a pedal travel when the rear wheels make 1 revolution?

7 FURTHER EXAMPLES OF FUNCTIONS AND THEIR GRAPHS

This section is designed to give you more practice in using the terminology associated with functions. Our examples, some of which may seem slightly bizarre, were actually chosen with an eye to our later work.

Example 7-1. Sketch the graph of the function that is defined by the equation
$$q(x) = \frac{|1 + x| - 1}{x}.$$

Solution. We take the domain D of a function that is defined in terms of a formula to be the set of numbers to which the formula applies, and so we see that for our function q, $D = (-\infty, 0) \cup (0, \infty)$. The fact that $0 \notin D$ means that there is no point of the form $(0, y)$ in the graph of q. If $x \geq -1$, then $|1 + x| = 1 + x$, and so for $x \geq -1$ (but not 0),

$$q(x) = \frac{1 + x - 1}{x} = 1.$$ The corre-

sponding part of the graph of q therefore appears as a horizontal line with a hole in it. For $x < -1$, $|1 + x| = -1 - x$, so $q(x) = \dfrac{-1 - x - 1}{x} = -\dfrac{2}{x} - 1.$ The graph of q is sketched in Fig. 7-1.

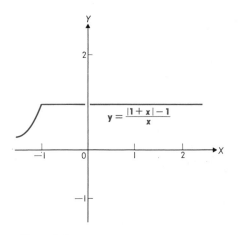

If (a, b) is a point of the graph of f, we know that there can be no other point (a, c) with the same first coordinate. There may, however, be other points with the same second coordinate. The geometric interpretation of these statements is that *vertical lines cannot intersect the graph of a function in more than one point, but horizontal lines can* (see Fig. 7-2).

Figure 7-1

Every function has a graph, but not all graphs are graphs of functions.

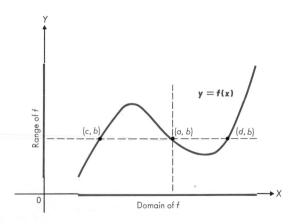

Figure 7-2

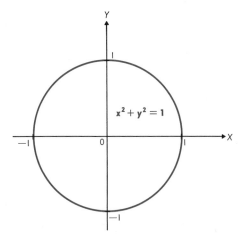

Figure 7-3

For example, vertical lines intersect the circle $x^2 + y^2 = 1$ (Fig. 7-3) in more than one point, so this graph is not the graph of a function. The two branches that we have drawn in Fig. 7-4, however, are the graphs of functions, the functions defined by the equations $y = -\sqrt{1 - x^2}$ and $y = \sqrt{1 - x^2}$. We could have selected

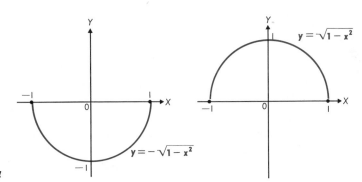

Figure 7-4

other subsets of our circle that are graphs of functions, too. Figure 7-5 shows two other possibilities. Although these choices don't appear to be as natural as the others, they *are* graphs of functions. The graph pictured on the left side of Fig. 7-5 is the graph of a function whose domain is the set [−1, 1] and whose range is the set (−1, 1], and the picture gives us an obvious rule for assigning a number of the range to each number of the domain. If we like, we can write that rule as the complicated equation $y = \sqrt{1 - x^2} \, (\llbracket x \rrbracket + \llbracket x + 1 \rrbracket)$, but this fearsome formula

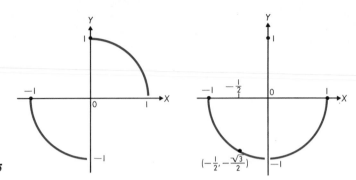

Figure 7-5

probably conceals more than it reveals. The domain of the function whose graph is illustrated on the right side of Fig. 7-5 is the set $[-1, 1]$, and its range is the set $(-1, 0] \cup [1, 1]$. Let us name this function h. Then the figure clearly shows that $h(-1) = 0$, $h(-\frac{1}{2}) = -\frac{1}{2}\sqrt{3}$, $h(0) = 1$, $h(1) = 0$, and so forth. If we insist on a formula for $h(x)$, we can use the equation $h(x) = \sqrt{1 - x^2}\,(1 + 2\,[\![x]\!] + 2\,[\![-x]\!])$. But a *formula* involving mathematical symbols is not a necessary part of a function. All we need is a *rule* that assigns to each element of the domain of the function an element in its range.

With this idea in mind, we turn now to the problem of combining given functions to produce new ones. One can make up an algebra of functions, giving rules for addition, multiplication, and division. Because the basic ideas that are involved are quite simple, we will leave their development to you in the problems. We will now consider an important way of combining functions that will be useful to us later.

Suppose the range of a given function g is a subset of the domain of another function f; that is, for each x in the domain of g, the element $g(x)$ belongs to the domain of f. Then the rule of the function f assigns to $g(x)$ a corresponding element $f(g(x))$ in the range of f. Thus we have a new function. This new function is "composed" of the functions f and g, and we call it the **composite function** formed by the **composition of g by f.** For example, if g is the absolute value function and if f is the tangent function, then the composition of g by f is the function defined by the equation $y = \tan |x|$. In symbols, if $g = \{(x, y) \,|\, y = |x|\}$, and $f = \{(y, z) \,|\, z = \tan y\}$, then the composition of g by f is the function $\{(x, z) \,|\, z = \tan |x|\}$. Just as we might expect a string quartet composed by a Mozart to be different from a Mozart composed by a string quartet, so do we expect that the compositions of f by g and of g by f (even when both are possible) will in general be different.

Example 7-3. Find the intersection of the graph of the composition of the tangent function by the absolute value function and the graph of the composition of the absolute value function by the tangent function. For brevity, let us restrict our domain to lie in the interval $(-\pi, \pi)$.

Solution.   On the left side of Fig. 7-6 we have pictured the graph of the composition of the absolute value function by the tangent function in dots, and the composition

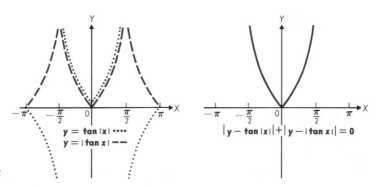

Figure 7-6

of the tangent function by the absolute value function in dashes. The intersection of the two graphs is illustrated in the sketch on the right.

The symbol $f(x)$ stands for the element in the range of the function f that corresponds to the element x in its domain. We now want to introduce a slight extension of this notation that will be useful to us later. *If A is a non-empty subset of the domain of a function f, then by f(A) we will mean the subset of the range of f that consists of the points of the form f(x), where $x \in A$.* In symbols,

$$f(A) = \{f(x) \mid x \in A\}.$$

For example, if f is the sine function and A is the interval $[\pi/6, \pi/2]$, then $f(A)$ is the interval $[\frac{1}{2}, 1]$. In this case we could write $\sin[\pi/6, \pi/2] = [\frac{1}{2}, 1]$. We see that the range R and the domain D of a function f are related by the equation $R = f(D)$. If our function f is a subset of R^2, so that D and R are sets of real numbers, we can picture the set A along the X-axis of a coordinate system and the set $f(A)$ along the Y-axis. To find $f(A)$ we simply project the points of the graph of f that lie directly above or below A onto the Y-axis, as shown in Fig. 7-7.

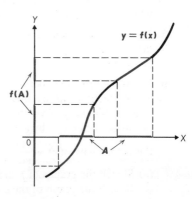

Figure 7-7

The following table shows other examples of the use of this notation.

The function f	The set A	The set $f(A)$
cosine	$\{0, \pi/2, \pi\}$	$\{-1, 0, 1\}$
greatest integer function	$(-\pi/2, \pi/2)$	$\{-2, -1, 0, 1\}$
tangent	$(-\pi/2, \pi/2)$	$(-\infty, \infty)$
sine	$(10, 17)$	$[-1, 1]$
logarithm	$(0, 1)$	$(-\infty, 0)$

P R O B L E M S   7

1. Sketch the graph of f if:

(a) $f(x) = |\sin x|$

(b) $f(x) = \frac{1}{2}(\cos x + |\cos x|)$

(c) $f(x) = \dfrac{|2 - x| - 2}{x}$

(d) $f(x) = \dfrac{x^2 - 3x + 2}{x - 2}$

(e) $f(x) = \dfrac{x - |x|}{x + |x|}$

(f) $f(x) = x - [x]$

2. Sketch the graphs of the following equations:

(a) $y = \cos \pi x$

(b) $y = [\cos \pi x]$

(c) $y = \cos^2 \pi x$

(d) $y = [\cos^2 \pi x]$

(e) $y = 2[\cos^2 \pi x] - 1$

(f) $y = \cos \dfrac{\pi}{2} [x]$

3. Let $f(x) = \sqrt{x^2 + 1}$. If the point (a, b) belongs to the graph of f, which of the following points also belong to the graph of f?

(a) (b, a) (b) $(-a, b)$ (c) $(a, -b)$ (d) $(-a, -b)$

4. Sketch the graph of the equation $y^2 = x^2$. Find 4 functions with domain $(-\infty, \infty)$ whose graphs are subsets of the graph of this equation.

5. Which of the following equations have graphs that are graphs of functions?

(a) $y^2 = x^3$

(b) $[x + y] = 0$

(c) $\log y = x$

(d) $y^2 = [x + 1] - [x]$

6. If f and g are two functions with the same domain, D, then we define their **sum** s as the function whose domain is D and whose rule of correspondence is $s(x) = f(x) + g(x)$. Similarly, if p is the **product** of f and g, then $p(x) = f(x) \cdot g(x)$. The domain of the **quotient** q of f by g is the subset of D for which $g(x) \neq 0$, and for each x in this set we have $q(x) = \dfrac{f(x)}{g(x)}$. Suppose that $f(x) = \sin \dfrac{\pi}{2} x$ and $g(x) = [x]$.

(a) Sketch the graphs of f and g.

(b) Sketch the graph of the sum of f and g.

(c) Sketch the graph of the product of f and g.

(d) Sketch the graph of the quotient of f by g.

(e) Sketch the graph of the composition of g by f.

(f) Sketch the graph of the composition of f by g.

7. Find an equation that defines the composition of g by f if:

(a) $f(x) = |x|, g(x) = x^2 + 1$ (b) $f(x) = \cos x, g(x) = [\![x]\!]$

(c) $f(y) = y, g(z) = z$ (d) $f(u) = \sin u, g(v) = \sin v$

8. A function q is called an **odd function** if for each x in its domain we have $q(-x) = -q(x)$. A function s is an **even function** if for each x in its domain we have $s(-x) = s(x)$.

(a) List three odd functions, three even functions, and three functions that are neither even nor odd.

(b) Show that the sum of two odd functions is odd.

(c) Show that the product of an odd function and an even function is odd.

(d) Show that the composition of an odd function by an odd function is even.

9. Find two different functions f and g such that the composition of f by g is the composition of g by f.

10. Given the formula for $f(x)$ and the set A, find $f(A)$ if:

(a) $f(x) = [\![x]\!], A = (-\infty, \infty)$ (b) $f(x) = |x|, A = (-3, 7)$

(c) $f(x) = x^{12}, A = (-1, \frac{1}{2})$ (d) $f(x) = \cot x, A = [\pi/4, 3\pi/4]$

(e) $f(x) = \log x, A = (\frac{1}{10}, 1000)$ (f) $f(x) = \tan x, A = (0, \pi/2) \cup (\pi/2, 4)$

11. Which of the following statements are true for every function f? (We assume, of course, that the sets A, B, $A \cup B$, and $A \cap B$ are nonempty subsets of the domain of f.)

(a) If $A \subseteq B$, then $f(A) \subseteq f(B)$ (b) $f(A \cup B) = f(A) \cup f(B)$

(c) $f(A \cap B) = f(A) \cap f(B)$

12. How do the graphs of the equations $y = f(x)$ and $y = (1 - 2[\![\cos^2 \pi x]\!])f(x)$ compare? Hint: Before you become too frightened at the complicated factor $(1 - 2[\![\cos^2 \pi x]\!])$, compute its value if x is an integer and its value if x is not an integer (see Number 2e).

13. Define the function f as follows: To the number x let there correspond the length of the line segment joining the points $(x, 1)$ and $(-1, 3)$. Sketch the graph of f. What is the range of f? Show that the graph of f is a subset of the graph of the equation $y^2 - (x + 1)^2 = 4$. Find at least two other functions whose graphs are subsets of this graph.

8 LINEAR FUNCTIONS

A function defined by an equation $y = mx + b$, where m and b are given numbers, is called a **linear function**. Linear functions are so named because the graph of a linear function is a line. The proof of this assertion will be easier to follow if we first consider an example.

Example 8-1. Suppose the function f is defined by the equation $y = 2x - 3$. Choose any three points of the graph of f and show that they lie in a line.

Solution. We were asked to choose any three points, so let us arbitrarily take $x = 0$, $x = 1$, and $x = 2$. Thus we find the three points $P_1(0, -3)$, $P_2(1, -1)$, and $P_3(2, 1)$ of the graph of f (see Fig. 8-1). The points will lie in a line if the distance $\overline{P_1P_3}$ is equal to the sum of the distances $\overline{P_1P_2}$ and $\overline{P_2P_3}$. (The shortest path between two points is a straight line; see Inequality 3-3.) Now

$$\overline{P_1P_3} = \sqrt{2^2 + 4^2} = \sqrt{20} = 2\sqrt{5}, \quad \overline{P_1P_2} = \sqrt{1^2 + 2^2} = \sqrt{5},$$

$$\overline{P_2P_3} = \sqrt{1^2 + 2^2} = \sqrt{5},$$

and therefore
$$\overline{P_1P_3} = \overline{P_1P_2} + \overline{P_2P_3}.$$

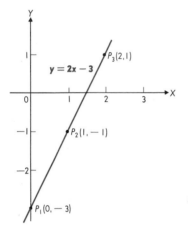

Figure 8-1

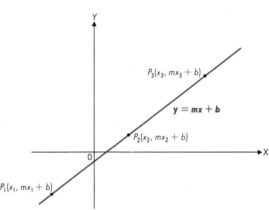

Figure 8-2

We shall now apply the same argument to the general linear function.

Theorem 8-1. *The graph of a linear function f is a line.*

Proof. Since f is a linear function, it is defined by an equation of the form $y = mx + b$. We have to show that any three points of the graph of f lie in a line, so suppose that x_1, x_2, and x_3 are three numbers such that $x_1 < x_2 < x_3$, and consider the corresponding three points of the graph of f. These three points are $P_1(x_1, mx_1 + b)$, $P_2(x_2, mx_2 + b)$, and $P_3(x_3, mx_3 + b)$ (see Fig. 8-2). These points lie in a line if the distance $\overline{P_1P_3}$ is equal to the sum of the distances $\overline{P_1P_2}$ and $\overline{P_2P_3}$.

Now

$$\overline{P_1 P_3} = \sqrt{(x_3 - x_1)^2 + [(mx_3 + b) - (mx_1 + b)]^2}$$
$$= \sqrt{(x_3 - x_1)^2 + m^2(x_3 - x_1)^2}$$
$$= \sqrt{(x_3 - x_1)^2(1 + m^2)}$$
$$= \sqrt{(x_3 - x_1)^2} \sqrt{1 + m^2}.$$

Since $x_3 > x_1$, $x_3 - x_1$ is positive, and hence

$$\sqrt{(x_3 - x_1)^2} = x_3 - x_1.$$

We therefore have

$$\overline{P_1 P_3} = (x_3 - x_1) \sqrt{(1 + m^2)}.$$

In exactly the same way we could calculate

$$\overline{P_1 P_2} = (x_2 - x_1) \sqrt{1 + m^2},$$

and

$$\overline{P_2 P_3} = (x_3 - x_2) \sqrt{1 + m^2}.$$

We can therefore write

$$\overline{P_1 P_2} + \overline{P_2 P_3} = (x_2 - x_1) \sqrt{1 + m^2} + (x_3 - x_2) \sqrt{1 + m^2}$$
$$= [(x_2 - x_1) + (x_3 - x_2)] \sqrt{1 + m^2}$$
$$= (x_3 - x_1) \sqrt{1 + m^2} = \overline{P_1 P_3},$$

and the theorem is proved.

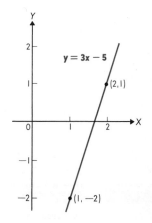

Figure 8-3

Example 8-2. Sketch the graph of the equation $y = 3x - 5$.

Solution. The graph in question is a line, and therefore it is only necessary to find two points of the graph in order to draw it. Two points are (2, 1) and (1, −2), and the graph is shown in Fig. 8-3.

Example 8-3. What can we say about a linear function f if $f(3) = f(1) + f(2)$?

Solution. Since f is a linear function, it must be defined by an equation of the form $y = mx + b$.

Therefore $f(3) = 3m + b$, $f(1) = m + b$, and $f(2) = 2m + b$. The equation $f(3) = f(1) + f(2)$ is valid only if $3m + b = (m + b) + (2m + b)$; that is, $3m + b = 3m + 2b$. But this equation means that $b = 2b$, and hence $b = 0$. Therefore the function f is defined by an equation of the form $y = mx$.

Example 8-4. If the temperature of a body is C degrees Centigrade, and if the corresponding Fahrenheit reading is F degrees, then the relation between these numbers is a linear one. Find it.

Solution. Since the relation is linear, we know that $F = mC + b$, so our problem is to determine the numbers m and b. Now $F = 32$ when $C = 0$, and $F = 212$ when $C = 100$; and therefore $32 = b$ and $212 = 100m + b$. Thus $212 = 100m + 32$, and we see that $m = \frac{9}{5}$. The formula connecting the two units of temperature measurements is therefore $F = \frac{9}{5}C + 32$.

The graph of an equation of the form $y = mx + b$ is a line. The question of whether or not every line must be the graph of such an equation is answered by the following theorem.

Theorem 8-2. *Any line not parallel to the Y-axis is the graph of an equation $y = mx + b$. A line parallel to the Y-axis is the graph of an equation $x = a$.*

Proof. First, let us consider the case of a line parallel to the Y-axis. A line parallel to the Y-axis must intersect the X-axis in some point $(a, 0)$. Then the X-coordinate of every point of the line must be $x = a$, which is the equation of the line. If a line is not parallel to the Y-axis, then it must intersect that axis and every line parallel to that axis. Suppose such a line intersects the Y-axis in the point $(0, b)$ and the line $x = 1$ in the point $(1, c)$, and let $c - b = m$. (See Fig. 8-4.) A given line therefore determines the numbers m and b, and we shall show that the equation of the line is $y = mx + b$. We already know that the graph of the equation $y = mx + b$ is a line. Furthermore, it is easy to establish that the graph of this equation contains the points $(0, b)$ and $(1, c)$. Since there is only one line containing these points, it follows that the graph of the equation $y = mx + b$ must be the line we started with.

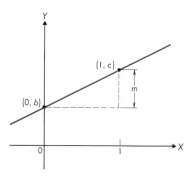

Figure 8-4

A linear function that is defined by an equation of the form $f(x) = mx$ (that is, a linear function in which $b = 0$) is a **homogeneous** linear function. The graph of a homogeneous linear function is a line that contains the origin. These functions are used in many scientific applications: distance = rate × time (constant rate), work = force × distance (constant force), force = mass × accelera- tion (constant mass), and so on. The key properties of homogeneous linear functions are given in the following theorem.

Theorem 8-3. *If f is a homogeneous linear function, and x and y are any numbers, then*

(8-1)
$$f(xy) = xf(y)$$

and

(8-2)
$$f(x + y) = f(x) + f(y).$$

Proof. We are told that f is a homogeneous linear function—in other words, that there is a number m such that for each number $z, f(z) = mz$. Therefore,

$$f(xy) = m \cdot (xy) = x \cdot (my) = xf(y).$$

Similarly,

$$f(x + y) = m \cdot (x + y) = mx + my = f(x) + f(y).$$

If we replace x in Equation 8-1 with 2, we obtain the equation $f(2y) = 2f(y)$. This equation tells us that if we double a number in the domain of f, then we double the corresponding number in the range. Equation 8-1 simply says that this statement applies to any multiple of a number in the domain of f. In the problems we will ask you to show that a homogeneous linear function is the only function for which this statement is true.

Equation 8-2 says that if we add two numbers in the domain of f and then find the corresponding number in the range, or if we find the corresponding numbers first and then add, we end up with the same number. It is a common mistake for students to think that *all* functions have this property. Under stress, many freshmen will equate $(a + b)^2$ and $a^2 + b^2$, or sin $(u + v)$ and sin u + sin v. But you know that these numbers are not in general equal; that is, the square function and the sine function do not possess the property expressed by Equation 8-2. The homo- geneous linear function is the only elementary function that possesses this property; you will study mathematics for some time before you meet another example of such a function.

P R O B L E M S   8

1. Suppose f is a linear function. Determine a formula for $f(x)$ if the graph of f contains the following points.

(a) $(1, 1)$ and $(2, 4)$ (b) $(0, 1)$ and $(1, 0)$

(c) $(1, 0)$ and $(-2, \pi)$ (d) (r, r) and $(2r, 3r)$

2. Sketch the graphs of the following equations. In each case let f be the function defined by the equation and find $f([1, 2])$.

(a) $y = 4x - 7$ (b) $y = 3 - 2x$

(c) $y = 2$ (d) $x = -4$

(e) $2x - 3y + 13 = 0$ (f) $y - 1 = \log 2^x$

(g) $y = [\![\frac{1}{2}x - 3]\!]$ (h) $y = |\frac{1}{2}x - 3|$

3. What can you say about a linear function f if:

(a) $2f(x) = f(2x)$ for every number x?

(b) $f(x + 1) = f(x) + 1$ for every number x?

(c) $f(2x + 1) = f(2x) + 1$ for every number x?

(d) $f(3) = 2$?

(e) $f(3) = 2$ and $f(-1) = 1$?

(f) $f(2) = -4$ and $f(-1) = -f(2)$?

(g) $|f(x)| = f(|x|)$ for every number x?

(h) $[\![f(x)]\!] = f([\![x]\!])$ for every number x?

4. What is the intersection of the graphs of the linear functions f and g that are defined by the equations $f(x) = 2x + 3$ and $g(x) = \frac{1}{2}(x + 3)$. Check your result with a sketch.

5. Find a linear function f such that

(a) $f([1, 2]) = [-1, 1]$ (b) $f([2, 3]) = [0, 1]$

(c) $f(A) = A$ for any set $A \subseteq R^1$ (d) $f(A) = \{1\}$ for any set $A \subseteq R^1$

(e) $f([0, 2]) \cup f([1, 3]) = [1, 4]$ (See Problem 7-11)

(f) $f([0, 2]) \cap f([1, 3]) = [1, 4]$ (See Problem 7-11)

6. If the number of calories of heat required to change 1 gram of solid ice at $0°$ C. to water at $T°$ C. is denoted by Q, then the relation between Q and T is linear when $0 \leq T \leq 100$. If $Q = 90$ when $T = 10$, and $Q = 150$ when $T = 70$, how much heat is required to transform ice into $0°$ water?

7. What is the linear function f for which the following statement is true for each positive number x: $\log 100x^3 = f(\log x)$?

8. Suppose that f and g are linear functions.

(a) Show that their sum is linear.

(b) Show that the composition of g by f is linear.

(c) Under what circumstances can you assert that the quotient of f by g is linear?

(d) Under what circumstances can you assert that the function L that is defined by the statement "$L(x)$ is the larger of $f(x)$ and $g(x)$" is linear? (Look at this question from a graphical point of view.)

9. Suppose that f is a function such that Equation 8-1 holds for each pair of real numbers x and y. Show that if we let $m = f(1)$, then $f(x) = mx$ for each real number x.

10. Suppose that f is a function such that Equation 8-2 holds for each pair of numbers x and y. Let $x = 0$ and $y = 0$ to show that $f(0) = 0$. Then let $y = -x$ to show that $f(-x) = -f(x)$. Now let us write $m = f(1)$ and let $x = 1$ and $y = 1$ to see that $f(2) = m \cdot 2$. Continue in this way to show that $f(3) = m \cdot 3$, $f(4) = m \cdot 4$, and so on. Can you use mathematical induction to show that $f(x) = mx$ for each positive integer x? Once this step has been taken, it is not difficult to show that $f(x) = mx$ for each *rational* number x.

11. Suppose that $f(x) = mx + b$ and A is the open interval $(a - r, a + r)$, where a is a given number and r is positive.
  (a) Show that if $m > 0$, then $f(A) = (f(a) - mr, f(a) + mr)$.
  (b) Show that if $m < 0$, then $f(A) = (f(a) + mr, f(a) - mr)$.

9 MORE ABOUT LINES. SLOPE

In the preceding section we have seen that if m and b are given numbers, then the graph of the equation

$$(9\text{-}1) \qquad\qquad y = mx + b$$

is a line that is not parallel to the Y-axis. The two numbers m and b determine this line, so let us see what geometric significance these numbers have. Since the point $(0, b)$ is one of the points of our line, we see that the number b is the Y-coordinate of the point of intersection of the line and the Y-axis. The number b is called the **Y-intercept** of the line.

To interpret the number m geometrically, let us choose two points (x_1, y_1) and (x_2, y_2) of our line. The coordinates of these points must satisfy Equation 9-1, and so

$$y_1 = mx_1 + b \text{ and } y_2 = mx_2 + b.$$

When we solve these equations for m, we find

$$(9\text{-}2) \qquad\qquad m = \frac{y_2 - y_1}{x_2 - x_1}.$$

Equation 9-2 tells us that the number m in the equation $y = mx + b$ is the ratio of the difference of the Y-coordinates to the difference of the X-coordinates of any two points of the line that is the graph of the equation. The number m is called the **slope** of the line. We also say that m is the slope of any line *segment* that contains the points (x_1, y_1) and (x_2, y_2). Equation 9-2 is meaningless if these points lie in a line (or line segment) that is parallel to the Y-axis. We shall simply say that such lines, or segments, *have no slope*. (This statement does not say that such lines have slope 0. What lines have slope 0?)

Figure 9-1 shows that if we move along our line from the point (x_1, y_1) to the point (x_2, y_2), then we move $y_2 - y_1$ units in the Y-direction and $x_2 - x_1$ units in the X-direction. Therefore, the quotient

$m = \dfrac{y_2 - y_1}{x_2 - x_1}$ is the number of units moved in the Y-direction for each unit moved in the X-direction, or as we say, the *rate* at which the line rises (or falls).

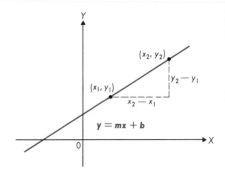

Figure 9-1

Example 9-1. The equation $F = \frac{9}{5}C + 32$ relates the Fahrenheit and Centigrade temperature scales. What do the numbers $\frac{9}{5}$ and 32 represent?

Solution. The number 32 tells us that when the Centigrade thermometer reads 0, the Fahrenheit thermometer reads 32. The number $\frac{9}{5}$ is the slope of the line we would obtain if we graphed our equation in an axis system in which Centigrade temperatures are measured on the horizontal axis and Fahrenheit temperatures are measured on the vertical axis. Thus the number $\frac{9}{5}$ is the number of units of Fahrenheit temperature rise per unit of Centigrade temperature rise. If a body's temperature increases $1°$ C., then it increases $\frac{9}{5}°$ F. If a body's temperature increases $-10°$ (decreases $10°$) C., then it increases $\frac{9}{5}(-10)° = -18°$ F.

Lines parallel to the Y-axis have equations of the form $x = a$, and lines not parallel to the Y-axis have equations of the form $y = mx + b$. Both these equations can be written in the form $Ax + By + C = 0$. Conversely, we have the following theorem.

Theorem 9-1. *If A, B, and C are three real numbers such that A and B are not both 0, then the graph of the equation $Ax + By + C = 0$ is a line.*

Proof. (i) Suppose $B \neq 0$. Then it is clear that our given equation is equivalent to the equation $y = -\dfrac{A}{B}x - \dfrac{C}{B}$. Since this latter equation is of the form

$y = mx + b \left(\text{with } m = -\dfrac{A}{B} \text{ and } b = -\dfrac{C}{B}\right)$, its graph is a line. Thus the graph of our given equivalent equation is a line.

(ii) If $B = 0$, then $A \neq 0$, since we have assumed that A and B are not both 0. The equation $Ax + By + C = 0$ then reduces to the equation

$x = -\dfrac{C}{A}$, which we know is the equation of a line parallel to the Y-axis.

Example 9-2.   Find the slope and Y-intercept of the line $2x + 3y + 4 = 0$.

Solution.   If we write this equation in the form $y = mx + b$, then we can read off the slope m and the Y-intercept b. Thus from the equation $y = -\frac{2}{3}x - \frac{4}{3}$, we see that $m = -\frac{2}{3}$ and $b = -\frac{4}{3}$.

Now let us consider two simple, but important, theorems about lines.

Theorem 9-2.   *Two lines $y = m_1x + b_1$ and $y = m_2x + b_2$ are parallel if, and only if, $m_1 = m_2$.*

Proof.   Non-parallel lines intersect in just one point. Let us find the condition under which the system of equations $y = m_1x + b_1$, $y = m_2x + b_2$ does *not* have just one solution. To solve this system we write $m_1x + b_1 = m_2x + b_2$; that is, $(m_1 - m_2)x = b_2 - b_1$. There is *just one* solution of this last equation if, and only if, $m_1 \neq m_2$. Otherwise, there are either no solutions ($m_1 = m_2$ and $b_1 \neq b_2$, in which case our lines are parallel) or infinitely many solutions ($m_1 = m_2$ and $b_1 = b_2$, in which case the equations are identical and represent the same line).

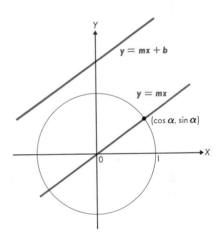

The line $y = mx$ has Y-intercept 0 and is parallel to the line $y = mx + b$ (see Fig. 9-2). The line $y = mx$ will intersect the unit circle in a point $(\cos \alpha, \sin \alpha)$, where $\alpha \in [0, \pi)$. Since the point $(\cos \alpha, \sin \alpha)$ belongs to the graph of the equation $y = mx$, we have $\sin \alpha = m \cos \alpha$; that is, $m = \tan \alpha$. The angle of α is the **angle of inclination** of the line $y = mx$, or of any parallel line $y = mx + b$, and so we see that *the slope of a line is the tangent of its angle of inclination.*

Figure 9-2

Theorem 9-3.   *Two lines $y = m_1x + b_1$ and $y = m_2x + b_2$ are perpendicular if, and only if, $m_1m_2 = -1$.*

Proof.   Figure 9-3 shows the two lines intersecting at a point $P(x, y)$. If we move along the line $y = m_1x + b_1$ one unit to the right, then we move m_1 units in the Y direction and arrive at the point $P_1(x + 1, y + m_1)$. Similarly, if we move along the line $y = m_2x + b_2$ one unit to the right, we arrive at the point $P_2(x + 1, y + m_2)$. The two lines are perpendicular if, and only if, the triangle PP_1P_2 is a right triangle with the right angle at P; that is, if

(9-3) $$\overline{P_1P_2^2} = \overline{PP_1^2} + \overline{PP_2^2}.$$

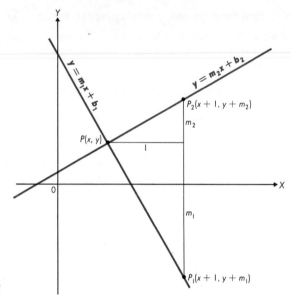

Figure 9-3

It is clear that

$$\overline{P_1P_2^2} = [(y + m_2) - (y + m_1)]^2 = (m_2 - m_1)^2.$$

From the distance formula, we have

$$\overline{PP_1^2} = [(x + 1) - x]^2 + [(y + m_1) - y]^2 = 1 + m_1^2,$$
$$\overline{PP_2^2} = [(x + 1) - x]^2 + [(y + m_2) - y]^2 = 1 + m_2^2,$$

so Equation 9-3 becomes

$$(m_2 - m_1)^2 = 1 + m_1^2 + 1 + m_2^2.$$

On simplifying this equation, we find that $-2m_2m_1 = 2$; that is, $m_1m_2 = -1$.

Example 9-3. Find the equation of the line that is perpendicular to the line $3x - y + 5 = 0$ at the point $(-1, 2)$.

Solution. The equation we seek has the form $y = mx + b$; we will find the numbers m and b. When we write our original equation in the form $y = 3x + 5$, we see that the slope of the given line is 3. Therefore, according to Theorem 9-3, $3m = -1$; that is, $m = -\frac{1}{3}$. Thus the equation we are looking for has the form $y = -\frac{1}{3}x + b$. This line must contain the point $(-1, 2)$, and therefore to find b we solve the equation $2 = -\frac{1}{3}(-1) + b$. Thus $b = \frac{5}{3}$, and we obtain the equation $y = -\frac{1}{3}x + \frac{5}{3}$. If we prefer, we can write this equation as $x + 3y - 5 = 0$.

We have seen that every line has an equation of the form $Ax + By + C = 0$, where A and B are not both zero. If a line has slope m, then it can be represented by an equation $y = mx + b$. This equation is called the **slope-intercept form** of the equation of a line. Another useful form of the equation of a line is the **point-slope form**

(9-4) $$y - y_1 = m(x - x_1).$$

Equation 9-4 is equivalent to the equation $y = mx + (y_1 - mx_1)$, so its graph is a line with slope m and Y-intercept $y_1 - mx_1$. You can readily verify that this line contains the point (x_1, y_1). Hence the graph of Equation 9-4 is *the line with slope m that contains the point (x_1, y_1).*

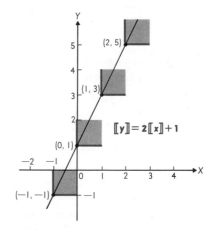

Figure 9-4

Example 9-4. Find the line with slope π that contains the point $(1, 2)$.

Solution. Using Equation 9-4 with $m = \pi$, $x_1 = 1$, and $y_1 = 2$, we find that $y - 2 = \pi(x - 1)$; that is, $y = \pi x + (2 - \pi)$. Notice that the Y-intercept is $2 - \pi$. Make a sketch of this line.

Example 9-5. Sketch the graph of the equation $[\![y]\!] = 2[\![x]\!] + 1$.

Solution. Let us first draw the line $y = 2x + 1$. Each point of this line with integer coordinates, such as the points $(0, 1)$, $(1, 3)$, and so on, belongs to the graph of our given equation. Let (a, b) be such a point. If $x \in [a, a + 1)$, then $[\![x]\!] = a$, and (x, y) is a point of the graph of our given equation if, and only if, $[\![y]\!] = 2a + 1 = b$; that is, $y \in [b, b + 1)$. Thus the graph consists of the collection of one-by-one squares whose lower left corners have integral coordinates $(a, 2a + 1)$ that we have sketched in Fig. 9-4.

PROBLEMS 9

1. Find the slope and Y-intercept of the following lines:
   (a) $y = 3x - 1$ (b) $y = 1 - 4x$
   (c) $2y = 4x + 7$ (d) $2y = 5 - 4x$
   (e) $2x + 4y + 1 = 0$ (f) $x + 4y + \pi = 0$

2. Explain why Theorem 9-3 does not apply to the case of a horizontal line and a vertical line.

3. Write an equation of the line of slope m that contains the listed point. In each case let f be the linear function defined by the equation and find $f([0, 1])$.

(a) $m = 4$, $(1, 3)$ (b) $m = -7$, $(1, -7)$

(c) $m = \frac{22}{7}$, $(1, \pi)$ (d) $m = \sqrt{2}$, $(1, 1.414)$

4. Is the Y-intercept positive or negative for the lines given in 3(c) and 3(d)?

5. Find the slope of the line that contains the given points.

(a) $(1, 2)$ and $(3, 4)$ (b) $(-2, 1)$ and $(2, 3)$

(c) $(4, 1)$ and $(\pi, 1)$ (d) $(-1, 5)$ and $(\pi, 2)$

6. Write an equation of each of the lines in the preceding question.

7. Find the line that contains the point $(-1, 2)$ and is parallel to the line $3x + 5y + 4 = 0$. Replace the word "parallel" with "perpendicular" and do the problem.

8. Use the idea of slope to determine if the triangle with vertices $(1, 1)$, $(3, 2)$, and $(-5, 17)$ is a right triangle.

9. A circle has a radius of 2 units, and its center is the origin. Find an equation of the line that is tangent to the circle at the point $(1, \sqrt{3})$.

10. Use the concept of slope to determine whether or not the following points are collinear:

(a) $(4, -3)$, $(-5, 4)$, $(0, 0)$ (b) $(3, 2)$, $(-\frac{4}{3}, \frac{5}{9})$, $(6, 3)$

11. Show that an equation of the line whose Y-intercept is $b \neq 0$ and whose X-intercept is $a \neq 0$ is $\dfrac{x}{a} + \dfrac{y}{b} = 1$.

This equation is called the **intercept form** of the equation of the line.

12. Use the equation of the preceding question to write an equation of the line that contains the points $(7, 0)$ and $(0, 11)$.

13. A circle is drawn so that it is tangent to the line $y = \frac{3}{4}x + 5$ at the point $(0, 5)$ and also tangent to the line $y = -4$. There are two possible choices for the center of such a circle. Find them.

14. What can you say about two lines if the product of their slopes is 1?

15. Given a triangle ABC, choose a coordinate plane so that the vertices are $A(-a, 0)$, $B(0, b)$, and $C(c, 0)$. For any point $P_1(x_1, y_1)$ of AB determine Q_1 of BC, and then R_1 of CA, such that P_1Q_1 is parallel to AC and Q_1R_1 is parallel to AB. Find the co-ordinates of P_2 of AB (in terms of x_1 and y_1) such that R_1P_2 is parallel to BC. If the above procedure is repeated, starting with P_2, to obtain a point P_3, what are the coordinates of P_3?

16. A "natural way" to find the perpendicular distance between the point $P(7, 2)$ and the line L: $3y = 4x + 3$ is to find the equation of the line N that contains P and is perpendicular to L. Then the distance between P and the intersection of N and L is the desired distance. Find it.

17. Sketch the graphs of the following relations.

(a) $|3x - 4y| = 5$ (b) $|3x - 4y| \leq 5$

(c) $[\![3x - 4y]\!] = 5$ (d) $[\![3x - 4y]\!] \leq 5$

18. Sketch the graphs of the following equations.

(a) $[\![x]\!] + [\![y]\!] = 0$ (b) $2[\![x]\!] - 3[\![y]\!] = 1$

(c) $2[\![x]\!] - 4[\![y]\!] = 1$ (d) $\pi[\![x]\!] - 2[\![y]\!] + 6 + 2\pi = 0$

10 LIMITS

When we sketch the graph of a function f, we can plot only a few points of the form $(x, f(x))$. Then we use the location of the plotted points to suggest where the other points "should" lie. In practice, of course, we fill in the other points "by eye," but in our study of calculus we need a mathematical formulation of what it means to say that certain points of a graph determine where other points "should" lie. Before we go into the theory, let us look at some examples. Although our first function will probably strike you as somewhat artificial, we introduce it here because it gives a particularly simple illustration of the fundamental basis of the limit concept, the subject of this section.

Example 10-1. Sketch the graph of $g = \{(x, y) \mid y = [\![\cos x]\!], \ x \in [-\pi, \pi]\}$.

Solution. The points that are listed in the table in Fig. 10-1 are plotted in the

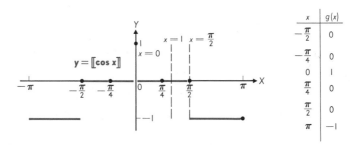

x	$g(x)$
$-\frac{\pi}{2}$	0
$-\frac{\pi}{4}$	0
0	1
$\frac{\pi}{4}$	0
$\frac{\pi}{2}$	0
π	-1

Figure 10-1

accompanying coordinate system. You will find it instructive to convince yourself that the other points we have filled in are indeed points of the graph of g.

Our next example is concerned with a type of function that arises frequently in the study of calculus. In this case we want to sketch the graph of the function, and also fill in an obvious "missing point."

Example 10-2. Sketch the graph of $s = \left\{(x, y) \mid y = \dfrac{\sin x}{x}, \ x \in (-\pi, 0) \cup (0, \pi)\right\}$.

Solution. The domain of this function does not contain 0, so no point of the graph of s will have first coordinate 0. We have sketched the graph in Fig. 10-2 in the usual way; that is, by plotting the points listed in the table and filling in the rest "by eye."

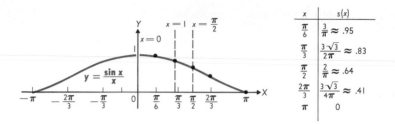

x	$s(x)$
$\frac{\pi}{6}$	$\frac{3}{\pi} \approx .95$
$\frac{\pi}{3}$	$\frac{3\sqrt{3}}{2\pi} \approx .83$
$\frac{\pi}{2}$	$\frac{2}{\pi} \approx .64$
$\frac{2\pi}{3}$	$\frac{3\sqrt{3}}{4\pi} \approx .41$
π	0

Figure 10-2

Now let us look at Figs. 10-1 and 10-2 and ask the question, "In what points 'should' the graphs of g and s intersect the Y-axis?" In Fig. 10-1 it is clear that the graph of g "should" intersect the Y-axis in the point whose Y-coordinate is 0. Actually, of course, the axis and graph intersect in the point whose Y-coordinate is 1; thus the graph is not "smooth." From Fig. 10-2 it appears that the graph of s should intersect the Y-axis in the point whose Y-coordinate is 1. In fact, the graph doesn't intersect the Y-axis at all, but the figure certainly suggests that if we were to adjoin a point of the Y-axis to the graph of s so as to obtain a "smooth curve," we would adjoin the point $(0, 1)$. Neither the graph of our function g nor the graph of our function s intersects the Y-axis in the "proper" point.

If we ask the same question with regard to the line $x = 1$, however, the situation is different. Figures 10-1 and 10-2 suggest that this line should and does intersect the graph of g in the point whose Y-coordinate is $g(1) = [\![\cos 1]\!] = 0$, and the graph of s in the point whose Y-coordinate is $s(1) = \sin 1 = .84147 \ldots$.

Let us now examine the intersections of the graphs and the line $x = \pi/2$. From Fig. 10-2 it appears that the graph of s should intersect the line $x = \pi/2$ in the point whose Y-coordinate is $s(\pi/2) = 2/\pi$, and it does. When we look at Fig. 10-1, however, we have a problem. The graph of g intersects the line $x = \pi/2$ in the point whose Y-coordinate is 0. That is as it should be—if we consider only those points of the graph that lie to the left of the given line. If we consider only the points that lie to the right of the line $x = \pi/2$, though, it would appear that the graph of g "should" intersect the line in the point whose Y-coordinate is -1. Thus, if we consider points on both sides of the line $x = \pi/2$, it is not clear what the point of intersection "should" be.

In the examples above we were given a function f and a point a, and we sought the Y-coordinate of the point in which the graph of f "should" intersect the line $x = a$. This number is called the **limit of f at a**, or the **limit of $f(x)$** as x approaches a, and we denote it by the symbol $\lim_{x \to a} f(x)$. In geometric terms, then, *the number $\lim_{x \to a} f(x)$ is the Y-coordinate of the point in which the graph of f should intersect the line $x = a$.* Of course, this notion is not mathematically precise because of the vagueness of the word "should" in this connection. However, it does convey the essential idea of what a limit is, and later in this section we will construct a mathematical definition of limit based on this idea. You should keep this intuitive idea firmly in mind. From our inspection of Figs. 10-1 and 10-2, we have concluded that $\lim_{x \to 0} [\![\cos x]\!] = 0$, $\lim_{x \to 0} \dfrac{\sin x}{x} = 1$, $\lim_{x \to 1} [\![\cos x]\!] = 0$, $\lim_{x \to 1} \dfrac{\sin x}{x} = \sin 1$, and $\lim_{x \to \frac{1}{2}\pi} \dfrac{\sin x}{x} = \dfrac{2}{\pi}$. There is no one point which is the "natural" point of intersection of the graph of the equation $y = [\![\cos x]\!]$ and the line $x = \pi/2$, so we say that $\lim_{x \to \frac{1}{2}\pi} [\![\cos x]\!]$ *does not exist.*

Because we are interested only in how other points determine what "should" be the point of intersection, the actual value of f at the point a plays no role in calculating the limit of f at a. For example, $\lim_{x \to 0} [\![\cos x]\!] = 0$, while $[\![\cos 0]\!] = 1$, and $\lim_{x \to 0} s(x) = 1$, even though $s(0)$ is not defined. The number $\lim_{x \to a} f(x)$ is determined by values of the function f that correspond to numbers in its domain that are close to, *but are not equal to,* a. We can summarize these remarks in another informal, but still highly useful, approach to the idea of a limit: *The number $\lim_{x \to a} f(x)$ is the number that is approximated by $f(x)$ when x is close to, but not equal to, a.*

Example 10-3. Find $\lim_{x \to 2} \dfrac{x^3 - 8}{x - 2}$.

Solution. When $x \neq 2$, we have $\dfrac{x^3 - 8}{x - 2} = x^2 + 2x + 4$, and when x is close to 2, this number is close to 12. Therefore, $\lim_{x \to 2} \dfrac{x^3 - 8}{x - 2} = 12$.

Although it is not necessary to take $f(a)$ into account when calculating $\lim_{x \to a} f(x)$, it may very well happen that $\lim_{x \to a} f(x) = f(a)$; that is, the limit of f at a is the value of f at a. We saw above, for example, that $\lim_{x \to 1} [\![\cos x]\!] = [\![\cos 1]\!] = 0$, and $\lim_{x \to \frac{1}{2}\pi} \dfrac{\sin x}{x} = \dfrac{\sin \frac{1}{2}\pi}{\frac{1}{2}\pi} = \dfrac{2}{\pi}$. When this situation occurs, we say that f is *continuous* at a in accordance with the following definition.

Definition 10-1. *The function f is continuous at the point a if $\lim_{x \to a} f(x) = f(a)$.*

In geometric terms, f is continuous at a if the graph of f does intersect the line $x = a$ in the point it "should."

Example 10-4. Is the function that is defined by the equation $f(x) = x^2 - 3$ continuous at the point -1?

Solution. Here $f(-1) = -2$, and so our question can be worded: Is $\lim\limits_{x \to -1} x^2 - 3 = -2$? In terms of our second informal idea of limit, we are asking if the number -2 is the number that is approximated by $x^2 - 3$ when x is close to the number -1. The answer to this question is clearly "yes," and so our function is continuous at the point -1.

We have given two informal definitions of the limit concept and some examples to make you familiar with it. Now we are ready for a more mathematical approach. Given a function f and a point a, we seek a mathematical statement that a number A is the Y-coordinate of the point in which the graph of f "should" intersect the line $x = a$. Thus the number $f(x)$ is to be close to A, provided that the number x is close to (but not equal to) a. As a measure of closeness to the point A, let us select a positive number p and construct about A the interval $(A - p, A + p)$ of radius p that we have shown on the Y-axis in Fig. 10-3. We will call this open

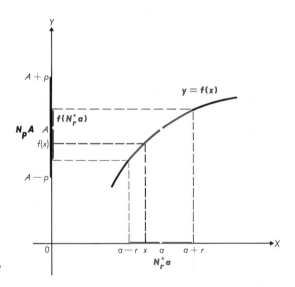

Figure 10-3

interval a **neighborhood of A of radius p** and write $N_p A = (A - p, A + p)$. We read the symbols $N_p A$ as "N sub p of A." If $f(x) \in N_p A$, then $f(x)$ is within p units of A, and so the choice of a small number p will ensure that $f(x)$ is close to A. We want the number $f(x)$ to be contained in the interval $N_p A$ for each x that is "sufficiently" close to (but not equal to) a. Specifically, we ask that there be a positive number r so that for each point x in the **punctured neighborhood** $N_r^* a = (a - r, a) \cup (a, a + r)$ of radius r about a we have $f(x) \in N_p A$, or symbolically, $f(N_r^* a) \subseteq N_p A$. The punctured neighborhood $N_r^* a$ is obtained by deleting the midpoint a from the open interval $(a - r, a + r)$. If we choose p to be a small number, that is, choose N_pA to be narrow, then it may be necessary to choose r to be small; that is, choose N_r^*a to be narrow. The essential idea is that no matter what choice of N_pA we make (first), there is a corresponding N_r^*a, as the following definition indicates.

Definition 10-2. *The equation* $\lim_{x \to a} f(x) = A$ *means that for each neighborhood* N_pA *there exists a punctured neighborhood* N_r^*a *such that* $f(N_r^*a) \subseteq N_pA$. (Notice that we are implicitly assuming that N_r^*a is a subset of the domain of f.)

It takes considerable practice to become proficient in the use of Definition 10-2, and we will begin by considering some examples.

Example 10-5. Apply Definition 10-2 to show that $\lim_{x \to 0} [\![\cos x]\!] = 0$.

Solution. Let $g(x) = [\![\cos x]\!]$. We must show that to an arbitrary neighborhood N_p0 there will correspond a punctured neighborhood N_r^*0 such that $g(N_r^*0) \subseteq N_p0$. So suppose that $N_p0 = (-p, p)$ is some neighborhood of 0. We determine the desired punctured neighborhood N_r^*0 by choosing its radius r. In this case, we may choose r to be any positive number that is less than $\frac{1}{2}\pi$; to be specific, let us take $r = 1$. We obtain the set N_1^*0 by deleting the point 0 from the interval $(-1, 1)$, and you can readily see from Fig. 10-1 that $g(N_1^*0) = \{0\}$. The set $\{0\}$ is contained in our interval $N_p0 = (-p, p)$, no matter what the number p is. Therefore $g(N_1^*0) \subseteq N_p0$, so Definition 10-2 tells us that $\lim_{x \to 0} [\![\cos x]\!] = 0$.

Definition 10-2 demands that to each neighborhood N_pA there correspond *at least* one punctured neighborhood N_r^*a. Actually, if we can find one, we can find infinitely many. For if s is any positive number that is less than r, then $N_s^*a \subseteq N_r^*a$, and so $f(N_s^*a) \subseteq f(N_r^*a) \subseteq N_pA$. In Example 10-5 we chose $r = 1$, but we could equally well have chosen $r = \frac{3}{2}$, $r = \frac{1}{2}$, or $r = .00001$. In most instances, the possible acceptable choices for r will depend on the radius p of N_pA, as we will see in Example 10-6. The fact that we could use the choice $r = 1$ for each N_p0 in Example 10-5 was exceptional.

In Example 10-1 there was no difficulty in deciding where the graph of g should intersect the line $x = \pi/2$, if we looked only at the part of the graph that lies on one side or the other of the line. For example, the part of the graph to the left of the line "should" intersect the line in the point whose Y-coordinate is 0. We call this number the **limit of g from the left** at $\pi/2$, and we denote it by the symbol $\lim_{x \uparrow \frac{1}{2}\pi} g(x)$. Similarly, we denote the **limit of g from the right** at $\pi/2$ by the symbol $\lim_{x \downarrow \frac{1}{2}\pi} g(x)$; it is the Y-coordinate of the point in which that portion of the graph of g that lies to the right of the line $x = \pi/2$ "should" intersect the line. In Example 10-1, $\lim_{x \downarrow \frac{1}{2}\pi} g(x) = -1$.

To modify Definition 10-2 to apply to limits from the left or from the right, we simply replace the general punctured neighborhood N_r^*a with a **left neighborhood** $L_r a = (a - r, a)$ or a **right neighborhood** $R_r a = (a, a + r)$. Thus $\lim\limits_{x \uparrow a} f(x) = B$ *if to each $N_p B$ there corresponds an $L_r a$ such that $f(L_r a) \subseteq N_p B$, and similarly for limits from the right.*

In Definition 10-1 we said that a function f is continuous at a point a provided that $\lim\limits_{x \to a} f(x) = f(a)$. Therefore, when testing for continuity we are concerned with the value of f at a, as well as at nearby points, and we needn't delete this point from our basic interval. Thus we use a neighborhood $N_r a$ in place of the punctured neighborhood $N_r^* a$, and our definition of continuity reads: *The function f is continuous at the point a if to each $N_p f(a)$ there corresponds an $N_r a$ such that $f(N_r a) \subseteq N_p f(a)$.*

Example 10-6. Show that the function q that is defined by the equation $q(x) = \dfrac{1}{x}$ is continuous at 1.

Solution. We are to show that to each neighborhood $N_p q(1) = N_p 1 = (1 - p, 1 + p)$ there corresponds a neighborhood $N_r 1$ such that $q(N_r 1) \subseteq N_p q(1)$. We determine this neighborhood by selecting its radius r. Figure 10-4 shows a typical $N_p q(1)$, and from this figure it appears that we can take r to be the distance between the points $1/(1 + p)$ and 1; that is, $r = p/(1 + p)$. Then $N_r 1 = \left(\dfrac{1}{1 + p}, \dfrac{1 + 2p}{1 + p} \right)$, and $q(N_r 1) = \left(\dfrac{1 + p}{1 + 2p}, 1 + p \right)$. To show that this interval is contained in the interval $N_p q(1) = (1 - p, 1 + p)$, we have only to show that $1 - p \leq \dfrac{1 + p}{1 + 2p}$. We leave this detail to you.

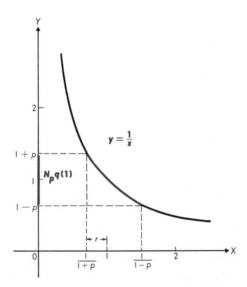

Figure 10-4

When testing to see if a number A is the limit of a function f at a point a, we start with an arbitrary neighborhood N_pA and search for a neighborhood N_r^*a such that $f(N_r^*a) \subseteq N_pA$. This neighborhood N_r^*a is determined by its radius r, so we are really searching for a positive number r. Demonstrating the existence of this number r is the goal of all proofs of limit theorems.

Example 10-7. Show that a linear function is continuous at each point of R^1.

Solution. Let $f(x) = mx + b$. We are to show that f is continuous at an arbitrary point a of R^1. Therefore, if $N_pf(a)$ is a neighborhood of $f(a)$, we seek a corresponding neighborhood N_ra such that

(10-1) $$f(N_ra) \subseteq N_pf(a).$$

Let us first find the set $f(N_ra)$ that is determined by an arbitrary positive number r, and then we will choose r so that Inclusion 10-1 holds. Fig. 10-5 shows the graph of

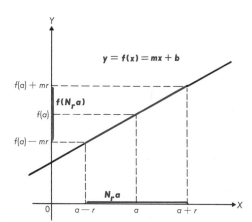

Figure 10-5

f in case m is a positive number, and with the help of this figure we see that $f(N_ra) = (f(a) - mr, f(a) + mr)$. If m is negative we can replace m with its absolute value; and so for each positive number r (see Problem 8-11),

$$f(N_ra) = (f(a) - |m|r, f(a) + |m|r) \quad \text{if } m \neq 0, \quad \text{and}$$
$$f(N_ra) = \{f(a)\} = \{b\} \quad \text{if } m = 0.$$

Now $N_pf(a) = (f(a) - p, f(a) + p)$, so Inclusion 10-1 will hold if r is chosen so that $|m|r \leq p$. If $m \neq 0$, we can take $r = p/|m|$, whereas if $m = 0$, any positive number, for instance 1, will do. Thus, in every case we see that to each neighborhood $N_pf(a)$ there corresponds a neighborhood N_ra such that Inclusion 10-1 holds, and so we have demonstrated that a linear function is continuous at each point of R^1.

PROBLEMS 10

1. Find the points, if any, at which the functions whose graphs are shown in the following figures are not continuous. Find the limits from the left and from the right at these points.
   (a) Fig. 4-3   (b) Fig. 5-1   (c) Fig. 5-2   (d) Fig. 5-3
   (e) Fig. 5-4   (f) Fig. 7-1   (g) Fig. 7-4 (left)   (h) Fig. 7-4 (right)
   (i) Fig. 7-5 (left)   (j) Fig. 7-5 (right)

2. By thinking of $\lim_{x \to a} f(x)$ as "the number that is approximated by $f(x)$ when x is close to, but not equal to, a," find the following limits:

   (a) $\lim_{x \to 2} \dfrac{x^2 - 4}{x - 2}$

   (b) $\lim_{x \to -1} \dfrac{x^3 + 1}{x + 1}$

   (c) $\lim_{x \to \pi} [x - 3] \csc x$

   (d) $\lim_{x \downarrow 0} [x] \cot x$

   (e) $\lim_{x \to 9} \dfrac{\sqrt{x} - 3}{x - 9}$

   (f) $\lim_{x \to -1} \dfrac{1 - |x|}{1 + x}$

   (g) $\lim_{x \to 0} x^0$

   (h) $\lim_{x \uparrow \frac{1}{2}} [4x - [x]]$

3. Interpret Example 10-7 geometrically in case $m = 0$.

4. For the following functions find $\lim_{x \uparrow 0} f(x)$, $\lim_{x \downarrow 0} f(x)$, and $\lim_{x \to 0} f(x)$ (if they exist.) Is f continuous at 0?
   (a) $f(x) = x - [x]$
   (b) $f(x) = [1 - x] + [x - 1]$
   (c) $f(x) = [x](3x + 4)$
   (d) $f(x) = 3x[x] + 4$
   (e) $f(x) = [|x|]$

5. Let f be the function that is defined in Illustration 5-5. Discuss the existence of $\lim_{x \uparrow \frac{1}{2}} f(x)$.

6. Sketch the portion of the graph of the function defined by the equation $h(x) = [\sin \pi x]$ that corresponds to the interval $(-2, 2)$. Use this sketch to help you answer the following questions.
   (a) At what points in our interval is h **discontinuous** (not continuous)?
   (b) Find the limit of h at $\frac{1}{2}$ and the value of h at $\frac{1}{2}$.
   (c) What can you say about the limit of h at 0 and the value of h at 0?
   (d) Find the sets $h(N_{1\frac{1}{2}}^*)$, $h(N_{1\frac{1}{2}}^*)$, and $h(N_{\frac{1}{4}\frac{1}{2}}^*)$.
   (e) Compare the sets $h(N_{1\frac{1}{2}}^*)$ and $h(N_{1\frac{1}{2}})$.
   (f) Find the sets $h(R_1 0)$, $h(L_1 0)$, $h(R_4 0)$, $h(L_4 0)$ and $h(N_4^* 0)$.

7. Let f be the function that is defined by the equation $f(x) = |2x - 4|$. As you answer the following questions, make a sketch to illustrate what is going on.
   (a) Find $f(N_2 3)$ and $f(N_1 3)$.
   (b) Show that if $r \in (0, 1]$, then $f(N_r 3) = (2 - 2r, 2 + 2r)$.
   (c) What is $\lim_{x \to 3} f(x)$?
   (d) Is f continuous at 3?

8. Show that the absolute value function is continuous at 0.

9. Let n be a positive integer, and suppose that $f(x) = x^n$. Show that if r is a positive number that is less than 1, then $f(N_r0) \subseteq (-r, r)$. Conclude that f is continuous at 0.

10. Conclude from Problem 6-9 that the sine function is continuous at 0.

11. (a) If $f(x) = \sin \dfrac{1}{x}$, show that for each positive number r, $f(N_r^*0) = [-1, 1]$. What can you conclude about the existence of $\lim\limits_{x \to 0} \sin \dfrac{1}{x}$?

(b) If $g(x) = x \sin \dfrac{1}{x}$, show that for each positive number r, $g(N_r^*0) \subseteq (-r, r)$. What can you conclude about $\lim\limits_{x \to 0} x \sin \dfrac{1}{x}$?

12. Let $f(x) = [\![x]\!](3 - x)$ and suppose that $r \in (0, 1)$.
(a) Find $f(L_r0)$, $f(R_r0)$, and $f(N_r^*0)$.
(b) From the results of part (a), what can you conclude about $\lim\limits_{x \uparrow 0} f(x)$, $\lim\limits_{x \downarrow 0} f(x)$, and $\lim\limits_{x \to 0} f(x)$?

13. Show that $\lim\limits_{x \to a} f(x) = A$ if, and only if, $\lim\limits_{x \uparrow a} f(x) = A$ and $\lim\limits_{x \downarrow a} f(x) = A$.

14. Show that if $\lim\limits_{x \to a} f(x) > 0$, there is a punctured neighborhood N_r^*a for which $f(N_r^*a) \subseteq (0, \infty)$. What is the corresponding inclusion if $\lim\limits_{x \to a} f(x) < 0$?

$\mathbf{II}$ GENERAL LIMIT THEOREMS

In the last section we found that every linear function is continuous at every point, and that the function q for which $q(x) = 1/x$ is continuous at the point 1. We might call these results *specific* limit theorems because they apply to particular types of functions. As we continue our study of calculus, we will have to calculate limits and check on the continuity of other specific functions, the trigonometric functions, the logarithmic functions, and so on. But before we go farther with specific cases, we will develop some *general* limit theorems, theorems that will enable us to calculate limits of sums, products, and so on, when we know the limits of the summands and the factors. The material in this section is expressed in quite formal language, and the proofs may appear to be harder than they really are because you do not yet feel comfortable with the language we use. But if you keep our informal definitions of limits in mind, and draw lots of pictures, you can get a good idea of what these theorems are all about.

Our first theorem is especially simple from an intuitive point of view.

Theorem 11-1. *Suppose that, for each number x in some punctured neighborhood of a point a, the number $g(x)$ is between the numbers $f(x)$ and $h(x)$, and suppose that $\lim\limits_{x \to a} f(x) = A$ and $\lim\limits_{x \to a} h(x) = A$. Then $\lim\limits_{x \to a} g(x) = A$.*

Proof. Intuitively, this theorem says that if $f(x)$ and $h(x)$ both approximate A when x is close to a, and if $g(x)$ is between $f(x)$ and $h(x)$, then $g(x)$ approximates A when x is close to a. To prove the theorem in terms of Definition 10-2, we suppose that we are given a neighborhood N_pA and we seek a positive number r that determines a punctured neighborhood N_r^*a such that $g(N_r^*a) \subseteq N_pA$. By hypothesis, $\lim\limits_{x \to a} f(x) = A$ and $\lim\limits_{x \to a} h(x) = A$, so we know that there are positive numbers r_1 and r_2 such that

$$f(N_{r_1}^*a) \subseteq N_pA \quad \text{and} \quad h(N_{r_2}^*a) \subseteq N_pA.$$

Now if we choose r to be the smaller of r_1 and r_2, then we will have

$$N_r^*a \subseteq N_{r_1}^*a \quad \text{and} \quad N_r^*a \subseteq N_{r_2}^*a,$$

and so

$$f(N_r^*a) \subseteq N_pA \quad \text{and} \quad h(N_r^*a) \subseteq N_pA.$$

Thus if $x \in N_r^*a$, we see that $f(x) \in N_pA$ and $h(x) \in N_pA$. Since N_pA is an interval, every number between the numbers $f(x)$ and $h(x)$ must also belong to N_pA. By hypothesis, $g(x)$ is such a number, so $g(x) \in N_pA$. Therefore, $g(N_r^*a) \subseteq N_pA$, and our theorem is proved.

Example 11-1. Let $g(x) = x^n$, where n is a positive integer. Show that g is continuous at 0.

Solution. For each $x \in (-1, 1)$, x^n is between $-x$ and x (why?). In Example 10-7 we saw that linear functions are continuous, so we know that $\lim\limits_{x \to 0} -x = 0$ and $\lim\limits_{x \to 0} x = 0$. Therefore, if we set $f(x) = -x$ and $h(x) = x$, the hypotheses of Theorem 11-1 are satisfied, and we have $\lim\limits_{x \to 0} x^n = 0 = 0^n$, which is what we were to show.

The next theorem tells us that if we add $f(x)$ and $g(x)$ and then find the limit, or first find the limits of $f(x)$ and $g(x)$ and then add them, we will end up with the same number.

Theorem 11-2.   *If $\lim\limits_{x \to a} f(x) = A$ and $\lim\limits_{x \to a} g(x) = B$, then $\lim\limits_{x \to a} [f(x) + g(x)] = A + B$.*
We often write this result as the equation

$$(11\text{-}1) \qquad \lim_{x \to a} [f(x) + g(x)] = \lim_{x \to a} f(x) + \lim_{x \to a} g(x).$$

It is a simple matter to extend the result to sums of any number of terms.

Proof. If we set $h(x) = f(x) + g(x)$, we are to show that $\lim\limits_{x \to a} h(x) = A + B$.
So suppose that $N_p(A + B)$ is a given neighborhood of $A + B$; we must

show that there is a punctured neighborhood N_r^*a such that $h(N_r^*a) \subseteq N_p(A + B)$. The neighborhood $N_p(A + B)$ is an interval whose center is the point $A + B$ and which is $2p$ units long. Now consider the neighborhoods $N_{p/2}A$ and $N_{p/2}B$ whose centers are A and B and which are p units long. Because we are told that $\lim_{x \to a} f(x) = A$ and $\lim_{x \to a} g(x) = B$, we know that to these neighborhoods of A and B there correspond punctured neighborhoods $N_{r_1}^*a$ and $N_{r_2}^*a$ such that $f(N_{r_1}^*a) \subseteq N_{p/2}A$ and $g(N_{r_2}^*a) \subseteq N_{p/2}B$. If we choose r to be the smaller of the numbers r_1 and r_2, then

(11-2) $f(N_r^*a) \subseteq N_{p/2}A$ and $g(N_r^*a) \subseteq N_{p/2}B$.

These inclusions show that N_r^*a is the punctured neighborhood we seek. For suppose that $x \in N_r^*a$. Then, according to Inclusions 11-2, $A - \frac{1}{2}p < f(x) < A + \frac{1}{2}p$ and $B - \frac{1}{2}p < g(x) < B + \frac{1}{2}p$. Therefore, $A + B - p < f(x) + g(x) < A + B + p$; in other words, $h(x) = f(x) + g(x) \in N_p(A + B)$. Thus we see that $h(N_r^*a) \subseteq N_p(A + B)$, the inclusion we were to demonstrate.

We will encounter many applications of Theorem 11-2 as we go along; let us now go on to our next theorem, which allows us to calculate limits of composite functions when we know how to find the limits of their components.

Theorem 11-3. *If the function g is continuous at the point L, and if* $\lim_{x \to a} f(x) = L$, *then* $\lim_{x \to a} g(f(x)) = g(L)$. *In other words,* $\lim_{x \to a} g(f(x)) = g(\lim_{x \to a} f(x))$.

Proof. Suppose we are given a neighborhood $N_p g(L)$; we are to show that there is a punctured neighborhood N_r^*a such that

(11-3) $g(f(N_r^*a)) \subseteq N_p g(L)$.

Because g is continuous at L, we know that to the neighborhood $N_p g(L)$ there corresponds a neighborhood $N_s L$ such that $g(N_s L) \subseteq N_p g(L)$. Furthermore, $\lim_{x \to a} f(x) = L$, so to the neighborhood $N_s L$ there corresponds a punctured neighborhood N_r^*a such that $f(N_r^*a) \subseteq N_s L$. We have now found the punctured neighborhood we sought. For from the inclusion $f(N_r^*a) \subseteq N_s L$ we see that $g(f(N_r^*a)) \subseteq g(N_s L)$. Since $g(N_s L) \subseteq N_p g(L)$, Inclusion 11-3 is established, and our proof is complete.

Example 11-2. Suppose that m and b are given numbers and that $\lim_{x \to a} f(x) = L$. Show that

(11-4) $\lim_{x \to a} [mf(x) + b] = mL + b$.

Solution. If we let g be the linear function that is defined by the equation $g(x) = mx + b$, Example 10-7 tells us that g is continuous at the point L. Therefore we obtain Equation 11-4 by an application of Theorem 11-3.

We can use the result of Example 11-2 to prove an extremely useful, though very simple, theorem.

Theorem 11-4. *The equations* $\lim_{x \to a} f(x) = A$ *and* $\lim_{x \to a} [f(x) - A] = 0$ *are equivalent.*

Proof. If $\lim_{x \to a} f(x) = A$, we simply set $m = 1$, $b = -A$ and $L = A$ in Equation 11-4 to see that $\lim_{x \to a} [f(x) - A] = 0$. Conversely, if we are given that $\lim_{x \to a} [f(x) - A] = 0$, we let $f(x) - A$ play the role of $f(x)$ in Equation 11-4. Then $L = 0$, and when we set $m = 1$ and $b = A$, we see that $\lim_{x \to a} f(x) = A$.

Theorem 11-4 allows us to restrict our attention to functions whose limit at a point is 0. Sometimes, as in the next example, it is easy to study the behavior of such functions.

Example 11-3. If $\lim_{x \to a} f(x) = 0$ and $\lim_{x \to a} g(x) = 0$, show that $\lim_{x \to a} f(x)g(x) = 0$.

Solution. Since the square function is continuous at 0 (Example 11-1 with $n = 2$), and $\lim_{x \to a} f(x) = 0$ and $\lim_{x \to a} g(x) = 0$, Theorem 11-3 tells us that $\lim_{x \to a} [f(x)]^2 = 0$ and $\lim_{x \to a} [g(x)]^2 = 0$. Furthermore we see from Theorem 11-2 that $\lim_{x \to a} [f(x) + g(x)] = \lim_{x \to a} f(x) + \lim_{x \to a} g(x) = 0 + 0 = 0$, so we also have $\lim_{x \to a} [f(x) + g(x)]^2 = 0$. Now

$$f(x)g(x) = \tfrac{1}{2}[f(x) + g(x)]^2 - \tfrac{1}{2}[f(x)]^2 - \tfrac{1}{2}[g(x)]^2,$$

so we may use the results we have just obtained, together with Equations 11-1 and 11-4, to see that $\lim_{x \to a} f(x)g(x) = 0$.

The product rule that we have just verified also holds when the limits of f and g are not 0.

Theorem 11-5. *If* $\lim_{x \to a} f(x) = A$ *and* $\lim_{x \to a} g(x) = B$, *then* $\lim_{x \to a} f(x)g(x) = AB$, *or*

(11-5) $$\lim_{x \to a} f(x)g(x) = \lim_{x \to a} f(x) \lim_{x \to a} g(x).$$

As with the sum rule, this result is true for any number of factors.

Proof. Let us write $f(x) g(x) = (f(x) - A)(g(x) - B) + Ag(x) + Bf(x) - AB$. According to Theorem 11-2, we can find the limit of this sum by separately calculating the limits of each of its terms. We find from Equation 11-4 that the limits of the second, third, and fourth terms are AB, AB, and $-AB$, and according to Theorem 11-4 and Example 11-3, the limit of the first term is 0. Therefore, the limit of the sum is $0 + AB + AB - AB = AB$, as we were to show.

With the natural restriction that we are not allowed to divide by 0, there is a quotient rule for limits, too.

Theorem 11-6. *If* $\lim_{x \to a} f(x) = A$ *and* $\lim_{x \to a} g(x) = B$, *where* $B \neq 0$, *then*

$$\lim_{x \to a} \frac{f(x)}{g(x)} = \frac{A}{B},$$

or,

$$(11\text{-}6) \qquad \lim_{x \to a} \frac{f(x)}{g(x)} = \frac{\lim_{x \to a} f(x)}{\lim_{x \to a} g(x)}, \qquad provided\ that\ \lim_{x \to a} g(x) \neq 0.$$

Proof. In order to apply our previous results, we write

$$\frac{f(x)}{g(x)} = \frac{f(x)}{B} \frac{B}{g(x)}.$$

From Equation 11-5 and our hypotheses, we have

$$\lim_{x \to a} \frac{f(x)}{g(x)} = \lim_{x \to a} \frac{f(x)}{B} \lim_{x \to a} \frac{B}{g(x)} = \frac{A}{B} \lim_{x \to a} \frac{B}{g(x)},$$

so our theorem will be proved if we can show that

$$(11\text{-}7) \qquad \lim_{x \to a} \frac{B}{g(x)} = 1.$$

Now $\lim_{x \to a} \frac{g(x)}{B} = \frac{B}{B} = 1$, and, as we saw in Example 10-6, the function q that is defined by the equation $q(x) = \frac{1}{x}$ is continuous at 1. Therefore Theorem 11-3 tells us that $\lim_{x \to a} q\left(\frac{g(x)}{B}\right) = q(1) = 1$. Since $q\left(\frac{g(x)}{B}\right) = \frac{B}{g(x)}$, we see that Equation 11-7 is true, and our proof is complete.

Example 11-4. A **rational function** r is one whose defining formula is the quotient of two polynomials; that is,

$$r(x) = \frac{a_n x^n + a_{n-1} x^{n-1} + \cdots + a_1 x + a_0}{b_m x^m + b_{m-1} x^{m-1} + \cdots + b_1 x + b_0}.$$

Discuss the continuity of r.

Solution. We will first show that every polynomial function is continuous at each point $u \in R^1$; that is, that $\lim_{x \to u} (a_n x^n + a_{n-1} x^{n-1} + \cdots + a_1 x + a_0) = a_n u^n + a_{n-1} u^{n-1} + \cdots + a_1 u + a_0$. This equation follows from our sum and product rules, together with the continuity of the identity and constant functions; for we have

$$\lim_{x \to u} (a_n x^n + \cdots + a_1 x + a_0)$$

$$= \lim_{x \to u} a_n \cdot \lim_{x \to u} x \cdot \cdots \cdot \lim_{x \to u} x + \cdots + \lim_{x \to u} a_1 \cdot \lim_{x \to u} x + \lim_{x \to u} a_0$$

$$= a_n u^n + \cdots + a_1 u + a_0.$$

Now we apply Theorem 11-6 to see that the limit of the quotient of two polynomials is the quotient of their limits, provided that the limit of the denominator is not 0. Therefore r is continuous at all points except those for which the denominator of $r(x)$ is 0.

P R O B L E M S   1 1

1. Use the definition of limit to show that $\lim_{x \to a} f(x) = \lim_{h \to 0} f(a + h)$. What does the statement $\lim_{h \to 0} f(a + h) = f(a)$ say about f?

2. Find the indicated limit and justify your reasoning by referring to theorems in this section.

(a) $\lim_{x \to 1} (x^2 - 5x + 2)$

(b) $\lim_{x \to 2} \dfrac{x^3 - 7}{x + 1}$

3. (a) Let $f(x) = x$ and $h(x) = -x$, and use Theorem 11-1 to find $\lim_{x \to 0} x \sin \left(\dfrac{1}{x} \right)$.

(b) Given that $F(x) = x \sin \left(\dfrac{1}{x} \right)$ for $x \neq 0$, and that F is continuous for all $x \in R^1$, what is $F(0)$?

4. Let $f(x) = \sqrt{x}$. The following steps prove that f is continuous at 1.
   (a) Let $u = 1 - p$ and $v = 1 + p$, where $p \in (0, 1)$. Show that $f((u^2, v^2)) = N_p 1$.
   (b) Let r be the smaller of the numbers $1 - u^2$ and $v^2 - 1$. Then $N_r 1 \subseteq (u^2, v^2)$.
   (c) From (a) and (b) conclude that $f(N_r 1) \subseteq N_p 1$, so that $\lim_{x \to 1} \sqrt{x} = 1$.

5. Using the preceding question, conclude that $\lim_{t \to 0} \sqrt{1 - t^2} = 1$.

6. From Problem 6-9 conclude that $\sqrt{1 - t^2} \leq |\cos t| \leq 1$. Now use the preceding problem and Theorem 11-1 to show that the cosine function is continuous at 0.

7. Justify the steps in the following argument (some of the results you need are developed in the problems in this and the preceding section): $\sin (x + h) = \sin x \cos h + \cos x \sin h$, so $\lim_{h \to 0} \sin (x + h) = \sin x \lim_{h \to 0} \cos h + \cos x \lim_{h \to 0} \sin h = \sin x$. Thus, the sine function is continuous at each point x.

8. Carry out an argument similar to that in the preceding problem to show that the cosine function is continuous at each point x. (Or use the identity $\cos x = \sin (\tfrac{1}{2}\pi - x)$.)

9. Use the results of the preceding two problems and our various limit theorems to deduce that the tangent, cotangent, secant, and cosecant functions are continuous at "most" points. Find the exceptional points.

10. At what points is the function s that is defined by the equation $s(x) = \dfrac{\sin x}{x}$ continuous? How does this fact show up in Fig. 10-2?

11. You will find the relations in Problems 1-15, 1-16, and 1-17 helpful in the following.
  (a) If $v(x) = |x|$, show that v is continuous at each point $a \in R^1$.
  (b) If $\lim_{x \to a} f(x) = A$, is it necessarily true that $\lim_{x \to a} |f(x)| = |A|$?
  (c) If $\lim_{x \to a} |f(x)| = |A|$, is it necessarily true that $\lim_{x \to a} f(x) = A$?

12. Suppose that $\lim_{x \to a} f(x) = A$. For what choices of A are you sure that the statement $\lim_{x \to a} [\![f(x)]\!] = [\![A]\!]$ is true? Can you find examples for which the statement is false?

13. Use our general limit theorems to show that $\lim_{x \to a} [f(x) - g(x)] = \lim_{x \to a} f(x) - \lim_{x \to a} g(x)$.

14. (a) Can you find two functions f and g such that $\lim_{x \to a} f(x)$ and $\lim_{x \to a} g(x)$ do not exist, but $\lim_{x \to a} [f(x) + g(x)]$ does exist?
  (b) Can you find two functions f and g such that $\lim_{x \to a} f(x)$ does not exist, but $\lim_{x \to a} g(x)$ and $\lim_{x \to a} [f(x) + g(x)]$ do exist?
  (c) Can you find two functions f and g such that $\lim_{x \to a} f(x)$ and $\lim_{x \to a} g(x)$ do not exist, but $\lim_{x \to a} [f(x)g(x)]$ does exist?
  (d) Can you find two functions f and g such that $\lim_{x \to a} f(x)$ does not exist, but $\lim_{x \to a} g(x)$ and $\lim_{x \to a} [f(x)g(x)]$ do exist?

15. In this problem we ask you to generalize the result of Number 4.
  (a) Let $f(x) = x^{1/q}$, where q is a positive integer. Now set $u = a^{1/q} - p$ and $v = a^{1/q} + p$, where $a > 0$ and $p \in (0, a^{1/q})$, and show that $f((u^q, v^q)) = N_p a^{1/q}$.
  (b) Let r be the smaller of the two numbers $a - u^q$ and $v^q - a$, and show that $N_r a \subseteq (u^q, v^q)$.
  (c) From (a) and (b) conclude that $f(N_r a) \subseteq N_p f(a)$, and hence that f is continuous at a.

16. Use the result of Number 15 and various other limit theorems to show that for any integers p and q $(q \neq 0)$, and any real number a for which $a^{p/q}$ is defined, we have $\lim_{x \to a} x^{p/q} = a^{p/q}$. (This limit may, in certain cases, be a one-sided limit.)

17. We proved that $\lim_{x \to a} [f(x) + g(x)] = \lim_{x \to a} f(x) + \lim_{x \to a} g(x)$. How does it follow that $\lim_{x \to a} [f(x) + g(x) + h(x)] = \lim_{x \to a} f(x) + \lim_{x \to a} g(x) + \lim_{x \to a} h(x)$? How do we continue with more terms? What is the situation for products?

18. The following "theorem" looks like Theorem 11-3, but this "theorem" is not true. Why not? If $\lim_{x \to a} F(x) = L$ and $\lim_{x \to L} G(x) = M$, then $\lim_{x \to a} G(F(x)) = M$.

19. Suppose that for each number x in some $N_r^* a$, $f(x) \le g(x)$, and that $\lim_{x \to a} f(x) = A$ and $\lim_{x \to a} g(x) = B$. Show that $A \le B$.

REVIEW PROBLEMS—CHAPTER ONE

You can use the following problems to test yourself on the material of this chapter.

1. Is it true that the sum of two rational numbers is a rational number? Is the sum of two irrational numbers necessarily an irrational number? Can the sum of a rational number and an irrational number be rational? Can the product of a rational number and an irrational number be rational?

2. How would you try to convince someone that every open interval contains a rational number? An irrational number?

3. Show that $x \in [a, b)$ if, and only if, $\left[\!\left[\dfrac{x - a}{b - a} \right]\!\right] = 0$.

4. Let f be a function whose range is a subset of R^1 and whose domain is R^1. Which of the following statements are surely true?

(a) $f(3 - 2) = f(3) - f(2)$ (b) $f(3 - 2) = f(1)$
(c) $f(\sqrt{2}) = \sqrt{f(2)}$ (d) $f(|-3|) = f(3)$
(e) $f(2)f(3) = f(6)$
(f) $f(x^2) = f(x)f(x)$

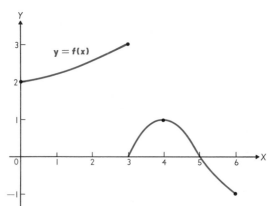

Figure 1-1

5. The graph of a function f is shown in Fig. I-1. Use this figure to answer the following questions as best you can.
   (a) What is the domain of f?
   (b) What is the range of f?
   (c) Find $f(\pi)$ and $f(3)$.
   (d) If $f(x) = \frac{1}{2}$, what is x?
   (e) Find $f(f(4))$.
   (f) Find $\lim_{x \uparrow 3} f(x) + \lim_{x \downarrow 3} f(x)$
   (g) If $f(f(x)) = 2$, what is x?

6. Define a function using the sets $\{a, b, c\}$ and $\{e, f, g, h\}$ as the domain and range (not necessarily in that order!).

7. Sketch the graphs of the following equations:
   (a) $(\sin \pi x)(\sin \pi y) = 0$
   (b) $|\sin \pi x| + |\sin \pi y| = 0$
   (c) $|\sin \pi y| - \sin \pi y + |\sin \pi x| - \sin \pi x = 0$

8. A perpendicular is dropped from the point $(1, 4)$ to the line $2y - 4x + 16 = 0$. Find the coordinates of the foot of the perpendicular.

9. Let $f(x)$ denote the distance between x and the nearest even integer. Thus $f(17) = 1$, $f(31\frac{1}{4}) = \frac{3}{4}$, and so on.
   (a) Sketch the graph of f.
   (b) Do you think f is continuous?
   (c) See if you can find a formula for $f(x)$.

10. Let f and g be linear functions. Show that the graphs of the composition of f by g and the composition of g by f are parallel lines.

11. Let $f(x) = x^2$, and in a ZY-coordinate system sketch the graph of the equation

$$y = \frac{f(z) - f(1)}{z - 1}.$$

12. A ferris wheel with a radius of 12 feet revolves at the rate of 3 revolutions per minute. Assume that the rays of the sun are parallel, and that the sun is directly overhead. Find a formula that gives the position of the shadow of the rider t minutes after he passes the lowest point of the wheel. Find the formula if the sun is not directly overhead but makes an angle of $45°$ with the horizontal (assume that the sun's rays are parallel to the plane of the wheel).

13. Solve for x.
   (a) $\sin [\sin (\sin x)] = 0$
   (b) $\cos (\cos x) = 0$
   (c) $\sin [\![x]\!] = [\![\sin x]\!]$
   (d) $\cos [\![x]\!] = [\![\cos x]\!]$

14. Show that the area of a regular polygon with n sides each of length a is $\frac{1}{4}na^2 \cot \left(\frac{\pi}{n}\right)$.

15. Show that $\cos 2t = \cos^4 t - \sin^4 t$ for each $t \in R^1$.

16. Find
   (a) $\lim_{x \to 0} \dfrac{x}{|x|} \sin x$
   (b) $\lim_{x \uparrow 0} \dfrac{x}{|x|} \cos x$

   (c) $\lim_{x \downarrow 0} \dfrac{x}{|x|} (3x - 2)$

17. Show that the function that is defined by the equation $f(x) = [\![x]\!](1 - 2x + [\![x]\!])$ is continuous at each point of R^1.

THE DERIVATIVE

T W O

The material concerning functions, graphs, slopes, and limits that we covered in Chapter 1 forms a necessary groundwork for the study of calculus, and we use it over and over again as we now move on to the study of calculus proper. One of the basic concepts of calculus, the derivative, will be introduced in this chapter. As we will soon see, a derivative is a rate, and we can gain some insight into the nature of the derivative by considering the following two problems:

Problem 1. A bottle is dropped into a stream that is flowing 3 miles per hour. Plot a graph showing the relationship between the distance the bottle has drifted and the time it has been drifting.

Problem 2. A bottle is dropped from rest in a vacuum. Plot a graph showing the relationship between the distance the bottle falls and the time during which it falls.

In order to solve these problems, we need only to recall a little elementary science. If s denotes the number of miles that the bottle in Problem 1 has drifted in t hours, then by applying the formula *distance* $=$ *rate* $\cdot$ *time* we obtain the equation $s = 3t$. The graph of this equation (Fig. II-1) is a line with slope 3. *The slope of the line is the velocity of the bottle.*

To solve Problem 2, let us recall from elementary physics that the relation between the number of units s of distance that a body falls from rest in t units of time is expressed by the equation $s = \frac{1}{2}gt^2$, where g is a number denoting the acceleration due to gravity. If we measure distance in feet and time in seconds,

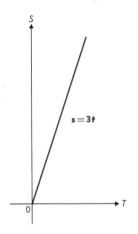

Figure II-1

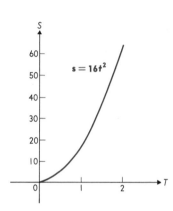

Figure II-2

then g is equal to 32 (approximately), and the relationship between s and t is expressed by the equation $s = 16t^2$. The graph of this equation is shown in Fig. II-2.

One obvious difference between the graph in Fig. II-1 and the graph in Fig. II-2 is that one is a line and the other isn't. The fact that the slope of the graph (line) in Fig. II-1 represents the velocity of the bottle in Problem 1 leads us to ask if the slope of the graph in Fig. II-2 represents the velocity of the bottle in Problem 2. But then we are faced with the question, "What do we mean by the 'slope of the graph'?," since we have, so far, only talked about slope in connection with lines. In this chapter we will answer this last question, and we will also learn how to calculate the slopes of the graphs of many of the elementary functions with which you are acquainted.

Later we will find that the concept of the slope of a graph has many applications in science. In particular, it does give us the velocity of our falling bottle.

12 A GEOMETRIC APPROACH TO THE DERIVATIVE

How, then, shall we define the slope of the graph of a function f? To each point $(x, f(x))$ of the graph we wish to assign a number that we can call the slope of the graph *at the point*. If the graph of f is a line, its slope at any point will turn out to be the slope of the line. Thus the slope of a line at one point is the same as its slope at any other point. For other graphs, though, the slope may be different at different points.

Since we have already defined the slope of a line, we might try to obtain the slope of a general graph at a point by first associating with the point of the graph a line that best "fits" the graph at the point and then assigning the slope of this line as the slope of the graph at the point. The line that best "fits" the graph at a point is called the **tangent line** to the graph at the point. The *slope of the graph at a point* is the *slope of this tangent line*.

Suppose we have a function f and that at each point of its graph we obtain the slope in the manner we have just indicated. Then with a number x of the domain of f we associate a number, the slope of the graph of f at the point $(x, f(x))$. We now have a new function. Its rule of correspondence is simple: To the number x there corresponds the slope of the graph at the point $(x, f(x))$. This new function is *derived* from f. We call it the **derived function** of f and designate it by the symbol f'. The value of the derived function at x is therefore denoted by $f'(x)$. Thus $f'(x)$ is the slope of the graph of f at the point $(x, f(x))$. The number $f'(x)$ is called the **derivative of $f(x)$**.

Our geometric definition of the derivative is not very precise. For one thing, we have not been very explicit about what a tangent line to a graph is. Nevertheless, we shall proceed with a few examples, using intuitive ideas concerning tangent lines, in order to illustrate the basic ideas involved. We will give a more precise definition of the derivative in the next section.

Example 12-1. Find $f'(x)$ if $f(x) = \sqrt{4 - x^2}$.

Solution. We first graph the equation $y = f(x)$; that is, $y = \sqrt{4 - x^2}$. If (x, y) is a point of this graph, then x belongs to the interval $[-2, 2]$, $y \geq 0$, and $\sqrt{x^2 + y^2} = 2$. Thus each point of the graph is two units from the origin and lies above the X-axis. The graph of f is therefore the upper semi-circle whose radius is 2 and whose center is the origin that is shown in Fig. 12-1.

Now we use this graph to find some values of the derived function f'. According to our definition of f', the number $f'(0)$ is the slope of the tangent line at the point $(0, f(0)) = (0, 2)$. The tangent line at this point is horizontal, and so it has slope 0. Therefore $f'(0) = 0$. When $x = 2$ or $x = -2$, the tangent line to the graph is vertical, and the slope of such a line in undefined (see Section 9). Thus the numbers 2 and -2 are not in the domain of the derived function f', though they are in the domain of f.

Now let us find a formula that gives us the number $f'(x)$ for any number x in the interval $(-2, 2)$. Suppose that (x, y) is a point of our graph. We know that the

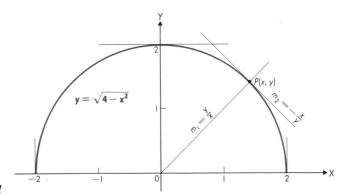

Figure 12-1

tangent line to a circle at a given point is perpendicular to the radius to that point; hence the slope of the tangent line is the negative reciprocal of the slope of the radius (Theorem 9-3). The slope of the radius to the point (x, y) is y/x (why?), and so we see that the slope of the tangent line is $-x/y$. Therefore, $f'(x) = -x/y$, or since $y = \sqrt{4 - x^2}$,

$$f'(x) = \frac{-x}{\sqrt{4 - x^2}}.$$

Notice that this formula gives us the value $f'(0) = 0$ that we found above.

Example 12-2.   If $f(x) = |x|$, find the derivative $f'(x)$.

Solution.   The graph of f is shown in Fig. 12-2. It is clear that for $x > 0$ the tangent line to the graph of f at the point $(x, |x|)$ is simply the line $y = x$. This line has slope 1. If $x < 0$, the equation of the tangent line is $y = -x$. The slope of this line is -1. At the point $(0, 0)$ there is no line that we consider to be a tangent line. It follows that the domain of f' is the set $(-\infty, 0) \cup (0, \infty)$, and that

$$f'(x) = 1 \text{ if } x > 0$$
$$f'(x) = -1 \text{ if } x < 0.$$

Thus we have found that $f'(x) = x / |x|$.

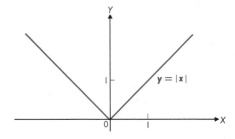

Figure 12-2

We shall use Fig. 12-3 to illustrate a number of points that we have considered in this section. The figure shows the graph of a certain function f. From it we see that the domain of f is the interval $[-1, 8]$, and we can read off some values

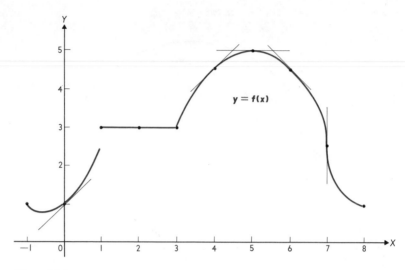

Figure 12-3

of the function; for example, $f(-1) = 1, f(1) = 3, f(5) = 5$, and so on. We have sketched in "tangent lines" at various points of the graph. The derivative $f'(x)$ at such a point is the slope of the tangent line. We read from the figure the following approximate values: $f'(2) = 0, f'(4) = 1, f'(5) = 0$, and $f'(6) = -1$. When $x = 7$, the graph has a vertical tangent; but since a vertical line has no slope assigned to it, we see that the number 7 is not in the domain of f'. Finally, there is no line that we consider to be a tangent line either at the point $(1, 3)$ or at the point $(3, 3)$. The numbers 1 and 3 are not in the domain of the derived function.

Example 12-3. If $f(x) = \sin x$, sketch an approximation to the graph of the derived function f' for the interval $[0, 1.6]$.

Solution. In Fig. 12-4 we have sketched the graph of the equation $y = \sin x$ as a solid curve, plotting the points in the accompanying table. The line segments joining these points are called "chords" of the graph, and because these points are quite close together it appears that the slopes of the chords should approximate the slopes of tangent lines. Thus as an approximation to the value of the derived function at one of our plotted points we take the slope of the chord that joins that point to the next point in the table. In this way, we see that the derivative at 0 is approximated by the number

$$\frac{.0998 - 0}{.1 - 0} = .998;$$

$f'(.1)$ is approximately

$$\frac{.1987 - .0998}{.2 - .1} = .989,$$

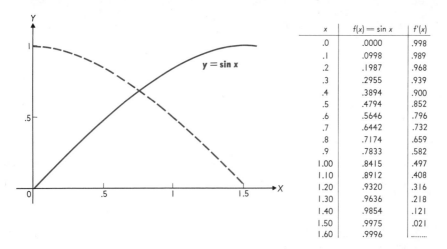

x	f(x) = sin x	f'(x)
.0	.0000	.998
.1	.0998	.989
.2	.1987	.968
.3	.2955	.939
.4	.3894	.900
.5	.4794	.852
.6	.5646	.796
.7	.6442	.732
.8	.7174	.659
.9	.7833	.582
1.00	.8415	.497
1.10	.8912	.408
1.20	.9320	.316
1.30	.9636	.218
1.40	.9854	.121
1.50	.9975	.021
1.60	.9996	....

Figure 12-4

and so on. The approximate values thus obtained are given in the third column of the table, and the dashed curve in Fig. 12-4 is (approximately) the graph of the derived function.

There are many notations commonly used in connection with the derivative. We shall use the "prime" notation for the present and introduce other notations later. If f is a function and x is a number in its domain, then we use either the symbol $f(x)$ or simply the letter y to represent the value of f at x. Similarly, the derived function of f is a function f', and the value of f' at the point x is denoted either by $f'(x)$ or by y'. The number y' is called the **derivative of y**. Thus, for example, the result of Example 12-1 can be written:

If $y = \sqrt{4 - x^2}$, then $y' = \dfrac{-x}{\sqrt{4 - x^2}}$.

P R O B L E M S   1 2

1. If $f(x)$ is given by one of the following equations, its graph will be found on some earlier page of the book. Use the graph to estimate the required number.
(a) $f(x) = \sin x$; find $2f'(0) - 3f'(\pi/2) + 4f'(\pi)$.
(b) $f(x) = x^{2/3}$; find $|f'(-1)| + f'(|-1|)$.
(c) $f(x) = \dfrac{|1 + x| - 1}{x}$; find $\frac{1}{2}(f(2) + f'(2))$.

(d) $f(x) = \dfrac{\sin x}{x}$; find $f'(1) + f'(-1)$.

(e) $f(x) = \dfrac{1}{x}$; find $f'(\frac{1}{2}) + \dfrac{1}{f'(2)}$.

(f) $f(x) = \tan x$; find $5f'(\pi) - f'(5\pi)$.

2. What is the derived function f' if f is a constant function?

3. If $f(x) = \cos x$, use a graph to solve the equation $f'(x) = 0$.

4. If $f(x) = \sin x$, its graph suggests that $f(x) > 0$ when x belongs to an interval of the form $\left(\dfrac{2k-1}{2}\pi, \dfrac{2k+1}{2}\pi \right)$, where k is an integer. Use graphs to find the sets for which f' is positive if:
   (a) $f(x) = \cos x$ (b) $f(x) = \tan x$
   (c) $f(x) = \cot x$ (d) $f(x) = \sec x$

5. Find the number y' if
   (a) $y = \frac{1}{2}(x - 1)$ (b) $3y = x - 4$
   (c) $2y = 4x - 7$ (d) $1 - y = 2 - x$

6. Let $f(x) = \cos x$. Use the procedure followed in Example 12-3 to sketch the graph of the derived function f' for the interval $[0, 1.6]$.

7. Draw a solid-line graph of the function f and a dashed-line graph of the derived function f' if:
   (a) $f(x) = 2x - 3$ (b) $f(x) = 4 - x$
   (c) $f(x) = [\![x]\!]$ (d) $f(x) = |x - 1|$
   (e) $f(x) = x - [\![x]\!]$ (f) $f(x) = |x| + |x - 2|$

8. Give a geometric explanation of why the number $\dfrac{f(1.1) - f(1)}{1.1 - 1}$ is an approximation to the number $f'(1)$. Use a set of tables to compute this approximation if
   (a) $f(x) = \tan x$ (b) $f(x) = \cos x$
   (c) $f(x) = \sin x^2$ (d) $f(x) = \sqrt[3]{x}$

9. Let $f(x) = |x| + |x - 1| + |x - 2| + |x - 3|$. What numbers are not in the domain of the derived function f'?

10. On the left side of Fig. 7-5 we have drawn the graph of a function we may call g. What is the domain of g'? Calculate $g'(\frac{1}{2})$ and $g'\left(-\dfrac{\sqrt{3}}{2}\right)$. Find a formula for $g'(x)$ if $x \in (0, 1)$. Find a formula for $g'(x)$ if $x \in (-1, 0)$.

11. Suppose that $f(x) = 3[\![x]\!]x + 4$.
   (a) Find $f'(\frac{1}{2}), f'(\pi)$, and $f'(-\sqrt{2})$.
   (b) What is the domain of f'?
   (c) Find a formula for $f'(x)$ that is valid for each x in the domain of f'.

12. Let $f(x)$ be the distance between x and the nearest prime number $(2, 3, 5, 7, \ldots)$. Thus $f(0) = 2$, $f(\pi) = .1415\ldots$, and so on. Sketch the graph of the equation $y = f(x)$ for x in the interval $[0, 5]$, and use this graph to help you calculate $f'(\sqrt{2})$, $f'(2.7)$, and $f'(\pi)$.

13. The equation $f(x) = 6 - \sqrt{21 + 4x - x^2}$ defines a function whose graph is a subset of the graph of the equation $(x - 2)^2 + (y - 6)^2 = 25$. Find a formula for $f'(x)$.

14. The graph of a certain function f whose domain is the interval $[1, \infty]$ consists of the straight-line segments that successively join the points $(1, 1)$, $(2, \frac{1}{2})$, $(3, \frac{1}{3})$, $\ldots$. Find $f'(\frac{1000}{3})$ and $f'(978\pi)$. Find a formula for $f'(x)$ if x is not an integer.

13 DEFINITION OF THE DERIVATIVE

Now we will explore more thoroughly the question of defining the derivative of $f(x)$. According to the remarks we made in the preceding section, if we want to calculate $f'(1)$, for example, we should sketch the graph of f and then draw the tangent line to this graph at the point where $x = 1$. The slope of this tangent line is then $f'(1)$. The device of using graphs and sketching in tangent lines "by eye" is useful for introducing the notion of the derivative, but it is not a very precise description of a mathematical concept. It has the obvious drawback that no two people are likely to get the same value of a derived function at a given point, since the tangent line that one person sketches "by eye" will probably not be exactly the same line that the other person sketches "by eye." Let us look for a method of calculating derivatives that will at least enable everyone to get the same answer.

For a clue to a "numerical" approach to the derivative, we return to Example 12-3. There we approximated the derivative at a point by finding the slope of the "chord" joining that point and a nearby point. It is certainly true that this chord is not the tangent line at the point, but we took the slope of the chord to be a satisfactory *approximation* to the slope of the tangent line. Notice that we assumed that there was a tangent line, that it had a slope, and it was this perfectly definite number (the slope of the tangent line) that we approximated.

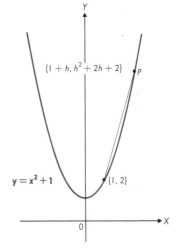

Figure 13-1

Let us apply this same idea to find $f'(1)$ when the function f is defined by the equation $f(x) = x^2 + 1$. We will arrive at the number $f'(1)$ indirectly. We will calculate approximations of $f'(1)$ and by looking at these approximations decide what number they approximate. Figure 13-1 shows the graph of f.

The number $f'(1)$ (the slope of the tangent line at the point $(1, 2)$) is approximated by the slope of the chord joining the point $(1, 2)$ and a second point P

of the graph of the equation $y = x^2 + 1$. If we want a "good" approximation, we should choose this second point P close to our point $(1, 2)$. Therefore we find it convenient to denote the X-coordinate of P by $1 + h$, a number that will be close to 1 when h is close to 0. Then the Y-coordinate of P is $(1 + h)^2 + 1 = h^2 + 2h + 2$, and so P is the point $(1 + h, h^2 + 2h + 2)$. The number h may be positive or negative; we have shown h as a positive number in Fig. 13-1. The slope of the chord that joins our points $(1, 2)$ and $(1 + h, h^2 + 2h + 2)$ is

$$(13\text{-}1) \qquad \frac{(h^2 + 2h + 2) - 2}{(1 + h) - 1} = \frac{h^2 + 2h}{h}.$$

Formula 13-1 yields an approximation of the number $f'(1)$ for each choice of h different from zero. For example, we get the approximations 3, 1, and $\frac{5}{2}$ by taking $h = 1, -1$, and $\frac{1}{2}$. We get "good" approximations to $f'(1)$ when we choose h close to 0. We cannot choose h *equal to* 0, for then Formula 13-1 is meaningless. Thus we can say that $f'(1)$ is the number that is approximated by the expression $\frac{2h + h^2}{h}$ when h is close to, but not equal to, 0. The preceding sentence is one of our informal definitions of the limit, and hence it appears that

$$f'(1) = \lim_{h \to 0} \frac{2h + h^2}{h}.$$

To calculate this limit, we write (since $h \neq 0$) $\dfrac{2h + h^2}{h} = 2 + h$, and from this expression we immediately see that $f'(1) = 2$. Therefore we should consider the line with slope 2 that contains the point $(1, 2)$ as the tangent line to our graph at that point. This line is the line $y = 2x$; we have sketched it in Fig. 13-2, and you will probably agree that the name "tangent line" is appropriate.

Let us continue to suppose that $f(x) = x^2 + 1$. For any $x \in R^1$, we can calculate $f'(x)$ by the same procedure we just used to determine $f'(1)$. We consider (see Fig. 13-3) the chord joining two points $(x, x^2 + 1)$ and $(x + h, (x + h)^2 + 1)$. The slope of this chord is given by the formula

$$(13\text{-}2) \qquad \frac{(x + h)^2 + 1 - (x^2 + 1)}{h} = \frac{2xh + h^2}{h}.$$

Geometric considerations suggest that the slope $f'(x)$ of the tangent line should be the number that is approximated by this expression when h is close to, but not equal to, 0. Therefore we define $f'(x)$ to be the number

$$(13\text{-}3) \qquad \lim_{h \to 0} \frac{2xh + h^2}{h} = \lim_{h \to 0} (2x + h) = 2x.$$

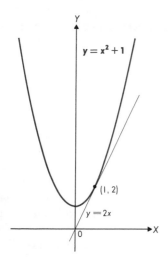

Figure 13-2

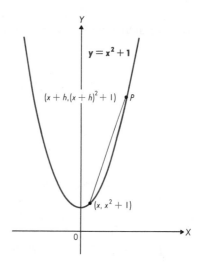

Figure 13-3

If you read the last sentence carefully, you noticed that we *defined* $f'(x)$ to be $2x$. We have reversed the position we took in Section 12. There we said that in order to calculate a derivative we should *first* draw a tangent line and *then* calculate its slope. Here we calculated a derivative without drawing a tangent line. And now we will *define* the tangent line to be the line that contains our given point and has the calculated derivative as its slope. This procedure eliminates the guess-work involved in fitting a tangent line to the curve "by eye"; now everyone will get the same tangent line.

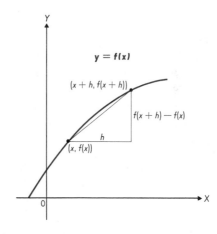

Figure 13-4

After looking at some examples, we are in a position to formulate a definition of the derivative in general terms. Let f be a function, and suppose that x is a point of an open interval in the domain of f. We find the number $f'(x)$ exactly as we did in the example we have just been considering. Thus we compute the slope of the chord that joins the point $(x, f(x))$ to a second point $(x + h, f(x + h))$ (see Fig. 13-4) by means of the formula

(13-4)
$$\frac{f(x + h) - f(x)}{h}.$$

Then we define the derivative $f'(x)$ to be the limit as h approaches 0 of the **Difference Quotient** 13-4 (if this limit exists, of course).

Definition 13-1. *If x is a number in the domain of a function f for which the following limit exists, then*

$$f'(x) = \lim_{h \to 0} \frac{f(x + h) - f(x)}{h}.$$

The above limit need not exist at every (or, indeed, any) point in the domain of a given function f. If it does exist at a particular point x, then we say f is **differentiable** at x. The process of finding the derivative $f'(x)$ is called **differentiation**. Notice that we are implicitly assuming that the domain of f contains some neighborhood of x; otherwise we couldn't even set up the difference quotient, much less find its limit.

We started our discussion of the derivative $f'(x)$ by regarding it as the slope of a tangent line to the graph of f. Definition 13-1, however, enables us to talk about $f'(x)$ without first introducing the tangent line, so now we will define the tangent line in terms of the derivative. The geometric discussion that led us to calculate $f'(x)$ as the limit of the Difference Quotient 13-4 makes the following definition a natural one.

Definition 13-2. *If a function f is differentiable at a point x, then the **tangent line** (or, simply, **tangent**) to the graph of f at the point $(x, f(x))$ is the line that contains the point $(x, f(x))$ and has slope $f'(x)$.*

It sometimes simplifies our algebraic manipulations if we let $z = x + h$ (and hence $h = z - x$) in the Difference Quotient 13-4 and thus obtain the expression

$$\frac{f(z) - f(x)}{z - x}.$$

Then the limit that defines $f'(x)$ is written

$$(13\text{-}5) \qquad\qquad f'(x) = \lim_{z \to x} \frac{f(z) - f(x)}{z - x}.$$

In the examples that follow, we will use whichever form of the difference quotient seems simplest. You should learn to use both forms.

Example 13-1. Find $f'(x)$ if $f(x) = 5x^2 - 3x$.

Solution. The difference quotient for f at x is

$$\frac{f(x+h) - f(x)}{h} = \frac{5(x+h)^2 - 3(x+h) - (5x^2 - 3x)}{h}$$

$$= \frac{5(x^2 + 2xh + h^2) - 3x - 3h - 5x^2 + 3x}{h}$$

$$= \frac{10xh + 5h^2 - 3h}{h}$$

$$= 10x - 3 + 5h.$$

Therefore, according to Definition 13-1,

$$f'(x) = \lim_{h \to 0} \frac{f(x+h) - f(x)}{h}$$

$$= \lim_{h \to 0} (10x - 3 + 5h)$$

$$= 10x - 3.$$

Example 13-2. Find $f'(x)$ if $f(x) = \dfrac{1}{x}$.

Solution. The difference quotient for f at x is

$$\frac{f(z) - f(x)}{z - x} = \frac{\dfrac{1}{z} - \dfrac{1}{x}}{z - x} = \frac{\dfrac{x - z}{xz}}{z - x} = -\frac{1}{xz}.$$

Therefore,

$$f'(x) = \lim_{z \to x} \frac{f(z) - f(x)}{z - x} = \lim_{z \to x} -\frac{1}{xz} = -\frac{1}{x^2}.$$

Example 13-3. Find the tangent to the graph of the function f in the preceding example at the point $(1, 1)$.

Solution. In Example 13-2 we found that $f'(1) = -1$. Therefore our desired line has slope -1, and it contains the point $(1, 1)$. Hence its equation is $y = -x + 2$.

When we find $f'(x)$ as the limit of a difference quotient we must use the limit theorems that we developed in Chapter 1. For instance, in Example 13-2 we know that $\lim\limits_{z \to x} -1/xz = -1/x^2$ because rational functions are continuous. Since the limit of the denominator of a difference quotient is zero, we cannot find the limit of the quotient by dividing the limit of the numerator by the limit of the denominator. We must first "manipulate" the quotient into a form to which the limit rules apply.

Example 13-4.   Find $f'(x)$ if $f(x) = \sqrt{x}$.

Solution.   Our difference quotient is

$$\frac{f(z) - f(x)}{z - x} = \frac{\sqrt{z} - \sqrt{x}}{z - x}.$$

Experience shows that the proper approach now is to "rationalize the numerator." Thus

$$\frac{f(z) - f(x)}{z - x} = \frac{\sqrt{z} - \sqrt{x}}{z - x} \cdot \frac{\sqrt{z} + \sqrt{x}}{\sqrt{z} + \sqrt{x}} = \frac{1}{\sqrt{z} + \sqrt{x}}.$$

In Problem 11-15 we showed that the square root function is continuous, and so we have

$$\lim_{z \to x} \frac{1}{\sqrt{z} + \sqrt{x}} = \frac{1}{\sqrt{x} + \sqrt{x}} = \frac{1}{2\sqrt{x}} = f'(x).$$

A differentiable function is quite "well-behaved." In particular, we will now show that a differentiable function is continuous. Notice that this theorem does *not* say that a continuous function must be differentiable.

Theorem 13-1.   *If f is differentiable at x, then f is continuous at x.*

Proof. According to Definition 10-1, f is continuous at x provided $\lim_{z \to x} f(z) = f(x)$; that is, $\lim_{z \to x} [f(z) - f(x)] = 0$. If $z \neq x$, we have

$$f(z) - f(x) = \frac{f(z) - f(x)}{z - x} (z - x).$$

Since $\lim_{z \to x} \dfrac{f(z) - f(x)}{z - x} = f'(x)$ by hypothesis, and $\lim_{z \to x} (z - x) = 0$, we may use our product rule for limits (Theorem 11-5) to see that $\lim_{z \to x} [f(z) - f(x)] = f'(x) \cdot 0 = 0$, and our theorem is proved.

If we are dealing with a function defined on an interval that contains an endpoint, we may wish to speak of its continuity or differentiability at the endpoint. Then we must consider the limit that appears in the definition of continuity or differentiability as a limit from the right or from the left. For example, if the domain of f is a closed finite interval $[a, b]$, then we say that f is continuous at a if $\lim\limits_{x \downarrow a} f(x) = f(a)$ and f is differentiable at b if $\lim\limits_{z \uparrow b} \dfrac{f(z) - f(b)}{z - b}$ exists. Here f is *continuous from the right* at a and *differentiable from the left* at b. We may also use the modifying phrases "from the left" or "from the right" at points other than endpoints. For instance, the function discussed in Example 10-1 is continuous and differentiable from the left at the point $\pi/2$, but it is not continuous from the right at that point.

P R O B L E M S   1 3

1. Use Definition 13-1 to find $f'(x)$ if

(a) $f(x) = 2x - 3$

(b) $f(x) = (x + 3)(x - 2)$

(c) $f(x) = \dfrac{1 - x}{1 + x}$

(d) $f(x) = x^{-2}$

(e) $f(x) = x^3 - 7x$

(f) $f(x) = |x - 1|^2$

2. If $f(x) = mx + b$, find $f'(x)$ by using Definition 13-1. What is the derived function of a constant function?

3. Find y' if

(a) $y = 2\sqrt{x}$

(b) $y = \sqrt{2x}$

(c) $y = \dfrac{1}{\sqrt{x + 1}}$

(d) $y = |x + 1|$

(e) $y = x - x^{-1}$

(f) $y = \dfrac{1 + x^2}{1 - x^2}$

4. Find $f'(2)$ if

(a) $f(x) = x\,|x|$

(b) $f(x) = x + |x - 1|$

(c) $f(x) = x\,|x - 1|$

(d) $f(x) = x[\![x - \frac{1}{2}]\!]$

(e) $f(x) = |x - 2|^3 + 4$

(f) $f(x) = (x - 2)\sin x$

5. Find the equations of the tangent lines to the graphs of the functions in Problem 3 at the point $(2, f(2))$.

6. Set up the difference quotient for each of the functions defined by the following equations, and note that its limit is not immediately apparent.

(a) $f(x) = \sin x$

(b) $f(x) = \sec x$

(c) $f(x) = \log x$

(d) $f(x) = 2^x$

7. Let $f(x) = \sin x$ and set up the difference quotient for f at 0. In Section 10 we found the limit of this quotient graphically; look up our result to find $f'(0)$. Does this number seem to be the slope of the sine curve at the origin?

8. Use limits from the right and from the left to find $f'(0)$ if

(a) $f(x) = [\![x]\!]x^3$

(b) $f(x) = (|x| - x)^2$

(c) $f(x) = x\,|x|$

9. Find an example of a function that is continuous at a certain point but is not differentiable there. How is this result related to Theorem 13-1?

10. If $g(x) = f(x) + x^2$, how are $g'(x)$ and $f'(x)$ related?

11. A 5-place table of common logarithms tells us that $\log 1.001 = .00043$. Use this fact to answer the following questions:
    (a) If $f(x) = \log x$, find approximations to $f'(1), f'(10), f'(100)$, and $f'(\frac{1}{10})$.
    (b) If $g(x) = 10^x$, find an approximation to $g'(0)$.
    (c) Use the result of part (b) to find an approximation to $g'(x)$.

12. Think through the following argument: suppose that f is a differentiable function such that $f(x + y) = f(x) + f(y)$. Then for each $x \in R^1$, $\dfrac{f(x + h) - f(x)}{h} = \dfrac{f(h)}{h}$, and so $f'(x) = f'(0)$. Therefore f' is a constant function. What is the graph of f?

13. Suppose that f and g are differentiable at a point a and that $f(a) = g(a)$. Furthermore, suppose that $f(x) \le g(x)$ if $x > a$ and $f(x) \ge g(x)$ if $x < a$. (For example, we might have $a = 0, f(x) = \sin x$, and $g(x) = \tan x$.) What is the relation between $f'(a)$ and $g'(a)$? (See Problem 11-19.)

14. If $f(x) = x^2 \sin \dfrac{1}{x}$ when $x \ne 0$ and $f(0) = 0$, show that $f'(0) = 0$. (See Problem 10-11.)

14 | THE RATE OF CHANGE

We interpret the slope m of the line $y = mx + b$ as the rate at which the line rises. Now the tangent line to a point of the graph of a function f is the line that best "fits" the graph at the point, so it is natural to say that the slope of the tangent line measures the rate at which the graph of the function rises. The slope of the tangent line at a point $(x, f(x))$ is the derivative $f'(x)$. Therefore we shall use the derivative $f'(x)$ as a measure of the rate at which the graph of f rises; that is, the rate at which the values of f change. In this connection it is customary to use a new notation for derivatives. If $y = f(x)$, then in addition to the notations y' and $f'(x)$ for the derivative of $f(x)$ we also write $D_x y$. We call $D_x y$ the derivative of y with respect to x. Thus

$$D_x y = f'(x) = y'.$$

The way the number $D_x y$ measures rate of change can be illustrated by considering the concept of velocity. When you ask the driver of a car, "How fast are you going now?" you are using a concept of velocity that is an extension of the concept of velocity ordinarily used in elementary science. A difficulty in answering your question arises from the use of the word "now." In elementary science you computed the velocity of a moving body by dividing the distance traveled by the time elapsed. Thus, if a car travels 100 miles in 2 hours, the velocity of the car is calculated as 50 miles per hour. This number is an *average* velocity, and we certainly do not imply that the speedometer of a car will register 50 miles per hour at all times during a 100-mile trip that takes 2 hours.

We define the velocity that the speedometer measures at a given instant in the following way. Let t denote the number of hours elapsed since the beginning of the trip, and s the number of miles traveled during this time. Then the relationship between s and t defines a function f so that $s = f(t)$. Let us now attempt to answer the question, "What is the velocity when $t = 1$?" The average velocity over any time interval beginning or ending at $t = 1$ can be calculated in the usual way. Thus we find the average velocity over the time interval between 1 and some other time z by dividing the distance traveled by the time elapsed. The distance traveled is $f(z) - f(1)$; that is, the distance traveled in z hours minus the distance traveled in 1 hour. The time elapsed is $z - 1$ hours, so the average velocity is given by the difference quotient

$$(14\text{-}1) \qquad \frac{f(z) - f(1)}{z - 1}.$$

We cannot set $z = 1$, for then the average velocity is not defined. But, as in the problem of finding the slope of a curve, it is perfectly clear that the velocity when $t = 1$ should be the number that is approximated by Difference Quotient 14-1 when z is a number near 1. Thus, using the concept of a limit, we *define* the velocity when $t = 1$ to be the number

$$\lim_{z \to 1} \frac{f(z) - f(1)}{z - 1} = f'(1).$$

In general, we have the following definition.

Definition 14-1. *If $s = f(t)$, then the **velocity** v at any time t is defined by the equation*

$$v = D_t s = f'(t).$$

In order to distinguish this velocity from the average velocity, the velocity defined in Definition 14-1 is sometimes called the **instantaneous velocity**.

Example 14-1. We noticed in the introduction to this chapter that if a body falls from rest in a vacuum a distance of s feet in t seconds, then the relationship between s and t is given by the equation $s = 16t^2$. How fast is the body falling at the end of 5 seconds? Express the velocity of the body in terms of the distance it has fallen.

Solution. According to Definition 14-1, we have to calculate $f'(5)$, where $f(t) = 16t^2$. You did many examples of this sort in the last section, and you may easily verify that here $v = f'(t) = 32t$. Therefore $f'(5) = 32 \cdot 5 = 160$, and so the velocity of the body at the end of 5 seconds is 160 feet per second. Since $s = 16t^2$, we see that $t = \frac{1}{4}\sqrt{s}$, and hence the equation $v = 32t$ can be written as $v = 8\sqrt{s}$ to give us an expression of the velocity of the body in terms of the distance it has fallen.

In Example 14-1 we measured distance in feet and time in seconds; hence the velocity is measured in feet per second. If distance has been measured in kilometers and time in hours, the velocity would be measured in kilometers per hour, and so on.

We use the concept of rate even though distance and time are not involved. For example, if y ergs of work are required to move a certain object x centimeters, then $D_x y$ is the number of ergs per centimeter (or dynes) of force applied at a given point during the motion. Similarly, if a house can be heated to a temperature of T degrees by burning p pounds of coal, then the number $D_p T$ measures the rate of change of temperature in degrees per pound.

An equation that involves derivatives is called a **differential equation**. For instance, in Example 14-1 we found that if $s = 16t^2$, then s *satisfies* the differential equations $D_t s = 32t$ and $D_t s = 8\sqrt{s}$. Because a derivative is a rate, a differential equation is an equation that involves rates, and such equations play important roles in science. We shall mention differential equations from time to time throughout this book, but a thorough study of them would require much more space than a calculus book has available.

Example 14-2. After t years from some initial date, the population of a certain country is P individuals, and it is increasing at the rate of 2% per year. What is the differential equation that is satisfied by P?

Solution. Our hypotheses tell us that the rate of change of the population at any particular time is $\frac{2}{100}$ of the population at that time, and so we have the equation $D_t P = .02P$. Now the question arises, "Can we find a P that satisfies this equation, and, if so, how?" We will have to defer the answer until we have quite a bit more calculus under our belts. We will solve this differential equation in Section 46.

P R O B L E M S   1 4

1. Compare:
   (a) $D_x(3x^2 + 2x)$ and $D_x(3x^2) + D_x(2x)$ (b) $D_x x^2$ and $(D_x x)^2$

   (c) $D_x\left(\dfrac{1}{x}\right)$ and $\dfrac{1}{D_x x}$ (d) $D_x\sqrt{x}$ and $\sqrt{D_x x}$

2. Would you expect $D_x y$ to be positive or negative if:
   (a) y is the number of miles traveled and x is the number of gallons of gas used?
   (b) y is the number of miles per gallon of gas that the car gets at a speed of x miles per hour?
   (c) y is the number of gallons of gas in the tank and x is the number of miles traveled?
   (d) y is the number of miles traveled and x is the number of gallons of gas in the tank?

3. A block slides down an inclined plane. At the end of t seconds the block is s feet from its starting point. Find the average velocity of the block for the first two seconds and its instantaneous velocity at $t = 2$ if:

(a) $s = 3t^2$ (b) $s = t^2 + t$ (c) $s = t^2 + \sqrt{t}$

4. A mass is connected to a certain spring. The mass moves along a line so that it is s inches from the equilibrium position t seconds after some moment, where $s = \sin t$. Use the graphs in Fig. 12-4 to estimate the velocity of the mass when $t = 0$, $t = .5$, and $t = 1$.

5. A steel ball is dropped in a glass tube that contains heavy oil. Suppose that the ball is s centimeters above the base of the tube t seconds after the ball enters the oil. The observed values of s and t are contained in the following table. From this table estimate the velocity of the ball when it strikes the bottom of the tube.

t	0	1	2	3	4	5
s	4	2.5	1.5	.75	.25	0

6. A penny expands when heated. Find the expression for the rate of change of the area of one side with respect to the radius.

7. At t minutes after noon the radius of a melting snowball is $60 - 3t$ inches. How fast is the volume changing at 12:10?

8. A machine rolls a wheel along a number scale marked off in centimeters in such a way that the coordinate of the center of the wheel t seconds after the start of the motion is given by the equation $x = t + \dfrac{1}{t}$.

(a) Find its velocity when $t = \frac{1}{2}$, $t = 1$, and $t = 2$.
(b) Which way is it moving at those times?
(c) If the wheel should break off the machine at one of those times and roll frictionlessly along the scale, where would it be 2 seconds later?

9. What does the graph of the equation $y = \log x$ suggest about the value of $[\![D_x \log x]\!]$ when $x \geq 1$?

10. Use the sine curve to graph as best you can the equation $y = [\![D_x \sin x]\!]$.

11. Suppose that x and y are related as follows. How are $D_x y$ and $D_y x$ related?
(a) $3x + 4y + 5 = 0$ (b) $y = x^2$ (c) $xy = 1$.

12. Boyle's Law says that the volume V of a given quantity of gas is inversely proportional to its pressure P. Show that V satisfies the differential equation $D_P V = -\dfrac{V}{P}$. (Hint: By hypothesis, $V = \dfrac{k}{P}$, where k is a number that is independent of P. Now find $D_P V$ and eliminate k.)

13. Show that $y = \sqrt{x}$ satisfies each of the differential equations (i) $y' = \dfrac{1}{2\sqrt{x}}$, (ii) $y' = \dfrac{1}{2y}$, and (iii) $y' = \dfrac{y}{2x}$. Show that $y = \sqrt{x} + 2$ satisfies (i), but not (ii) and (iii); $y = \sqrt{x} + 2$ satisfies (ii), but not (i) and (iii); and $y = 2\sqrt{x}$ satisfies (iii), but not (i) and (ii).

15 THE POWER FORMULA

The routine of setting up a difference quotient and then finding its limit every time we wish to calculate a derivative soon becomes unduly time consuming, so it is worthwhile to establish (and memorize) certain differentiation rules. These rules are of two types—specific and general. The specific rules are formulas for derivatives of certain basic functions. The general rules enable us to find derivatives for complicated functions that are built up out of basic functions. In this section we will begin the task of proving one of the most important specific differentiation formulas, the **Power Formula.**

Theorem 15-1.   *If r is any real number, then*

$$(15\text{-}1) \qquad\qquad D_x x^r = rx^{r-1}.$$

The proof of this theorem is complicated because the way the expression x^r is defined depends on the "kind" of number r is. For instance, you know that

$$x^3 = x \cdot x \cdot x, \quad x^{1/3} = \sqrt[3]{x}, \quad x^{-3} = \frac{1}{x \cdot x \cdot x}, \quad x^0 = 1, \text{ and } x^{4/3} = \sqrt[3]{x^4} = (\sqrt[3]{x})^4.$$

When we prove Theorem 15-1, we have to take each of these possibilities into account. Furthermore, the theorem is also true when r is an irrational number, such as π, and you have probably had no occasion even to see a definition of what the symbol x^π is supposed to represent. We won't get around to it until Section 48. So our proof of Theorem 15-1 will be given in steps as we treat the different possibilities for the number r at different points in the book. At the end of this section we will prove the theorem in case r is a positive integer and in case r is the reciprocal of a positive integer. Now let us give a few examples to show how we use it in those two cases.

Example 15-1.   Find the equation of the tangent line to the graph of the function f at the point $(-1, f(-1))$ if $f(x) = x^4$.

Solution.   The slope of the tangent at the point $(-1, f(-1)) = (-1, 1)$ is $f'(-1)$. Using Rule 15-1 we find that

$$f'(x) = D_x x^4 = 4x^3,$$

and so

$$f'(-1) = -4.$$

Thus the equation of our tangent line is $y - 1 = -4(x + 1)$.

Example 15-2.   Show that the tangent to the graph of the equation $y = x^5$ at the point $(2, 32)$ is parallel to the tangent to the graph of the equation $y = x^{80}$ at the point $(1, 1)$.

Solution. On applying Rule 15-1, we see that if $y = x^5$, then $D_x y = 5x^4$, and if $y = x^{80}$, then $D_x y = 80x^{79}$. Thus the slope of the tangent to the curve $y = x^5$ at a point (x, y) is $5x^4$, and therefore at the point $(2, 32)$ the slope of the tangent is $5 \cdot 2^4 = 80$. Similarly, the slope of the tangent to the curve $y = x^{80}$ at the point $(1, 1)$ is $80 \cdot 1^{79} = 80$. Since the two tangents have the same slope, 80, they are parallel (Theorem 9-2).

Let P be a point of the graph of a function f. The line that contains P and is perpendicular to the tangent line to the graph of f at P is called the **normal line** (or **normal**) to the graph at the point P.

Example 15-3. Find the equation of the normal line to the graph of the equation $y = \sqrt{x}$ at the point $(9, 3)$.

Solution. Since $\sqrt{x} = x^{1/2}$, we have $y = x^{1/2}$, so we may use Equation 15-1 to calculate the slope of the tangent at a point:

$$D_x y = D_x x^{1/2} = \frac{1}{2} x^{1/2-1} = \frac{1}{2} x^{-1/2} = \frac{1}{2\sqrt{x}}.$$

When $x = 9$, we see that the slope of the tangent is $\frac{1}{6}$. Thus the slope of the normal line at the point $(9, 3)$ is -6, and its equation is $y - 3 = -6(x - 9)$.

Although we stated Rule 15-1 in terms of the letters x and r, it is clear that the same formula is applicable if other letters are used. For example:

$$D_y y^s = sy^{s-1};$$

$$D_u u^7 = 7u^6;$$

$$D_t \sqrt[5]{t} = D_t t^{1/5} = \frac{1}{5} t^{-4/5} = \frac{1}{5\sqrt[5]{t^4}}.$$

Example 15-4. Suppose a body moves s feet in t seconds, where s and t are related by the equation $s = t^2$. When does the velocity reach 10 feet per second?

Solution. We use Rule 15-1 to find $v = D_t s = 2t$. Now we must find the number t such that $2t = 10$, and that number clearly is $t = 5$. Thus, 5 seconds after the start of the motion, the body is traveling 10 feet per second.

Now we will begin the proof of Theorem 15-1. We first treat the case in which r is a positive integer n. Let us write $f(x) = x^n$ and set up the difference quotient

$$\frac{f(z) - f(x)}{z - x} = \frac{z^n - x^n}{z - x}.$$

It is a matter of long division to show that

$$(15\text{-}2) \quad \frac{z^n - x^n}{z - x} = \underbrace{z^{n-1} + z^{n-2}x + z^{n-3}x^2 + \cdots + zx^{n-2} + x^{n-1}}_{n \text{ terms}}.$$

(You can verify Equation 15-2 by multiplying the right side by $z - x$ and obtaining $z^n - x^n$.) The right side of Equation 15-2 is a polynomial in z, and since polynomial functions are continuous, we obtain its limit as z approaches x by replacing z with x:

$$\lim_{z \to x} \frac{z^n - x^n}{z - x} = \underbrace{x^{n-1} + x^{n-1} + x^{n-1} + \cdots + x^{n-1} + x^{n-1}}_{n \text{ terms}} = nx^{n-1}.$$

This equation tells us that $D_x x^n = nx^{n-1}$, which of course, is Equation 15-1 with r replaced by n.

If r is the reciprocal of a positive integer, that is, $r = 1/n$, we proceed as follows. Equation 15-2 is valid for any two unequal numbers z and x, so in that equation let us replace z with $z^{1/n}$ and x with $x^{1/n}$ and invert both sides to obtain the equation

$$(15\text{-}3) \quad \frac{z^{1/n} - x^{1/n}}{z - x} = \frac{1}{\underbrace{z^{(n-1)/n} + z^{(n-2)/n}x^{1/n} + \cdots + z^{1/n}x^{(n-2)/n} + x^{(n-1)/n}}_{n \text{ terms}}}$$

In Problem 11-16 we showed that $\lim_{z \to x} z^{p/q} = x^{p/q}$, so from Equation 15-3 we find that

$$\lim_{z \to x} \frac{z^{1/n} - x^{1/n}}{z - x} = \frac{1}{x^{(n-1)/n} + x^{(n-2)/n}x^{1/n} + \cdots + x^{1/n}x^{(n-2)/n} + x^{(n-1)/n}}$$

$$= \frac{1}{nx^{(n-1)/n}} = \frac{1}{n} x^{\frac{1}{n} - 1}.$$

This equation says that $D_x x^{\frac{1}{n}} = \frac{1}{n} x^{\frac{1}{n} - 1}$, which is Equation 15-1 with r replaced by $\frac{1}{n}$.

We will now feel free to use Equation 15-1 in case n is a positive integer or the reciprocal of a positive integer, but we will refrain from using it in other cases until we have verified it.

P R O B L E M S   1 5

1. Find y' if:

(a) $y = x^7$

(b) $y = \sqrt[4]{x}$

(c) $y = \sqrt[5]{t}$

(d) $y = (u^3)^2$

(e) $y = \sqrt{\sqrt{\sqrt{x}}}$

(f) $y = \left(\dfrac{|x| + x}{2}\right)^6$

2. Find the equation of the tangent and of the normal at the point $(1, 1)$ if:

(a) $y = \sqrt[3]{x}$

(b) $y = x^3$

(c) $y = x^{[\![x+(5/2)]\!]}$

(d) $y = x^{1/[\![x+(5/2)]\!]}$

3. Suppose that n and m are positive integers and $n > m$. Does $D_x(x^n \cdot x^m) = (D_x x^n)(D_x x^m)$? Does $D_x\left(\dfrac{x^n}{x^m}\right) = \dfrac{D_x x^n}{D_x x^m}$?

4. Prove Theorem 15-1 for the case $r = 0$.

5. Use Example 13-2 to show that Theorem 15-1 is true if $r = -1$.

6. Find the points of the graphs of the two equations listed that have the same X-coordinate and at which the tangent lines are parallel.

(a) $y = x^2$ and $y = x^3$

(b) $y = \sqrt{x}$ and $y = \sqrt[3]{x}$

(c) $y = \sqrt{x}$ and $y = x^2$

7. Prove that if n is an odd positive integer, the lines tangent to the graph of the equation $y = x^n$ at the points $(1, 1)$ and $(-1, -1)$ are parallel.

8. Prove that if n is an even positive integer, the line tangent to the graph of the equation $y = \sqrt[n]{x}$ at the point $(1, 1)$ is perpendicular to the line tangent to the graph of the equation $y = x^n$ at the point $(-1, 1)$.

9. Suppose $y = x^n$, where n is a positive integer. What is the relation between $D_x y$ and $D_y x$?

10. Show that $y = x^r$ satisfies the differential equation $D_x y = r\dfrac{y}{x}$.

11. What is the radius of the circle whose center is a point of the X-axis and which is tangent to the curve $y = x^{1/4}$ at the point $(16, 2)$?

12. A particle starts at the origin and moves along the graph of the equation $y = x^r$ in the direction of increasing x. When its X-coordinate is 8, it flies off on a tangent and hits a man standing at the point $(32, 4)$. What is r?

13. Show that the tangent line to the graph of the equation $y = x^r$ (r a positive integer or the reciprocal of a positive integer) at the point $(1, 1)$ intersects the Y-axis at a point that is $|r - 1|$ units away from the origin.

14. Show that the Y-intercept of the tangent line to the graph of the equation $y = x^r$ (r a positive integer or the reciprocal of a positive integer) at the point (a, b) is $(1 - r)a^r$.

15. Suppose that the tangent line to the graph of the equation $y = x^2$ at the point (a, b) intersects the Y-axis at the point P and that the normal line to the graph at the point (a, b) intersects the Y-axis at the point Q. Show that the coordinates of P are $(0, -b)$ and that the distance between the points P and Q is $2b + \frac{1}{2}$.

16. What is the distance between the points P and Q in the preceding question if you consider the graph of the equation $y = x^r$ (r a positive integer or the reciprocal of a positive integer)?

16 THE CHAIN RULE

We turn now from a specific differentiation formula to a general one, the rule by which we calculate derivatives for a composite function in terms of derivatives of its components.

Theorem 16-1.   The Chain Rule. *If f and g are differentiable functions, and $u = g(x)$, then*

$$(16\text{-}1) \qquad\qquad D_x f(u) = D_u f(u) D_x u.$$

We will delay the proof of this theorem until the end of the section; let us first see how we use it.

One of the first things we do with any specific differentiation formula is to "build it into the Chain Rule." Thus the Power Formula tells us that $D_u u^r = r u^{r-1}$, so if we replace $f(u)$ with u^r in Equation 16-1, we obtain the equation

$$(16\text{-}2) \qquad\qquad D_x u^r = r u^{r-1} D_x u.$$

Since we have verified the Power Formula only in case r is a positive integer or the reciprocal of a positive integer, it appears that we must restrict our applications of Equation 16-2 to these cases. But actually we can pull ourselves up by our boot straps and use Equation 16-2 for these special exponents to extend the validity of the Power Formula to all rational exponents.

Example 16-1.   Find $D_x x^{p/q}$, where p and q are positive integers.

Solution.   Let us set $r = 1/q$ and $u = x^p$ in Equation 16-2 to obtain

$$D_x x^{p/q} = \frac{1}{q} x^{p\left(\frac{1}{q}-1\right)} D_x x^p = \frac{1}{q} x^{\frac{p}{q}-p} \cdot p x^{p-1} = \frac{p}{q} x^{\frac{p}{q}-1}.$$

This equation is simply the Power Formula with r replaced by the positive rational exponent p/q, so we have extended the applicability of the Power Formula considerably.

Example 16-2. Find $D_x x^{-s}$, where s is a positive rational number.

Solution. We note that $x^{-s} = (1/x)^s$. Since the Power Formula is valid for positive rational exponents, we may replace r with s in Equation 16-2, and we will set $u = 1/x$, to obtain the equation

$$D_x x^{-s} = D_x \left(\frac{1}{x}\right)^s = s\left(\frac{1}{x}\right)^{s-1} D_x \frac{1}{x}.$$

In Example 13-2 we found that $D_x \dfrac{1}{x} = -\dfrac{1}{x^2}$, so we have

$$D_x x^{-s} = s\left(\frac{1}{x}\right)^{s-1}\left(-\frac{1}{x^2}\right) = -s\left(\frac{1}{x}\right)^{s+1} = -sx^{-s-1},$$

which is simply the Power Formula with r replaced by the negative rational exponent $-s$.

We have now completely verified the Power Formula for rational exponents, and we will use it freely for such exponents. For irrational exponents we will have to wait until Section 48.

Let us introduce here a simple, but extremely useful, formula: *If m is a number and g is a differentiable function, then*

(16-3) $$D_x mg(x) = m D_x g(x).$$

We can use the definition of the derivative to prove this formula directly, but it is also a simple consequence of the Chain Rule. In Problem 13-2 we asked you to verify the geometrically obvious fact that if $f(u) = mu$, then $D_u f(u) = m$. Thus when we replace $f(u)$ with mu in Equation 16-1 we find that $D_x mu = m D_x u$. Now we replace u with $g(x)$ to obtain Equation 16-3.

Example 16-3. Find $D_x \sqrt{4x^3}$ in two ways.

Solution. If in Equation 16-2 we replace u with $4x^3$ and r with $\frac{1}{2}$, we have

$$D_x \sqrt{4x^3} = \tfrac{1}{2}(4x^3)^{-(1/2)} D_x 4x^3 = \frac{1}{2\sqrt{4x^3}} D_x 4x^3.$$

Now we use Equation 16-3 to see that $D_x 4x^3 = 4D_x x^3 = 4 \cdot 3x^2 = 12x^2$, and hence

$$D_x \sqrt{4x^3} = \frac{12x^2}{2\sqrt{4x^3}} = \frac{3x^2}{x^{3/2}} = 3\sqrt{x}.$$

On the other hand, we could first write $\sqrt{4x^3} = 2x^{3/2}$, and therefore

$$D_x\sqrt{4x^3} = D_x2x^{3/2} = 2D_xx^{3/2} = 2 \cdot \tfrac{3}{2}x^{1/2} = 3\sqrt{x},$$

as before. Here we used Equation 16-3 when we said that $D_x2x^{3/2} = 2D_xx^{3/2}$.

We can write the Chain Rule Equation in many different ways. For example, if we replace $f(u)$ in Equation 16-1 with y, we obtain a more symmetric form: *If $y = f(u)$, where $u = g(x)$, then*

(16-4) $$D_xy = D_uyD_xu.$$

Or suppose we denote by p the composite function formed by the composition of g by f. Thus $p(x) = f(g(x))$. Since $D_uf(u) = f'(u)$, and so on, we can write Equation 16-1 in either of the forms

(16-5) $$p'(x) = f'(u)g'(x)$$

or

(16-6) $$p'(x) = f'(g(x))g'(x).$$

Example 16-4. Suppose that f is a differentiable function and let p be the composition of the cosine function by f; that is, $p(x) = f(\cos x)$. Use a graphical argument to show that $p'(0) = 0$.

Solution. According to Equation 16-6, we have $p'(0) = f'(g(0))g'(0)$, where, in our example, g is the cosine function. Therefore $g(0) = 1$, and from the graph of the cosine function it is apparent that $g'(0) = 0$. Thus $p'(0) = f'(1) \cdot 0 = 0$, as we were to show.

For the purposes of its proof, it seems easiest to express the Chain Rule in the form of Equation 16-5. We suppose that x is a point in the domain of the composite function p and that the function g is differentiable at x and the function f is differentiable at u, where $u = g(x)$. We must show that p is differentiable at x and that $p'(x)$ is given by Equation 16-5. Thus we must find the limit of the difference quotient

(16-7) $$\frac{p(z) - p(x)}{z - x} = \frac{f(g(z)) - f(g(x))}{z - x}$$

as z approaches x. It is not clear from this formula what the limit is; our first task is to rewrite the difference quotient in such a way that we can use our limit theorems to find its limit. Therefore we introduce the "quotient function" q, where

$$q(w) = \frac{f(w) - f(u)}{w - u} \quad \text{if } w \neq u.$$

This equation does not define $q(u)$, of course. We note, however, that the limit of $q(w)$ as w approaches u is $f'(u)$, so we make the "natural" definition

$$q(u) = f'(u).$$

By defining the function q so that its value at u is its limit at u, we obtain a function that is continuous at u. From our defining equations we see that for every choice of w in the domain of f (whether $w = u$ or not),

$$f(w) - f(u) = q(w)(w - u).$$

In this equation we replace w with $g(z)$ and, since $u = g(x)$, we obtain the equation

$$f(g(z)) - f(g(x)) = q(g(z)) [g(z) - g(x)].$$

Now we substitute this result in the numerator of the right-hand side of the Difference Quotient 16-7, and we have

$$\frac{p(z) - p(x)}{z - x} = q(g(z)) \frac{g(z) - g(x)}{z - x}.$$

Our general limit theorems apply to this form of the difference quotient; the Product Rule tells us that its limit is the product of the numbers $\lim_{z \to x} q(g(z))$ and $\lim_{z \to x} \frac{g(z) - g(x)}{z - x}$. The second of these numbers is, by definition, $g'(x)$. To find $\lim_{z \to x} q(g(z))$, we note that g is continuous at x, since it is differentiable there (Theorem 13-1), and we have already remarked that q is continuous at $g(x) = u$. Hence Theorem 11-3 applies to tell us that $\lim_{z \to x} q(g(z)) = q(g(x)) = q(u) = f'(u)$. It follows that

$$\lim_{z \to x} \frac{p(z) - p(x)}{z - x} = f'(u)g'(x),$$

which is just Equation 16-5.

P R O B L E M S   1 6

1. Find $D_x y$ if

(a) $y = 6x^{-(7/2)}$

(b) $y = \sqrt[3]{5x^2}$

(c) $y = 5(\sqrt[3]{x})^2$

(d) $y = \dfrac{2}{3\sqrt[5]{x^3}}$

(e) $y = \pi x^{3.1416}$

(f) $y = [\![x]\!]x^{-(4/5)}$

2. Find the equation of the tangent line to the graphs of the following functions at the point $(1, f(1))$.

(a) $f(x) = \sqrt{2x + 7}$

(b) $f(x) = \sqrt{\dfrac{1}{2x + 7}}$

(c) $f(x) = (3 + 5x)^{2/3}$

(d) $f(x) = x^{[3 \sin x]/3}$

3. (a) Use the equation $|x| = \sqrt{x^2}$ and the Chain Rule to obtain the differentiation formula $D_x |x| = \dfrac{x}{|x|}$ for $x \neq 0$ (see Example 12-2).

(b) Incorporate this differentiation formula into the Chain Rule to obtain the equation

$$D_x |u| = \frac{u}{|u|} D_x u \quad (u \neq 0).$$

(c) Suppose that f is differentiable on a certain interval. At what points of the interval could $D_x |f(x)|$ fail to exist?

(d) Explain why $|D_x |f(x)|| = |D_x f(x)|$ when all the derivatives involved exist.

4. In Example 16-1 set $r = p$ and $u = x^{1/q}$ to get the same result that we obtained with a different substitution.

5. A point P moves along the graph of $y = x^2$ so that the time rate of change of the X-coordinate of P is v. What is the time rate of change of the Y-coordinate?

6. Find a formula for the rate of change of volume of a spherical soap bubble whose radius is increasing according to the equation $r = g(t)$.

7. A pebble dropped in a lake creates an expanding ripple whose radius increases at the rate of $g(t)$ feet per second. Find a formula for the rate at which the area of the region enclosed by the ripple is increasing.

8. In Problem 7-8 we said that a function s is even if $s(-x) = s(x)$ and a function q is odd if $q(-x) = -q(x)$. Show that the derived function of an even function is odd and the derived function of an odd function is even.

9. A function f is **periodic** if there is a number p such that for each x, $f(x + p) = f(x)$. For example, the sine function is periodic, since $\sin (x + 2\pi) = \sin x$. Show that the derived function of a differentiable periodic function is periodic.

10. What is the difference between $D_x f(3x + 4)$ and $f'(3x + 4)$? Between $D_x f(x + 4)$ and $f'(x + 4)$?

11. Show that if $y = f(x)$ satisfies the differential equation $y' = 3y$, then $y = f(x + 4)$ also satisfies it. How about $y = 5f(x + 6)$?

12. Which of the following are correct statements of the Chain Rule equation: $D_y x = D_u x D_y u$; $D_u y = D_x y D_x u$; $D_x u = D_x v D_v u$?

13. Suppose that $p(x) = f(g(x))$, where f is an arbitrary differentiable function and g is as given. Show that $p'(0) = 0$.

(a) $g(x) = \sqrt{4 - x^2}$ (See Example 12-1)

(b) $g(x) = \sec x$ (look at the graph)

(c) g is any even differentiable function (See Number 8)

14. Use Equation 16-2 and the sine curve to solve the equation $D_x \sin^{13} x = 0$.

17 DERIVATIVES OF SUMS, PRODUCTS, AND QUOTIENTS

Our next general differentiation theorem states that the differential operator D_x is *distributive* with respect to addition. Thus it is immaterial whether we first add and then apply the operator D_x or first apply the operator and then add. We get the same result in either case.

Theorem 17-1. *If f and g are differentiable at x, then*

(17-1) $$D_x[f(x) + g(x)] = D_x f(x) + D_x g(x).$$

It is a simple matter to extend this rule to the sum of any number of terms.

Proof. To prove this theorem, we go back to the definition of the derivative and use our limit theorems. We have

$$D_x[f(x) + g(x)] = \lim_{z \to x} \frac{[f(z) + g(z)] - [f(x) + g(x)]}{z - x} \quad \text{(Definition 13-1)}$$

$$= \lim_{z \to x} \left[\frac{f(z) - f(x)}{z - x} + \frac{g(z) - g(x)}{z - x} \right] \quad \text{(Algebra)}$$

$$= \lim_{z \to x} \frac{f(z) - f(x)}{z - x} + \lim_{z \to x} \frac{g(z) - g(x)}{z - x} \quad \text{(Theorem 11-2)}$$

$$= D_x f(x) + D_x g(x) \quad \text{(Definition 13-1),}$$

and our theorem is proved.

Example 17-1. Find $D_x (\sqrt{x} + 3x^2)$.

Solution. Normally we won't be so formal with a simple problem like this one, but here we have listed the rules by which we justify each of our steps in finding the derivative:

$$D_x(\sqrt{x} + 3x^2) = D_x\sqrt{x} + D_x 3x^2 \text{ (Equation 17-1)}$$

$$= D_x\sqrt{x} + 3D_x x^2 \text{ (Equation 16-3)}$$

$$= \frac{1}{2\sqrt{x}} + 3 \cdot 2x \quad \text{(The Power Formula)}$$

$$= \frac{1}{2\sqrt{x}} + 6x.$$

Example 17-2. Show that

(17-2) $D_x[f(x) + g(x)]^2 = 2[f(x) + g(x)][D_x f(x) + D_x g(x)]$.

Solution. We simply replace u with $f(x) + g(x)$ and r with 2 in Equation 16-2, and we have

$$D_x[f(x) + g(x)]^2 = 2[f(x) + g(x)] \, D_x[f(x) + g(x)].$$

Now we apply Equation 17-1 to obtain Equation 17-2.

The rule for differentiating products is more complicated than the rule for differentiating sums. *It is not true, in general, that the derivative of a product is the product of the derivatives of its factors.* Instead, we have the following theorem.

Theorem 17-2. *If f and g are differentiable at x, then*

(17-3) $$D_x[f(x)g(x)] = f(x)D_x g(x) + g(x)D_x f(x).$$

Proof. You can easily verify that

$$f(x)g(x) = \tfrac{1}{2}[f(x) + g(x)]^2 - \tfrac{1}{2}f(x)^2 - \tfrac{1}{2}g(x)^2.$$

Then according to the Sum Rule and Equation 16-3,

$$D_x[f(x)g(x)] = \tfrac{1}{2}D_x[f(x) + g(x)]^2 - \tfrac{1}{2}D_x f(x)^2 - \tfrac{1}{2}D_x g(x)^2.$$

We have already calculated the first of the derivatives on the right side of this equation (Equation 17-2), and Equation 16-2 immediately gives us $D_x f(x)^2 = 2f(x)D_x f(x)$ and $D_x g(x)^2 = 2g(x)D_x g(x)$. Therefore,

$$D_x[f(x)g(x)] = [f(x) + g(x)][D_x f(x) + D_x g(x)] - f(x)D_x f(x) - g(x)D_x g(x),$$

which you can quickly reduce to Equation 17-3.

Example 17-3. Find $D_x[x(4x + 3)]$.

Solution. We may proceed in either of two ways, the easiest is to perform the indicated multiplication first and obtain $D_x(4x^2 + 3x) = D_x 4x^2 + D_x 3x = 8x + 3$. But we could use Theorem 17-2 to write

$$D_x[x(4x + 3)] = xD_x(4x + 3) + (4x + 3)D_x x = x \cdot 4 + (4x + 3) \cdot 1 = 8x + 3.$$

Example 17-4. Extend the Product Rule to find a rule for differentiating a product of 3 factors.

Solution. We can think of the product $f(x)g(x)h(x)$ as the product of the two factors $f(x)$ and $g(x)h(x)$. Therefore Theorem 17-2 applies, and we have

$$D_x[f(x)g(x)h(x)] = f(x)D_x[g(x)h(x)] + g(x)h(x)D_x f(x).$$

Now we use Theorem 17-2 again, this time to show that

$$D_x[g(x)\,h(x)] = g(x)D_xh(x) + h(x)D_xg(x),$$

and so we see that

$$D_x[f(x)\,g(x)h(x)] = f(x) \cdot g(x) \cdot D_xh(x) + f(x) \cdot D_xg(x) \cdot h(x)$$
$$+ D_xf(x) \cdot g(x) \cdot h(x).$$

It is a simple matter to extend the rule to products containing any number of factors.

As is the case with multiplication, the order in which we apply the operations of division and differentiation is important. If we divide and then differentiate or differentiate and then divide, we will usually get different results. The rule for differentiating a quotient is the following.

Theorem 17-3. *If f and g are differentiable at x, and if $g(x) \neq 0$, then*

(17-4)
$$D_x\left(\frac{f(x)}{g(x)}\right) = \frac{g(x)D_xf(x) - f(x)D_xg(x)}{g(x)^2}.$$

Proof. We use the Product Rule and the Power Formula:

$$D_x\left(\frac{f(x)}{g(x)}\right) = D_x[f(x)g(x)^{-1}] \qquad \text{(Algebra)}$$
$$= f(x)D_xg(x)^{-1} + g(x)^{-1}D_xf(x) \qquad \text{(Product Rule)}$$
$$= -f(x)g(x)^{-2}D_xg(x) + g(x)^{-1}D_xf(x) \quad \text{(Power Formula, } r = -1),$$

and simple algebra reduces this equation to Equation 17-4.

Example 17-5. Find y' if $y = \dfrac{x - 1}{\sqrt{x + 1}}$.

Solution. We have

$$D_x\left(\frac{x - 1}{\sqrt{x + 1}}\right) = \frac{\sqrt{x + 1}\,D_x(x - 1) - (x - 1)D_x\sqrt{x + 1}}{x + 1} \quad \text{(Quotient Rule)}$$

$$= \frac{\sqrt{x + 1} \cdot 1 - \dfrac{x - 1}{2\sqrt{x + 1}}}{x + 1} \qquad \begin{array}{l}\text{(Power Formula to find}\\ D_x\sqrt{x + 1})\end{array}$$

$$= \frac{x + 3}{2(x + 1)^{3/2}} \qquad \text{(Algebra).}$$

Let us summarize the differentiation rules we have developed in this section. If f and g are differentiable functions and $u = f(x)$ and $v = g(x)$, then for any given numbers m and n,

$$(17\text{-}5) \qquad\qquad D_x(mu + nv) = mD_xu + nD_xv.$$

This rule, a combination of the Sum Rule and Equation 16-3, says that D_x is a **linear operator.** We also have

$$(17\text{-}6) \qquad\qquad D_x(uv) = uD_xv + vD_xu \quad \text{(Product Rule)}$$

and

$$(17\text{-}7) \qquad\qquad D_x\left(\frac{u}{v}\right) = \frac{vD_xu - uD_xv}{v^2} \quad \text{(Quotient Rule)}.$$

PROBLEMS 17

1. Find and simplify D_xy.

(a) $y = \sqrt{2x} - \sqrt{2}x$

(b) $y = \sqrt{x+3} - \sqrt{x} - \sqrt{3}$

(c) $y = \sqrt{2x} + \dfrac{1}{\sqrt{2x}}$

(d) $y = \dfrac{x-1}{x+1}$

(e) $y = x\,|x|$

(f) $y = \left(x + \dfrac{1}{x}\right)^2 - x^2 - x^{-2}$

(g) $y = \sqrt{\dfrac{x}{1+x}}$

(h) $y = x^4(x-5)^6$

(i) $y = (x-1)^4(x+2)^5(x-3)^6$

(j) $y = \dfrac{(x-1)^4(x-3)^6}{(x+2)^5}$

(k) $y = (x^2+1)\left(x + \dfrac{1}{x}\right)$

(l) $y = (x^2+1)\Big/\left(x + \dfrac{1}{x}\right)$

(m) $y = \dfrac{x}{\sqrt{16-x^2}}$

(n) $y = \dfrac{\sqrt{16-x^2}}{x}$

2. Find $f'(-2)$ if:

(a) $f(x) = \sqrt[3]{3x-2} + 3x^3 - 2$

(b) $f(x) = (x+2)^5(x+5)^2$

(c) $f(x) = |x| + x^2$

(d) $f(x) = [\![x + \tfrac{1}{2}]\!] + \sqrt[5]{16x}$

(e) $f(x) = [\![x + \tfrac{1}{2}]\!]\,\sqrt[5]{16x}$

(f) $f(x) = (|x| + x)\sqrt[5]{16x}$

(g) $f(x) = (|x| - x)\sqrt[5]{16x}$

(h) $f(x) = [\![\sin x]\!]\,\sqrt[5]{16x}$

3. Find the points of the graphs of the following equations at which the tangent lines are perpendicular to the line $4y + x - 8 = 0$.

(a) $y = x^2 - 4x + 1$

(b) $y = \dfrac{x^2 - 3}{x}$

(c) $y = 3 + 2\sqrt{x}$

(d) $y = |x + 1|\,(x+1)$

4. What is the rate of change of volume with respect to the radius of

(a) A sphere?

(b) A circular cylinder with fixed height?

(c) A cone with fixed height?

5. A point moves along a number scale and is s feet from the origin t seconds after a given moment. Find the equation that gives the velocity of the moving point if

(a) $s = \dfrac{1 + t + t^2}{\sqrt{t}}$

(b) $s = \dfrac{\sqrt{t}}{1 + t + t^2}$

(c) $s = \sqrt{t}(1 + t + t^2)$

6. (a) Suppose that r is a rational number and $f(x) = x^{-r}$ and $g(x) = (x + r)^r$. Show that $D_x[f(x)g(x)] = D_x f(x) D_x g(x)$. Can you find other pairs of functions for which this equation holds?

(b) Let r be a rational number and $f(x) = \left(\dfrac{x + r}{x}\right)^r$ and $g(x) = x^{-r}$. Show that $D_x\left(\dfrac{f(x)}{g(x)}\right) = \dfrac{D_x f(x)}{D_x g(x)}$. Can you find other pairs of functions for which this equation holds?

7. Let f and g be differentiable functions and define functions l and s by the equations $l(x) = \frac{1}{2}[f(x) + g(x) + |f(x) - g(x)|]$ and $s(x) = \frac{1}{2}[f(x) + g(x) - |f(x) - g(x)|]$. Show that for each x, $l(x)$ is the larger and $s(x)$ is the smaller of $f(x)$ and $g(x)$. Show that at a point x for which $f(x) \neq g(x)$ we have

$$l'(x) = \frac{1}{2}\left[f'(x) + g'(x) + \frac{f(x) - g(x)}{|f(x) - g(x)|}(f'(x) - g'(x))\right].$$

What is the corresponding formula for $s'(x)$? What is the relation between $l'(x)$ and the larger of $f'(x)$ and $g'(x)$?

8. Write a product rule for a product of 4 factors; that is, find a formula for

$$D_x[a(x)b(x)c(x)d(x)].$$

What is the rule for any number of factors?

18 DERIVATIVES OF THE TRIGONOMETRIC FUNCTIONS

Now let us return to the task of finding specific differentiation formulas and develop the differentiation formulas for the trigonometric functions. To find the derivative of $f(x)$ when $f(x) = \sin x$, we set up the difference quotient

$$\frac{f(x + h) - f(x)}{h} = \frac{\sin (x + h) - \sin x}{h}$$

and compute its limit as h approaches 0. In order to reduce this difference quotient to a more manageable form, we replace $\sin (x + h)$ with $\sin x \cos h + \cos x \sin h$

(see Formula A-2 in the Appendix). Our difference quotient then becomes

$$\frac{\sin x \cos h + \cos x \sin h - \sin x}{h} = \cos x \frac{\sin h}{h} + \sin x \frac{\cos h - 1}{h}.$$

Therefore, according to the definition of the derivative and our theorems on limits,

$$(18\text{-}1) \qquad D_x \sin x = \cos x \lim_{h \to 0} \frac{\sin h}{h} + \sin x \lim_{h \to 0} \frac{\cos h - 1}{h}.$$

Thus, in order to calculate $D_x \sin x$, we need to calculate the two limits that appear in Equation 18-1. Our next two examples are devoted to finding those limits.

Example 18-1. Find $\lim\limits_{h \to 0} \dfrac{\sin h}{h}$.

Solution. In Section 10 we gave a graphical argument to show that $\lim\limits_{h \to 0} \dfrac{\sin h}{h} = 1$.
An analytic proof of this result requires more of a discussion of what we mean by the length of a circular arc than we care to undertake here, but we can show the basic idea by referring to a picture. In Fig. 18-1 we have sketched the unit circle,

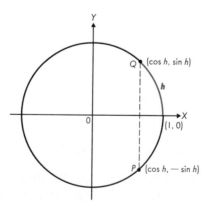

Figure 18-1

showing the points $P(\cos h, -\sin h)$ and $Q(\cos h, \sin h)$ that correspond to a small positive number h. Thus the length of the *segment* PQ is $2 \sin h$ units, while the *arc* PQ is $2h$ units long. Since $\dfrac{\sin h}{h} = \dfrac{2 \sin h}{2h}$, we therefore see that the quotient $\dfrac{\sin h}{h}$ is the ratio of the length of a chord of a circle to the length of the corresponding arc. (If h were negative, we would get exactly the same result.) It is a consequence of the definition of arclength that the limit of the ratio of chordlength to arclength is 1, and hence $\lim\limits_{h \to 0} \dfrac{\sin h}{h} = 1$. (We will discuss arclength in Section 71. At that point it would be possible to put the derivation of this limit, as well as our entire discussion of trigonometry, on a firmer theoretical basis.)

Example 18-2. Find $\lim\limits_{h \to 0} \dfrac{\cos h - 1}{h}$.

Solution. From the definition of the derivative, we see that the derivative of $\cos x$ at 0 is the number

$$\lim_{h \to 0} \frac{\cos h - \cos 0}{h} = \lim_{h \to 0} \frac{\cos h - 1}{h}.$$

Thus the limit we are to find is the derivative of $\cos x$ at 0, and from the cosine curve (Fig. 6-5) it appears that this derivative is 0.

We can also use the limit we found in Example 18-1 to obtain this result. For

$$\frac{\cos h - 1}{h} = \frac{\cos h - 1}{h} \frac{\cos h + 1}{\cos h + 1} = -\frac{1 - \cos^2 h}{h(\cos h + 1)} = -\frac{\sin^2 h}{h(\cos h + 1)}$$

$$= -\frac{\sin^2 h}{h^2} \frac{1}{\cos h + 1} h.$$

Therefore we can find our desired limit by finding the limits of the three factors in this last product. In Example 18-1 we found that the limit of the first factor is 1. Since the cosine function is continuous at 0 (Problem 11-6), the limit of the second factor is $\dfrac{1}{\cos 0 + 1} = \tfrac{1}{2}$. The limit of the third factor, of course, is 0. Therefore our required limit is $-1 \cdot \tfrac{1}{2} \cdot 0 = 0$.

From the results of Examples 18-1 and 18-2 we see that Equation 18-1 becomes $D_x \sin x = \cos x \cdot 1 + \sin x \cdot 0 = \cos x$; that is,

(18-2) $$\boldsymbol{D_x \sin x = \cos x.}$$

Recall that we used a geometric argument to obtain a rough sketch of the equation $y = D_x \sin x$ in Fig. 12-4. Now that we have a differentiation formula for the sine function, you might re-examine that graph to see if our approximation agrees with Equation 18-2.

As usual with specific differentiation formulas, we now incorporate Equation 18-2 into the Chain Rule. Thus in Equation 16-1 we replace $f(u)$ with $\sin u$ to obtain the equation $D_x \sin u = D_u \sin u\, D_x u$. Equation 18-2 tells us that $D_u \sin u = \cos u$, so we have the equation

(18-3) $$\boldsymbol{D_x \sin u = \cos u\, D_x u.}$$

Example 18-3.   Find $D_x \sin x^2$ and $D_x \sin^2 x$.

Solution.   We find $D_x \sin x^2$ by replacing u with x^2 in Equation 18-3:

$$D_x \sin x^2 = \cos x^2 \, D_x x^2 = 2x \cos x^2.$$

On the other hand, $\sin^2 x$ means $(\sin x)^2$, and therefore we use the Power Formula to find $D_x \sin^2 x$. Thus in Equation 16-2, with $r = 2$, we replace u with $\sin x$, and then use Equation 18-2 to calculate $D_x \sin x$:

$$D_x \sin^2 x = 2 \sin x \, D_x \sin x = 2 \sin x \cos x = \sin 2x.$$

We can use the rules we have developed so far to obtain the derivatives for the other trigonometric functions. For example, since $\cos x = \sin \left(\frac{\pi}{2} - x \right)$, we have $D_x \cos x = D_x \sin \left(\frac{\pi}{2} - x \right)$, and we can find this last derivative by replacing u with $\frac{\pi}{2} - x$ in Equation 18-3. Thus

$$D_x \cos x = D_x \sin \left(\frac{\pi}{2} - x \right) = \cos \left(\frac{\pi}{2} - x \right) D_x\left(\frac{\pi}{2} - x \right) = -\cos \left(\frac{\pi}{2} - x \right).$$

But $\cos \left(\frac{\pi}{2} - x \right) = -\sin x$, and so

(18-4) $$\mathbf{D}_x \cos x = -\sin x.$$

We find the derivative of $\tan x$ by applying the Quotient Rule to the right side of the identity $\tan x = \dfrac{\sin x}{\cos x}$ and using Equations 18-2 and 18-4:

$$D_x \tan x = D_x \frac{\sin x}{\cos x} = \frac{\cos x \, D_x \sin x - \sin x \, D_x \cos x}{\cos^2 x}$$

$$= \frac{\cos^2 x + \sin^2 x}{\cos^2 x} = \frac{1}{\cos^2 x} = \sec^2 x.$$

Therefore we have the differentiation formula

(18-5) $$\mathbf{D}_x \tan x = \sec^2 x.$$

We find $D_x \sec x$ by writing $\sec x = (\cos x)^{-1}$ and applying the Power Formula:

$$D_x(\cos x)^{-1} = -(\cos x)^{-2} D_x \cos x = \frac{\sin x}{\cos^2 x} = \frac{1}{\cos x} \frac{\sin x}{\cos x} = \sec x \tan x.$$

Similar tricks yield derivatives for the other trigonometric functions, and we obtain the following formulas:

(18-6) $$D_x \cot x = -\csc^2 x,$$

(18-7) $$D_x \sec x = \sec x \tan x,$$

(18-8) $$D_x \csc x = -\csc x \cot x.$$

And, of course, we immediately incorporate these formulas into the Chain Rule:

(18-9) $$D_x \cos u = -\sin u \, D_x u,$$

(18-10) $$D_x \tan u = \sec^2 u \, D_x u,$$

(18-11) $$D_x \cot u = -\csc^2 u \, D_x u,$$

(18-12) $$D_x \sec u = \sec u \tan u \, D_x u,$$

(18-13) $$D_x \csc u = -\csc u \cot u \, D_x u.$$

Perhaps you are beginning to wonder just how many differentiation formulas we are going to develop (and ask you to memorize). The answer appears in Table IV in the back of the book, where we have listed all of the specific differentiation formulas that we will introduce.

Example 18-4. If $f(x) = \csc \dfrac{1}{x}$, find $f'\left(\dfrac{2}{\pi}\right)$.

Solution. According to Equation 18-13, with $u = \dfrac{1}{x}$, we have

$$D_x \csc \frac{1}{x} = -\csc \frac{1}{x} \cot \frac{1}{x} D_x \frac{1}{x} = -\left(\csc \frac{1}{x} \cot \frac{1}{x}\right)\left(-\frac{1}{x^2}\right).$$

Therefore, $f'(x) = \dfrac{1}{x^2} \csc \dfrac{1}{x} \cot \dfrac{1}{x}$, and so $f'\left(\dfrac{2}{\pi}\right) = \left(\dfrac{\pi}{2}\right)^2 \csc \dfrac{\pi}{2} \cot \dfrac{\pi}{2} = 0.$

Example 18-5. Find the points of the graph of the equation $y = x + \cot x$ at which the tangent line is horizontal.

Solution. With the help of our differentiation formulas, we see that

$$y' = 1 - \csc^2 x = -\cot^2 x.$$

The slope of the tangent line is y', so the tangent line is horizontal at those points where $y' = 0$. To find those points, we must therefore solve the equation

$$-\cot^2 x = 0.$$

The solutions to this equation have the form $x = \dfrac{\pi}{2} + k\pi$, where k can be any integer—positive, negative, or 0. Thus the points where the tangent line is horizontal form the set

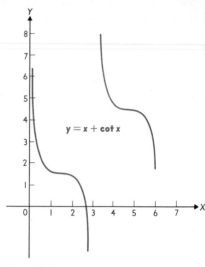

$y = x + \cot x$

Figure 18-2

$$\left\{ (x, x) \mid x = \frac{\pi}{2} + k\pi, k = 0, \pm1, \pm2, \ldots \right\}.$$

The graph of the equation $y = x + \cot x$ is illustrated in Fig. 18-2. Does the figure agree with the fact that y' is never positive?

P R O B L E M S   1 8

1. Find $D_x y$.

(a) $y = \sqrt{\sin x} - \sin \sqrt{x}$

(b) $y = \tan x^2 - \tan^2 x$

(c) $y = \sec 2x - 2 \sec x$

(d) $y = \cot (x + 2) - (\cot x + \cot 2)$

(e) $y = \cos 2x - (\cos 2)(\cos x)$

(f) $y = \csc \dfrac{3}{x} - \dfrac{\csc 3}{\csc x}$

(g) $y = \dfrac{\sin x}{x}$

(h) $y = \cos (\sin x)$

(i) $y = \sin^2 (\cos^2 x^2)$

(j) $y = \sqrt[3]{\sec^2 2x}$

(k) $y = |\cot |x| |$

(l) $y = |x| \sin |x|$

2. Derive Formulas 18-6 and 18-8.

3. Find the equations of the tangent line and the normal line to the sine curve at the following points:

(a) $(0, 0)$

(b) $\left(\dfrac{\pi}{4}, \dfrac{\sqrt{2}}{2} \right)$

(c) $\left(\dfrac{\pi}{2}, 1 \right)$

4. (a) Find a point of the sine curve at which the tangent is parallel to the line $x + 2y + 3 = 0$.

(b) Find a point of the sine curve at which the normal is parallel to the line $2x + y + 3 = 0$.

5. Differentiate both sides of the identity $\sin 2x = 2 \sin x \cos x$ to obtain an identity involving $\cos 2x$.

6. Show that there are no points of the graph of the equation $y = \sec x - \tan x$ at which the tangent line is horizontal.

7. Show that $y = \tan x$ satisfies the differential equations (i) $y' \sin 2x = 2y$ and (ii) $y' = 1 + y^2$. Show that $y = 3 \tan x$ satisfies (i) but not (ii) and $y = \tan (x + 3)$ satisfies (ii) but not (i).

8. If the displacement of a moving body is related to the time by the equation $s = A \sin (bt + c)$, where A, b, and c are given numbers, then the motion of the body is termed *simple harmonic motion*. Find an expression for the velocity in simple harmonic motion.

9. Let $\sin \theta°$ and $\cos \theta°$ denote the sine and cosine of an angle of θ degrees. Show that

$$D_\theta \sin \theta° = \frac{\pi}{180} \cos \theta°.$$

10. A point P moves along a circle of radius 1 whose center is the origin at the rate of 1 rpm. Let Q denote the point at which the tangent to the circle at P intersects the X-axis. How fast is the point Q moving along the X-axis when Q is 2 units to the right of the origin?

11. Let $f(x) = x^2 \sin \dfrac{1}{x}$ if $x \neq 0$ and $f(0) = 0$. In Problem 13-14 we asked you to show that f is differentiable at 0. Show that f' is not continuous at 0.

19 SOME BASIC THEOREMS

Calculus is an old subject, and in the many years that it has been intensively studied certain theorems have emerged as fundamental. In this section we will present some of these basic theorems. At this early stage of the course it will not be apparent to you why we single out these particular theorems for special attention; their importance will only become clear as you see them used over and over again in our development of calculus later on in the book. Though you will temporarily have to accept the importance of the theorems of this section on faith, you will find that, geometrically speaking, they are quite reasonable assertions.

In Section 10 we said that a function is continuous at a point of its domain if its limit at the point is its value at the point. A function is **continuous in an interval** if it is continuous at each point of the interval. Geometrically, this statement says that each point of the graph of the function is where it "should" be. Thus if a function is continuous in an interval, then its graph has no "breaks" in the interval.

For example, the greatest integer function is not continuous in the interval $(0, 2)$—its graph has a break as it crosses the line $x = 1$. But the greatest integer function *is* continuous in the interval $[\frac{1}{4}, \frac{1}{2}]$—its graph in that interval has no breaks. The following theorem tells us the basic things about continuous functions that we need to know in calculus.

Theorem 19-1.   *If f is a function that is continuous in the closed finite interval $[a, b]$, then there are numbers A and B such that $f([a, b]) = [A, B]$.*

Figure 19-1 graphically illustrates the content of this theorem. The theorem says that if we project onto the Y-axis the part of the graph that lies above the interval $[a, b]$ of the X-axis, we obtain the interval $[A, B]$. From our remarks about the geometric implications of continuity, this theorem may seem quite natural. An analytic proof, however, is both long and difficult. It depends on basic properties of the real number system (for example, the Completeness Property 2-1), and of course we must use our analytic definition of the limit. The reasoning gets a little subtle, too. For instance, in the problems at the end of the section we will ask you to look at some examples that show that the conclusion of the theorem need

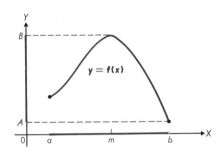

Figure 19-1

not follow if we do not require the interval $[a, b]$ to be a finite interval, or if we replace it with an interval that is not closed. Furthermore, the converse of the theorem is false; the conclusion holds for some discontinuous functions. We are not going to prove Theorem 19-1. Every advanced calculus book contains a proof, though usually these key results are stated as several theorems.

The numbers A and B are the least and greatest values of the function f in the interval $[a, b]$. For the function whose graph is shown in Fig. 19-1, the greatest value B corresponds to a point m in the open interval (a, b). In this case the graph suggests that $f'(m) = 0$, and this simple observation leads us to some of the most important theorems in calculus. Before we turn to these theorems, however, let us show that $f'(m) = 0$ by a method that is somewhat more mathematical than just looking at a picture.

Theorem 19-2.   *Suppose that the greatest (or least) value that a function f takes in a set that contains an open interval (a, b) is the number $f(m)$, where $m \in (a, b)$, and suppose that f is differentiable at m. Then $f'(m) = 0$.*

Proof. Suppose $f(m)$ is the greatest value of f. (It is a simple matter to replace the word "greatest" with the word "least.") Therefore for each point

$x \in (a, b)$ that is different from m, $f(x) - f(m) \le 0$. Hence

$$\frac{f(x) - f(m)}{x - m} \ge 0 \quad \text{if} \quad x < m \quad \text{and} \quad \frac{f(x) - f(m)}{x - m} \le 0 \quad \text{if} \quad x > m.$$

From these inequalities it is clear (see Problem 11-19) that

$$\lim_{x \uparrow m} \frac{f(x) - f(m)}{x - m} \ge 0 \quad \text{and} \quad \lim_{x \downarrow m} \frac{f(x) - f(m)}{x - m} \le 0.$$

Since f is differentiable at m, these limits are both equal to $f'(m)$, and so we have $f'(m) \ge 0$ and $f'(m) \le 0$. These inequalities tell us that $f'(m) = 0$, as we were to show.

We now use the result we have just established to prove one of our fundamental theorems.

Theorem 19-3. Rolle's Theorem. *If f is differentiable in the open interval (a, b) and continuous in the closed interval $[a, b]$, and if $f(a) = f(b)$, then there is at least one number $m \in (a, b)$ such that $f'(m) = 0$.*

Proof. As a result of Theorem 19-2, we see that it will be sufficient for us to show that either the greatest or the least value that f takes in the closed interval $[a, b]$ is taken at a point m in the open interval (a, b). But this fact is immediately apparent. For if f does not take its least value at a point of (a, b), then the number $f(a)$ ($=f(b)$) must be the least value of f. Hence for each $x \in (a, b)$, we have $f(x) \ge f(a)$ ($=f(b)$), and so f takes its greatest value in (a, b).

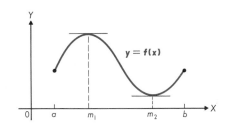

Figure 19-2

If you sketch the graphs of a few functions that satisfy the hypotheses of Rolle's Theorem, you will see that it is geometrically obvious. Thus the theorem simply says that if the graph of f intersects a horizontal line when $x = a$, and again when $x = b$, then at some point m between a and b the tangent line to the graph is horizontal. For the function whose graph is shown in Fig. 19-2, there are two points at which the tangent line is horizontal, and hence we can choose either m_1 or m_2 as the number m of Rolle's Theorem. For other functions there may be 5, 100, or even infinitely many choices for m. But if the conditions of Rolle's Theorem are satisfied, then there must be *at least one choice for m.*

By itself, Rolle's Theorem does not seem to deserve much attention; anyone can see that it is true. But there are clever ways of exploiting this simple theorem to obtain some of the important results of calculus. Our next theorem is essentially just another form of Rolle's Theorem, a form tailored to fit later applications. You won't find this theorem as obvious as Rolle's Theorem (although we will be able to give a simple geometric interpretation of it after we have studied vectors).

Theorem 19-4.   The Extended Theorem of the Mean.   *If f and g are differentiable in the open interval (a, b) and continuous in the closed interval $[a, b]$, and if $g'(x) \neq 0$ for $x \in (a, b)$, then there is a point $m \in (a, b)$ such that*

(19-1)
$$\frac{f(b) - f(a)}{g(b) - g(a)} = \frac{f'(m)}{g'(m)}.$$

Proof. To prove this theorem, we construct a function h that satisfies the conditions of Rolle's Theorem; our defining equation is

$$h(x) = [f(b) - f(a)]g(x) - [g(b) - g(a)]f(x).$$

Since $h(a) = f(b)g(a) - g(b)f(a)$ and $h(b) = -f(a)g(b) + g(a)f(b)$, we see that $h(a) = h(b)$, and so Rolle's Theorem tells us that there is a point $m \in (a, b)$ such that $h'(m) = 0$. But

$$h'(x) = [f(b) - f(a)]g'(x) - [g(b) - g(a)]f'(x),$$

and therefore the equation $h'(m) = 0$ can be written as

(19-2) $[f(b) - f(a)]g'(m) = [g(b) - g(a)]f'(m).$

So far, we have not used the hypothesis that $g'(x) \neq 0$. This assumption, of course, tells us that $g'(m) \neq 0$, and it also assures us that $g(b) \neq g(a)$. Otherwise, according to Rolle's Theorem, there would be a point of (a, b) at which g' takes the value 0. Thus we can divide both sides of Equation 19-2 by $g'(m)[g(b) - g(a)]$ and obtain the desired Equation 19-1.

A special case of Theorem 19-4 is so important that we list it as a separate theorem, the (ordinary) **Theorem of the Mean** or the **Mean Value Theorem.**

Theorem 19-5.   Theorem of the Mean.   *If f is differentiable in the open interval (a, b) and continuous in the closed interval $[a, b]$, then there is a point $m \in (a, b)$ such that*

(19-3)
$$\frac{f(b) - f(a)}{b - a} = f'(m).$$

Proof. If $g(x) = x$, then f and g satisfy the hypotheses of Theorem 19-4 (check this statement), and Equation 19-3 follows from Equation 19-1.

The Theorem of the Mean has a very simple geometric interpretation. The left-hand side of Equation 19-3 is the slope of the line segment that terminates at the points $(a, f(a))$ and $(b, f(b))$ of the graph of f, and the right-hand side is the slope of the tangent line at a point of the curve between these two points (see Fig. 19-3). Thus the Theorem of the Mean states that *there is at least one point of any arc of the graph of f at which the tangent line is parallel to the chord that joins the endpoints of the arc.*

There are many important applications of the Theorem of the Mean (and the Extended Theorem of the Mean) to the "theoretical side" of calculus, but there are applications to "practical" problems, too.

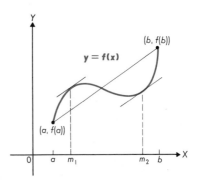

Figure 19-3

Example 19-1. Use the Theorem of the Mean to find an approximate value of $\sqrt{101}$.

Solution. We will let $f(x) = \sqrt{x}$, $a = 100$, and $b = 101$ in the statement of the Theorem of the Mean. Here $f'(x) = \dfrac{1}{2\sqrt{x}}$, and so Equation 19-3 becomes

$$\frac{\sqrt{101} - \sqrt{100}}{101 - 100} = \frac{1}{2\sqrt{m}},$$

where m is a number between 100 and 101. On simplifying this last equation, we have

$$\sqrt{101} = 10 + \frac{1}{2\sqrt{m}}.$$

Now since $100 < m < 101$, then $10 < \sqrt{m} < \sqrt{101}$, and so

$$20 < 2\sqrt{m} < 2\sqrt{101} = \sqrt{404}.$$

We note that $404 < 21^2 = 441$, and hence

$$20 < 2\sqrt{m} < 21.$$

Therefore

$$\frac{1}{21} < \frac{1}{2\sqrt{m}} < \frac{1}{20}.$$

Thus 101 is a number between $10 + \frac{1}{21}$ and $10 + \frac{1}{20}$, or in terms of decimals,

$$10.047 < \sqrt{101} < 10.050.$$

So we see that if we take $\sqrt{101} = 10.05$, our error will be less than .003.

Our next example uses both Theorem 19-1 and Rolle's Theorem.

Example 19-2. Show that the equation $x^5 + 2x^3 - 5x - 10 = 0$ has exactly one solution that lies in the interval $(1, 2)$.

Solution. Let $f(x) = x^5 + 2x^3 - 5x - 10$. We must show (i) that the equation $f(x) = 0$ has *at least* one solution in the interval $(1, 2)$, and (ii) that the equation has *no more than* one solution in the interval. To show that the equation $f(x) = 0$ has at least one solution, we use Theorem 19-1 as follows. First we observe that the polynomial function f is continuous in the interval $[1, 2]$, and so Theorem 19-1 tells us that $f([1, 2])$ is a closed interval $[A, B]$. Since $f(1) = -12$ and $f(2) = 28$, we see that $[A, B]$ contains the points -12 and 28. Now if two points belong to an interval, then every point between them belongs to the interval, so the point 0 (which is between -12 and 28) belongs to the interval $[A, B] = f([1, 2])$. Thus there is at least one point $a \in [1, 2]$ such that $f(a) = 0$. We have already seen that a is not one of the endpoints, so $a \in (1, 2)$. Suppose that there were another point b in the interval $(1, 2)$ such that $f(b) = 0$. Then, according to Rolle's Theorem, there would be a point m between a and b—and hence in the interval $(1, 2)$—such that $f'(m) = 0$. But $f'(x) = 5x^4 + 6x^2 - 5$, and so if $m > 1$ we have $f'(m) = 5m^4 + 6m^2 - 5$, which is positive. Therefore there cannot be a second point b in the interval $(1, 2)$ at which f takes the value 0.

Now let us turn to a theoretical consequence of the Theorem of the Mean. A given differentiable function f gives rise to *just one* derived function f'. This statement does *not* say that two different functions cannot have the same derived function, however. Thus, for example, if $f(x) = x^3 + 3$ and $g(x) = x^3 - 5$, then f and g are different functions. But $f'(x) = g'(x) = 3x^2$, and so the derived functions f' and g' are the same. Nevertheless, if two functions have the same derived functions, they can't be too different, as our next theorem shows. We will have more to say on this point later.

Theorem 19-6. *Let f and g be functions that are differentiable in some interval I, and suppose that at each point $x \in I$, $f'(x) = g'(x)$. Then there is a number C (independent of x) such that for each $x \in I$, $f(x) = g(x) + C$.*

Proof. Let us write $F(x) = f(x) - g(x)$, and choose any point $a \in I$. Then according to the Theorem of the Mean, for each other point $x \in I$ there is a point m between a and x such that

$$\frac{F(x) - F(a)}{x - a} = F'(m).$$

Now $F'(m) = f'(m) - g'(m)$, and by hypothesis this number is 0. Therefore $F(x) - F(a) = 0$; that is, $F(x) = F(a)$. If we write $C = F(a)$, and recall that $F(x) = f(x) - g(x)$, we see that the equation $F(x) = F(a)$ asserts that $f(x) = g(x) + C$, as we were to prove.

Geometrically, we can look at Theorem 19-6 as follows. The statement $f'(x) = g'(x)$ means that the graphs of the functions f and g are "parallel." Any vertical line intersects the two graphs in points at which they have the same slope. Theorem 19-6 tells us that the two graphs therefore cut segments of equal lengths from such vertical lines (see Fig. 19-4).

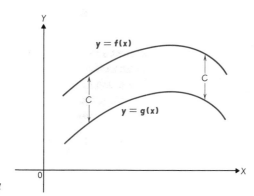

Figure 19-4

P R O B L E M S   1 9

1. The functions defined by the following equations are continuous in the interval $[0, 1]$, so Theorem 19-1 asserts that $f([0, 1])$ is a closed interval. Find it.
(a) $f(x) = \sin \pi x$
(b) $f(x) = 2x - 1$
(c) $f(x) = (2x - 1)^2$
(d) $f(x) = |2x - 1|$
(e) $f(x) = \cos x$
(f) $f(x) = [\frac{1}{4}x + \pi]$

2. Suppose that $f(x) = \dfrac{1}{1 + x^2}$.
(a) What theorems tell us that f is continuous in R^1?
(b) What theorem tells us that $f([-1, 1])$ is a closed interval?

(c) Is $f([-\infty, \infty])$ a closed interval?   (d) Is $f((-1, 1))$ a closed interval?
(e) Is $f((-1, 1))$ an open interval?

3. Find an example of a continuous function f such that $f((0, 1))$ is a closed interval.

4. Find an example of a function f such that $f([0, 1])$ is not an interval.

5. Is the function defined by the equation $f(x) = x + [x](x - \frac{3}{2})$ continuous in the interval $[0, \frac{3}{2}]$? Is $f([0, \frac{3}{2}])$ a closed interval?

6. Find a number that can be chosen as the number m in the Theorem of the Mean if $f(x)$ and the interval $[a, b]$ are
   (a) $f(x) = \sin x$, $[0, \pi]$ (b) $f(x) = x$, $[0, 1]$

   (c) $f(x) = x^2$, $[0, 1]$ (d) $f(x) = x + \dfrac{1}{x}$, $[p^2, q^2]$

   (e) $f(x) = x^3 + 2x^2 + 1$, $[0, 3]$ (f) $f(x) = \sin x + \cos x$, $[0, 2\pi]$

7. In each of the following cases show that $f'(x) = g'(x)$. What is the relation between $f(x)$ and $g(x)$?
   (a) $f(x) = \sin^2 x$, $g(x) = -(\cos 2x)/2$ (b) $f(x) = (x - 2)^2$, $g(x) = x(x - 4)$

   (c) $f(x) = \dfrac{x}{1 + x}$, $g(x) = \dfrac{-1}{1 + x}$ (d) $f(x) = x(1 + x + x^2)$, $g(x) = \dfrac{1 + x^4}{1 - x}$

   (e) $f(x) = \sec^2 x$, $g(x) = \tan^2 x$

8. Suppose $f(x) = \log x$ and $g(x) = \log 3x$. What is the relation between $f'(x)$ and $g'(x)$?

9. Suppose that f is continuous in $N_r a$, and differentiable in $N_r^* a$, and that $\lim_{x \to a} f'(x)$ exists. Use the Theorem of the Mean to prove that $f'(a)$ exists. Is f' continuous at a?

10. Suppose that for each $x \in [0, \infty]$, we have $f'(x) \geq 0$. Show that for each such x, $f(x) \geq f(0)$.

11. (a) Suppose that, for every number $x \in R^1$, $D_x[10^x f(x)] = 0$. If $f(0) = 3$, what is $f(x)$?
    (b) Suppose that, for every number $x \geq 0$, $D_x[10^x f(x)] \geq 0$. If $f(0) = 3$, what can you say about $f(x)$ for a number $x \geq 0$?

12. We have listed below some functions and intervals for which the hypotheses of the Theorem of the Mean are not satisfied. Explain why not. Does the conclusion of the theorem hold?
    (a) $f(x) = |x|$, $[-1, 1]$ (b) $f(x) = x - [x]$, $[0, 1]$
    (c) $f(x) = \tan x$, $[0, \pi]$ (d) $f(x) = [\cos x]$, $[0, 2\pi]$

13. Suppose that y satisfies the differential equation $xy' + y = 3x^2$ and that $y = 3$ when $x = 1$. Show that $D_x(xy - x^3) = 0$, and hence deduce that $xy - x^3 = 2$; that is, $y = x^2 + \dfrac{2}{x}$.

20 DERIVATIVES OF HIGHER ORDER

With a differentiable function f we associate its derived function f'. Now f' may very well be a differentiable function itself. That is, we may be able to associate with it another function $(f')'$—the derived function of f'. The derived function of f' is the **second derived function of f** and is denoted by f''. We have called $f'(x)$ the derivative of $f(x)$. We can call $f'(x)$ the **first derivative of $f(x)$** to distinguish it from the **second derivative $f''(x)$**. Just as we use the notation $D_x y$ for the first derivative of y with respect to x, so the symbol $D_x^2 y$ represents the second derivative of y with respect to x, and so on.

Example 20-1. If $y = x^2 + \sin x$, find y''.

Solution. We calculate $y' = 2x + \cos x$ in the usual way. To find y'' we simply differentiate $2x + \cos x$. Thus $y'' = 2 - \sin x$.

We don't stop with the concept of second derivative, but consider third, fourth, and higher derivatives, as well. The derivative of $f''(x)$ is the third derivative of $f(x)$, which we write as $f'''(x)$. Similarly, $f^{iv}(x)$ is the fourth derivative of $f(x)$ (and, incidentally, the second derivative of $f''(x)$), and so on. The notation $f^{(n)}$ is also used to denote the derived function of order n of a given function f. Thus we obtain $f^{(12)}(x)$ by differentiating $f(x)$, differentiating the result, and so on, for a total of 12 differentiations.

Example 20-2. Find $D_x^4(x^2 \sin x)$.

Solution. We must perform four successive differentiations. First we find that

$$D_x(x^2 \sin x) = 2x \sin x + x^2 \cos x.$$

Then

$$D_x^2(x^2 \sin x) = D_x(2x \sin x + x^2 \cos x)$$
$$= 2 \sin x + 2x \cos x + 2x \cos x - x^2 \sin x$$
$$= 2 \sin x + 4x \cos x - x^2 \sin x.$$

Now

$$D_x^3(x^2 \sin x) = D_x(2 \sin x + 4x \cos x - x^2 \sin x)$$
$$= 2 \cos x + 4 \cos x - 4x \sin x - 2x \sin x - x^2 \cos x$$
$$= 6 \cos x - 6x \sin x - x^2 \cos x.$$

And finally,

$$D_x^4(x^2 \sin x) = D_x(6 \cos x - 6x \sin x - x^2 \cos x)$$
$$= -6 \sin x - 6 \sin x - 6x \cos x - 2x \cos x + x^2 \sin x$$
$$= -12 \sin x - 8x \cos x + x^2 \sin x.$$

Example 20-3.   Find $D_x^{27} \sin x$.

Solution.   Let us look at the first four of the indicated 27 differentiations.

$$D_x \sin x = \cos x,$$
$$D_x^2 \sin x = D_x \cos x = -\sin x,$$
$$D_x^3 \sin x = D_x(-\sin x) = -\cos x,$$
$$D_x^4 \sin x = D_x(-\cos x) = \sin x.$$

These four differentiations lead us back to our starting point. Hence we conclude that $D_x^8 \sin x = \sin x$, $D_x^{12} \sin x = \sin x$, and so on, till finally $D_x^{24} \sin x = \sin x$. Now it is clear that $D_x^{27} \sin x = D_x^3 \sin x = -\cos x$.

In Section 14 we used the first derivative to measure rate of change. In particular, if a moving point is displaced s units of distance from a given reference point t time units from some initial instant, then $D_t s$ measures the rate of change of distance with respect to time; that is, $D_t s$ measures the velocity of the moving point. So we write $v = D_t s$. Now the second derivative of s with respect to t, $D_t^2 s$, is equal to $D_t(D_t s) = D_t v$. Thus $D_t^2 s$ *measures the rate of change of velocity with respect to time.* This rate is called the **acceleration** of the moving point. For example, in the formula $s = 16t^2$ (the relation between displacement measured in feet and time measured in seconds for a body falling from rest near the surface of the earth) we see that $v = D_t s = 32t$ and $D_t^2 s = 32$. Thus the number 32 measures the acceleration of the body. Acceleration is measured in units of velocity per unit of time, so the acceleration of our falling body is 32 feet per second per second.

Example 20-4.   If a point moves along a line in such a way that its displacement s from some reference point after t units of time have elapsed is given by the formula $s = A \sin(at + b)$, then we call the motion of the point **simple harmonic motion** (see Problem 18-8). Show that the acceleration of the point is proportional to its displacement.

Solution.   We are to show that the acceleration $D_t^2 s$ and the displacement s are related by an equation of the form $D_t^2 s = ks$, for some number k. You may readily verify that $D_t s = aA \cos(at + b)$, and $D_t^2 s = -a^2 A \sin(at + b)$. Thus $D_t^2 s = -a^2 s$, so the number $-a^2$ is our constant of proportionality, and our assertion is verified.

We have already pointed out that equations involving rates—that is, differential equations—are of great importance in science. If a differential equation contains first, but not higher derivatives, it is called a *differential equation of the first order*. Similarly, *differential equations of the second order* contain second, but not higher, derivatives, and so on. For example, we have just seen that if $s = A \sin(at + b)$, then s satisfies the differential equation of the second order $s'' + a^2 s = 0$.

Example 20-5.   Show that $y = \dfrac{1}{x}$ satisfies the differential equation of the first order
(i) $xy' + y = 0$ and the differential equation of the second order (ii) $x^2 y'' + xy' - y = 0$. Show that $y = x$ satisfies (ii) but not (i).

Solution.   It is a simple matter to make the required substitutions, and we leave it to you. As you can see, however, we would have much more of a problem on our hands if the question read, "Solve equations (i) and (ii) for y." This question belongs to a course in differential equations.

Example 20-6.   Show that if $f''(x) = 0$ for each $x \in R^1$, then f is a linear function.

Solution.   It is easy to show that *if* f is linear; that is, $f(x) = mx + b$, then $y = mx + b$ satisfies the differential equation $y'' = 0$. We are asking the more difficult converse; namely, to show that the only possible solutions are determined by linear functions. Thus we are to find numbers m and b such that $f(x) = mx + b$. The equation $f''(x) = 0$ says that $f'(x)$ and 0 have the same derivative, and therefore Theorem 19-6 tells us that there is a number m such that $f'(x) = 0 + m = m$. This equation, in turn, says that $f(x)$ and mx have the same derivative, so we can again apply Theorem 19-6 to see that there is a number b such that $f(x) = mx + b$, as we were to show.

P R O B L E M S   2 0

1. Find y'' if

(a) $y = \dfrac{1 - x}{1 + x}$ (b) $y = x + \dfrac{1}{x}$ (c) $y = \sin^2 x$

(d) $y = \tan \dfrac{1}{x}$ (e) $y = x\,|x|$ (f) $y = x[\![x]\!]$

2. Find $f''(3)$ if

(a) $f(x) = \sin \dfrac{\pi x}{9}$ (b) $f(x) = x \cos \dfrac{\pi}{x}$

(c) $f(x) = \dfrac{1 - x^2}{1 + x^2}$ (d) $f(x) = x^3[\![x + \tfrac{1}{2}]\!] + x\,[\![x^3 + \tfrac{1}{2}]\!]$

3. Let $f(x) = x^{13}$ and show that

$$f^{(n)}(x) = \frac{13!}{(13 - n)!}\,x^{13-n}, \text{ if } n \leq 13 \text{ and } f^{(n)}(x) = 0, \text{ if } n > 13.$$

4. Show that if $f'''(x) = 0$ for each $x \in R^1$, then f is a quadratic function; that is, that there are numbers a, b, and c such that $f(x) = ax^2 + bx + c$.

5. (a) Show that for any pair of numbers a and b, $y = ax^2 + bx$ satisfies the differential equation $x^2 y'' - 2xy' + 2y = 0$.
   (b) Choose numbers a and b so that y also satisfies the conditions $y = 3$ when $x = 1$ and $y' = 8$ when $x = 1$.

6. Show that $D_x^n |f(x)| = \dfrac{f(x)}{|f(x)|} D_x^n f(x)$.

7. Determine k so that $y = \sec kx$ satisfies the differential equation $y'' + y = 2y^3$.

8. Show that $y = t \sin t$ satisfies the differential equations

    (a) $y'' + y = 2 \cos t$ (b) $y^{(4)} - y = -4 \cos t$.

9. Show that

    (a) $D_x^n \cos x = \cos\left(x + \dfrac{n\pi}{2}\right)$ (b) $D_x^n \sin x = \sin\left(x + \dfrac{n\pi}{2}\right)$

10. Show that $(uv)'' = u''v + 2u'v' + uv''$ and $(uv)''' = u'''v + 3u''v' + 3u'v'' + uv'''$. Do these formulas remind you of the Binomial Theorem? If so, see if you can guess the formulas for $(uv)^{(4)}$, $(uv)^{(5)}$, and so on.

11. Suppose that $f(a) = f(b) = f'(a) = f'(b) = 0$. Show that there are at least two points in the interval (a, b) that are solutions to the equation $f''(x) = 0$. Illustrate this result with the function defined by the equation $f(x) = (x^2 - 1)^2$ in the interval $[-1, 1]$.

12. Show that $y = \sin kx$ satisfies the differential equation $y'' + k^2y = 0$. For what choices of k is it also true that $y = 0$ when $x = 0$ and $y = 0$ when $x = \pi$?

13. The Chain Rule says that $D_x f(u) = f'(u)D_x u$. Replace u with y' to get the formula for $D_x f(y')$. Use this formula to find

    (a) $D_x y'^r$ (b) $D_x \sin y'$ (c) $D_x \sec y'$ (d) $D_x \cot y'$

14. (a) Show that $D_x^2 y$ and $(D_x y)^2$ are not always the same.

    (b) Show that if $D_x^2 y = (D_x y)^2$; that is, $y'' = y'^2$, then $D_x\left(x + \dfrac{1}{y'}\right) = 0$. What does this equation tell us about y'? Does it tell us anything about y?

21   INCREASING FUNCTIONS. CONCAVITY

    Some students get little more from their study of calculus than an ability to find the derivatives of complicated expressions. But differentiation formulas, though important, are technical details. We study calculus in order to gain a better understanding of functional relationships, and one of the best ways to increase this understanding is to apply our knowledge of calculus to the graphs of functions. We will devote this section to some geometric consequences of the Theorem of the Mean and a geometric interpretation of the second derivative.

    Figure 21-1 shows the graph of a function f, typical of the kind of functions we have in mind. Let us think of a point traveling along this curve from left to right. The point goes up as its X-coordinate increases from 0 to 2, and then down as its X-coordinate increases from 2 to 5. We say that f is *increasing* in the interval $(0, 2)$ and *decreasing* in the interval $(2, 5)$ in accordance with the following formal definition.

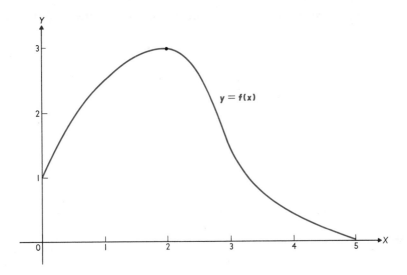

Figure 21-1

Definition 21-1. *A function f is **increasing in an interval** I if for each pair of points a and b in I such that a < b, we have f(a) < f(b). Similarly, f is **decreasing in an interval** I if for each pair of points a and b in I such that a < b, we have f(a) > f(b).*

In more informal terms than we used in Definition 21-1, we say that *f is increasing if the graph of f "rises to the right," and f is decreasing if the graph of f "falls to the right."* Notice that we cannot say that *f* is decreasing or increasing in the entire interval (0, 5) in Fig. 21-1.

Now we will develop a simple test that shows if a given function *f* is increasing or decreasing. We first recall that the graph of a linear function *f* is a line, and we see immediately that if the line has a positive slope, then *f* is increasing. If the line has a negative slope, then *f* is decreasing. This same rule applies to functions in general, as we see from the following theorem.

Theorem 21-1. *Suppose f is continuous in an interval I. If f'(x) > 0 at every interior point (that is, not an endpoint) x of I, then f is increasing in I. If f'(x) < 0 at every interior point x of I, then f is decreasing in I.*

Proof. We shall only write out the proof for the first case and leave the other case for the problems. Thus, we are assuming that *f'(x)* > 0 for every interior point *x* of *I*, and we are to show that if *a* and *b* are two numbers in *I* such that

$a < b$, then $f(a) < f(b)$. Now, according to the Theorem of the Mean (Theorem 19-5), there is a number m between a and b such that

$$\frac{f(b) - f(a)}{b - a} = f'(m).$$

Since m is an interior point of I, our hypothesis tells us that $f'(m) > 0$. Thus

$$\frac{f(b) - f(a)}{b - a} > 0,$$

and since $b - a > 0$, we have $f(b) - f(a) > 0$; that is, $f(a) < f(b)$.

Example 21-1. Show that if $f(x) = 3x^3 + 2x - 7$, then f is increasing in any interval.

Solution. Since $f'(x) = 9x^2 + 2 > 0$ for any real number x, it follows from Theorem 21-1 that f is an increasing function in any interval.

Example 21-2. Determine the intervals in which f is decreasing if $f(x) = 2x^3 + 3x^2 - 12x + 5$.

Solution. Here we have $f'(x) = 6x^2 + 6x - 12 = 6(x - 1)(x + 2)$. So Theorem 21-1 tells us that f is decreasing in intervals whose interior points satisfy the inequality

$$(x - 1)(x + 2) < 0.$$

The product $(x - 1)(x + 2)$ is negative if, and only if, the factors $(x - 1)$ and $(x + 2)$ have opposite signs. Thus we are looking either for an interval in which $(x - 1)$ is positive and $(x + 2)$ is negative, or an interval in which $(x - 1)$ is negative and $(x + 2)$ is positive. We must rule out the first possibility, for if there were a number x such that $(x - 1)$ is positive and $(x + 2)$ is negative, then x would be both greater than 1 and less than -2. There is no such number x. However, we *can* find an interval in which $(x - 1) < 0$ and $(x + 2) > 0$. These two inequalities are equivalent to the inequalities $x < 1$ and $x > -2$, which hold when x is a number in the interval $(-2, 1)$. Therefore, f is decreasing in any interval whose interior points belong to the interval $(-2, 1)$; the largest such interval is the closed interval $[-2, 1]$.

Now let us see what geometric information is conveyed by the sign of $f''(x)$. Since $f''(x)$ is the derivative of $f'(x)$, Theorem 21-1 tells us that if $f''(x) > 0$ in some interval, then f' is increasing in that interval. Fig. 21-2 is designed to show how we can translate this statement into a statement about the graph of f. Suppose that the points P_1, P_2, and P_3 are the points of the graph of f that correspond to numbers x_1, x_2, and x_3 such that $x_1 < x_2 < x_3$. Then, since f' is increasing, the tangent line at P_2 has a larger slope than the tangent line at P_1, and the tangent line at P_3 has a still larger slope. The segments we have drawn at P_1, P_2, and P_3 show this behavior. Since a curve is closely approximated in a neighborhood of one of its points by the tangent line at the point, Fig. 21-2 suggests that our function f has a graph of the form shown in Fig. 21-3.

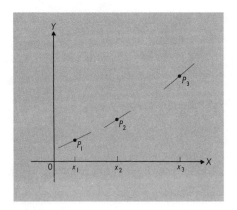

Figure 21-2

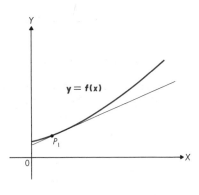

Figure 21-3

The arc in Fig. 21-3 has the following property: If we draw the tangent line at any point of the arc, then the entire arc (with the exception of the point of tangency) lies above the tangent line. Such an arc is said to be **concave up.** If an arc lies below every tangent line, then we say that the arc is **concave down.** The part of the curve in Fig. 21-1 for which $0 < x < 3$, for example, is concave down.

We were led to the arc shown in Fig. 21-3 by trying to find the geometric implications of the inequality $f''(x) > 0$. From our informal analysis above it looks as if the inequality implies that the graph of f is concave up, and the following theorem confirms this result. The proof of the theorem is rather long, but it gives us good practice in dealing with some of the fundamentals of calculus.

Theorem 21-2. *If $f''(x) > 0$ at every interior point x of an interval I, then the graph of f is concave up in I. If $f''(x) < 0$ at every interior point x of an interval I, then the graph of f is concave down in I.*

Proof. We shall only write out the proof for the case $f''(x) > 0$; the case $f''(x) < 0$ is similar. You will want to refer to Fig. 21-4 as we go along. We are to show that if we draw the tangent line at any point $(a, f(a))$, then the curve lies above this line. In other words, if the line $x = b$, where b is a point of I that is different from a, intersects our tangent line in the point (b, c), we are to show that $c < f(b)$; that is,

Figure 21-4

(21-1) $f(b) - c > 0$.

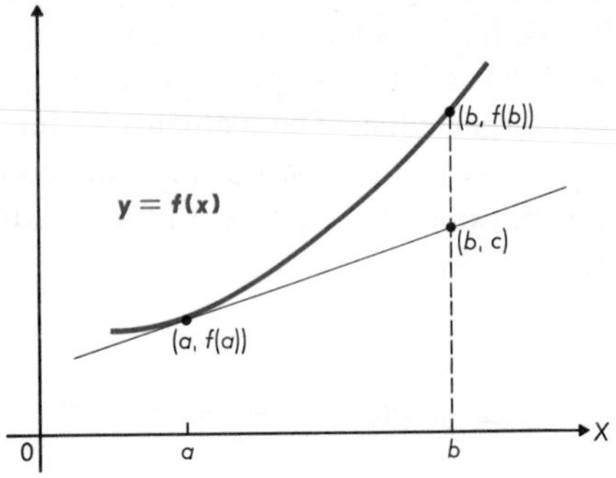

We first observe that the slope of the line that contains the points $(a, f(a))$ and (b, c) is $\dfrac{c - f(a)}{b - a}$, and since this line is a tangent line, this number must equal $f'(a)$. Therefore,

(21-2) $$c - f(a) = f'(a)(b - a).$$

According to the Theorem of the Mean, there is a point m between a and b such that $\dfrac{f(b) - f(a)}{b - a} = f'(m)$; that is,

(21-3) $$f(b) - f(a) = f'(m)(b - a).$$

Now we subtract the sides of Equation 21-2 from the corresponding sides of Equation 21-3, and we have

(21-4) $$f(b) - c = [f'(m) - f'(a)](b - a).$$

At this point we apply the Theorem of the Mean to the function f' to see that there is a number n between a and m such that $\dfrac{f'(m) - f'(a)}{m - a} = f''(n)$, and when we substitute this result into Equation 21-4, we obtain the equation

(21-5) $$f(b) - c = f''(n)(m - a)(b - a).$$

Since n is an interior point of I, our hypothesis tells us that $f''(n)$ is a positive number. Furthermore, since m is between a and b, we see that the product $(m - a)(b - a)$ is positive, regardless of the relative positions of a and b. Therefore, the right-hand side of Equation 21-5 is positive, which verifies Inequality 21-1 and completes our proof.

Our results concerning the increasing and decreasing nature of a function and the concavity of its graph are briefly summarized in the following table:

$f'(x) > 0$	f increasing
$f'(x) < 0$	f decreasing
$f''(x) > 0$	graph of f concave up
$f''(x) < 0$	graph of f concave down.

Example 21-3. Discuss the graph of the equation $y = \frac{1}{2}x + \sin x$, $x \in [0, 2\pi]$.

Solution. We can get quite a bit of information about our graph by considering the derivatives

$$D_x y = \frac{1}{2} + \cos x \text{ and } D_x^2 y = -\sin x.$$

From the first of these equations we find that for $x \in (0, \frac{2}{3}\pi) \cup (\frac{4}{3}\pi, 2\pi)$, we have $D_x y > 0$, so the curve rises to the right in that set. For $x \in (\frac{2}{3}\pi, \frac{4}{3}\pi)$, the derivative is negative and the curve falls to the right. We see that $D_x^2 y < 0$ in the interval $(0, \pi)$, and so the curve is concave down. For the interval $(\pi, 2\pi)$ we see that $D_x^2 y > 0$, and so the curve is concave up. Using the preceding information and plotting a few points enables us to sketch the graph of our equation as shown in Fig. 21-5.

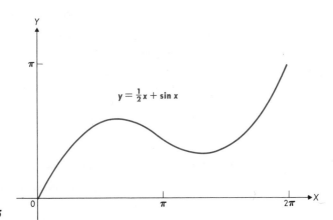

$y = \frac{1}{2}x + \sin x$

Figure 21-5

PROBLEMS 21

1. Find the intervals in which f is increasing and the intervals in which f is decreasing if
(a) $f(x) = x^3 - 6x^2 + 9x + 3$ (b) $f(x) = (x + 1)^2(x - 2)$

(c) $f(x) = \dfrac{x - 2}{(x + 1)^2}$ (d) $f(x) = \dfrac{x^2 + 1}{x}$

(e) $f(x) = \dfrac{x}{x^2 + 1}$ (f) $f(x) = \sin x + \cos x,\ x \in [0, 2\pi]$

(g) $f(x) = |\sin x| + |\cos x|,\ x \in [0, 2\pi]$ (h) $f(x) = \sin x\, |\sin x|,\ x \in [0, 2\pi]$

(i) $f(x) = \cos x + \sqrt{3}\, \sin x,\ x \in [0, 2\pi]$

2. Discuss the concavity of the graphs of the following equations:

   (a) $y = x^3 + 2x^2 + 5$ (b) $y = \sin x$

   (c) $y = x^4 - 4x^3 + 6x^2 + 12x$ (d) $y = x^4 - 4x^3 - 18x^2 + 12x - 9$

   (e) $y = \tan x$ (f) $y = |x^2 - 1|$

   (g) $y = |x^3 + 2x^2|$

   (h) $y = x^{p/q}$, where p and q are integers with no common factor

   (i) $y = 16 \sin x + \sin 2x$

3. Show that if f is increasing in some interval I, then $-f$ and $\dfrac{1}{f}$ are decreasing in I.

4. Show that if f is increasing in some interval I and if g is increasing, then the composition of f by g (assuming it exists) is increasing in I.

5. Show that

   (a) If $f'(x)g(x) > -f(x)g'(x)$ for each point x in an interval I, then the product of f and g is increasing in I.

   (b) If $f'(x)g(x) > f(x)g'(x)$ for each point x in an interval I, then the quotient of f by g is increasing in I.

6. Prove Theorem 21-1 in case $f'(x) < 0$ for each interior point of I.

7. Prove Theorem 21-2 in case $f''(x) < 0$ for each interior point of I.

8. Suppose that f is differentiable and increasing in an interval I. Show that for each interior point of I, $f'(x) \geq 0$. Can you assert that $f'(x) > 0$?

9. If $f''(x) > 0$ for every number x in the interval $[a, b]$, then we know from Theorem 21-2 that the graph of f lies above any tangent line. Show that the graph lies below the chord that joins the points $(a, f(a))$ and $(b, f(b))$.

10. If $f'(0) > 0$, show that there is a positive number r such that for $x \in (0, r)$, $f(x) > f(0)$. (Hint: See Problem 10-14.)

11. If $f(x) = \dfrac{x}{10} + x^2 \sin \dfrac{1}{x}$ for $x \neq 0$, and $f(0) = 0$, then (see Problem 13-14) $f'(0) = \dfrac{1}{10} > 0$. Is there a positive number r such that f is increasing in $(0, r)$?

REVIEW PROBLEMS—CHAPTER TWO

You can use the following problems to test yourself on the material of this chapter.

1. Let $f(x)$ be the distance between x and the nearest perfect square. Thus, $f(17) = 17 - 16 = 1$, $f(\pi) = 4 - \pi = .85840\ldots$, and so on. Find $f'(\pi)$ and $f'(1776)$. What is $f''(x)$? At what points do $f'(x)$ and $f''(x)$ fail to exist?

2. Which of the following are the same?
   (a) $D_x f(x^2)$ and $f'(x^2)$
   (b) $D_x[f(x) + g(x)]$ and $f'(x) + g'(x)$
   (c) $D_x[f(x)g(x)]$ and $f'(x)g'(x)$
   (d) $D_x f(2)$ and $f'(D_x 2)$

3. Answer the following questions as best you can by referring to the graph of f that appears in Fig. II-3. The light lines are supposed to be tangent lines.

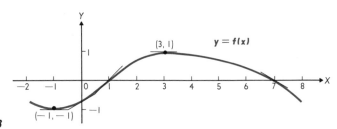

Figure II-3

(a) Find $3f(7) - 7f(3)$.

(b) Find $3f'(7) - 7f'(3)$.

(c) Find $\dfrac{f''(2)}{|f''(2)|}$.

(d) Find $g'(1)$ if $g(x) = f(x)^2$.

(e) Find $h'(-1)$ if $h(x) = f(x^2)$.

(f) Find $q'(3)$ if $q(x) = \dfrac{f(x)}{x}$.

(g) What is the largest interval in which $f'(x) > 0$?
(h) What is the largest interval in which $f''(x) < 0$?
(i) Find $T'(1)$ if $T(x) = \tan f(x)$.   (j) Find $c'(1)$ if $c(x) = f(f(x))$.
(k) The Theorem of the Mean says that there is at least one point m in the interval $(-2, 1)$ such that $\dfrac{f(1) - f(-2)}{3} = f'(m)$. Actually, how many such points are there?

4. In Chapter 6 we are going to find that $D_x 2^x = .69 \, 2^x$ (the number .69 is only approximately correct, but it will suffice for the purposes of this problem). Use this fact and the Chain Rule to find $D_x 4^x$.

5. Is there a function f for which $D_x\left(\dfrac{1}{f(x)}\right) = \dfrac{1}{D_x f(x)}$?

6. Suppose that for each $x \in R^1$, $f(x)g'(x) = f'(x)g(x)$ and that $g(x) \neq 0$. Furthermore, suppose that $f(0) = 5g(0)$. Then show that for each $x \in R^1$, $f(x) = 5g(x)$. $\left(\text{Hint: Consider the quotient} \dfrac{f(x)}{g(x)}.\right)$

7. If f is continuous in the finite interval $[a, b]$, Theorem 19-1 tells us that $f([a, b])$ is an interval. If we also know that f is increasing in $[a, b]$, show that $f([a, b]) = [f(a), f(b)]$. If f is decreasing, what is $f([a, b])$? If $f''(x) > 0$ for each $x \in [a, b]$, what is $f'([a, b])$?

8. If $f''(x) > 0$ for each x in an interval $[a, b]$, can you conclude that f is increasing in (a, b)? What if you also know that $f'(a) \geq 0$?

9. Use elementary algebra to show that between each pair of numbers a and b, with $a < b$, there is a number m such that $m^2 = \frac{1}{3}(b^2 + ab + a^2)$ and then obtain the same result from the Theorem of the Mean. Which method is easier? Notice that a and b may have opposite signs.

10. The Remainder Theorem of elementary algebra says that if $P(x)$ is a polynomial in x and r is any number, then there is a polynomial $Q(x)$ such that $P(x) = Q(x)(x - r) + P(r)$. What is $\lim\limits_{x \to r} Q(x)$?

APPLICATIONS

OF THE DERIVATIVE

T H R E E

Attempts to solve the problems that arise in natural science, from Newton's study of gravity to the present research in nuclear physics, have required the development of suitable mathematical tools. Calculus ranks high among these mathematical tools, and it is easy to see why. In science we study relationships. For example, we might be interested in the relationship between the velocity of an earth satellite and its distance from the earth. We would ask such questions as, "At what distances is the velocity increasing, at what distances it it decreasing?" "At what distances is the velocity greatest, at what distances is it least?" Calculus can help us to answer such questions.

In this chapter we will look at some of the simpler applications of calculus to geometry, and to some problems in natural science. Our object, obviously, is not to teach physics but to increase your understanding of calculus and its applications. You will see many other applications of calculus in courses in natural science and, nowadays, in the social sciences as well.

129

22 CURVE SKETCHING

Calculus is a study of functions, and functions are represented geometrically by means of graphs. It helps us visualize the concepts of calculus if we use them in sketching the graphs of equations. So in this section we are going to see what some facts we already know can tell us about curves. These facts are:

(1) *The number y' is the slope of the tangent to the graph of the equation $y = f(x)$ at the point (x, y).*

(2) *The graph of f rises to the right in an interval in which $f'(x) > 0$ and falls to the right in an interval in which $f'(x) < 0$.*

(3) *The graph of f is concave up in an interval in which $f''(x) > 0$ and concave down in an interval in which $f''(x) < 0$.*

Example 22-1.   Sketch the graph of the function f defined by the equation

$$f(x) = \frac{x^2}{8} - \frac{1}{x}.$$

Solution.   For a given number x we calculate both the number

$$y = \frac{x^2}{8} - \frac{1}{x}, \quad \text{and the number} \quad y' = \frac{x}{4} + \frac{1}{x^2}.$$

We have tabulated the results of some of these calculations in Fig. 22-1. In the coordinate system on the left side of Fig. 22-1 we have plotted the points in the table. In the coordinate system on the right, we have drawn through each of the points (x, y) a short segment with slope y'. These segments are tangent to the graph of our function.

Next we calculate

$$y'' = \frac{1}{4} - \frac{2}{x^3} = 2\left(\frac{1}{8} - \frac{1}{x^3}\right).$$

From this equation, we find that $y'' < 0$ if $0 < x < 2$, while $y'' > 0$ if $x < 0$ or if $x > 2$. Thus our curve will be concave up when $x < 0$ or when $x > 2$, and it will be concave down when x is in the interval $(0, 2)$. The curve therefore lies above the tangent lines for points to the left of the Y-axis and for points to the right of the vertical line $x = 2$. The curve lies below the tangent lines for points between the Y-axis and the vertical line $x = 2$. Figure 22-2 shows the graph of our function.

The point labeled P in Fig. 22-2 is lower (its Y-coordinate is smaller) than every other point "near" it. We call such a point a *minimum point* in accordance with the following definition.

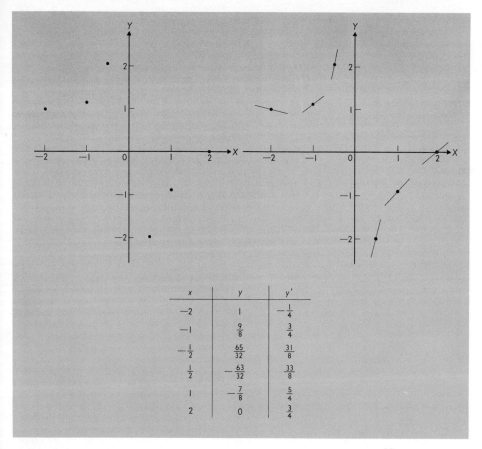

x	y	y'
-2	1	$-\frac{1}{4}$
-1	$\frac{9}{8}$	$\frac{3}{4}$
$-\frac{1}{2}$	$\frac{65}{32}$	$\frac{31}{8}$
$\frac{1}{2}$	$-\frac{63}{32}$	$\frac{33}{8}$
1	$-\frac{7}{8}$	$\frac{5}{4}$
2	0	$\frac{3}{4}$

Figure 22-1

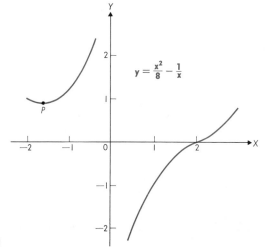

$$y = \frac{x^2}{8} - \frac{1}{x}$$

Figure 22-2

Definition 22-1. *A point $(a, f(a))$ is a **minimum point** of the graph of a function f with domain D if there is some punctured neighborhood $N_r^* a$ such that $f(x) > f(a)$ for $x \in N_r^* a \cap D$. The number $f(a)$ is called a **minimum value** of f. If the inequality sign $>$ is replaced by the sign $<$, then the point is called a **maximum point,** and $f(a)$ is a **maximum value** of f.*

Many authors use the term *relative* minimum point where we have simply said minimum point, because the Y-coordinate of a minimum point is only compared with the Y-coordinates of nearby points, not *all* the Y-coordinates. For example, there are points of the graph in Fig. 22-2 that are lower than the minimum point P, so P is not an "absolute" minimum point; it is just the lowest point in its vicinity.

From Theorem 19-2 we know that: *If a belongs to an open interval in the domain of a differentiable function f, and if $(a, f(a))$ is a maximum or a minimum point of the graph of f, then $f'(a) = 0$.* This fact is illustrated in Fig. 22-2, where it is clear that the slope of the graph at the point P is 0. Thus, to find the X-coordinate of P, we will solve the equation $f'(x) = 0$. Since $f'(x) = \dfrac{x}{4} + \dfrac{1}{x^2}$, this equation is

$$\frac{x}{4} + \frac{1}{x^2} = 0,$$

from which we find $x = -\sqrt[3]{4} = -1.6$. Now we calculate $f(-1.6) = \dfrac{(-1.6)^2}{8} + \dfrac{1}{1.6} = .95$, to see that P is the point $(-1.6, .95)$.

The equation $f'(a) = 0$ is neither a necessary nor a sufficient condition that the point $(a, f(a))$ be a maximum or a minimum point. Figure 22-3 illustrates various possibilities. At the maximum point P and the minimum point Q, the curve has a horizontal tangent. But the tangent is also horizontal at the point R, which is neither a maximum nor a minimum point. Furthermore, if we confine our search

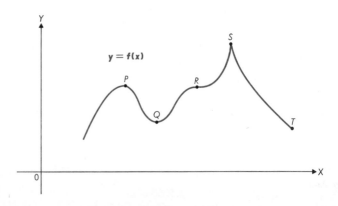

Figure 22-3

for maximum and minimum points to those points whose X-coordinates satisfy the equation $f'(x) = 0$, we will miss the maximum point S and the minimum point T. The graph doesn't have a slope at S (so it cannot have slope 0 there), and the point T is an **endpoint**.

The above remarks tell us that we are to look for maximum and minimum points of the graph of a function f among the points (x, y) such that

(1) $f'(x) = 0$,
(2) $f'(x)$ does not exist, or
(3) (x, y) is an endpoint of the graph.

We will call a point that satisfies one of these conditions a **critical point**. *A maximum or a minimum point must be a critical point, but critical points need not be maximum or minimum points.*

Example 22-2. Find the maximum and minimum points and sketch the graph of f if $f(x) = 2\sqrt{x} - x$.

Solution. The domain of f is the interval $[0, \infty)$. The derivative exists at all points in $(0, \infty)$, and

$$f'(x) = \frac{1}{\sqrt{x}} - 1.$$

Thus the only solution to the equation $f'(x) = 0$ is 1, so the critical points of our graph are the point $(1, 1)$ at which the tangent is horizontal and the endpoint $(0, 0)$. When we write $f(x)$ in the form $f(x) = \sqrt{x}(2 - \sqrt{x})$, it is clear that if x is slightly larger than 0, then $f(x) > 0$, and so $(0, 0)$ is a minimum point. On the other hand, $1 - f(x) = 1 - 2\sqrt{x} + x = (1 - \sqrt{x})^2$, which is positive if $x \neq 1$. Therefore $f(x) < 1$ if $x \neq 1$, and we see that $(1, 1)$ is a maximum point. Since $f''(x) = -x^{-3/2}$, a negative number, the curve is concave down. A sketch of the graph f appears in Fig. 22-4.

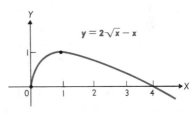

Figure 22-4

To find a rule for selecting maximum and minimum points from among the critical points of the graph of a function f, let us again refer to Fig. 22-3. At points to the left of the maximum points P and S, the derived function f' takes positive values (the graph has positive slope), while for points to the right of P and S, f' takes negative values. The situation is reversed at the minimum point Q. In a neighborhood of a critical point such as R, the derivatives of $f(x)$ have the same signs. The following theorem, the **First Derivative Test,** tells this story in more formal terms.

Theorem 22-1.   *If the function f is continuous at the point a and is differentiable in some punctured neighborhood N_r^*a, then,*

(i)   *$f(a)$ is a maximum value of f if $f'(x)$ is positive for $x \in (a - r, a)$ and $f'(x)$ is negative for $x \in (a, a + r)$.*

(ii)   *$f(a)$ is a minimum value of f if $f'(x)$ is negative for $x \in (a - r, a)$ and $f'(x)$ is positive for $x \in (a, a + r)$.*

(iii)   *$f(a)$ is neither a maximum nor a minimum value of f if $f'(x) > 0$ for $x \in N_r^*a$ or $f'(x) < 0$ for $x \in N_r^*a$.*

Proof. This theorem is a direct consequence of Theorem 21-1. For example, suppose the hypotheses of statement (i) are satisfied. Then Theorem 21-1 tells us that f is increasing in the interval $(a - r, a]$ and decreasing in the interval $[a, a + r)$, so $f(a)$ is clearly a maximum value. Statements (ii) and (iii) are equally easy to deduce.

Remark. It is clear how to modify statements (i) and (ii) to make them apply to the case in which $(a, f(a))$ is an endpoint.

Example 22-3.   Apply the First Derivative Test (Theorem 22-1) to the function f of Example 22-2.

Solution. As our punctured neighborhood of the point 1, we choose $N_1^*1 = (0, 1) \cup (1, 2)$ (other choices are possible, but we only need one). We see that if $x \in (0, 1)$, then $f'(x) = \dfrac{1}{\sqrt{x}} - 1 > 0$, while if $x \in (1, 2)$, $f'(x) < 0$. Therefore statement (i) of our theorem applies, and says that $f(1)$ is a maximum value of f. For each point $x \in (0, 1)$, $f'(x) > 0$, so statement (ii) (modified for the endpoint case) applies to tell us that $(0, 0)$ is a minimum point of the graph of f.

To apply the First Derivative Test to a critical point $(a, f(a))$, we must consider signs of values of f' in a punctured neighborhood of a. Now we will introduce a test for maxima and minima that requires us to check the sign of only one number, the number $f''(a)$. This test is called the **Second Derivative Test.** It applies, you will notice, only to those critical points at which the first derivative is 0, whereas the First Derivative Test applies to other types of critical points as well.

Theorem 22-2.   *Suppose that f is differentiable in an open interval that contains the point a and that $f'(a) = 0$. Then,*

(i)   *$f(a)$ is a maximum value of f if $f''(a) < 0$, and*

(ii)   *$f(a)$ is a minimum value of f if $f''(a) > 0$.*

If $f''(a) = 0$, this test does not apply.

Proof. By definition, $f''(a) = \lim\limits_{x \to a} \dfrac{f'(x) - f'(a)}{x - a}$. We are assuming that $f'(a) = 0$, so our difference quotient simplifies to $\dfrac{f'(x)}{x - a}$. Suppose, for the moment, that $f''(a) > 0$. Then we have $\lim\limits_{x \to a} \dfrac{f'(x)}{x - a} > 0$. In Problem 10-14 we asked you to show that this inequality implies that there is a punctured neighborhood N_r^*a such that if $x \in N_r^*a$, then $\dfrac{f'(x)}{x - a} > 0$. This last inequality tells us that if $x \in (a - r, a)$, then $f'(x) < 0$, whereas if $x \in (a, a + r)$, then $f'(x) > 0$. The conditions of Statement (ii) of Theorem 22-1 are therefore satisfied, and so $(a, f(a))$ is a minimum point. If $f''(a) < 0$, we prove our present theorem by applying statement (i) of Theorem 22-1 in a similar way.

Our discussion has shown that there are two steps in finding the maximum and minimum points of the graph of a given function:

(1) We first locate the critical points, and then
(2) We test each critical point—perhaps by using the First or Second Derivative Test—to see which are maximum points, minimum points, or neither.

Example 22-4. Test the function that is defined by the equation $f(x) = \sin^{2/3} x$ in the interval $[0, 2\pi]$ for maximum and minimum points.

Solution. For each point x at which f is differentiable, we have

$$f'(x) = \tfrac{2}{3} \sin^{-1/3} x \cos x;$$

f is not differentiable at the points for which $\sin x = 0$. Thus in this example we have critical points of all three kinds; $f'(x) = 0$ when $x = \dfrac{\pi}{2}$ and $\dfrac{3\pi}{2}$, $f'(x)$ does not exist when $x = \pi$, and we must consider the endpoints $(0, 0)$ and $(2\pi, 0)$. The signs of $f'(x)$, for $x \in (0, 2\pi)$, are indicated in Fig. 22-5 ($*$ means that $f'(x)$ does not exist;

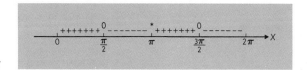

Figure 22-5

0 means that $f'(x) = 0$), and from this figure and Theorem 22-1 we see that $(0, 0)$ $(\pi, 0)$, and $(2\pi, 0)$ are minimum points, whereas $\left(\dfrac{\pi}{2}, 1\right)$ and $\left(\dfrac{3\pi}{2}, 1\right)$ are maximum

points. We find, furthermore, that $f''(x) = -\frac{2}{9} \sin^{-4/3} x \cos^2 x - \frac{2}{3} \sin^{2/3} x$. Therefore $f''\left(\frac{\pi}{2}\right) = f''\left(\frac{3\pi}{2}\right) = -\frac{2}{3}$, and the fact that the second derivatives of f are negative at the points at which f' is 0 also shows, according to Theorem 22-2, that $f\left(\frac{\pi}{2}\right)$ and $f\left(\frac{3\pi}{2}\right)$ are maximum values of f.

PROBLEMS 22

1. Let $y = x + \dfrac{1}{x}$.

(a) Complete the following table.

x	-2	-1	$-\frac{1}{2}$	$\frac{1}{2}$	1	2
y						
y'						
y''						

(b) Discuss the concavity of the graph of the equation.
(c) Find the maximum and minimum points.
(d) Sketch the graph of the equation, showing the tangent lines at the points of the table, for x in the set $[-2, 0) \cup (0, 2]$.

2. Sketch the graphs of the following equations for x in the interval $[0, 2\pi]$, making use of your knowledge of maximum and minimum points, concavity, and so on.
  (a) $y = \sin^{1/3} x$ (b) $y = \sin^{2/3} x$ (c) $y = \sin^4 x$ (d) $y = \sin^{4/3} x$

3. Find the maximum and minimum points, discuss the concavity, and sketch the graph of the equation $y = x^4 - 2x^3 - 12x^2 + 26x - 13$.

4. Find the maximum and minimum points of the graph of f.
  (a) $f(x) = |x^2 - 1|$ (b) $f(x) = |\sin x|$
  (c) $f(x) = \dfrac{x(x - 2)}{(x + 1)^2}$ (d) $f(x) = x^{3/2}(x - 1)^{2/3}$
  (e) $f(x) = 1 - |\sin x|$ (f) $f(x) = \cos x + \sin x + |\cos x - \sin x|$
  (g) $f(x) = \sqrt{x} \cos x,\ x \in [0, \pi/2]$ (h) $f(x) = \sqrt{2 - x} - \sqrt{x + 1}$

5. Suppose that f is an increasing function. Show that the maximum and minimum values of the composite function defined by the equation $y = f(g(x))$ occur at the points at which g takes its maximum and minimum values.

6. Discuss completely the graph of the general quadratic equation $y = ax^2 + bx + c$.

7. Let $f(x) = (x - a)^m(x - b)^n$, where m and n are integers and $a \neq b$. Discuss the maximum and minimum points of the graph of f, considering the different cases that occur when m and n are even or odd integers.

8. Prove Statement (iii) of Theorem 22-1.

9. Discuss the problem of finding the maximum and minimum values of the function f that is defined by the equation $f(x) = \dfrac{\sin x}{x}$.

10. If a function f is differentiable in a right and a left neighborhood of a point a at which f is continuous, and if the values of f'' are all positive in one of the two neighborhoods and negative in the other, then the point $(a, f(a))$ is a **point of inflection** of the graph of f. Find points of inflection for the following functions.

(a) $f(x) = \tan x + \cot x$ (b) $f(x) = \sqrt{x} + \dfrac{1}{\sqrt{x}}$

(c) $f(x) = \cos x + \sin x + |\cos x - \sin x|$

11. Find $f([a, b])$ for the following functions and intervals

(a) $f(x) = x + \dfrac{1}{x}$, $[\frac{1}{2}, 3]$ (b) $f(x) = \dfrac{\sqrt{x}}{1 + x^2}$, $[0, \infty]$

12. What is the range of the function f defined by the equation $f(x) = \sqrt{3 - x} - \sqrt{x + 2}$?

23 PROBLEMS INVOLVING MAXIMA AND MINIMA

Some of the most important problems in mathematics and in the applications of mathematics can be solved by finding maximum or minimum values of functions. We will devote this section to some examples.

In Section 5 (Illustration 5–4) we showed that if a cylindrical tin can with a capacity of 54π cubic inches is constructed from material costing .012¢ per square inch for the sides and .021¢ per square inch for the top and bottom then the relation between the cost c in cents and the base radius r in inches is given by the equation

(23-1) $$c = \frac{108\pi}{r}(.012) + 2\pi r^2(.021).$$

For each choice of r we obtain a number c. Thus, for example, if we select $r = 2$, we obtain $c = 2.57$, so a can with a 2-inch base radius costs 2.57 cents; a can with a base radius of 3 inches costs 2.54 cents, and so on. Since each different choice of a number r as radius yields a different number c as cost, a natural question to ask is, "What choice of r results in the *smallest* number c?"—that is, "What is the radius of the cheapest can?"

Our knowledge of the maximum and minimum points of graphs will help us answer this question. Figure 23-1 shows the graph of Equation 23-1 for

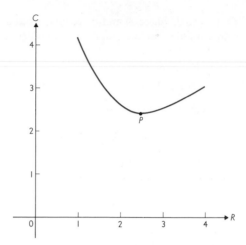

Figure 23-1

$r > 0$. If (r, c) is a point of this graph, then a can with a radius of r inches costs c cents. The point labeled P in Fig. 23-1 has the smallest C-coordinate of any point of the graph. Therefore the R-coordinate of P represents the radius, and the C-coordinate of P represents the cost, of the cheapest can. So our question, "What is the radius of the cheapest can?" will be answered when we find the R-coordinate of the minimum point P.

It is clear from Fig. 23-1 that we can find the R-coordinate of P by solving the equation $D_r c = 0$. From Equation 23-1 we find that

$$(23\text{-}2) \qquad D_r c = -\frac{108\pi(.012)}{r^2} + 4\pi r(.021).$$

Therefore, the equation $D_r c = 0$ becomes

$$4\pi r(.021) - \frac{108\pi}{r^2}(.012) = 0.$$

It is a simple matter to solve this last equation for r:

$$r = \sqrt[3]{\frac{108\pi(.012)}{4\pi(.021)}} = 2.49.$$

Thus the radius of the cheapest can is 2.49 inches. To find its cost, we simply replace r in Equation 23-1 with 2.49, and find that $c = 2.45$. The cheapest can has a radius of 2.49 inches and costs 2.45 cents.

Notice that we only used the graph in Fig. 23-1 to convince ourselves that we could find the coordinates of the minimum point P by solving the equation

$D_r c = 0$. Actually, we could have relied on our previous theory and dispensed altogether with drawing the picture. The only critical points of the graph of Equation 23-1 are those at which $D_r c = 0$. If we have any doubts whether such a critical point is a maximum point, or a minimum point, or neither, we can consider the second derivative. It is easy to see that

$$D_r^2 c = 4\pi(.021) + (216\pi)(.012)/r^3.$$

Thus $D^2 c > 0$ for every $r > 0$. It follows that the graph of Equation 23-1 is concave up, and hence it is clear that a point at which $D_r c = 0$ is a minimum point. The First Derivative Test or The Second Derivative Test could also be used to verify that we have a minimum point.

In order to solve the "word problems" of this section, it will pay you to proceed according to the following steps:

(i) Read the problem carefully, and draw a sketch to illustrate it if you can.

(ii) Determine exactly what quantity you want to be a maximum or a minimum.

(iii) Use the data of the problem to express the quantity to be maximized or minimized in terms of some one other quantity, thus obtaining an equation of the form $y = f(x)$, $A = g(r)$, or the like.

(iv) Find the critical points of the graph of the equation found in the preceding step and determine the nature of these critical points—maximum points, minimum points, or neither.

(v) Re-read the problem to see explicitly what question was asked and then see if you can answer the question with the information you now have.

We will devote the remainder of this section to examples that show how to use these steps in solving maximum and minimum problems.

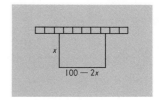

Figure 23-2

Example 23-1. A farmer has 100 yards of fencing. He wishes to construct a rectangular enclosure along a long stone wall, using the wall as one side of the enclosure and fencing in the other three sides. What is the largest area he can enclose?

Solution. We follow the five steps listed above.

(i) From the description, we sketch the drawing of the enclosure shown in Fig. 23-2.

(ii) We wish to find the maximum area.

(iii) If the side of the enclosure perpendicular to the wall is x yards long, then the side parallel to the wall is $100 - 2x$ yards long. So if the area is A square yards, then

(23-3) $A = x(100 - 2x) = 100x - 2x^2.$

(iv) From the nature of the problem, we see that x must be a number satisfying the inequalities $0 < x < 50$ in order to obtain a proper rectangle. So there are no endpoints to consider, and the X-coordinate of the critical point is found from the equation

$$D_xA = 100 - 4x = 0.$$

Thus $x = 25$. We see that $D_x^2A = -4 < 0$, and hence The Second Derivative Test tells us that we have found a maximum point.

(v) Finally, the question asked us to find the maximum area. We know that the maximum area is attained when $x = 25$. So we set $x = 25$ in Equation 23-3 to find that

$$A_{max} = 25(100 - 50) = 1,250 \text{ square yards.}$$

Example 23-2. A man who can swim 20 feet per second and run 25 feet per second stands at the edge of a circular swimming pool that has a radius of 50 feet. He wishes to reach a point one-quarter of the way around the pool in the least possible time, and he plans to run along the edge of the pool for a way and then dive in and swim straight to his destination. What is the shortest possible time required for this maneuver?

Solution. Again we follow our five steps.

(i) In Fig. 23-3 we have sketched a quarter circle that represents the perimeter of the pool. Our man will run along the circle from A to P, a distance of s feet, and then swim from P to B, a distance of c feet.

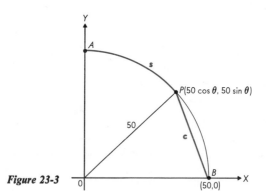

Figure 23-3

(ii) We wish to minimize the time it takes him to get from A to B.

(iii) The total number of seconds, t, that it takes our man to go from A to B is the sum of the time required to go from A to P and the time required to go from

P to B. It takes $\dfrac{s}{25}$ seconds to run from A to P and then $\dfrac{c}{20}$ seconds to swim to B, and hence

(23-4)
$$t = \frac{s}{25} + \frac{c}{20}.$$

We have now expressed t in terms of s and c, and to complete this step we must express t in terms of *some one* quantity. So let us write both s and c in terms of the number θ, the radian measure of $\angle BOP$. The coordinates of P are $(50 \cos \theta, 50 \sin \theta)$, and so the Distance Formula gives the distance between P and the point $B(50, 0)$ as

$$c = \sqrt{(50 \cos \theta - 50)^2 + (50 \sin \theta)^2}$$
$$= 50 \sqrt{\cos^2 \theta - 2 \cos \theta + 1 + \sin^2 \theta}$$
$$= 50 \sqrt{2(1 - \cos \theta)}$$
$$= 50 \sqrt{4 \sin^2 \frac{\theta}{2}}$$
$$= 100 \sin \frac{\theta}{2}.$$

Furthermore, since $\angle POA$ is an angle of $\dfrac{\pi}{2} - \theta$ radians, we have $s = 50\left(\dfrac{\pi}{2} - \theta\right)$. Now we can replace s and c in Equation 23-4 with their expressions in terms of θ, and we obtain the following expression for t in terms of the single quantity θ:

(23-5)
$$t = \frac{50\left(\dfrac{\pi}{2} - \theta\right)}{25} + \frac{100 \sin \dfrac{\theta}{2}}{20} = \pi - 2\theta + 5 \sin \frac{\theta}{2}.$$

The statement of the problem tells us that $\theta \in \left[0, \dfrac{\pi}{2}\right]$.

(iv) The critical points of the graph of Equation 23-5 are the endpoints—the points at which $\theta = 0$ and $\theta = \dfrac{\pi}{2}$—and the points at which $D_\theta t = 0$. We have

$$D_\theta t = -2 + \frac{5}{2} \cos \frac{\theta}{2} \quad \text{and} \quad D_\theta^2 t = -\frac{5}{4} \sin \frac{\theta}{2}.$$

Thus we see that $D_\theta^2 t < 0$ for $\theta \in \left(0, \dfrac{\pi}{2}\right)$, and therefore our curve is concave down. Hence the only minimum points are the endpoints of the arc.

(v) From Equation 23-5 we find that $t = \pi$ when $\theta = 0$, and $t = \dfrac{5\sqrt{2}}{2}$ when $\theta = \dfrac{\pi}{2}$. Since $\dfrac{5\sqrt{2}}{2} > \pi$, we see that our man uses the least time when $\theta = 0$; that is, he runs all the way and doesn't swim at all, and this minimum time is π seconds.

P R O B L E M S   2 3

1. A rectangular box with a square base is to be made from 300 square inches of tin. Find the dimensions of the box of maximum volume if:
   (a) The box has a top.   (b) The box has no top.

2. If our man in Example 23-2 takes the longest possible time to get from A to B, at what point does he dive in?

3. Equal squares are cut from each corner of a piece of tin measuring 6 inches by 6 inches, and the edges are then turned up to form a rectangular box with no lid. What is the volume of the largest such box?

4. A triangle whose base angles are acute has an altitude of h inches and a base of b inches. A rectangle is placed inside the triangle with one side on the base of the triangle. Show that the maximum possible area of such a rectangle is one-half the area of the triangle.

5. Suppose it requires S square inches of tin to make a cylindrical can with a top and bottom. Show that for such a can to be of maximum volume, the diameter of the base must equal the altitude.

6. Prove that the product of two positive real numbers whose nth powers add up to 1 is a maximum when they are equal.

7. A rectangular wall is to have an area of 12 square yards. What should be the height and width of the wall so that a brace from one base corner to the midpoint of the opposite vertical side is of minimum length?

8. An irrigation ditch is to have a cross section in the shape of an isosceles trapezoid, wider at the top than at the bottom, and with a horizontal base. The bottom and the equal sides of the trapezoid are each to be L feet long. Suppose the side of the ditch makes an acute angle of θ with the horizontal.
   (a) Show that the cross-sectional area of the ditch is given by the equation $A = L^2(\sin \theta + \sin \theta \cos \theta)$.
   (b) For what angle will the carrying capacity of the ditch be a maximum?

9. A page is to contain 24 square inches of print. The margins at the top and bottom are each to be one and a half inches. Each margin at the side is to be 1 inch. What are the dimensions of the smallest such page?

10. An E-volt battery has an internal resistance of r ohms. If a resistor of R ohms is connected across the battery terminals, then a current of I amps will flow and generate P watts of power, where

$$I = \frac{E}{R + r}, \quad \text{and} \quad P = I^2 R.$$

For what resistance R will the power generated be a maximum?

11. While driving through the north woods, Bill runs out of gas. He can reach the nearest gas station either by walking 1 mile north and 10 miles east along paved roads, or by walking through the woods in a northeasterly direction until he

reaches the paved road and then proceeding east along the road to the gas station. Suppose he can walk 5 miles per hour along the paved roads, and 3 miles per hour through the woods. Describe the path he should follow in order to reach the gas station in the shortest time.

12. Two cottages are located on the shores of a circular lake that is two miles in diameter. Cottage A is one-fourth of the way around the lake from Cottage B. Where should a third cottage be located so that the sum of its distances from Cottages A and B is a maximum?

13. An experiment is performed n times, and n numbers (measurements) $x_1, x_2, \ldots, x_n$ are obtained. In order to obtain an "average" number, we choose the number x that makes the sum of the squares of the differences between x and each x_i the least; that is, we choose the number x that makes $s = (x - x_1)^2 + (x - x_2)^2 + \cdots + (x - x_n)^2$ a minimum. Show that we get the usual arithmetic mean as our "average" number.

14. A wall h feet high stands d feet away from a tall building. A ladder L feet long reaches from the ground outside the wall to the building. Let the acute angle between the ladder and the horizontal be an angle of θ.
    (a) Show that if the ladder touches the top of the wall, $L = h \csc \theta + d \sec \theta$.
    (b) Find the shortest ladder that will reach the building if $h = 8$ and $d = 24$.

24 LINEAR MOTION AND RELATED RATES

If a projectile fired vertically upward with an initial velocity of 96 feet per second reaches a height of s feet above its launching site after t seconds, then the numbers s and t are related by the formula

$$(24\text{-}1) \qquad s = -16t^2 + 96t.$$

We have already defined velocity as the rate of change of distance with respect to time; that is, $v = D_t s$. For our projectile, $D_t s = -32t + 96$ and so v is expressed in terms of t by the equation

$$(24\text{-}2) \qquad v = -32t + 96.$$

Here we are measuring distance in feet and time in seconds, and hence velocity is measured in feet per second. The absolute value $|v|$ is called the **speed** of the projectile.

We saw in Section 21 that the inequality $D_t s > 0$ implies that distance is increasing, and the inequality $D_t s < 0$ implies that distance is decreasing. In our present example, then, we see that when $v > 0$, the distance between the projectile and the launching site is increasing (the projectile is moving up), while if $v < 0$, the distance is decreasing (the projectile is moving down).

The number $a = D_t v$ measures the rate of change of velocity with respect to time, that is, the **acceleration** of the projectile. For our projectile,

(24-3) $a = D_t v = -32.$

Acceleration is measured in units of velocity per unit of time. Here it is measured in feet per second per second.

Equation 24-3 tells us that the derivative $D_t v$ is negative. Hence the velocity of our projectile decreases as time increases. The projectile starts at a velocity of 96 feet per second and slows down to 0 feet per second. Then it begins to fall, *but its velocity continues to decrease* through negative values. The *speed* of the projectile increases as the body falls.

Example 24-1. For the projectile whose motion is described by Equation 24-1 find the maximum height, the total time of flight, and the maximum velocity.

Solution. The projectile reaches its maximum height when $D_t s = v = -32t + 96 = 0$; that is, 3 seconds after launching. According to Equation 24-1, $s = -16 \cdot 3^2 + 96 \cdot 3 = 144$ feet at that moment. We will assume that a projectile fired vertically upward will return to its starting point. Hence the duration of its flight is found by solving the equation $s = 0$; that is, $-16t^2 + 96t = 0$. There are two solutions to this equation: $t = 0$ and $t = 6$. When $t = 0$, the projectile is at its launching point at the start of the flight, and when $t = 6$ the projectile is at its launching point after completing its flight. Thus its total time of flight is 6 seconds. The projectile's velocity is decreasing during its flight, so the maximum value of the velocity occurs when $t = 0$, and is 96 feet per second.

In general we will picture a body moving along a line as a point moving along a number scale (Fig. 24-1). Let s denote the coordinate of the point t seconds

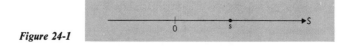

Figure 24-1

after some initial instant of time. The number s is positive if the point is on the positive side of the origin. In our projectile problem we placed the number scale so that the "up" direction was positive, and $s = 0$ when $t = 0$. In general, we do not insist that s be 0 when $t = 0$. If the velocity of our moving point is measured by the number v, the acceleration by the number a, and the speed by the number r, then, by definition,

$$v = D_t s,$$

(24-4) $$a = D_t v = D_t^2 s,$$

$$r = |v|.$$

Example 24-2.   Discuss the motion of a particle that moves along the number scale of Fig. 24-1 in accordance with the equation $s = t + \dfrac{1}{t}$ for $t > 0$.

Solution.   We have

$$s = t + \frac{1}{t},$$

$$v = D_t s = 1 - \frac{1}{t^2},$$

$$a = D_t^2 s = \frac{2}{t^3}.$$

For t close to 0, the number s is very large, and hence our particle is very far from the origin. For t in the interval $(0, 1)$, v is negative, and hence s is decreasing. Thus the particle moves to the left. When $t = 1$, $v = 0$, and for $t > 1$, $v > 0$. Thus our particle stops and reverses direction when $t = 1$. At this instant $s = 2$, so the closest the particle comes to the origin is the point two units to the right of it. For $t > 1$, the particle moves to the right, and as time goes on it recedes indefinitely. The acceleration is always positive; that is, the velocity is continually increasing. However, notice that the velocity always remains less than 1.

Example 24-3.   Show that a particle moving along a line is speeding up in time intervals in which its velocity and acceleration have the same sign and slowing down in time intervals in which they have opposite signs.

Solution.   We are to show that the speed r is increasing or decreasing in the indicated intervals, so we look at the sign of its derivative $D_t r$. From the definitions of r and a, we have

$$D_t r = D_t |v| = \frac{v}{|v|} D_t v = \frac{va}{|v|}.$$

Since this number will be positive (hence r is increasing) when v and a have the same sign, and negative (hence r is decreasing) when they have opposite signs, our original statement is verified.

In Examples 24-1 and 24-2 we found the rate of change of s with respect to t in a straightforward way; we had an expression for s in terms of t, and we differentiated it. Sometimes, however, we want the rate of change of a quantity that we cannot, or at least find it inconvenient to, express in terms of time. Let us look at an example.

Suppose a spherical snowball melts in such a way that at the instant its radius is 4 inches its volume is decreasing at the rate of 2 cubic inches per minute. How fast is the radius changing at that instant? If the snowball has a radius of r inches t minutes after some initial time, the problem amounts to finding the number $D_t r$ when $r = 4$. So if we could express r in terms of t, we would simply have a problem in differentiation. But we are not given enough information to write r in terms of t, and therefore we must attack the problem differently.

At the instant we are interested in, the volume of the snowball is decreasing at the rate of 2 cubic inches per minute. Therefore if the volume is V cubic inches, then $D_tV = -2$ at our given instant (the minus sign indicates that the volume is decreasing then). Thus we are given D_tV, and we are asked to find D_tr. To solve the problem, we will find the relation between these two rates. We first find a relation between V and r and then differentiate to find out how the rates of change of V and of r are related. Because the snowball is spherical, the relation between V and r is

$$V = \frac{4\pi r^3}{3}.$$

Now we differentiate (using the Power Formula 16-2) to find the equation

$$D_tV = 4\pi r^2 \, D_tr.$$

Since we are interested in the value of D_tr when $r = 4$, we replace r with 4 and D_tV with -2 in this equation and obtain the equation $-2 = 64\pi \, D_tr$. It follows that

$$D_tr = -\frac{1}{32\pi} \text{ inches per minute when } r = 4,$$

which answers our original question.

In a typical problem in related rates, we are given one of two rates D_tx or D_ty (or two of three, D_tx, D_ty, or D_tz, and so on) and are asked to find the other rate at some particular instant of time. Of course we may use letters other than x and y as, for example, we used V and r in the problem above. We follow these steps:

(i) Find an equation that expresses y in terms of x; a figure is often helpful.

(ii) Differentiate with respect to t to obtain the relation between the given and the desired rates.

(iii) Substitute in the equation found in Step (ii) the data given in the problem and evaluate the unknown rate.

Example 24-4. A television cameraman is televising a 100-yard dash. He is located 10 yards away from the track in line with the finish line (Fig. 24-2). When the runners are 10 yards from the finish line, his camera is turning at the rate of $\frac{2}{5}$ radians per second. How fast are the runners moving at that instant?

Solution. Figure 24-2 shows the situation at the instant the runners

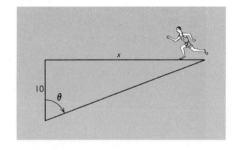

Figure 24-2

are x yards from the finish line, at which time θ is the radian measure of the angle between the line joining the camera and the runners and the finish line extended to the camera. We are told that $D_t\theta = -\frac{3}{5}$ radians per second when $x = 10$. Our steps in the solution are:

(i) From Fig. 24-2, we see that $x = 10 \tan \theta$.

(ii) Therefore, according to the rule for differentiating $\tan \theta$, we have

(24-5) $D_t x = 10 \sec^2 \theta \; D_t\theta.$

(iii) We are interested in the speed of the runners when $x = 10$. At that point we clearly have $\theta = \frac{\pi}{4}$, and therefore $\sec \theta = \sqrt{2}$. So Equation 24-5 becomes $D_t x = 10(\sqrt{2})^2(-\frac{3}{5}) = -12$, and we see that our runners are approaching the finish line at the rate of 12 yards per second.

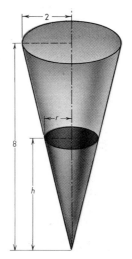

Example 24-5. A freshman is drinking a soda through a straw from a conical cup 8 inches deep and 4 inches in diameter at the top. At the instant the soda is 5 inches deep, he is drinking at the rate of 3 cubic inches per second. How fast is the level of the soda dropping at that time?

Figure 24-3

Solution. Suppose that t seconds after the freshman starts drinking, the soda is h inches deep and V cubic inches in volume. We know that $D_t V = -3$ when $h = 5$, and we are asked to find $D_t h$. We follow our three steps.

(i) In Fig. 24-3 we have illustrated the situation at some instant of time. The formula for the volume of a cone gives us

(24-6) $V = \dfrac{\pi r^2 h}{3}.$

Furthermore, from the similar triangles in the figure we see that $\dfrac{r}{2} = \dfrac{h}{8}$; that is,

(24-7) $r = \tfrac{1}{4}h.$

We can substitute this expression for r in Equation 24-6 to obtain the equation

$$V = \pi \frac{h^2}{16} \cdot \frac{h}{3} = \frac{\pi h^3}{48}.$$

(ii) Therefore, from the Power Rule, $D_t V = \dfrac{\pi h^2}{16} D_t h.$

(iii) We substitute the given values $D_t V = -3$ and $h = 5$ in the equation we found in Step (ii), and we have $-3 = \frac{\pi}{16} 5^2 D_t h$, from which it follows that $D_t h = -48/25\,\pi$. Thus the level of the soda is dropping at the rate of $48/25\pi$ inches per second.

We could also have proceeded as follows. If we apply the Product Rule to Equation 24-6, we find that

$$D_t V = \frac{2\pi rh}{3} D_t r + \frac{\pi r^2}{3} D_t h.$$

Also, Equation 24-7 gives us

$$D_t r = \tfrac{1}{4} D_t h.$$

Now we substitute our given values $D_t V = -3$ and $h = 5$ in these equations and Equation 24-7 and solve for $D_t h$. For our present problem this second method is slightly more complicated than our first solution. There are problems, however, for which it is superior.

P R O B L E M S   2 4

1. For the indicated time, find the position, velocity, speed, and acceleration of a point moving along a number scale if:

(a) $s = t + \dfrac{2}{t^2}$, $t = \tfrac{1}{2}$

(b) $s = \tan \dfrac{\pi t}{3}$, $t = 2$

(c) $s = |t - 1| + |t - 3|^3$, $t = 2$

(d) $s = |\tfrac{1}{2} - \sin t|$, $t = \dfrac{41\pi}{4}$

2. Discuss the motion of a point that moves along the number scale in accordance with the given equation.

(a) $s = 9t + \dfrac{4}{t}$, $t \in (0, \infty)$

(b) $s = \sin t + \csc t$, $t \in (0, \pi)$

(c) $s = t^{2[\![t]\!]}$, $t \in (0, 2)$

(d) $s = t^2 + \dfrac{1}{t} - \left| t^2 - \dfrac{1}{t} \right|$, $t \in (0, \infty)$

3. A projectile is fired from a balloon in such a way that it is s feet above the ground t seconds after firing, and $s = -16t^2 + 96t + 256$.
   (a) How high was the balloon when the projectile was fired?
   (b) What is the maximum height reached by the projectile?
   (c) How fast is the projectile going when it hits the earth?

4. A rocket travels upward from the surface of the earth and is s miles high t minutes after lift-off. Suppose that $s = 200 + 100 \sec\left(2t + \dfrac{2\pi}{3}\right)$.

   (a) How high does the rocket go?
   (b) How fast is the rocket going when it hits the earth?
   (c) What is the duration of the flight?
   (d) What is the maximum speed of the rocket?

5. A point moves along the number scale in accordance with the equation $s = 3t^4 - 4t^3 + 2$. How close does the point come to the origin? What is its minimum speed? What is its minimum velocity?

6. A conical soda cup is 4 inches across the top and 6 inches deep. A soda jerk fills it at the rate of 2 cubic inches per second. What is the vertical velocity of a bubble on the top of the liquid when the soda is halfway to the top?

7. Find the vertical velocity of the bubble in the preceding problem when $h = 3$ if the soda cup has a leak in it through which the soda is running out at the rate of 1 cubic inch per second as it is being filled.

8. A horizontal eaves trough 10 feet long has a triangular cross section 4 inches across the top and 4 inches deep. During a rainstorm, the water in the trough is rising at the rate of $\frac{1}{4}$ inch per minute when the depth is 2 inches. How fast is the volume of water in the trough increasing? After the rain has stopped, the water drains out of the trough at the rate of 40 cubic inches per minute. How fast is the surface of the water falling when the depth is 1 inch?

9. A 13-foot ladder leans against the wall of a house. Someone pulls the base of the ladder away from the house at the rate of 2 feet per second. How fast is the top of the ladder sliding down the wall when it is 5 feet from the ground?

10. An airplane is flying at an altitude of 10,000 feet so as to pass directly over an observer on the ground. The observer notices that the angle between his line of sight to the plane and the horizontal measures $\frac{\pi}{3}$ radians and is increasing at the rate of .06 radians per second. How fast is the plane flying? How fast is the distance between the plane and the observer changing?

11. A man 6 feet tall walks at the rate of 5 feet per second directly away from a lamp 15 feet above the ground. Find the rate at which the end of his shadow is moving and the rate at which his shadow is lengthening when he is 20 feet away from the lamp post.

12. A boat is moored to a dock by a 13-foot rope fastened 5 feet above the bow of the boat. A man pulls in the rope at the rate of 1 foot per second. What is the horizontal velocity of the boat at the instant he starts pulling?

13. A marble is dropped from a tall building, and T seconds later a second marble is dropped. Does the distance between the marbles remain constant? What is the rate of change of distance between the marbles?

14. Show that the inequality $sv > pv$ indicates that our moving point is moving *away* from a point p of the number scale, whereas the inequality $sv < pv$ indicates that the moving point is moving *toward p*.

25 APPROXIMATIONS. NEWTON'S METHOD

We first introduced the concept of the derived function in connection with the problem of drawing the tangent line to the graph of a function at a point.

We will now return to this idea as we study problems such as the following two: (1) Find $\sqrt{10}$, approximately; (2) Find an approximate solution to the equation $\sin x - \dfrac{1}{x} = 0$.

In Fig. 25-1 we have drawn a somewhat exaggerated view of the graph of the function f defined by the equation $f(x) = \sqrt{x}$. In geometric language, the problem of finding $\sqrt{10}$ amounts to finding the Y-coordinate of the point $R(10, \sqrt{10})$ of this graph. We have drawn the tangent line to our graph at the point $P(9, 3)$,

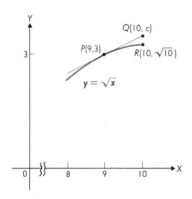

Figure 25-1

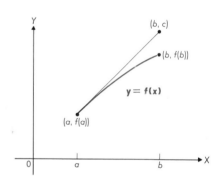

Figure 25-2

and this tangent line approximates the graph of the function for nearby points. In particular, we might agree that the Y-coordinate of the point labeled $Q(10, c)$ of the tangent line is a close approximation of the Y-coordinate of the point $R(10, \sqrt{10})$. In other words, we may be satisfied to use this number c as an approximation of $\sqrt{10}$.

This number c is easy to calculate. The line containing P and Q is tangent to the graph of the equation $y = f(x)$ at the point $P(9, 3)$, so its slope is $f'(9)$. On the other hand, since $(9, 3)$ and $(10, c)$ are points of the line, its slope is also given by the quotient $\dfrac{c - 3}{10 - 9}$, which simplifies to $c - 3$. Thus we have

$$(25\text{-}1) \qquad\qquad c - 3 = f'(9).$$

Since $f(x) = \sqrt{x}$, we find that $f'(x) = \dfrac{1}{2\sqrt{x}}$, and so $f'(9) = \frac{1}{6}$. Therefore Equation 25-1 becomes $c - 3 = \frac{1}{6}$, and hence $c = \frac{19}{6}$. To two decimal places, the actual value of $\sqrt{10}$ is 3.16, so our approximate value of $\frac{19}{6} = 3.17$ is quite close.

We can use this line of reasoning to develop a general approximation formula. Suppose we know the value of a given function f and its derived function f' at a point a and wish to approximate the value of f at another point b. Figure 25-2 shows the arc of the graph of f that joins the points $(a, f(a))$ and $(b, f(b))$. We will approximate the number $f(b)$ by the Y-coordinate of the point (b, c) of the tangent line at the point $(a, f(a))$. To find the number c, we simply equate two expressions for the slope of this line. Since it is a tangent line, its slope is $f'(a)$, and since it contains the points $(a, f(a))$ and (b, c), its slope is $\dfrac{c - f(a)}{b - a}$. Therefore,

$$\frac{c - f(a)}{b - a} = f'(a),$$

and so

(25-2) $$c = f(a) + f'(a)(b - a).$$

To indicate that $f(b)$ is approximated by the number c, we write

(25-3) $$f(b) \approx f(a) + f'(a)(b - a),$$

which is our desired approximation formula. If we let $b = a + h$, we can write this formula in a slightly different form:

$$f(a + h) \approx f(a) + f'(a)h.$$

Example 25-1. A cubical box with inside dimensions of 4 inches × 4 inches × 4 inches is made of lead $\frac{1}{32}$ inch thick. If lead weighs 5 pounds per cubic inch, approximately how much does the box weigh?

Solution. We will define the function f by means of the equation $f(x) = x^3$. Then the exterior of our box encloses a volume of

$$(4\tfrac{1}{16})^3 = f(4\tfrac{1}{16}) \text{ cubic inches.}$$

On the other hand, the volume of the interior of the box is $4^3 = f(4)$ cubic inches. Therefore, the volume of lead used to make our box is

$$f(4\tfrac{1}{16}) - f(4) \text{ cubic inches.}$$

Now according to Formula 25-3, we see that

$$f(4\tfrac{1}{16}) - f(4) \approx f'(4) \cdot \tfrac{1}{16}$$
$$= 3 \cdot 4^2 \cdot \tfrac{1}{16} = 3.$$

Our box is made out of about 3 cubic inches of lead and therefore weighs approximately 15 pounds.

If the number A is an approximation of a number N, then we shall call the number $E = N - A$ the **error** of the approximation, and the number $|E|$ the **absolute error** of the approximation. The number $R = |E/N|$ is called the **relative error**, and $100R\%$ is termed the **percentage error.** In practice, of course, we usually do not know the number N that we approximate with a number A. Hence the error is not known. What we try to do is to find a **bound** on $|E|$; that is, a number that we know is not exceeded by $|E|$.

The error we make when we use Formula 25-3 to approximate $f(b)$ is

$$(25\text{-}4) \qquad E = f(b) - c = f(b) - f(a) - f'(a)(b - a),$$

and in Section 21 (Equation 21-5) we applied the theorem of the mean twice and found that this number is equal to $f''(n)(m - a)(b - a)$, where m and n are points between a and b. Therefore, if we know a bound M for the second derivative of $f(x)$ in the interval (a, b); that is, a number M such that $|f''(x)| \leq M$ for each $x \in (a, b)$, then we see that $|E| \leq M(b - a)^2$. Actually, we can get a bound that is exactly twice as good. Suppose we let $F(x) = f(x) + f'(x)(b - x)$ and $G(x) = (b - x)^2$. The Extended Theorem of the Mean (Theorem 19-4) tells us that for some number m between a and b

$$\frac{F(b) - F(a)}{G(b) - G(a)} = \frac{F'(m)}{G'(m)}.$$

You can easily see that $F'(x) = f''(x)(b - x)$ and $G'(x) = -2(b - x)$, so when we substitute the values for F and G and their derivatives, our equation becomes

$$\frac{f(b) - f(a) - f'(a)(b - a)}{0 - (b - a)^2} = \frac{f''(m)(b - m)}{-2(b - m)}.$$

The numerator of the left-hand side of this equation (see Equation 25-4) is just E; therefore our equation simplifies to

$$E = \tfrac{1}{2}f''(m)(b - a)^2.$$

We are assuming that $|f''(m)| \leq M$, and so we have the error bound

$$(25\text{-}5) \qquad\qquad |E| \leq \tfrac{1}{2}M(b - a)^2.$$

Let us see what Inequality 25-5 tells us about the accuracy of our computation in Example 25-1.

> *Example 25-2.*   Find a bound on the accuracy of our approximation of the volume of lead used to construct the box in Example 25-1.

Solution. In Example 25-1 we dealt with the function f for which $f(x) = x^3$, with x in the interval $[4, 4\frac{1}{16}]$. In this case

$$|f''(x)| = |6x| \leq 6 \cdot 4\tfrac{1}{16} = \tfrac{195}{8}.$$

So Inequality 25-5 becomes

$$|E| \leq \tfrac{195}{16} (\tfrac{1}{16})^2 = \tfrac{195}{4096} < .05.$$

The absolute error in our calculation is less than .05 cubic inches, and our relative error is bounded by $\dfrac{.05}{3}$; that is, we are in error by no more than about 2 parts in a hundred, or 2%.

The problem of solving equations is an important one in mathematics and its applications. Some equations—linear and quadratic equations, for example—can be solved by straightforward methods. Other equations, such as

$$(25\text{-}6) \qquad\qquad \sin x - \frac{1}{x} = 0,$$

cannot be solved by simple formulas. If we define the function f by means of the equation $f(x) = \sin x - 1/x$, then Equation 25-6 is the equation $f(x) = 0$. The solutions to this equation are called **zeros** of the function f. One useful method for finding an approximation to a zero of a function is known as **Newton's Method.**

Newton's Method is best described in geometric language. A zero of a function f is the X-coordinate of a point in which the graph of the equation $y = f(x)$ cuts the X-axis. Thus the number r is a zero of the function whose graph appears in Fig. 25-3. We will suppose that we don't know r, but that graphically, or by using tables, we have found a number x_0 that approximates r. We wish to

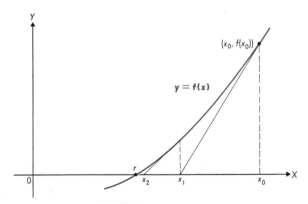

Figure 25-3

improve upon this approximation. From Fig. 25-3 we see that the tangent line at $(x_0, f(x_0))$ intersects the X-axis in a point x_1 that is a closer approximation of r than is x_0. We find the number x_1 in much the same way that we derived Formula 25-3. Thus the slope of the line joining $(x_0, f(x_0))$ and $(x_1, 0)$ is

$$\frac{f(x_0) - 0}{x_0 - x_1}.$$

On the other hand, this line is the tangent line at $(x_0, f(x_0))$, so its slope is $f'(x_0)$. Hence we have

$$f'(x_0) = \frac{f(x_0)}{x_0 - x_1},$$

from which it follows that

(25-7)
$$x_1 = x_0 - \frac{f(x_0)}{f'(x_0)}.$$

This equation gives us a rule that "transforms" an approximation x_0 into another approximation x_1. We can use the same rule to transform the approximation x_1 into a better approximation x_2; thus $x_2 = x_1 - \dfrac{f(x_1)}{f'(x_1)}$. The point x_2, of course, is the point in which the tangent to the graph of f at the point $(x_1, f(x_1))$ intersects the X-axis, as shown in Fig. 25-3. We can repeat this procedure as often as we please and obtain a sequence of numbers $x_1, x_2, x_3, \ldots$, each number being a closer approximation of r than the preceding number.

We based our discussion of Newton's Method on Fig. 25-3, which shows a somewhat special graph. Our arguments don't apply to graphs that are too "wiggly." To be sure that Newton's Method will always yield a sequence of numbers such that x_2 is a closer approximation of the desired zero than is x_1, x_3 is a closer approximation than is x_2, and so on, we should stay in an interval in which $f'(x) \neq 0$ and every number $f''(x)$ has the same sign. Then the curve is either concave up (as in Fig. 25-3) or concave down. You might experiment with a few graphs to see how the sequence of numbers $x_1, x_2, \ldots$ "converges" toward r.

Example 25-3. Use Newton's Method to find a solution to the equation $\sin x - \dfrac{1}{x} = 0$ that is near $x_0 = \pi$.

Solution. Here we have $f(x) = \sin x - \dfrac{1}{x}$ and $x_0 = \pi \approx 3.142$. Equation 25-7 gives us the first approximation

$$x_1 = \pi - \frac{\sin \pi - (1/\pi)}{\cos \pi + (1/\pi)^2} \approx 2.789.$$

If we apply our transformation equation again, we get a second approximation:

$$x_2 = 2.789 - \frac{\sin 2.789 - (1/2.789)}{\cos 2.789 + (1/2.789)^2} \approx 2.776,$$

and additional approximations can be found in the same manner.

We can get an idea of how the accuracy of our approximations $x_1, x_2, \ldots$ is improved at each step by means of the following analysis. We let the numbers x_0 and r play the roles of a and b in Equation 25-4 and recall that $f(r) = 0$, and we see that $E = -f(x_0) - f'(x_0)(r - x_0)$. From this equation we find that

$$r = x_0 - \frac{f(x_0)}{f'(x_0)} - \frac{E}{f'(x_0)}, \quad \text{or}$$

in view of Equation 25-7, $r = x_1 - \dfrac{E}{f'(x_0)}$. Thus we have

$$|r - x_1| = \frac{|E|}{|f'(x_0)|}.$$

Now we use Inequality 25-5 (still with x_0 and r replacing a and b) to replace $|E|$ with a number that is certainly not smaller, and we have

$$|r - x_1| \leq \frac{M}{2\,|f'(x_0)|}\,|r - x_0|^2.$$

Here, of course, we are assuming that M is a number that is not exceeded by $|f''(x)|$ for any x between x_0 and r. If we can also find a positive number m such that $|f'(x)| \geq m$ for every number x in the interval in which we are working, then we will have $|f'(x_0)| \geq m$, and therefore $\dfrac{M}{2\,|f'(x_0)|} \leq \dfrac{M}{2m}$. Thus we see that the absolute errors $|r - x_1|$ and $|r - x_0|$ are related by the inequality

$$(25\text{-}8) \qquad\qquad |r - x_1| \leq \frac{M}{2m}\,|r - x_0|^2.$$

Clearly, this inequality applies to any two consecutive terms of the sequence $x_0, x_1, x_2, \ldots$, not just the first two.

Example 25-4. To two decimal places, $\sqrt{45} \approx 6.71$. Use Newton's Method to find a closer approximation.

Solution. The number $\sqrt{45}$ is a zero of the function f defined by the equation $f(x) = x^2 - 45$. Here $f'(x) = 2x$, and if we use $x_0 = 6.71$, Equation 25-7 gives us

$$x_1 = 6.71 - \frac{(6.71)^2 - 45}{2(6.71)} \approx 6.70820.$$

Since $f''(x) = 2$, $M = 2$. Surely we need only consider numbers greater than $x = 6$, so that $f'(x) = 2x > 2 \cdot 6 = 12$. Therefore we can take $m = 12$, and Inequality 25-8 reads

$$|\sqrt{45} - x_1| \leq \tfrac{1}{12}|\sqrt{45} - 6.71|^2.$$

We said that 6.71 approximates $\sqrt{45}$ to two decimal places, and that statement means that

$$|\sqrt{45} - 6.71| \leq .005 = \tfrac{1}{2} \cdot 10^{-2}.$$

Therefore

$$|\sqrt{45} - 6.71|^2 \leq \tfrac{1}{4} \cdot 10^{-4},$$

and we have

$$|\sqrt{45} - x_1| \leq \tfrac{1}{12} \cdot \tfrac{1}{4} \cdot 10^{-4} < \tfrac{1}{4} \cdot 10^{-5}.$$

We can conclude from this last inequality and our expression for x_1 that to five decimal places, $\sqrt{45} \approx 6.70820$.

P R O B L E M S   2 5

1. Use Formula 25-3 to find approximations to the following numbers.

   (a) $\sqrt{26}$ (b) $\sqrt{120}$

   (c) $\sqrt[5]{34}$ (d) $\sqrt[3]{9}$

   (e) $\dfrac{1}{\sqrt[3]{65}}$ (f) $\sin 1°$

   (g) $\dfrac{1}{\sqrt[4]{85}}$ (h) $\cos 1°$

2. A flat circular ring with an outside radius of b inches and an inside radius of a inches has an area of A square inches. Let $f(r) = \pi r^2$, and use Formula 25-3 to find a formula for a number A_1 that is an approximation to A. What is the formula for A? Show that $A_1 < A$. If $b = 10$ and $a = 9$, compute the percentage error of the approximation.

3. Use $\sqrt{2} \approx 1.4142$ and $\pi/4 \approx .7854$ to compute an approximation to $\sin .78$ with the aid of Formula 25-3.

4. Find a formula for the approximate volume of material in a thin cylindrical shell h inches tall with an inside radius of r inches and a wall thickness of t inches.

5. Find a formula for the approximate volume of material in a thin spherical shell with an inside radius of r inches and a wall thickness of t inches.

6. In each case use Newton's Method to find a solution to the given equation.
(a) $x^3 - 12x^2 + 45x - 35 = 0$ (b) $x^3 + x - 1 = 0$
(c) $x + \cos 2x = 0$ (d) $x + 1 = \tan x$
(e) $3 \sin x = x^2$ (f) $x^2 = 2 \cos x$
(g) $x - 2 \sin x = 0$ (h) $\cos t = \sin 3t$

7. A limber stick 8 feet long is bent into a circular arc by tying the ends together with a piece of string 6 feet long. What is the radius of the arc?

8. To find an approximation to the number $f(b)g(b)$ in terms of the values of f, g, f', and g' at the point a, we could proceed in two ways. We could write $p(x) = f(x)g(x)$ and apply Formula 25-3 with f replaced by p. Or we could use Formula 25-3 to obtain approximation to $f(b)$ and $g(b)$ and then multiply the results. How do the answers obtained by these two methods differ?

9. Suppose you let x_0 be an approximation of the number $\sqrt{a}$; that is, we are approximating a zero of $x^2 - a$. Show that Newton's Method leads you to take $\frac{1}{2}\left(x_0 + \frac{a}{x_0}\right)$ as your next approximation. In words, this rule reads, "To find a second approximation to the square root of a number a, divide a by your first approximation and average the resulting quotient and the first approximation." Apply this rule for a step or two to approximate a few square roots, such as $\sqrt{10}$, and see how well it works.

10. Generalize the result in the preceding problem to take care of the case in which we approximate $\sqrt[n]{a}$, where n is an arbitrary positive integer.

11. Find the point of the graph of the equation $y = x^2$ that is closest to the point $(1, 0)$.

12. We say that a number A approximates a number N to **within p decimal places** if $|N - A| \le \frac{1}{2}10^{-p}$ (why?). Use Inequality 25-8 to show that if f is a function for which $M/m \le 4$, and if x_0 approximates r to within p decimal places, then x_1 will approximate r to within $2p$ decimal places.

26 IMPLICIT DIFFERENTIATION

In Section 7 we saw some examples in which the graph of a function; that is, the graph of an equation of the form

(26-1) $$y = f(x),$$

was a subset of the graph of a more general equation

(26-2) $$A(x, y) = B(x, y).$$

For example, we pointed out that the graphs of the functions that are shown in Figs. 7–4 and 7–5 are all subsets of the graph of the equation

(26-3) $$x^2 + y^2 = 1.$$

To find the derivative of y at a point at which f is differentiable, we would naturally expect to use Equation 26-1, which expresses y in terms of x. However, we can often find this derivative directly from Equation 26-2. For example, if $y = f(x)$ and satisfies Equation 26-3, we simply differentiate both sides of this latter equation:

$$D_x x^2 + D_x y^2 = D_x 1.$$

Of course, $D_x x^2 = 2x$ and $D_x 1 = 0$. We find that $D_x y^2 = 2y D_x y$ by applying the Power Formula as built into the Chain Rule (Equation 16-2). Therefore we have

$$2x + 2y D_x y = 0,$$

and so

$$D_x y = -\frac{x}{y}.$$

Notice that this formula gives us the slopes of the tangent lines to any one of the graphs shown in Figs. 7–4 and 7–5; indeed, it gives us the slope of the tangent line to any point of the circle $x^2 + y^2 = 1$.

Although we didn't use Equation 26-1 explicitly when we found $D_x y$ in the example we just completed, we did use it implicitly. For example, the equation $D_x y^2 = 2y D_x y$ makes no sense unless x and y are related by an equation such as Equation 26-1. As we apply our general differentiation rules in the following problems, we will always assume that such a relationship exists between x and y, although we won't always mention it. In the usual applications of this process of *implicit differentiation*, Equation 26-2 itself determines the relation between y and x. Thus in some neighborhood of a point (a, b) of the graph of Equation 26-2 we can (theoretically, at least) solve for y in terms of x and find Equation 26-1. We then say that our function f is *defined implicitly* by Equation 26-2. The question of when and how such an equation implicitly defines differentiable functions is one that we can leave for advanced calculus.

Example 26-1.   The point $\left(\sqrt{2}, \dfrac{\pi}{4} \right)$ belongs to the graph of the equation $x \sin y = 2x^2 - 3$. Find the slope of the graph at this point.

Solution.   We differentiate both sides of our given equation with respect to x:

(26-4) $$D_x(x \sin y) = D_x(2x^2 - 3).$$

The right-hand side of this last equation is clearly $4x$. To calculate the left-hand side we use the Product Rule. Thus

$$D_x (x \sin y) = (D_x x) \sin y + x D_x \sin y$$
$$= \sin y + (x \cos y) D_x y.$$

Equation 26-4 now becomes

$$\sin y + x \cos y \, D_x y = 4x.$$

We are interested in the point $(\sqrt{2}, \pi/4)$, so we substitute these coordinates and obtain the equation

$$\frac{1}{\sqrt{2}} + \frac{\sqrt{2}}{\sqrt{2}} D_x y = 4\sqrt{2}.$$

This equation yields

$$D_x y = 4\sqrt{2} - \frac{1}{\sqrt{2}} = \frac{7}{\sqrt{2}}.$$

Example 26-2. At what points of the graph of the equation $\dfrac{x^2}{4} - y^2 = 1$ are the tangent lines parallel to the line $y = x + 3$?

Solution. Since the slope of the line $y = x + 3$ is 1, we are looking for those points of the graph at which the tangent lines have slope 1. If we differentiate both sides of our given equation with respect to x, we obtain the equation

$$D_x\left(\frac{x^2}{4} - y^2\right) = D_x 1.$$

As we perform the various differentiations, this equation becomes

$$D_x\left(\frac{x^2}{4}\right) - D_x y^2 = 0,$$

and then

$$\frac{x}{2} - 2y \, D_x y = 0,$$

so the tangent line at a point (x, y) has slope

$$D_x y = \frac{x}{4y}.$$

We are interested in finding those points at which the slope is 1. If (x, y) is such a point, $x/4y = 1$, or

$$(26\text{-}5) \qquad\qquad\qquad x = 4y.$$

But the points must also belong to our curve, and so their coordinates must satisfy the equation of the curve

(26-6)
$$\frac{x^2}{4} - y^2 = 1.$$

Equations 26-5 and 26-6 form a system of simultaneous equations whose solutions are the answers to our original question. You may verify that the solutions of this system are the points $(4/\sqrt{3}, 1/\sqrt{3})$ and $(-4/\sqrt{3}, -1/\sqrt{3})$.

Example 26-3. Sketch the graph of the equation

$$y^2 = 2x^2 - x^4 + 8.$$

Solution. When $x = 0$, we have $y = \sqrt{8}$ or $y = -\sqrt{8}$. The X-coordinates of the points at which $y = 0$ satisfy the equation $2x^2 - x^4 + 8 = 0$. It is easy to solve this equation and find that $x = 2$ or $x = -2$ when $y = 0$. We find $D_x y$ by implicit differentiation:

$$2yD_x y = 4x - 4x^3$$

and hence

$$D_x y = \frac{2x(1 - x^2)}{y}.$$

We see that $D_x y = 0$ when $x = 0, 1,$ or -1. Our results are summarized in the table in Fig. 26-1, which also shows the graph of the given equation.

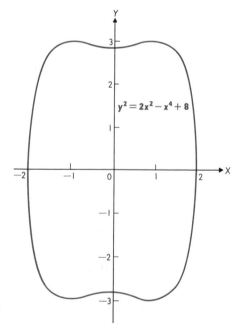

x	y	$D_x y$
0	$\sqrt{8}$	0
0	$-\sqrt{8}$	0
-1	3	0
-1	-3	0
1	3	0
1	-3	0
-2	0	—
2	0	—

Figure 26-1

Example 26-4. When we replace the *parameter c* in the equation

(26-7)
$$y^2 + (x - c)^2 = c^2$$

with numbers such as 1, π, -3, and so on, we obtain various members of the *family of equations* whose "general member" is Equation 26-7. Show that if f is a differentiable function whose graph is a subset of any member of this family, then $y = f(x)$ satisfies the differential equation

(26-8)
$$1 + y'^2 = \left(\frac{x}{y} + y'\right)^2.$$

Solution. Let c be any number and differentiate both sides of Equation 26-7:

$$D_x y^2 + D_x(x - c)^2 = D_x c^2,$$
$$2y D_x y + 2(x - c) = 0,$$
$$yy' + (x - c) = 0.$$

This last equation tells us that $x - c = -yy'$ and $c = x + yy'$, and when we substitute these expressions for $x - c$ and c in Equation 26-7 and simplify, we obtain Equation 26-8.

P R O B L E M S   2 6

1. Use implicit differentiation to compute $D_x y$ if:
  (a) $3y^5 + 5y^3 + 15y = 15x$
  (b) $2x^2 - 5y^2 - 8 = 0$
  (c) $x^3 + y^3 - 20x = 5$
  (d) $x^2 y + y^3 - 4 = 0$
  (e) $xy^3 - 2xy + y^2 = 7$
  (f) $\sqrt{xy} + x^4 y = 3$
  (g) $x^2 = (x - y)/(x + y)$
  (h) $\sin xy = \sin x \sin y$
  (i) $x^2 y^2 = x^2 + y^2$
  (j) $y^2 = |x^2 - x|$

2. Find the slope of each of the following curves at the given point.
  (a) $x^2 + xy + 2y^2 = 28$; (2, 3)
  (b) $(x - y)/(x - 2y) = 2$; (3, 1)
  (c) $b^2 x^2 + a^2 y^2 = a^2 b^2$; (x_0, y_0)
  (d) $|x^3 - 3xy^2| + y^3 = 1$; (2, -1)

3. Show that the graphs of the following pairs of equations intersect at right angles.
  (a) $y^2 = 6x + 9$ and $y^2 = 9 - 6x$
  (b) $x^2 - y^2 = 5$ and $4x^2 + 9y^2 = 72$

4. Find the equation of the tangent to the graph of the equation $x^m y^n = a^{m+n}$ at the point (x_0, y_0) of the graph.

5. Find the equations of the two tangents to the graph of the equation $4x^2 + y^2 = 72$ that intersect in the point (4, 4).

6. (a) Show that if (i) $x^2 - 2y^2 = 4$, then (ii) $D_x y = x/2y$.
  (b) Differentiate both sides of Equation (ii) to obtain

(iii)
$$D_x^2 y = \frac{y - x D_x y}{2y^2}.$$

(c) Use Equation (ii) to transform Equation (iii) into the equation
$$D_x^2 y = -1/y^3.$$

7. Use the method employed in Problem 6 to compute $D_x^2 y$ if:
(a) $x^2 + y^2 = 1$ (b) $x^3 + y^3 = 1$
(c) $y^2 = 4ax$ (d) $x^4 + 2x^2 y^2 = \pi$

8. Sketch the graph of the following equations. Use calculus to check on maximum and minimum points, concavity, and so on.
(a) $x^4 + y^4 = 1$ (b) $x^3 + y^3 = 1$
(c) $x^{2/3} + y^{2/3} = 1$ (d) $4x^2 - 4xy + y^2 - 10x + 5y + 6 = 0$

9. By "eliminating the parameter c" as we did in Example 26-4, show that $y = f(x)$ satisfies the given differential equation if the graph of f is a subset of one of the members of the given family of equations.
(a) $x(3 + y^2)y' = y(y^2 - 3)$; $y^2 + 2cxy = 3$

(b) $(y - xy')^2 = y^2 y'^2 (y^2 - x^2)$; $\sin(y + c) = \dfrac{x}{y}$

10. Show that the graph of the function defined by the equation $f(x) = \sin\sqrt{-x} - 3$ is a subset of the graph of the equation $|y| + y = |x| + x$. What happens when we try to compute $f'\left(-\dfrac{\pi}{2}\right)$ from this latter equation by implicit differentiation?

11. Sketch the graphs of the following equations.
(a) $y^2(2 - x) = x^3$ (b) $x\sqrt{1 + y} = x^2 - y$
(c) $(x^2 + y^2)^2 = (x^2 - y^2)$ (d) $y + \sqrt{xy} = x^2$

REVIEW PROBLEMS—CHAPTER THREE

You can use the following problems to test yourself on the material of this chapter.

1. For x in the interval $[0, 2\pi]$, sketch the graphs of the members of the family of equations $y = x + c\sin x$ for which $c = 2, 1, 0, -1$, and -2. Find maximum and minimum points, check the concavity, and so on. Show that, regardless of the choice of c, y satisfies the differential equation $y' = 1 + (y - x)\cot x$.

2. If $(a, f(a))$ and $(b, f(b))$ are two maximum points of the graph of a function f that is continuous in the interval $[a, b]$, is it necessarily true that there is a point $c \in (a, b)$ such that $(c, f(c))$ is a minimum point of the graph of f?

3. A point is moving along the number scale in accordance with the equation $s = |t^2 - 5| + \sqrt{t + 2}$ for t in the interval $(0, \infty)$ (distance measured in feet, time in seconds). When $t = 2$, where is the point, which way is it moving, and how fast (in feet per second) is it moving? At that instant, is it speeding up or slowing down? At what time is the point closest to the origin? At what time in the first second of motion is the point farthest from the origin. (You might want to use Newton's Method to calculate this number.)

4. A particle moves along a line in such a way that its acceleration is given by the equation $a = \sin t^2$. At what times $(t > 0)$ is the velocity a maximum?

5. Suppose you are told that there are no maximum or minimum points of the graph of the equation $y = ax^3 + bx^2 + cx + d$. What can you conclude about the numbers a, b, and c?

6. A rectangle is to have one side along the X-axis and two vertices on the circle with a radius of 5 whose center is the origin. What is the largest possible perimeter that such a rectangle can have?

7. Find the point of the unit circle whose center is the origin that is closest to the point $(3, 4)$.

8. Find the slope of the tangent to the graph of the equation $x^2 - |3y^2 - x\sqrt{xy}| = 11$ at the point $(4, 1)$.

9. The graph of the identity $\cos(x + y) - \cos x \cos y + \sin x \sin y = 0$ is the entire XY-plane, so of course the graph of any equation of the form $y = f(x)$, where f is a differentiable function, is a subset of it. What happens when we try to use implicit differentiation to find $D_x y$ from our identity?

10. A line segment is to join the point $(0, \frac{1}{2})$ to a first quadrant point P that belongs to the graph of the equation $y = 1/x^2$. Locate P so that the line segment is as short as possible.

11. A cylindrical tin can, closed at the top and bottom, is to be made to contain a volume of 24 cubic inches. No waste is involved in cutting the tin for the vertical side of the can, but each circular end piece is to be stamped from a square, and the "corners" of the square are wasted. Find the radius of the most economical can that can be manufactured in this way.

12. Suppose we mail a rectangular package with one square side that measures x by x inches and whose other dimension is such that the package barely meets the post-office requirements that the sum of its length and girth not exceed 72 inches: (a) show that its volume is given by the formula $V = \dfrac{x^2}{4}[216 - 11x + |5x - 72|]$; (b) find the dimensions of the largest such package; (c) sketch the graph of the equation of part (a), taking note of such things as concavity.

13. A large cylindrical glass of radius R inches is partly filled with water. A second cylindrical glass of radius $R/2$ inches is pushed down into the large glass at the rate of K inches per second while both glasses are in an upright position. How fast is the level of the water rising when the bottom of the smaller glass is 1 inch below the surface of the water?

14. Work the preceding problem using in place of the smaller glass a conical paper cup whose radius and height are both $R/2$ inches.

THE CONICS

F O U R

The fundamental idea of analytic geometry is that a point set in the coordinate plane can be thought of as a subset of R^2, the set of pairs of real numbers, and so it can be specified by giving a numerical relation that is satisfied by the coordinates of its points. Thus a numerical relation of the form $Ax + By + C = 0$ represents a geometric line, and so on. Now we are ready for a systematic study of more complicated plane point sets and their numerical representations. In this chapter we will take up the circle, the ellipse, the hyperbola, and the parabola. First we will treat these curves individually; then in Section 31 we will show how the last three, which are collectively known as *conics*, are related.

27   THE CIRCLE. TRANSLATION OF AXES

Geometrically speaking, a circle is a point set in the plane, each of whose members is the same distance from a given point called the center of the circle. We wish to translate this geometric statement into analytic language, so let us suppose we are talking about a circle whose radius is a given positive number r and whose center is a point (h, k) of the coordinate plane. If (x, y) is a point of our circle, then its distance from (h, k) is the number $\sqrt{(x - h)^2 + (y - k)^2}$, and hence the statement that this distance is r can be expressed as the equation $\sqrt{(x - h)^2 + (y - k)^2} = r$. This equation will look a little nicer if we square both sides, and when we do we get the following result: *The equation of the circle with a radius of r and with the point (h, k) as center is*

(27-1)
$$(x - h)^2 + (y - k)^2 = r^2.$$

For example, the equation of the circle with a radius of 3 and $(0, -1)$ as center is $x^2 + (y + 1)^2 = 9$; that is $x^2 + y^2 + 2y - 8 = 0$.

Example 27-1. Find the center and radius of the circle

$$x^2 - 4x + y^2 + 8y - 5 = 0.$$

Solution. We can find the radius and the coordinates of the center by inspection (and, incidentally, verify the fact that the graph of the given equation *is* a circle) if we write the equation in the form of Equation 27-1. In order to do so we "complete the square" as follows:

$$(x^2 - 4x \qquad) + (y^2 + 8y \qquad) = 5,$$
$$(x^2 - 4x + 4) + (y^2 + 8y + 16) = 5 + 4 + 16,$$
$$(x - 2)^2 + (y + 4)^2 = 25.$$

From our final form of the given equation, we see that its graph is the circle with a radius of 5 and with the point $(2, -4)$ as its center.

Example 27-2. Find the center of the circle that contains the three points $(0, 0)$, $(1, 0)$, and $(1, 4)$.

Solution. If we denote the coordinates of the center of our circle by (h, k) and its radius by r, then its equation will be Equation 27-1; we are to find the numbers h and k. Since the three given points are to be points of the circle, the coordinates of each must satisfy this equation. So we substitute the coordinates of our three points in Equation 27-1 to obtain the three equations

$$(0 - h)^2 + (0 - k)^2 = r^2,$$
$$(1 - h)^2 + (0 - k)^2 = r^2,$$

and

$$(1 - h)^2 + (4 - k)^2 = r^2.$$

In other words,

$$h^2 + k^2 = r^2,$$
$$1 - 2h + h^2 + k^2 = r^2,$$

and

$$1 - 2h + h^2 + 16 - 8k + k^2 = r^2.$$

Now we subtract the first equation from the second and the second equation from the third and find that

$$1 - 2h = 0$$

and

$$16 - 8k = 0.$$

Thus $h = \frac{1}{2}$ and $k = 2$, so the center of our circle is the point $(\frac{1}{2}, 2)$.

For the circle with a radius of r and with the origin as center, Equation 27-1 reduces to

(27-2) $$x^2 + y^2 = r^2.$$

This equation is "simpler" than Equation 27-1. When dealing with geometric problems in terms of coordinates, it is wise to choose the coordinate axes so as to make your equation as simple as possible. Sometimes it is even convenient to change coordinate axes in order to simplify things. One method of changing the coordinate axes is to perform a *translation of axes*, as we shall now illustrate.

Let us suppose that we have chosen a set of coordinate axes, shown in Fig. 27-1 as solid lines. We have labeled these axes the X-axis and Y-axis. Let us

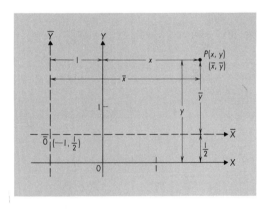

Figure 27-1

now select another set of coordinate axes, shown in Fig. 27-1 as dashed lines. We have labeled these axes the $\bar{X}$-axis and the $\bar{Y}$-axis. The $\bar{X}$-axis is parallel to the X-axis and $\frac{1}{2}$ unit above it. The $\bar{Y}$-axis is parallel to the Y-axis and 1 unit to the left of it. We say we have obtained the $\bar{X}\bar{Y}$-axes by a *translation*. Any point P in the plane can be described by either its XY-coordinates (x, y) or its $\overline{X}\overline{Y}$-coordinates $(\bar{x}, \bar{y})$. From Fig. 27-1 we see that the relation between the numbers x and $\bar{x}$ is $\bar{x} = x + 1$ and between the numbers y and $\bar{y}$ is $\bar{y} = y - \frac{1}{2}$. Let us write these equations in the form

(27-3)
$$\bar{x} = x - (-1)$$
$$\bar{y} = y - \tfrac{1}{2}.$$

In particular, we notice that the origin of the $\overline{X}\overline{Y}$-coordinate system has $\overline{X}\overline{Y}$-coordinates $(0, 0)$ and XY-coordinates $(-1, \frac{1}{2})$. Thus to obtain the $\overline{X}\overline{Y}$-coordinates of a point P, we subtract the XY-coordinates of the origin of the $\overline{X}\overline{Y}$-coordinate system from the XY-coordinates of P.

Let us generalize the problem we have just been looking at and consider a coordinate change in which we obtain new coordinates $(\bar{x}, \bar{y})$ for a point with original coordinates (x, y) by using the formulas

(27-4)
$$\bar{x} = x - h$$
$$\bar{y} = y - k,$$

in which h and k are given numbers. It is clear from Equations 27-4 that the origin of the $\overline{X}\overline{Y}$-coordinate system—that is, the point whose $\overline{X}\overline{Y}$-coordinates are $(0, 0)$—is the point whose XY-coordinates are (h, k). Furthermore, every point whose $\overline{X}$-coordinate is zero belongs to the line $x = h$; that is, *the line $x = h$ is the $\overline{Y}$-axis.* Similarly, *the line $y = k$ is the $\overline{X}$-axis.* Thus we see that the coordinate change described by Equations 27-4 is a translation; the $\overline{X}$- and $\overline{Y}$-axes are parallel to the X- and Y-axes and have the same directions, and their intersection is the point whose XY-coordinates are (h, k). Equations 27-4 are called the **transformation of coordinate equations** for a **translation** of axes.

Example 27-3. Find a translation of axes that simplifies the equation

$$xy + 3x - 4y = 5.$$

Solution. We will replace x with $\bar{x} + h$ and y with $\bar{y} + k$ in the given equation and then choose h and k so that the resulting equation is simpler than the

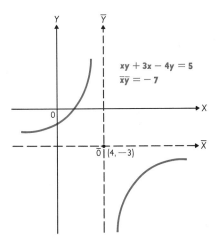

Figure 27-2

original. When we make the replacement, our equation becomes

$$(\bar{x} + h)(\bar{y} + k) + 3(\bar{x} + h) - 4(\bar{y} + k) = 5,$$
$$\bar{x}\bar{y} + (k + 3)\bar{x} + (h - 4)\bar{y} + hk + 3h - 4k = 5.$$

Now if we set $h = 4$ and $k = -3$, this equation takes the simple form $\bar{x}\bar{y} - 12 + 12 + 12 = 5$, or $\bar{x}\bar{y} = -7$. With our present knowledge of calculus and analytic geometry, it is very easy to sketch the graph of this final equation, as shown in Fig. 27-2.

P R O B L E M S   2 7

1. Find the equations of the circles with the given points as centers and the given numbers as radii.
(a) $(3, -2), 5$ (b) $(-1, -1), 2$
(c) $(\cos(-2), \sin(-2)), 1$ (d) $(\log \frac{1}{2}, \log 2), \log 100$

2. Complete the square to find the center and radius of each of the following circles.
(a) $x^2 + y^2 - 4x + 2y - 4 = 0$ (b) $x^2 + y^2 + 6x + 5 = 0$
(c) $4x^2 + 4y^2 - 4x - 3 = 0$ (d) $9x^2 + 9y^2 - 18x + 36y + 44 = 0$

3. Find the equation of the circle C in the following cases.
(a) $(0, 0), (0, 1),$ and $(1, 0)$ are points of C.
(b) $(0, 0)$ is a point of C and $(2, 3)$ is the center of C.
(c) The center of C is a point of the X-axis, the radius of C is $\sqrt{17}$, and $(0, 1) \in C$.
(d) The center of C is the point $(10, -1)$ and C "touches" the circle $x^2 + y^2 + 4x - 8y = 5$.
(e) C is inscribed in the triangle whose vertices are $(0, 0), (2, 0)$ and $(0, 2)$.
(f) C lies below the X-axis and "touches" the X-axis, the line $x - y = 0$, and the line $x + y - 2 = 0$.

4. Suppose we construct an $\bar{X}\bar{Y}$-coordinate system from an XY-coordinate system by translating the axes so that the origin is translated to the point $(2, -3)$. First consider the following elements of R^2 as XY-coordinates of points and find the $\bar{X}\bar{Y}$-coordinates of the points, and then consider the elements of R^2 as $\bar{X}\bar{Y}$-coordinates of points and find the XY-coordinates of the points.
(a) $(-5, 1)$ (b) $(5, -1)$ (c) $(\llbracket a \rrbracket, \llbracket b \rrbracket)$ (d) $(\log 3, \log 2)$

5. (a) Find one pair of numbers h and k so that after a translation of axes that translates the origin to the point (h, k), the equation $y = 3x - 2$ becomes $\bar{y} = m\bar{x}$. Find this number m.
(b) Find a translation of axes such that the lines whose equations are $x - 3y + 7 = 0$ and $2x - y + 4 = 0$ intersect in the new origin. What are the equations of the lines in the $\bar{X}\bar{Y}$-coordinate system?

6. What are the transformation of coordinate equations under which a sine curve in the XY-system becomes a cosine curve in the $\bar{X}\bar{Y}$-system?

7. A point moves so that it is always three times as far from the point $(0, -4)$ as it is from the point $(0, 4)$. Find the equation of the curve traced out by the point, sketch the curve, and perform a translation so as to simplify the equation of the curve.

(b) In part (a) replace "three" with r, where r is any positive number. Describe the path of the point in each of the following cases: $0 < r < 1; r = 1; r > 1$.

8. What relation among the coefficients a, b, and c is necessary in order that the graph of the equation $x^2 + y^2 + ax + by + c = 0$ be a circle? Describe the graph of the inequality $x^2 + y^2 + ax + by + c < 0$.

9. Sketch the graphs of the following equations.

(a) $[x]^2 + [y]^2 = 13$ (b) $[x^2 + y^2] = 13$ (c) $[x^2] + [y^2] = 2$

(d) $(x - [x])^2 + y^2 = 1$ (e) $(|x| + x)^2 + (|y| + y)^2 = 36$

10. Show that if the graph of the equation $y = f(x)$ is an arc of the circle $x^2 + y^2 = r^2$, then y satisfies the differential equation $y' = -\dfrac{x}{y}$. Conversely, if $y' = -\dfrac{x}{y}$, then show that $D_x(x^2 + y^2) = 0$ and hence $x^2 + y^2 = r^2$ for some number r that is independent of x.

11. Let C_1 be the circle whose radius is 3 and whose center is the origin of an XY-coordinate system. Let C_2 be the circle whose center is the point $(5, 0)$ and is such that at each point of $C_1 \cap C_2$ the tangents to C_1 and C_2 are perpendicular.

(a) Find the equation of the line determined by the points of $C_1 \cap C_2$.

(b) Construct an $\bar{X}\bar{Y}$-coordinate system by translating the axes so that the $\bar{Y}$-axis is the line determined by $C_1 \cap C_2$ and the origin is the point of $C_1 \cap C_2$ with negative Y-coordinate. Find the equation of C_1 in the $\bar{X}\bar{Y}$-system.

28 THE ELLIPSE. SYMMETRY

A circle can be thought of as a special case of a curve known as an **ellipse**. To describe a circle, we start with a given point and a given positive number, and we say that the circle is the set of points whose distance from the given point is the given number. To describe an ellipse, we start with *two* points and a positive number, and we say that *the ellipse is the set of points, the average of whose distances from the two given points is the given number.* In set notation, if F_1 and F_2 are the two given points, and a is the given positive number, then the ellipse is the set of points $\{P \mid \frac{1}{2}(\overline{PF_1} + \overline{PF_2}) = a\}$. The points F_1 and F_2 are called the **foci** (singular, *focus*) of the ellipse. If the two foci coincide, the ellipse becomes a circle.

To translate our geometric description of an ellipse into analytic terms, we introduce a coordinate system into the plane, and it will simplify our formulas if we set up the coordinate system so that our foci are the points $(-c, 0)$ and $(c, 0)$, as shown in Fig. 28-1. For each point (x, y) of the ellipse, the average of the distances r_1 and r_2 is the given number a; that is, $\dfrac{r_1 + r_2}{2} = a$, or

(28-1) $r_1 + r_2 = 2a.$

The foci are $2c$ units apart, so since the sum of the lengths of two sides of a triangle is greater than the length of the third side, $r_1 + r_2 > 2c$. When we compare this inequality with Equation 28-1, we see that $a > c$.

A simple way to construct our ellipse is to stick thumbtacks into each focus and then place a loop of string $2a + 2c$ units long around the tacks. Now put your pencil point inside the loop of string and draw it taut, thus obtaining the triangle shown in Fig. 28-1. As you move your pencil, keeping the string taut, you will trace out the ellipse.

To find the equation of our ellipse, we use the distance formula to express r_1 and r_2:

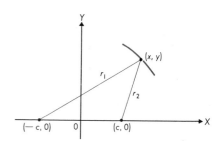

$$r_1 = \sqrt{(x + c)^2 + y^2}$$

and

$$r_2 = \sqrt{(x - c)^2 + y^2}.$$

Figure 28-1

When we substitute these numbers in Equation 28-1, we find that a point (x, y) is one of the points of our ellipse if, and only if, its coordinates satisfy the equation

(28-2) $$\sqrt{(x + c)^2 + y^2} + \sqrt{(x - c)^2 + y^2} = 2a.$$

We could consider Equation 28-2 as the equation of our ellipse, but a little algebra enables us to reduce this equation to a much simpler form. To eliminate radicals, we transpose the term $\sqrt{(x - c)^2 + y^2}$ and square, thus obtaining

$$(x + c)^2 + y^2 = 4a^2 - 4a\sqrt{(x - c)^2 + y^2} + (x - c)^2 + y^2.$$

When we simplify the last equation, we have $a\sqrt{(x - c)^2 + y^2} = a^2 - cx$, so we square again to get

$$a^2[(x - c)^2 + y^2] = a^4 - 2a^2cx + c^2x^2.$$

Simplification now yields

$$(a^2 - c^2)x^2 + a^2y^2 = a^2(a^2 - c^2).$$

We noticed that $a > c$, so $a^2 - c^2 > 0$. We can therefore introduce the number $b = \sqrt{a^2 - c^2}$, and our equation becomes

$$b^2x^2 + a^2y^2 = a^2b^2.$$

Now we divide both sides of this equation by a^2b^2 to get the final form of the equation of our ellipse:

(28-3)
$$\frac{x^2}{a^2} + \frac{y^2}{b^2} = 1.$$

The graph of this equation is shown in Fig. 28-2.

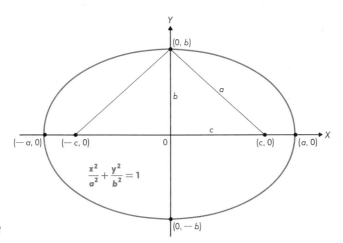

Figure 28-2

An ellipse is a highly symmetrical figure, and this fact is very useful in constructing its graph. Before we discuss the symmetry of the ellipse in particular, let us say a few words about the symmetry of graphs in general.

A plane point set S is **symmetric with respect to a line** L if for each point $P \in S$ there is a point $Q \in S$ such that the line L is the perpendicular bisector of the segment PQ. In particular, a set S of the coordinate plane is symmetric with respect to the Y-axis if whenever $(x, y) \in S$, we also have $(-x, y) \in S$, because, as you can see, the Y-axis is the perpendicular bisector of the segment joining the points (x, y) and $(-x, y)$. Thus *the graph of a relation is symmetric with respect to the Y-axis if whenever the pair (x, y) satisfies the relation, the pair $(-x, y)$ also satisfies it.*

A set S is **symmetric with respect to a point** Q if for each point $P \in S$ there is a point $R \in S$ such that the point Q is the midpoint of the segment PR. In particular, a set S of the coordinate plane is symmetric with respect to the origin if whenever $(x, y) \in S$, we also have $(-x, -y) \in S$. Thus *the graph of a relation is symmetric with respect to the origin if whenever the pair (x, y) satisfies the relation, the pair $(-x, -y)$ also satisfies it.*

We see immediately that if the pair (x, y) satisfies Equation 28-3, then the pairs $(-x, y)$, $(x, -y)$, and $(-x, -y)$ do too, so our ellipse is symmetric with respect to the Y-axis, the X-axis, and the origin. The point of symmetry of an ellipse (here the origin) is called the **center** of the ellipse. An ellipse has two lines of symmetry, and the four points of intersection of the ellipse with its lines of symmetry are the **vertices** (singular, *vertex*) of the ellipse. The vertices of the ellipse whose equation is Equation 28-3 are the points $(a, 0)$, $(-a, 0)$, $(0, b)$, and $(0, -b)$. A line segment that contains the center of an ellipse and whose terminal points are points of the ellipse is called a **diameter** of the ellipse. The longest diameter of an ellipse is its **major diameter**, and the shortest diameter is its **minor diameter**. Figure 28-2 shows (in Problem 28-12 we ask you to use analytic methods to verify these statements) that the major diameter of our ellipse joins the vertices $(a, 0)$ and $(-a, 0)$ and is $2a$ units long, whereas the minor diameter joins the vertices $(0, b)$ and $(0, -b)$ and is $2b$ units long. Notice that the foci are points of the major diameter.

The graph of Equation 28-3 is also an ellipse if $b > a$. In that case, the roles of b and a are interchanged. The foci are the points $(0, -c)$ and $(0, c)$, where $c = \sqrt{b^2 - a^2}$, of the Y-axis. The major diameter is now the segment terminating at the points $(0, -b)$ and $(0, b)$, while the minor diameter terminates at $(-a, 0)$ and $(a, 0)$. The average of the distances of a point of this ellipse from the two foci is b, rather than a.

Example 28-1.   Find the equation of the ellipse whose foci are the points $(0, 4)$ and $(0, -4)$ and which has $(0, 5)$ and $(0, -5)$ as vertices.

Solution.   The desired equation takes the form of Equation 28-3; we are to find the numbers a and b. Because the foci are points of the Y-axis, $b > a$. Here $b = 5$ and $c = 4$, and so $a = \sqrt{25 - 16} = 3$. The equation of our ellipse is

$$\frac{x^2}{9} + \frac{y^2}{25} = 1,$$

and a sketch is shown in Fig. 28-3.

Equation 28-3 represents an ellipse whose center is the origin. Now let us suppose that we have an ellipse whose center is the point (h, k). We still assume that the major and minor diameters of the ellipse are parallel to the coordinate axes. If we choose a translated $\overline{X}\overline{Y}$-coordinate system whose origin is the point (h, k), then the equation of the ellipse relative to this new coordinate system takes the form of Equation 28-3; that is,

$$\frac{\bar{x}^2}{a^2} + \frac{\bar{y}^2}{b^2} = 1.$$

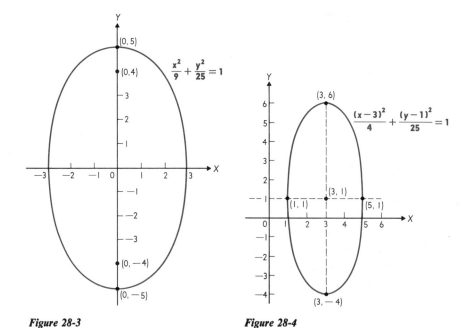

Figure 28-3   **Figure 28-4**

Now we use the translation equations $\bar{x} = x - h$ and $\bar{y} = y - k$ to find the equation of our ellipse in the XY-coordinate system:

(28-4)
$$\frac{(x - h)^2}{a^2} + \frac{(y - k)^2}{b^2} = 1.$$

Example 28-2. Write the equation of the ellipse whose vertices are the points $(1, 1)$, $(5, 1)$, $(3, 6)$, and $(3, -4)$, and sketch its graph.

Solution. We first plot the given vertices (Fig. 28-4). These four points are the ends of the major and minor diameters of the ellipse. The diameter that is parallel to the Y-axis is 10 units long, and the diameter that is parallel to the X-axis is 4 units long. Thus $a = 2$ and $b = 5$. The center of an ellipse is the point in which its major and minor diameters intersect. In this case, the center is the point $(3, 1)$. Thus $h = 3$ and $k = 1$, and Equation 28-4 becomes

$$\frac{(x - 3)^2}{4} + \frac{(y - 1)^2}{25} = 1.$$

Example 28-3. Reduce the equation $9x^2 + 4y^2 + 18x - 16y - 11 = 0$ to a simpler form by a translation of axes. What can you say about its graph?

Solution. We first rewrite our equation by completing the square:

$$9x^2 + 4y^2 + 18x - 16y - 11 = 0,$$
$$9(x^2 + 2x \quad) + 4(y^2 - 4y \quad) - 11 = 0,$$
$$9(x^2 + 2x + 1) + 4(y^2 - 4y + 4) - 11 = 9 + 16,$$
$$9(x + 1)^2 + 4(y - 2)^2 = 36.$$

So if we set $\bar{x} = x + 1$ and $\bar{y} = y - 2$, our equation becomes $9\bar{x}^2 + 4\bar{y}^2 = 36$, which reduces to the standard form (relative to the $\bar{X}\bar{Y}$-coordinate system) of the equation of an ellipse:

$$\frac{\bar{x}^2}{4} + \frac{\bar{y}^2}{9} = 1.$$

Here $a = 2$, $b = 3$, and $c = \sqrt{b^2 - a^2} = \sqrt{5}$. The coordinates of the vertices of our ellipse in the $\bar{X}\bar{Y}$-coordinate system are $(-2, 0)$, $(2, 0)$, $(0, -3)$, and $(0, 3)$, and its foci are the points with $\bar{X}\bar{Y}$-coordinates $(0, -\sqrt{5})$ and $(0, \sqrt{5})$. The XY- and $\bar{X}\bar{Y}$-coordinates are related by the equations $x = \bar{x} - 1$ and $y = \bar{y} + 2$. Therefore the XY-coordinates of the vertices are $(-3, 2)$, $(1, 2)$, $(-1, -1)$, and $(-1, 5)$. The foci are the points $(-1, 2 - \sqrt{5})$ and $(-1, 2 + \sqrt{5})$.

Example 28-4. At what point of the first quadrant is the tangent to the ellipse

$$\frac{x^2}{16} + \frac{y^2}{9} = 1$$

parallel to the chord that joins the vertices $(4, 0)$ and $(0, 3)$?

Solution. To find the slope of the tangent at a point (x, y), we use implicit differentiation. Thus we differentiate both sides of the equation $\dfrac{x^2}{16} + \dfrac{y^2}{9} = 1$ with respect to x to obtain the equation

$$\frac{2x}{16} + \frac{2yy'}{9} = 0,$$

from which we see that

$$y' = \frac{-9x}{16y}.$$

The slope of the chord that joins the vertices $(4, 0)$ and $(0, 3)$ is $-\frac{3}{4}$. Since the tangent line is to be parallel to this chord, their slopes must be equal. Therefore the coordinates (x, y) of our desired point satisfy the equation

$$\frac{-9x}{16y} = \frac{-3}{4}; \text{ that is, } y = \tfrac{3}{4}x.$$

The numbers x and y also satisfy the equation of the ellipse, so

$$\frac{x^2}{16} + \frac{(3x/4)^2}{9} = 1,$$

and hence $x^2 = 8$. Thus (since (x, y) is in the first quadrant) $x = 2\sqrt{2}$, and $y = 3x/4 = 3\sqrt{2}/2$.

P R O B L E M S   2 8

1. Find the equation of, and sketch, the ellipses that satisfy the following conditions.
   (a) Center $(0, 0)$; major diameter along the X-axis and 6 units long; minor diameter 4 units long.
   (b) Center $(-3, 1)$; major diameter parallel to the Y-axis and 5 units long; minor diameter 1 unit long.
   (c) Foci $(-2, 0)$ and $(2, 0)$; major diameter 8 units long.
   (d) Foci $(-1, -1)$ and $(-1, 7)$, major diameter 16 units long.
   (e) Vertices $(-3, 0)$, $(3, 0)$, $(0, -5)$, $(0, 5)$.
   (f) Vertices $(0, -1)$, $(12, -1)$, $(6, -4)$, $(6, 2)$.

2. Suppose we want to use the string and thumbtack method to construct an ellipse on an $8\frac{1}{2}$ inch $\times$ 11 inch sheet of paper so that its major diameter is parallel to the 11-inch edge. Where should we place the tacks, and how long a piece of string should we use in order to draw the largest possible ellipse on the paper?

3. Find the foci of each of the following ellipses.
   (a) $9x^2 + 25y^2 - 18x + 100y - 116 = 0$
   (b) $16x^2 + 4y^2 - 32x - 4y + 13 = 0$

4. Find the equation of the tangent and normal lines to the given ellipses at the indicated points.

   (a) $4x^2 + 9y^2 = 72$, $(3, 2)$
   (b) $\dfrac{(x + 1)^2}{8} + \dfrac{(y - 2)^2}{2} = 1$, $(-3, 1)$

5. Discuss the graphs of the following equations
   (a) $\sin \pi \sqrt{x^2 + 4y^2} = 0$
   (b) $4x^2 + 9y^2 - 8\,|x| - 36\,|y| + 4 = 0$

   (c) $x(x + |x|) + 4y(y - |y|) = 8$
   (d) $\left[\!\left[\dfrac{x^2}{25} + \dfrac{y^2}{16}\right]\!\right] = 0$

6. Compare the graphs of the equations $y = \sin x$, $y = \sin |x|$, $|y| = \sin |x|$, and $|y| = |\sin |x||$.

7. Show that the points (a, b) and (b, a) are symmetric with respect to the line $y = x$. What point is symmetric to (a, b) with respect to the line $y = -x$?

8. Use calculus to discuss the concavity of an ellipse.

9. The segment that an ellipse cuts from a line that contains a focus and is perpendicular to the major diameter is called a **latus rectum** of the ellipse. Show that the

length of a latus rectum of the ellipse whose equation is Equation 28-3 (with $a > b$) is $\dfrac{2b^2}{a}$. Find the slope of the tangent to this ellipse at the point of the first quadrant that is an endpoint of a latus rectum. Show that this tangent cuts off a segment of the positive Y-axis that is half as long as the major diameter of the ellipse.

10. Equation 28-3 is the equation of an ellipse. A rectangle is to be inscribed in this ellipse so that its sides are parallel to the major and minor diameters of the ellipse. Show that the largest area that such a rectangle can have is $2ab$.

11. (a) A point moves so that the line segments joining it to two given points are always perpendicular. Describe the path of the point.

   (b) Now suppose that the point moves so that the product of the slopes of the line segments joining it to the two given points is $-k^2$, where k is a given number. Describe the path of the point.

12. A **semi-diameter** of an ellipse is a segment whose terminal points are the center and a point of the ellipse. Thus if the semi-diameter that contains a point (x, y) of the ellipse $\dfrac{x^2}{a^2} + \dfrac{y^2}{b^2} = 1$ is S units long, we have

$$S^2 = x^2 + y^2 = x^2 + b^2\left(1 - \frac{x^2}{a^2}\right) = b^2 + \frac{a^2 - b^2}{a^2}\, x^2.$$

Use this equation to find the major and minor diameters of our ellipse.

29 THE HYPERBOLA

As with the ellipse, the geometric definition of the hyperbola starts with two given points F_1 and F_2 (again called the **foci**) and a given positive number a. An ellipse is the set of points, the sum of whose distances from the foci is $2a$, and *a hyperbola is the set of points, the differences of whose distances from the foci is $2a$.* In set notation, if F_1 and F_2 are the foci, and a is a positive number, the hyperbola is the set of points $\{P \mid |\overline{PF_1} - \overline{PF_2}| = 2a\}$. In Fig. 29-1 we have chosen our coordinate system so that the foci of the hyperbola are the points $(-c, 0)$ and $(c, 0)$. A point (x, y) at distances of r_1 and r_2 from the foci is a point of our hyperbola if, and only if,

(29-1) $|r_1 - r_2| = 2a.$

The sides of the triangle whose vertices are the points $(-c, 0)$, $(c, 0)$, and (x, y) have lengths of $2c$, r_1, and r_2. Since the difference in the lengths of two sides of a triangle is less than the length of the third side, $|r_1 - r_2| < 2c$. When we compare this inequality with Equation 29-1, we see that for a hyperbola, $a < c$.

Just as in the case of the ellipse, we can construct an arc of a hyperbola by using a pencil, some string, and two thumbtacks. The tacks are placed at the foci, and the pencil is tied in the middle of the string. Then the string is looped around

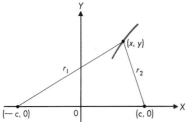

Figure 29-1

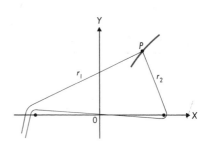

Figure 29-2

the tacks as shown in Fig. 29-2 (the pencil point is at P). We keep the string taut and move the pencil, paying out both strands of the string together. Thus the difference $r_1 - r_2$ is the same for any two points of the arc traced out by the pencil, so the arc must be part of a hyperbola.

We see that Equation 29-1 is equivalent to the equation

$$(r_1 - r_2)^2 = 4a^2.$$

Since

$$r_1 = \sqrt{(x + c)^2 + y^2} \quad \text{and} \quad r_2 = \sqrt{(x - c)^2 + y^2},$$

we find (after a little simplification) that a point (x, y) is one of the points of our hyperbola if, and only if, its coordinates satisfy the equation

$$x^2 + y^2 + c^2 - 2a^2 = \sqrt{(x + c)^2 + y^2} \sqrt{(x - c)^2 + y^2}.$$

Now we square and simplify to find that

(29-2) $$(c^2 - a^2)x^2 - a^2y^2 = a^2(c^2 - a^2).$$

Since $c > a$, the equation $b = \sqrt{c^2 - a^2}$ defines a positive number b, in terms of which we can write Equation 29-2 as $b^2x^2 - a^2y^2 = a^2b^2$; that is,

(29-3) $$\frac{x^2}{a^2} - \frac{y^2}{b^2} = 1.$$

Replacing x with $-x$ and y with $-y$, separately or together, in Equation 29-3 does not alter the equation, so we see that our hyperbola is symmetric with respect to the Y-axis, the X-axis, and the origin. The point of symmetry of a hyperbola (in this case the origin) is the **center** of the hyperbola. From Equation 29-3 we see that our hyperbola intersects one of its lines of symmetry, the X-axis, in the points $(-a, 0)$ and $(a, 0)$. These points are the **vertices** of the hyperbola. The line segment joining the two vertices is the **transverse diameter** of the hyperbola. Since there is no real number y that satisfies Equation 29-3 when $x = 0$, we see that our hyperbola does not intersect its other line of symmetry, the Y-axis. Figure 29-3 shows the graph of Equation 29-3.

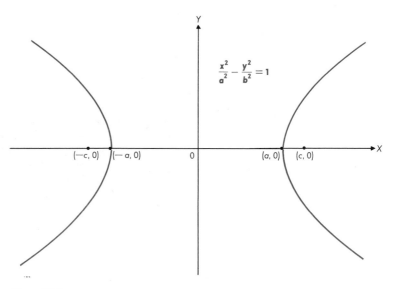

Figure 29-3

Let us suppose for the moment that we consider only points in the first quadrant and solve Equation 29-3 for y to obtain $y = \dfrac{b}{a}\sqrt{x^2 - a^2}$, or equivalently,

$$(29\text{-}4) \qquad\qquad y = \frac{bx}{a}\sqrt{1 - \frac{a^2}{x^2}}.$$

Since $\sqrt{1 - a^2/x^2} < 1$, we see that $y < bx/a$. Hence the arc of the hyperbola that lies in the first quadrant is below the line whose equation is $y = (b/a)x$ (Fig. 29-4). But if x is very large, $\sqrt{1 - a^2/x^2}$ is close to 1, and Equation 29-4 suggests that the equation of our hyperbola does not differ a great deal from the linear equation $y = (b/a)x$. Let us show that the hyperbola does in fact approximate (for large x)

the line $y = (b/a)x$. Let x be a large number and suppose that (x, y_1) is the corresponding point of the hyperbola. We wish to show that the (perpendicular) distance d between this point and our line is small. Now if (x, y_2) is the point of the line that corresponds to x, it is clear (Fig. 29-4) that

(29-5) $$d < y_2 - y_1.$$

We have $y_2 = (b/a)x$ and, according to Equation 29-4,

(29-6) $$y_1 = \frac{b}{a}\sqrt{x^2 - a^2}.$$

Hence

$$y_2 - y_1 = \frac{b}{a}(x - \sqrt{x^2 - a^2})$$

$$= \frac{b}{a}(x - \sqrt{x^2 - a^2})\left[\frac{x + \sqrt{x^2 - a^2}}{x + \sqrt{x^2 - a^2}}\right]$$

$$= \frac{b}{a}\left[\frac{x^2 - (x^2 - a^2)}{x + \sqrt{x^2 - a^2}}\right]$$

$$= \frac{ab}{x + \sqrt{x^2 - a^2}} < \frac{ab}{x}.$$

Therefore, $d < ab/x$, and we see that d is small when x is large. Thus for points in the first quadrant far to the right on our graph, the hyperbola practically coincides with the line $y = (b/a)x$. This line is called an **asymptote** of the hyperbola. It is not hard to see that for points in the third quadrant remote from the origin, the hyperbola also practically coincides with the line $y = (b/a)x$, whereas for points in the second and fourth quadrants, the line $y = -(b/a)x$ is an asymptote of the hyperbola.

The rectangle whose sides are parallel to the axes and contain the points $(-a, 0), (a, 0), (0, -b)$, and $(0, b)$ is called the **auxiliary rectangle** of our hyperbola. The asymptotes of the hyperbola are extensions of the diagonals of this rectangle.

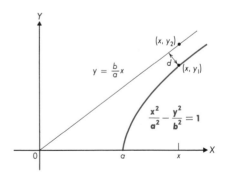

Figure 29-4

Our hyperbola, with the asymptotes drawn in, is the curve on the left in Fig. 29-5. If the auxiliary rectangle is a square, then the hyperbola is an **equilateral hyperbola**.

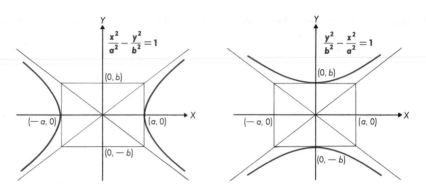

Figure 29-5

If we choose the coordinate axes so that the foci of a hyperbola are the points $(0, c)$ and $(0, -c)$, then its vertices are points of the Y-axis. We use $2b$ (rather than $2a$) to denote the difference of the focal distances of a point of this hyperbola, and we obtain the following equation:

(29-7) $$\frac{y^2}{b^2} - \frac{x^2}{a^2} = 1,$$

where again $a^2 + b^2 = c^2$. The points $(0, -b)$ and $(0, b)$ are the vertices of this hyperbola. We also see that there is no number x for which $y = 0$; that is, the curve does not intersect the X-axis. The graph of Equation 29-7 is shown on the right in Fig. 29-5. The asymptotes of both the hyperbolas in Fig. 29-5 are the same lines, and we say that these hyperbolas form a pair of **conjugate hyperbolas**.

Example 29-1. Find the equation of the hyperbola whose foci are the points $(5, 0)$ and $(-5, 0)$, and whose vertices are $(4, 0)$ and $(-4, 0)$.

Solution. We obtain the equation of this hyperbola by setting $c = 5$, $a = 4$, and $b = \sqrt{c^2 - a^2} = 3$ in Equation 29-3:

$$\frac{x^2}{16} - \frac{y^2}{9} = 1.$$

Its asymptotes are the lines $y = \frac{3}{4}x$ and $y = -\frac{3}{4}x$, and it looks like the hyperbola on the left in Fig. 29-5.

Now suppose we have a hyperbola whose center is the point (h, k) and whose transverse diameter is parallel to the X-axis. If we choose a translated

$\overline{X}\overline{Y}$-coordinate system whose origin is the point (h, k), then the equation of the hyperbola relative to this coordinate system is

$$\frac{\bar{x}^2}{a^2} - \frac{\bar{y}^2}{b^2} = 1.$$

Since $\bar{x} = x - h$ and $\bar{y} = y - k$, the equation of the hyperbola in the XY-coordinate system is

(29-8) $$\frac{(x - h)^2}{a^2} - \frac{(y - k)^2}{b^2} = 1.$$

In a similar manner, the equation of a hyperbola whose center is the point (h, k) and whose transverse diameter is parallel to the Y-axis is

(29-9) $$\frac{(y - k)^2}{b^2} - \frac{(x - h)^2}{a^2} = 1.$$

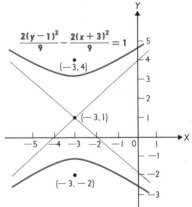

Example 29-2. The foci of an equilateral hyperbola are the points $(-3, 4)$ and $(-3, -2)$. Find the equation of the hyperbola and sketch its graph.

Solution. We are to replace the letters a, b, h, and k in Equation 29-9 with appropriate numbers. The center of the hyperbola is midway between the two foci, so it is the point $(-3, 1)$; hence $h = -3$ and $k = 1$ (Fig. 29-6). Since the hyperbola is equilateral, $a = b$. Now c

Figure 29-6

is the distance between the center of the hyperbola and a focus, so in the present case, $c = 3$. Hence the equation $c^2 = a^2 + b^2$ becomes $9 = 2a^2$, and therefore $a^2 = b^2 = \frac{9}{2}$. The equation of our hyperbola is

$$\frac{2(y - 1)^2}{9} - \frac{2(x + 3)^2}{9} = 1;$$

its graph is shown in Fig. 29-6.

PROBLEMS 29

1. Find the foci, vertices, and asymptotes of the following hyperbolas, and sketch them.

(a) $x^2 - 4y^2 = 4$

(b) $4x^2 - y^2 = 4$

(c) $x^2 - 4y^2 = -4$

(d) $4x^2 - y^2 = -4$

(e) $\dfrac{(x + 1)^2}{16} - \dfrac{(y - 2)^2}{9} = 1$

(f) $\dfrac{(y + 2)^2}{9} - \dfrac{(x - 1)^2}{16} = 1$

2. Find the equations of, and sketch, the hyperbolas that satisfy the following conditions.

(a) Foci $(-3, 0)$ and $(3, 0)$; vertices $(-2, 0)$ and $(2, 0)$.

(b) Foci $(-5, 1)$ and $(7, 1)$; vertices $(-3, 1)$ and $(5, 1)$.

(c) Asymptotes $y = 2x$ and $y = -2x$, contains the point $(1, 1)$.

(d) Asymptotes $y = x + 1$ and $y = -x + 3$, contains the point $(2, 4)$.

3. (a) Find the equation of the hyperbola whose foci are the vertices of the ellipse $11x^2 + 7y^2 = 77$ and whose vertices are the foci of this ellipse.

(b) Find the equation of the ellipse whose vertices are the foci of the hyperbola $11x^2 - 7y^2 = 77$ and whose foci are the vertices of this hyperbola.

4. Are there points of a hyperbola at which the tangent line is parallel to an asymptote? Are there tangent lines that contain the origin?

5. Find the tangent and normal lines to the hyperbolas at the given point.

(a) $8x^2 - 6y^2 = 48$, $(3, 2)$

(b) $(y - 1)^2 - 12(x + 2)^2 = 24$, $(-1, 7)$

6. Use calculus to discuss the concavity of a hyperbola.

7. Sketch the graphs of the following equations.

(a) $\left| \dfrac{x^2}{4} - y^2 \right| = 1$

(b) $\sin \pi \sqrt{x^2 - 4y^2} = 0$

(c) $\dfrac{x|x|}{4} + y|y| = 1$

(d) $\left[\dfrac{x^2}{4} - y^2 \right] = 0$

8. Describe the graph of the equation $\dfrac{x^4}{a^4} - \dfrac{y^4}{b^4} + \dfrac{2y^2}{b^2} = 1$.

9. The segment cut by a hyperbola from a line that contains a focus and is perpendicular to the transverse diameter is called a **latus rectum** of the hyperbola. Show that the length of a latus rectum of the hyperbola whose equation is Equation 29-3 is $\dfrac{2b^2}{a}$. Find the slope of the tangent at the point of the first quadrant that is an endpoint of a latus rectum. Show that this tangent line cuts off a segment of the negative Y-axis that is half as long as the transverse diameter.

10. A point moves so that the product of the slopes of the line segments that join it to two given points is k^2. Describe the curve traced out by the point.

11. Consider the tangent to the hyperbola $\dfrac{x^2}{a^2} - \dfrac{y^2}{b^2} = 1$ at a point (h, k) of the hyperbola.

Show that this tangent line intersects the asymptotes of the hyperbola in the points $\left(\dfrac{bh + ak}{b}, \dfrac{bh + ak}{a}\right)$ and $\left(\dfrac{bh - ak}{b}, \dfrac{ak - bh}{a}\right)$. Use this result to prove the following theorem. If the tangent to a hyperbola at a point A intersects the asymptotes of the hyperbola in the points P and Q, then A is the midpoint of the line segment PQ.

12. A **semi-diameter** of a hyperbola is a segment whose terminal points are the center and a point of the hyperbola. Thus if the semi-diameter that contains a point (x, y) of the hyperbola $\dfrac{x^2}{a^2} - \dfrac{y^2}{b^2} = 1$ is S units long, we have

$$S^2 = x^2 + y^2 = a^2\left(1 + \frac{y^2}{b^2}\right) + y^2 = a^2 + y^2\left(1 + \frac{a^2}{b^2}\right).$$

From this equation, conclude that the transverse diameter is the shortest diameter of the hyperbola. Is there a longest diameter?

30 THE PARABOLA

For our geometric descriptions of the ellipse and the hyperbola, we started with two given points and a given positive number. In the case of the **parabola**, we start with a given point and a given line. The point is the **focus** of the parabola, the line is its **directrix**, and the *parabola is the set of points, each of which is equidistant from the focus and the directrix.*

To translate this geometric description of a parabola into an analytic one, let us choose our coordinate axes so that the focus is the point $(c, 0)$ and the directrix is the line $x = -c$. In Fig. 30-1 we have shown the focus and directrix if $c > 0$, but our discussion is valid if c is either positive or negative. The (perpendicular) distance between a point (x, y) and the directrix is $|x + c|$. The distance formula tells us that the

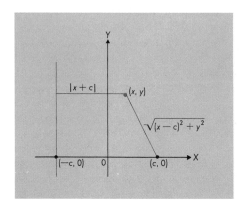

Figure 30-1

distance between the points (x, y) and $(c, 0)$ is $\sqrt{(x - c)^2 + y^2}$, so (x, y) is a point of our parabola if, and only if,

$$\sqrt{(x - c)^2 + y^2} = |x + c|.$$

When we square both sides of this equation and simplify, we get the equation

(30-1) $$y^2 = 4cx.$$

Since we can replace y with $-y$ without changing Equation 30-1, we see that our parabola is symmetric with respect to the X-axis. The line of symmetry of a parabola (in this case the X-axis) is called the **axis** of the parabola. The axis of a parabola contains the focus and is perpendicular to the directrix.

The point of intersection of a parabola with its axis (in this case the origin) is the **vertex** of the parabola. The **focal length** of the parabola is the distance between the vertex and the focus (in this case $|c|$).

We shall now draw the parabola $y^2 = 4cx$. Let us suppose for the moment that $c > 0$. Since the curve is symmetric about the X-axis, we need only plot those points for which $y > 0$, for we can obtain the remainder of the graph by reflecting this part about the X-axis. So we can suppose that

$$y = 2\sqrt{cx}.$$

Then it is easy to calculate that

$$y' = \sqrt{\frac{c}{x}} \quad \text{and} \quad y'' = -\frac{1}{2x}\sqrt{\frac{c}{x}}.$$

From the equation for y', we see that the slope is always positive (except where it is undefined at the origin), so the curve rises to the right. On the other hand, $y'' < 0$, so our parabola is concave down. Its graph is shown in Fig. 30-2.

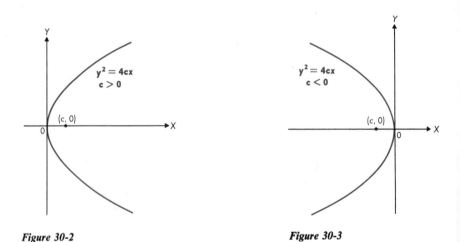

Figure 30-2   Figure 30-3

When we sketched the parabola in Fig. 30-2, we assumed that $c > 0$. If $c < 0$, the parabola opens to the left, rather than to the right. The graph in this case is shown in Fig. 30-3.

If we choose the coordinate axes so that the focus of the parabola is the point

$(0, c)$ of the Y-axis and the directrix is the line $y = -c$ parallel to the X-axis, then the vertex of the parabola is again the origin. However, the roles of x and y are now interchanged, so the line of symmetry of the parabola is the Y-axis, and its equation is

(30-2) $$x^2 = 4cy.$$

If $c > 0$, the parabola opens up as shown on the left in Fig. 30-4. If $c < 0$, the parabola opens down as shown on the right in Fig. 30-4.

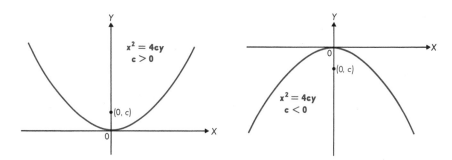

Figure 30-4

Example 30-1. The vertex of a parabola is the origin, and it is symmetric with respect to the X-axis. The slope of the parabola is -1 where it intersects the line $y = 6$. What is the equation of the parabola?

Solution. The equation of a parabola that is symmetric with respect to the X-axis and has the origin as vertex has the form $y^2 = 4cx$. We must determine the number c. We use implicit differentiation to find that $2yy' = 4c$, and when we substitute $y = 6$ and $y' = -1$, we find that $c = -3$. The equation of our parabola is therefore $y^2 = -12x$.

The equation

(30-3) $$(y - k)^2 = 4c(x - h)$$

is also an equation of a parabola. If we use the translation equations $\bar{y} = y - k$ and $\bar{x} = x - h$ to introduce an $\overline{X}\overline{Y}$-coordinate system, our equation becomes $\bar{y}^2 = 4c\bar{x}$, which tells us that the vertex of the parabola is the origin of the $\overline{X}\overline{Y}$-system (that is, the point (h, k) of the XY-system) and the directrix is the line $\bar{x} = -c$ (that is, the line $x = h - c$ in the XY-system). Figure 30-5 shows what the parabola looks like if $c > 0$. Similarly the equation

(30-4) $(x - h)^2 = 4c(y - k)$

represents a parabola whose vertex is the point (h, k) and whose directrix is the line $y = k - c$ (see Fig. 30-6 for the case $c > 0$).

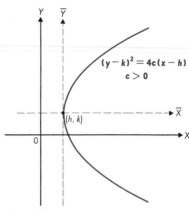

Example 30-2. Write the equation of the parabola whose directrix is the line $y = -5$ and whose focus is the point $(4, -1)$.

Figure 30-5

Solution. Since the directrix is horizontal, the axis of our parabola is vertical. The vertex is midway between the focus and the point in which the axis intersects the directrix. In this case the vertex is the point $(4, -3)$. Clearly (see Fig. 30-7),

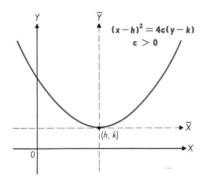

Figure 30-6

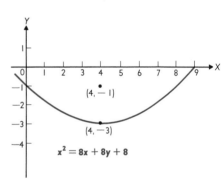

Figure 30-7

the focal length is $c = 2$. Thus we obtain the equation of our parabola from Equation 30-4 by taking $h = 4$, $k = -3$ and $c = 2$; that is,

$$(x - 4)^2 = 8(y + 3).$$

This equation can also be written

$$x^2 = 8x + 8y + 8.$$

Example 30-3. Show that the graph of the equation $y = ax^2 + bx + c$ is a parabola if $a \neq 0$.

Solution. We replace x with $\bar{x} + h$ and y with $\bar{y} + k$, where h and k are numbers to be determined, and obtain the equation

$$\bar{y} + k = a(\bar{x} + h)^2 + b(\bar{x} + h) + c$$

$$= a\bar{x}^2 + (2ah + b)\bar{x} + ah^2 + bh + c.$$

Now if we let $h = -b/2a$ and then $k = ah^2 + bh + c = \dfrac{4ac - b^2}{4a}$, we obtain the standard form of the equation of a parabola,

$$\bar{x}^2 = \frac{1}{a}\,\bar{y}.$$

If $a > 0$, the parabola opens up; if $a < 0$, the parabola opens down.

P R O B L E M S   3 0

1. Find the focus and directrix of each of the following parabolas and sketch.
(a) $y^2 = 8x$
(b) $(x + 3)^2 = 24(y - 2)$
(c) $x^2 - 2x + 4y + 5 = 0$
(d) $y^2 - 12x + 2y + 1 = 0$

2. Find the equations of the parabolas that satisfy the following conditions.
(a) Focus $(3, 0)$; directrix $x = -3$.
(b) Focus $(-3, 2)$; directrix $y = -4$.
(c) Vertex $(1, -3)$; focal length 5; opens down.
(d) Vertex $(-1, 3)$; contains the point $(1, 1)$; axis parallel to the X-axis.

3. Discuss the graphs of the following equations.
(a) $y^2 = 8\,|x|$
(b) $y\,|y| = 8x$
(c) $y^2 = [\![x]\!]x$
(d) $y^2 - 12\,|x| + 2\,|y| + 1 = 0$

4. Let (x_1, y_1) and (x_2, y_2) be any two points of the parabola $x^2 = 4cy$. Show that the chord joining these two points is parallel to the tangent to the parabola at the point whose X-coordinate is the midpoint of the interval $[x_1, x_2]$.

5. The axis of the parabola $y = ax^2 + bx + c$ is parallel to the Y-axis. Therefore its vertex is a maximum or a minimum point. Use derivatives to find the vertex of the parabola and compare your result with the result in Example 30-3. Use the second derivative to discuss the concavity of the parabola.

6. The segment that a parabola cuts from the line that contains the focus and is perpendicular to the axis is called the **latus rectum** of the parabola. (a) Show that the length of the latus rectum of a parabola whose focal length is c is $4c$. (b) Determine the length of the latus rectum for each of the parabolas in Number 2.

7. Find the slopes of the tangents to the parabola $y^2 = 4cx$ at the endpoints of the latus rectum. What is the angle between these tangents? Show that these tangents intersect on the directrix of the parabola.

8. Find the equation of the circle that contains the vertex and the two endpoints of the latus rectum of the parabola $y^2 = 4cx$.

9. The vertex of the parabola $x^2 = 8y$ is the center of an ellipse, and the focus of the parabola is an endpoint of the minor diameter of the ellipse. The parabola and ellipse intersect at right angles. Find the equation of the ellipse.

10. One focus and one vertex of the hyperbola $b^2x^2 - a^2y^2 = a^2b^2$ are points of the positive X-axis. Find the equation of the parabola with the same vertex and focus. Show that the parabola is "eaten by" the right-hand branch of the hyperbola.

11. Let $a > b$ so that one focus and one vertex of the ellipse $b^2x^2 + a^2y^2 = a^2b^2$ are points of the positive X-axis. Find the equation of the parabola with the same vertex and focus. Show that the parabola "eats" the ellipse.

12. Show that if the graph of the equation $y = f(x)$ is a subset of the parabola $y^2 = 4cx$, then y satisfies the differential equation $2xy' = y$. Conversely, show that if y satisfies the differential equation, then $D_x\left(\dfrac{y^2}{x}\right) = 0$, so $y^2 = 4cx$, where c is a number that is independent of x.

31 CONICS

We have defined a parabola as the set of points, each of which is equidistant from a given point (the focus) and a given line (the directrix). Another way to word this definition is to say that the ratio of the distance between a point of our parabola and the focus to the distance between the point and the directrix is 1 for each point of the parabola.

A similar property is possessed by ellipses and hyperbolas. Associated with each focus of an ellipse or a hyperbola is a line (called a *directrix*) such that the ratio of the distance between a point of the curve and the focus to the distance between the point and the directrix is a number e that is the same for every point of the curve.

Let us look at a hyperbola to see exactly what we mean. In Fig. 31-1 we have drawn the hyperbola whose equation is

(31-1)
$$\frac{x^2}{a^2} - \frac{y^2}{b^2} = 1.$$

We have also shown the focus $(c, 0)$, where

(31-2)
$$c = \sqrt{a^2 + b^2}.$$

Let us compute the number r_1^2, where r_1 is the distance between a point (x, y) of our hyperbola and the focus $(c, 0)$. Even though we have shown (x, y) as a point of the "right branch" in our figure, it could be a point of either branch of the

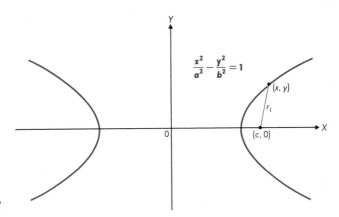

Figure 31-1

hyperbola. According to the distance formula,

$$r_1^2 = (x - c)^2 + y^2 = x^2 - 2cx + c^2 + y^2.$$

In this equation we may replace y^2 with $\dfrac{b^2x^2}{a^2} - b^2$ (from Equation 31-1), and get

$$r_1^2 = x^2 - 2cx + c^2 + \frac{b^2x^2}{a^2} - b^2$$

$$= \left(\frac{a^2 + b^2}{a^2}\right)x^2 - 2cx + c^2 - b^2.$$

Equation 31-2 tells us that $a^2 + b^2 = c^2$, and $c^2 - b^2 = a^2$, so

$$r_1^2 = \frac{c^2}{a^2}x^2 - 2cx + a^2$$

$$= \frac{c^2}{a^2}\left(x^2 - \frac{2a^2}{c}x + \frac{a^4}{c^2}\right)$$

$$= \frac{c^2}{a^2}\left(x - \frac{a^2}{c}\right)^2.$$

Thus we see that

(31-3)
$$r_1 = \frac{c}{a}\left| x - \frac{a^2}{c} \right|.$$

The number $\left| x - \dfrac{a^2}{c} \right|$ is the distance r_2 between the point (x, y) and the line parallel

to the Y-axis and a^2/c units to the right of it (Fig. 31-2). Therefore, Equation 31-3

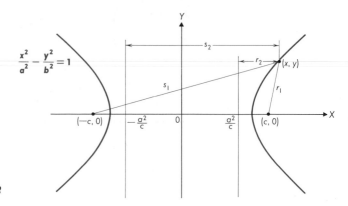

Figure 31-2

can be written as

(31-4)
$$\frac{r_1}{r_2} = \frac{c}{a}.$$

Thus, associated with the focus $(c, 0)$ we have found a line, $x = a^2/c$, such that the ratio of the distance between a point of our hyperbola and the focus to the distance between the point and the line is a number, $\frac{c}{a}$, that is independent of the choice of the point of the hyperbola. It is easy to show that the line a^2/c units to the left of the Y-axis is associated with the focus $(-c, 0)$ in the same way. That is, if s_1 is the distance between the point (x, y) and the focus $(-c, 0)$ and s_2 is the distance between the point and the associated line, then the ratio s_1/s_2 is again the number c/a. The lines $x = a^2/c$ and $x = -a^2/c$ are called the **directrices** of the hyperbola, and the ratio $e = c/a$ is the **eccentricity** of the hyperbola.

The same reasoning that we used above leads to similar results in the case of an ellipse. Let us consider the ellipse whose equation is

(31-5)
$$\frac{x^2}{a^2} + \frac{y^2}{b^2} = 1,$$

where $a > b$. This ellipse is shown in Fig. 31-3. Associated with the focus $(c, 0)$ is the directrix parallel to the Y-axis and a^2/c units to the right of it. The directrix a^2/c units to the left of the Y-axis is associated with the focus $(-c, 0)$. In the problems at the end of the section, we ask you to show that if (x, y) is any point of our ellipse, then the ratio r_1/r_2 of the distance between (x, y) and $(c, 0)$ to the distance between (x, y) and the associated directrix is the eccentricity $e = c/a$. The ratio s_1/s_2 of the distances to the other focus and directrix is also e.

We have shown that the ellipse, parabola, and hyperbola all share a common "ratio" property. Associated with a focus of one of these curves is a line, called a directrix, such that the ratio of the distance between a point of the curve and the focus to the distance between the point and the directrix is a number e (the eccentricity) that is independent of the choice of the point of the curve. In the case of our ellipse and hyperbola, we saw that the number e was given by the formula $e = c/a$. Since $c < a$ for an ellipse and $c > a$ for a hyperbola, we see that *the eccentricity of an ellipse is a number that is less than* 1, *the eccentricity of a hyperbola is greater than* 1, *and the eccentricity of a parabola is equal to* 1.

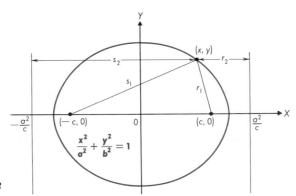

Figure 31-3

Ellipses, parabolas, and hyperbolas make up the family of curves known as *conics*. The members of this family can be geometrically described as follows: *A* **conic** *is determined by a given point F (a* **focus**), *a given line d not containing F (the* **directrix** *associated with F), and a number e (the* **eccentricity**). *A point P is a point of the conic if, and only if, the ratio of the distance* $\overline{FP}$ *to the distance between P and the line d is the number e.*

A conic is an ellipse, parabola, or hyperbola depending on whether $e < 1$, $e = 1$, or $e > 1$. In the case of our hyperbola of Equation 31-1 and of our ellipse of Equation 31-5 (in which $a > b$), the directrices are the lines

$$(31\text{-}6) \qquad x = -\frac{a^2}{c} \quad \text{and} \quad x = \frac{a^2}{c},$$

and the eccentricity is the number

$$(31\text{-}7) \qquad e = \frac{c}{a}.$$

If a hyperbola or ellipse has a different orientation, these formulas must be modified accordingly. For example, if $b > a$ in Equation 31-5 of the ellipse, then $e = c/b$, and the directrices are the lines $y = -b^2/c$ and $y = b^2/c$.

Example 31-1. Find the equation of the conic that has an eccentricity of 2 and has the point (3, 0) as a focus for which the corresponding directrix is the *Y*-axis.

Solution. In Fig. 31-4 we show the typical point (x, y) of our conic and also the focus $(3, 0)$. The geometric description of a conic tells us that $r_1/r_2 = 2$; that is,

$$r_1^2 = 4r_2^2.$$

Since $r_1^2 = (x - 3)^2 + y^2$ and $r_2^2 = x^2$, the equation of our conic is

$$(x - 3)^2 + y^2 = 4x^2.$$

This equation can be written as

$$3x^2 - y^2 + 6x - 9 = 0,$$

or, after completing the square

$$\frac{(x + 1)^2}{4} - \frac{y^2}{12} = 1.$$

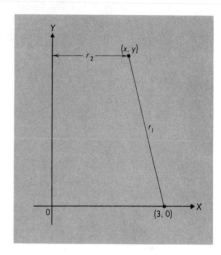

Figure 31-4

In this form, it is plain that the equation represents a hyperbola; we knew from the start that our conic was a hyperbola, since its eccentricity is greater than 1.

Example 31-2. Find the eccentricity and locate the directrices of the conic whose equation is $9x^2 + 25y^2 = 1$.

Solution. If we write this equation as

$$\frac{x^2}{\frac{1}{9}} + \frac{y^2}{\frac{1}{25}} = 1,$$

we recognize it as the standard form of the equation of an ellipse for which $a^2 = \frac{1}{9}$ and $b^2 = \frac{1}{25}$. Hence

$$c = \sqrt{a^2 - b^2} = \sqrt{\tfrac{1}{9} - \tfrac{1}{25}} = \sqrt{\tfrac{16}{225}} = \tfrac{4}{15}.$$

Equation 31-7 gives the eccentricity of our ellipse as $e = \dfrac{c}{a} = \dfrac{\frac{4}{15}}{\frac{1}{3}} = \dfrac{4}{5}$, and we see from Equations 31-6 that the directrices are the lines with equations $x = -\frac{5}{12}$ and $x = \frac{5}{12}$.

The use of the word "focus" for certain points connected with the conics is related to the fact that these points play the role of focal points in a physical sense. To demonstrate this fact in the case of the parabola, we find it convenient to choose the coordinate axes so that the equation of the parabola is $y^2 = 4cx$, with $c > 0$. Figure 31-5 shows the upper half of the parabola; the point $F(c, 0)$ is its focus. If the figure represents the upper half of the cross section of a parabolic reflector, then we will show that a ray of light parallel to the X-axis will strike a point P of the parabola and be reflected to the focus F. The tangent to the parabola at P is the line TP in Fig. 31-5, and it is a law of optics that the reflected beam and the incident beam will make equal angles with this line. From elementary geometry, we see that the acute angle between the incident beam and the tangent line is equal to $\angle PTF$. The reflected beam will travel the path PF

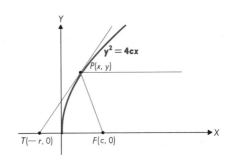

Figure 31-5

if, and only if, $\angle FPT = \angle PTF$. These angles will be equal if, and only if, the triangle TFP is an isosceles triangle with $\overline{PF} = \overline{TF}$. It is this equation that we shall now verify.

If the coordinates of P are (x, y), then the distance formula yields

$$\overline{PF} = \sqrt{(x - c)^2 + y^2} = \sqrt{x^2 - 2cx + c^2 + y^2}.$$

Since P is a point of our parabola, $y^2 = 4cx$, and hence we may replace y^2 with $4cx$ in the last radical to obtain

(31-8) $$\overline{PF} = \sqrt{x^2 + 2cx + c^2} = x + c.$$

Calculating the distance $\overline{TF}$ is somewhat more complicated. From Fig. 31-5 we see that $\overline{TF} = c + r$, where r is the positive number such that the tangent line at P intersects the X-axis in the point T with coordinates $(-r, 0)$. To find this number r, we first note that the slope of the segment TP is $y/(x + r)$. The slope of this segment may also be found from the equation $y^2 = 4cx$ by implicit differentiation: $2yy' = 4c$. Hence $y' = 2c/y$, and we equate our two expressions for the slope of the segment TP to obtain the equation

$$\frac{y}{x + r} = \frac{2c}{y}.$$

Then

$$x + r = \frac{y^2}{2c} = \frac{4cx}{2c} = 2x,$$

and so $r = x$. It then follows that

$$\overline{TF} = c + r = c + x.$$

When we compare this equation with Equation 31-8, we see that $\overline{PF} = \overline{TF}$, and our result is proved.

We won't go into quite so much detail with regard to the focusing property of the ellipse. Figure 31-6 shows an ellipse whose equation has the standard form

$$\frac{x^2}{a^2} + \frac{y^2}{b^2} = 1,$$

with $a > b$. We have drawn a tangent line to the curve at an arbitrary point P of the ellipse. Now we assert that the segments SP and RP (S and R are the foci

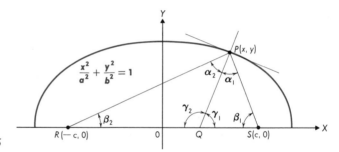

Figure 31-6

of the ellipse) make equal angles with the tangent line at P (or equivalently, with the normal line QP). Thus, if our figure is the cross section of an elliptical reflector, we are saying that a ray of light emanating from the focus S will be reflected at P to the other focus R.

To prove this assertion, we must show that the angles of α_1 and α_2 in Fig. 31-6 are equal. These angles will be equal if $\beta_1 + \gamma_1 = \beta_2 + \gamma_2$, and in this situation this equation is equivalent to the equation

$$\tan (\beta_1 + \gamma_1) = \tan (\beta_2 + \gamma_2).$$

We can verify the preceding equation by first expanding the two sides to obtain the equation

$$\frac{\tan \beta_1 + \tan \gamma_1}{1 - \tan \beta_1 \tan \gamma_1} = \frac{\tan \beta_2 + \tan \gamma_2}{1 - \tan \beta_2 \tan \gamma_2},$$

and then calculating these tangents in terms of the coordinates of P. For example, $\tan \beta_2 = y/(x + c)$, and $\tan \gamma_1$ times the slope of the ellipse at P is -1. We will leave the details of verifying this equation for the problems.

PROBLEMS 31

1. Find the eccentricity and the directrices of the hyperbola $a^2y^2 - b^2x^2 = a^2b^2$.

2. Use our geometric description to find the conic with the given focus, corresponding directrix, and eccentricity.
(a) Focus $(2, 0)$; directrix $x = -2$; $e = 2$.
(b) Focus $(2, 0)$; directrix $x = -2$; $e = 1$.
(c) Focus $(2, 0)$; directrix $x = -2$; $e = \frac{1}{2}$.
(d) Focus $(0, 4)$; directrix $y = 0$; $e = 3$.
(e) Focus $(1, 0)$; directrix $x = 2$; $e = 1$.
(f) Focus $(1, 0)$; directrix $x = 4$; $e = \frac{1}{2}$.
(g) Focus $(1, 2)$; directrix $y = -2$; $e = \frac{1}{3}$.
(h) Focus $(0, 4)$; directrix $y = 1$; $e = 2$.

3. Find the eccentricity and the directrices of the following conics.
(a) $3x^2 + 4y^2 = 12$ (b) $3y^2 = 2x$
(c) $y^2 - 2x^2 + 8 = 0$ (d) $y^2 - 2x^2 - 8 = 0$
(e) $y^2 - 2x^2 - 6y - 4x + 15 = 0$ (f) $3x^2 + 4y^2 + 6x + 24y - 9 = 0$

4. (a) Tell how the shape of an ellipse changes as the eccentricity varies from near 0 to near 1.
(b) Tell how the shape of a hyperbola changes as the eccentricity varies from near 1 to a very large number.

5. Suppose you are told that the Y-axis is a directrix of an equilateral hyperbola and that the corresponding focus is a point of the X-axis that is 3 units away from this directrix. Can you find the equation of the hyperbola?

6. What is the eccentricity of an ellipse in which the distance between its foci is one-half the distance between its directrices?

7. The vertex of a parabola is the origin, and its focus is the point $(1, 1)$. What is the equation of its directrix?

8. The vertex of the parabola $x^2 = 4cy$ is the center of an ellipse. The focus of the parabola is an endpoint of the minor diameter of the ellipse, and the parabola and ellipse intersect at right angles. Find the eccentricity of the ellipse. (See Problem 30-9.)

9. The vertex of the parabola $y^2 = 4cx$ is the center of an ellipse. The latus rectum of the parabola is a latus rectum of the ellipse. What is the eccentricity of the ellipse? Change the word "ellipse" to "hyperbola" and do the problem.

10. Fill in the details concerning the focusing property of the ellipse.

11. Use algebra to show that the distance d between a point (x, y) of the ellipse $\dfrac{x^2}{a^2} + \dfrac{y^2}{b^2} = 1$ (with $a > b$) and the focus $(c, 0)$ is given by the equation

$$d = e \left| x - \frac{a^2}{c} \right|.$$

REVIEW PROBLEMS—CHAPTER FOUR

You can use the following problems to test yourself on the material of this chapter.

1. An ellipse is tangent to the circle $x^2 + y^2 = 4$ at the points of intersection of the circle and the Y-axis, and its foci are the points of intersection of the circle and the X-axis. Find the equation of the ellipse. What is its eccentricity?

2. Consider a hyperbola whose transverse diameter lies along the X-axis. Show that the slope of a tangent at an endpoint of a latus rectum is either e or $-e$.

3. Find the slope of the tangent line to the ellipse $b^2x^2 + a^2y^2 = a^2b^2$ (where $a > b$) at the point of the first quadrant that is an endpoint of a latus rectum. How is this slope related to the eccentricity of the ellipse?

4. An artificial earth satellite moves in an elliptical orbit with the center of the earth as one focus. The minimum distance from the center of the earth to the satellite's path is d_1 miles, and the maximum distance is d_2 miles. Find the formula for the eccentricity of the elliptical path in terms of d_1 and d_2.

5. The slope of the segment that joins a point P to the origin is 4 times the X-co-ordinate of P. Where is P?

6. A man walks directly from the point $(4, 0)$ to a point $P(x, y)$ of the curve $x^2/25 + y^2/9 = 1$, and then walks twice as fast directly to the point $(-4, 0)$. How far does he walk? To which point P should he go to complete his trip in minimum time?

7. Show that if the graph of the equation $y = f(x)$ is a subset of an ellipse or a hyperbola in "standard position," then y satisfies the differential equation $xyy'' + xy'^2 - yy' = 0$.

8. Show that if the graph of the equation $y = f(x)$ is a subset of the graph of one of Equations 30-1, 29-3, 29-7, or 28-3, then y^3y'' is independent of x.

9. What conditions must a, b, c, d, and e satisfy in order that the graph of the equation $ax^2 + by^2 + 2cx + 2dy + e = 0$ be an ellipse? a hyperbola? or a parabola?

10. Sketch the graphs of the following equations.

(a) $y = (|x| + x)^2$
(b) $x^2 + [x]y^2 = 1$
(c) $\dfrac{x^2}{[x]^2} + y^2 = 1$
(d) $[y] = 4x^2$

11. The equations of ellipses, hyperbolas, and parabolas in standard position can be written as $\dfrac{xx}{a^2} + \dfrac{yy}{b^2} = 1$, $\dfrac{xx}{a^2} - \dfrac{yy}{b^2} = 1$, $yy = 4c\left(\dfrac{x+x}{2}\right)$, and so on, where we replace x^2 and y^2 with xx and yy, and replace x and y with $\dfrac{x+x}{2}$ and $\dfrac{y+y}{2}$. Show that the tangents to these curves at the point (x_1, y_1) have the equations $\dfrac{xx_1}{a^2} + \dfrac{yy_1}{b^2} = 1$, $\dfrac{xx_1}{a^2} - \dfrac{yy_1}{b^2} = 1$, $yy_1 = 4c\left(\dfrac{x+x_1}{2}\right)$, and so on.

THE INTEGRAL

F I V E

The two most important concepts in calculus can be introduced by a study of geometric problems. We have seen how the concept of the *derivative* arose when we considered the problem of finding the tangent line to a curve at a point. In this chapter we shall see how the problem of finding the area of a plane region with a given curve as part of its boundary leads us to the second major concept of calculus—the *integral*.

Of course, we don't restrict our interpretation of the derivative to the geometric idea of slope. A derivative is a rate, and as such we can use it to discuss problems involving the velocity and acceleration of moving bodies, and so on. Similarly, although we shall introduce the integral as a solution to the problem of finding the areas of certain regions, we shall also see that other interpretations are possible. Our applications of integrals will range from finding the work required to pump out a tank of water to providing a new approach to the definition of logarithms.

197

32 APPROXIMATING AREAS

Before we introduce the concept of the integral of a function over an interval, let us briefly recall how we introduced the concept of the derivative of a function at a point. In geometric terms, the derivative $f'(x)$ of a function f at the point x is the slope of the line that is tangent to the graph of f at the point $(x, f(x))$. Thus our first method of calculating the derivative $f'(x)$ was to draw "by eye" a line for which the name "tangent line" seemed appropriate and then measure its slope. This procedure suffers because the phrase "by eye" is vague; it is not good practice to define a mathematical concept such as the tangent line to a graph as the "line that seems to the eye to fit the curve best at the given point." Therefore, we turned to an analytical approach as follows.

(i) In order to get started, we assumed that there *is* a tangent line to the graph of the given function f at the given point.

(ii) Then we used geometric reasoning to convince ourselves that the slope of that line is approximated by some slopes that we can calculate analytically— namely, the slopes of certain chords. These slopes are calculated from our difference quotient $\dfrac{f(z) - f(x)}{z - x}$.

(iii) Lastly, we examined these approximating slopes to see what number they approximate; that is, we found the limit of the difference quotient. This number we took to be the number $f'(x)$ that we were seeking.

Notice that from a strictly logical point of view we don't need steps (i) and (ii). Their only purpose is to suggest why it might be useful to study the difference quotient. We could bypass these steps and simply define $f'(x)$ as $\lim\limits_{z \to x} \dfrac{f(z) - f(x)}{z - x}$. Thus we can formulate a precise definition of the derivative without first having a precise definition of a tangent line. In fact, we introduced our definition of the tangent line *after* we had defined $f'(x)$.

We will follow a similar sequence of steps as we introduce the integral of a function over an interval $[a, b]$. As a first geometric approach to this concept, we will think of the integral as the area A of the region that is bounded by the graph of f, the X-axis, and the lines $x = a$ and $x = b$, the shaded region in Fig. 32-1. (For the moment, we will consider regions that lie wholly above the X-axis.) Therefore, we could calculate the integral A by sketching the graph of f on graph paper and counting the squares that are contained in the shaded region. In general, the curve would cut some of the squares, so we would have to estimate "by eye" the fractions of squares that lie under the curve. Thus this graphical calculation of A suffers from difficulties that are similar to those we encountered when we tried to calculate $f'(x)$ by sketching a tangent line "by eye." To avoid these difficulties, we turn to an analytic approach.

(i) In order to get started, we *assume* that there is a number A that we can say is the area of our region.

(ii) Then we use geometric reasoning to develop an analytical method of calculating approximations of this number A.

(iii) Lastly, we examine these approximations to find the number that they approximate; that is, we find their limit.

As in the case of the derivative, the purpose of steps (i) and (ii) is simply to suggest the analytic expression whose limit we will take to be the integral. Thus we will be able to formulate a precise definition of the integral without first having a

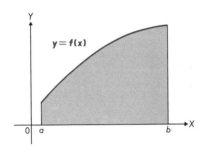

Figure 32-1

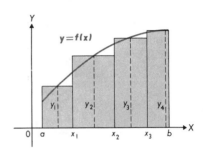

Figure 32-2

precise definition of the area of a plane region. We will have more to say about the connection between integrals and areas later; now we will concentrate on step (ii), approximating the number that we think should measure the area of a region such as the one shown in Fig. 32-1.

Figure 32-2 shows how we make the approximations. We have drawn some rectangles in the figure in such a way that the sum of their areas seems to approximate the area A we seek. To construct these approximating rectangles, we simply chose three points, x_1, x_2, and x_3 between a and b. In this way the interval $[a, b]$ is divided into four smaller intervals called **subintervals** of $[a, b]$. In each subinterval we erected a vertical segment from the X-axis to the curve. The lengths of these segments are $y_1, y_2, y_3,$ and y_4. The areas of our four rectangles are $y_1(x_1 - a)$, $y_2(x_2 - x_1)$, $y_3(x_3 - x_2)$, and $y_4(b - x_3)$. From the figure, it appears that the sum of these areas, the number

$$s = y_1(x_1 - a) + y_2(x_2 - x_1) + y_3(x_3 - x_2) + y_4(b - x_3),$$

approximates our desired area A.

Example 32-1. Suppose that

$$f(x) = \frac{1}{1 + x^2}.$$

Approximate the area A of the region bounded by the graph of f, the X-axis, and the lines $x = 0$ and $x = 1$.

Solution. Fig. 32-3 shows the graph of f in the interval $[0, 1]$. Let us divide this interval into the two subintervals $[0, \frac{1}{2}]$ and $[\frac{1}{2}, 1]$, and then construct rectangles with these subintervals as bases. The bases of these rectangles are each $\frac{1}{2}$ unit long.

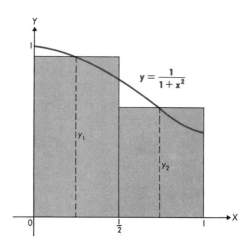

$$y = \frac{1}{1 + x^2}$$

Figure 32-3

For the altitudes of the rectangles, we will arbitrarily choose the values of f at the midpoints of the subintervals. Thus

$$y_1 = f(\tfrac{1}{4}) = \frac{1}{1 + \frac{1}{16}} = \tfrac{16}{17}$$

and

$$y_2 = f(\tfrac{3}{4}) = \tfrac{16}{25}.$$

The area A is therefore approximated by the sum

$$s = \tfrac{16}{17} \cdot \tfrac{1}{2} + \tfrac{16}{25} \cdot \tfrac{1}{2} = .79... .$$

Later we shall find that $A = \pi/4 \approx .78$, so our approximation is quite close.

Now let us go into a little more detail on how we calculate the sums that approximate the area of a region like the one illustrated in Fig. 32-1. First we divide our basic interval $[a, b]$ into a number of subintervals. To form n subintervals we choose $n - 1$ points $x_1, x_2, \ldots, x_{n-1}$ lying between a and b such that $a < x_1 < x_2 < \cdots < x_{n-1} < b$. These points determine a **partition** of (that is, a "division of") the interval $[a, b]$ into the subintervals $[a, x_1], [x_1, x_2], \ldots, [x_{n-1}, b]$. In order to simplify notation, we write $x_0 = a$ and $x_n = b$, and then we can talk about a sub-interval $[x_{i-1}, x_i]$, where i is one of the numbers $1, 2, \ldots, n$. In Example 32-1, we chose $n = 2$, $x_0 = 0$, $x_1 = \frac{1}{2}$, and $x_2 = 1$; these division points determined the subintervals $[0, \frac{1}{2}]$, and $[\frac{1}{2}, 1]$.

Now we construct a rectangle on each of the subintervals in such a way that the sum of the areas of the rectangles approximates the area of the region under the graph of f. It seems reasonable to choose as the altitude of each rectangle the value of f at a point of the subinterval that forms the base of the rectangle. And that is exactly what we do. In each subinterval $[x_{i-1}, x_i]$, we choose a number x_i^*. (In Example 32-1, for instance, we chose $x_1^* = \frac{1}{4}$ in the subinterval $[0, \frac{1}{2}]$ and $x_2^* = \frac{3}{4}$ in the subinterval $[\frac{1}{2}, 1]$.) Then we erect a rectangle whose altitude is $f(x_i^*)$ and whose base is the subinterval $[x_{i-1}, x_i]$; the area of this rectangle is $f(x_i^*)(x_i - x_{i-1})$. The sum of the areas of all the rectangles will approximate the area A. Thus if $n = 4$, for example, we will have the **approximating sum**

$$(32\text{-}1) \quad s = f(x_1^*)(x_1 - x_0) + f(x_2^*)(x_2 - x_1)$$
$$+ f(x_3^*)(x_3 - x_2) + f(x_4^*)(x_4 - x_3).$$

If we had partitioned the interval $[a, b]$ into 104 subintervals, our number s would have been the sum of 104 terms. In order to condense our formulas for approximating sums to a manageable length when n is a large number, we must introduce some notation. The sum in Equation 32-1 may be obtained by carrying out the following directions: "Replace the letter i in the expression $f(x_i^*)(x_i - x_{i-1})$ with each of the numbers 1, 2, 3, and 4 in turn, and add up the terms that result." Directions such as these occur so often in mathematics that we have a special symbol for them. If $P(i)$ is some mathematical expression and n is a positive integer, then the symbol

$$\sum_{i=1}^{n} P(i)$$

means, "Successively replace the letter i in the expression $P(i)$ with the numbers $1, 2, 3, \ldots, n$ and add up the resulting terms." The symbol Σ is the Greek letter **sigma**, and it is used to suggest "sum", since we are to add a number of terms. Thus, for example,

$$\sum_{i=1}^{6} i^2 = 1^2 + 2^2 + 3^2 + 4^2 + 5^2 + 6^2 = 91;$$

$$\sum_{i=1}^{5} 2^i = 2^1 + 2^2 + 2^3 + 2^4 + 2^5 = 62.$$

In this Σ-notation, Equation 32-1 can be written as

$$s = \sum_{i=1}^{4} f(x_i^*)(x_i - x_{i-1}).$$

The letter *i* is called the **index of summation**, and in the above sum the numbers 1, 2, 3, and 4 constitute the **range** of *i*. Other letters may be used as indices of summation, and the range of the index need not start at 1. Thus, for example,

$$\sum_{r=3}^{5} \log r = \log 3 + \log 4 + \log 5 = \log 60,$$

and so on. In the Σ-notation, an approximating sum based on a partition of the interval into *n* subintervals takes the form

(32-2)
$$s = \sum_{i=1}^{n} f(x_i^*)(x_i - x_{i-1}).$$

The length of the subinterval $[x_{i-1}, x_i]$; that is, the number $x_i - x_{i-1}$, occurs so often in our formulas that it is worth our while to introduce an abbreviation for it. We write

$$\Delta x_i = x_i - x_{i-1}.$$

The symbol Δ is the Greek letter **delta**, and it is supposed to suggest the word "difference." In this Δ-notation, Equation 32-2 for an approximating sum becomes

(32-3) $$s = \sum_{i=1}^{n} f(x_i^*)\Delta x_i.$$

Example 32-2. Approximate the area of the region between the graph of the equation $y = \sin x$ and the interval $[0, \pi/2]$ of the X-axis (Fig. 32-4).

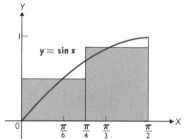

Figure 32-4

Solution. The statement of the problem allows us considerable freedom to choose the number of intervals into which the basic interval $[0, \pi/2]$ is to be partitioned and the points that determine the partition. Suppose we decide to partition the interval into $n = 2$ subintervals by selecting the point $x_1 = \pi/4$. Therefore, $x_0 = 0$, $x_1 = \pi/4$, and $x_2 = \pi/2$, and so $\Delta x_1 = \pi/4 - 0$, and $\Delta x_2 = \pi/2 - \pi/4$. Now let us arbitrarily select the point $x_1^* = \pi/6$ in the interval $[0, \pi/4]$ and the point $x_2^* = \pi/3$ in the interval $[\pi/4, \pi/2]$. Thus Equation 32-3 becomes in this case

$$s = \left(\sin \frac{\pi}{6}\right) \cdot \left(\frac{\pi}{4}\right) + \left(\sin \frac{\pi}{3}\right) \cdot \left(\frac{\pi}{4}\right)$$

$$= \left(\frac{1}{2}\right)\left(\frac{\pi}{4}\right) + \left(\frac{\sqrt{3}}{2}\right)\left(\frac{\pi}{4}\right) \approx 1.1.$$

It appears from Fig. 32-4 that our approximation is probably a number that is too large. Later we will find that half the area bounded by an arch of the sine curve and the X-axis is 1 square unit.

In both Example 32-1 and Example 32-2 we partitioned the interval into subintervals of equal length. Thus in Example 32-1, $\Delta x_1 = \Delta x_2 = \frac{1}{2}$; and in Example 32-2, $\Delta x_1 = \Delta x_2 = \pi/4$. Choosing equal subintervals may make it easier to calculate an approximating sum, but is is not necessary to make such a choice. In fact, in some cases it is not even desirable. We conclude this section with an example of such a case.

Example 32-3. Approximate the area of the region under the graph of f in the interval $[0, 4]$ if $f(x) = 2x^4/(1 + x^4)$.

Solution. Fig. 32-5 shows the graph of f for the interval $[0, 4]$. This graph suggests that we partition the basic interval $[0, 4]$ into subintervals that are shortest when

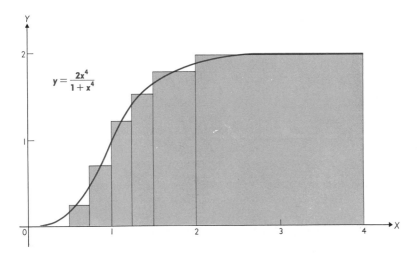

Figure 32-5

the graph is steepest. So let us partition the interval $[0, 4]$ by means of the following points: $0, \frac{1}{2}, \frac{3}{4}, 1, \frac{5}{4}, \frac{3}{2}, 2$, and 4. If we then pick the number x_i^* to be the midpoint of the subinterval $[x_{i-1}, x_i]$, our approximating sum is

$$s = \tfrac{1}{2}f(\tfrac{1}{4}) + \tfrac{1}{4}f(\tfrac{5}{8}) + \tfrac{1}{4}f(\tfrac{7}{8}) + \tfrac{1}{4}f(\tfrac{9}{8}) + \tfrac{1}{4}f(\tfrac{11}{8}) + \tfrac{1}{2}f(\tfrac{7}{4}) + 2f(3) \approx 5.81$$

If we use the techniques of Section 58, we can show that the actual area of our region is 5.79 square units.

You should notice that Formula 32-3 applies to discontinuous functions as well as to continuous ones. In case the function f has some discontinuities in the interval $[a, b]$ (for instance, the greatest integer function as shown in Fig. 32-6), it is not strictly correct to talk about the region that is bounded by the graph of f, the X-axis, and the lines $x = a$ and $x = b$, but we will do so, and you will know what we mean (the shaded region in Fig. 32-6.).

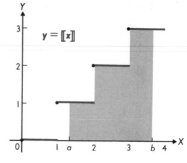

Figure 32-6

P R O B L E M S   3 2

1. Find the points that partition the following intervals into 5 equal subintervals:
   (a) [2, 12]   (b) [−5, 10]
   (c) [−3, 5]   (d) [log 3, log 96]

2. Approximate the area of the region that is bounded by the graph of f, the X-axis, and the lines $x = 2$ and $x = 10$ by partitioning the interval [2, 10] into 4 equal subintervals and using rectangles based on these subintervals, with altitudes equal to the values of f at the midpoints of the subintervals. Use a figure to judge if your approximation is too large or too small.
   (a) $f(x) = 20 - 2x$ (b) $f(x) = 3 + |x - 6|$
   (c) $f(x) = x[x]$ (d) $f(x) = (x - 6)^2$
   (e) $f(x) = \sqrt{16 - (x - 6)^2}$ (f) $f(x) = mx + b$

3. The area of the disk bounded by the circle $x^2 + y^2 = 1$ is π square units. It follows that the area of the region in the first quadrant bounded by the X-axis, the Y-axis, and the graph of the equation $y = \sqrt{1 - x^2}$ is $\pi/4$ square units. Partition the interval [0, 1] into 4 equal subintervals and erect altitudes at the midpoints of the subintervals so as to obtain an approximating sum of 4 terms that approximates the area of this region, and hence obtain an approximation of the number π.

4. Use the ideas in this section to approximate the area of the region under the graph of f and above the indicated interval.
   (a) $f(x) = 3[2x]$, [0, 2]   (b) $f(x) = 2 + [\sin \pi x]$, [−1, 1]
   (c) $f(x) = \tan x$, [0, $\pi/3$] (d) $f(x) = |\tan x|$, [−$\pi/3$, $\pi/3$]
   (e) $f(x) = \cos^2 x$, [0, 2π] (f) $f(x) = \sin x + \cos x$, [0, $\pi/2$]

5. Suppose that the interval [−1, 1] is partitioned into 4 equal subintervals. What is the largest and the smallest (if there are such) sums that we can get from Equation 32-3 (by various choices of x_1^*, x_2^*, x_3^*, and x_4^*) in the following cases. Can you find the set of all such sums?
   (a) $f(x) = \sin \pi x$ (b) $f(x) = |\sin \pi x|$ (c) $f(x) = [\sin \pi x]$ (d) $f(x) = x - [x]$

6. Find the following sums.

(a) $\sum_{i=1}^{4} \sin(\pi/i)$

(b) $\sum_{i=2}^{5} (1 + i)^2$

(c) $\sum_{i=1}^{100} [F(i) - F(i - 1)]$

(d) $\sum_{i=1}^{100} (3i + 2)$

7. With the aid of the formula for the area of a trapezoid, compute the area of the triangle whose vertices are the points $(1, 1)$, $(3, 5)$, and $(7, 3)$. (Drop perpendiculars from the vertices to the X-axis and find the algebraic sum of the areas of the three trapezoids that are formed.)

8. Let $n = 3$, $x_0 = 0$, $x_i = 2^i$ for $i = 1, 2, 3$, $x_i^* = \frac{1}{2}(x_i + x_{i-1})$ and $f(x) = x^2$. Find $\sum_{i=1}^{n} f(x_i^*)\Delta x_i$.

9. Show that if for each $x \in [a, b]$ it is true that $f(x) \in [A, B]$, then for each sum s that we can obtain from Equation 32-3 we have $s \in [A(b - a), B(b - a)]$.

10. Suppose we are given two functions f and g that are defined in a certain interval $[a, b]$, and a number c. Let h and k be the functions that are defined by the equations $h(x) = f(x) + g(x)$ and $k(x) = cf(x)$. Now choose a particular partition of $[a, b]$ and a set of points $x_1^*, x_2^* \ldots, x_n^*$ and denote by F, G, H, and K the sums that we obtain using Equation 32-3 for the functions f, g, h, and k.
(a) Show that $H = F + G$.
(b) Show that $K = cF$.
(c) Show that if we further assume that for each $x \in [a, b]$ we have $f(x) \le g(x)$, then $F \le G$.

11. Suppose that f is an increasing function in the interval $[a, b]$. Let s and t be two sums that are given by Equation 32-3 for the same partition of $[a, b]$ but using different choices of the points $x_1^*, x_2^*, \ldots, x_n^*$. Show that $|s - t| \le [f(b) - f(a)]u$, where u is the length of the longest subinterval of our partition of $[a, b]$.

33 THE INTEGRAL

In the preceding section we used sums of the form

(33-1)
$$s = \sum_{i=1}^{n} f(x_i^*) \Delta x_i$$

to approximate the area A of the region that is bounded by the graph of a function f that takes positive values, the X-axis, and the lines $x = a$ and $x = b$. When we look at the figures in that section, it appears that we can get a close approximation of A by choosing the partition points $x_1, x_2, \ldots, x_{n-1}$ to be close together. Then the rectangles that approximate the region under the graph of f will be narrow, and we feel that the narrower the rectangles, the more nearly they "fill up" the region. Thus a "fine" partition of the interval $[a, b]$ should lead to a close approximation of the area, regardless of our choice of the points $x_1^*, x_2^*, \ldots, x_n^*$ at which we compute the functional values $f(x_1^*), f(x_2^*), \ldots, f(x_n^*)$ that serve as the altitudes of our approximating rectangles.

We measure the "fineness" of a partition by means of a number called the **norm** of the partition, which is the largest of the numbers Δx_i, $i = 1, 2, \ldots, n$. Thus the norm of a partition of the interval $[a, b]$ is the length of the longest subinterval into which the interval is divided. For example, the norm of the partition in Example 32-3 is 2, and the norm of the partition in Example 32-2 is $\pi/4$. If the norm of a partition is small, then *all* the subintervals into which the basic interval is divided are short. These remarks suggest that, intuitively speaking, the area of the region under the graph of f is approximated by Sum 33-1, and a close approximation can be assured by using a partition with a small norm when we form this approximating sum.

The number s is not determined simply by specifying the norm of the partition that we use when we calculate it. For one thing, we may choose many different partitions with the same norm. Secondly, even after the partition is fixed we must choose a number x_i^* in each subinterval, and in general we should not expect to get the same sum s for each choice. Thus for a given norm, Equation 33-1 yields a whole set of numbers. Still it seems reasonable to suppose that if f is a moderately "well-behaved" function, every number of the set will be a close approximation to the area A, if we choose a sufficiently small norm.

Let us put these remarks on a more formal basis. The norm of a partition of $[a, b]$ can be any positive number u that does not exceed $b - a$. With each such number u we will associate the set $S(u)$ of all the sums that Equation 33-1 yields when we use a partition of norm u. Thus

$$(33\text{-}2) \qquad S(u) = \left\{ s \mid s = \sum_{i=1}^{n} f(x_i^*) \Delta x_i, \text{ maximum } \Delta x_i = u \right\}.$$

This equation defines a *set-valued* function S that is basic to our mathematical development of the integral. Notice that all the ingredients of a function are here. The domain of the function S is the half-open interval $(0, b - a]$, its range is a family of sets of numbers, and we have a rule that pairs with each number in the domain one of the sets of numbers in the range. In most of the functions we have dealt with up to now, the elements of the range have been numbers. Here they are sets of numbers, but a set of numbers is a perfectly respectable mathematical entity, so S is a respectable function. To sketch the graph of the function S, we plot all pairs of the form (u, s), where u is a number in the interval $(0, b - a]$, and s is one of the numbers we can get from Equation 33-1 when we use a partition of norm u. In other words, to sketch the graph of the function S we plot the points of the set

$$\left\{ (u, s) \mid u \in (0, b - a], s = \sum_{i=1}^{n} f(x_i^*) \Delta x_i, \text{ maximum } \Delta x_i = u \right\}.$$

Figure 33-1 shows what the result might look like. From that figure, for example, it appears that $S(2) = [1, 3]$; that is, the *set* that corresponds to the *number* 2 is the interval [1, 3].

Since we are interested in the approximating sums that we get when the norm of our partition is small, we will want to know what the set $S(u)$ is like when u is a

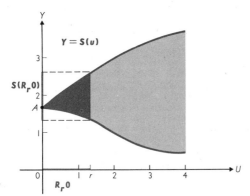

Figure 33-1

number that is close to 0. To be specific, we will want to find the limit of S from the right at 0; that is, the number $\lim_{u \downarrow 0} S(u)$. Although our set-valued function S differs somewhat from the numerical-valued functions we treated earlier, our definition of what it means to say that a number A is the limit of S from the right at 0 is essentially unchanged. Figure 33-1 illustrates this meaning graphically; formally, we say that $\lim_{u \downarrow 0} S(u) = A$ if for each neighborhood $N_p A$ there is a right neighborhood $R_r 0$ such that $S(R_r 0) \subseteq N_p A$. A right neighborhood $R_r 0$ is just an open interval of the form $(0, r)$, and the symbol $S(R_r 0)$ stands for the union of all the sets of the form $S(u)$, where $u \in R_r 0$. We have illustrated such a set in Fig. 33-1. Now we can give our mathematical definition of the integral.

Definition 33-1. *Let f be a function whose domain contains an interval* [a, b], *and use Equation 33-2 to define the set-valued function S. Then if* $\lim_{u \downarrow 0} S(u)$ *exists we say that f is **integrable** on the interval* [a, b]. *The limit is called the **integral** of f over* [a, b], *and we denote this number by the symbol* $\displaystyle\int_a^b f(x)\, dx$.

Before we say more about the meaning of the integral, let us discuss the symbol $\displaystyle\int_a^b f(x)\, dx$. The symbol $\int$ is an elongated S; it is called an **integral sign**. It suggests that the integral is the limit of "sums." The numbers a and b are called, respectively, the lower and upper **limits of integration**, but here the word "limit" is used in a new sense. The limits of integration are analogous to the numbers determining the range of the index in a summation —for example, the numbers r and n in the sum $\sum_{i=r}^{n} P(i)$. The letter x in the symbol $\int_{a}^{b} f(x)\, dx$ plays a role that is similar to the role played by the index of summation. The letter i in the sum $\sum_{i=r}^{n} P(i)$ can be replaced by another letter without altering the sum. The letter x in the symbol $\int_{a}^{b} f(x)\, dx$ is called the **variable of integration**, and it can be replaced by other letters without altering the integral. Thus, for example,

$$\int_{a}^{b} f(x)\, dx = \int_{a}^{b} f(t)\, dt = \int_{a}^{b} f(z)\, dz.$$

The "dx" or "dt" or "dz" tells us what the variable of integration is. For example,

$$\int_{0}^{1} x^2 t\, dx \text{ and } \int_{0}^{1} x^2 t\, dt$$

are different integrals. Finally, we refer to $f(x)$ as the **integrand** of $\int_{a}^{b} f(x)\, dx$. Thus $\sqrt{x}$ is the integrand of $\int_{2}^{3} \sqrt{x}\, dx$.

To see how Definition 33-1 applies in a specific case, let us take f to be the greatest integer function, $[a, b]$ to be the interval $[1, 2]$, and construct our set function S and calculate its limit from the right at 0. On the left-hand side of Fig. 33-2 we have sketched the given function f, together with a typical partition of the basic interval $[a, b]$ and a choice of the points $x_1^*, \ldots, x_n^*$. We are to calculate sums of the form

$$s = \sum_{i=1}^{n} f(x_i^*)\, \Delta x_i = f(x_1^*)\, \Delta x_1 + f(x_2^*)\, \Delta x_2 + \cdots + f(x_{n-1}^*)\, \Delta x_{n-1} + f(x_n^*)\, \Delta x_n.$$

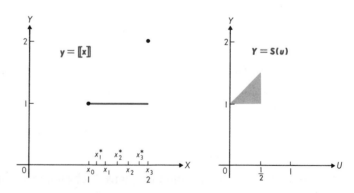

Figure 33-2

No matter how we choose the points $x_1^*, \ldots, x_{n-1}^*$, the corresponding functional values will be 1. The number $f(x_n^*)$ will either be 1 (if we choose x_n^* to be a number other than 2) or 2 (if we choose $x_n^* = 2$). Therefore, our sum s will either be

$$s = \Delta x_1 + \Delta x_2 + \cdots + \Delta x_{n-1} + \Delta x_n = 1$$

or

$$s = \Delta x_1 + \Delta x_2 + \cdots + \Delta x_{n-1} + 2\,\Delta x_n = \Delta x_1 + \cdots + \Delta x_n + \Delta x_n = 1 + \Delta x_n.$$

Since we are interested in the limit of S at 0, we need only consider $S(u)$ when u is close to 0. We will therefore only sketch the graph of S in case $u < \frac{1}{2}$. (It would be a good exercise for you to complete this graph for the whole domain of S, the interval $(0, 1]$.) If u is any number less than $\frac{1}{2}$, then we can choose a partition of the basic interval $[1, 2]$ so that Δx_n is any number that satisfies the inequalities $0 < \Delta x_n \leq u$. Therefore, our formulas for s tell us that s may be any number such that $1 \leq s \leq 1 + u$; in other words, $S(u) = [1, 1 + u]$. Thus the graph of S for u near 0 is the shaded region in the figure on the right-hand side of Fig. 33-2. From this figure it is apparent that $\lim_{u \downarrow 0} S(u) = 1$, so we see that $\int_1^2 [\![x]\!]\, dx = 1$, exactly the result we would expect from our area interpretation of the integral.

Although the example we have just completed was quite complicated, it is really one of the simplest illustrations of how to evaluate an integral *directly from our definition*. In practice, we don't evaluate integrals this way; we will find efficient methods of evaluating integrals later. Here we are not so much concerned with *evaluating* integrals as we are with their *definition*.

In the geometric discussion suggesting that the sums given by Equation 33-1 are approximations to the area of the region between the graph of f and the interval $[a, b]$ of the X-axis, we assumed that f does not take negative values. But we don't need this restriction to form these sums and hence construct our set-valued function S and take its limit. In other words, Definition 33-1 permits us to talk about $\int_a^b f(x)\, dx$ even though the graph of f crosses the X-axis between a and b. We will interpret such integrals in terms of area in Section 39.

To help fix the definition of the integral in our minds, and also to provide us with a useful fact about integrals, we now state and prove a simple theorem.

Theorem 33-1. *If f is integrable on an interval $[a, b]$, and if $f(x) \geqslant 0$ for each point $x \in [a, b]$, then $\int_a^b f(x)\, dx \geq 0$.*

Proof. Since f does not take negative values in $[a, b]$, it is clear that each sum s that we can form from Equation 33-1 is greater than or equal to 0. The number $\int_a^b f(x)\, dx$ is approximated by such sums, so from our intuitive notion of what a limit is, it is clear that this integral cannot be negative. A formal proof is more complicated. We use the method of "proof by contradiction," where we suppose that the conclusion of our theorem is false and show that this supposition leads to a contradiction of the hypotheses. Our integral is the limit of a set-valued function S, so we will suppose that this limit is negative; that is, that there is a positive number p such that $\lim_{u \downarrow 0} S(u) =$ $-p$. According to the definition of a limit, corresponding to this positive number p there is a right neighborhood $R_r 0$ such that $S(R_r 0) \subseteq N_p(-p) =$ $(-2p, 0)$. This inclusion says that for each $u \in R_r 0$, $S(u) \subseteq (-2p, 0)$, and so if $s \in S(u)$, $s < 0$. But we have already remarked that our hypotheses imply that *no* sum s can be negative, so we have reached a contradiction, and our theorem is established.

Definition 33-1 deals with an integral $\int_a^b f(x)\, dx$ in which the upper limit b is larger than the lower limit a. In order to complete our definition of the integral, we add the following definition.

Definition 33-2. *For any function f whose domain contains a point a,*

$$\int_a^a f(x)\, dx = 0.$$

If $a < b$ and if f is integrable on the interval $[a, b]$, then

$$\int_b^a f(x)\, dx = -\int_a^b f(x)\, dx.$$

We have been careful to point out that our formal definition of the integral is logically independent of the concept of the area of a plane region. Nevertheless, the discussion that led to this formal definition makes it clear that if the mathematical concept of area is to agree with our common-sense notions about area, then the area of the region between the graph of a function f that takes non-negative values and an interval $[a, b]$ of the X-axis must be the number $\int_a^b f(x)\, dx$. One way to assure this result is simply to *define* the area of the region to be the integral. This approach, however, merely gives us the areas of geometric figures that have the form of "rectangles with one curved side." It is not a simple process to extend this definition to make it cover other geometric shapes, and therefore most mathematicians prefer a definition of area that applies directly to more complicated regions. We will have to leave a full explanation of the mathematical definition of area to some later course. Here we will only say that one aspect of finding the area of a plane figure consists of "packing" it with simple figures whose areas we can compute (such as rectangles) and then calculating a limit of the sums of these areas. This process is closely related to the way we might "pack" one of our regions with rectangles before taking the limit that is the integral, so it turns out that the integral really is the area (in the sense in which mathematicians use the term) of our region. Furthermore, the mathematical definition of area has all the properties you would expect; that is, the area of a rectangle is the product of its base and its altitude, the area of a circular disk of radius r is πr^2, the area of the union of two sets that have no common points is the sum of their areas, and so on. Because integrals do give areas, we will use areas to calculate integrals and integrals to calculate areas.

Example 33-1.   Suppose that a is a positive number. Evaluate the integral

$$\int_0^a \sqrt{a^2 - x^2}\, dx.$$

Solution.   You can easily verify that the graph of the equation $y = \sqrt{a^2 - x^2}$ is a semicircle with a radius of a units whose center is the origin. This semicircle and the interval $[-a, a]$ of the X-axis bound a region with an area of $\dfrac{\pi a^2}{2}$ square units. It is clear that our integral represents the area of one-half of this region, so we have the important formula

(33-3)
$$\int_0^a \sqrt{a^2 - x^2}\, dx = \frac{\pi a^2}{4}.$$

P R O B L E M S   3 3

1. Use the geometric interpretation of $\displaystyle\int_a^b f(x)\, dx$ as an area to evaluate the following.

(a) $\displaystyle\int_0^{5/2} [\![x]\!]\, dx$

(b) $\displaystyle\int_{-3}^5 |x|\, dx$

(c) $\displaystyle\int_{-1}^2 (|x| + x)\, dx$

(d) $\displaystyle\int_{-1}^3 (2x + 3)\, dx$

(e) $\displaystyle\int_0^4 (|x - 1| + |x - 2|)\, dx$

(f) $\displaystyle\int_0^2 -[\![\cos \pi x]\!]\, dx$

(g) $\displaystyle\int_{-1}^1 (1 + \sqrt{1 - x^2})\, dx$

(h) $\displaystyle\int_{-1}^1 (1 - \sqrt{1 - x^2})\, dx$

(i) $\displaystyle\int_1^5 (5 + \sqrt{4 - (x - 3)^2})\, dx$

(j) $\displaystyle\int_0^3 ([\![x]\!]x + 2)\, dx$

(k) $\displaystyle\int_1^3 [\![\tfrac{1}{3}(-2x^2 + 11x - 9)]\!]\, dx$

(l) $\displaystyle\int_{-1}^3 (x + 1 + 3|1 - x|)\, dx$

2. Find $\displaystyle\int_2^9 f(x)\, dx$ if $f(x)$ is the distance between x and the nearest prime number.

3. Show that none of the following integrals is negative.

(a) $\displaystyle\int_0^3 (4 + 3x - x^2)\, dx$

(b) $\displaystyle\int_{-1}^0 (z^3 - z^2 - 2z)\, dz$

(c) $\displaystyle\int_0^1 (t - \sin t)\, dt$

(d) $\displaystyle\int_{\frac{1}{2}}^2 \left(u + \frac{1}{u} - 2\right) du$

4. By an argument that is similar to the proof of Theorem 33-1, show that if $f(x) \leq 0$ for each point $x \in [a, b]$, then $\displaystyle\int_a^b f(x)\, dx \leq 0$.

5. Use a graph and an area estimate to find $\left[\left[\displaystyle\int_0^2 |\cos x|\, dx\right]\right]$.

6. Suppose that f has positive values in the interval $[1, 10]$.

(a) Use the area interpretation of $\displaystyle\int_1^{10} f(x)\, dx$ to conclude that if f is an increasing function in $[1, 10]$, then

$$\sum_{k=1}^9 f(k) \leq \int_1^{10} f(x)\, dx \leq \sum_{k=2}^{10} f(k).$$

(b) Write a set of inequalities similar to those in part (a) if f is decreasing in the interval $[1, 10]$.

7. Suppose that f is the constant function with value c. Show that for each partition of an interval $[a, b]$ and each choice of points $x_1^*, x_2^*, \ldots, x_n^*$ from the partition, Equation 33-1 gives us $s = c(b - a)$. What is the set $S(u)$ for any $u \in (0, b - a]$? What is $\displaystyle\int_a^b f(x)\, dx$? (This simple problem is to help you get acquainted with our terminology.)

8. Let f be the greatest integer function, $[a, b]$ the interval $[0, 1]$, and S the function defined by Equation 33-2. What is the set $S(1)$? Graph the function $S(u)$ for $0 < u \leq \frac{1}{2}$. Is $\lim_{u \downarrow 0} S(u)$ the number you would expect to get from the area interpretation of an integral?

9. Let f be defined, as in Illustration 5-5, by the statements:
(i) $f(x) = 0$ if there is a decimal expression for x that has all 0's after a certain stage and (ii) $f(x) = 1$ otherwise; and let $[a, b]$ be the interval $[0, 2]$.
Show that the corresponding set function S is given by the equations $S(u) = [0, 2]$ if $u \in (0, 1]$ and $S(u) = [0, 2 - u] \cup [u, 2]$ if $u \in (1, 2]$. Sketch the graph of S. What does your figure tell you about the integrability of f on the interval $[0, 2]$?

10. Show that if for each x in the interval $[a, b]$ we have $f(x) \in [A, B]$, then for each $u \in (0, b - a]$, $S(u) \subseteq [A(b - a), B(b - a)]$. If you also know that f is integrable on $[a, b]$, show that $\displaystyle\int_a^b f(x)\, dx \in [A(b - a), B(b - a)]$.

11. Let f be the greatest integer function, and let $[a, b]$ be the interval $[0, 2]$. If S is the function defined by Equation 33-2, what is the set $S(2)$? What is the set $S(1)$? Graph $S(u)$ for $0 < u \leq 1$. What is $\lim_{u \downarrow 0} S(u)$?

34 GENERAL INTEGRAL THEOREMS

When we consider the integral of a function f on an interval $[a, b]$, we raise two questions:

(i) Is f integrable on $[a, b]$; that is, does the integral (a limit) exist?

(ii) If so, what is the value of the integral; that is, what is the number

$$\int_a^b f(x)\, dx?$$

In this first course in calculus we will concentrate most of our attention on the second question. Because of its difficulty, we must leave a full discussion of question (i) to a later course. Here we can only state and briefly explain what the answer is.

It is not hard to show that the answer to question (i) is "no" if f is *unbounded* in the interval $[a, b]$; that is, if the set $f([a, b])$ is not contained in some finite interval. For example, if $f(x) = \tan x$ for $x \in [0, \tfrac{1}{2}\pi)$ and $f(\tfrac{1}{2}\pi) = 37$, then f is unbounded in the interval $[0, \tfrac{1}{2}\pi]$, and it is *not* integrable on that interval.

Question (i) only becomes difficult in case f is bounded in the interval $[a, b]$. Then the answer depends on the "measure" of the set of points in $[a, b]$ at which f is discontinuous. If this set has measure 0, f is integrable; otherwise not. The measure of a set is a technical term whose strict definition is part of the "full discussion" that we are omitting. We will simply say that the measure of a set of real numbers is a generalization of the idea of the length of an interval. In particular, the measure of a finite interval is its length. Every set that consists of only a finite number of points (maybe no points, maybe one, maybe a billion) has measure 0. (It turns out that some infinite sets have measure 0, too, but we will not have to concern ourselves with this problem.) The union and intersection of two sets of measure 0 also have measure 0, and every subset of a set of measure 0 has measure 0. With this brief description of measure, we will state without proof the existence theorem that furnishes a complete answer to question (i).

Theorem 34-1. *A function f that is bounded in the interval $[a, b]$ is integrable on $[a, b]$ if, and only if, the set of points in $[a, b]$ at which f is discontinuous has measure 0. In particular, a bounded function is integrable on an interval if it has only a finite number of points of discontinuity. If f is unbounded in $[a, b]$, then it is not integrable on $[a, b]$.*

Example 34-1. Show that if f is continuous in an interval $[a, b]$, then f is integrable on $[a, b]$.

Solution. According to Theorem 19-1, a function that is continuous in a closed, finite interval is bounded in the interval. Therefore, since our function has only a finite number (none) of points of discontinuity, Theorem 34-1 tells us that it is integrable.

Example 34-2. Explain how you know that the following integrals exist:

$$\int_0^\pi \sin x \, dx, \quad \int_{-10}^{17} [\![x]\!] \, dx, \quad \text{and} \quad \int_{-3\pi}^{3\pi} \frac{\sin x}{x} \, dx. \quad \text{What about} \quad \int_0^1 \frac{1}{x} \, dx?$$

Solution. The sine function is continuous in the interval $[0, \pi]$, so the result of Example 34-1 tells us that the first integral exists. The greatest integer function is bounded in the interval $[-10, 17]$ and has only a finite number (27) of points of discontinuity there. Therefore, the existence of the second integral is an immediate consequence of our existence theorem. The equations $s(x) = \dfrac{\sin x}{x}$ and $q(x) = \dfrac{1}{x}$ define functions whose domains do not contain the point 0. Strictly speaking, therefore, we should not talk about the integrals of these functions over any interval that contains 0, unless we first extend their definitions so that their domains do contain 0. If we choose $s(0)$ to be 1, then s is continuous at 0 and at every other point of the X-axis. If we take $s(0)$ to be a number other than 1, then s will not be continuous at 0, but it will be continuous everywhere else. In either case, s has only a finite number (0 or 1) of points of discontinuity; it is also bounded in the interval $[-3\pi, 3\pi]$, and hence s is integrable on this interval. (Incidentally, the value of the integral is the same, whatever number we choose as $s(0)$.)

No matter what number we choose as $q(0)$, the function q will be discontinuous at 0. But it will be continuous at every other point, and so it has only a finite number (1) of points of discontinuity. Nevertheless, since q is unbounded in the interval $[0, 1]$, the integral $\int_0^1 \dfrac{1}{x} \, dx$ does not exist.

The function that is defined (Problem 33-9) by the statements (i) $f(x) = 0$ if there is a decimal expression for x that has all 0's after a certain stage, and (ii) $f(x) = 1$ otherwise, is discontinuous at each point of the interval $[0, 2]$. The measure of this interval is its length, 2, so this set of points of discontinuity is *not* of measure 0. Thus, even though f is bounded in the interval $[0, 2]$, it is not integrable on the interval. This function is not likely to arise in the usual applications of mathematics; practically all the bounded functions you will ever meet will be integrable.

The integral of a function f over an interval $[a, b]$ is the limit of S from the right at 0, where S is the set-valued function defined by Equation 33-2. Therefore, we can derive relations between integrals from limit relations for set-valued functions. In order to state the limit relations we will use, we first introduce some special notation. Let S and T be set-valued functions with a common domain. If u is a point of this domain, $S(u)$ and $T(u)$ are sets of numbers, and we denote by $S(u) + T(u)$ the set of all the sums that we can form by adding an element of $S(u)$ and an element of $T(u)$. Thus

$$S(u) + T(u) = \{x + y \mid x \in S(u), y \in T(u)\}.$$

Similarly, if c is a number, we denote by $cS(u)$ the set of all products that we can obtain by multiplying elements of $S(u)$ by c. In other words,

$$cS(u) = \{cx \mid x \in S(u)\}.$$

Now we can state the theorem on set-valued functions from which we will derive our general integral theorems.

Theorem 34-2. *Let S and T be set-valued functions with limits from the right at* 0, *and suppose that c is a given number. Then*

(34-1) $$\lim_{u \downarrow 0} [S(u) + T(u)] = \lim_{u \downarrow 0} S(u) + \lim_{u \downarrow 0} T(u)$$

and

(34-2) $$\lim_{u \downarrow 0} cS(u) = c \lim_{u \downarrow 0} S(u).$$

If $S(u) \subseteq T(u)$ for each number u in some interval $(0, h)$, then

(34-3) $$\lim_{u \downarrow 0} S(u) = \lim_{u \downarrow 0} T(u).$$

The proof of this theorem is easy; we leave the details to you in the problems. For example, Equation 34-1 can be established by the same arguments that we used to prove the corresponding theorem about limits of numerical-valued functions (Theorem 11-2), and the other two equations are even easier to verify. Theorem 34-2 will be the key to the formal proofs of the fundamental integral theorems that follow. Before you work through these formal proofs, however, you should look at what the theorems say from an intuitive viewpoint and see how reasonable they are.

Theorem 34-3. *If f is integrable on an interval $[a, b]$ and c is a given number, then*

(34-4) $$\int_a^b cf(x)\, dx = c \int_a^b f(x)\, dx.$$

Proof. As usual, we use Equation 33-2 to associate with each number u in the interval $(0, b - a]$ the set $S(u)$ of sums of the form $\sum_{i=1}^{n} f(x_i^*) \Delta x_i$. Then the set $cS(u)$ consists of numbers of the form $\sum_{i=1}^{n} cf(x_i^*) \Delta x_i$. But these sums are exactly the ones we must form when we calculate the integral $\int_a^b cf(x)\, dx$;

that is, $\displaystyle\int_a^b cf(x)\,dx = \lim_{u\downarrow 0} cS(u)$. According to Equation 34-2, this last expression equals $c\lim_{u\downarrow 0} S(u)$. Therefore, since $\lim_{u\downarrow 0} S(u) = \displaystyle\int_a^b f(x)\,dx$, we have established Equation 34-4.

Theorem 34-4. *If the functions f and g are integrable on the interval $[a, b]$, then*

$$(34\text{-}5) \qquad \int_a^b [f(x) + g(x)]\,dx = \int_a^b f(x)\,dx + \int_a^b g(x)\,dx.$$

Proof. We use Equation 33-2 to associate with each point u in the interval $(0, b - a]$ the set $S(u)$ of sums of the form $\displaystyle\sum_{i=1}^n f(x_i^*)\,\Delta x_i$. Let $T(u)$ be the corresponding set that we obtain when f is replaced by g, and $R(u)$ be a similar set of sums of the form $\displaystyle\sum_{i=1}^n [f(x_i^*) + g(x_i^*)]\,\Delta x_i$. Then

$$\int_a^b f(x)\,dx = \lim_{u\downarrow 0} S(u), \qquad \int_a^b g(x)\,dx = \lim_{u\downarrow 0} T(u),$$

$(34\text{-}6)$

and

$$\int_a^b [f(x) + g(x)]\,dx = \lim_{u\downarrow 0} R(u).$$

Since $\displaystyle\sum_{i=1}^n [f(x_i^*) + g(x_i^*)]\,\Delta x_i = \sum_{i=1}^n f(x_i^*)\,\Delta x_i + \sum_{i=1}^n g(x_i^*)\Delta x_i$, we see that every member of $R(u)$ can be expressed as a sum of members of $S(u)$ and $T(u)$; that is, $R(u) \subseteq S(u) + T(u)$. Now Equations 34-3 and 34-1 tell us that

$$\lim_{u\downarrow 0} R(u) = \lim_{u\downarrow 0} [S(u) + T(u)] = \lim_{u\downarrow 0} S(u) + \lim_{u\downarrow 0} T(u),$$

and reference to Equations 34-6 shows that we have established Equation 34-5.

Example 34-3. Find $\displaystyle\int_0^2 (3[\![x]\!] - 2\sqrt{4 - x^2})\,dx$.

Solution. We have

$$\int_0^2 (3[\![x]\!] - 2\sqrt{4 - x^2})\,dx = \int_0^2 3[\![x]\!]\,dx + \int_0^2 (-2)\sqrt{4 - x^2}\,dx \text{ (Equation 34-5)}$$

$$= 3\int_0^2 [\![x]\!]\,dx - 2\int_0^2 \sqrt{4 - x^2}\,dx \text{ (Equation 34-4)}$$

$$= 3\cdot 1 - 2\pi \text{ (Evaluate the integrals geometrically; see}$$
$$\text{Example 33-1)}$$

$$= 3 - 2\pi \approx -3.28.$$

Example 34-4.   If $f(x) \le g(x)$ for each $x \in [a, b]$, show that $\int_a^b f(x)\, dx \le \int_a^b g(x)\, dx$.

Solution.   Since $g(x) - f(x) \ge 0$, Theorem 33-1 tells us that

$$\int_a^b [g(x) - f(x)]\, dx \ge 0.$$

Now we apply Theorems 34-4 and 34-3 to rewrite this integral:

$$\int_a^b [g(x) - f(x)]\, dx = \int_a^b g(x)\, dx + (-1)\int_a^b f(x)\, dx.$$

Therefore, we have obtained the inequality $0 \le \int_a^b g(x)\, dx - \int_a^b f(x)\, dx$, from which the inequality we were to verify follows immediately.

We now turn to a theorem that has an especially simple geometric interpretation. Geometrically, we think of the integral $\int_a^b f(x)\, dx$ of the function whose graph is shown in Fig. 34-1 as the area of the shaded region. From the figure, it seems reasonable to suppose that there is a point $m \in [a, b]$ such that the area of the rectangle of altitude $f(m)$ whose base is the interval $[a, b]$ (and hence is $b - a$ units long) has the same area as our shaded region. Thus we would have

$$(b - a)f(m) = \int_a^b f(x)\, dx.$$

The number $f(m)$ is called the **mean** or **average** value of f in the interval $[a, b]$. Our next theorem tells us that our geometric intuition is correct; in fact, if f is any function that is continuous in the interval $[a, b]$, then there is such a point m.

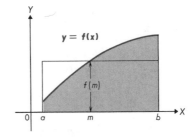

Figure 34-1

Theorem 34-5.   **A Mean Value Theorem for Integrals.** *If f is continuous in the interval $[a, b]$, then there is a point $m \in [a, b]$ such that*

(34-7)
$$f(m) = \frac{1}{b - a}\int_a^b f(x)\, dx.$$

Proof. Since f is continuous in $[a, b]$, Example 34-1 tells us that it is integrable on this interval, and Theorem 19-1 tells us that there are numbers A and B such that $f([a, b]) = [A, B]$. From this equation, it follows that for each $x \in [a, b]$ we have the inequalities

$$A \leq f(x) \leq B.$$

As we saw in Example 34-4, these inequalities are preserved when we integrate over the interval $[a, b]$:

$$\int_a^b A \, dx \leq \int_a^b f(x) \, dx \leq \int_a^b B \, dx.$$

Since

$$\int_a^b A \, dx = A(b - a) \text{ and } \int_a^b B \, dx = B(b - a) \quad \text{(Problem 33-7),}$$

the preceding inequalities tell us that

$$A(b - a) \leq \int_a^b f(x) \, dx \leq B(b - a);$$

that is,

$$\frac{1}{b - a} \int_a^b f(x) \, dx \in [A, B].$$

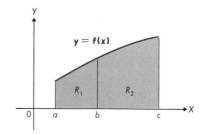

Figure 34-2

Again we make use of the equation $f([a, b]) = [A, B]$. It says that each point of the interval $[A, B]$ is a value of f at some (at least one) point of $[a, b]$. In particular, then, the num..

$$\frac{1}{b - a} \int_a^b f(x) \, dx \text{ is equal to } f(m) \text{ for some point } m \in [a, b].$$

The final theorem of this section is also strongly suggested by our geometric interpretation of the integral. Because the union of the regions R_1 and R_2 of Fig. 34-2 is the entire shaded region, it appears that the integral of f over the interval $[a, c]$ is the sum of the integrals of f over the intervals $[a, b]$ and $[b, c]$. Again our intuition is correct, and we have the following theorem.

Theorem 34-6.   *Let a, b, and c be three points of an interval that is contained in the domain of a function f. Then if any two of the following integrals exist, so does the third, and we have the equation*

(34-8) $$\int_a^c f(x) \, dx = \int_a^b f(x) \, dx + \int_b^c f(x) \, dx.$$

Proof. The fact that all three integrals exist if two of them do is a simple consequence of Theorem 34-1 and the facts about sets of measure 0 that we mentioned earlier; the thing for us to do is to verify Equation 34-8. We will assume first that the numbers a, b, and c are in the order $a < b < c$. Then let u be a number that is so small that it belongs to all three of the intervals $(0, b-a]$, $(0, c-b]$, and $(0, c-a]$. We use Equation 33-2 to associate with u the set $S(u)$ of sums of the form $\sum_{i=1}^{n} f(x_i^*)\,\Delta x_i$ that we obtain from partitions with norm u of the interval $[a, b]$. Let $T(u)$ and $R(u)$ be similar sets of sums that are computed from partitions with norm u of the intervals $[b, c]$ and $[a, c]$. Since each pair of partitions with norm u of $[a, b]$ and $[b, c]$ determines a partition with norm u of $[a, c]$, it follows that $S(u) + T(u) \subseteq R(u)$. Therefore, according to Equations 34-1 and 34-3, $\lim_{u \downarrow 0} S(u) + \lim_{u \downarrow 0} T(u) = \lim_{u \downarrow 0} R(u)$. This equation is equivalent to Equation 34-8 (why?), so the first part of our proof is complete.

Now suppose that the numbers a, b, and c are in some other order—for example, $b < c < a$. Our work in the preceding paragraph shows that

(34-9) $$\int_b^a f(x)\,dx = \int_b^c f(x)\,dx + \int_c^a f(x)\,dx.$$

Now we use Definition 33-2 to write

$$\int_b^a f(x)\,dx \text{ as } -\int_a^b f(x)\,dx \text{ and } \int_c^a f(x)\,dx \text{ as } -\int_a^c f(x)\,dx,$$

and so transform Equation 34-9 into Equation 34-8. Clearly, this same type of argument will work for any ordering of the numbers a, b, and c.

Example 34-5. Explain why $\int_{-\pi}^{\pi} \sin x\,dx = 0$.

Solution. According to Equation 34-8,

(34-10) $$\int_{-\pi}^{\pi} \sin x\,dx = \int_{-\pi}^{0} \sin x\,dx + \int_{0}^{\pi} \sin x\,dx.$$

Let us look at the number $\int_{-\pi}^{0} \sin x\,dx$ from a geometric point of view. We first use Equation 34-4 to write this integral as $-\int_{-\pi}^{0} (-\sin x)\,dx$. Then we consider the integral $\int_{-\pi}^{0} (-\sin x)\,dx$ to be the area of the region bounded by the X-axis

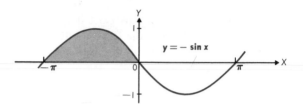

Figure 34-3

and the graph of the equation $y = -\sin x$ that is shaded in Fig. 34-3. Since this region is the region under one arch of the sine curve, its area is $\int_0^\pi \sin x \, dx$. Thus we see that $\int_{-\pi}^0 (-\sin x) \, dx = \int_0^\pi \sin x \, dx$, and hence Equation 34-10 becomes

$$\int_{-\pi}^\pi \sin x \, dx = -\int_0^\pi \sin x \, dx + \int_0^\pi \sin x \, dx = 0.$$

P R O B L E M S   3 4

1. Determine which of the following integrals exist. If the integral does exist, use general integral theorems and geometric arguments to evaluate it.

(a) $\displaystyle\int_0^\pi \sec x \, dx$

(b) $\displaystyle\int_{-2}^3 \left(2 + \frac{x}{|x|}\right) dx$

(c) $\displaystyle\int_{-1}^1 \frac{1}{x^3} \, dx$

(d) $\displaystyle\int_{-1}^1 \left(4 + \frac{x}{|x|} \sqrt{1 - x^2}\right) dx$

(e) $\displaystyle\int_0^3 (2x + 1 + 4\sqrt{9 - x^2}) \, dx$

(f) $\displaystyle\int_0^2 \frac{x^2 - 1}{x - 1} \, dx$

(g) $\displaystyle\int_{-1}^2 (\llbracket x \rrbracket^2 + 2\llbracket x \rrbracket + 3) \, dx$

(h) $\displaystyle\int_0^{10} \sin \frac{\llbracket x \rrbracket \pi}{2} \, dx$

2. Use Theorem 34-3 to show that $\displaystyle\int_a^b 0 \, dx = 0$.

3. What is the mean value of the sine function in the interval $[-\pi, \pi]$?

4. Let $f(x) = \sqrt{16 - x^2}$. What is the mean value of f in the interval $[-4, 4]$? At what points does f take its mean value?

5. Let f be a linear function, $f(x) = mx + b$. What is the mean value of f over the interval $[c, d]$? At what point does f take this average value?

6. Use an argument similar to that in Example 34-5 to evaluate $\displaystyle\int_{-\pi}^\pi \sin 3x \, dx$.

7. Use the formula $2 \sin mx \cos nx = \sin (m + n)x + \sin (m - n)x$ and some general integral theorems to evaluate $\displaystyle\int_{-\pi}^\pi \sin 2x \cos x \, dx$. (You need the result of the preceding problem here.)

8. Show that:

(a) $\int_0^1 x^2\,dx \le \int_0^1 x\,dx$ 　　　　　　(b) $\int_0^1 x^4\,dx \le \int_0^1 y^2\,dy$

(c) $\int_0^1 (x^2 - 2x - 3)\,dx \le \int_0^{-1} (t^2 - 2t - 3)\,dt$

9. If f and g are integrable on the interval $[a, b]$, is it necessarily true that

(a) $\int_a^b f(x)g(x)\,dx = \int_a^b f(x)\,dx \int_a^b g(x)\,dx$?

(b) $\int_a^b [f(x) - g(x)]\,dx = \int_a^b f(x)\,dx - \int_a^b g(x)\,dx$?

(c) $\int_a^b \dfrac{f(x)}{g(x)}\,dx = \dfrac{\displaystyle\int_a^b f(x)\,dx}{\displaystyle\int_a^b g(x)\,dx}$?

10. Give an example, using a discontinuous function, of course, for which Equation 34-7 does not hold. Find a discontinuous function for which it does hold.

11. Extend Theroem 34-4 to show that

$$\int_a^b [f(x) + g(x) + h(x)]\,dx = \int_a^b f(x)\,dx + \int_a^b g(x)\,dx + \int_a^b h(x)\,dx.$$

12. Use Example 34-4 to show that if f is integrable on $[a, b]$, then $\left| \int_a^b f(x)\,dx \right| \le \int_a^b |f(x)|\,dx$. Hence conclude that if $|f(x)| \le M$ for each point $x \in [a, b]$, then $\left| \int_a^b f(x)\,dx \right| \le M(b - a)$.

13. Evaluate the integral $\int_0^2 (x - [\![x^2]\!])\,dx$.

14. (a) Write out a proof for Equation 34-3.
(b) Write out a proof for Equation 34-2.
(c) Write out a proof for Equation 34-1.

35 INTEGRALS OF SOME PARTICULAR FUNCTIONS

We have used geometric reasoning to find a few specific integrals. In addition, in Problem 33-7 we asked you to use the formal definition of the integral to show that for each number c, and every choice of limits a and b,

(35-1) $$\int_a^b c\,dx = c(b - a).$$

The next theorem provides us with a basic tool for finding the integrals of other functions.

Theorem 35-1. *Suppose that the function f is integrable on the interval [a, b]. If there is a number A such that for every partition of [a, b] we can choose the numbers $x_1^*, x_2^*, \ldots, x_n^*$ so that the approximating sum $\sum_{i=1}^{n} f(x_i^*) \Delta x_i$ is equal to A, then $\int_a^b f(x)\, dx = A$.*

Proof. As usual, we will use Equation 33-2 to define our set-valued function S whose limit from the right at 0 is the integral $\int_a^b f(x)\, dx$. Let us also introduce a constant set-valued function R, defined by the equation $R(u) = \{A\}$. The hypotheses of our theorem tell us that for each partition of [a, b], A is one of our approximating sums. Thus $A \in S(u)$ for each norm u. We can write this inclusion as $\{A\} \subseteq S(u)$; that is, $R(u) \subseteq S(u)$. Therefore, according to Theorem 34-1, $\lim_{u \downarrow 0} R(u) = \lim_{u \downarrow 0} S(u)$. By definition, $\lim_{u \downarrow 0} S(u) = \int_a^b f(x)\, dx$, and it is obvious that $\lim_{u \downarrow 0} R(u) = A$. Thus we have shown that $\int_a^b f(x)\, dx = A$, and our proof is complete.

Example 35-1. Show that for any finite interval [a, b],

(35-2)
$$\int_a^b x\, dx = \frac{b^2}{2} - \frac{a^2}{2}.$$

Solution. We know that the integral exists, because the function we are integrating (the identity function) is continuous at every point. Our problem is to find its value. According to Theorem 35-1, we need only show that for each partition of the interval [a, b] there is an approximating sum

$$s = \frac{b^2}{2} - \frac{a^2}{2}.$$

So suppose we have a partition of the interval [a, b] determined by the points $x_0 = a, x_1, x_2, \ldots, x_{n-1}, x_n = b$. Every approximating sum will take the form

$$s = \sum_{i=1}^{n} f(x_i^*) \Delta x_i = \sum_{i=1}^{n} x_i^* \Delta x_i,$$

and we must show that a suitable choice of the numbers $x_1^*, x_2^*, \ldots, x_n^*$ will give us $s = \frac{b^2}{2} - \frac{a^2}{2}$. In this example the "suitable choice" consists of taking x_i^* to be the midpoint of the interval $[x_{i-1}, x_i]$, that is, $x_i^* = \frac{1}{2}(x_i + x_{i-1})$. For then

$$s = \sum_{i=1}^{n} \frac{1}{2}(x_i + x_{i-1})(x_i - x_{i-1})$$

$$= \sum_{i=1}^{n} \left(\frac{x_i^2}{2} - \frac{x_{i-1}^2}{2} \right)$$

$$= \left(\frac{x_1^2}{2} - \frac{x_0^2}{2} \right) + \left(\frac{x_2^2}{2} - \frac{x_1^2}{2} \right) + \cdots + \left(\frac{x_n^2}{2} - \frac{x_{n-1}^2}{2} \right)$$

$$= \frac{x_n^2}{2} - \frac{x_0^2}{2} = \frac{b^2}{2} - \frac{a^2}{2} .$$

Example 35-2. Show that for any pair of numbers a and b,

(35-3)
$$\int_a^b x^2 \, dx = \frac{b^3}{3} - \frac{a^3}{3} .$$

Solution. In order to avoid some algebraic complications that arise when a and b have opposite signs, we first write

$$\int_a^b x^2 \, dx = \int_a^0 x^2 \, dx + \int_0^b x^2 \, dx = - \int_0^a x^2 \, dx + \int_0^b x^2 \, dx.$$

Our problem is now reduced to showing that for each number c,

(35-4)
$$\int_0^c x^2 \, dx = \frac{c^3}{3} .$$

We will verify this equation in case $c > 0$; similar methods apply when $c \leq 0$, so we leave this case to you in the problems. For each partition of the interval $[0, c]$ our approximating sums take the form $s = \sum_{i=1}^{n} x_i^{*2} \, \Delta x_i$, and Theorem 35-1 tells us that we can verify Equation 35-4 by showing that there is a set of numbers $x_1^*, x_2^*, \ldots, x_n^*$ such that this sum is $\frac{c^3}{3}$.

For each i, let us choose

$$x_i^* = \sqrt{\frac{1}{3}(x_i^2 + x_i x_{i-1} + x_{i-1}^2)}.$$

You can readily show that $x_i^* \in [x_{i-1}, x_i]$. Furthermore,

$$x_i^{*2} \, \Delta x_i = \frac{1}{3}(x_i^2 + x_i x_{i-1} + x_{i-1}^2)(x_i - x_{i-1}) = \frac{x_i^3}{3} - \frac{x_{i-1}^3}{3},$$

and so

$$\sum_{i=1}^{n} x_i^{*2} \, \Delta x_i = \sum_{i=1}^{n} \left(\frac{x_i^3}{3} - \frac{x_{i-1}^3}{3} \right)$$

$$= \left(\frac{x_1^3}{3} - \frac{x_0^3}{3} \right) + \left(\frac{x_2^3}{3} - \frac{x_1^3}{3} \right) + \cdots + \left(\frac{x_n^3}{3} - \frac{x_{n-1}^3}{3} \right)$$

$$= \frac{x_n^3}{3} - \frac{x_0^3}{3} = \frac{c^3}{3} - \frac{0^3}{3} = \frac{c^3}{3}.$$

Together, the *specific* Integration Formulas 35-1, 35-2, and 35-3 and the *general* Integration Formulas 34-4 and 34-5 furnish the tools we need to evaluate the integral of any quadratic function; that is, a function f defined by an equation of the form $f(x) = Ax^2 + Bx + C$.

Example 35-3.   Evaluate $\displaystyle\int_2^3 (6x^2 + 2x - 5) \, dx$.

Solution.   Using Equation 34-5, we can write

$$\int_2^3 (6x^2 + 2x - 5) \, dx = \int_2^3 6x^2 \, dx + \int_2^3 2x \, dx + \int_2^3 (-5) \, dx.$$

Now we use Equation 34-4 to obtain the equation

$$\int_2^3 (6x^2 + 2x - 5) \, dx = 6 \int_2^3 x^2 \, dx + 2 \int_2^3 x \, dx + \int_2^3 (-5) \, dx.$$

We use Equations 35-1, 35-2, and 35-3 to evaluate the last three integrals:

$$\int_2^3 (6x^2 + 2x - 5) \, dx = 6 \left(\frac{3^3}{3} - \frac{2^3}{3} \right) + 2 \left(\frac{3^2}{2} - \frac{2^2}{2} \right) - 5(3 - 2) = 38.$$

We will use the result of our next example in the following section.

Example 35-4.   Show that

$$(35\text{-}5) \qquad \int_a^b (Ax^2 + Bx + C) \, dx = \frac{b-a}{6} \left[g(a) + 4g\left(\frac{a+b}{2} \right) + g(b) \right],$$

where $g(x) = Ax^2 + Bx + C$.

Solution.   We can evaluate the given integral just as we did the integral in the last example. Thus

$$\int_a^b (Ax^2 + Bx + C) \, dx = A \int_a^b x^2 \, dx + B \int_a^b x \, dx + \int_a^b C \, dx,$$

and hence

$$(35\text{-}6) \qquad \int_a^b (Ax^2 + Bx + C)\, dx = A\left(\frac{b^3}{3} - \frac{a^3}{3}\right) + B\left(\frac{b^2}{2} - \frac{a^2}{2}\right) + C(b - a).$$

Simple algebra shows that the right sides of Equations 35-5 and 35-6 are the same. Thus since

$$4g\left(\frac{a + b}{2}\right) = 4A\left(\frac{a + b}{2}\right)^2 + 4B\left(\frac{a + b}{2}\right) + 4C$$

$$= A(b^2 + 2ab + a^2) + 2B(b + a) + 4C,$$

you can easily verify that

$$g(a) + 4g\left(\frac{a + b}{2}\right) + g(b) = 2A(b^2 + ab + a^2) + 3B(b + a) + 6C.$$

So

$$\frac{b - a}{6}\left[g(a) + 4g\left(\frac{a + b}{2}\right) + g(b)\right] = \frac{A(b^3 - a^3)}{3} + \frac{B(b^2 - a^2)}{2} + C(b - a),$$

and therefore Equation 35-6 can be expressed in the form of Equation 35-5.

P R O B L E M S   3 5

1. We verified Formula 35-2 in case $a < b$; show that it is also valid if $b < a$.

2. Evaluate the following integrals.

(a) $\displaystyle\int_{-1}^{7} x\, dx$

(b) $\displaystyle\int_{-3}^{-1} t\, dt$

(c) $\displaystyle\int_{-2}^{4} z^2\, dz$

(d) $\displaystyle\int_{-3}^{-5} x^2\, dx$

(e) $\displaystyle\int_{0}^{2} (x - 4x^2)\, dx$

(f) $\displaystyle\int_{1}^{4} (3t^2 - 6t)\, dt$

(g) $\displaystyle\int_{-1}^{0} (1 - r^2)\, dr$

(h) $\displaystyle\int_{6}^{6} (s^2 + 6s - 7)\, ds$

3. Suppose that $mx + b > 0$ for $x \in [c, d]$. Use the area interpretation of the integral to compute $\displaystyle\int_c^d (mx + b)\, dx$, and show that you get the same result when you evaluate the integral by using our integration formulas.

4. Compute the following numbers.

(a) $\displaystyle\int_{-1}^{3} (t + 1)^2\, dt$

(b) $\displaystyle\int_{-2}^{-1} (2s^2 - 3s + 4)\, ds$

(c) $\displaystyle\int_{-2}^{3} (x + 2)(x - 3)\, dx$

(d) $\int_{-2}^{3} |x|\,(2x+3)\,dx$ (e) $\int_{-1}^{2} [\![x]\!](x^2 - 4x)\,dx$ (f) $\int_{-2}^{1} \dfrac{4x^3 - x^2}{|x|}\,dx$

(g) $\int_{-1}^{0} (\tan x + 3x^2)\,dx + \int_{0}^{1} (\tan y - 3y^2)\,dy + \int_{1}^{-1} (\tan z + 3z^2)\,dz$

(h) $\int_{0}^{4} \dfrac{x^3 - 2x^2}{|x - 2|}\,dx$ (i) $\int_{-a}^{a} [(x+a)^3 - (x-a)^3]\,dx$ (j) $\int_{0}^{4} |x^2 - 1|\,dx$

5. (a) Show that for each pair of numbers a and b, $\displaystyle\int_{a}^{b} |x|\,dx = \dfrac{|b|\,b - |a|\,a}{2}$.

(b) Use Part (a) and Problem 34-12 to show that $|b^2 - a^2| \leq |b|\,b - |a|\,a$, if $a \leq b$.

6. Show that $\displaystyle\int_{a}^{b} (x - c)^2\,dx = \dfrac{(b-c)^3}{3} - \dfrac{(a-c)^3}{3}$.

7. Follow the method used in Example 35-2 and show that

$$\int_{a}^{b} x^3\,dx = \frac{b^4}{4} - \frac{a^4}{4}.$$

Choose $x_i^* = \sqrt[3]{\tfrac{1}{4}(x_i^3 + x_i^2 x_{i-1} + x_i x_{i-1}^2 + x_{i-1}^3)}$.

8. Use the formula we developed in the preceding problem to evaluate the following integrals.

(a) $\displaystyle\int_{1}^{6} x^3\,dx$ (b) $\displaystyle\int_{-1}^{0} t^3\,dt$ (c) $\displaystyle\int_{-1}^{2} (4x^3 - 2x + 1)\,dx$

(d) $\displaystyle\int_{-1}^{2} |x(x-1)(x-2)|\,dx$ (e) $\displaystyle\int_{-1}^{2} \dfrac{x^4}{|x|}\,dx$ (f) $\displaystyle\int_{-1}^{2} (4|x|^3 - 2|x| + 1)\,dx$

9. Complete the solution of Example 35-2 by verifying Equation 35-4 in case $c \leq 0$.

10. (a) Show that for each pair of numbers a and b, $\displaystyle\int_{a}^{b} |x|^3\,dx = \tfrac{1}{4}(b\,|b|^3 - a\,|a|^3)$.

(b) Use Part (a) and Problem 34-12 to show that

$$|b^4 - a^4| \leq b\,|b|^3 - a\,|a|^3, \text{ if } a \leq b.$$

11. (a) What is the average height of a castle door that is bounded by the parabola $y = 8x(2 - x)$ and the X-axis?

(b) What is the average depth of a river whose cross section is the part of the third quadrant that is bounded by the X-axis and the curve $y = 10x(2 + x - x^2)$?

12. Verify Formula 35-5 if $a = 0$, $b = 2$, $A = 3$, $B = 4$, and $C = 5$.

13. In Example 35-4 we showed that

$$\int_{a}^{b} g(x)\,dx = \frac{b-a}{6}\left[g(a) + 4g\left(\frac{a+b}{2}\right) + g(b) \right]$$

when $g(x) = Ax^2 + Bx + C$. Show that this equation is also valid when $g(x) = Ax^3 + Bx^2 + Cx + D$.

36 NUMERICAL INTEGRATION

An integral of a function f over an interval $[a, b]$ is a *number*. In the case of certain simple functions, we have formulas (Equations 35-1, 35-2, and 35-3, for example) with which we can compute this number very easily. Soon we will have many more such formulas. All these formulas may obscure the fact that, in principle anyway, we already have the tools at our disposal to compute integrals to whatever degree of accuracy we may desire. In this section we are going to use these tools to develop two of the simpler methods of numerical integration. We introduce numerical integration at this point (before going on to new integration formulas of the type we developed in Section 35) for two reasons:

(i) No matter how many integration formulas we develop, they cannot apply to all possible integrals, and

(ii) The widespread use of modern computing equipment has brought numerical methods to a central place in the various applications of mathematics; no present-day student can afford to remain unaware of them.

We will use an example to introduce our first method of numerical integration.

Example 36-1. Find an approximation to $\int_0^4 \sqrt{x}\,dx$.

Solution. Fig. 36-1 shows the graph of the equation $y = \sqrt{x}$ for $x \in [0, 4]$.
The number $\int_0^4 \sqrt{x}\,dx$ that we seek is the area of the region that lies between this arc and the X-axis. As an approximation to this number, we will find the sum of

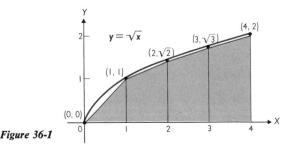

Figure 36-1

the areas of the shaded trapezoidal regions that are shown in the figure. The parallel sides of the four trapezoids have lengths 0 and 1, 1 and $\sqrt{2}$, $\sqrt{2}$ and $\sqrt{3}$, and $\sqrt{3}$ and 2, and each trapezoid has an altitude (the distance between the parallel sides) of 1. Since the area A of a trapezoid with altitude h and parallel sides a and

b is $A = \frac{1}{2}(a + b)h$, we find that the area of the entire shaded region is

$$\frac{0 + 1}{2} \cdot 1 + \frac{1 + \sqrt{2}}{2} \cdot 1 + \frac{\sqrt{2} + \sqrt{3}}{2} \cdot 1 + \frac{\sqrt{3} + 2}{2} \cdot 1 \approx \frac{0 + 1}{2} + \frac{1 + 1.4}{2}$$

$$+ \frac{1.4 + 1.7}{2} + \frac{1.7 + 2}{2} = 5.1.$$

Therefore, $\int_0^4 \sqrt{x}\, dx \approx 5.1$. From the figure it appears that this number is too small, and we will soon find (Example 37-1) that the actual value of the integral is $\frac{16}{3} \approx 5.3$. It is apparent that we could get a more accurate approximation with our "trapezoidal rule" by choosing trapezoids of smaller altitudes, such as $\frac{1}{2}$, $\frac{1}{4}$, .1, and so on.

The way we approximated the integral in the last example suggests a general method of approximating an integral $\int_a^b f(x)\, dx$. We pick an integer n and partition the interval $[a, b]$ into n subintervals of equal length. Each of these subintervals will therefore be $h = \dfrac{b - a}{n}$ units long, and the points that determine our partition will be

$x_0 = a,\ x_1 = a + h,\ x_2 = a + 2h,\ \ldots ,$

$x_n = a + nh = b.$

Now we join the successive points (x_0, y_0), $(x_1, y_1),\ \ldots ,\ (x_n, y_n)$, where $y_i = f(x_i)$, to obtain a polygonal (broken line) arc that approximates the graph of f (Fig. 36-2). Because this arc approximates the graph of f, it seems reasonable to suppose that

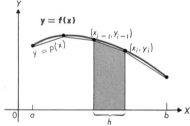

Figure 36-2

the integral $\int_a^b p(x)\, dx$, where $y = p(x)$ is the equation of the polygonal arc, approximates the given integral $\int_a^b f(x)\, dx$. So now we will evaluate the integral $\int_a^b p(x)\, dx$; our first step is to write it as a sum:

$$(36\text{-}1) \quad \int_a^b p(x)\, dx = \int_{x_0}^{x_1} p(x)\, dx + \int_{x_1}^{x_2} p(x)\, dx + \cdots + \int_{x_{n-1}}^{x_n} p(x)\, dx.$$

The integrand of a typical term $\int_{x_{i-1}}^{x_i} p(x)\, dx$ of this sum is linear, so it has the form $p(x) = m_i x + b_i$. Therefore,

$$\int_{x_{i-1}}^{x_i} p(x)\, dx = m_i\left(\frac{x_i^2}{2} - \frac{x_{i-1}^2}{2}\right) + b_i(x_i - x_{i-1}) \quad \begin{array}{l}\text{(which of our integration}\\ \text{formulas did we use?)}\end{array}$$

$$= \tfrac{1}{2}(m_i x_i + m_i x_{i-1} + 2b_i)(x_i - x_{i-1}) \quad \text{(algebra)}.$$

We recall that $x_i - x_{i-1} = h$, $y_i = m_i x_i + b_i$, and $y_{i-1} = m_i x_{i-1} + b_i$, so this equation takes the simple form

$$\int_{x_{i-1}}^{x_i} p(x)\, dx = \frac{y_i + y_{i-1}}{2}\, h.$$

When we substitute these expressions in the right-hand side of Equation 36-1, we obtain the value of $\int_a^b p(x)\, dx$:

$$\frac{y_0 + y_1}{2}\, h + \frac{y_1 + y_2}{2}\, h + \cdots + \frac{y_{n-2} + y_{n-1}}{2}\, h + \frac{y_{n-1} + y_n}{2}\, h$$

$$= \left(\frac{y_0}{2} + \frac{y_1}{2} + \frac{y_1}{2} + \frac{y_2}{2} + \cdots + \frac{y_{n-2}}{2} + \frac{y_{n-1}}{2} + \frac{y_{n-1}}{2} + \frac{y_n}{2}\right)h$$

$$= \left(\frac{y_0}{2} + y_1 + y_2 + \cdots + y_{n-1} + \frac{y_n}{2}\right)h.$$

We are assuming that this number approximates our given integral, so we have the following numerical integration rule, whose name stems from the type of geometric argument we used in Example 36-1.

The Trapezoidal Rule. *Let n be a positive integer and take* $h = \dfrac{b-a}{n}$. *If we write* $y_i = f(a + ih)$ *for* $i = 0, 1, 2, \ldots, n,$ *then*

$$(36\text{-}2) \quad \int_a^b f(x)\, dx \approx \left(\frac{y_0}{2} + y_1 + y_2 + \cdots + y_{n-1} + \frac{y_n}{2}\right)h.$$

Example 36-2. Use the Trapezoidal Rule with $n = 4$ to approximate the integral $\int_1^2 \dfrac{1}{x}\, dx.$

Solution. We divide the basic interval $[1, 2]$ into 4 parts, each with a length of $h = (2 - 1)/4 = \tfrac{1}{4}$, by means of the points $x_0 = 1$, $x_1 = \tfrac{5}{4}$, $x_2 = \tfrac{3}{2}$, $x_3 = \tfrac{7}{4}$, and $x_4 = 2$. Since $y_i = 1/x_i$, then $y_0 = 1$, $y_1 = \tfrac{4}{5}$, $y_2 = \tfrac{2}{3}$, $y_3 = \tfrac{4}{7}$, and $y_4 = \tfrac{1}{2}$. Thus, according to Formula 36-2,

$$\int_1^2 \frac{1}{x}\,dx \approx \left(\frac{1}{2} + \frac{4}{5} + \frac{2}{3} + \frac{4}{7} + \frac{1}{4}\right)\frac{1}{4}$$

$$= \frac{1171}{1680} \approx .697.$$

The actual value of this integral, correct to 3 decimal places, is .693.

To approximate an integral by means of the Trapezoidal Rule, we divide the interval of integration into equal subintervals and replace our given function with a function that is linear over each of the subintervals. Often we get an even closer approximation of the integral by replacing the given function with a function that is quadratic over certain subintervals of the interval of integration.

To approximate the number $\int_a^b f(x)\,dx$ by this method, we divide the interval $[a, b]$ into an *even* number n of equal subintervals, each with a length of $h = \dfrac{b-a}{n}$ (Fig. 36-3). Suppose that the points of subdivision are $x_0 = a$, $x_1 = a + h$,

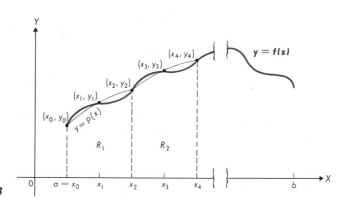

Figure 36-3

$x_2 = a + 2h$, and so on, and that we denote the corresponding function values by y_0, y_1, y_2, and so on. It is a matter of simple algebra to find numbers A, B, and C such that the graph of the equation $y = Ax^2 + Bx + C$ contains the points (x_0, y_0), (x_1, y_1), and (x_2, y_2). Since this graph is a parabola, we say that we have "passed a parabola through the points." Through the points (x_2, y_2), (x_3, y_3), and (x_4, y_4) we pass another parabola whose equation is $y = Dx^2 + Ex + F$, and so on, for each successive group of three points.

Together, these parabolic arcs form the graph of an equation $y = p(x)$, and because this graph approximates the graph of f, it seems reasonable to suppose that the integrals $\int_a^b f(x)\, dx$ and $\int_a^b p(x)\, dx$ are also approximately equal. Again we evaluate our approximating integral by writing it as a sum, but not the same sum that we used in Equation 36-1; here we cover two subintervals at a time:

$$(36\text{-}3) \quad \int_a^b p(x)\, dx = \int_{x_0}^{x_2} p(x)\, dx + \int_{x_2}^{x_4} p(x)\, dx + \cdots + \int_{x_{n-2}}^{x_n} p(x)\, dx.$$

To evaluate the integrals on the right-hand side of this equation, we replace $p(x)$ in each integral with the appropriate quadratic expression. Thus we replace the first integral with $\int_{x_0}^{x_2}(Ax^2 + Bx + C)\, dx$, the second with $\int_{x_2}^{x_4}(Dx^2 + Ex + F)\, dx$, and so on.

Now we evaluate the integrals of these quadratic expressions. From Formula 35-5 we see that

$$(36\text{-}4) \quad \int_{x_0}^{x_2}(Ax^2 + Bx + C)\, dx = \frac{x_2 - x_0}{6}\left[p(x_0) + 4p\left(\frac{x_0 + x_2}{2}\right) + p(x_2)\right],$$

where $p(x) = Ax^2 + Bx + C$. We are supposing that $x_2 - x_0 = 2h$, and $\dfrac{x_0 + x_2}{2} = x_1$, so the right-hand side of Equation 36-4 can be written as

$$\frac{h}{3}\left[p(x_0) + 4p(x_1) + p(x_2)\right].$$

Furthermore, since the graph of the function p contains the three points (x_0, y_0), (x_1, y_1), and (x_2, y_2), we have $p(x_0) = y_0, p(x_1) = y_1$, and $p(x_2) = y_2$. Thus Equation 36-4 can be written as

$$\int_{x_0}^{x_2}(Ax^2 + Bx + C)\, dx = \frac{h}{3}(y_0 + 4y_1 + y_2).$$

In exactly the same way we find that

$$\int_{x_2}^{x_4}(Dx^2 + Ex + F)\, dx = \frac{h}{3}(y_2 + 4y_3 + y_4),$$

and so on. We now replace the terms in the right-hand side of Equation 36-3 with these expressions, and we obtain

$$\frac{h}{3}(y_0 + 4y_1 + y_2) + \frac{h}{3}(y_2 + 4y_3 + y_4) + \cdots + \frac{h}{3}(y_{n-2} + 4y_{n-1} + y_n)$$

$$= \frac{h}{3}(y_0 + 4y_1 + 2y_2 + 4y_3 + \cdots + 2y_{n-2} + 4y_{n-1} + y_n).$$

Our result is another method for calculating integrals numerically.

Simpson's Parabolic Rule. *Let n be a positive even integer and take* $h = (b-a)/n$. *Then*

$$(36\text{-}5) \quad \int_a^b f(x)\,dx \approx \frac{h}{3}(y_0 + 4y_1 + 2y_2 + 4y_3 + \cdots$$

$$+ 2y_{n-2} + 4y_{n-1} + y_n),$$

where $y_i = f(a + ih)$, $i = 0, 1, \ldots, n$. *Notice that inside the parentheses the numbers y_0 and y_n are multiplied by 1, whereas the other y's with even subscripts are multiplied by 2. All the y's with odd subscripts are multiplied by 4.*

Example 36-3.   Use Simpson's Rule with $n = 4$ to approximate $\int_1^2 \frac{1}{x}\,dx$.

Solution.   We use the numbers y_0, y_1, y_2, y_3, and y_4 that we calculated in Example 36-2, together with Formula 36-5, to get

$$\int_1^2 \frac{1}{x}\,dx \approx \frac{\frac{1}{4}}{3}\left[1 + 4\cdot\left(\frac{4}{5}\right) + 2\cdot\left(\frac{2}{3}\right) + 4\cdot\left(\frac{4}{7}\right) + \frac{1}{2}\right] = \frac{1747}{2520} \approx .6933.$$

The value of the integral, correct to 4 decimal places, is .6931. Our new approximation is somewhat more accurate than the result we obtained with the Trapezoidal Rule in Example 36-2.

As with any approximation method, we would naturally like to know how accurate the Trapezoidal Rule and Simpson's Parabolic Rule are. We won't go into the details, which are more tedious than difficult, but by methods very similar to those we used to find Formula 25-5 we can prove the following theorem.

Theorem 36-1.   *Let M and N be numbers such that for each $x \in [a, b]$ we have the inequalities $|f''(x)| \leq M$ and $|f^{(4)}(x)| \leq N$. If the Trapezoidal Rule gives the number T, and Simpson's Rule gives the number S as approximations to* $\int_a^b f(x)\,dx$, *then*

$$(36\text{-}6) \quad \left|\int_a^b f(x)\,dx - T\right| \leq \frac{b-a}{12} Mh^2$$

and

$$(36\text{-}7) \quad \left|\int_a^b f(x)\,dx - S\right| \leq \frac{b-a}{180} Nh^4.$$

Example 36-4   Use the error bounds of Theorem 36-1 to test the accuracy of the approximations we found in Examples 36-2 and 36-3.

Solution.   Here $f(x) = x^{-1}$, so $f''(x) = 2x^{-3}$ and $f^{(4)}(x) = 24x^{-5}$. Therefore, $|f''(x)| \leq 2$ and $|f^{(4)}(x)| \leq 24$ in the interval $[1, 2]$, so we set $M = 2$ and $N = 24$

in Formulas 36-6 and 36-7. In both our examples, $h = \frac{1}{4}$ and $b - a = 1$. Thus we see that the error we made in Example 36-2 was no greater than $\frac{1}{12} \cdot 2 \cdot (\frac{1}{4})^2 = 1/96 \approx .01$, while the error we made in Example 36-3 was no greater than $\frac{1}{180} \cdot 24 \cdot (\frac{1}{4})^4 = \frac{1}{1820} \approx .0005$.

To a student doing a long list of problems with only a pencil and paper to help him, the Trapezoidal Rule and Simpson's Rule appear tedious indeed. They don't look so tedious to a modern computing machine!

PROBLEMS 36

1. Compare your results when you compute $\int_0^2 (2x - x^2 + 1)\, dx$ using (a) integration formulas and (b) the Trapezoidal Rule with $n = 4$. Sketch a figure showing the curve and the trapezoids involved.

2. Compute an approximation to the integral, using the Trapezoidal Rule with the number n as indicated.

(a) $\int_0^2 (1 + x^3)\, dx;\ n = 4$ (b) $\int_1^2 x^{-2}\, dx;\ n = 2$

(c) $\int_0^2 \sqrt{x}\, dx;\ n = 4$ (d) $\int_1^5 \sqrt{126 - x^3}\, dx;\ n = 4$.

3. Compute an approximation of the integral, using Simpson's Parabolic Rule with the number n as indicated.

(a) $\int_0^\pi \sin x\, dx;\ n = 4$ (b) $\int_0^\pi (2 + \cos x)^{-1}\, dx;\ n = 4$

(c) $\int_0^1 (1 + x^2)^{-1}\, dx;\ n = 2$ (d) $\int_2^8 x(4 + x^2)^{-1/3}\, dx;\ n = 6$

(e) $\int_0^{\pi/2} (1 - \frac{1}{2}\sin^2 x)^{-1/2}\, dx;\ n = 4$ (f) $\int_2^{10} (1 + x)^{-1}\, dx;\ n = 8$.

4. Show that the equation of the parabola that contains the points (x_0, y_0), (x_1, y_1), and (x_2, y_2) is

$$y = \frac{y_0(x - x_1)(x - x_2)}{(x_0 - x_1)(x_0 - x_2)} + \frac{y_1(x - x_0)(x - x_2)}{(x_1 - x_0)(x_1 - x_2)} + \frac{y_2(x - x_0)(x - x_1)}{(x_2 - x_0)(x_2 - x_1)}$$

5. Use Simpson's Parabolic Rule with $n = 4$, and the tables in the back of the book, to approximate $\int_0^{.4} \sin x\, dx$. Use Formula 36-7 to show that your calculation is as exact as the tables will allow. Use the same technique to approximate $\int_0^{.4} \frac{\sin x}{x}\, dx$.

6. Does Simpson's Rule always give a better approximation than the Trapezoidal Rule?

7. Suppose that $f(x)$ is a polynomial of degree 3. What can you conclude from Formula 36-7 about the accuracy of the Simpson Rule Approximation? (See Problem 35-13.)

8. When we derived the Trapezoidal Rule, we replaced the function in an interval $[x_{i-1}, x_i]$ by a linear function whose graph was the line segment joining the point (x_{i-1}, y_{i-1}) to the point (x_i, y_i). Replace this line segment with a segment of the tangent line to the graph of f at the midpoint $m_i = \dfrac{x_{i-1} + x_i}{2}$ to obtain the **Tangent Rule:**

$$\int_a^b f(x)\, dx \approx h \sum_{i=1}^{n} f(m_i).$$

Compare the approximations to $\displaystyle\int_0^{.4} \frac{\sin x}{x}\, dx$ that you get by using the Trapezoidal Rule and the Tangent Rule, with $n = 2$.

9. From our geometric interpretation of the integral, we know that $\displaystyle\int_0^1 \sqrt{1 - x^2}\, dx = \frac{\pi}{4}.$ Find approximate values of π by using this equation, $n = 4$, and (a) The Trapezoidal Rule, (b) Simpson's Parabolic Rule, (c) The Tangent Rule (see the preceding problem).

10. Can you choose a value of n for which the Trapezoidal Rule gives the exact value of $\displaystyle\int_0^4 [\![x]\!]\, dx$?

37 THE FUNDAMENTAL THEOREM OF CALCULUS

So far, we have kept the concepts of the derivative and the integral separate. In Chapter 2 we found out what a derivative is and how to calculate it. In the early sections of this chapter we learned what an integral is and acquired some techniques for calculating integrals. Nothing we have said up to now suggests that the processes of differentiation and integration are not independent. But they aren't. In a sense, they are inverses of each other. This fact, as we shall see, enables us to use our differentiation formulas to calculate integrals. Let us first write the relationship between the derivative and the integral as a formal theorem, and then we will discuss what this theorem says. We will delay its proof until the end of the section.

Theorem 37-1.   The Fundamental Theorem of Calculus. *If a function f is integrable on the interval $[a, b]$ and if F is a function that is continuous in $[a, b]$ and is such that $D_x F(x) = f(x)$ for each $x \in (a, b)$, then*

(37-1) $$\int_a^b f(x)\, dx = F(b) - F(a).$$

We can make the connection between differentiation and integration seem more direct if we write Equation 37-1 in a different form. We are supposing that $D_x F(x) = f(x)$, and hence Equation 37-1 can be written as

$$\int_a^b D_x F(x)\, dx = F(b) - F(a).$$

This equation shows us how integration "undoes" the operation of differentiation. When you remember that we introduced the process of differentiation in terms of finding a tangent line to a curve and the process of integration in terms of the apparently unrelated problem of finding the area of a region under a curve, you will probably agree that the Fundamental Theorem is not an obvious result!

Now let us see how we can use our theorem to calculate integrals. In essence, the Fundamental Theorem tells us that we can evaluate integrals very simply if we know our rules of differentiation backwards as well as forwards. For to evaluate the integral $\int_a^b f(x)\, dx$, we need only to find a function F such that $D_x F(x) = f(x)$ and then compute the number $F(b) - F(a)$. Of course, it is not always a simple matter to solve the equation $D_x F(x) = f(x)$ for $F(x)$, but we shall find that in many cases our familiarity with the rules of differentiation will enable us to solve this equation by inspection. If $D_x F(x) = f(x)$, then $f(x)$ is called the derivative of $F(x)$, and $F(x)$ is called an **antiderivative** of $f(x)$. The Fundamental Theorem tells us how to evaluate integrals of a function f if we can find an antiderivative of $f(x)$. It is customary to use the notation

$$F(x)\,\Big|_a^b = F(b) - F(a).$$

In that notation Equation 40-1 becomes

(37-2)
$$\int_a^b f(x)\, dx = F(x)\,\Big|_a^b.$$

Now let us apply the Fundamental Theorem to derive a most useful integration formula. In the notation of Equation 37-2, our earlier integration formulas can be written as

$$\int_a^b 1\, dx = x\,\Big|_a^b,$$

(37-3)
$$\int_a^b x\, dx = \frac{x^2}{2}\,\Big|_a^b,$$

$$\int_a^b x^2\, dx = \frac{x^3}{3}\,\Big|_a^b.$$

These equations suggest that

$$(37\text{-}4) \qquad \int_a^b x^r \, dx = \frac{x^{r+1}}{r+1} \Big|_a^b,$$

where r is any rational number other than -1. It is an easy matter to *verify* Equation 37-4. For according to the Fundamental Theorem, we need only show that $\dfrac{x^{r+1}}{r+1}$ is an antiderivative of x^r; that is, that the derivative of $\dfrac{x^{r+1}}{r+1}$ is x^r. Our rules of differentiation immediately yield

$$D_x\left(\frac{x^{r+1}}{r+1}\right) = \left(\frac{r+1}{r+1}\right)x^r = x^r,$$

and so the verification of Formula 37-4 is complete. When we see how easily the Fundamental Theorem yields Equation 37-4 (which includes Formulas 37-3 that we so laboriously derived, as well as many others) we begin to see what a valuable tool it really is.

Example 37-1. Evaluate the integral $\int_0^4 \sqrt{x} \, dx$ that we approximated in Example 36-1.

Solution. Our given integral can be written as $\int_0^4 x^{1/2} \, dx$, so we apply Formula 37-4 with $r = \frac{1}{2}$:

$$\int_0^4 x^{1/2} \, dx = \frac{x^{3/2}}{\frac{3}{2}} \Big|_0^4 = \frac{2}{3}(4^{3/2} - 0^{3/2}) = \frac{2}{3} \cdot 8 = \frac{16}{3}.$$

Example 37-2. How do we use the Fundamental Theorem to evaluate $\int_{-1}^8 \dfrac{1}{\sqrt[3]{t^5}} \, dt$?

Solution. We don't! You might be tempted to use Equation 37-4 with $r = -5/3$ to obtain the answer

$$\frac{t^{-\frac{5}{3}+1}}{-\frac{5}{3}+1} \Big|_{-1}^8 = -\frac{3}{2} t^{-2/3} \Big|_{-1}^8 = -\frac{3}{2}\left(\frac{1}{4} - 1\right) = \frac{9}{8}.$$

But the integrand is not bounded in the interval $[-1, 8]$, so our integral does not exist. Obviously, the Fundamental Theorem does not apply.

We can evaluate many integrals by combining Equation 37-4 with general integration rules such as Equations 34-4 and 34-5.

Example 37-3. Evaluate the integral $\int_1^2 \left(2z^3 - \dfrac{3}{z^2}\right) dz$.

Solution. We have

$$\int_1^2 \left(2z^3 - \frac{3}{z^2}\right) dz = \int_1^2 (2z^3 - 3z^{-2}) \, dz$$

$$= 2\int_1^2 z^3 \, dz - 3\int_1^2 z^{-2} \, dz$$

$$= 2\left(\frac{z^4}{4}\right)\Big|_1^2 - 3\left(\frac{z^{-1}}{-1}\right)\Big|_1^2$$

$$= 2\left(\frac{16}{4} - \frac{1}{4}\right) - 3\left(\frac{2^{-1}}{-1} - \frac{1}{-1}\right) = 6.$$

We conclude this section with a proof of the Fundamental Theorem of Calculus.

Proof. According to Theorem 35-1, the number $F(b) - F(a)$ is the integral of f over the interval $[a, b]$ if for *each* partition of the interval $[a, b]$ we can find an approximating sum such that

(37-5)
$$\sum_{i=1}^n f(x_i^*)\Delta x_i = F(b) - F(a).$$

So our problem is to find numbers $x_1^*, x_2^*, \ldots, x_n^*$ for which Equation 37-5 is valid. We are assuming that F is continuous in every interval $[x_{i-1}, x_i]$ and that $F'(x)$ is defined at each point in the open interval (x_{i-1}, x_i). Therefore, according to the Theorem of the Mean (Theorem 19-5), there is a number m_i in the interval (x_{i-1}, x_i) such that

(37-6)
$$F(x_i) - F(x_{i-1}) = F'(m_i)(x_i - x_{i-1}).$$

Since $F'(x) = f(x)$ by assumption, $F'(m_i) = f(m_i)$. Also, $x_i - x_{i-1} = \Delta x_i$, so Equation 37-6 can be written as

(37-7)
$$F(x_i) - F(x_{i-1}) = f(m_i)\,\Delta x_i.$$

Therefore, if we choose $x_i^* = m_i$, the left-hand side of Equation 37-5 becomes

$$\sum_{i=1}^n f(m_i)\,\Delta x_i = \sum_{i=1}^n [F(x_i) - F(x_{i-1})]$$

$$= [F(x_1) - F(x_0)] + [F(x_2) - F(x_1)] + \cdots + [F(x_n) - F(x_{n-1})]$$

$$= F(x_n) - F(x_0) = F(b) - F(a).$$

We have found numbers $x_1^*, x_2^*, \ldots, x_n^*$ for which Equation 37-5 is valid, and have thereby completed the proof of the Fundamental Theorem of Calculus.

PROBLEMS 37

1. Compute.

(a) $\displaystyle\int_0^2 10x^4\,dx$

(b) $\displaystyle\int_0^1 \sqrt[4]{t^3}\,dt$

(c) $\displaystyle\int_{-4}^{-2} \frac{1}{t^2}\,dt$

(d) $\displaystyle\int_0^{-1} \sqrt[3]{z}\,dz$

(e) $\displaystyle\int_1^4 \frac{1}{\sqrt{z}}\,dz$

(f) $\displaystyle\int_1^8 \frac{1}{3\sqrt[3]{x^2}}\,dx$

2. Compute.

(a) $\displaystyle\int_0^1 (w^4 - \sqrt{w})\,dw$

(b) $\displaystyle\int_0^a (a^2x - x^3)\,dx$

(c) $\displaystyle\int_{-1}^3 (3 + 2x - x^2)\,dx$

(d) $\displaystyle\int_0^{-4} x(\sqrt[3]{x} + x^3)\,dx$

(e) $\displaystyle\int_{-2}^2 x(x^2 + 3x)\,dx$

(f) $\displaystyle\int_1^4 (\sqrt{t} + 2)(2t - 1)\,dt$

3. Compute.

(a) $\displaystyle\int_0^4 |4 - x^2|\,dx$

(b) $\displaystyle\int_0^2 x\,|1 - x|\,dx$

(c) $\displaystyle\int_{-1}^1 \sqrt{|x| + x}\,dx$

(d) $\displaystyle\int_{-1}^5 \sqrt[3]{4(|x| - x)}\,dx$

4. Compute.

(a) $\displaystyle\int_0^2 [\![x]\!]x^2\,dx$

(b) $\displaystyle\int_{\frac{1}{2}}^2 \frac{x^2 + 1}{x^2}\,dx$

(c) $\displaystyle\int_1^{16} \frac{5\sqrt[4]{x^3} - 3x}{\sqrt{x}}\,dx$

(d) $\displaystyle\int_{-8}^{-1} \left(\sqrt[3]{8x} + \frac{1}{\sqrt[3]{8x}}\right)^2\,dx$

(e) $\displaystyle\int_{-1}^1 \sqrt[3]{4(|x| + x)}\,dx$

(f) $\displaystyle\int_{-1}^4 \sqrt{|x|}\,dx$

(g) $\displaystyle\int_1^4 x^{\sin\,(\pi/[\![x]\!])}\,dx$

(h) $\displaystyle\int_1^{a^{16}} \sqrt{x\sqrt{x\sqrt{x}}}\,dx$

5. Show that if p and q are positive integers, then $\displaystyle\int_0^1 (x^{p/q} + x^{q/p})\,dx = 1$.

6. Find the area of the region that is bounded by the X-axis and the graph of the given equation.
(a) $y = 16 - x^2$
(b) $y = 2x^2 - x^3$
(c) $y = 4a^3x - 6a^2x^2 + 4ax^3 - x^4$
(d) $y = \sqrt{x} + 2 - x - |\sqrt{x} + x - 2|$

7. Find the average value of f in the interval $[1, 4]$ if $f(x) = 3\sqrt{x} + \dfrac{2}{\sqrt{x}}$. Find a point at which f takes this mean value.

8. Find a positive number x such that

$$\int_0^x (2 - t + t^2)\, dt = \tfrac{14}{3}.$$

Interpret this problem geometrically.

9. Are there any positive rational numbers r and s such that

$$\int_0^1 x^r\, dx \cdot \int_0^1 x^s\, dx = \int_0^1 x^r \cdot x^s\, dx?$$

10. Compute.

(a) $\displaystyle\int_0^1 D_x\sqrt{x^2 + 8}\, dx$

(b) $\displaystyle\int_{-1}^1 D_t \sin t^2\, dt$

(c) $\displaystyle\int_0^{\pi/4} D_t \tan t\, dt$

(d) $\displaystyle\int_2^8 D_x \log x\, dx$

11. Show that for a rational number r, $\displaystyle\int_a^b |x|^r\, dx = \dfrac{b\,|b|^r - a\,|a|^r}{r + 1}$ $(r \neq -1)$.

12. If the position of a point along the number scale is given by the equation $s = f(t)$, then its *average velocity* in a time interval $[t_1, t_2]$ is $\dfrac{f(t_2) - f(t_1)}{t_2 - t_1}$. In the terminology of the Theorem of the Mean for Integrals, the *average of the velocity v* is the number $\dfrac{1}{t_2 - t_1}\displaystyle\int_{t_1}^{t_2} v\, dt$. Show that these two average velocities are the same.

38 INTEGRATION FORMULAS

The Fundamental Theorem of Calculus tells us that

$$(38\text{-}1) \qquad\qquad \int_a^b f(x)\, dx = F(x)\,\Big|_a^b$$

whenever f is integrable and F is continuous in $[a, b]$, and

$$(38\text{-}2) \qquad\qquad D_x F(x) = f(x)$$

for each $x \in (a, b)$. For example,

$$\int_a^b 6x^5\, dx = x^6\,\Big|_a^b, \quad \text{since} \quad D_x x^6 = 6x^5.$$

Here the limits of integration a and b are arbitrary. They could be the numbers 2 and 3, $-\pi$ and π, or any other pair of real numbers. Thus

$$\int_2^3 6x^5\, dx = x^6\,\Big|_2^3 = 665, \quad \int_{-\pi}^{\pi} 6x^5 = x^6\,\Big|_{-\pi}^{\pi} = 0, \text{ and so on.}$$

In general, when we use the Fundamental Theorem to evaluate integrals of a function f that is integrable on an interval I, we look for a function F that is continuous in I and that satisfies Equation 38-2 at each point of I. Then Equation 38-1 is valid for arbitrary points a and b of I. Thus, in a sense, Equation 38-1 is independent of the limits a and b, and to save space we drop them and simply write

$$(38\text{-}3) \qquad \int f(x)\,dx = F(x).$$

Integration Formula 38-3 is merely an abbreviated form of Equation 38-1. When we say that Formula 38-3 holds in an interval I we mean that Equation 38-1 is valid for each pair of points a and b of I. We get Equation 38-1 from Formula 38-3 by inserting the limits a and b.

With each specific differentiation formula we can now associate an integration formula. Thus, because

$$D_x \frac{x^{r+1}}{r+1} = x^r,$$

we have the integration formula that we introduced in the preceding section,

$$(38\text{-}4) \quad \int x^r\,dx = \frac{x^{r+1}}{r+1} \text{ (r a rational number, not equal to -1).}$$

Our differentiation formulas for the various trigonometric functions lead to the following integration formulas:

$$(38\text{-}5) \qquad \int \sin x\,dx = -\cos x$$

$$(38\text{-}6) \qquad \int \cos x\,dx = \sin x$$

$$(38\text{-}7) \qquad \int \sec^2 x\,dx = \tan x$$

$$(38\text{-}8) \qquad \int \csc^2 x\,dx = -\cot x$$

$$(38\text{-}9) \qquad \int \sec x \tan x\,dx = \sec x$$

$$(38\text{-}10) \qquad \int \csc x \cot x\,dx = -\csc x$$

To verify one of these formulas, we need only show that the expression on the right is an antiderivative of the integrand. Thus, for example, Formula 38-9 is valid because $D_x \sec x = \sec x \tan x$. You should memorize these integration formulas and realize that they are nothing but our old differentiation formulas written in a new form

Example 38-1. Find the area of the region bounded by an arch of the sine curve and the *X*-axis

Solution. If we look at the graph of the equation $y = \sin x$, we see that the area we seek is given by the integral $\int_0^\pi \sin x \, dx$. This integral is evaluated by inserting the limits 0 and π into Formula 38-5:

$$\int_0^\pi \sin x \, dx = -\cos x \Big|_0^\pi = (-\cos \pi) - (-\cos 0)$$

$$= 2.$$

(In Example 32-2 we used rectangles to find an approximation of the area of one-half of this region.)

In addition to the integration formulas listed above, which deal with specific functions, there are a number of general integration rules, two of which we already know (Theorems 34-3, 34-4, and 34-6):

(38-11) $\qquad \int_a^b [mf(x) + ng(x)] \, dx = m \int_a^b f(x) \, dx + n \int_a^b g(x) \, dx$

and

(38-12) $\qquad \int_a^c f(x) \, dx = \int_a^b f(x) \, dx + \int_b^c f(x) \, dx.$

In these equations, f and g are assumed to be integrable functions, and m and n are real numbers.

The best way to become familiar with integration formulas is to use them.

Example 38-2. Evaluate the integral $\int_0^1 (8t^3 - \sec^2 t) \, dt.$

Solution. Here we have

$$\int_0^1 (8t^3 - \sec^2 t) \, dt = 8 \int_0^1 t^3 \, dt - \int_0^1 \sec^2 t \, dt \qquad \text{(Equation 38-11)}$$

$$= 8 \frac{t^4}{4} \Big|_0^1 - \tan t \Big|_0^1 \qquad \text{(Formulas 38-4 and 38-7)}$$

$$= 8(\tfrac{1}{4} - 0) - (\tan 1 - \tan 0)$$

$$= 2 - \tan 1.$$

From Table I we find that tan $1 = 1.557$, so

$$\int_0^1 (8t^3 - \sec^2 t)\, dt = .443.$$

Example 38-3. Evaluate the integral $\displaystyle\int_{-\pi}^{2\pi} \sin |x|\, dx$.

Solution. None of the Formulas 38-4 to 38-10 applies directly to this case. However, since $|x| = -x$ when $x \in [-\pi, 0]$ and $|x| = x$ when $x \in [0, 2\pi]$, we can use these formulas if we first apply Equation 38-12:

$$\int_{-\pi}^{2\pi} \sin |x|\, dx = \int_{-\pi}^{0} \sin |x|\, dx + \int_{0}^{2\pi} \sin |x|\, dx \qquad \text{(Equation 38-12)}$$

$$= \int_{-\pi}^{0} \sin(-x)\, dx + \int_{0}^{2\pi} \sin x\, dx \qquad \text{(Definition of } |x|)$$

$$= -\int_{-\pi}^{0} \sin x\, dx + \int_{0}^{2\pi} \sin x\, dx \qquad \begin{array}{l}(\sin(-x) = -\sin x \text{ and} \\ \text{Equation 38-11)}\end{array}$$

$$= \cos x \Big|_{-\pi}^{0} - \cos x \Big|_{0}^{2\pi} = 2. \qquad \text{(Formula 38-5)}.$$

You will often find the following generalizations of Formulas 38-5 and 38-6 useful. If a and b are any numbers ($a \neq 0$), then

$$(38\text{-}13) \qquad \int \cos(ax + b)\, dx = \frac{1}{a} \sin(ax + b)$$

and

$$(38\text{-}14) \qquad \int \sin(ax + b)\, dx = -\frac{1}{a} \cos(ax + b).$$

We verify these integration formulas by using our rules of differentiation to show that

$$D_x \left[\frac{1}{a} \sin(ax + b) \right] = \cos(ax + b),$$

and

$$D_x \left[-\frac{1}{a} \cos(ax + b) \right] = \sin(ax + b).$$

It is not hard to write similar generalizations of the other formulas on our list.

Finally, notice that the Fundamental Theorem tells how to evaluate the integral of a function f by using any antiderivative of $f(x)$. We get the value of the integral no matter which of the antiderivatives of $f(x)$ we choose. For example, if we evaluate the integral $\int_a^b \cos x \, dx$ by choosing the antiderivative $\sin x$, we obtain the number $\sin b - \sin a$. On the other hand, since $D_x(\sin x + 7) = \cos x$, we see that $\sin x + 7$ is also an antiderivative of $\cos x$ and hence

$$\int_a^b \cos x \, dx = (\sin x + 7) \Big|_a^b = (\sin b + 7) - (\sin a + 7)$$
$$= \sin b - \sin a.$$

Since it makes no difference which of the antiderivatives of $f(x)$ we use when we apply the Fundamental Theorem, we normally choose the "simplest" antiderivative when we state an integration formula. Thus we write $\int \cos x \, dx = \sin x$, for example, although it would be equally correct to write $\int \cos x \, dx = \sin x + 7$. We cannot infer from these two formulas that $\sin x$ and $\sin x + 7$ are equal, of course. These integration formulas are simply abbreviated forms of the equations $\int_a^b \cos x \, dx = \sin x \Big|_a^b$ and $\int_a^b \cos x \, dx = (\sin x + 7) \Big|_a^b$; it is the numbers $\sin x \Big|_a^b$ and $(\sin x + 7) \Big|_a^b$ that are the same.

PROBLEMS 38

1. Evaluate the following integrals.

(a) $\int_0^{\pi/2} (\sin x + 2 \cos x) \, dx$

(b) $\int_{-\pi/4}^0 \sec^2 x \, dx$

(c) $\int_0^1 (x + \sin x) \, dx$

(d) $\int_{1/2}^1 (2x + \csc^2 x) \, dx$

(e) $\int_{-1}^1 \sec t \tan t \, dt$

(f) $\int_{\pi/4}^{3\pi/4} \csc z \cot z \, dz$

2. Evaluate the following integrals.

(a) $\int_{-\pi/4}^0 (2 \sin x + 4 \sec^2 x) \, dx$

(b) $\int_0^1 (4x + \sin x) \, dx$

(c) $\int_{\pi/4}^{3\pi/4} \csc z \cot z \, dz$

(d) $\int_{-\pi/2}^{\pi/2} (\cos 2x - 2 \cos x) \, dx$

(e) $\int_{-\pi}^{\pi} \sin (|x| + x) \, dx$

(f) $\int_0^{5\pi} (|\sin x| + \sin x) \, dx$

(g) $\int_{-2\pi}^{2\pi} (\sin |x| + |\sin x|) \, dx$

(h) $\int_0^4 [\![x]\!] \cos \pi [\![x]\!] x \, dx$

3. Find the area of the region bounded by the X-axis and an arch of the curve whose equation is given.

(a) $y = 2 \cos x$

(b) $y = \sin \dfrac{\pi x}{2}$

(c) $y = \sin \left(\dfrac{x}{2} - \pi \right)$

(d) $y = \cos \left(2x - \dfrac{\pi}{6} \right)$

4. Determine the positive number c such that the region in the first quadrant that is bounded by the graph of the equation $y = \cos x$, the X-axis, the Y-axis, and the line $x = c$ has the same area as the region in the first quadrant that is bounded by the graph of the equation $y = 2 \sin 2x$, the X-axis, and the line $x = c$.

5. Verify the following integration formulas.

(a) $\displaystyle \int \sin^2 x \cos x \, dx = \dfrac{\sin^3 x}{3}$

(b) $\displaystyle \int \cos^3 x \sin x \, dx = -\dfrac{\cos^4 x}{4}$

(c) $\displaystyle \int \sec^2 (ax + b) \, dx = \dfrac{1}{a} \tan (ax + b)$

(d) $\displaystyle \int (x + a)^r \, dx = \dfrac{(x + a)^{r+1}}{r + 1}$

(e) $\displaystyle \int \sqrt[n]{x + c} \, dx = \dfrac{n}{n + 1} (x + c)^{(n+1)/n}$

(f) $\displaystyle \int \sqrt{ax + b} \, dx = \dfrac{2}{3a} (ax + b)^{3/2}$

6. State and prove two general integration formulas suggested by formulas (a) and (b) in the preceding problem.

7. Prove that there is a point $x \in [0, \pi]$ at which the value of the sine function is equal to the average value of the sine function in the interval $[0, x]$. Use Newton's Method to find this point (approximately).

8. Find a number r that makes the integration formula correct.

(a) $\displaystyle \int x(x^2 + 3)^3 \, dx = r(x^2 + 3)^4$

(b) $\displaystyle \int \sec 3x \tan 3x \, dx = r \sec 3x$

(c) $\displaystyle \int x^3 \sec^2 x^4 \, dx = r \tan x^4$

(d) $\displaystyle \int \dfrac{1}{(x \cos x)^2} \, dx = \tan \dfrac{r}{x}$

9. Suppose that a and b are given numbers, with $a \neq 0$. Show that if $F'(x) = f(x)$, then $\displaystyle \int f(ax + b) \, dx = \dfrac{1}{a} F(ax + b)$.

10. Show that $\displaystyle \int_a^b \dfrac{x}{|x|} \, dx = |x| \Big|_a^b$ for every pair of numbers a and b and hence the integration formula $\displaystyle \int \dfrac{x}{|x|} \, dx = |x|$ is valid in R^1. Is the equation $D_x |x| = \dfrac{x}{|x|}$ true for every number x? Does the equation $\displaystyle \int_{-1}^3 \dfrac{x}{|x|} \, dx = |x| \Big|_{-1}^3$ follow from the Fundamental Theorem of Calculus?

11. (a) Show that $\displaystyle \int_0^c [\![x]\!] \, dx = c[\![c]\!] - \tfrac{1}{2}[\![c]\!][\![c + 1]\!]$ for each real number c.

(b) Use part (a) to show that the integration formula

$$\int [\![x]\!] \, dx = x[\![x]\!] - \tfrac{1}{2}[\![x]\!][\![x + 1]\!]$$

is valid in R^1.

39 USING INTEGRATION TO FIND AREAS

To help fix the idea of the integral in your mind, we are now going to take up some applications of this concept. Although you can find applications of the integral in almost any scientific subject you choose to study, we will mostly restrict ourselves to geometric problems. Thus we avoid the necessity of introducing specialized terminology from physics, economics, and the like. But even in our relatively simple geometric problems we will be basing our discussion on intuitive ideas rather than strict mathematical definitions. As we said before, a beginning calculus course is no place for a digression into the fine points of what a mathematician means by area and volume. As far as these concepts are concerned, we ask you to proceed on the principle that, "What seems reasonable, is reasonable."

If $f(x) \geq 0$ for each $x \in [a, b]$, then $R = \{(x, y) \mid a \leq x \leq b, \ 0 \leq y \leq f(x)\}$ is the region that is bounded by the graph of f, the X-axis, and the lines $x = a$ and $x = b$. The area of R is the number

(39-1)
$$A = \int_a^b f(x)\, dx.$$

In the graphical argument that makes this equation seem reasonable, we divide the basic interval $[a, b]$ into a set of subintervals of lengths $\Delta x_1, \Delta x_2, \ldots, \Delta x_n$, such as the "typical subinterval" shown in Fig. 39-1. Then we choose a point x_i^* in our typical subinterval and drop a perpendicular from the curve to the X-axis at this point. Let us denote the length of this segment by h_i. Next we draw the rectangle whose base is our subinterval and whose altitude is this perpendicular. The area of this rectangle is $h_i \Delta x_i$. Since $h_i = f(x_i^*)$, the formula for the area of our typical rectangle can be written as $f(x_i^*) \Delta x_i$. The sum of the areas of all the

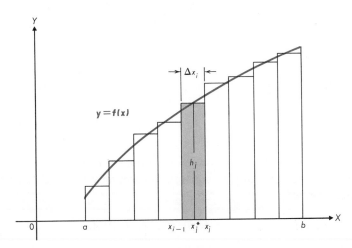

Figure 39-1

rectangles,

$$\sum_{i=1}^{n} f(x_i^*) \Delta x_i,$$

approximates the area of our region R. This sum also approximates the integral

$$\int_a^b f(x) \, dx,$$

which we therefore take to be the area of R.

Whenever we use integrals to compute areas, we shall follow the sequence of steps that we used in the example above:

(i) Draw a figure that shows the region whose area we are to find.

(ii) In the figure show a typical subinterval with a length of Δx_i on the X-axis and a point x_i^* in this subinterval.

(iii) Find the segment with a length of h_i that is perpendicular to the X-axis at x_i^* and which serves as the altitude of our typical rectangle; then draw in the typical rectangle.

(iv) Express h_i in terms of x_i^*, and hence derive an expression for the area $h_i \Delta x_i$ of our typical rectangle.

(v) Form the sum of these areas and then write down the integral that this sum suggests.

(vi) Evaluate this integral and take it to be the area of the region.

Let us see how these steps apply to a region such as the one shown in Fig. 39-2. Here we are considering a function f that takes only negative values in the interval $[a, b]$, and we wish to find the area of the region R that is bounded by the graph of f, the X-axis, and the lines $x = a$, $x = b$. Figure 39-2 shows how we have carried out steps (i) to (iii) above. Clearly the altitude h_i of our typical rectangle is the number $h_i = -f(x_i^*)$. Thus our approximating sum is

$$\sum_{i=1}^{n} -f(x_i^*) \Delta x_i,$$

and this sum suggests that the area A of our region is given by the equation

$$(39\text{-}2) \qquad A = \int_a^b -f(x) \, dx = -\int_a^b f(x) \, dx.$$

Equation 39-1 applies when f is a function whose graph lies above the X-axis, and Equation 39-2 applies when f is a function whose graph lies below the X-axis. The formula

$$(39\text{-}3) \qquad A = \int_a^b |f(x)| \, dx$$

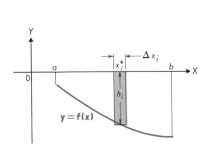

Figure 39-2

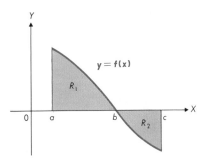

Figure 39-3

covers both cases. Furthermore, Equation 39-3 gives us the area of the region bounded by the graph of a function f, the X-axis, and the lines $x = a$ and $x = b$ even when this region lies partly above and partly below the X-axis. Thus if f is the function whose graph is shown in Fig. 39-3, then

$$\int_a^c |f(x)| \, dx = \int_a^b |f(x)| \, dx + \int_b^c |f(x)| \, dx.$$

The first integral on the right-hand side of this equation gives us the area of the region R_1; the second integral gives us the area of R_2, and so their sum is the area of $R_1 \cup R_2$.

   The graphical interpretation of the integral $\int_a^c f(x) \, dx$ for the function whose graph appears in Fig. 39-3 is the following. We have

$$\int_a^c f(x) \, dx = \int_a^b f(x) \, dx + \int_b^c f(x) \, dx.$$

The first integral on the right-hand side of this equation gives us the area of the region R_1. The second integral is the *negative* of the area of R_2, since $f(x) \leq 0$ if $x \in [b, c]$. Therefore, the integral $\int_a^b f(x) \, dx$ represents the *difference* in the areas of the regions R_1 and R_2. In general, the integral $\int_a^b f(x) \, dx$ represents the number of square units by which the part of the region bounded by the graph of f, the X-axis, and the lines $x = a$ and $x = b$ that lies above the X-axis exceeds the part that lies below the X-axis. In other words, $\int_a^b f(x) \, dx$ represents a "net" area.

   Example 39-1.   Compute the area of the region between the X-axis and the graph of the function defined by the equation $f(x) = \frac{1}{4}(x^3 + x - 2)$ in the interval $[0, 2]$.

Solution.   The graph of the given function is shown in Fig. 39-4. Because the curve lies below the X-axis for x in the interval $(0, 1)$, the area A_1 of the region R_1 is

$$A_1 = \int_0^1 |f(x)|\, dx = -\tfrac{1}{4}\int_0^1 (x^3 + x - 2)\, dx = \tfrac{5}{16}.$$

The area of the region R_2 is

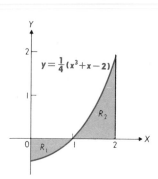

$$A_2 = \int_1^2 |f(x)|\, dx = \tfrac{1}{4}\int_1^2 (x^3 + x - 2)\, dx = \tfrac{13}{16}.$$

Hence the area of the shaded region, $R_1 \cup R_2$, is the number

$$A_1 + A_2 = \tfrac{5}{16} + \tfrac{13}{16} = \tfrac{9}{8}.$$

Notice that

Figure 39-4

$$\tfrac{1}{4}\int_0^2 (x^3 + x - 2)\, dx = \tfrac{1}{2}.$$

This number is the amount by which A_2 exceeds A_1; that is,

$$A_2 - A_1 = \tfrac{13}{16} - \tfrac{5}{16} = \tfrac{1}{2}.$$

Instead of Equation 39-3, we frequently write the formula for the area of the region between the graph of the equation $y = f(x)$ and the interval $[a, b]$ of the X-axis as

(39-4) $$A = \int_a^b |y|\, dx$$

or, if $f(x) \geq 0$ in the interval $[a, b]$, simply as

(39-5) $$A = \int_a^b y\, dx.$$

We understand, of course, that we must replace y with $f(x)$ when we evaluate the integral.

Example 39-2.   Find the area of the region interior to an ellipse whose diameters have lengths of $2a$ and $2b$.

Solution.   Fig. 39-5 shows one quarter of our ellipse; so Formula 39-5 gives us

$$\frac{A}{4} = \int_0^a y\, dx.$$

Since the equation of our ellipse is $\dfrac{x^2}{a^2} + \dfrac{y^2}{b^2} = 1$, we have $y = \dfrac{b}{a}\sqrt{a^2 - x^2}$. Hence

$$A = \frac{4b}{a}\int_0^a \sqrt{a^2 - x^2}\, dx.$$

We have already seen (Equation 33-3)

that $\displaystyle\int_0^a \sqrt{a^2 - x^2}\, dx = \frac{\pi a^2}{4}$, and therefore

the area of the region bounded by the

ellipse is $\dfrac{4b}{a}\dfrac{\pi a^2}{4}$; that is,

$$A = \pi ab.$$

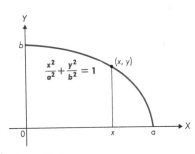

Figure 39-5

When we use our six steps to find
an area by integration, we usually use a
simplified notation in which we write Δx rather than Δx_i for the length of a typical
subinterval, x rather than x_i^* for a point in the subinterval, and h rather than h_i
for the altitude of a typical rectangle. The next example illustrates this simplified
notation.

Example 39-3.   Find the area of the region between the sine and cosine curves in
the interval $[\pi/4, 5\pi/4]$.

Solution.   Fig. 39-6 shows the region whose area we are to find. A typical rectangle
whose altitude is h and base is Δx is also shown. Now we must express h in terms

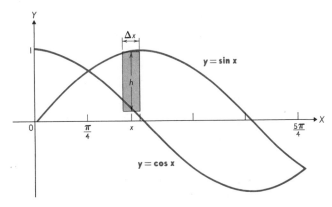

Figure 39-6

of x and substitute the result in the formula $h\,\Delta x$ for the area of the typical rectangle.
Since the upper boundary of our region is an arc of the sine curve and the lower
boundary is an arc of the cosine curve, $h = \sin x - \cos x$. Therefore, the area of

our typical rectangle is $(\sin x - \cos x)\,\Delta x$, and a sum of such terms, indicated as

$$\sum (\sin x - \cos x)\,\Delta x,$$

approximates the area of our region. This indicated sum is the simplified notation for the sum

$$\sum_{i=1}^{n} (\sin x_i^* - \cos x_i^*)\,\Delta x_i,$$

and this latter sum suggests that the area we seek is given by the equation

$$A = \int_{\pi/4}^{5\pi/4} (\sin x - \cos x)\,dx = -\cos x \Big|_{\pi/4}^{5\pi/4} - \sin x \Big|_{\pi/4}^{5\pi/4} = 2\sqrt{2}.$$

Example 39-4.   Find the area A of the region bounded by the Y-axis and the curve whose equation is $y^2 - 4y + 2x = 0$.

Solution.   Figure 39-7 shows the region whose area we are to find. A typical rectangle is also shown, and now we must express the altitude h of this rectangle in terms of x. In this case $h = y_2 - y_1$, where y_2 is the larger and y_1 is the smaller solution of the equation $y^2 - 4y + 2x = 0$. Thus

$$y_2 = \frac{4 + \sqrt{16 - 8x}}{2} = 2 + \sqrt{4 - 2x},$$

and

$$y_1 = 2 - \sqrt{4 - 2x}.$$

Therefore, $h = y_2 - y_1 = 2\sqrt{4 - 2x}$, so the area of our typical rectangle is $2\sqrt{4 - 2x}\,\Delta x$. The indicated sum $\Sigma\, 2\sqrt{4 - 2x}\,\Delta x$ suggests that the area of our

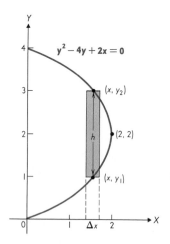

Figure 39-7

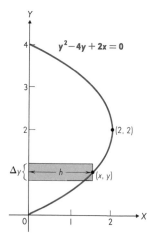

Figure 39-8

region is given by the equation

$$A = 2\int_0^2 \sqrt{4 - 2x}\, dx.$$

In Problem 38-5(f) we have an integration formula that applies in this case; if you use it you will find that $A = \frac{16}{3}$.

Instead of using "vertical rectangles" to approximate our region, a simpler method is to use "horizontal rectangles" such as the one shown in Fig. 39-8. In this case we are subdividing an interval of the Y-axis rather than an interval of the X-axis. Hence we must express the altitude h of our typical rectangle in terms of y. It is clear that h is the X-coordinate of the point of the graph of the equation $y^2 - 4y + 2x = 0$ that corresponds to y, so we find h by solving the equation of our curve for x. We find that

$$h = x = 2y - \frac{y^2}{2},$$

and therefore the area of our typical rectangle is

$$h\,\Delta y = \left(2y - \frac{y^2}{2}\right)\Delta y.$$

A sum of such terms,

$$\Sigma\left(2y - \frac{y^2}{2}\right)\Delta y,$$

approximates the area of our region, and this sum suggests that the area A we seek is given by the equation

$$A = \int_0^4\left(2y - \frac{y^2}{2}\right)dy = y^2\Big|_0^4 - \frac{y^3}{6}\Big|_0^4 = \frac{16}{3}.$$

P R O B L E M S   39

1. Compute the area of the region bounded by the X-axis and the parabola

$$y = 2 + x - x^2.$$

2. Compute the area of the region bounded by the X-axis and the parabola whose vertex is the point $(2, -1)$ and whose directrix is the line $y = -2$.

3. Compute the area of the region between the curve $y = f(x)$ and the X-axis in the given interval.
(a) $f(x) = \sin x$, $[0, 2\pi]$
(b) $f(x) = \cos x$, $[0, \pi]$
(c) $f(x) = x^3$, $[-1, 1]$
(d) $f(x) = 3x^5 - x$, $[-2, 2]$
(e) $f(x) = [\![x]\!]$, $[-1, 2]$
(f) $f(x) = 1 - |x|$, $[-2, 2]$

4. Find the area of the region bounded by the given curves. Draw pictures!

(a) $y = \frac{1}{4}x^2$ and $y = \frac{1}{2}x + 2$

(b) $y^2 = 6x$ and $x^2 = 6y$

(c) $y^2 = 2x$ and $x - y = 4$

(d) $\sqrt{x} + \sqrt{y} = \sqrt{a}$ and the coordinate axes

(e) $x = y^3 - 4y$, $x = 4 - y^2$

(f) $y = x^3$, $y = (2 - x)^2$, and the X-axis.

5. Sketch the region in the first quadrant between the circles $x^2 + y^2 = a^2$ and $x^2 + y^2 = b^2$. Draw an arc of the ellipse $x^2/a^2 + y^2/b^2 = 1$. Show that your arc divides the region between the two circles into two regions whose areas are in the ratio a/b.

6. Through opposite corners of a rectangle draw an arc of a parabola whose vertex is one of the corner points and whose axis lies along one side of your rectangle. Show that you have formed two regions such that the area of one is twice the area of the other.

7. If f is integrable on the interval $[a, b]$, what is the area of the region

$$\left\{ (x, y) \mid x \in [a, b],\ y \in \left[\frac{f(x) - |f(x)|}{2},\ \frac{f(x) + |f(x)|}{2} \right] \right\}?$$

8. Draw the rectangle formed by the two coordinate axes and the lines $x = a$ and $y = b$. The curve $y = bx^n/a^n$ (n a positive integer) divides the rectangle into two regions. Show that the area of one region is n times the area of the other region.

9. Let k be a positive integer, and let $A(k)$ denote the area of the region bounded by the graphs of $y = x^k$ and $y = x^{k+1}$. Find an expression for $\sum_{k=1}^{n} A(k)$. What number does this sum approximate if n is very large? Interpret your result geometrically.

10. Use geometric reasoning to evaluate the following integrals.

(a) $\displaystyle\int_0^8 (-1)^{[\![x]\!]} [\![x]\!]\, dx$

(b) $\displaystyle\int_0^{-5} (-1)^{[\![x]\!]} [\![x]\!]\, dx$

11. Let $pn(x)$ denote the prime number that is nearest to x (if there are two equally near, choose the smaller). Determine m such that the region bounded by the X-axis, the line $x = 10$, and the line $y = mx$ has the same area as the region bounded by the X and Y-axes, the line $x = 10$, and the graph of $y = pn(x)$.

40 VOLUME OF A SOLID OF REVOLUTION

In the preceding section we used our knowledge of calculus to compute the areas of various plane regions. These regions were somewhat more complicated than the triangles, trapezoids, and other figures whose areas you learned to measure in plane geometry. In your elementary geometry course you were told formulas that give the volume of various solid figures such as spheres, cylinders, and cones. We shall now find that calculus can help us determine these formulas and the volumes of other solids as well. We shall first consider the problem of computing the volume of a solid obtained by rotating a plane region about a line. Such a solid is called a **solid of revolution.**

Let f be a function whose domain contains the interval $[a, b]$. We obtain a solid of revolution by rotating the region bounded by the graph of f, the X-axis, and the lines $x = a$ and $x = b$ about the X-axis. Figure 40-1 shows such a solid.

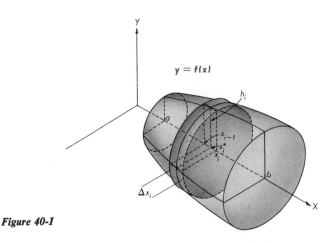

Figure 40-1

To find the volume of this solid, we proceed as we did in the area problem we have just covered. We partition the interval $[a, b]$ into n subintervals; in each subinterval $[x_{i-1}, x_i]$ we choose a point x_i^* and erect a rectangle with an altitude of $h_i = |f(x_i^*)|$, as shown in Fig. 40-1. When we rotate this "typical rectangle" about the X-axis, we obtain a circular disk with a radius of h_i and a thickness of $\Delta x_i = x_i - x_{i-1}$. The volume of this disk is therefore $\pi h_i^2 \, \Delta x_i = \pi f(x_i^*)^2 \, \Delta x_i$, and the sum of these volumes,

$$\sum_{i=1}^{n} \pi f(x_i^*)^2 \, \Delta x_i,$$

approximates the volume of our solid of revolution. Now we find the limit of this sum as the norm of the partition of the interval $[a, b]$ approaches zero (if this limit exists), and we take this limit to be the volume of our solid of revolution. If f is an integrable function, then the limit of this sum will be (as the form of its terms suggests) $\int_a^b \pi f(x)^2 \, dx$. So we take the volume of our solid of revolution to be the number

(40-1) $$V = \pi \int_a^b f(x)^2 \, dx.$$

Instead of Equation 40-1, we frequently write the formula for the volume of the solid obtained by rotating the graph of the equation $y = f(x)$ about the X-axis as

(40-2)
$$V = \pi \int_a^b y^2 \, dx.$$

Of course, before we evaluate the integral in Formula 40-2, we must replace y with $f(x)$.

Example 40-1. Use Equation 40-2 to compute the volume of a solid sphere whose radius is r.

Solution. The graph of the equation $y = \sqrt{r^2 - x^2}$ is a semicircle with a radius of r and with its diameter along the X-axis. We obtain our sphere by rotating this arc about the X-axis. Now we make use of Equation 40-2 with $y = \sqrt{r^2 - x^2}$, $a = -r$, and $b = r$ to obtain

$$V = \pi \int_{-r}^r y^2 \, dx = \pi \int_{-r}^r (r^2 - x^2) \, dx = \pi \left(r^2 x \Big|_{-r}^r - \frac{x^3}{3} \Big|_{-r}^r \right) = \frac{4\pi r^3}{3}.$$

Rather than rely on formulas such as Equation 40-1, you should follow the steps we used in arriving at the formula:

(i) Draw a figure that includes a sketch of a "typical rectangle."

(ii) Write a formula that expresses in terms of x and Δx the volume of the disk obtained by rotating this typical rectangle. (We usually use the simplified notation x and Δx instead of x_i^* and Δx_i.)

(iii) Take the volume of the solid of revolution to be the integral that is suggested by a sum of the volumes of these disks.

(iv) Evaluate the integral.

Example 40-2. Find the volume of a solid right-circular cone with an altitude of h and a base radius of r.

Solution. The surface of the cone can be obtained by rotating the line segment joining the origin and the point (h, r) about the X-axis (Fig. 40-2). The altitude of our illustrated rectangle is y, and its base is Δx. Therefore the volume of the disk that it generates is $\pi y^2 \Delta x$. In order to write this formula in terms of x and Δx, we must express y in terms of x. The numbers x and y are related by the equation of the line that contains the point (h, r) and the origin. Thus $y = \frac{r}{h} x$, and the volume of our disk is $\pi \left(\frac{r}{h} \right)^2 x^2 \Delta x$. The sum of these volumes has the form

$$\sum \pi \left(\frac{r}{h} \right)^2 x^2 \Delta x,$$

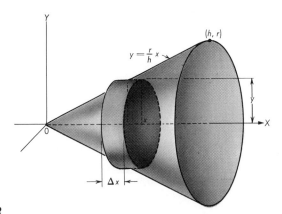

Figure 40-2

and the volume of our cone is given by the integral suggested by this sum:

$$V = \pi \frac{r^2}{h^2} \int_0^h x^2 \, dx = \pi \left(\frac{r^2}{h^2}\right)\left(\frac{h^3}{3}\right) = \pi \frac{r^2 h}{3}.$$

No essentially new ideas are involved when we consider solids of revolution obtained by rotating plane regions about the *Y*-axis.

Example 40-3. The region bounded by the *Y*-axis, the line $y = 1$, and the graph of the equation $y = \sqrt{x}$ (Fig. 40-3) is rotated about the *Y*-axis. What is the volume of the solid that is generated?

Solution. A "typical rectangle" is shown in Fig. 40-3. The volume of the disk generated by this rectangle is $\pi x^2 \, \Delta y$. Here we will express this volume in terms of y and Δy, and to do so we must express x in terms of y. The numbers x and y are related by the equation of our curve; that is, $y = \sqrt{x}$. Therefore, $x^2 = y^4$, so the volume of our typical disk is $\pi y^4 \, \Delta y$. A sum of such volumes has the form

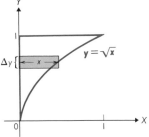

Figure 40-3

$$\sum \pi y^4 \, \Delta y,$$

which suggests that the volume of our solid of revolution is:

$$V = \pi \int_0^1 y^4 \, dy = \frac{\pi y^5}{5} \bigg|_0^1 = \frac{\pi}{5}.$$

The next example is somewhat more complicated than the preceding one, but we analyze it in much the same way.

Example 40-4. Find the volume of the solid obtained by rotating the region described in Example 40-3 about the *X*-axis.

Solution. When we rotate the typical rectangle shown in Fig. 40-4, it generates a solid "washer," not a disk. An end view of half this washer is shown on the right

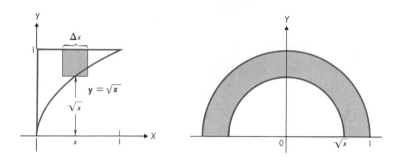

Figure 40-4

in Fig. 40-4. From this figure we see that the area of the base of the washer is $\pi \cdot 1^2 - \pi(\sqrt{x})^2 = \pi(1 - x)$. Since the washer is Δx units thick, its volume is $\pi(1 - x)\,\Delta x$. A sum of such terms, indicated by $\Sigma\pi(1 - x)\,\Delta x$, approximates the volume of the solid under consideration. The volume is given by the integral suggested by this sum:

$$V = \pi \int_0^1 (1 - x)\, dx = \pi\left(x\,\Big|_0^1 - \frac{x^2}{2}\,\Big|_0^1\right) = \frac{\pi}{2}.$$

Example 40-5. Find the volume obtained by rotating the region of the last two examples about the line $y = 1$.

Solution. When we rotate the typical rectangle shown in Fig. 40-4 about the line $y = 1$, it generates a disk with a radius of $(1 - \sqrt{x})$ and a thickness of Δx. Therefore, its volume is $\pi(1 - \sqrt{x})^2\,\Delta x$, and a sum of terms of the form $\Sigma\pi(1 - \sqrt{x})^2\,\Delta x$ approximates the volume of our solid. The volume of our solid is the integral suggested by this sum:

$$V = \pi \int_0^1 (1 - \sqrt{x})^2\, dx = \pi \int_0^1 (1 - 2\sqrt{x} + x)\, dx$$

$$= \pi \int_0^1 (1 - 2x^{1/2} + x)\, dx$$

$$= \pi\left[x\,\Big|_0^1 - \tfrac{4}{3}x^{3/2}\,\Big|_0^1 + \frac{x^2}{2}\Big|_0^1\right] = \frac{\pi}{6}.$$

P R O B L E M S   4 0

1. Find the volume of the solid ellipsoid generated by rotating the region bounded by the ellipse $b^2x^2 + a^2y^2 = a^2b^2$ about the X-axis.

2. Find the volume of the solid generated by rotating about the X-axis the region bounded by the curves given below.
(a) $y = x^3$, $x = 2$, and the X-axis.
(b) $y = -4x^2 + 8x - 1$, $x = 1$, and the coordinate axes.
(c) $\sqrt{x} + \sqrt{y} = \sqrt{a}$ and the coordinate axes.
(d) $y = x^{2/3}$, $x = -1$, $x = 1$, and the X-axis.

3. Find the volume of the solid generated by rotating about the X-axis the region in the first quadrant bounded by the Y-axis and the sine and cosine curves. (Use the identity $\cos^2 x - \sin^2 x = \cos 2x$.)

4. Find the volume of the solid obtained by rotating about the Y-axis the region bounded by the curves given.
(a) $y = x^3$, $y = 8$, and the Y-axis.
(b) $y = x^3$, $x = 2$, and the X-axis.
(c) $2y^2 = x^3$ and $x = 2$.
(d) $y = 1 + x^2$, $x = 2$, and the coordinate axes.

5. Let a be a positive number and let n be a positive integer. The curve $y = x^n$ divides the rectangle formed by the coordinate axes and the lines $x = a$ and $y = a^n$ into two regions. Two solids are obtained by rotating these regions about the X-axis. What is the ratio of their volumes? What is the ratio of the volumes of the solids obtained by rotating the two regions about the Y-axis?

6. Derive the formula for the volume of a solid truncated cone whose height is h and whose two radii are a and b.

7. Find the volume of the solid obtained by rotating about the line $x = 4$ the region bounded by the curves given below.
(a) $y = x$, $y = 3 - x$, and $x = 4$.   (b) $y = x^{3/2}$, $y = 0$, and $x = 4$.
(c) $y = x^{3/2}$, $x = 0$, and $y = 8$.   (d) $y = x$, and $y = x^2/2$

8. Find the volume of the solid generated by rotating, one arch of the sine curve about the X-axis. (Use the identity $\sin^2 x = \frac{1}{2}(1 - \cos 2x)$.)

9. Find the volume of the "torus" obtained by rotating the circle $x^2 + (y - b)^2 = a^2$ about the X-axis (assume $0 < a < b$).

10. The region common to the two ellipses $a^2x^2 + b^2y^2 = a^2b^2$ and $b^2x^2 + a^2y^2 = a^2b^2$ is rotated about the X-axis. Find the volume of the resulting solid.

11. (a) Show that the volume of a right circular cylindrical shell of altitude h, inner radius x_1, and outer radius x_2 is $2\pi \bar{x}_2 h \, \Delta x_2$, where $\bar{x}_2 = \dfrac{x_1 + x_2}{2}$ and $\Delta x_2 = x_2 - x_1$.

(b) Let f be a function that is integrable on an interval $[a, b]$ that lies to the right of the origin ($a \geq 0$), and suppose that $f(x) \geq 0$ for each $x \in [a, b]$. We are going to find a formula for the volume of the solid that is obtained by rotating the region

$\{(x, y) \mid 0 \leq a \leq x \leq b, 0 \leq y \leq f(x)\}$ about the Y-axis. We partition the interval $[a, b]$ into n subintervals, and on each subinterval $[x_{i-1}, x_i]$ erect a rectangle with an altitude of $f(\bar{x}_i)$. When a typical rectangle is rotated about the Y-axis, a cylindrical shell is formed. Use part (a) to show that it is reasonable to expect that the volume of the solid is given by the formula

$$V = 2\pi \int_a^b xf(x) \, dx = 2\pi \int_a^b xy \, dx.$$

12. Use the formula in the preceding problem to compute the volume of the solid obtained by rotating the given region about the Y-axis.

(a) $\{(x, y) \mid 0 \leq x \leq 1, 0 \leq y \leq x^2\}$

(b) $\{(x, y) \mid 0 \leq x \leq 4, 0 \leq y \leq (x - 2)^2\}$

(c) $\{(x, y) \mid 0 \leq x \leq \pi, 0 \leq y \leq (\sin x)/x\}$

(d) $\{(x, y) \mid 0 \leq x \leq 3, 0 \leq y \leq [\![2 \sin x]\!] x^2\}$

41 VOLUMES BY SLICING

We can generalize the methods of the last section so that they apply to solids other than solids of revolution. The integral $\pi \int_a^b f(x)^2 \, dx$ that is the volume of the solid of revolution shown in Fig. 40-1 is the limit of sums of the form

$$\sum \pi f(x)^2 \, \Delta x.$$

In each term of this sum, the number $\pi f(x)^2$ is the area of the base of a cylindrical disk "sliced" from our solid. If we denote this area by $A(x)$, then our sum takes the form $\sum A(x) \, \Delta x$. In the case of a solid of revolution, the cross-sectional area $A(x)$ is easy to calculate because the cross sections are circles. But even when the cross sections are not circles, we can still find the volume of a solid by slicing if we can calculate the cross-sectional area $A(x)$.

In Fig. 41-1 we have shown a solid whose volume we wish to determine. This solid projects onto an interval $[a, b]$ of a conveniently chosen X-axis. We

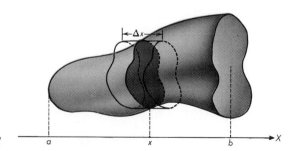

Figure 41-1

partition this interval into subintervals—a typical subinterval having a length of Δx. Through a point x in this sub-interval we pass a plane perpendicular to the X-axis. This plane intersects our solid in the shaded region, whose area we will denote by $A(x)$. The volume of the cylindrical "slice" whose thickness is Δx and which has the shaded region as a cross section is $A(x)\,\Delta x$. A sum of such volumes approximates the volume of our solid and is indicated by

$$\sum A(x)\,\Delta x.$$

We take the integral that is suggested by this sum to *be* the volume:

(41-1) $$V = \int_a^b A(x)\,dx.$$

In order to apply Equation 41-1 to find the volume of a given figure, we need only find the expression $A(x)$ for the cross-sectional area and then evaluate the integral, as in the following examples.

Example 41-1. The plans for a wave guide antenna are shown in Fig. 41-2. Each cross section in a plane perpendicular to the central axis of the wave guide (here the X-axis) is an ellipse whose major diameter is twice as long as its minor diameter. The upper boundary of the widest longitudinal cross section is the parabola $y = \dfrac{x^2}{3} + 1$. The entire antenna is 3 feet long. Find the volume of the region enclosed by the wave guide.

Solution. In order to use Equation 41-1 to find the volume, we must find the area $A(x)$ of a cross section cut from the antenna by a plane perpendicular to the axis at a point x. This cross section

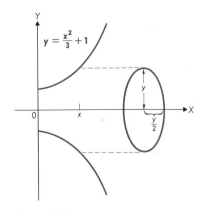

Figure 41-2

is the elliptical region shown in Fig. 41-2. In Example 39-2 we found that an elliptical region with diameters of $2a$ and $2b$ has an area of πab square units. Therefore, the area of our illustrated cross section is $\frac{1}{2}\pi y^2$ square feet. Since $y = \dfrac{x^2}{3} + 1$,

$$A(x) = \frac{\pi}{2}\left(\frac{x^2}{3} + 1\right)^2 = \pi\left(\frac{x^4}{18} + \frac{x^2}{3} + \frac{1}{2}\right).$$

Thus Formula 41-1 gives us

$$V = \pi\int_0^3\left(\frac{x^4}{18} + \frac{x^2}{3} + \frac{1}{2}\right)dx = \frac{36\pi}{5} \text{ cubic feet.}$$

Example 41-2. A regular pyramid is 100 feet high and has a base 100 feet square. If it is made of rock weighing 100 pounds per cubic foot, how much does it weigh?

Solution. We will first find the volume, in cubic feet, of the pyramid and then multiply this result by 100 to get its weight. Figure 41-3 shows the entire pyramid

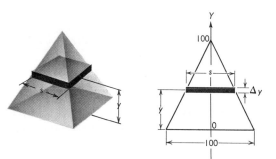

Figure 41-3

and also a triangular cross section. At a height y feet above the base we have shaded a "typical slice." If we denote the area of a face of this slice by $A(y)$, then the volume of our pyramid is

$$V = \int_0^{100} A(y)\, dy.$$

Therefore, in order to find V we must find an expression for $A(y)$. A face of our typical slice is obviously square; let s denote the length of a side. Then from similar triangles in Fig. 41-3 we see that

$$\frac{s}{100 - y} = \frac{100}{100}.$$

Therefore, $s = 100 - y$ and $A(y) = (100 - y)^2$. Hence,

$$V = \int_0^{100} (100 - y)^2\, dy$$

$$= \int_0^{100} (100^2 - 200y + y^2)\, dy = 100^3/3.$$

The weight W of the pyramid is 100 times this amount, so

$$W = 100^4/3 = 10^8/3.$$

The pyramid weighs $10^8/3$ pounds or nearly 17,000 tons.

The next example tests your ability to visualize three-dimensional figures.

Example 41-3.   The base of a certain solid is a circular disk with a 2-inch radius. Cross sections perpendicular to one of the diameters of the disk are square. Find the volume of the solid.

Solution.   On the left side of Fig. 41-4 we have shown a top view of our solid with the mentioned diagonal lying along the *X*-axis. On the right of the figure is the

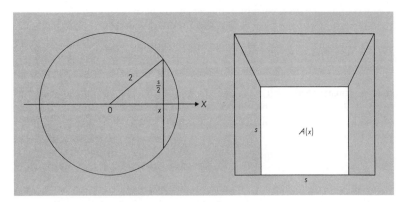

Figure 41-4

view we would see if we cut the solid at the point *x* and looked at it down the *X*-axis. Our cross section is an *s* by *s* square, and we will be able to find its area $A(x)$ as soon as we find *s* in terms of *x*. From the right triangle of hypotenuse 2 and legs *s*/2 and *x* that we see inside the circle, we obtain the relation $4 = (s/2)^2 + x^2$. Hence $s^2 = 16 - 4x^2$. But $A(x) = s^2$, so

$$V = \int_{-2}^{2} A(x)\,dx = \int_{-2}^{2} (16 - 4x^2)\,dx$$

$$= (16x - \tfrac{4}{3}x^3)\Big|_{-2}^{2} = \tfrac{128}{3} \text{ cubic inches.}$$

P R O B L E M S   4 1

1. A four-sided solid is formed by sawing a corner off a rectangular block. The base of the figure is a right triangle whose legs are 3 and 4 inches long, and the altitude of the figure is 5 inches. Use Equation 41-1 to find its volume.

2. Use Equation 41-1 to compute the volume of a slice taken from a spherical orange with a radius of *r* inches that contains *k* identical slices.

3. A cylindrical hole with a radius of 1 inch is drilled along the diameter of a solid metal sphere whose radius is 4 inches. Find the volume of the part of the sphere that remains.

4. Calculate the volume of a solid ellipsoid such that three mutually perpendicular cross sections are bounded by ellipses whose diameters are $2a$, $2b$, and $2c$ units long.

5. A solid is constructed with a circular base of radius 4 and such that every cross section perpendicular to a certain diameter of the base is bounded by an equilateral triangle. Find the volume of the solid.

6. A solid is constructed with a circular base of radius 2 and such that every cross section perpendicular to a certain diameter of the base is an isosceles right triangle with its hypotenuse in the base plane. Find the volume of the solid.

7. A solid is constructed with a circular base of radius 1 and such that every cross section perpendicular to a certain diameter of the base is an isosceles triangle whose altitude is 2. Find the volume of the solid.

8. A solid is constructed with a base that is bounded by an ellipse whose major diameter is $2a$ units long and whose minor diameter is $2b$ units long such that every cross section perpendicular to the major diameter is a square. Find the volume of the solid.

9. When two pieces of 1-inch quarter round are cut so as to fit together in the corner of a room, how much material is cut away from each piece?

10. The axes of two right-circular cylinders with equal radii of r inches intersect at right angles. Find the volume of the region common to both cylinders.

42 WORK

The Fundamental Theorem of Calculus states that

$$(42\text{-}1) \qquad \int_a^b F'(x)\,dx = F(b) - F(a).$$

Naturally we view this equation as a means of evaluating an integral by subtraction, but we could perfectly well consider it as a means of replacing a problem in subtraction with a problem in integration. If we know the numbers $F(b)$ and $F(a)$, of course, it is foolish to find their difference by integrating. But we will now give some examples in which it is easier to find a formula for $F'(x)$ than it is to find a formula for $F(x)$ itself, and in these cases "subtraction by integration" is quite appropriate.

Suppose that one end of a spring is fixed at a point of the negative side of a number scale and that the free end is at the origin when the spring is in its natural (unstretched) position. Let us denote by $F(x)$ the work performed in pulling the free end to the point x of the number scale (as in Fig. 42-1). Thus if a and b are two points, we perform $F(a)$ units of work to pull the free end of the spring from its rest position to the point a and $F(b)$ units to pull it from its rest position to the point b. Therefore, if we denote by W the amount of work that is done in moving

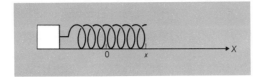

Figure 42-1

the free end from a to b, we see that

$$W = F(b) - F(a).$$

But we cannot find W from this equation as it stands because we don't have a formula for $F(x)$ from which to calculate $F(b)$ and $F(a)$.

Instead of finding a formula for $F(x)$, we will find a formula for $F'(x)$, and then we will find the number $F(b) - F(a)$ by evaluating the integral $\int_a^b F'(x)\, dx$. Suppose that x is a point in the interval $[a, b]$ and z is a nearby point, as shown in Fig. 42-2. We will denote by $f(x)$ the force that is required to hold the free end of

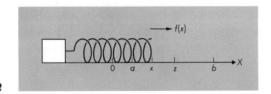

Figure 42-2

the spring at the point x. Then the work that is performed in pulling the free end from x to z is approximately $f(x) \cdot (z - x)$ units. We say "approximately" because the force that we must apply varies as we move from x to z, so strictly speaking the elementary formula *work = force × distance* is not applicable. But if z is close to x, the variation in the force will be slight, and we may use this formula to find an approximation to the work done. On the other hand, the work is the difference $F(z) - F(x)$, so we have the approximation

$$F(z) - F(x) \approx f(x) \cdot (z - x);$$

that is,

$$\frac{F(z) - F(x)}{z - x} \approx f(x).$$

Since this approximation is good when z is near x, it appears reasonable that

$$\lim_{z \to x} \frac{F(z) - F(x)}{z - x} = f(x).$$

The left side of this equation is $F'(x)$—by the definition of the derivative—so we see that $F'(x) = f(x)$. Therefore, the work W that is performed in moving the free end of the spring from a to b is given by the equation $W = F(b) - F(a) = \int_a^b F'(x)\,dx = \int_a^b f(x)\,dx$. Thus we have the equation

(42-2)
$$W = \int_a^b f(x)\,dx,$$

where $f(x)$ is the force that holds the free end of the spring x units from its rest position. Hooke's Law gives us the formula for this force,

$$f(x) = kx,$$

where k is a number, called the **spring constant,** that depends on the spring. Therefore, the work that we do when we stretch the free end of our spring from the point a to the point b is

$$W = \int_a^b kx\,dx = \frac{k}{2}(b^2 - a^2).$$

Example 42-1. If it requires a force of 10 pounds to hold a certain spring when it is stretched 2 inches, how much work is performed in pulling the free end 6 inches from its natural position?

Solution.   Here $a = 0$ and $b = 6$, so $W = \int_0^6 kx\,dx = 18k$. Now we must find the spring constant k. We know that $f(2) = 10$, and therefore the equation $f(x) = kx$ tells us that $2k = 10$. Thus $k = 5$, so $W = 18 \cdot 5 = 90$ inch pounds $= 7.5$ foot pounds.

When we derived Equation 42-2, we assumed that we knew what we were talking about when we spoke of the work that is done in stretching the spring a distance of x units. We took it for granted that this work could be measured by a differentiable function F and that the elementary formula *work = force × distance* is approximately correct for small displacements. We are in somewhat the same position we were when we talked about area and volume earlier. If the quantity under discussion (here work, there area and volume) is defined in a "reasonable" way, then we have a formula for it. In the case of area and volume, we had to refer to mathematical definitions and tell you that they are reasonable. In the case of work, things are simpler. We consider Equation 42-2 as the *definition* of the work that is done as a point moves from a to b, at each point $x \in [a, b]$ being subjected to a force of $f(x)$. Thus work is the integral of force. If the force function f is a constant function with value c, then the amount of work that is done as the force is applied to a point that moves from a to b is given by the formula

$$W = \int_a^b c\,dx = c(b - a).$$

This equation is our old formula *work = force × distance*, and so we see that the integral definition of work agrees with the elementary definition when both apply.

The next example is another typical work problem that we can solve with calculus.

Example 42-2.   A vat has the shape of a paraboloid of revolution. It is 2 feet high, and the radius of its top is 1 foot. It is filled with water which weighs 62.5 pounds per cubic foot. How much work is required to pump the contents of the vat through a nozzle 4 feet above the top?

Solution.   Fig. 42-3 shows our vat and its exhaust pipe. We have drawn in a coordinate system to help us formulate our problem mathematically. Suppose that $F(y)$ foot pounds of work are required to empty the tank if it is filled to a depth of y feet. Then $F(2)$ is the number we want, and since $F(0) = 0$, we can write this number as a difference: $F(2) = F(2) - F(0)$. Now according to the Fundamental Theorem of Calculus, we can write this difference as an integral,

$$F(2) - F(0) = \int_0^2 F'(y)\,dy,$$

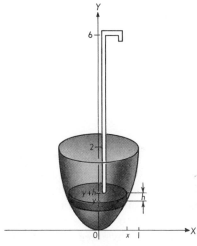

Figure 42-3

and so we may solve our given problem by finding $F'(y)$ and integrating. If h is some given number, then the number $F(y + h) - F(y)$ is the difference between the work required to pump out the tank when it is filled to a depth of $y + h$ feet and the work required when the water in the tank is y feet deep. In other words, $F(y + h) - F(y)$ is the work required to remove the part of the water in the tank that lies between the two horizontal planes that are y and $y + h$ feet above the bottom. This work is approximately the work required to remove the "disk of water" with a radius of x feet and a thickness of h feet that is shown in Fig. 42-3. The volume of this disk is $\pi x^2 h$ cubic feet, and since the density of water is 62.5 pounds per cubic foot, we see that the disk weighs $62.5\pi x^2 h$ pounds. The disk must be lifted about $6 - y$ feet, so the work required to lift the disk out through the nozzle is about $62.5\pi x^2(6 - y)h$ foot pounds. Thus

$$F(y + h) - F(y) \approx 62.5\pi x^2(6 - y)h$$

or

$$\frac{F(y + h) - F(y)}{h} \approx 62.5\pi x^2(6 - y).$$

Since the quotient $\dfrac{F(y + h) - F(y)}{h}$ also approximates the derivative $F'(y)$ when h is small, we conclude that

$$F'(y) = 62.5\pi x^2(6 - y).$$

Before we can compute its integral, we must express $F'(y)$ entirely in terms of y, so let us now replace x^2 with an expression in y. We chose the coordinate system of Fig. 42-3 so that our parabola would be in standard position, and hence its equation is $x^2 = 4cy$, where c is a number that we will now determine. Since the vat is 2 feet tall, and the radius of its top is 1 foot, we see that the point $(1, 2)$ belongs to the parabola. Hence $1 = 4c \cdot 2$, so $4c = \frac{1}{2}$, and the equation of our parabola is $x^2 = \frac{1}{2}y$. Therefore, $F'(y) = \dfrac{62.5\pi}{2} y(6 - y)$, and so

$$F(2) = F(2) - F(0) = \frac{62.5\pi}{2} \int_0^2 y(6 - y)\, dy$$

$$= \frac{875\pi}{3} \text{ foot pounds.}$$

We can use the same techniques to compute work that we have already employed to compute areas and volumes. Thus we can partition our basic interval, construct an approximating sum, and find an integral that is suggested by this sum. We based our discussion of work on "subtraction by integration" because we wanted you to see this method in operation, too. Of course, we can also apply "subtraction by integration" to find areas and volumes, and it would be most instructive for you to try it in a few examples.

P R O B L E M S   4 2

1. A force of 50 pounds stretches a spring two inches beyond its natural length. How much work is required to stretch it those 2 inches?

2. A spring is stretched 1 inch beyond its natural length by a force of 100 pounds. How much work is done in stretching it 4 inches?

3. A 1-ton elevator is lifted from the bottom of a 50-foot shaft by means of a cable that weighs 10 pounds per foot. Find the work done in lifting the elevator to the top of the shaft.

4. How much work is required to empty a tankful of water by pumping it over the rim if the tank is a hemisphere with a radius of 2 feet?

5. A tank in the shape of a paraboloid of revolution is 6 feet deep, has a radius on the top of 3 feet, and is full of water. How much work must be done to lower the water level 2 feet by pumping the water over the rim?

6. How much work is required to construct the pyramid in Example 41-2?

7. A conical cistern is 20 feet across the top, 15 feet deep, and is filled to within 5 feet of the top with water. Find the work done in pumping the water over the top to empty the tank.

8. An empty tank that is a right-circular cone with its vertex down has a base radius of 3 feet, an altitude of 8 feet, and stands on a platform 30 feet above the ground. The tank is filled by pumping water from ground level through a pipe that enters the bottom of the tank. How much work is done?

9. The weight of a body varies inversely as the square of its distance from the center of the earth. A satellite weighs 10 tons on the surface of the earth. Neglecting the atmospheric resistance, compute the work done in propelling the satellite to a height of 1000 miles. (Assume the radius of the earth is 4000 miles.)

10. A rocket is loaded with 1000 pounds of fuel at the surface of the earth. The fuel is burned at a steady rate with respect to distance and is entirely consumed when the rocket reaches a height of 10 miles. Neglecting the variation in the force of gravity, how much work is required just to lift the rocket's fuel?

REVIEW PROBLEMS—CHAPTER FIVE

You can use the following problems to test yourself on the material of this chapter.

1. Evaluate the following integrals.

(a) $\int_0^1 x^2 t \, dt - \int_0^1 x^2 t \, dx$

(b) $\int_{3\pi/4}^{\pi} [(-2)\cos x + \cos(-2x) + (\cos x)^{-2}] \, dx$

(c) $\int_{\pi/6}^{\pi/3} [D_x(\sin x)^{-2} - (D_x \sin x)^{-2}] \, dx$

(d) $\int_0^{2\pi} (|2\cos x + 1| + [\![2\cos x + 1]\!]) \, dx$

2. Determine numbers p and q that make the following integration formulas correct.

(a) $\int \frac{1}{(1+x)^2} \, dx = p(1+x)^q$

(b) $\int \frac{\sin \sqrt{x}}{\sqrt{x}} \, dx = p \cos \sqrt{x}$

(c) $\int x^{-2} \sec \frac{1}{x} \tan \frac{1}{x} \, dx = p \cos^q \frac{1}{x}$

(d) $\int \sqrt{8x} \, dx = px^q$

3. Use the inequality $[f(x) - g(x)]^2 \geq 0$ together with some general integral theorems to show that if f and g are integrable on an interval $[a, b]$, then

$$\int_a^b f(x)^2\, dx + \int_a^b g(x)^2\, dx \geq 2 \int_a^b f(x)\, g(x)\, dx.$$

4. Let R be the region between the parabolas $y = x^2$ and $y = \sqrt{8x}$. (a) Find the area of R. (b) Find the volume of the solid of revolution that we obtain when we rotate R about the X-axis. (c) Find the volume of the solid of revolution that we obtain when we rotate R about the Y-axis.

5. An oil drum 4 feet long and 2 feet in diameter is lying on its side. If the oil in the drum is $1\frac{1}{2}$ feet deep at the deepest point, how many cubic feet of oil are in the drum? (Use Simpson's Parabolic Rule with $n = 4$ to evaluate the integral you get.)

6. A 5-pound bucket, originally containing 100 pounds of water, is hoisted at a steady rate from a 50-foot well. The bucket leaks so fast that it becomes empty just as it gets to the top of the well. How much work is required to get the bucket to the surface?

7. Show that for each number x in the interval $[0, 1]$ we have

$$1 - x + x^2 - x^3 \leq \frac{1}{1 + x} \leq 1 - x + x^2 - x^3 + x^4.$$

What do these inequalities tell us about the number $\int_0^1 \dfrac{1}{1 + x}\, dx$? Can you improve the accuracy of this approximation by increasing the number of terms in the expressions on the left and right sides of the above inequalities? Use a geometric argument to convince yourself that $\int_0^1 \dfrac{1}{1 + x}\, dx = \int_1^2 \dfrac{1}{x}\, dx$, and then look at Example 36-3 to find an approximate value of this integral.

8. Suppose that $f''(x) > 0$ for each $x \in [a, b]$. Use the result of Problem 21-9 to show that the Trapezoidal Rule always yields a number that is larger than $\int_a^b f(x)\, dx$. What about the Tangent Rule (Problem 36-8)?

9. If m and n are integers, show that $\int_m^n [\![x]\!]\, dx = \frac{1}{2}[|n|\,(n - 1) - |m|\,(m - 1)]$. (Hint: First verify this formula in case $m = 0$. Recall that $\sum_{k=1}^n k = \frac{1}{2}n(n + 1)$.)

10. (a) Show that $\int_a^b [f(x) - u]^2\, dx$ is a minimum when the number u is the mean value of f in the interval $[a, b]$.

(b) Use the result of Part (a) to show that for any function f that is integrable on $[a, b]$, $\left(\displaystyle\int_a^b f(x)\, dx\right)^2 \leq (b - a) \int_a^b f(x)^2\, dx.$

(c) Let S_1 be the solid we generate when we rotate the graph of f about the X-axis and let S_2 be the solid we generate when we rotate the graph of the constant function whose value is the mean value of f about the X-axis. Use the result of Part (b) to find which of these solids has the larger volume.

EXPONENTIAL,

LOGARITHMIC,

INVERSE TRIGONOMETRIC,

AND HYPERBOLIC

FUNCTIONS

S I X

In the preceding chapter we introduced the concept of the integral and gave a few examples to show how useful this concept is. In the next chapter we shall consider in some detail some further techniques of calculating integrals. But before we go into this detailed study, we will use the concept of the integral to define the *exponential* and *logarithmic* functions and the associated *hyperbolic* functions.

43 FUNCTIONS DEFINED BY INTEGRALS

We have used the fundamental process of differentiation to construct a derived function f' from a given function f. Now we are going to use the fundamental process of integration to construct a function F from a given function f. Here is an example to illustrate what we have in mind.

269

Example 43-1. Let F be the function defined by the equation

$$F(x) = \int_0^x |\sin t| \, dt.$$

Find $F(0)$, $F(\pi/2)$, $F(3\pi/2)$, and $F(27\pi)$.

Solution. We can interpret the functional values of F graphically as follows. In Fig. 43-1 we have drawn a graph of the equation $y = |\sin t|$. Graphically speaking,

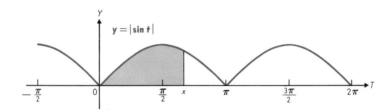

Figure 43-1

$F(x)$ is the area of the region between this curve and the interval $[0, x]$ of the T-axis. This region is shaded in the figure. We have

$$F(0) = \int_0^0 |\sin t| \, dt = 0,$$

and

$$F(\pi/2) = \int_0^{\pi/2} |\sin t| \, dt = \int_0^{\pi/2} \sin t \, dt = 1.$$

To calculate $F(3\pi/2)$ and $F(27\pi)$, we see from the graph that

$$F(3\pi/2) = 3F(\pi/2) = 3,$$

and

$$F(27\pi) = 54F(\pi/2) = 54.$$

In general, if f is a function that is integrable on an interval that contains a point c, then we can define a function F in this interval by means of the equation

(43-1) $$F(x) = \int_c^x f(t) \, dt.$$

We may be forced to evaluate functional values such as $F(3)$, $F(5)$, and so on, by approximation methods such as Simpson's Rule or the Trapezoidal Rule. But Equation 43-1 does assign a number $F(x)$ to each number x in the given interval, and this correspondence defines a function, even though it may be a function whose values are hard to find.

Our function F is determined by the function f and the number c. We are free to choose whatever letters we wish to indicate the variable of integration and to denote a number in the domain of F. To avoid confusion, however, the same letter should not be used to indicate both. Thus, for example, the equations

$$F(u) = \int_0^u |\sin v|\, dv,$$

$$F(t) = \int_0^t |\sin u|\, du,$$

and

$$F(t) = \int_0^t |\sin x|\, dx$$

all define the function F that we discussed in Example 43-1.

To get an idea of the properties of functions that are defined by integrals, let us turn now to another example.

Example 43-2. Let f be the greatest integer function; that is $f(u) = [\![u]\!]$, and let the equation $F(x) = \int_0^x f(u)\, du$ define the function F. Sketch the graphs of the functions f and F for the interval $[0, 2]$.

Solution. The graph of the greatest integer function for the interval $[0, 2]$ is shown on the left in Fig. 43-2. The number $F(x)$ is the area of the region under this graph

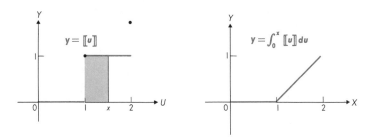

Figure 43-2

and above the interval $[0, x]$ of the horizontal axis. It is clear that if $0 \le x \le 1$, the area is zero, so that $F(x) = 0$ for $x \in [0, 1]$. If $1 < x \le 2$, $F(x)$ is the area of the shaded rectangular region in Fig. 43-2. The area of this shaded region is $(x - 1) \cdot 1 = x - 1$ square units. Thus $F(x) = x - 1$ if $x \in (1, 2]$. The graph of F appears on the right-hand side of Fig. 43-2.

The graphs of the functions f and F in the preceding example illustrate two important facts. First, we see that the function f is not continuous at 1 and 2. This fact is illustrated by the breaks in the graph of f at those points. On the other hand, the graph of the function F has no breaks; F is a continuous function in the interval [0, 2]. This example illustrates the following theorem.

Theorem 43-1. *If f is integrable on an interval I that contains a point c, then the function F that is defined by the equation*

$$(43-2) \qquad F(x) = \int_c^x f(t)\, dt$$

is continuous in I.

Proof. According to the definition of continuity, we must show that

$$\lim_{z \to x} F(z) = F(x);$$

that is, $\lim\limits_{z \to x} [F(z) - F(x)] = 0$, for each point $x \in I$. We use our general integral theorems to write

$$(43-3) \quad F(z) - F(x) = \int_c^z f(t)\, dt - \int_c^x f(t)\, dt$$
$$= \int_c^z f(t)\, dt + \int_x^c f(t)\, dt = \int_x^z f(t)\, dt.$$

Theorem 34-1 tells us that if a function is integrable on an interval, then it must be bounded in the interval. Thus there is a number M such that for each point $t \in I$, $-M \le f(t) \le M$. In the proof of Theorem 34-5 we showed that these inequalities imply that the number $\int_x^z f(t)\, dt$ is between $-M(z - x)$ and $M(z - x)$. Thus we have "trapped" the difference $F(z) - F(x)$ between $-M(z - x)$ and $M(z - x)$, and so it follows from Theorem 11-1 that $\lim\limits_{z \to x} [F(z) - F(x)] = 0$, as we were to show.

Figure 43-2 also shows that the derivative $F'(x)$, the slope of the graph of F, is defined at every point of $(0, 2)$, except the point 1. Furthermore, we see that $F'(x) = 0$ when x is between 0 and 1, and $F'(x) = 1$ when x is between 1 and 2. Thus, $F'(x) = f(x)$ wherever f is continuous. If you were given the graph on the right-hand side of Fig. 43-2 and were asked to make a graph showing its slope, you would draw the graph on the left-hand side of Fig. 43-2.

This behavior is typical of a function F defined by an integral, as in Equation 43-2. We have the following theorem.

Theorem 43-2. *Suppose that f is integrable on an interval I that contains a point c, and F is the function defined by the equation* $F(x) = \int_c^x f(t)\, dt$. *Then if f is continuous at a point* $x \in I$, *F is differentiable at* x, *and* $F'(x) = f(x)$.

Proof. According to the definition of the derivative, we must show that

$$\lim_{z \to x} \frac{F(z) - F(x)}{z - x} = f(x).$$

From Equation 43-3 we see that our difference quotient can be written as $\dfrac{1}{z - x} \displaystyle\int_x^z f(t)\, dt$, so we must show that for a given neighborhood $N_p f(x)$ there exists a punctured neighborhood $N_r^* x$ such that for each $z \in N_r^* x$, $\dfrac{1}{z - x} \displaystyle\int_x^z f(t)\, dt \in N_p f(x)$. Because f is continuous at x, we know that there is a neighborhood $N_r x$ such that $f(N_r x) \subseteq N_p f(x)$; let us show that $N_r^* x$ is the punctured neighborhood we seek. For suppose $z \in N_r^* x$ and $z > x$. Then $[x, z] \subseteq N_r x$, and so $f([x, z]) \subseteq N_p f(x)$. In the proof of Theorem 34-5 we showed that if $f([a, b]) \subseteq [A, B]$, then $\dfrac{1}{b - a} \displaystyle\int_a^b f(t)\, dt \in [A, B]$. This reasoning, with the interval $[x, z]$ playing the role of $[a, b]$ and the interval $N_p f(x)$ in place of $[A, B]$, gives us the inclusion $\dfrac{1}{z - x} \displaystyle\int_x^z f(t)\, dt \in N_p f(x)$. If we interchange x and z on the left-hand side of this inclusion we get the inclusion that follows from our arguments when $z < x$. But this interchange does not alter the value of the left-hand side, so we see that the inclusion holds for every $z \in N_r^* x$, and our proof is complete.

The essential content of Theorem 43-1 can be summed up in the equation

$$(43\text{-}4) \qquad D_x \int_c^x f(t)\, dt = f(x) \quad (\text{if } f \text{ is continuous at } x).$$

This equation shows us how differentiation "undoes" integration, just as integration "undoes" differentiation. Theorem 43-2 is in a sense the converse of the Fundamental Theorem of Calculus (Theorem 37-1). The Fundamental Theorem tells us that if we have an antiderivative $F(x)$ of $f(x)$, then we can evaluate integrals of f. Theorem 43-2 tells us that if we can evaluate integrals of f, then we can calculate an antiderivative $F(x)$ of $f(x)$.

Example 43-3. Find the number x for which the function F defined in the interval $[-1, 1]$ by the equation $F(x) = \displaystyle\int_{-1}^x \tan t\, dt$ takes its minimum value.

Solution. According to Theorem 43-2, $F'(x) = \tan x$. We see that $F'(x) > 0$ if $x > 0$, and $F'(x) < 0$ if $x < 0$. Therefore the point $(0, F(0))$ is a minimum point on the graph of F (see Theorem 22-1). To find the minimum *value* of F (that is, the number $F(0) = \int_{-1}^{0} \tan t \, dt$), it would be necessary for us (at the moment) to use some approximation technique such as Simpson's Rule. We would find that $F(0) \approx -.62$.

P R O B L E M S   4 3

1. Let $f(x)$ be the distance between x and the nearest prime number, for $x \in [0, 5]$. Sketch the graphs of f, f', and F, where $F(x) = \int_{0}^{x} f(t) \, dt$. How does the concavity of the graph of F show up in the graph of f'?

2. Let $F(x) = \int_{0}^{x} \sin^3 t \, dt$.

   (a) Use a graphical argument to find $F(2\pi)$.

   (b) For what numbers does F take maximum values? minimum values?

   (c) Convince yourself that $0 \le F(x) \le 2$.

   (d) In what intervals is the graph of F concave up? concave down?

3. Sketch the graph of the equation $y = \int_{0}^{x} (1 + 2[\![\cos t]\!]) \, dt$ for $x \in [0, 2\pi]$. Find the maximum and minimum points of the graph.

4. The equation $f(x) = \int_{-3}^{x} \sqrt{9 - t^2} \, dt$ defines a function f. Use the area interpretation of the integral to determine the domain and range of f.

5. Let $F(x) = \int_{x}^{c} f(u) \, du$. Show that $F'(x) = -f(x)$.

6. Find $D_x y$:

   (a) $y = \int_{3}^{x} (5^t + t^5) \, dt$ (b) $y = \int_{-7}^{x} \sqrt[4]{|\sin u|} \, du$

   (c) $y = \int_{x}^{3} (1 + r^2)^{-1} \, dr$ (d) $y = \int_{x}^{2} (3z + 1)^{12} \, dz$

7. If we incorporate Equation 43-4 into the Chain Rule, assuming that $u = g(x)$, we obtain the equation

$$D_x \int_{c}^{u} f(t) \, dt = f(u) D_x u.$$

Use this result to find $D_x y$ if:

   (a) $y = \int_{2}^{x^2} t^2 \, dt$ (b) $y = \int_{0}^{\sin x} 2^t \, dt$

   (c) $y = \int_{-x}^{0} f(t) \, dt$ (d) $y = \int_{3x+2}^{x^2} \sin t^2 \, dt$

8. Let x be a number in the interval $[-1, 1]$ and let $F(x)$ be twice the area of the region that is bounded by the semi-circle $y = \sqrt{1 - x^2}$ and the line segments joining the origin to the points $(x, \sqrt{1 - x^2})$ and $(1, 0)$.

(a) Show that $F(x) = x\sqrt{1 - x^2} + 2\int_x^1 \sqrt{1 - t^2}\, dt$.

(b) Use the equation in Part (a) to show that F is a decreasing function for $x \in [-1, 1]$.

(c) Discuss the concavity of the graph of F and sketch it.

(d) Let $S(x) = F(x) + F(-x)$. Show that $S'(x) = 0$ for $-1 < x < 1$, and hence S is a constant function. What is its value? Interpret this result geometrically.

9. Let x be a number in the interval $[1, \infty]$ and let $G(x)$ be twice the area of the region that is bounded by the hyperbola $x^2 - y^2 = 1$ and the line segments joining the origin to the points $(x, \sqrt{1 + x^2})$ and $(1, 0)$. (Notice the analogy to the function F in the preceding problem.)

(a) Show that $G(x) = x\sqrt{x^2 - 1} - 2\int_1^x \sqrt{t^2 - 1}\, dt$.

(b) Use the equation in Part (a) to show that G is a decreasing function for $x \in [1, \infty]$.

(c) Discuss the concavity of the graph of G.

10. For what numbers does the function F defined by the equation

$$F(x) = \int_0^x (2^t + 2^{1-t} - 3)\, dt$$

take maximum values? minimum values?

11. Show that

$$D_x \int_c^x f(t)\, dt = \int_c^x D_t f(t)\, dt + f(c).$$

12. Let $F(x) = \int_{-x}^x f(t)\, dt$, where f is a continuous, odd function (that is, $f(-t) = -f(t)$). Show that $F'(x) = 0$ for each number x. Then use Theorem 19-3 to see that $F(x) = 0$ for each x.

13. Let $F(x) = \int_{-x}^x f(t)\, dt$ and $G(x) = 2\int_0^x f(t)\, dt$, where f is a continuous, even function (that is, $f(-t) = f(t)$). Show that $F'(x) = G'(x)$. Does it follow that $F(x) = G(x)$?

14. Suppose that the integration formula $\int f(x)\, dx = F(x)$ is valid in an interval I in which f is continuous. Show that $D_x F(x) = f(x)$ for each $x \in I$. Could we make this assertion if we did not assume that f is continuous? (See Problem 38-10.)

44 THE FUNCTION *In*

In the last section we took up the general problem of defining functions by means of integrals; now we will turn our attention to a particular example. Instead of denoting our new function by a single letter such as F, as we did in the preceding section, we will use the two lettered symbol ln and call the function, for the moment, the "ell-en" function. As we develop its properties, the function ln will look more and more familiar, and in fact it will turn out to be a logarithmic function.

Definition 44-1. *The function* ln *is defined by the rule of correspondence,*

$$(44\text{-}1) \qquad\qquad \ln x = \int_1^x \frac{1}{t}\, dt.$$

Since $1/t$ is unbounded in any interval that contains 0, we see that the integral that defines $\ln x$ exists only in case x is a point of the interval $(0, \infty)$. *In other words, the domain of the function* ln *is the set of positive numbers.* We will find that its range is the set of all real numbers. Furthermore, it follows from Theorem 43-1 that ln is continuous at each point of the interval $(0, \infty)$.

Let us see what we can say about the values of ln. Since $\int_1^1 \frac{1}{t}\, dt = 0$, we have $\ln 1 = 0$. If $x > 1$, then $\int_1^x \frac{1}{t}\, dt > 0$, and the integral is the area of the region between the curve $y = 1/t$ and the interval $[1, x]$. On the other hand, if $x \in (0, 1)$, then $\int_1^x \frac{1}{t}\, dt = -\int_x^1 \frac{1}{t}\, dt$, and we see that the integral defining $\ln x$ is negative. This negative number is the negative of the area of the shaded region that is shown in Fig. 44-1. Thus our function ln has the following properties:

$$
\begin{aligned}
&\ln x < 0 \quad \text{if} \quad x \in (0, 1), \\
(44\text{-}2) \qquad &\ln x = 0 \quad \text{if} \quad x = 1, \quad \text{and} \\
&\ln x > 0 \quad \text{if} \quad x \in (1, \infty).
\end{aligned}
$$

We could use Simpson's Parabolic Rule, the Trapezoidal Rule, or some other method of numerical integration to calculate values of the function ln. For example, we have already found in Example 36-2 that $\ln 2 \approx .6933$. The function ln is an important function, as we shall soon see, and its values have been tabulated. Table II in the back of this book is a table of values of ln.

The function q that is defined by the equation $q(t) = 1/t$ is continuous in the interval $(0, \infty)$. Therefore, according to Theorem 43-2,

$$D_x \ln x = D_x \int_1^x \frac{1}{t}\, dt = \frac{1}{x}.$$

We now have another specific differentiation formula:

$$(44\text{-}3) \qquad\qquad D_x \ln x = \frac{1}{x}.$$

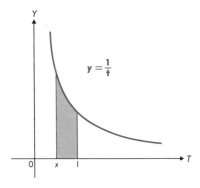

Figure 44-1   **Figure 44-2**

It follows from Equation 44-3 that

$$D_x^2 \ln x = D_x x^{-1} = -\frac{1}{x^2}.$$

Thus $D_x \ln x > 0$ and $D_x^2 \ln x < 0$ for every number in the domain of the function In. Therefore, In is an *increasing* function and its graph is *concave down* in the interval $(0, \infty)$. Using this information and some values from Table II, we can plot the graph of ln shown in Fig. 44-2.

To make Formula 44-3 apply more generally, we incorporate it into the Chain Rule equation $D_x f(u) = D_u f(u) D_x u$. When we replace $f(u)$ with $\ln u$, this equation becomes $D_x \ln u = D_u \ln u\, D_x u$, and from Equation 44-3 we see that $D_u \ln u = 1/u$. Therefore, if $u = g(x)$, we have the differentiation formula

(44-4) $$D_x \ln u = \frac{1}{u} D_x u.$$

Example 44-1.   Let a be a positive number and r a rational number.   Show that

(44-5) $$D_x \ln ax = \frac{1}{x}$$

and

(44-6) $$D_x \ln x^r = \frac{r}{x}.$$

Solution.   To verify Equation 44-5, we simply replace u with ax in Equation 44-4:

$$D_x \ln ax = \frac{1}{ax} D_x(ax) = \frac{1}{ax} \cdot a = \frac{1}{x}.$$

Similarly, to verify Equation 44-6, we replace u with x^r:

$$D_x \ln x^r = \frac{1}{x^r} D_x x^r = \frac{1}{x^r} r x^{r-1} = \frac{r}{x}.$$

We can use the results of the preceding example to show that our function ln behaves like a logarithmic function.

Theorem 44-1. *If a and b are positive numbers, and r is a rational number, then*

(44-7) $$\ln ab = \ln a + \ln b$$

and

(44-8) $$\ln a^r = r \ln a.$$

Proof. According to Definition 44-1, $\ln b = \int_1^b \frac{1}{x} \, dx$. Equation 44-5 tells us that $\ln ax$ is an antiderivative of $\frac{1}{x}$, so we can use the Fundamental Theorem of Calculus to express this integral as

$$\int_1^b \frac{1}{x} \, dx = \ln ax \Big|_1^b = \ln ab - \ln a.$$

Thus we have shown that $\ln b = \ln ab - \ln a$, which is equivalent to Equation 44-7.

Similarly, to verify Equation 44-8, we use Definition 44-1 to write

$$r \ln a = r \int_1^a \frac{1}{x} \, dx = \int_1^a \frac{r}{x} \, dx.$$

Equation 44-6 tells us that $\ln x^r$ is an antiderivative of $\frac{r}{x}$, so we can use the Fundamental Theorem to express this integral as

$$\int_1^a \frac{r}{x} \, dx = \ln x^r \Big|_1^a = \ln a^r - \ln 1.$$

But $\ln 1 = 0$, so our integral equals $\ln a^r$, and Equation 44-8 is established.

We can use Theorem 44-1 to find values of the function ln outside the range of Table II.

Example 44-2. Find ln .045.

Solution. We have

$$\ln .045 = \ln(4.5)(10)^{-2} = \ln 4.5 + \ln 10^{-2} \qquad \text{(Equation 44-7)}$$
$$= \ln 4.5 - 2\ln 10 \qquad \text{(Equation 44-8)}$$
$$= 1.5041 - 2(2.3026) \qquad \text{(Table II)}$$
$$= 1.5041 - 4.6052 = -3.1011.$$

P R O B L E M S   4 4

1. Compute ln 3 from the definition of the function ln, using $n = 4$ and (a) The Trapezoidal Rule, (b) Simpson's Parabolic Rule, and (c) The Tangent Rule (Problem 36-8). Check your results with Table II.

2. Use Theorem 44-1 and the values ln 2 $= .69$ and ln $= 1.10$ to compute the following numbers.
   (a) ln 6   (b) ln $\frac{1}{2}$ (c) ln 27   (d) ln 108   (e) ln $\sqrt[3]{12}$ (f) ln $\sqrt{6}$

3. Use Theorem 44-1 to show that for positive numbers A and B, $\ln \dfrac{A}{B} = \ln A - \ln B$.

4. Use Table II, the rules of logarithms (Theorem 44-1), and linear interpolation to calculate the following.
   (a) ln .541   (b) ln 541   (c) $\dfrac{\sqrt[3]{53.1}}{135\sqrt{.315}}$ (d) $\dfrac{1}{\sqrt{\ln 351}}$

5. If we use linear interpolation to find logarithms of numbers that lie between two numbers that are listed in Table II, do we get a number that is too large or too small? If we use Formula 25-3 as an interpolation formula, do we get a number that is too large or too small?

6. Use a graphical argument to show that ln $\frac{1}{3}$ $= -\ln 3$.

7. Find $D_x y$ if:
   (a) $y = \ln \sqrt{x} - \sqrt{\ln x}$
   (b) $y = \ln |x| - |\ln x|$
   (c) $y = \ln \sin x - \sin \ln x$
   (d) $y = \ln \dfrac{1}{x} - \dfrac{1}{\ln x}$
   (e) $y = \ln |\sec x + \tan x|$
   (f) $y = \ln (|\sec x| + |\tan x|)$.

8. Let $G(x) = \displaystyle\int_{1}^{x} \ln t \, dt$ and use Fig. 44-2 to estimate $G(2)$ and $G(\frac{1}{2})$. Check your result by using a numerical integration technique and Table II.

9. Find the mean value of the function q on the interval $[5, 10]$ if $q(x) = 1/x$.

10. In each case determine how the functions defined by the following equations are related to the function ln.

(a) $F(x) = \int_2^x \frac{1}{t}\,dt$

(b) $G(x) = \int_{1/x}^1 \frac{1}{t}\,dt$

(c) $H(x) = \int_2^x \frac{1}{t-1}\,dt$

(d) $K(x) = \int_{x^4}^{x^5} \frac{1}{t}\,dt.$

11. Show graphically that (See Problem 33-6)

$$\tfrac{1}{2} + \tfrac{1}{3} + \tfrac{1}{4} + \tfrac{1}{5} < \ln 5 < 1 + \tfrac{1}{2} + \tfrac{1}{3} + \tfrac{1}{4}.$$

12. Find the following numbers, using Table II as necessary.
(a) The area of the region that is bounded by the graphs of the following equations: $y = 1/x$, $y = 0$, $x = -10$, and $x = -7$.
(b) The volume of the solid that is obtained by rotating about the X-axis the region that is bounded by the graphs of the following equations: $y = x^{-1/2}$, $x = 1$, $x = 4$, and $y = 0$.

13. Show that, if $x > -1$, then

$$\frac{x}{x+1} \leq \ln(1+x) \leq x.$$

Use Table II to check this inequality when $x = .1$.

45   INVERSE FUNCTIONS

A function whose domain and range are sets of real numbers is a subset of R^2; that is, a collection of pairs of numbers. If we pick a number x from the domain, there corresponds a number y of the range; it is this rule of correspondence that is the heart of the function. For many important functions we can pick the number y in the range first, apply the rule of correspondence backwards, and obtain the number x in the domain. As an example, let us look at the function whose domain is the interval $(0, \infty)$, whose range is the interval $(0, 1)$, and in which a number y of the range is paired with a given number x of the domain by the equation $y = \frac{x}{1+x}$. Thus if we start with the number $x = 2$, we obtain the number $y = \frac{2}{3}$. Conversely, if we start by setting $y = \frac{2}{3}$, we can solve the equation $\frac{2}{3} = \frac{x}{1+x}$ to obtain $x = 2$. In fact, if y is any number of the interval $(0, 1)$ we can solve the equation $y = \frac{x}{1+x}$ for the number $x = \frac{y}{1-y}$ in the interval $(0, \infty)$. Thus we can interchange the roles of domain and range and still obtain a rule of correspondence. We have a new function, the *inverse* of the one we started with. In this section we want to discuss the inverses of functions in general, and then in later sections we will apply our results to the inverses of specific functions, such as the function ln and the trigonometric functions.

So suppose we have a function f whose domain and range are sets of numbers. We know that the equation $y = f(x)$ determines the number y in the range of f that corresponds to a given number x of the domain; now we want to know if this equation also determines x when y is given. If for each given y in the range of f there is just one number x in the domain such that $y = f(x)$, then we have a rule that pairs with the numbers of the range of f the numbers of its domain. We therefore have all the ingredients of a function. Since we obtained this new function by interchanging the domain and range of f and reading its rule of correspondence backwards, we naturally call this new function the inverse of f, in accordance with the following definition.

Definition 45-1. *If for each number y in the range of a function f there is exactly one number x in the domain of f such that $y = f(x)$, then f has an **inverse function** f^{-1}. The domain of f^{-1} is the range of f, and the range of f^{-1} is the domain of f. The number that corresponds to a given number y in the range of f is the number x that satisfies the equation $y = f(x)$. Thus*

$$(45\text{-}1) \qquad x = f^{-1}(y) \quad \textit{if, and only if,} \quad y = f(x).$$

If we view our given function f as a collection of pairs of numbers, it is easy to construct the set of pairs that make up the inverse function f^{-1}. We simply interchange the members of each pair of f:

$$f^{-1} = \{(y, x) \mid (x, y) \in f\}.$$

To say that for each number y in the range of f the equation $y = f(x)$ has *just one* solution x in the domain means that two different pairs in the set f^{-1} do not have the same first member, which is our criterion that a subset of R^2 should constitute a function.

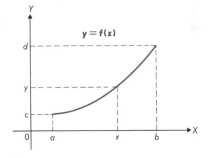

Figure 45-1

Obviously not every function has an inverse. For example, the equation $f(x) = 3$ defines a function whose domain is the entire set of real numbers and whose range is the set $\{3\}$. If we pick the number 5 in the domain, we obtain the number 3 in the range, but of course we can't go backwards. The question of whether or not a given function has an inverse has a simple graphical answer. Figure 45-1 shows the graph of a function f whose domain is the interval (a, b) and whose range is the interval (c, d). As with the graph of any function, a line parallel to the Y-axis and intersecting the X-axis in a point of the domain intersects the graph of f in just one point, which is a graphical expression of the statement that a point x of the domain determines the pair (x, y) of f. For a function with an inverse, the number y also determines this pair. Thus, lines parallel to the X-axis and intersecting the Y-axis in a point of the range also intersect the graph of f in just one point. For a function without an inverse there is at least one line parallel to the X-axis and intersecting the graph in more than one point. Horizontal lines do not intersect the graph in Fig. 45-1 more than once, so our function f has an inverse. Notice that f is an increasing function in the interval (a, b). Every increasing function has an inverse (why?). So does every decreasing function.

Example 45-1. Let f be the linear function defined by the equation $f(x) = 3x + 2$. Find the equation that defines the inverse function f^{-1}.

Solution. It is clear from the graph of f (a straight line with positive slope) that f is an increasing function in any interval and therefore has an inverse. To find the value of f^{-1} at a given number y, we must solve the equation $y = f(x)$ (that is, $y = 3x + 2$) for x. Thus we have $x = \frac{1}{3}y - \frac{2}{3}$; or in other words, $f^{-1}(y) = \frac{1}{3}y - \frac{2}{3}$. Of course, the letter that we use to denote a number in the domain of the inverse function is of no importance whatsoever, so this last equation can be rewritten $f^{-1}(u) = \frac{1}{3}u - \frac{2}{3}$, or $f^{-1}(s) = \frac{1}{3}s - \frac{2}{3}$, or even $f^{-1}(x) = \frac{1}{3}x - \frac{2}{3}$, and it will still define the same function f^{-1}.

Example 45-2. Does the sine function have an inverse?

Solution. No. The domain of the sine function is the interval $(-\infty, \infty)$, and its range is the interval $[-1, 1]$. For each number $y \in [-1, 1]$, the equation $y = \sin x$ has not just one but infinitely many solutions. Therefore, the conditions of Definition 45-1 are violated, so the sine function does not have an inverse. Later we will introduce a modification of the sine function that does have an inverse.

Suppose now that f is a function that has an inverse. Since

$$f^{-1} = \{(y, x) \mid (x, y) \in f\},$$

we see that (u, v) is a point of the graph of f^{-1} if, and only if, (v, u) is a point of the graph of f. You can easily see (Problem 28-7) that the points (u, v) and (v, u) are symmetric with respect to the line $y = x$, and so *the graph of f^{-1} is obtained by reflecting the graph of f about the line that bisects the first and third quadrants.* Figure 45-2 illustrates what we mean for the function whose

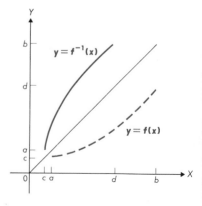

Figure 45-2

graph appears in Fig. 45-1. It is clear that if we reflect the graph of f^{-1} about the line $y = x$, we will come back to the graph of f, which is a geometric way of saying that *the inverse of the function f^{-1} is the function f*.

Suppose that u is a point in the domain of a function f that has an inverse, and v is the corresponding point in its range; that is, $v = f(u)$. Then we have $u = f^{-1}(v)$, and by replacing v with $f(u)$ we obtain the identity

$$(45\text{-}2) \qquad\qquad u = f^{-1}(f(u)),$$

which is valid for each point u in the domain of f. We can also use the pair of equations $v = f(u)$ and $u = f^{-1}(v)$ to obtain the identity

$$(45\text{-}3) \qquad\qquad v = f(f^{-1}(v)),$$

which is valid for each point v in the range of f (the domain of f^{-1}).

Example 45-3. Show how Equations 45-2 and 45-3 apply to the function that is defined by the equation $f(x) = 3x + 2$.

Solution. In Example 45-1 we saw that

$$f^{-1}(x) = \frac{x}{3} - \frac{2}{3},$$

and so

$$f^{-1}(f(u)) = \frac{f(u)}{3} - \frac{2}{3} = \frac{3u + 2}{3} - \frac{2}{3} = u.$$

Similarly,

$$f(f^{-1}(v)) = 3f^{-1}(v) + 2 = 3\left(\frac{v}{3} - \frac{2}{3}\right) + 2 = v - 2 + 2 = v.$$

We pointed out earlier that if a function f is continuous in an interval I, then its graph has no breaks in it. Reflecting a curve about a line cannot introduce breaks into a graph that doesn't already have them, so it seems reasonable to suppose that if f is continuous in I, then f^{-1} is continuous in $f(I)$. Similarly, if a graph is smooth enough so that we can draw a tangent at each point, then we should also be able to draw tangent lines to its reflection about a line. This argument suggests that the inverse of a differentiable function is also differentiable (except at points where $f'(x) = 0$). The geometric reasoning we have just used is not, of course, a mathematical proof of the conclusions we drew from it. It is relatively easy, but quite tedious, to turn this geometric argument into a proof that continuity of f implies the continuity of f^{-1}. Once we establish the continuity of f^{-1}, an argument very similar to our proof of the Chain Rule can be used to find the derivative of $f^{-1}(x)$. In Problem 45-14 we give you a hint about how this argument runs; here let us collect the essential results as a theorem whose precise proof we will omit.

Theorem 45-1. *If f is differentiable in an interval I, and $f'(x) \neq 0$ for each $x \in I$, then f^{-1} exists and is a differentiable function.*

Our theorem tells us that the derivative of $f^{-1}(x)$ exists; it doesn't tell us how to find it. Instead of calculating $D_x y$ directly from the equation $y = f^{-1}(x)$, let us apply implicit differentiation to the equivalent equation $x = f(y)$. When we differentiate both sides of this equation with respect to x, using the Chain Rule, we obtain the equation

$$1 = D_x f(y) = D_y f(y) D_x y = f'(y) D_x y.$$

Then we solve for $D_x y$, and we obtain the following important result. If $y = f^{-1}(x)$, then

$$(45\text{-}4) \qquad\qquad D_x y = \frac{1}{f'(y)}.$$

It is frequently helpful to have this equation written in different, but equivalent, forms. Thus let us replace y with $f^{-1}(x)$ to obtain the equation

$$(45\text{-}5) \qquad\qquad D_x f^{-1}(x) = \frac{1}{f'(f^{-1}(x))}.$$

Also, since $x = f(y)$, we see that $D_y x = f'(y)$, and so Equation 45-4 can be written in the symmetric form

$$(45\text{-}6) \qquad\qquad D_x y = \frac{1}{D_y x}.$$

Example 45-4. Show that Equation 45-5 yields the correct answer when $f(x) = x^3$.

Solution. The inverse of the cube function is the cube root function, so $f^{-1}(x) = x^{1/3}$. Therefore

$$D_x f^{-1}(x) = D_x x^{1/3} = \tfrac{1}{3} x^{-2/3}.$$

On the other hand, $f'(x) = 3x^2$, and when we substitute in Equation 45-5 we have

$$D_x f^{-1}(x) = \frac{1}{3(f^{-1}(x))^2} = \frac{1}{3(x^{1/3})^2} = \frac{1}{3} x^{-2/3},$$

as before.

Example 45-5. Let F be the function that is defined by the equation

$$F(x) = \int_0^x \frac{1}{1 + t^2}\, dt.$$

Show that if $y = F^{-1}(x)$, then y satisfies the differential equation $y' = 1 + y^2$.

Solution. According to Theorem 43-2, $F'(x) = 1/(1 + x^2)$. Thus we see that F is an increasing function in any interval and hence has an inverse. If we set $y = F^{-1}(x)$, we find from Equation 45-4 that $D_x y = \dfrac{1}{F'(y)} = \dfrac{1}{1/(1 + y^2)} = 1 + y^2$, as we were to show.

P R O B L E M S   4 5

1. Each of the functions defined by the following equations has an inverse. Find the equation that defines the inverse function and show how Equations 45-2 and 45-3 apply. Find $D_x f^{-1}(x)$ from your expression for $f^{-1}(x)$, and compare the result with what you get when you use Equation 45-5.

(a) $f(x) = x^3 - 1$ (b) $f(x) = \dfrac{2 - x}{3 + x}$ (c) $f(x) = \dfrac{4 - 4x}{5x + 4}$ (d) $f(x) = \dfrac{8}{x^3 + 1}$

2. Determine whether or not the function f has an inverse, and if it does, determine the domain of the inverse function.

(a) $f(x) = x^5 + 5x^3 - 23$ (b) $f(x) = \dfrac{x}{1 + |x|}$

(c) $f(x) = 3|x| + x$ (d) $f(x) = \displaystyle\int_0^x (1 + \sin^2 t)\, dt$

3. Find an example of a function whose domain is an interval I, which has an inverse, but which is neither increasing nor decreasing in I.

4. Show that if $y = F^{-1}(x)$, where $F(x) = \displaystyle\int_c^x f(t)\, dt$, then y satisfies the differential equation $y' = \dfrac{1}{f(y)}$ and the initial condition $y = c$ when $x = 0$. Use this fact to find y if it satisfies the given differential equation and the initial condition $y = 1$ when $x = 0$.

(a) $y' = \tfrac{1}{3} y^{-2}$ (b) $y' = y^4$

5. Without using calculus, show that if we interchange x and y in the equation $y = mx + b$, we obtain the equation of a line whose slope is the reciprocal of the slope of our given line. How is this fact related to Equation 45-6?

6. Under what conditions on a, b, c, and d, can you be sure that a function f defined by an equation of the form $f(x) = ax^3 + bx^2 + cx + d$ has an inverse?

7. Sketch the graph of f and of f^{-1} if $f(x) = 3(x - 2)|x - 2| + 4$.

8. Let F be the function defined in Problem 43-8. Use the equation defining F to show that $y = F^{-1}(x)$ satisfies the differential equation $y^2 + (y')^2 = 1$. Sketch the graph of F^{-1}. Do you recognize the function F^{-1}?

9. Let G be the function defined in Problem 43-9. Show that $y = G^{-1}(x)$ satisfies the differential equation $y^2 - (y')^2 = 1$.

10. The Chain Rule Equation reads $D_x z = D_y z D_x y$. If we replace z with $D_x y$, we have $D_x^2 y = D_y(D_x y)D_x y$, and in this equation we may, according to Equation 45-6, replace $D_x y$ with $\dfrac{1}{D_y x}$ and obtain $D_x^2 y = D_y\left(\dfrac{1}{D_y x}\right)D_x y$. Continue this computation and obtain the formula

$$D_x^2 y = \frac{-D_y^2 x}{(D_y x)^3}.$$

See how this formula applies if (a) $y = x^{1/5}$ (b) $y = x^3$.

11. Use the formula we developed in the preceding problem to compute $D_x^2 y$ if $y = f^{-1}(x)$ and $f(x) = x^3 + x + 2$. (You will get $D_x^2 y$ expressed in terms of y.)

12. Suppose that f^{-1} exists and that $F(x) = \displaystyle\int_0^x f(t)\,dt$. Show that

$$D_x(xf^{-1}(x) - F(f^{-1}(x))) = f^{-1}(x).$$

13. Suppose that $F(x) = \displaystyle\int_0^x \frac{1}{\sqrt{1 - t^2}}\,dt$. Use the equation in Number 10, above, to show that $y = F^{-1}(x)$ satisfies the differential equation $y'' + y = 0$. (In Section 51 we will see that $F^{-1}(x) = \sin x$.)

14. To show that f^{-1} is differentiable under the assumption that f' does not take the value 0, and after we have proved that f^{-1} is continuous, you may take g to be f^{-1}, and hence p to be the identity function, in Equation 16-7. The next steps in the proof of the Chain Rule give you an expression for the difference quotient $\dfrac{f^{-1}(z) - f^{-1}(x)}{z - x}$, and when you take the limit of this difference quotient you will obtain Equation 45-5. Work through the details of this argument.

46 THE FUNCTION *exp* AND THE NUMBER *e*

Now we will apply our knowledge of inverse functions to the function ln that we defined in Section 44 by the equation

$$\ln x = \int_1^x \frac{1}{t}\,dt \quad \text{for } x > 0.$$

Since $D_x \ln x = 1/x > 0$, we see that ln is an increasing function, and hence it has an inverse. We shall denote this inverse function by the three-lettered symbol **exp.** (The letters "exp" form an abbreviation of the work "exponent," and we will soon see why this choice is appropriate.) Thus we have

(46-1) $\qquad\qquad y = \ln x \quad \textit{if, and only if,} \quad x = \textbf{exp } y.$

From our knowledge of inverse functions in general, we see that not only is the function exp the inverse of the function ln, but ln is also the inverse of exp.

We can find some values of exp by reading Table II "backwards"; that is, from right to left. For example, since ln 8 = 2.0794, exp 2.0794 = 8. The function exp is such an important function that it is tabulated directly. You will shortly see that Table III gives values of exp.

According to our remarks in the preceding section concerning the graph of an inverse function, we need only reflect the graph of the function ln about the line that bisects the first and third quadrants to obtain the graph of the equation $y =$ exp x that is shown in Fig. 46-1. The graph of the equation $y = \ln x$ is shown as a dashed curve in that figure. From the graph of the function exp we see that:

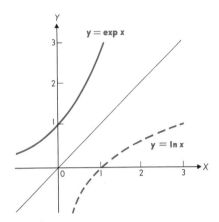

$$0 < \exp x < 1 \quad \text{if} \quad x < 0,$$
$$\exp x = 1 \quad \text{if} \quad x = 0,$$
$$\exp x > 1 \quad \text{if} \quad x > 0.$$

Figure 46-1

These relations correspond to Relations 44-2 for the function ln. Just as you should know how to sketch the graphs of the trigonometric functions, so should you know what the graphs of the functions ln and exp look like.

We have already shown that the function ln has the basic logarithmic properties:

(46-2) $$\ln ab = \ln a + \ln b,$$

and

(46-3) $$\ln a^r = r \ln a.$$

Furthermore, since the functions exp and ln are inverses of each other, we have (see Equations 45-2 and 45-3).

(46-4) $$\exp (\ln u) = u$$

for any positive number u, and

(46-5) $$\ln (\exp v) = v$$

for any number v. These equations enable us to express the logarithmic properties of ln as exponential properties of exp.

Theorem 46-1. *If x and y are any two numbers, and if r is a rational number, then*

(46-6) $\exp (x + y) = (\exp x)(\exp y),$

and

(46-7) $\exp rx = (\exp x)^r.$

Proof. We will verify Equation 46-6 and leave the verification of Equation 46-7 for the problems:

$$\exp (x + y) = \exp [\ln (\exp x) + \ln (\exp y)] \quad \text{(Eq. 46-5 applied}$$
twice, once with
$v = x$ and once
with $v = y$)

$$= \exp [\ln (\exp x \cdot \exp y)] \quad \text{(Eq. 46-2)}$$
$$= (\exp x)(\exp y) \quad \text{(Eq. 46-4 with}$$
$u = \exp x \cdot \exp y).$

Equations 46-6 and 46-7 tell us that our function exp shares certain properties with exponential functions. For instance, if r is a rational number and if the function f is defined by the equation $f(x) = 2^x$, then $f(x + y) = f(x) \cdot f(y)$ and $f(rx) = [f(x)]^r$ so that the functions f and exp both satisfy the same functional equations (Equations 46-6 and 46-7). The fact that our function exp satisfies functional equations that are also satisfied by exponential functions makes us suspect that exp is itself an exponential function. We shall now see that it is.

If we set $x = 1$ in Equation 46-7 we see that

(46-8) $\exp r = (\exp 1)^r.$

Therefore, the value of exp for the rational number r is the rth power of the number exp 1. The number exp 1 is such an important number in mathematics that we use a particular letter for it, just as we use the letter π for the number 3.14159 .... We make the following definition.

Definition 46-1.

$$\exp 1 = e.$$

From the graph in Fig. 46-1 it appears that the number e is slightly smaller than 3. It can be shown that to 5 decimal places

$$e = 2.71828 \ldots$$

Now that we have agreed to write e in place of exp 1, Equation 46-8 becomes

(46-9) $$\exp r = e^r.$$

Thus the function exp and the exponential function with base e take the same values at the rational numbers, and we are left with the question of whether or not the numbers exp a and e^a are the same for each irrational number a, too. When we try to answer this question, we discover, as we pointed out in Section 15, that we have never defined what we mean by the irrational power of a number. One good definition suggests itself now. If we want e^a to be equal to exp a, we may *define e^a to be equal to exp a for each irrational number a.*

Then we see that exp is an exponential function whose domain is the set of all real numbers. For if x is any real number, then Equation 46-9 tells us that exp $x = e^x$ if x is a rational number, and our definition of irrational powers of e tells us that exp $x = e^x$ if x is irrational. Therefore, the equation

(46-10) $$\mathbf{exp}\; x = e^x$$

is true for every real number x. Because of this equation we can write Equations 46-6 and 46-7 in the form

$$e^{x+y} = e^x e^y \quad \text{and} \quad e^{rx} = (e^x)^r.$$

These equations are two of the basic laws of exponents, so our definition of irrational powers of e does not violate these two fundamental laws.

According to Equation 46-10, we have exp $y = e^y$, so we see that Equations 46-1 can be written

$$y = \ln x \quad \textit{if, and only if,} \quad x = e^y.$$

Let us recall that the logarithm of a positive number x to a positive base $b \neq 1$ was defined in elementary mathematics as follows:

$$y = \log_b x \quad \text{if, and only if,} \quad x = b^y.$$

This definition assumes that we know what the symbol b^y means for each real number y, irrational as well as rational. We will take up this point in Section 48. If we set $b = e$, however, we have just defined what we mean by the symbol e^y for every real number y, and so we have the statement

$$y = \log_e x \quad \text{if, and only if,} \; x = e^y.$$

Thus we see that $\ln x$ and $\log_e x$ are the same number; namely, the solution to the equation $x = e^y$. Hence

$$(46\text{-}11) \qquad\qquad\qquad \ln x = \log_e x.$$

From now on we will call **ln** the **logarithmic function (with base e)** and **exp** the **exponential function (with base e).** We shall continue to use the notation $\ln x$, but many authors simply write $\log x$ for $\log_e x$. The number $\ln x$ is called the **natural logarithm of x,** and Table II is a table of natural logarithms. We will use the notation e^x more often than exp x. Table III contains some values of the exponential function with base e.

In Section 44 we found that $D_x \ln x = \dfrac{1}{x}$. We can use this formula and the differentiation rules for inverse functions that we gave in the preceding section to find $D_x e^x$. We have

$$y = e^x \quad \text{if, and only if,} \quad x = \ln y.$$

Therefore, $D_y x = \dfrac{1}{y}$, and so Equation 45-6 gives us

$$D_x y = \frac{1}{D_y x} = \frac{1}{1/y} = y.$$

In other words, we have found another specific differentiation formula,

$$(46\text{-}12) \qquad\qquad\qquad D_x e^x = e^x.$$

We might interpret Formula 46-12 by saying that e^x is "immune" to differentiation! We can incorporate this formula into our Chain Rule Equation $D_x f(u) = D_u f(u) D_x u$. Thus we set $f(u) = e^u$, where we suppose that $u = g(x)$, to obtain the equation $D_x e^u = D_u e^u D_x u$. Since $D_u e^u = e^u$, we have the differentiation formula

$$(46\text{-}13) \qquad\qquad\qquad D_x e^u = e^u D_x u.$$

Example 46-1.   Find $D_x e^{\sqrt{x}}$.

Solution.   According to Equation 46-13, with $u = \sqrt{x}$,

$$D_x e^{\sqrt{x}} = e^{\sqrt{x}} D_x \sqrt{x} = \frac{e^{\sqrt{x}}}{2\sqrt{x}}.$$

In Example 14-2 we met the differential equation $D_t P = .02P$ and were unable to solve it. Now we can.

Example 46-2.   Find P if $D_t P = .02P$ for $t \geq 0$, and $P = P_0$ when $t = 0$.

Solution.   We write $D_t P - .02P = 0$ and multiply by $e^{-.02t}$ to get

(46-14) $e^{-.02t} D_t P - .02 e^{-.02t} P = 0.$

Now we observe that

$$D_t(e^{-.02t}P) = e^{-.02t} D_t P + PD_t(e^{-.02t}) \qquad \text{(Product Rule)}$$
$$= e^{-.02t} D_t P - .02 e^{-.02t} P \qquad \text{(Equation 46-13)}$$
$$= 0 \qquad \text{(Equation 46-14).}$$

We have shown that the derivative of $e^{-.02t}P$ is 0. Thus the value of this expression does not change; its value for any t is its value at $t = 0$. In other words, for each t we have $e^{-.02t}P = e^{(-.02)0}P_0 = P_0$. This equation tells us that $P = P_0 e^{.02t}$, and so we have solved our differential problem.

PROBLEMS   46

1. Solve for x.

(a) $\displaystyle\int_1^x \frac{1}{t}\,dt = 1$ (b) $\displaystyle\int_{x^2}^{x^5} \frac{2}{t}\,dt = 54$ (c) $\displaystyle\int_5^{1/x} \frac{1}{t}\,dt = \ln 5$ (d) $\displaystyle\int_{e^{3x}}^{e^{x^2}} \frac{1}{t}\,dt = 4$

2. Use the tables in the back of the book to find the following numbers.

(a) $e^{2.35}$ (b) $\sqrt{e^{\sin 1}}$ (c) $1/e^e$ (d) $(e^{\sin \frac{1}{4}}) \cos \frac{1}{2}$

3. Verify Equation 46-7.

4. Find the maximum and minimum points, investigate the concavity, and sketch the graph of f.
(a) $f(x) = x^2 e^{-x}$ (b) $f(x) = x \ln x$

5. Find $D_x y$.
(a) $y = e^{x^2} - (e^x)^2$ (b) $y = (e^{\sin x})(\sin e^x)$
(c) $y = \exp(e^x)$ (d) $y = \ln \sqrt{e^x} - \exp(\ln \sqrt{x})$
(e) $y = \sqrt{\ln e^x} - \ln e^{\sqrt{x}}$ (f) $x = \exp(e^y)$

6. Let $f(x) = e^x - \ln x$. For what number x is the value of f a minimum? (Use Newton's Method to approximate the solution.)

7. Show that $y = e^{-x} \sin 2x$ satisfies the differential equation $y'' + 2y' + 5y = 0$.

8. (a) Show that if $y = Ae^{mx}$, then $D_x^n y = m^n y$.
(b) Find m such that $y = Ae^{mx}$ satisfies the differential equation $2y'' + 3y' - 2y = 0$.

9. Draw graphs of the equations $y = e^{-x}$ and $y = \sin x$. Use these graphs to graph the equation $y = e^{-x} \sin x$ for $x > 0$. Find the X-coordinates of the maximum points of this graph. Discuss the concavity of your graph.

10. (a) Show that $\displaystyle\int_1^2 \frac{1}{t}\,dt < 1$ and explain why you can conclude from this inequality that $e > 2$.

(b) Use an approximating sum based on 8 equal subintervals with the point x_i^* as the right endpoint of the subinterval $[x_{i-1}, x_i]$ to conclude that $\int_1^3 \frac{1}{t}\, dt > 1$, and hence $e < 3$.

11. Suppose that a certain population increases at the rate of 3% a year and reaches a figure of 1000 when $t = 0$. Use the methods of Examples 14-2 and 46-2 to find a formula for the population P at the end of t years. Use the tables in the back of the book to find the population after 10 years, and the number of years that it will take the population to double.

12. Let $A(x) = \int_0^x p(t)\, dt$, and $B(x) = \int_0^x e^{A(t)} q(t)\, dt$.

(a) Show that for any choice of the number C, $y = Ce^{-A(x)}$ satisfies the differential equation $y' + p(x)y = 0$. Find a solution to $y' - xy = 0$.

(b) Show that for any choice of the number C, $y = Ce^{-A(x)} + e^{-A(x)}B(x)$ satisfies the differential equation $y' + p(x)y = q(x)$. Find a solution to $y' - y = e^{2x}$.

47   INTEGRATION FORMULAS FOR EXPONENTS AND LOGARITHMS

In the preceding sections we developed the differentiation formulas

$$(47\text{-}1) \qquad\qquad D_x \ln u = \frac{1}{u} D_x u$$

and

$$(47\text{-}2) \qquad\qquad D_x e^u = e^u D_x u.$$

Because of the Fundamental Theorem of Calculus, differentiation formulas are always accompanied by integration formulas; these two give us the integration formulas we will introduce now.

Our first integration formula is

$$(47\text{-}3) \qquad\qquad \int e^{ax}\, dx = \frac{e^{ax}}{a} \quad (a \neq 0).$$

To verify this formula, we simply use Equation 47-2 to show that $D_x \dfrac{e^{ax}}{a} = e^{ax}$.

Example 47-1. The region that is bounded by the graph of the equation $y = e^x$, the X-axis, the Y-axis, and the line $x = 1$ is rotated about the X-axis. What is the volume of the resulting solid of revolution?

Solution. Our formula for the volume of a solid of revolution tells us that

$$V = \pi \int_0^1 y^2\, dx = \pi \int_0^1 (e^x)^2\, dx = \pi \int_0^1 e^{2x}\, dx.$$

Now we use Formula 47-3 with $a = 2$:

$$V = \pi \int_0^1 e^{2x}\, dx = \tfrac{1}{2}\pi e^{2x}\Big|_0^1 = \tfrac{1}{2}\pi(e^2 - 1) \approx 10.$$

Our next integration formula is

(47-4) $$\int \frac{1}{x}\, dx = \ln|x|.$$

To verify this formula, we replace u with $|x|$ in Equation 47-1, and we have

(47-5) $$D_x \ln|x| = \frac{1}{|x|} D_x |x| = \frac{1}{|x|} \cdot \frac{x}{|x|} = \frac{x}{x^2} = \frac{1}{x}.$$

Example 47-2. Evaluate the integral $\int_{-8}^{-4} \frac{1}{x}\, dx.$

Solution. According to Formula 47-4,

$$\int_{-8}^{-4} \frac{1}{x}\, dx = \ln|x|\,\Big|_{-8}^{-4} = \ln|-4| - \ln|-8| = \ln 4 - \ln 8$$

$$= \ln \tfrac{4}{8} = \ln \tfrac{1}{2} = -\ln 2 = -.6931.$$

(Explain the geometric significance of the negative answer.)

Our final integration formula of this section is

(47-6) $$\int \ln|x|\, dx = x \ln|x| - x.$$

To verify this formula, we must show that $D_x[x \ln|x| - x] = \ln|x|$. We have

$$D_x[x \ln|x| - x] = x D_x \ln|x| + \ln|x|\, D_x x - D_x x.$$

We have just seen that $D_x \ln|x| = \dfrac{1}{x}$, and $D_x x = 1$, so

$$D_x[x \ln|x| - x] = \frac{x}{x} + \ln|x| - 1 = \ln|x|,$$

which verifies Formula 47-6.

Usually Formulas 47-4 and 47-6 are applied in intervals in which x is positive, and in that case the absolute value signs in the formulas can be deleted.

Example 47-3. Evaluate the integral $\int_1^2 \ln x^2 \, dx$.

Solution. We do not have an integration formula in which the integrand is $\ln x^2$. However, $\ln x^2 = 2 \ln x$, so we can evaluate the given integral as follows:

$$\int_1^2 \ln x^2 \, dx = 2 \int_1^2 \ln x \, dx = 2(x \ln x - x)\Big|_1^2$$
$$= 2[(2 \ln 2 - 2) - (1 \ln 1 - 1)]$$
$$= 2[2 \ln 2 - 1] \approx .77.$$

Before we close this section, we will obtain one more formula from Equation 47-1, a limit relation that we will need in the next section.

Example 47-4. Show that $\lim\limits_{h \to 0} \dfrac{\ln (1 + h)}{h} = 1$.

Solution. If we let $f(x) = \ln x$, then we see from Equation 47-1 that $f'(1) = 1$. But the definition of a derivative tells us that

$$f'(1) = \lim_{h \to 0} \frac{\ln (1 + h) - \ln 1}{h} = \lim_{h \to 0} \frac{\ln (1 + h)}{h},$$

and so our conclusion follows.

P R O B L E M S   4 7

1. Sketch the graph of the equation $y = \ln |x|$. Draw in a few tangent lines to verify graphically that $D_x y = \dfrac{1}{x}$.

2. Use a method similar to that used in Example 47-4 to show that $\lim\limits_{h \to 0} \dfrac{e^h - 1}{h} = 1$.

3. Compute
   (a) $D_x[e^x(x - 1)]$
   (b) $D_t[-e^{-t}(2 + 2t + t^2)]$
   (c) $D_x[e^x/(1 + x)]$
   (d) $D_x(\frac{1}{2}x^2 \ln x - \frac{1}{4}x^2)$

4. Write integration formulas that "correspond to" the differentiation formulas developed in the preceding problem.

5. Evaluate the following integrals.

   (a) $\int_{-8}^{-4} \dfrac{1}{|x|} \, dx$

   (b) $\int_0^{\ln 2} e^{3t} \, dt$

   (c) $\int_0^1 [(e^{2x} + 1)^2/e^x] \, dx$

   (d) $\int_1^2 \dfrac{x^3 + x^2 + x + 1}{x^2} \, dx$

   (e) $\int_1^2 e^{\ln 2x} \, dx$

   (f) $\int_1^2 e^{-2 \ln x} \, dx$

(g) $\displaystyle\int_1^2 \ln(v^2 e^{v^2})\,dv$ (h) $\displaystyle\int_{1/2}^2 \ln x\,dx$ (i) $\displaystyle\int_{1/2}^2 |\ln x|\,dx$

(j) $\displaystyle\int_{1/2}^2 [\![\ln x]\!]\,dx$

6. Use the fact that $\ln ax = \ln a + \ln x$ to find an integration formula whose left-hand side is $\int \ln ax\,dx$.

7. Find the volume of the solid that is obtained by rotating about the X-axis the region that is bounded by the graphs of the following equations: $y = e^{-x}$, $y = 0$, $x = -\frac{1}{2}$, and $x = \frac{1}{2}$.

8. Show that $\int \ln|x|\,dx = x \ln \dfrac{|x|}{e}$.

9. Use Simpson's Rule with 4 subintervals to compute

(a) $\displaystyle\int_1^5 (\ln x)^2\,dx$ (b) $\displaystyle\int_0^2 e^{-x^2}\,dx$

10. Find the minimum value of the function f if $f(x) = e^{5x} - 20e^{2x}$.

11. Find the maximum value of the product xe^{-x} for $x > 0$.

12. Prove that the equation $e^x = 1 + x$ has only one real solution.

13. (a) Show that if $y > 0$ and n is a positive integer, then

$$n(1 - y^{-1/n}) \le \ln y \le n(y^{1/n} - 1).$$

(Hint: Consider the integrals $\displaystyle\int_1^y t^{-(1/n)-1}\,dt,\ \int_1^y t^{-1}\,dt,\ \text{and}\ \int_1^y t^{(1/n)-1}\,dt$ in case $0 < y < 1$ and in case $y \ge 1$.)

(b) Suppose that x is a given number, and set $y = e^x$ in the inequalities of Part (a). If we choose n to be a positive integer that is larger than $|x|$, show that these inequalities yield the inequalities

$$\left(1 + \frac{x}{n}\right)^n \le e^x \le \left(1 - \frac{x}{n}\right)^{-n}.$$

(c) Set $x = 1$ and $n = 5$ in the inequalities of Part (b) to show that $2.4 \le e \le 3.2$.

14. Show that if f' is an odd function, then $D_x f(|x|) = f'(x)$.

48   **EXPONENTIAL AND LOGARITHMIC FUNCTIONS
(WITH BASES OTHER THAN e)**

We defined irrational powers of e in Section 46 in terms of the expression $\exp x$. In this expression we can replace x with any real number, and when we replace x with a rational number r, we obtain e^r. Therefore, it was natural, when a is an irrational number, to *define* e^a to be the number $\exp a$. We will use this same idea to define irrational powers of an arbitrary positive number b. That is, we will start with a function f whose domain is the set of all real numbers and is such that for each rational number r we have $f(r) = b^r$. Then for each irrational number a we will *define* b^a to be the number $f(a)$. Logically, we have considerable freedom in our choice of f, but there is only one practical possibility. We want the usual laws of exponents (for example, the rule $(x^m)^n = x^{mn}$) to apply to all exponents, rational and irrational. By insisting on this rule, we restrict the possible definitions of b^a to just one. For we know (Equation 46-4) that $b = e^{\ln b}$. Therefore, however we define b^a, we will have $b^a = (e^{\ln b})^a$. Thus, in order to preserve the rule $(x^m)^n = x^{mn}$, we must have $b^a = e^{a \ln b}$, and so we will take $f(x) = e^{x \ln b}$ as the equation that defines our "generating" function f. This function f has the properties we want. Its domain is the entire set of real numbers, and for each rational number r we obtain the right answer: $f(r) = b^r$ (why?). Therefore, if a is an irrational number, we will define b^a to be the number $f(a)$ as follows.

Definition 48-1. *If b is a positive number and a is an irrational number, then*

$$(48\text{-}1) \qquad\qquad b^a = e^{a \ln b} = \exp{(a \ln b)}.$$

For example, $\pi^{\sqrt{2}} = e^{\sqrt{2} \ln \pi}$. From our table of logarithms, we find $\ln \pi \approx 1.144$, so $\sqrt{2} \ln \pi \approx 1.62$. From Table III, $e^{1.62} \approx 5.05$. Thus $\pi^{\sqrt{2}} \approx 5.05$. Notice that Equation 48-1 is true for each real number a, rational or irrational. If a is irrational, the equation is true by definition, whereas if a is rational, it is a consequence of the formulas of Section 46.

We were forced to make Definition 48-1 to keep from violating *just one* rule of exponents, and now it is natural to ask whether, with this definition, all the rules of exponents and logarithms hold. The answer is "yes," but of course it requires demonstration. For example, we must show that $\ln x^r = r \ln x$ when r is any real number. (We already know that this equation is valid if r is a *rational* number.) We have

$$\ln x^r = \ln{[\exp{(r \ln x)}]} \qquad \text{(Equation 48-1)}$$
$$= r \ln x \qquad \text{(Equation 46-5 with } v = r \ln x\text{).}$$

Furthermore, we must show that $b^a \cdot b^c = b^{a+c}$, when a and c are any real numbers. Here we have

$$b^a \cdot b^c = (e^{a \ln b})(e^{c \ln b}) \qquad \text{(Equation 48-1)}$$
$$= e^{a \ln b + c \ln b} \qquad \text{(Equation 46-6)}$$
$$= e^{(a+c) \ln b}$$
$$= b^{a+c} \qquad \text{(Equation 48-1).}$$

We will leave the proofs of the laws $(b^a)^c = b^{ac}$ and $(ab)^c = a^c b^c$ to you in the problems.

When we started the proof of the Power Formula $D_x x^r = rx^{r-1}$ in Section 15, we pointed out that its details would vary, depending on the "kind" of number r is. We have already proved this formula in case r is a rational number, and now we have the tools at hand to prove it in case r is *any* real number, rational or irrational. According to Equation 48-1,

$$x^r = e^{r \ln x}.$$

Thus we can find the derivative of x^r by setting $u = r \ln x$ in the formula $D_x e^u = e^u D_x u$. We have

$$D_x e^{r \ln x} = e^{r \ln x} D_x(r \ln x) = x^r \cdot \frac{r}{x} = rx^{r-1}.$$

Therefore, the formula

$$\boldsymbol{D_x x^r = rx^{r-1}}$$

is valid for any real number.

We have just seen how to differentiate x to a real power. Now let us consider the case in which x is the exponent.

Example 48-1. Find $D_x 10^x$.

Solution. According to Equation 48-1, $10^x = e^{x \ln 10}$. Now we use the formula $D_x e^u = e^u D_x u$ with $u = x \ln 10$ and we have

$$D_x e^{x \ln 10} = e^{x \ln 10} D_x(x \ln 10) = (\ln 10)10^x.$$

Thus

$$D_x 10^x = (\ln 10)10^x \approx (2.303)10^x.$$

We can use the method of the preceding example to derive a more general differentiation formula. If b is any positive number,

$$D_x b^x = D_x e^{x \ln b} = e^{x \ln b} D_x(x \ln b) = e^{x \ln b} \ln b = b^x \ln b.$$

Thus

(48-2)
$$\boldsymbol{D_x b^x = b^x \ln b}.$$

We incorporate this specific differentiation formula into the Chain Rule Equation $D_x f(u) = D_u f(u) D_x u$ in the usual way. Thus if $u = g(x)$, then $D_x b^u = D_u b^u D_x u$; we have just seen that $D_u b^u = b^u \ln b$, and so

(48-3)
$$\boldsymbol{D_x b^u = b^u \ln b\, D_x u}.$$

It follows from Equation 48-2 that if $b \neq 1$, then

$$D_x\left(\frac{b^x}{\ln b}\right) = \frac{1}{\ln b} D_x b^x = b^x,$$

so $\dfrac{b^x}{\ln b}$ is an antiderivative of b^x. Thus we have the integration formula

(48-4)
$$\int b^x \, dx = \frac{b^x}{\ln b} \quad (b \neq 1).$$

Example 48-2. The graph of the equation $y = 3^x$, the lines $x = -1$ and $x = 1$, and the X-axis enclose a region R. Find the volume of the solid obtained by rotating this region about the X-axis.

Solution. The volume we seek is given by the integral

$$V = \pi \int_{-1}^{1} y^2 \, dx = \pi \int_{-1}^{1} (3^x)^2 \, dx = \pi \int_{-1}^{1} 3^{2x} \, dx = \pi \int_{-1}^{1} 9^x \, dx.$$

Now Formula 48-4 (with $b = 9$) applies and we have

$$V = \frac{\pi}{\ln 9} \, 9^x \, \bigg|_{-1}^{1} = \frac{\pi}{\ln 9} \left(9 - \frac{1}{9} \right) \approx 13.$$

Now let us consider logarithmic functions with bases other than e. Suppose that b is a positive number, and let $y = \log_b x$. We wish to find $D_x y$. We first notice that, by definition,

$$y = \log_b x \quad \text{if, and only if,} \quad b^y = x.$$

From the equation $b^y = x$ it follows that $\ln b^y = \ln x$; that is, $y \ln b = \ln x$. Thus $y = \dfrac{\ln x}{\ln b}$, so that

(48-5)
$$\log_b x = \frac{\ln x}{\ln b} \, .$$

From this equation we get

$$D_x \log_b x = D_x \left(\frac{\ln x}{\ln b} \right) = \frac{1}{\ln b} \, D_x \ln x = \frac{1}{x \ln b} \, .$$

Since $\dfrac{1}{\ln b} = \log_b e$ (Equation 48-5 with $x = e$), we can write our differentiation formula as

(48-6)
$$D_x \log_b x = \frac{1}{x \ln b} = \frac{\log_b e}{x} \, .$$

When we incorporate this formula into the Chain Rule Equation, we obtain the formula

(48-7) $$D_x \log_b u = \frac{D_x u}{u \ln b} = \frac{\log_b e}{u} D_x u.$$

Example 48-3. Verify the following integration formula:

(48-8) $$\int \log_b x \, dx = x \log_b \frac{x}{e}.$$

Solution. We need only show that $\log_b x$ is the derivative of $x \log_b \dfrac{x}{e}$. We have

$$D_x \left[x \log_b \frac{x}{e} \right] = D_x (x \log_b x - x \log_b e)$$

$$= (D_x x) \log_b x + x D_x \log_b x - (D_x x) \log_b e$$

$$= \log_b x + \frac{x \log_b e}{x} - \log_b e$$

$$= \log_b x.$$

Thus we see that the Integration Formula 48-8 is valid.

Example 48-4. Find $D_x y$ if $y = x^{e^x}$.

Solution. We can write

$$y = e^{e^x \ln x} = e^u, \text{ where } u = e^x \ln x,$$

and use the formula $D_x e^u = e^u D_x u$. You may verify that

$$D_x u = e^x \ln x + \frac{e^x}{x},$$

and so we have

$$D_x y = e^u \left(e^x \ln x + \frac{e^x}{x} \right)$$

$$= y e^x \left(\ln x + \frac{1}{x} \right)$$

$$= x^{e^x} e^x \left(\ln x + \frac{1}{x} \right).$$

Example 48-5. Show that

(48-8) $$\lim_{h \to 0} (1 + h)^{1/h} = e.$$

Solution. If we let $f(h) = (1 + h)^{1/h}$, then $\ln f(h) = \dfrac{1}{h} \ln (1 + h)$. We substitute this result in the identity $f(h) = \exp (\ln f(h))$ and obtain the equation $f(h) = \exp \left(\dfrac{1}{h} \ln (1 + h) \right)$. Thus

$$\lim_{h \to 0} f(h) = \lim_{h \to 0} \exp \left(\frac{1}{h} \ln (1 + h) \right)$$

$$= \exp \left(\lim_{h \to 0} \frac{\ln (1 + h)}{h} \right) \qquad \text{(exp is a continuous function)}$$

$$= \exp 1 \qquad\qquad \text{(Example 47-4)}$$

$$= e.$$

In many books you will find the number e *defined* by Equation 48-8.

PROBLEMS 48

1. Find $D_x y$.
(a) $y = 3^{2x-1}$
(b) $x = 3^{2y-1}$
(c) $y = x^\pi \pi^x$
(d) $y = \log_3 (\ln x) - \ln (\log_3 x)$
(e) $y = 2^{5x^2} - (5x^2)^2$
(f) $y = x^x$
(g) $y = x^{\sqrt{x}}$
(h) $y = x^{x^x}$
(i) $y = \sqrt{x^x}$

2. (a) Show that $(ab)^c = a^c b^c$.
(b) Show that $(b^a)^c = b^{ac}$.

3. Compute π^e and e^π.

4. Show that $\lim\limits_{h \to 0} \dfrac{b^h - 1}{h} = \ln b$. (*Hint:* Let $f(x) = b^x$ and write out the definition of $f'(0)$.)

5. What is the minimum value of x^x (for $x > 0$)?

6. Evaluate the following integrals.

(a) $\displaystyle\int_0^1 e^\pi \, dx$
(b) $\displaystyle\int_0^1 e^{\pi x} \, dx$
(c) $\displaystyle\int_0^1 \pi^{ex} \, dx$
(d) $\displaystyle\int_0^1 x^{\pi e} \, dx$

(e) $\displaystyle\int_{-1}^1 3^{-t} \, dt$
(f) $\displaystyle\int_0^2 (2^x - x^2) \, dx$
(g) $\displaystyle\int_e^{10e} \log_{10} x \, dx$
(h) $\displaystyle\int_1^{10} \log_{10} \sqrt{xe} \, dx$

7. Let $f(x) = 4x^\pi + x^{-\pi}$ for $x > 0$. What is the minimum value of f?

8. Let $g(x) = 4\pi^x + \pi^{-x}$. What is the minimum value of g?

9. Find the mean value of f on the given interval.
(a) $f(x) = 2^x$ on $[0, 2]$
(b) $f(x) = \log_{10} x$ on $[e/10, 100e]$

10. Sketch the graph of the equation $y = (1 + x)^{1/x}$.

11. Find $D_x \log_x 3$.

12. Suppose $u = f(x)$ and $v = g(x)$, and that for each x, $f(x) > 0$. Show that

$$D_x u^v = u^v \left[\frac{v}{u} D_x u + (\ln u) D_x v \right]$$

Apply this formula to solve Example 48-4.

In Example 45-2 we pointed out that the sine function does not have an inverse. In fact, no trigonometric function does. For if f is a trigonometric function and y is a given number of its range, then to each solution of the equation $y = f(x)$ we can add 2π, 4π, -2π, and so on, and obtain other solutions. Thus the equation $y = f(x)$ does not have *just one* solution for each choice of y in the range of f, and so f does not have an inverse. But we can construct, by "restricting the domain" of the trigonometric functions, new functions that do have inverses.

We define the **Sine function** (the capital letter S distinguishes this new function from the sine function) as the function whose domain is the interval $[-\frac{1}{2}\pi, \frac{1}{2}\pi]$, and whose rule of correspondence is expressed by the equation $y = \sin x$. The colored curve in Fig. 49-1 is the graph of the Sine function. We obtain this graph simply by removing the black portion of the sine curve.

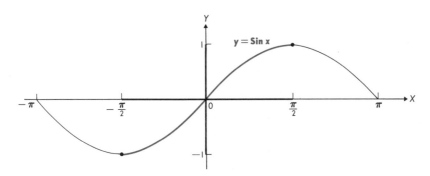

Figure 49-1

From the graph it is clear that the Sine function has an inverse; we call this inverse function the **Arcsine function**. The range of the Sine function is the interval $[-1, 1]$, so this interval serves as the domain of the Arcsine function. The number that the Arcsine function associates with a given number y of its domain is commonly denoted either by Arcsin y or by $\text{Sin}^{-1} y$. If we think of our functions as subsets of R^2, then Sine $= \{(x, y) \mid x \in [-\frac{1}{2}\pi, \frac{1}{2}\pi], y = \sin x\}$. We obtain its inverse by interchanging the numbers in each pair; that is, Arcsine $= \{(y, x) \mid x \in [-\frac{1}{2}\pi, \frac{1}{2}\pi],$ $y = \sin x\}$. Our formal definition of the Arcsine function states the conditions under which a point belongs to this set.

Definition 49-1.   *The equation*

$$x = \mathbf{Arcsin}\, y = \mathbf{Sin^{-1}}\, y$$

is equivalent to the two statements

(i) $y = \sin x$ *and*   (ii) $x \in [-\frac{1}{2}\boldsymbol{\pi}, \frac{1}{2}\boldsymbol{\pi}]$.

Example 49-1.   Find Arcsin $\frac{1}{2}$.

Solution.   We know from our study of trigonometry that $\frac{1}{2} = \sin \frac{1}{6}\pi$. Furthermore, $\frac{1}{6}\pi \in [-\frac{1}{2}\pi, \frac{1}{2}\pi]$, so both Conditions (i) and (ii) of Definition 49-1 are satisfied, and hence $\frac{1}{6}\pi = $ Arcsin $\frac{1}{2}$.

Example 49-2.   Show that $\cos (\mathrm{Sin^{-1}}\, x) = \sqrt{1 - x^2}$ for each $x \in [-1, 1]$.

Solution.   If we write $t = \mathrm{Sin^{-1}}\, x$, then according to Definition 49-1,

(i) $x = \sin t$ and   (ii) $t \in [-\frac{1}{2}\pi, \frac{1}{2}\pi]$.

We are to find $\cos t$. Now since $\cos^2 t + \sin^2 t = 1$, and since $\sin t = x$, we have $\cos^2 t = 1 - x^2$. Therefore, $\cos t = \sqrt{1 - x^2}$ or $\cos t = -\sqrt{1 - x^2}$. Because $t \in [-\frac{1}{2}\pi, \frac{1}{2}\pi]$, it follows that $\cos t \geq 0$, and so $\cos t = \sqrt{1 - x^2}$.

From our discussion of the graphs of inverse functions in Section 45, we see that we can obtain the graph of the Arcsine function by reflecting the graph of the Sine function about the line $y = x$. The resulting graph of the equation $y = \mathrm{Sin^{-1}}\, x$ is shown in Fig. 49-2. We treat the cosine function as we have just treated the sine function. We first define the **Cosine function** (again using a capital letter to distinguish this new function from the cosine function) as the function whose domain is the interval $[0, \pi]$ and whose rule of correspondence is expressed by the equation $y = \cos x$. The graph of the Cosine function is the colored curve in Fig. 49-3; it shows that the Cosine function has an inverse whose domain is the interval $[-1, 1]$. This inverse is called the **Arccosine function**, and

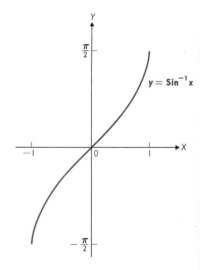

Figure 49-2

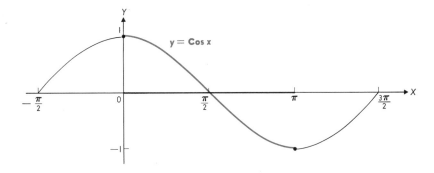

Figure 49-3

the number corresponding to a given number y in the domain of the Arc-cosine function is denoted either by Arccos y or by Cos^{-1} y. Since Cosine $=$ $\{(x, y) \mid x \in [0, \pi], y = \cos x\}$, we have Arccosine $= \{(y, x) \mid x \in [0, \pi], y = \cos x\}$. Our formal definition of the Arccosine function states the conditions under which a point belongs to this set.

Definition 49-2. *The equation*

$$x = \text{Arccos } y = \text{Cos}^{-1} y$$

is equivalent to the two statements

$$\text{(i) } y = \cos x \quad and \quad \text{(ii) } x \in [0, \pi].$$

The graph of the equation $y = \text{Cos}^{-1} x$ is shown in Fig. 49-4.

Now let us turn to the tangent function. We first restrict its domain to the interval $(-\tfrac{1}{2}\pi, \tfrac{1}{2}\pi)$, thereby obtaining a new function called the **Tangent function.** Thus Tangent $= \{(x, y) \mid x \in (-\tfrac{1}{2}\pi, \tfrac{1}{2}\pi), y = \tan x\}$. We have drawn the graph of this function in Fig. 49-5. We see that the Tangent function has an inverse whose *domain is the set of all real numbers.* This inverse function is called the **Arctangent function,** and the number that it associates with a given real number y is denoted by Arctan y or by Tan^{-1} y. From our description of the function Tangent as a subset of R^2, we obtain the equation Arctangent $= \{(y, x) \mid x \in (-\tfrac{1}{2}\pi, \tfrac{1}{2}\pi), y = \tan x\}$. Our formal definition of the Arctangent function states the conditions under which a point belongs to this set.

Definition 49-3. *The equation*

$$x = \text{Arctan } y = \text{Tan}^{-1} y$$

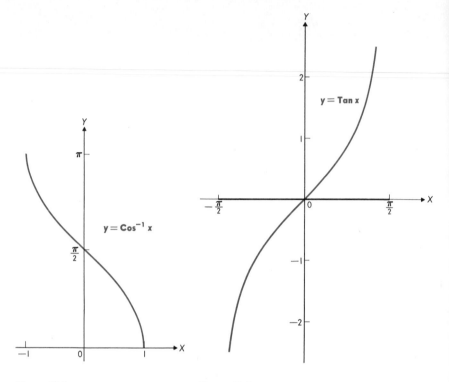

Figure 49-4   **Figure 49-5**

is equivalent to the two statements

$$\text{(i)} \quad y = \tan x \quad \text{and} \quad \text{(ii)} \quad x \in (-\tfrac{1}{2}\pi, \tfrac{1}{2}\pi).$$

We obtain the graph of the Arctangent function (Fig. 49-6) by reflecting the graph of the Tangent function about the line $y = x$. It is important that you know what this graph looks like.

Example 49-3. Calculate

$$\operatorname{Tan}^{-1} x \, \Big|_{-\sqrt{3}/3}^{\sqrt{3}/3}.$$

Solution. We have

$$\operatorname{Tan}^{-1} x \, \Big|_{-\sqrt{3}/3}^{\sqrt{3}/3} = \operatorname{Tan}^{-1}(\sqrt{3}/3) - \operatorname{Tan}^{-1}(-\sqrt{3}/3)$$

$$= \frac{\pi}{6} - \left(-\frac{\pi}{6}\right)$$

$$= \frac{\pi}{3}.$$

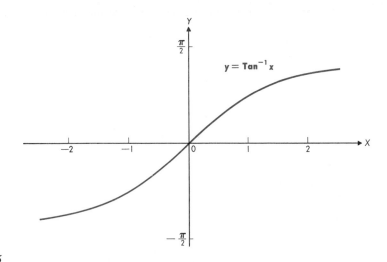

Figure 49-6

P R O B L E M S   4 9

1. Evaluate:

(a) $\operatorname{Sin}^{-1} x \Big|_{1/2}^{1}$

(b) $\operatorname{Cos}^{-1} t \Big|_{1/2}^{1}$

(c) $\operatorname{Tan}^{-1} u \Big|_{-1}^{1}$

(d) $\operatorname{Sin}^{-1} x \Big|_{-\sqrt{2}/2}^{\sqrt{3}/2}$

(e) $\operatorname{Tan}^{-1} x \Big|_{.4228}^{.6841}$

(f) $\operatorname{Sin}^{-1} (\sin x) \Big|_{\pi/2}^{3\pi/2}$

2. Verify the following equalities. (We will need results (a) and (b) in the next section.)

(a) $\sin (\operatorname{Cos}^{-1} x) = \sqrt{1 - x^2}$

(b) $\sec^2 (\operatorname{Tan}^{-1} x) = 1 + x^2$

(c) $\operatorname{Tan}^{-1} x = \operatorname{Sin}^{-1} (x/\sqrt{1 + x^2})$

(d) $\tan (\tfrac{1}{2} \operatorname{Cos}^{-1} x) = \sqrt{1 - x}/\sqrt{1 + x}$

3. Use the graphs in this section to determine which number is larger if $x > 0$.

(a) x or $\operatorname{Sin} x$

(b) x or $\operatorname{Sin}^{-1} x$

(c) $\operatorname{Tan}^{-1} x$ or $\operatorname{Sin}^{-1} x$

(d) $\exp (\operatorname{Sin} x)$ or $\exp (\operatorname{Sin}^{-1} x)$

4. From the graphs in this section determine whether the following numbers are positive or negative.

(a) $D_x \operatorname{Sin}^{-1} x$

(b) $D_x \operatorname{Cos}^{-1} x$

(c) $D_x \operatorname{Tan}^{-1} x$

(d) $D_x (\operatorname{Cos}^{-1} x)^2$

(e) $D_x (\operatorname{Sin}^{-1} x)^2$ for $x < 0$

(f) $D_x (\operatorname{Tan}^{-1} x)^2$ for $x < 0$.

5. Use the graphs of the inverse trigonometric functions to help you evaluate the following integrals.

(a) $\displaystyle\int_0^1 \text{Sin}^{-1} x \, dx$ (b) $\displaystyle\int_0^1 \text{Cos}^{-1} t \, dt$

(c) $\displaystyle\int_0^{1/2} \text{Sin}^{-1} u \, du$ (d) $\displaystyle\int_{-1}^0 \text{Cos}^{-1} u \, du$

6. Verify the following identities.
  (a) $\text{Arctan}\,(-x) = -\text{Arctan}\,x$ (b) $\text{Arcsin}\,(-x) = -\text{Arcsin}\,x$
  (c) $\text{Arccos}\,(-x) = \pi - \text{Arccos}\,x.$

7. Solve for t: $\text{Arctan}\,\frac{1}{3} + \text{Arctan}\,\frac{1}{2} = \text{Arcsin}\,t.$

8. The **Arccotangent function** is defined as follows: $x = \text{Arccot}\,y = \text{Cot}^{-1}\,y$ if, and only if, (i) $y = \cot x$ and (ii) $x \in (0, \pi)$. Show that if $x > 0$, then $\text{Arctan}\,x = \text{Arccot}\,\dfrac{1}{x}.$

9. Explain the difference, if any, between:
  (a) $\sin\,(\text{Sin}^{-1} x)$ and $\text{Sin}^{-1}\,(\sin x)$.   (b) $\text{Tan}^{-1}\,(\text{Tan}\,x)$ and $\text{Tan}\,(\text{Tan}^{-1} x)$.
  (c) $\cos\,(\text{Cos}^{-1} x)$ and $\text{Cos}^{-1}\,(\cos x)$.   (d) $\cot\,(\text{Cot}^{-1} x)$ and $\text{Cot}^{-1}\,(\cot x)$.

10. Find the point of intersection of the graphs of the Arccosine function and the Arctangent function.

11. Explain why we write $D_x \text{Sin}\,x = \cos x$, and do *not* say that $D_x \text{Sin}\,x$ is $\text{Cos}\,x$. What is $D_x \text{Cos}\,x$?

50   DIFFERENTIATION OF THE INVERSE TRIGONOMETRIC FUNCTIONS

In Section 45 we found that if $y = f^{-1}(x)$, then $D_x y = 1/f'(y)$. Now we will use this result, successively replacing f with the Sine, Cosine, and Tangent functions, to find differentiation formulas for the inverse trigonometric functions. When we take f to be the Sine function, we have $f'(y) = \cos y$, and so we see that if $y = \text{Sin}^{-1} x$, then $D_x y = 1/\cos y$. If we replace y with $\text{Sin}^{-1} x$, this last equation takes the form $D_x \text{Sin}^{-1} x = 1/\cos\,(\text{Sin}^{-1} x)$. But $\cos\,(\text{Sin}^{-1} x) = \sqrt{1 - x^2}$ (see Example 49-2), so we have derived the differentiation formula

(50-1) $$D_x \text{Sin}^{-1} x = \frac{1}{\sqrt{1 - x^2}}.$$

Let us incorporate this differentiation formula for the Arcsine function into the Chain Rule Equation $D_x f(u) = D_u f(u) D_x u$. Since $D_u \text{Sin}^{-1} u = 1/\sqrt{1 - u^2}$, replacing $f(u)$ with $\text{Sin}^{-1} u$ gives us the differentiation formula

(50-2) $$D_x \text{Sin}^{-1} u = \frac{D_x u}{\sqrt{1 - u^2}}.$$

Example 50-1. Show that if a is any positive number,

(50-3) $$D_x \operatorname{Sin}^{-1} \frac{x}{a} = \frac{1}{\sqrt{a^2 - x^2}}.$$

Solution. If we replace u with x/a in Formula 50-2, we have

$$D_x \operatorname{Sin}^{-1} \frac{x}{a} = \frac{D_x(x/a)}{\sqrt{1 - (x/a)^2}} = \frac{1}{a\sqrt{1 - (x/a)^2}} = \frac{1}{\sqrt{a^2 - x^2}}.$$

At what point did we use the assumption that a is positive?

In the differentiation rule for inverse functions, let us now replace the function f with the Cosine function. Here we have $f'(y) = -\sin y$, and so we see that if $y = \operatorname{Cos}^{-1} x$, then $D_x y = -1/\sin y$. When we replace y with $\operatorname{Cos}^{-1} x$, this last equation takes the form $D_x \operatorname{Cos}^{-1} x = -1/\sin(\operatorname{Cos}^{-1} x)$. It is easy to show (Problem 49-2a) that $\sin(\operatorname{Cos}^{-1} x) = \sqrt{1 - x^2}$, so we have derived the formula

(50-4) $$D_x \operatorname{Cos}^{-1} x = -\frac{1}{\sqrt{1 - x^2}}.$$

When we incorporate this formula into the Chain Rule Equation, we obtain the differentiation formula

(50-5) $$D_x \operatorname{Cos}^{-1} u = -\frac{D_x u}{\sqrt{1 - u^2}}.$$

Example 50-2. From Equations 50-1 and 50-4 we see that $D_x \operatorname{Cos}^{-1} x = -D_x \operatorname{Sin}^{-1} x$. Does this equation imply that $\operatorname{Cos}^{-1} x$ is merely the negative of $\operatorname{Sin}^{-1} x$?

Solution. No; $\operatorname{Cos}^{-1} x$ and $-\operatorname{Sin}^{-1} x$ have the same derivative, but as we know from Theorem 19-6 this fact merely implies that there is a number c such that

$$\operatorname{Cos}^{-1} x = -\operatorname{Sin}^{-1} x + c \quad \text{for each } x \in [-1, 1].$$

To find c, we will set $x = 0$. Thus $\operatorname{Cos}^{-1} 0 = -\operatorname{Sin}^{-1} 0 + c$. But we know (see Figs. 49-2 and 49-4, for instance) that $\operatorname{Cos}^{-1} 0 = \pi/2$ and $\operatorname{Sin}^{-1} 0 = 0$. Hence $c = \pi/2$, and so we see that $\operatorname{Cos}^{-1} x = \frac{1}{2}\pi - \operatorname{Sin}^{-1} x$ for each $x \in [-1, 1]$. You can also verify this equation by referring to the definitions of the Arccosine and Arcsine functions.

Finally, in the differentiation rule for inverse functions we will replace f with the Tangent function. Here we have $f'(y) = \sec^2 y$, and so we see that if $y = \operatorname{Tan}^{-1} x$, then $D_x y = 1/\sec^2 y$. When we replace y with $\operatorname{Tan}^{-1} x$, this last equation takes the form $D_x \operatorname{Tan}^{-1} x = 1/\sec^2(\operatorname{Tan}^{-1} x)$. In Problem 49-2b we asked you to show that $\sec^2 (\text{Tan}^{-1} x) = 1 + x^2$, and when we make use of this fact, our differentiation formula becomes

$$(50\text{-}6) \qquad\qquad D_x \text{Tan}^{-1} x = \frac{1}{1 + x^2}.$$

Now we incorporate this formula into the Chain Rule Equation, and we obtain the differentiation formula

$$(50\text{-}7) \qquad\qquad D_x \text{Tan}^{-1} u = \frac{D_x u}{1 + u^2}.$$

Example 50-3. Show that if $a \neq 0$, then

$$(50\text{-}8) \qquad\qquad D_x \text{Tan}^{-1} \frac{x}{a} = \frac{a}{a^2 + x^2}.$$

Solution. When we replace u with x/a, Formula 50-7 becomes

$$D_x \text{Tan}^{-1} \frac{x}{a} = \frac{1/a}{1 + (x/a)^2} = \frac{a}{a^2 + x^2}.$$

Example 50-4. Find $D_x[\text{Tan}^{-1} (\cot x)]$.

Solution. If we replace u with $\cot x$, Formula 50-7 becomes

$$D_x[\text{Tan}^{-1} (\cot x)] = \frac{D_x \cot x}{1 + \cot^2 x} = \frac{-\csc^2 x}{1 + \cot^2 x}.$$

Now we use the trigonometric identity $1 + \cot^2 x = \csc^2 x$, and we see that

$$D_x[\text{Tan}^{-1} (\cot x)] = -1.$$

It would be a good test of your understanding of the trigonometric functions and the inverse trigonometric functions to verify that the graph of the equation $y = \text{Tan}^{-1} (\cot x)$ is the one shown in Fig. 50-1.

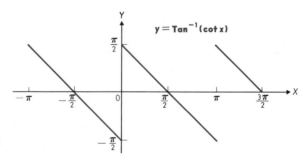

Figure 50-1

Example 50-5. A searchlight 40 feet from the base of a building makes a spot 30 feet up on the side of the building. Approximately how much must the searchlight be rotated in order to raise the spot 1 foot?

Solution. Fig. 50-2 illustrates the situation; we are to find the number α. From elementary trigonometry we see that

$$\tan(\theta + \alpha) = \tfrac{31}{40}$$

and

$$\tan\theta = \tfrac{3}{4},$$

so

$$\alpha = (\theta + \alpha) - \theta$$

$$= \text{Tan}^{-1}\tfrac{31}{40} - \text{Tan}^{-1}\tfrac{3}{4}.$$

Now we will set $f(x) = \text{Tan}^{-1}\dfrac{x}{40}$, and so our solution α can be expressed as

$$\alpha = f(31) - f(30).$$

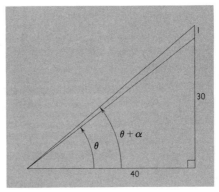

Figure 50-2

According to Formula 25-3, this difference is approximated by the formula

$$f(31) - f(30) \approx f'(30)(31 - 30) = f'(30),$$

so let us calculate $f'(30)$. When we set $a = 40$ in Equation 50-8, we find that $f'(x) = 40/(40^2 + x^2)$, and hence $f'(30) = 40/(40^2 + 30^2) \approx .016$. Therefore, the searchlight must be rotated upward approximately .016 radians, or .9°.

P R O B L E M S   5 0

1. Find $D_x y$.
  (a) $y = \text{Arctan } x^2 - (\text{Arctan } x)^2$ (b) $y = \sqrt{\text{Sin}^{-1} x} - \text{Sin}^{-1}\sqrt{x}$
  (c) $y = \text{Cos}^{-1} e^x$ (d) $y = \text{Sin}^{-1} x - (\text{Sin } x)^{-1}$
  (e) $y = \ln(\text{Cos}^{-1} x)$ (f) $y = \text{Tan}^{-1} e^{-x^2}$
  (g) $y = \text{Sin}^{-1}(\cos x) - \cos(\text{Sin}^{-1} x)$ (h) $y = (\text{Tan}^{-1} x^{-1})^{-1}$

2. Use implicit differentiation to calculate $D_x y$ from the equation given.
  (a) $\text{Sin}^{-1} x + \text{Sin}^{-1} y = \pi/2$ (b) $\text{Tan}^{-1} x + \text{Tan}^{-1} y = \pi/2$
  (c) $\text{Sin}^{-1} x + \text{Tan}^{-1} y = 0$.

3. Compute $D_x y$ and sketch the graph of the equation.
  (a) $y = \text{Sin}^{-1}(\sin x)$ (b) $y = \sin(\text{Sin}^{-1} x)$
  (c) $y = \text{Cos}^{-1}(\cos x)$ (d) $y = \text{Tan}^{-1}(\tan x)$

4. Verify the following identities. Would they still be true if we "canceled" the symbol D_x?

(a) $D_x \operatorname{Sin}^{-1}(-x) = -D_x \operatorname{Sin}^{-1} x$

(b) $D_x \operatorname{Cos}^{-1}(-x) = -D_x \operatorname{Cos}^{-1} x$

(c) $D_x \operatorname{Tan}^{-1}\left(\dfrac{2x}{1 - x^2}\right) = D_x(2 \operatorname{Tan}^{-1} x)$

(d) $D_x \operatorname{Cos}^{-1} \dfrac{\sqrt{1 - x^2} - x\sqrt{3}}{2} = D_x \operatorname{Sin}^{-1} x$

5. Let $y = \operatorname{Sin}^{-1}(\cos x) + \operatorname{Cos}^{-1}(\sin x)$. Find $D_x y$ and sketch the graph of the equation for $x \in [0, 2\pi]$.

6. What is the relation between $D_x \operatorname{Arctan} \dfrac{1}{x}$ and $D_x \operatorname{Arctan} x$? Use this result to find the relation between $\operatorname{Arctan} \dfrac{1}{x}$ and $\operatorname{Arctan} x$. (You will want to look at the case $x > 0$ and the case $x < 0$ separately.)

7. A statue 7 feet high is placed on a pedestal so that the base of the statue is 9 feet above your eye level. How far back should you stand from the base of the statue in order to get the "best" view?

8. Two guy wires are to be fastened at the same point P which is h feet up a pole. The wires and the pole are in the same vertical plane, and one wire is to be fastened to the ground at a point x feet from the base of the pole and the other to a point on the same side of the pole and $2x$ feet from its base. Determine x so that the angle between the wires at the point P is a maximum.

9. Find: $\lim\limits_{h \to 0} \dfrac{\operatorname{Sin}^{-1} h}{h}$. (Write out the definition of $f'(0)$ if $f(x) = \operatorname{Sin}^{-1} x$.)

10. Use the graph of the Arcsine function to show that:

$$\int_0^x \operatorname{Sin}^{-1} t\, dt = x \operatorname{Sin}^{-1} x - \int_0^{\operatorname{Sin}^{-1} x} \sin t\, dt$$

$$= x \operatorname{Sin}^{-1} x + \cos(\operatorname{Sin}^{-1} x) - 1$$

$$= x \operatorname{Sin}^{-1} x + \sqrt{1 - x^2} - 1.$$

Verify this equation by differentiation.

11. Use calculus to help you sketch the graph of the equation $y = \operatorname{Arcsin}(\cos x)$.

12. Let $F(x) = \displaystyle\int_0^x \operatorname{Tan}^{-1}(\cot t)\, dt$ (see Fig. 50-1).

(a) Sketch the graph of F.   (b) Evaluate the integral $\displaystyle\int_{-10\pi}^{10\pi} F(x)\, dx$.

13. Let F be the function defined in Problem 43-8. Prove that $F(x) = \operatorname{Cos}^{-1} x$. (Hint: First show that $F'(x) = D_x \operatorname{Cos}^{-1} x$.) Check your work in Problem 45-8 now!

51   INTEGRATION FORMULAS THAT INVOLVE INVERSE TRIGONOMETRIC FUNCTIONS

According to the Fundamental Theorem of Calculus, we can write an integration formula $\int f(x)\,dx = F(x)$ for each differentiation formula $D_x F(x) = f(x)$. Thus the Differentiation Formulas 50-3 and 50-8 lead to the integration formulas

$$(51\text{-}1) \qquad \int \frac{1}{\sqrt{a^2 - x^2}}\,dx = \operatorname{Sin}^{-1} \frac{x}{a} \qquad (a > 0)$$

and

$$(51\text{-}2) \qquad \int \frac{1}{a^2 + x^2}\,dx = \frac{1}{a}\operatorname{Tan}^{-1} \frac{x}{a} \qquad (a \neq 0).$$

Notice that there is a factor $\dfrac{1}{a}$ on the right-hand side of Formula 51-2 that is not present in Formula 51-1 and that we require a to be positive in Formula 51-1 but not in Formula 51-2.

Example 51-1.   Evaluate the integral

$$\int_{-3}^{3} \frac{1}{\sqrt{12 - x^2}}\,dx.$$

Solution.   We may use Formula 51-1 with $a = \sqrt{12} = 2\sqrt{3}$ to find that

$$\int_{-3}^{3} \frac{1}{\sqrt{12 - x^2}}\,dx = \operatorname{Sin}^{-1} \frac{x}{2\sqrt{3}} \Big|_{-3}^{3} = \operatorname{Sin}^{-1} \frac{\sqrt{3}}{2} - \operatorname{Sin}^{-1}\left(-\frac{\sqrt{3}}{2}\right)$$

$$= \frac{\pi}{3} - \left(-\frac{\pi}{3}\right) = \frac{2\pi}{3}.$$

Example 51-2.   Use Simpson's Rule with $n = 4$ to find π from the equation

$$(51\text{-}3) \qquad \frac{\pi}{4} = \int_{0}^{1} \frac{1}{1 + x^2}\,dx.$$

Solution.   First, let us use Formula 51-2 to verify that Equation 51-3 is correct:

$$\int_{0}^{1} \frac{1}{1 + x^2}\,dx = \operatorname{Tan}^{-1} x \Big|_{0}^{1} = \frac{\pi}{4} - 0 = \frac{\pi}{4}.$$

Now we will approximate the integral by Simpson's Rule. We partition the interval $[0, 1]$ into four subintervals by the points $x_0 = 0$, $x_1 = \frac{1}{4}$, $x_2 = \frac{1}{2}$, $x_3 = \frac{3}{4}$, and $x_4 = 1$. The corresponding numbers obtained from the equation $y = 1/(1 + x^2)$ are $y_0 = 1$, $y_1 = \frac{16}{17}$, $y_2 = \frac{4}{5}$, $y_3 = \frac{16}{25}$, and $y_4 = \frac{1}{2}$. In this case, $h = \frac{1}{4}$, and

Simpson's Rule gives us

$$\tfrac{1}{4}\pi \approx \tfrac{1}{12}[1 + 4(\tfrac{16}{17}) + 2(\tfrac{4}{5}) + 4(\tfrac{16}{25}) + \tfrac{1}{2}] = .785392.$$

Hence $\pi \approx 3.14157$. Since the value of π, correct to 5 decimal places, is 3.14159, we see that our approximation is a good one.

Example 51-3. Verify the following integration formula:

$$(51\text{-}4)\qquad \int \sqrt{a^2 - x^2}\, dx = \frac{1}{2}\left[x\sqrt{a^2 - x^2} + a^2\,\text{Sin}^{-1}\frac{x}{a}\right]\qquad (a > 0).$$

Solution. To verify an integration formula, we must differentiate the expression on the right-hand side and obtain the integrand. We first differentiate $x\sqrt{a^2 - x^2}$:

$$
\begin{aligned}
D_x(x\sqrt{a^2 - x^2}) &= (D_x x)\sqrt{a^2 - x^2} + x D_x\sqrt{a^2 - x^2} \\
&= \sqrt{a^2 - x^2} - x^2/\sqrt{a^2 - x^2} \\
&= (a^2 - 2x^2)/\sqrt{a^2 - x^2}.
\end{aligned}
$$

From Formula 50-3 we see that

$$D_x[a^2\,\text{Sin}^{-1}(x/a)] = a^2/\sqrt{a^2 - x^2}.$$

Thus

$$D_x\frac{1}{2}\left[x\sqrt{a^2 - x^2} + a^2\,\text{Sin}^{-1}\frac{x}{a}\right] = \frac{1}{2}\left(\frac{a^2 - 2x^2}{\sqrt{a^2 - x^2}} + \frac{a^2}{\sqrt{a^2 - x^2}}\right)$$
$$= \sqrt{a^2 - x^2},$$

and Formula 51-4 is verified.

Example 51-4. Derive a formula for the area of the smaller region cut from a circle whose radius is r by a chord s units from the center of the circle.

Solution. Let us choose our circle with the origin as its center so that its equation is $x^2 + y^2 = r^2$. Then we will choose our chord to lie along the line $x = s$, where $s > 0$ (see Fig. 51-1). In view of the symmetry of the circle, we see that the area we are seeking is given by the equation

$$A = 2\int_s^r \sqrt{r^2 - x^2}\, dx\,.$$

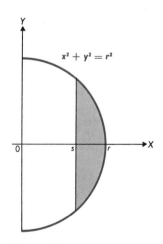

Figure 51-1

We use Formula 51-4 to evaluate the integral:

$$A = \left[x\sqrt{r^2 - x^2} + r^2 \operatorname{Sin}^{-1} \frac{x}{r} \right]\Big|_{s}^{r}$$

$$= r^2 \operatorname{Sin}^{-1} 1 - s\sqrt{r^2 - s^2} - r^2 \operatorname{Sin}^{-1} \frac{s}{r}$$

$$= \frac{\pi r^2}{2} - s\sqrt{r^2 - s^2} - r^2 \operatorname{Sin}^{-1} \frac{s}{r}.$$

P R O B L E M S   5 1

1. Find the area of the region that is bounded by the circle $x^2 + y^2 = 25$ and the lines $x = -3$ and $x = 4$.

2. Find the area of the region under the curve $y = 10/(9 + x^2)$ and above the interval $[-\sqrt{3}, \sqrt{3}]$.

3. Find the mean value of the function f on the indicated interval.
   (a) $f(x) = 3/\sqrt{12 - x^2}$, $[-3, 3]$ (b) $f(x) = 5/\sqrt{8 - x^2}$, $[0, 2]$
   (c) $f(x) = 7/(3 + x^2)$, $[-1, 1]$ (d) $f(x) = 7/(3 + x^2)$, $[0, 3]$
   (e) $f(x) = 1/(4 + x^2)$, $[-1, 1]$

4. Let x be a number in the interval $(0, \pi/2)$. Compute:

   (a) $\displaystyle\int_{\sin x}^{\cos x} \frac{1}{\sqrt{1 - t^2}}\, dt$ (b) $\displaystyle\int_{\cot x}^{\tan x} \frac{1}{1 + t^2}\, dt$

5. Show that for any numbers a and b the area of the region bounded by the graph of the equation $y = 1/(1 + x^2)$, the X-axis, and the lines $x = a$ and $x = b$ is less than π.

6. The region bounded by the graph of the equation $y = 1/\sqrt{1 + x^2}$, the line $x = 1$, and the coordinate axes is rotated about the X-axis. What is the volume of the resulting solid of revolution?

7. Find the area of the region interior to the ellipse $x^2/16 + y^2/9 = 1$ and to the right of the line $x = 2$.

8. The equation $f(x) = 1/\sqrt{1 - x^2}$ defines a function f such that if b is a number between 0 and 1 but "close" to 1, then $f(b)$ is a large number. Show that the mean value of f on the interval $[0, b]$ is a number close to $\pi/2$.

9. Draw the graph of the equation $y = 1/\sqrt[4]{1 - x^2}$. The region bounded by this graph, the X-axis, and the lines $x = a$ and $x = b$, where $-1 < a < b < 1$, is rotated about the X-axis. Show that the volume of the solid obtained is less than π^2.

10. The region bounded by the graph of the equation $x\sqrt{4 + y^2} = 1$, the coordinate axes, and the line $y = 100$ is rotated about the Y-axis. Find, approximately, the volume of the solid thus obtained.

52 THE HYPERBOLIC FUNCTIONS

Certain combinations of e^x and e^{-x} occur so often in mathematical applications that they are used to define new functions. The **hyperbolic cosine** function and the **hyperbolic sine** function are defined by the equations

(52-1) $$\cosh x = \frac{e^x + e^{-x}}{2}$$

and

(52-2) $$\sinh x = \frac{e^x - e^{-x}}{2}.$$

These functions are called "hyperbolic" functions because their values are related to the coordinates of the points of a hyperbola in somewhat the same way that the values of the trigonometric functions are related to the coordinates of points of a circle. We won't go into the details of this relationship, but the following example will give you the essential idea. (Also see Problems 43-8, 43-9, 50-13, and 53-9.)

Example 52-1.   Show that for any number t

(52-3) $$\cosh^2 t - \sinh^2 t = 1.$$

Solution.   According to our definitions of the hyperbolic functions,

$$\cosh^2 t - \sinh^2 t = \left(\frac{e^t + e^{-t}}{2}\right)^2 - \left(\frac{e^t - e^{-t}}{2}\right)^2.$$

It is a matter of simple algebra to expand the terms on the right-hand side of this equation and see that the resulting number is 1. Equation 52-3 tells us that the point $(\cosh t, \sinh t)$ belongs to the hyperbola $x^2 - y^2 = 1$, just as the point $(\cos t, \sin t)$ belongs to the circle $x^2 + y^2 = 1$.

The remaining hyperbolic functions can be defined in terms of the hyperbolic sine and cosine functions as follows:

(52-4) $$\tanh x = \frac{\sinh x}{\cosh x} = \frac{e^x - e^{-x}}{e^x + e^{-x}}$$

(52-5) $$\coth x = \frac{1}{\tanh x} = \frac{e^x + e^{-x}}{e^x - e^{-x}}$$

(52-6) $$\operatorname{sech} x = \frac{1}{\cosh x} = \frac{2}{e^x + e^{-x}}$$

(52-7) $$\operatorname{csch} x = \frac{1}{\sinh x} = \frac{2}{e^x - e^{-x}}.$$

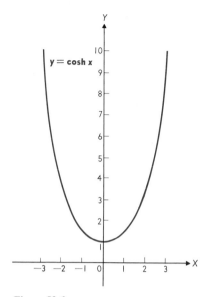

Figure 52-1

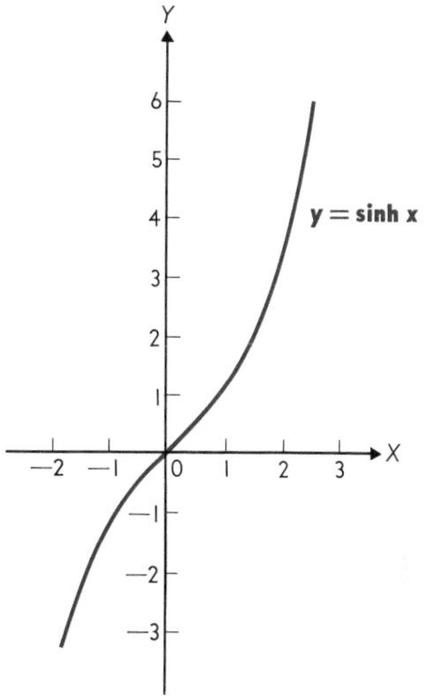

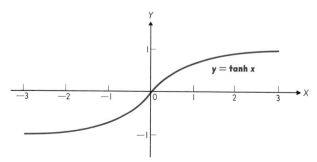

Figure 52-2

Figures 52-1, 52-2, and 52-3 show the graphs of the hyperbolic cosine, sine, and tangent functions. These functions are tabulated in Table III.

The values of the hyperbolic functions satisfy many identities similar to those satisfied by the trigonometric functions. In addition to Equation 52-3, which is a fundamental identity, we have:

(52-8) $1 - \tanh^2 x = \operatorname{sech}^2 x,$

(52-9) $\coth^2 x - 1 = \operatorname{csch}^2 x,$

(52-10) $\sinh (u + v) = \sinh u \cosh v + \cosh u \sinh v,$

(52-11) $\cosh (u + v) = \cosh u \cosh v + \sinh u \sinh v.$

These identities can be verified by straightforward algebraic manipulation.

Figure 52-3

Example 52-2. Find expressions for sinh $2x$ and cosh $2x$.

Solution. By setting $u = x$ and $v = x$ in Equations 52-10 and 52-11, we obtain the equations

(52-12) $$\textbf{sinh } 2x = 2 \textbf{ sinh } x \textbf{ cosh } x.$$

and

(52-13) $$\textbf{cosh } 2x = \textbf{cosh}^2\, x + \textbf{sinh}^2\, x.$$

To find the derivatives of cosh x, sinh x, tanh x, and so on, we make use of our defining equations. For example,

$$D_x \cosh x = D_x\left(\frac{e^x + e^{-x}}{2}\right) = \frac{D_x e^x + D_x e^{-x}}{2}$$

$$= \frac{e^x - e^{-x}}{2} = \sinh x.$$

Thus we find that

(52-14) $$\textbf{\textit{D}}_x \textbf{ cosh } x = \textbf{sinh } x.$$

When we incorporate this differentiation formula into the Chain Rule Equation $D_x f(u) = D_u f(u) D_x u$ we obtain the formula

(52-15) $$\textbf{\textit{D}}_x \textbf{ cosh } u = \textbf{sinh } u \, \textbf{\textit{D}}_x u.$$

We will leave to you, in the problems at the end of this section, the verification of the following differentiation formulas:

(52-16) $$\textbf{\textit{D}}_x \textbf{ sinh } u = \textbf{cosh } u \, \textbf{\textit{D}}_x u,$$
(52-17) $$\textbf{\textit{D}}_x \textbf{ tanh } u = \textbf{sech}^2\, u \, \textbf{\textit{D}}_x u,$$
(52-18) $$\textbf{\textit{D}}_x \textbf{ coth } u = -\textbf{csch}^2\, u \, \textbf{\textit{D}}_x u,$$
(52-19) $$\textbf{\textit{D}}_x \textbf{ sech } u = -\textbf{sech } u \textbf{ tanh } u \, \textbf{\textit{D}}_x u,$$
(52-20) $$\textbf{\textit{D}}_x \textbf{ csch } u = -\textbf{csch } u \textbf{ coth } u \, \textbf{\textit{D}}_x u.$$

Example 52-3. Compute $D_x \ln (\cosh x)$.

Solution. In the differentiation formula for the function ln, $D_x \ln u = \dfrac{D_x u}{u}$, we replace u with cosh x and use Formula 52-14:

$$D_x \ln (\cosh x) = \frac{D_x \cosh x}{\cosh x} = \frac{\sinh x}{\cosh x}.$$

Thus we obtain the formula

(52-21) $$D_x \ln (\cosh x) = \tanh x.$$

Example 52-4. Show that if

$$y = A \sinh kx + B \cosh kx,$$

then y satisfies the differential equation $y'' - k^2 y = 0$.

Solution. From Formulas 52-15 and 52-16, with $u = kx$, we see that

$$y' = Ak \cosh kx + Bk \sinh kx$$

and

$$y'' = Ak^2 \sinh kx + Bk^2 \cosh kx.$$

Thus

$$y'' = k^2 y, \text{ or in other words, } y'' - k^2 y = 0.$$

Example 52-5. Show that the graph of the function defined by the equation

$$y = 8 \sinh x - 17 \cosh x$$

is concave down everywhere, and find the maximum value of the function.

Solution. We have

$$y' = 8 \cosh x - 17 \sinh x$$

and

$$y'' = 8 \sinh x - 17 \cosh x.$$

To show that our graph is concave down, we will show that $y'' < 0$; that is, that $8 \sinh x < 17 \cosh x$. This last inequality is equivalent to the inequality $\tanh x < \frac{17}{8}$, which is clearly true since (see Fig. 52-3) $\tanh x \leq 1$. At the maximum point of the graph, $y' = 0$; that is,

$$8 \cosh x = 17 \sinh x.$$

This equation is equivalent to the equation $\tanh x = \frac{8}{17}$, and we see from Fig. 52-3 that its solution is a number x_0 approximately equal to .5. The maximum value of our function is therefore

$$y_0 = 8 \sinh x_0 - 17 \cosh x_0,$$

and we will now proceed to calculate this number. First of all, $\tanh x_0 = \frac{8}{17}$, and therefore it follows from Equations 52-6 and 52-8 that $\cosh x_0 = \frac{17}{15}$. Now we have

$$y_0 = 8 \sinh x_0 - 17 \cosh x_0$$
$$= \cosh x_0 (8 \tanh x_0 - 17)$$
$$= \tfrac{17}{15}[8(\tfrac{8}{17}) - 17] = -15.$$

Corresponding to each of the differentiation formulas for the hyperbolic functions is an integration formula. Thus, corresponding to Formula 52-14 is the integration formula

(52-22) $\int \sinh x \ dx = \cosh x.$

Similarly, corresponding to the other differentiation formulas (with $u = x$) are the following integration formulas:

(52-23) $\int \cosh x \ dx = \sinh x,$

(52-24) $\int \text{sech}^2 x \ dx = \tanh x,$

(52-25) $\int \text{csch}^2 x \ dx = -\coth x,$

(52-26) $\int \text{sech } x \tanh x \ dx = -\text{sech } x,$

(52-27) $\int \text{csch } x \coth x \ dx = -\text{csch } x.$

Example 52-6. Find the area of the region in the first quadrant that is bounded by the graph of the equation $y = \cosh x$ and the line $x = 1$.

Solution. We are to find the area of the shaded region in Fig. 52-4, and therefore we must evaluate the integral $\int_0^1 \cosh x \ dx$.

Using Integration Formula 52-23,

$$\int_0^1 \cosh x \ dx = \sinh x \ \Big|_0^1$$
$$= \sinh 1 - \sinh 0$$
$$= 1.1752$$

We can immediately state another integration formula from the Differentiation Formula 52-21 that we found in Example 52-3:

(52-28) $\int \tanh x \ dx = \ln (\cosh x).$

We will leave the verification of the following integration formula for the problems:

(52-29) $\int \coth x \ dx = \ln |\sinh x \cdot|.$

P R O B L E M S   5 2

1. Show that:
(a) $\sinh (u - v) = \sinh u \cosh v - \cosh u \sinh v$.
(b) $\cosh (u - v) = \cosh u \cosh v - \sinh u \sinh v$.
(c) $\tanh (u + v) = (\tanh u + \tanh v)/(1 + \tanh u \tanh v)$

2. (a) Verify Formula 52-16.   (b) Verify Formula 52-17.
(c) Verify Formula 52-18.   (d) Verify Formula 52-19.
(e) Verify Formula 52-20.

3. Find $D_x y$.
(a) $y = \cosh e^x - e^{\cosh x}$ (b) $y = \sinh^2 x - \sinh x^2$
(c) $y = \ln (\operatorname{csch} x) - \ln (\operatorname{sech} x)$ (d) $y = \operatorname{csch} (\ln x) - \operatorname{sech} (\ln x)$
(e) $y = \sin (\cosh x) - \cos (\sinh x)$ (f) $y = \operatorname{sech} x \operatorname{csch} x$

4. (a) If $a \neq 0$, show that $\int \sinh ax\, dx = \dfrac{1}{a} \cosh ax$ and $\int \cosh ax\, dx = \dfrac{1}{a} \sinh ax$.

(b) Use the results of Part (a) and suitable identities to find integration formulas whose left-hand members are $\int \cosh^2 x\, dx$ and $\int \sinh x \cosh x\, dx$.
(c) Use the results of Part (b) to find the volume of the solid that is generated by rotating the region of Example 52-6 about the X-axis.

5. Show that for each number u, $\cosh u + \sinh u = e^u$. Use this fact to verify the identity

$$(\cosh x + \sinh x)^n = \cosh nx + \sinh nx.$$

6. Show that if $y = e^{ax} \sinh bx$, then y satisfies the differential equation $y'' - 2ay' + (a^2 - b^2)y = 0$.

7. Verify Formula 52-29.

8. Show that $\operatorname{Tan}^{-1} (\sinh x) = \operatorname{Sin}^{-1} (\tanh x)$. (Hint: First show that their derivatives are equal.)

9. (a) Show that $D_x(2 \operatorname{Tan}^{-1} e^x) = D_x \operatorname{Tan}^{-1} (\sinh x)$.
(b) Is the equation we found in Part (a) still valid if we "cancel" D_x?
(c) State two integration formulas with $\operatorname{sech} x$ as the integrand.

10. Show that for each pair of numbers a and b.

$$\int_a^b \cosh x\, dx = 2 \cosh \frac{b + a}{2} \sinh \frac{b - a}{2}.$$

53 INVERSE HYPERBOLIC FUNCTIONS

You can see from Figures 52-1, 52-2, and 52-3 that the hyperbolic sine and hyperbolic tangent functions have inverses but that the hyperbolic cosine function doesn't. We may restrict the domain of the hyperbolic cosine function to obtain a new function with an inverse in much the same way that we restricted the domains of the trigonometric functions to obtain functions with inverses. Thus we define the **Hyperbolic Cosine** function as the function whose domain is the interval $[0, \infty]$ and whose rule of correspondence is $y = \cosh x$. This function has an inverse. In a similar manner we may restrict the domain of the hyperbolic secant function in order to obtain the **Hyperbolic Secant** function that has an inverse. The inverse hyperbolic functions are thus defined by the following equations:

(53-1) $y = \sinh^{-1} x$ if, and only if, $x = \sinh y$.

(53-2) $y = \cosh^{-1} x$ if, and only if, $x = \cosh y$ and $y \geq 0$.

(53-3) $y = \tanh^{-1} x$ if, and only if, $x = \tanh y$.

(53-4) $y = \coth^{-1} x$ if, and only if, $x = \coth y$.

(53-5) $y = \text{Sech}^{-1} x$ if, and only if, $x = \text{sech } y$ and $y \geq 0$.

(53-6) $y = \text{csch}^{-1} x$ if, and only if, $x = \text{csch } y$.

Since the hyperbolic functions are defined in terms of exponentials with base e, it is not surprising that we can express the values of the inverse hyperbolic functions in terms of logarithms with base e.

Example 53-1. Show that

(53-7) $$\tanh^{-1} x = \frac{1}{2} \ln\left(\frac{1 + x}{1 - x}\right), \quad |x| < 1.$$

Solution. If we let $y = \tanh^{-1} x$, then

$$x = \tanh y = \frac{e^y - e^{-y}}{e^y + e^{-y}}.$$

Thus

$$xe^y + xe^{-y} = e^y - e^{-y},$$

and so

$$(x - 1)e^y = -(1 + x)e^{-y}.$$

When we multiply both sides of this equation by e^y, we obtain

$$(x - 1)e^{2y} = -(1 + x),$$

and thus

$$e^{2y} = (1 + x)/(1 - x).$$

Now we take the logarithm of both sides and remember that $y = \tanh^{-1} x$ to obtain Equation 53-7.

By proceeding as we did in the preceding example, you can verify that the following formulas are valid:

(53-8)
$$\sinh^{-1} x = \ln (x + \sqrt{x^2 + 1}),$$

(53-9)
$$\mathrm{Cosh}^{-1} x = \ln (x + \sqrt{x^2 - 1}),$$

(53-10)
$$\coth^{-1} x = \frac{1}{2} \ln \left(\frac{x+1}{x-1}\right), \quad |x| > 1.$$

To find differentiation formulas for the inverse hyperbolic functions, we may either use the rules for finding derived functions of inverse functions that we developed in Section 45, or we may differentiate the logarithmic expressions for the inverse hyperbolic functions. These two methods are illustrated in the following example.

Example 53-2. Show in two ways that

(53-11)
$$D_x \sinh^{-1} x = \frac{1}{\sqrt{x^2 + 1}}.$$

Solution. *Method 1.* By definition, $y = \sinh^{-1} x$ if, and only if, $x = \sinh y$. Thus

$$
\begin{aligned}
D_y x &= \cosh y && \text{(Equation 52-16)} \\
&= \sqrt{\sinh^2 y + 1} && \text{(Equation 52-3)} \\
&= \sqrt{x^2 + 1} && (\sinh y = x).
\end{aligned}
$$

Therefore (see Equation 45-6)

$$D_x y = \frac{1}{D_y x} = \frac{1}{\sqrt{x^2 + 1}}.$$

Method 2. According to Equation 53-8,

$$
\begin{aligned}
D_x \sinh^{-1} x &= D_x \ln (x + \sqrt{x^2 + 1}) \\
&= \frac{D_x(x + \sqrt{x^2 + 1})}{x + \sqrt{x^2 + 1}} \\
&= \frac{1 + \dfrac{x}{\sqrt{x^2 + 1}}}{x + \sqrt{x^2 + 1}} \\
&= \frac{1}{\sqrt{x^2 + 1}},
\end{aligned}
$$

and so we again have Equation 53-11.

When we incorporate Equation 53-11 into the Chain Rule Equation $D_x f(u) = D_u f(u) D_x u$, we obtain the equation

$$(53\text{-}12) \qquad D_x \sinh^{-1} u = \frac{D_x u}{\sqrt{u^2 + 1}}.$$

The following differentiation formulas for the other inverse hyperbolic functions may be obtained in the same way that we obtained Equation 53-12:

$$(53\text{-}13) \qquad D_x \operatorname{Cosh}^{-1} u = \frac{D_x u}{\sqrt{u^2 - 1}} \quad (u > 1),$$

$$(53\text{-}14) \qquad D_x \tanh^{-1} u = \frac{D_x u}{1 - u^2} \quad (|u| < 1),$$

$$(53\text{-}15) \qquad D_x \coth^{-1} u = \frac{D_x u}{1 - u^2} \quad (|u| > 1),$$

$$(53\text{-}16) \qquad D_x \operatorname{Sech}^{-1} u = \frac{-D_x u}{u\sqrt{1 - u^2}} \quad (0 < u < 1),$$

$$(53\text{-}17) \qquad D_x \operatorname{csch}^{-1} u = \frac{-D_x u}{|u|\sqrt{1 + u^2}}.$$

These differentiation formulas enable us to state some integration formulas. For example, let us use Formula 53-12 to verify the integration formula

$$(53\text{-}18) \qquad \int \frac{1}{\sqrt{x^2 + a^2}} \, dx = \sinh^{-1} \frac{x}{a} \quad (a > 0).$$

To verify this formula, we use Formula 53-12 with $u = x/a$:

$$D_x \sinh^{-1} \frac{x}{a} = \frac{D_x(x/a)}{\sqrt{(x/a)^2 + 1}} = \frac{1}{a\sqrt{(x/a)^2 + 1}} = \frac{1}{\sqrt{x^2 + a^2}}.$$

(Where did we use the fact that $a > 0$?)

In exactly the same way we can use Differentiation Formula 53-13 to verify the integration formula

$$(53\text{-}19) \qquad \int \frac{1}{\sqrt{x^2 - a^2}} \, dx = \operatorname{Cosh}^{-1} \frac{x}{a} \quad (0 < a < x).$$

Differentiation Formulas 53-14 and 53-15 enable us to verify the integration formulas

(53-20)
$$\int \frac{1}{a^2 - x^2}\, dx = \begin{cases} \dfrac{1}{a} \tanh^{-1} \dfrac{x}{a} & \text{if } |x| < |a|, \\[2mm] \dfrac{1}{a} \coth^{-1} \dfrac{x}{a} & \text{if } |x| > |a|. \end{cases}$$

Equation 53-7 shows us the relation between the inverse hyperbolic tangent and the natural logarithm, and we could use such equations, together with Equations 53-20, to obtain the integration formula

(53-21)
$$\int \frac{1}{a^2 - x^2}\, dx = \frac{1}{2a} \ln \left| \frac{a + x}{a - x} \right| \quad (a \neq 0).$$

We can also verify this integration formula directly. In Section 47 we showed that $D_u \ln |u| = \dfrac{1}{u}$, and hence $D_x \ln |u| = \dfrac{D_x u}{u}$. Therefore,

$$D_x \left[\frac{1}{2a} \ln \left| \frac{a + x}{a - x} \right| \right] = \frac{1}{2a} D_x [\ln |a + x| - \ln |a - x|]$$

$$= \frac{1}{2a} \left[\frac{D_x(a + x)}{a + x} - \frac{D_x(a - x)}{a - x} \right]$$

$$= \frac{1}{2a} \left[\frac{1}{a + x} + \frac{1}{a - x} \right]$$

$$= \frac{1}{a^2 - x^2},$$

and this result verifies Integration Formula 53-21.

P R O B L E M S   5 3

1. Sketch the graphs of the following equations.
(a) $y = \sinh^{-1} x$ (b) $y = \text{Cosh}^{-1} x$
(c) $y = \tanh^{-1} x$ (d) $y = \coth^{-1} x$

2. Use Tables II and III to verify that:
(a) $\sinh^{-1} \frac{3}{4} = \ln 2$ (b) $\tanh^{-1} .5 = \frac{1}{2} \ln [(1 + .5)/(1 - .5)]$
(c) $\text{Cosh}^{-1} 2 = \ln (2 + \sqrt{2^2 - 1})$ (d) $\coth^{-1} 3 = \frac{1}{2} \ln [(3 + 1)/(3 - 1)]$

3. Either use algebra, as we did in Example 53-1, or use calculus (Equations 53-12, 53-13, 53-15, and the differentiation rules for logarithms) to verify Formulas 53-8, 53-9, and 53-10.

4. Show that if $b > 1$, then $\sinh^{-1} \sqrt{b^2 - 1} = \mathrm{Cosh}^{-1} b$.

5. Find $\lim\limits_{h \to 0} \dfrac{\sinh^{-1} h}{h}$.

6. Compute $D_x y$.
   (a) $y = \tanh^{-1}(\cos x)$ (b) $y = \mathrm{csch}^{-1}(\tan x)$ (c) $y = \coth^{-1}(\cosh x)$
   (d) $y = \sinh^{-1}(\tan x)$ (e) $y = \mathrm{Cosh}^{-1}(\cos x)$ (f) $y = \mathrm{Cosh}^{-1}(\sec x)$

7. Evaluate the following integrals.

   (a) $\displaystyle\int_0^2 \frac{1}{\sqrt{x^2 + 4}}\, dx$

   (b) $\displaystyle\int_0^1 \frac{1}{\sqrt{1 + x^2}}\, dx$

   (c) $\displaystyle\int_2^3 \frac{1}{\sqrt{x^2 - 1}}\, dx$

   (d) $\displaystyle\int_5^7 \frac{1}{\sqrt{x^2 - 9}}\, dx$

   (e) $\displaystyle\int_{-1/2}^{1/2} \frac{1}{1 - x^2}\, dx$

   (f) $\displaystyle\int_{-1}^1 \frac{1}{2 - x^2}\, dx$

   (g) $\displaystyle\int_4^5 \frac{1}{x^2 - 9}\, dx$

   (h) $\displaystyle\int_{-1}^1 \frac{1}{\sqrt{2 - x^2}}\, dx$

8. Show that if $-\pi/2 < x < \pi/2$, then $\sinh^{-1}(\tan x) = \tanh^{-1}(\sin x)$.

9. Let G be the function defined in Problem 43-9. Prove that $G(x) = \mathrm{Cosh}^{-1} x$. (Hint: See Problem 50-13.)

10. Verify the following integration formulas.

    (a) $\displaystyle\int \sqrt{x^2 + a^2}\, dx = \frac{1}{2}\left(x\sqrt{x^2 + a^2} + a^2 \sinh^{-1}\frac{x}{a}\right)$

    (b) $\displaystyle\int \sqrt{x^2 - a^2}\, dx = \frac{1}{2}\left(x\sqrt{x^2 - a^2} - a^2 \mathrm{Cosh}^{-1}\frac{x}{a}\right),\ (x > a).$

11. Verify that:
    (a) $D_x[x \sinh^{-1} x - \sqrt{1 + x^2}] = \sinh^{-1} x.$
    (b) $D_x[x \mathrm{Cosh}^{-1} x - \sqrt{x^2 - 1}] = \mathrm{Cosh}^{-1} x.$
    (c) $D_x[x \tanh^{-1} x - \ln\sqrt{x^2 - 1}] = \tanh^{-1} x$

REVIEW PROBLEMS—CHAPTER SIX

You can use the following problems to test yourself on the material of this chapter.

1. Find $D_x y$.
   (a) $y = x^{a^2} + a^{x^2} + 2^{a^x}$ (b) $y = \ln(\ln x) + \exp(\exp x)$

   (c) $y = \displaystyle\int_{-x^2}^{x^2} e^{t^2}\, dt$ (d) $y = |\ln|x||$

2. Verify the following integration formulas.

(a) $\displaystyle \int e^{ax} \cos bx \, dx = \left(\frac{a \cos bx + b \sin bx}{a^2 + b^2} \right) e^{ax}$

(b) $\displaystyle \int e^{ax} \sin bx \, dx = \left(\frac{a \sin bx - b \cos bx}{a^2 + b^2} \right) e^{ax}$

3. Sketch the graph of the equation $y = \displaystyle \int_1^{3^x} \frac{1}{t} \, dt$.

4. How many solutions does the equation $e^x = ex$ have?

5. Sketch the graph of the equation $y = x^2 \ln \dfrac{1}{|x|}$. Check for maximum and minimum points, concavity, and so on.

6. Evaluate the integral $\displaystyle \int_0^{e^{100}} [\![\ln x]\!] \, dx$.

7. Sketch the graph of the equation $y = \displaystyle \int_0^x \text{Arccos} (\cos t) \, dt$.

8. Suppose that $u = f(x)$ and $v = g(x)$, where $f(x) > 1$ and $g(x) > 0$. Show that
$$D_x \log_u v = \left(\frac{D_x v}{v} - \log_u v \, \frac{D_x u}{u} \right) \log_u e.$$

9. Evaluate the following integrals.

(a) $\displaystyle \int_{-b}^b \frac{1}{\sqrt{4b^2 - x^2}} \, dx$

(b) $\displaystyle \int_0^4 \cosh^2 x \, dx$

(c) $\displaystyle \int_0^1 e^{-x} \sinh 2x \, dx$

(d) $\displaystyle \int_{-b}^b \frac{1}{4b^2 - x^2} \, dx$

10. Let $f(x) = |x - 1| + |x - 2|$ and $F(x) = \displaystyle \int_0^x f(t) \, dt$.

(a) Sketch the graph of f.
(b) Find $F(0)$, $F(1)$, $F(2)$, and $F(3)$.
(c) Find $F'(1)$ and $F'(3)$.
(d) Sketch the graph of F.
(e) Does f have an inverse? If so, sketch the graph of f^{-1}.
(f) Does F have an inverse? If so, sketch the graph of F^{-1}.

11. Suppose that $0 < x < \pi/2$, $y > 0$, and $\cos x \cosh y = 1$.
(a) Show that $y = \ln (\sec x + \tan x)$.
(b) Compute $D_x y$.

TECHNIQUES

OF INTEGRATION

SEVEN

In the preceding two chapters we developed a number of specific integration formulas, rules that tell us how to find integrals of polynomials, some trigonometric functions, logarithmic functions, and so on. In order to utilize these formulas fully, we will now develop some additional general techniques of integration. Our sampling of integration techniques will be far from exhaustive. Not many years ago, a large part of the standard calculus course was devoted to various integration tricks. Today, we restrict our presentation of methods of integration to a few essentials, thereby freeing time to spend on more important topics. You can look in almost any older calculus book and find some tricks that we have left out.

54 USING INTEGRATION FORMULAS

An integral $\int_a^b f(x)\,dx$ is the limit of sums of the form $\sum_{i=1}^{n} f(x_i^*)\,\Delta x_i$. In some cases we must use numerical methods such as Simpson's Parabolic Rule or The Trapezoidal Rule to evaluate an integral, but often an integration formula

$$(54\text{-}1) \qquad\qquad \int f(x)\,dx = F(x)$$

applies in some interval I. Formula 54-1 means that the integral $\int_a^b f(x)\,dx$ is the number $F(x)\Big|_a^b = F(b) - F(a)$ for each pair of numbers a and b of I. We also extend this convention to more general integration formulas, such as Formula 54-2. In formulas like this, the limits of integration have again been dropped, and you are to think of expressions like $\int f(x)\,dx$ and $F(x)$ as abbreviations for $\int_a^b f(x)\,dx$ and $F(x)\Big|_a^b$. In particular, when you use an integration formula such as Formula 54-1 to replace $\int f(x)\,dx$ with $F(x)$, you must realize that you are really replacing $\int_a^b f(x)\,dx$ with $F(x)\Big|_a^b$.

The Fundamental Theorem of Calculus and its converse, Theorems 37-1 and 43-2, tell us that if f is continuous in an interval I, then Formula 54-1 is equivalent to saying that $D_x F(x) = f(x)$ for each $x \in I$. In other words, $F(x)$ is an antiderivative of $f(x)$. Thus differentiation formulas and integration formulas are equivalent when the functions we are dealing with are continuous.

We have listed a number of differentiation formulas in Table IV and integration formulas in Table V in the back of the book. The first 25 formulas of Table V are labeled Basic Integration Formulas. They are essentially the differentiation formulas in Table IV read from right to left. You should learn most of these basic formulas by heart. Table V is actually a very short list of integration formulas. Longer lists can be found in the standard collections of mathematical tables, and you can find extensive "tables of integrals" in any mathematics library. Since the most practical way to find an integral you don't know is to look it up in a table, you should learn how to use these tables. Notice that the tables use the abbreviation $\int \dfrac{du}{f(u)}$ for $\int \dfrac{1}{f(u)}\,du$.

We have simply set down a list of integration formulas in Table V, many of which you have not seen before. What assurance have we that these formulas are correct? Because of the relation between differentiation and integration formulas that we mentioned above, it is easy to answer this question for any of our integration formulas. *To verify a specific integration formula in Table V, we differentiate the right-hand side to obtain the integrand.*

Example 54-1. Verify Integration Formulas V-20.

Solution. We must show that

$$D_u \sinh^{-1} \frac{u}{a} = \frac{1}{\sqrt{u^2 + a^2}},$$

and

$$D_u \ln \left[\frac{u + \sqrt{u^2 + a^2}}{a} \right] = \frac{1}{\sqrt{u^2 + a^2}}.$$

According to Formula IV-21,

$$D_u \sinh^{-1} \frac{u}{a} = \frac{D_u(u/a)}{\sqrt{(u/a)^2 + 1}}$$

$$= \frac{1/a}{\sqrt{(u/a)^2 + 1}} = \frac{1}{\sqrt{u^2 + a^2}}.$$

(Notice that we are assuming that $a > 0$ in these integration formulas.) We use Formula IV-9 to show that

$$D_u \ln \left[\frac{u + \sqrt{u^2 + a^2}}{a} \right] = \frac{D_u(u + \sqrt{u^2 + a^2})}{u + \sqrt{u^2 + a^2}} = \frac{1 + u/\sqrt{u^2 + a^2}}{u + \sqrt{u^2 + a^2}} = \frac{1}{\sqrt{u^2 + a^2}}.$$

Example 54-2. Evaluate the integral $\displaystyle\int_1^{100} \frac{dx}{x(4x + 3)}$.

Solution. We set $a = 4$, $b = 3$, and $u = x$ in Formula V-28 to obtain the equation

$$\int_1^{100} \frac{dx}{x(4x + 3)} = \frac{1}{3} \ln \left| \frac{x}{4x + 3} \right| \Big|_1^{100}$$

$$= \tfrac{1}{3}(\ln \tfrac{100}{403} - \ln \tfrac{1}{7})$$

$$= \tfrac{1}{3} \ln \tfrac{700}{403} \approx .1826.$$

Some of the formulas in Table V are *reduction formulas.* They may not give us the answer we seek directly, but they help us proceed one step in the right direction.

Example 54-3. Find $\displaystyle\int \frac{x \, dx}{(x^2 - 2x + 2)^2}$. That is, find an integration formula whose left-hand side is the given expression.

Solution. Here we apply Formula V-50 to obtain the formula

$$(54\text{-}2) \qquad \int \frac{x \, dx}{(x^2 - 2x + 2)^2} = \frac{-(4 - 2x)}{4(x^2 - 2x + 2)} - \left(-\frac{2}{4} \right) \int \frac{dx}{(x^2 - 2x + 2)}$$

$$= \frac{x - 2}{2(x^2 - 2x + 2)} + \frac{1}{2} \int \frac{dx}{x^2 - 2x + 2}.$$

Our reduction Formula V-50 has reduced the exponent of the term $(x^2 - 2x + 2)$ from 2 in our original integrand to 1 in the new integrand. Now we may use Formula V-47 to find that

$$\int \frac{dx}{x^2 - 2x + 2} = \frac{2}{\sqrt{4}} \, \text{Tan}^{-1} \frac{2x - 2}{\sqrt{4}} = \text{Tan}^{-1}(x - 1).$$

We substitute this result in Formula 54-2 and obtain the integration formula we were seeking:

$$\int \frac{x \, dx}{(x^2 - 2x + 2)^2} = \frac{x - 2}{2(x^2 - 2x + 2)} + \frac{1}{2} \, \text{Tan}^{-1}(x - 1).$$

The content of the general integration Theorems 34-3 and 34-4 can be summed up in the equation $\int_a^b [mf(x) + ng(x)] \, dx = m \int_a^b f(x) \, dx + n \int_a^b g(x) \, dx$. Here we assume that m and n are given numbers, and f and g are integrable functions. When we drop the limits of integration, we obtain the integration formula

$$(54\text{-}3) \qquad \int [mf(x) + ng(x)] \, dx = m \int f(x) \, dx + n \int g(x) \, dx,$$

which we can use to reduce complicated integrands to simple ones. Thus in Section 58 we shall have to find integration formulas whose left-hand sides are of the form $\int \frac{Bx + C}{(x^2 + bx + c)^2} \, dx$, where $B, C, b,$ and c are given real numbers, with $b^2 - 4c < 0$, and r is a positive integer. According to Formula 54-3, this problem reduces to finding $\int \frac{x}{(x^2 + bx + c)^2} \, dx$ and $\int \frac{1}{(x^2 + bx + c)^2} \, dx$. Example 54-3 illustrates how we use our integral tables to handle such problems.

Here is an example of how we might use Formula 54-3 to find an antiderivative.

Example 54-4.   Find an antiderivative of $3 \cos x - 2xe^x$.

Solution.   We have

$$\int (3 \cos x - 2x \, e^x) \, dx = 3 \int \cos x \, dx - 2 \int x \, e^x \, dx \qquad \text{(Formula 54-3)}$$

$$= 3 \sin x - 2x \, e^x + 2 \int e^x \, dx \qquad \text{(Formulas V-2 and V-44)}$$

$$= 3 \sin x - 2x \, e^x + 2 \, e^x \qquad \text{(Formula V-8).}$$

Since the function defined by the equation $f(x) = 3 \cos x - 2x \, e^x$ is continuous, this integration formula tells us that an antiderivative of $3 \cos x - 2x \, e^x$ is

$3 \sin x + 2(1 - x)e^x$. It is always wise to check such a result by differentiating, and when we check now, we find that

$$D_x[3 \sin x + 2(1 - x)e^x] = 3 \cos x - 2x\, e^x,$$

as it should.

P R O B L E M S   5 4

1. Determine k so that the given integration formula is correct.

(a) $\displaystyle\int xe^{3x^2}\, dx = ke^{3x^2}$

(b) $\displaystyle\int \frac{dx}{x(\ln x)^{2/3}} = k\sqrt[3]{\ln x}$

(c) $\displaystyle\int \sin x \cos (\cos x)\, dx = k \sin (\cos x)$

(d) $\displaystyle\int \frac{2^{1/x}}{x^2}\, dx = k2^{1/x}$

2. Verify the following formulas from Table V.
   (a) V-26   (b) V-29   (c) V-30   (d) V-35   (e) V-37   (f) V-38

3. Use Table V and Formula 54-3 to find the following.

(a) $\displaystyle\int (e^{x+2} + x^{e+2})\, dx$

(b) $\displaystyle\int \left(\ln w^4 + \ln \frac{4}{w}\right) dw$

4. Show that $\displaystyle\int \sec u\, du = -\ln |\sec u - \tan u|$. Does this formula agree with Formula V-35?

5. Use Table V to find an antiderivative of $f(x)$.
   (a) $f(x) = 1/x(3x - 4)^2$
   (c) $f(x) = x^2\sqrt{5 - x^2}$
   (e) $f(x) = x^3 \ln x^x$
   (b) $f(x) = \tan^2 x$
   (d) $f(x) = e^{3x+4} \sin (5x + \pi/3)$
   (f) $f(x) = (x^2 - 2x + 2)^{-2}$

6. Evaluate the following integrals.

(a) $\displaystyle\int_0^{\pi/2} \sin^8 x\, dx$

(b) $\displaystyle\int_0^{\pi/2} \sin^9 x\, dx$

(c) $\displaystyle\int_0^1 x^4 e^x\, dx$

(d) $\displaystyle\int_0^{\pi/2} x^9 \sin x\, dx$

7. Evaluate the following integrals with the aid of reduction formulas.

(a) $\displaystyle\int_0^2 \frac{dx}{(x^2 + 4)^3}$

(b) $\displaystyle\int_0^2 \frac{x\, dx}{(x^2 + 4)^3}$

(c) $\displaystyle\int_1^3 \frac{x\, dx}{(x^2 - 4x + 5)^2}$

(d) $\displaystyle\int_{-2}^{-1} \frac{dx}{(x^2 + 4x + 5)^2}$

8. Find the area of the region bounded by the X-axis, the lines $x = 1$ and $x = 2$, and the graph of the equation $x^2y + xy = 1$.

9. The region in the first quadrant bounded by the Y-axis, the lines $y = 1$ and $y = 4$, and the graph of the equation $yx^2(y + 1)^2 = 1$ is rotated about the Y-axis. Find the volume of the resulting solid.

10. If you know that the integration formula $\int f(x)\, dx = \int g(x)\, dx$ is valid in an interval I, can you necessarily conclude that $f(x) = g(x)$ for each point $x \in I$?

11. Prove, taking care to use all symbols correctly, that the integration formula $\int f(x)\, dx = H(x) + \int g(x)\, dx$ is valid in an interval I if, and only if, the formula $\int [f(x) - g(x)]\, dx = H(x)$ is valid in I.

55 CHANGE OF VARIABLE OF INTEGRATION

We have seen how the Chain Rule greatly extends the applicability of specific differentiation formulas. Now let us see how we can also use it to increase the range of specific integration formulas. If g is a continuous function and c is a number, Theorem 43-2 tells us that we find the derivative of $\int_c^v g(u)\, du$ with respect to v by deleting the symbols of integration and replacing the variable of integration with v. In other words, $D_v \int_c^v g(u)\, du = g(v)$. When we incorporate this differentiation formula into the Chain Rule equation $D_x f(v) = D_v f(v) D_x v$, we see that

$$D_x \int_c^v g(u)\, du = g(v) D_x v.$$

Thus if h is a differentiable function,

$$D_x \int_c^{h(x)} g(u)\, du = g(h(x)) h'(x).$$

This equation says that $\int_c^{h(x)} g(u)\, du$ is an antiderivative of $g(h(x)) h'(x)$, and so (if h' is integrable), the Fundamental Theorem of Calculus tells us that

$$\int_a^b g(h(x)) h'(x)\, dx = \int_c^{h(x)} g(u)\, du \,\Big|_a^b$$

$$= \int_c^{h(b)} g(u)\, du - \int_c^{h(a)} g(u)\, du = \int_{h(a)}^{h(b)} g(u)\, du;$$

that is,

$$(55\text{-}1) \qquad \int_a^b g(h(x)) h'(x)\, dx = \int_{h(a)}^{h(b)} g(u)\, du.$$

We will shortly introduce some notational conventions that make this complicated looking equation appear a little simpler, but before we do, let us use it to calculate an integral that we couldn't have computed before.

Example 55-1. Evaluate the integral $\displaystyle\int_{\sqrt{\pi}}^{2\sqrt{\pi}} 2x \sin x^2 \, dx$.

Solution. Since we are going to apply Equation 55-1, we want to write our integrand $2x \sin x^2$ as $g(h(x))h'(x)$ for some functions g and h. If we choose $h(x) = x^2$, then $h'(x) = 2x$, and so $2x \sin x^2 = \sin (h(x))h'(x)$. Thus the form of our integrand is $g(h(x))h'(x)$ if we take g to be the sine function; that is, $g(u) = \sin u$. Here $a = \sqrt{\pi}$ and $b = 2\sqrt{\pi}$, so $h(a) = \pi$ and $h(b) = 4\pi$. Therefore, when we substitute in Equation 55-1 we find that

$$\int_{\sqrt{\pi}}^{2\sqrt{\pi}} 2x \sin x^2 \, dx = \int_{\pi}^{4\pi} \cos u \, du.$$

It is easy to evaluate this last integral; the answer is -2. Therefore our original integral (which we can't find in Table V) is also -2.

Example 55-1 shows how we use Equation 55-1 to evaluate a given integral $\displaystyle\int_a^b f(x) \, dx$. We try to find functions g and h such that

(55-2) $f(x) = g(h(x))h'(x).$

Then according to Equation 55-1, the problem of finding $\displaystyle\int_a^b f(x) \, dx$ becomes the problem of finding $\displaystyle\int_{h(a)}^{h(b)} g(u) \, du$. Therefore, we want g to be a function such that we know $\int g(u) \, du$, or can find it in a table. We can choose h freely, but once we have picked it, we are committed. Then g is determined, and the question of whether or not our choice of h was a good one depends on whether or not we can find $\int g(u) \, du$. Let us look at another example.

Example 55-2. Suppose $f(x) = e^x \tan e^x$. Find four pairs of functions g and h such that Equation 55-2 holds.

Solution. By direct substitution, you can readily verify Equation 55-2 for each pair in the following table.

	$h(x)$	$g(u)$
1	e^x	$\tan u$
2	$\sec e^x$	$\dfrac{1}{u}$
3	$\ln \sec e^x$	1
4	x	$e^u \tan e^u$

Choice 1 is perhaps the most natural, and it is a good one because $\int \tan u\, du$ is listed in Table V. Choice 2 is much less natural, but it is certainly as good as or better than Choice 1, because the resulting integrand is so simple. Choice 3 is the best of all, in the sense that it results in the simplest possible $g(u)$, but it is most unlikely that you would hit upon it as your first choice for $h(x)$. Of course, it really makes no sense to say that one of the first three choices is better than another. We can use any one of them to evaluate integrals of f. Choice 4 is a correct, but trivial, choice. We can always satisfy Equation 55-2 with $h(x) = x$ and $g(u) = f(u)$, but then Equation 55-1 becomes $\displaystyle\int_c^b f(x)\, dx = \int_a^b f(u)\, du$—our new integral is the one we started with.

If we keep Equation 55-2 in mind, we can write Equation 55-1 as

(55-3)
$$\int_a^b f(x)\, dx = \int_{h(a)}^{h(b)} g(u)\, du.$$

Let us now introduce a mechanical routine by which we can produce the integral on the right-hand side of Equation 55-3 from the one on the left, via Equation 55-2. We proceed by *changing the variable of integration* from x to u by means of the equation $u = h(x)$. With this substitution, we can write Equation 55-2 as $f(x) = g(u)D_x u$. Now let us formally multiply this equation by dx to obtain the equation

(55-4)
$$f(x)\, dx = g(u)D_x u\, dx.$$

At this point we write

(55-5)
$$du = D_x u\, dx;$$

then Equation 55-4 becomes $f(x)\, dx = g(u)\, du$, and so we have transformed the expression that appears under the integral sign on the left-hand side of Equation 55-3 to the expression that appears under the integral sign on the right-hand side. Now we insert the integral signs and the proper limits of integration, and we have Equation 55-3. Because we have not assigned any meaning to the symbols dx and du (except as "indicators"), we really should not treat "Equation" 55-5 as a true equality between numbers. Nevertheless, it will be very convenient—and it will not lead us into error here—to proceed formally as if we were dealing with a real equation, and we shall do so. Our steps in changing the variable of integration may be summarized as follows:

   (i) Choose a function h and set $u = h(x)$.
   (ii) Calculate $D_x u$ from this equation and write $du = D_x u\, dx$.
   (iii) Use the equations from steps (i) and (ii) to write $f(x)\, dx = g(u)\, du$.

(iv) Calculate the new limits of integration, $h(a)$ and $h(b)$, from the equation $u = h(x)$, and write the equation $\displaystyle\int_a^b f(x)\,dx = \int_{h(a)}^{h(b)} g(u)\,du.$

(v) Evaluate the new integral.

Let us emphasize that the success or failure of this method hinges on our choice of h in step (i). We don't know whether or not it is a good choice until we try to evaluate our new integral in step (v). If we can't evaluate that integral, then we either have to start over with another substitution or admit defeat. Your percentage of success with this method should improve with experience.

Example 55-3. Evaluate the integral $\displaystyle\int_3^5 x\sqrt{x^2 - 9}\,dx.$

Solution. We follow our listed steps.

(i) Set $u = x^2 - 9$.

(ii) Then $D_x u = 2x$, and so $du = 2x\,dx$.

(iii) From the equations in steps (i) and (ii), we see that $x\sqrt{x^2-9}\,dx = \frac{1}{2}\sqrt{u}\,du$.

(iv) Our new limits of integration are $3^2 - 9 = 0$ and $5^2 - 9 = 16$, and so

$$\int_3^5 x\sqrt{x^2-9}\,dx = \frac{1}{2}\int_0^{16}\sqrt{u}\,du.$$

(v) From our earlier work with integrals we find:

$$\frac{1}{2}\int_0^{16}\sqrt{u}\,du = \frac{1}{3}u^{3/2}\Big|_0^{16} = \frac{64}{3}.$$

Example 55-4. Compute $\displaystyle\int_0^{\pi/6} \sin^2 x \cos x\,dx.$

Solution. We set $u = \sin x$, and so $du = \cos x\,dx$. Therefore $\sin^2 x\,dx = u^2\,du$. We see that $u = 0$ when $x = 0$ and $u = \frac{1}{2}$ when $x = \pi/6$, so our new limits of integration are 0 and $\frac{1}{2}$, and

$$\int_0^{\pi/6} \sin^2 x \cos x\,dx = \int_0^{1/2} u^2\,du = \frac{1}{3}u^3\Big|_0^{1/2} = \frac{1}{24}.$$

We already know that the letter we use as the variable of integration has nothing to do with the value of an integral. Thus, for example,

$$\int_a^b \sin x\,dx = \int_a^b \sin u\,du = \cos a - \cos b.$$

This equality agrees with what we said earlier in this section because we can go from the integral on the left to the one on the right by means of the substitution

$u = x$. But sometimes when we deal with several integrals at once it is easy to lose sight of the basic fact that the value of an integral is independent of the letter that is used as the variable of integration. Our next example illustrates this kind of problem. To work out such a problem is a real test of your understanding of the nature of the variable of integration.

Example 55-5. Show that for any continuous function f,

$$\int_0^\pi \theta f(\sin \theta)\, d\theta = \frac{\pi}{2} \int_0^\pi f(\sin \theta)\, d\theta.$$

Solution. If we make the substitution $\phi = \pi - \theta$, we have $d\phi = -d\theta$ and $\sin \theta = \sin \phi$. Furthermore, $\phi = \pi$ when $\theta = 0$, and $\phi = 0$ when $\theta = \pi$. Thus

$$\int_0^\pi \theta f(\sin \theta)\, d\theta = -\int_\pi^0 (\pi - \phi) f(\sin \phi)\, d\phi$$

$$= \pi \int_0^\pi f(\sin \phi)\, d\phi - \int_0^\pi \phi f(\sin \phi)\, d\phi.$$

Therefore,

(55-5)
$$\int_0^\pi \theta f(\sin \theta)\, d\theta + \int_0^\pi \phi f(\sin \phi)\, d\phi$$

$$= \pi \int_0^\pi f(\sin \phi)\, d\phi.$$

Now remember that it makes no difference which letter we use as the variable of integration. In particular, we may replace all the ϕ's, letter by letter, with θ's. If we make this replacement, Equation 55-5 can be written,

$$2 \int_0^\pi \theta f(\sin \theta)\, d\theta = \pi \int_0^\pi f(\sin \theta)\, d\theta,$$

and the desired equation follows immediately.

P R O B L E M S   5 5

1. Use the indicated change of variable of integration to evaluate the integral.

(a) $\displaystyle\int_0^{\pi/6} \cos 2x\, dx,\ u = 2x$

(b) $\displaystyle\int_0^2 x e^{x^2}\, dx,\ u = x^2$

(c) $\displaystyle\int_0^1 x\sqrt{x^2 + 1}\, dx,\ u = x^2 + 1$

(d) $\displaystyle\int_0^{\pi/2} \cos x \sin (\sin x)\, dx,\ u = \sin x$

(e) $\displaystyle\int_1^4 \frac{e^{\sqrt{x}}}{\sqrt{x}}\, dx,\ u = \sqrt{x}$

(f) $\displaystyle\int_0^{\pi/6} \frac{\cos x - \sin x}{\sin x + \cos x}\, dx,\ u = \sin x + \cos x$

(g) $\int_0^1 (2x - 3)\sqrt{x^2 - 3x + 5}\, dx$, $u = x^2 - 3x + 5$

(h) $\int_0^1 \text{sech}^5 x \sinh x\, dx$, $u = \cosh x$

2. Evaluate the integral $\int_{\sqrt{\pi/6}}^{\sqrt{\pi/2}} x \cot x^2\, dx$ by means of the following changes of variable of integration.
   (a) $u = x^2$ (b) $u = \sin x^2$ (c) $u = \ln \sin x^2$ (d) $u = \ln \sqrt{\sin x^2}$

3. By making a suitable change of variable of integration, each of the following integrals can be evaluated by using an integration formula for $c \int u^r\, du$, where c and r are appropriate numbers.

   (a) $\int_3^4 x\sqrt{25 - x^2}\, dx$ (b) $\int_0^1 \dfrac{x + 4}{(x^2 + 8x + 1)^2}\, dx$ (c) $\int_0^{\ln 5} \tanh x\, dx$

   (d) $\int_0^\pi \sin x\, (\cos^{13} x + 6 \cos^8 x - 2 \cos^5 x + 3)\, dx$ (e) $\int_1^e \dfrac{(\ln x)^5}{x}\, dx$

   (f) $\int_0^{\sqrt{3}} \dfrac{(\text{Arctan } x)^3}{1 + x^2}\, dx$

4. Find $\int_{2\sqrt{2}}^4 \dfrac{dx}{x\sqrt{x^2 - 4}}$ in two ways. In one case, use the change of variable

   $u = \sqrt{x^2 - 4}$, and in the other set $v = 1/x$.

5. Evaluate the following integrals.

   (a) $\int_{\ln 2}^{\ln 7} e^x e^{e^x}\, dx$ (b) $\int_0^{\pi/2} \dfrac{\sin t}{1 + \cos^2 t}\, dt$ (c) $\int_0^1 \sin \dfrac{\pi}{2}(x + 3)\, dx$

   (d) $\int_{\pi/4}^{\pi/2} \cot x \ln (\sin x)\, dx$

6. Find the area of the region enclosed by the curve whose equation is $y^2 + x^4 = 4x^2$.

7. Show that the following equations hold for arbitrary continuous functions f and g.

   (a) $\int_2^3 f(x + 3)\, dx = \int_5^6 f(x)\, dx$

   (b) $\int_0^1 f(x)g(1 - x)\, dx = \int_0^1 f(1 - x)g(x)\, dx$

   (c) $\int_a^b f(x)\, dx = \int_a^b f(a + b - x)\, dx$

8. Use a change of variable of integration to show that $\int_{-a}^a f(x)\, dx$ is $2\int_0^a f(x)\, dx$ if f is an even continuous function, and 0 if f is an odd continuous function.

9. Evaluate $\int_0^{2\pi} |\cos nx|\, dx$, where n is a positive integer.

10. Sketch the graph of the equation $y = (\ln x)/\sqrt{x}$. The region bounded by this curve, the X-axis, and a vertical line through the maximum point of the curve is rotated about the X-axis. Find the volume of the solid that is generated.

11. Find the volume of the solid formed by rotating the first quadrant region that is bounded by the graph of the equation $y = x\sqrt[3]{1 - x^3}$ and the X-axis about the X-axis.

56 THE METHOD OF SUBSTITUTION

In the last section we saw how to substitute a new variable of integration by means of the equation $u = h(x)$ to produce the equation

$$(56\text{-}1) \qquad\qquad \int_a^b f(x)\, dx = \int_{h(a)}^{h(b)} g(u)\, du.$$

Since the limits of integration on these two integrals are different, we would lose the meaning of the equation if we simply dropped them. Instead, we write

$$(56\text{-}2) \qquad\qquad \int f(x)\, dx = \int g(u)\, du, \qquad u = h(x).$$

The substitution equation $u = h(x)$ tells us how to put in the limits of integration, so there is no difference in content between Equation 56-1 and Formula 56-2. We simply use these two equations in different situations, employing Equation 56-1 when we want to evaluate integrals and turning to Formula 56-2 when we want to find antiderivatives or integration formulas.

Example 56-1. Find an antiderivative of $\sin (x + 2)$.

Solution. Since the sine function is continuous, we know that if we can find an integration formula $\int \sin (x + 2)\, dx = F(x)$, then $F(x)$ is an antiderivative of $\sin (x + 2)$. To find such an integration formula, let us set $u = x + 2$. Then $du = dx$, and $\sin (x + 2)\, dx = \sin u\, du$. Therefore, as in formula 56-2, we write

$$\int \sin (x + 2)\, dx = \int \sin u\, du, u = x + 2.$$

Now $\int \sin u\, du = -\cos u$, and when we replace u with $x + 2$, we find that

$$\int \sin (x + 2)\, dx = -\cos (x + 2).$$

This integration formula tells us that an antiderivative of $\sin (x + 2)$ is $-\cos (x + 2)$.

Example 56-2. Find $\displaystyle\int \frac{x\,dx}{\sqrt{x+1}}$.

Solution. We will indicate two different substitutions that could be used to solve this problem.

Substitution 1. Set $u = \sqrt{x+1}$. Then $du = \dfrac{1}{2\sqrt{x+1}}\,dx$, and $x = u^2 - 1$. Therefore,

$$\int \frac{x\,dx}{\sqrt{x+1}} = \int 2(u^2 - 1)\,du,\ u = \sqrt{x+1}.$$

Now $\displaystyle\int 2(u^2 - 1)\,du = 2\left(\dfrac{u^3}{3} - u\right)$, and so

$$\int \frac{x\,dx}{\sqrt{x+1}} = \tfrac{2}{3}(x+1)^{3/2} - 2(x+1)^{1/2}.$$

Substitution 2. Set $u = x + 1$. Then $du = dx$, $x = u - 1$, and we have

$$\int \frac{x\,dx}{\sqrt{x+1}} = \int \frac{u-1}{\sqrt{u}}\,du = \int (u^{1/2} - u^{-1/2})\,du,\ u = x + 1.$$

Now $\int (u^{1/2} - u^{-1/2})\,du = \tfrac{2}{3}u^{3/2} - 2u^{1/2}$, and so

$$\int \frac{x\,dx}{\sqrt{x+1}} = \tfrac{2}{3}(x+1)^{3/2} - 2(x+1)^{1/2}.$$

This "method of substitution" is more of an art than a science. There are no simple rules that tell us what substitution to make so that $f(x)$ becomes $g(u)D_xu$, with g being a function for which we know an integration formula. Since both u and D_xu appear, we try to pick out certain expressions and their derivatives, such as $\sin x$ and $\cos x$, $\ln |x|$ and $1/x$, and so on. For example, to find $\int f(\sin x)\cos x\,dx$, we naturally think of the substitution $u = \sin x$. Then $du = \cos x\,dx$, and

$$\int f(\sin x)\cos x\,dx = \int f(u)\,du, \qquad u = \sin x.$$

Example 56-3. Find $\displaystyle\int \frac{\cos x}{\sqrt{9 - \sin^2 x}}\,dx$.

Solution. From what we said above, we see that

$$\int \frac{\cos x}{\sqrt{9 - \sin^2 x}}\,dx = \int \frac{du}{\sqrt{9 - u^2}},\ u = \sin x.$$

From Formula V-12, we have $\displaystyle\int \frac{du}{\sqrt{9 - u^2}} = \text{Sin}^{-1}(u/3)$, and so

$$\int \frac{\cos x}{\sqrt{9 - \sin^2 x}}\, dx = \text{Sin}^{-1}\left(\frac{\sin x}{3}\right).$$

It sometimes helps us to decide on a particular substitution if we first perform certain algebraic or trigonometric manipulations on our given integrand. In the next section, we will look at some trigonometric examples; here is a standard algebraic manipulation.

Example 56-4.   Find $\displaystyle\int \frac{dx}{3x^2 - 12x + 15}$.

Solution.   We factor and complete the square in the denominator of the integrand, which gives us

$$\int \frac{dx}{3x^2 - 12x + 15} = \frac{1}{3}\int \frac{dx}{(x - 2)^2 + 1}.$$

This form suggests the substitution $u = x - 2$. Then $du = dx$, and so

$$\int \frac{dx}{3x^2 - 12x + 15} = \frac{1}{3}\int \frac{du}{u^2 + 1}, \; u = x - 2.$$

Since $\displaystyle\int \frac{du}{u^2 + 1} = \text{Tan}^{-1} u$, we obtain the integration formula

$$\int \frac{dx}{3x^2 - 12x + 15} = \frac{1}{3}\text{Tan}^{-1}(x - 2).$$

P R O B L E M S   5 6

1. Use the indicated substitution to find an integration formula with the given left-hand side.

(a) $\displaystyle\int 3x^2 e^{x^3}\, dx, \; u = x^3$

(b) $\displaystyle\int 3^{x^2} x\, dx, \; u = x^2$

(c) $\displaystyle\int x^2 \sin x^3\, dx, \; u = x^3$

(d) $\displaystyle\int x \ln x^2\, dx, \; u = x^2$

(e) $\displaystyle\int \frac{dx}{4 + 9x^2}, \; u = 3x$

(f) $\displaystyle\int \frac{x\, dx}{3 + 4x^2}, \; u = 3 + 4x^2$

(g) $\displaystyle\int \frac{(\ln x)^3}{x}\, dx, \; u = \ln x$

(h) $\displaystyle\int \sin^2 x \cos x\, dx, \; u = \sin x$

(i) $\displaystyle\int \tan x\, dx, \; u = \cos x$

(j) $\displaystyle\int e^x \cos e^x\, dx, \; u = e^x$

2. What are the "natural" substitutions in the following cases? What do you get when you make this substitution?

(a) $\displaystyle\int e^x f(e^x)\,dx$

(b) $\displaystyle\int \frac{1}{x}\,f(\ln |x|)\,dx$

(c) $\displaystyle\int \frac{f(\sqrt{x})}{\sqrt{x}}\,dx$

(d) $\displaystyle\int \frac{f(1/x)}{x^2}\,dx$

(e) $\displaystyle\int x^{r-1} f(x^r)\,dx$

(f) $\displaystyle\int \frac{f(\mathrm{Tan}^{-1} x)}{1+x^2}\,dx$

(g) $\displaystyle\int f(mx + b)\,dx$

(h) $\displaystyle\int g(x) f\left(\int_c^x g(t)\,dt\right)\,dx.$

3. Find an antiderivative of each of the following.

(a) $e^{\sin x} \cos x$

(b) $\cos (3x - 4)$

(c) $\sec^2 (2x + 3)$

(d) $x^{-1} \sin (\ln x)$

(e) $\dfrac{x^2}{\sqrt{x^3 - 5}}$

(f) $\dfrac{3x - 1}{3x^2 - 2x + 1}$

(g) $e^x \sec e^x \tan e^x$

(h) $\dfrac{e^x - e^{-x}}{e^x + e^{-x}}$

4. Find an integration formula with the given left-hand side.

(a) $\displaystyle\int \sec^3 x \tan x\,dx$

(b) $\displaystyle\int \frac{\cos 2x}{3 + 4 \sin 2x}\,dx$

(c) $\displaystyle\int \frac{3 + 4 \sin 2x}{\cos 2x}\,dx$

(d) $\displaystyle\int \ln e^{3x^2}\,dx$

(e) $\displaystyle\int \frac{e^{2x}}{e^x + 1}\,dx$

(f) $\displaystyle\int \exp (e^x + x)\,dx$

5. When finding integration formulas for the following, manipulate the integrand algebraically before deciding on your substitution.

(a) $\displaystyle\int \frac{dx}{x^2 + 4x + 13}$

(b) $\displaystyle\int \frac{dx}{\sqrt{6x - x^2 - 8}}$

(c) $\displaystyle\int \frac{dx}{\sqrt{8x - 4x^2}}$

(d) $\displaystyle\int \frac{(x + 2)\,dx}{x^2 - 6x + 10}$

6. Find an antiderivative of $\sec^6 x$ by first writing

$$\sec^6 x = \sec^4 x \sec^2 x = (1 + \tan^2 x)^2 \sec^2 x$$

and then letting $u = \tan x$.

7. (a) Explain how the substitution $u = ax^2 + b$ could be used to find

$$\int \frac{x^{2n} - 1}{\sqrt{ax^2 + b}}\,dx,$$

where n is a positive integer.

(b) Show how the substitution $u = 1/x$ reduces the problem of finding

$$\int \frac{dx}{x^{2n}\sqrt{ax^2 + b}},$$

where n is a positive integer, to the problem of Part (a).

57 INTEGRANDS INVOLVING TRIGONOMETRIC FUNCTIONS

If an integrand contains values of the trigonometric functions, we can often use appropriate trigonometric identities to help us as we search for an integration formula. Some of the most useful trigonometric identities for this purpose are

(57-1)
$$\cos^2 x + \sin^2 x = 1,$$
$$\tan^2 x = \sec^2 x - 1,$$
$$\cot^2 x = \csc^2 x - 1,$$

and

(57-2)
$$\sin^2 x = \frac{1 - \cos 2x}{2},$$
$$\cos^2 x = \frac{1 + \cos 2x}{2}.$$

Example 57-1. Find an antiderivative of $\tan^2 x$.

Solution. When we use the second of Equations 57-1, we obtain the integration formula

$$\int \tan^2 x \, dx = \int (\sec^2 x - 1) \, dx = \tan x - x,$$

which tells us that an antiderivative of $\tan^2 x$ is $\tan x - x$.

We often use our trigonometric identities to write a given integrand in the form $f(\sin x) \cos x$ or $f(\cos x) \sin x$; the first form suggests the substitution $u = \sin x$, and the second, the substitution $u = \cos x$.

Example 57-2. Evaluate the integral

$$\int_0^{\pi/2} \sin^4 x \cos^5 x \, dx.$$

Solution. In order to write $\sin^4 x \cos^5 x$ in the form $f(\sin x) \cos x$, we first express $\cos^4 x$ in terms of $\sin x$. Since $\cos^2 x = 1 - \sin^2 x$, we see that $\cos^4 x = (1 - \sin^2 x)^2$. Therefore,

$$\int_0^{\pi/2} \sin^4 x \cos^5 x \, dx = \int_0^{\pi/2} \sin^4 x (1 - \sin^2 x)^2 \cdot \cos x \, dx.$$

Now we let $u = \sin x$. Then $du = \cos x \, dx$, and $u = 0$ when $x = 0$ and $u = 1$ when $x = \pi/2$. Therefore, our integral becomes

$$\int_0^1 u^4 (1 - u^2)^2 \, du = \int_0^1 (u^4 - 2u^6 + u^8) \, du$$
$$= \tfrac{8}{315}.$$

We can use the method illustrated in the preceding example to find

$$\int \sin^n x \cos^m x \, dx$$

if at least one of the exponents is an odd positive integer. If $m = 2k + 1$, we write

$$\sin^n x \cos^m x = \sin^n x \cos^{2k} x \cos x = \sin^n x (1 - \sin^2 x)^k \cos x,$$

and we use the substitution $u = \sin x$. If $n = 2k + 1$, the integrand can be written as

$$\sin^n x \cos^m x = (1 - \cos^2 x)^k \cos^m x \sin x,$$

and we use the substitution $u = \cos x$.

If both exponents m and n are even, we can use Equations 57-2 (several times, if necessary) to reduce the problem to similar problems in which one of the exponents is odd. The next example shows how.

Example 57-3. Find $\int \sin^6 x \, dx$.

Solution. Here the form of the integrand is $\sin^n x \cos^m x$, where the exponents are the even integers $n = 6$ and $m = 0$. We use the first of Equations 57-2 to write

$$\sin^6 x = (\sin^2 x)^3 = \tfrac{1}{8}(1 - \cos 2x)^3 = \tfrac{1}{8}(1 - 3 \cos 2x + 3 \cos^2 2x - \cos^3 2x).$$

Thus

$$(57\text{-}3) \quad \int \sin^6 x \, dx = \tfrac{1}{8}\int 1 \, dx - \tfrac{3}{8}\int \cos 2x \, dx + \tfrac{3}{8}\int \cos^2 2x \, dx - \tfrac{1}{8}\int \cos^3 2x \, dx.$$

The first two terms on the right-hand side of this formula are easy to handle, and in the integrand of the fourth term there is the odd exponent 3. Therefore, we write

$$\int \cos^3 2x \, dx = \int (1 - \sin^2 2x) \cos 2x \, dx$$

and use the substitution $u = \sin 2x$. The integrand of the third term in Formula 57-3 has the even exponent 2, so we apply the second of Equations 57-2 to write

$$\int \cos^2 2x \, dx = \tfrac{1}{2}\int (1 + \cos 4x) \, dx = \tfrac{1}{2}x + \tfrac{1}{8} \sin 4x.$$

When we substitute the results of our calculations in Formula 57-3 and combine terms, we find that

$$\int \sin^6 x \, dx = \tfrac{5}{16} x - \tfrac{1}{4} \sin 2x + \tfrac{3}{64} \sin 4x - \tfrac{1}{48} \sin^4 2x.$$

Of course, there are many trigonometric identities in addition to Equations 57-1 and 57-2, and many of them are useful for finding integration formulas. We will mention just one more set of identities, the equations

$$2 \sin A \cos B = \sin (A + B) + \sin (A - B),$$

(57-4) $$2 \sin A \sin B = \cos (A - B) - \cos (A + B),$$

$$2 \cos A \cos B = \cos (A - B) + \cos (A + B).$$

Example 57-4. In certain applications of mathematics we meet the expression

$$B(m, n) = \int_{-\pi}^{\pi} \sin mx \sin nx \, dx,$$

where m and n are positive integers. Evaluate $B(5, 3)$ and $B(5, 5)$.

Solution. From the second of Equations 57-4 we have

$$\sin mx \sin nx = \frac{\cos (m - n)x - \cos (m + n)x}{2},$$

and so

(57-5) $$B(m, n) = \tfrac{1}{2} \int_{-\pi}^{\pi} [\cos (m - n)x - \cos (m + n)x] \, dx.$$

Therefore,

$$B(5, 3) = \tfrac{1}{2} \int_{-\pi}^{\pi} (\cos 2x - \cos 8x) \, dx$$

$$= \frac{1}{2} \left[\frac{\sin 2x}{2} - \frac{\sin 8x}{8} \right] \Big|_{-\pi}^{\pi}$$

$$= \frac{\sin 2\pi}{4} - \frac{\sin 8\pi}{16} + \frac{\sin 2\pi}{4} - \frac{\sin 8\pi}{16} = 0.$$

Equation 57-5 also gives us

$$B(5, 5) = \tfrac{1}{2} \int_{-\pi}^{\pi} (1 - \cos 10x) \, dx$$

$$= \frac{1}{2} \left[x - \frac{\sin 10x}{10} \right] \Big|_{-\pi}^{\pi} = \pi.$$

You should be able to show that $B(m, n) = 0$ if m and n are unequal positive integers, while $B(m, m) = \pi$ for every positive integer m.

Now let us look at some situations in which the methods of this section can be applied, even though we start with algebraic, rather than trigonometric, integrands. The trick is to change the algebraic integrands to trigonometric ones by means of a substitution suggested by the Theorem of Pythagoras and our knowledge of right triangle trigonometry. We apply this technique to integrands that contain powers of x and expressions of the form $(a^2 + x^2)^r$, $(a^2 - x^2)^r$, or $(x^2 - a^2)^r$. Figure 57-1 shows the right triangles that we draw in these cases. We use the Pythagorean Theorem to label the legs and hypotenuse of each triangle, the

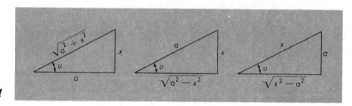

Figure 57-1

largest number being the length of the hypotenuse, of course. The first triangle suggests the substitution $u = \text{Tan}^{-1}\dfrac{x}{a}$, the second $u = \text{Sin}^{-1}\dfrac{x}{a}$, and the third $u = \text{Sin}^{-1}\dfrac{a}{x}$. Here is an example.

Example 57-5.   Find $\displaystyle\int \frac{\sqrt{9 - x^2}}{x}\, dx$.

Solution.   In this case we refer to the middle triangle in Fig. 57-1, with $a = 3$. The triangle suggests the substitution $u = \text{Sin}^{-1}\dfrac{x}{3}$, from which we calculate $du = \dfrac{dx}{\sqrt{9 - x^2}}$. We could also use the substitution equation to establish that $\sqrt{9 - x^2} = 3\cos u$ and $x = 3\sin u$, but it is easier to read these equations directly from the figure. Thus we have

$$\int \frac{\sqrt{9 - x^2}}{x}\, dx = \int \frac{3\cos u}{3\sin u}\, 3\cos u\, du = 3\int \frac{\cos^2 u}{\sin u}\, du, \quad u = \text{Sin}^{-1}\frac{x}{3}.$$

Now we find $3\displaystyle\int \frac{\cos^2 u}{\sin u}\, du$:

$$3\int \frac{\cos^2 u}{\sin u}\, du = 3\int \frac{1 - \sin^2 u}{\sin u}\, du$$

$$= 3\int (\csc u - \sin u)\, du$$

$$= 3(\ln |\csc u - \cot u| + \cos u).$$

To get our answer in terms of x, we again refer to Fig. 57-1, which tells us that $\csc u = \dfrac{3}{x}$, $\cot u = \dfrac{\sqrt{9 - x^2}}{x}$, and $\cos u = \dfrac{\sqrt{9 - x^2}}{3}$. Now we make the proper substitutions and write our integration formula:

$$\int \frac{\sqrt{9 - x^2}}{x}\, dx = 3 \ln \left| \frac{3 - \sqrt{9 - x^2}}{x} \right| + \sqrt{9 - x^2}.$$

To make sure that we didn't make a mistake in the course of our complicated calculations, you should check our final formula by differentiating the right-hand side.

PROBLEMS 57

1. Find the following.
 (a) $\int \cot^2 x\, dx$
 (b) $\int \sin x \cos^2 x\, dx$
 (c) $\int \cos^3 x \sin^2 x\, dx$
 (d) $\int \tan^2 x \sec^2 x\, dx$
 (e) $\int \sin x \sqrt{\cos x}\, dx$
 (f) $\int \sqrt[3]{\cos^2 x} \sin^5 x\, dx$

2. Find antiderivatives of the following.
 (a) $\sin^4 x$
 (b) $\sin^2 x \cos^2 x$
 (c) $\sin^2 x \cos^4 x$
 (d) $\sin^4 x \cos 2x$

3. Apply Formula V-41 to find an integration formula whose left-hand side is $\int \sin^6 x\, dx$, and compare the result with what we found in Example 57-3.

4. Find the following.
 (a) $\int \sec^5 x \sin x\, dx$
 (b) $\int \ln (\sin x) \cot x\, dx$
 (c) $\int \tan^2 x \cos x\, dx$
 (d) $\int \tan^4 x\, dx$

5. (a) Show that $\displaystyle\int_{-\pi}^{\pi} \cos mx \sin nx\, dx = 0$ if m and n are integers.

 (b) Set $A(m, n) = \displaystyle\int_{-\pi}^{\pi} \cos mx \cos nx\, dx$, where m and n are positive integers, and show that $A(m, n) = 0$ if $m \neq n$, while $A(m, m) = \pi$.

6. Find:
 (a) $\displaystyle\int \frac{dx}{x^2 \sqrt{x^2 + 25}}$
 (b) $\displaystyle\int \frac{dx}{(9 + x^2)^{3/2}}$
 (c) $\displaystyle\int \frac{dx}{x^2 \sqrt{9 - x^2}}$
 (d) $\displaystyle\int \frac{dx}{(1 + x^2)^2}$

7. Evaluate the following integrals.
 (a) $\displaystyle\int_{-\pi}^{\pi} |\cos^3 t|\, dt$
 (b) $\displaystyle\int_{-\pi}^{\pi} |\sin^5 t|\, dt$
 (c) $\displaystyle\int_{-\pi}^{\pi} |\cos^3 t + \sin^3 t|\, dt$
 (d) $\displaystyle\int_{0}^{\pi} \cos[\![x]\!] x\, dx$

8. Evaluate the integral $\displaystyle\int_0^{\pi/2} \sqrt{2 - \sin^2 x}\,\cos^3 x\,dx$.

9. The region bounded by the X-axis and the graphs of the equations $y = \operatorname{Sin}^{-1} x$ and $y = \operatorname{Cos}^{-1} x$ is rotated about the Y-axis. Find the volume of the resulting solid.

58 INTEGRANDS THAT ARE RATIONAL EXPRESSIONS

Up to now the algebraic operations we have performed on a given integrand have involved nothing more complicated than completing the square. Now we will introduce some deeper algebraic theory that will enable us to handle a very broad class of algebraic integrands.

If n is a positive integer or 0 and if $a_0, a_1, \ldots, a_n$ are $n + 1$ real numbers, where $a_n \neq 0$, then the expression

$$P(x) = a_n x^n + a^{n-1} x^{n-1} + \cdots + a_0$$

is called a **polynomial of degree n in x** with real **coefficients** $a_0, a_1, \ldots, a_n$. A *ratio* of two polynomials is termed a **rational expression.** For example $\dfrac{3x^2 + 2x - 1}{x - 2}$ and $\dfrac{1}{x^2 + 1}$ are rational expressions. In general, a rational expression takes the form

$$(58\text{-}1) \qquad F(x) = \frac{a_n x^n + a_{n-1} x^{n-1} + \cdots + a_0}{b_m x^m + b_{m-1} x^{m-1} + \cdots + b_0} = \frac{P(x)}{D(x)}.$$

You have studied polynomials in your earlier mathematics courses. You know how to add, subtract, and multiply two polynomials, and you know that there are theorems about factoring polynomials, and so on. We will now discuss a method of finding antiderivatives of rational expressions that is based on this algebraic theory. Since rational functions are continuous (Example 11-4), our differentiation formulas and integration formulas are equivalent; we will use this fact freely.

The basic algebraic fact that we use here is that every rational expression $F(x)$ can be written as a sum of terms of the forms

$$(58\text{-}2) \qquad q_r x^r + q_{r-1} x^{r-1} + \cdots + q_0, \qquad \frac{A}{(x - a)^r},$$

and

$$\frac{Bx + C}{(x^2 + bx + c)^r}, \qquad \text{where} \quad b^2 - 4c < 0.$$

For example,

$$(58-3) \quad \frac{x^9 - 6x^8 + 19x^7 - 35x^6 + 34x^5 - 5x^4 - 30x^3 + 48x^2 - 39x + 12}{x^7 - 6x^6 + 17x^5 - 28x^4 + 28x^3 - 16x^2 + 4x}$$

$$= x^2 + 2 + \frac{3}{x} + \frac{2}{x-1} - \frac{1}{(x-1)^2} + \frac{1}{x^2 - 2x + 2} + \frac{-8x + 11}{(x^2 - 2x + 2)^2}.$$

It is easy to find antiderivatives of Expressions 58-2. Polynomials present no problem, and we reduce $\int \frac{A}{(x-a)^r} dx$ to $A \int u^{-r} du$ by means of the substitution $u = x - a$. Expressions of the third type are most easily disposed of by referring to various formulas in Table V; see Example 54-3, for instance.

We know how to find antiderivatives of the individual terms of the decomposition of a rational expression; let us see how to obtain the decomposition. Suppose we have a rational expression such as $F(x)$ of Equation 58-1. If the degree of the numerator is as large as or larger than the degree of the denominator; that is, $n \geq m$, then we can use long division to write

$$(58-4) \qquad\qquad F(x) = Q(x) + \frac{R(x)}{D(x)},$$

where $Q(x)$ is a polynomial, $q_r x^r + \cdots + q_0$, and $R(x)$ is a polynomial whose degree is actually less than the degree of $D(x)$. The first step in finding the decomposition of a rational expression $F(x)$ is to write it in the form indicated in Equation 58-4.

Example 58-1. Perform the first step in the decomposition of $\dfrac{x^3 + 1}{x - 2}$ and find $\int \dfrac{x^3 + 1}{x - 2} dx$.

Solution. We use long division

$$
\begin{array}{r}
x^2 + 2x + 4 \\
x - 2 \overline{\smash{)}\, x^3 + 1 } \\
\underline{x^3 - 2x^2 } \\
2x^2 + 1 \\
\underline{2x^2 - 4x } \\
4x + 1 \\
\underline{4x - 8} \\
9
\end{array}
$$

to find the quotient $Q(x) = x^2 + 2x + 4$ and the remainder 9 that enable us to write

$$\frac{x^3 + 1}{x - 2} = x^2 + 2x + 4 + \frac{9}{x - 2}.$$

Notice that the degree of the remainder is 0, a number less than the degree (1) of the denominator $x - 2$. From this last equation we find that

$$\int \frac{x^3 + 1}{x - 2}\, dx = \int (x^2 + 2x + 4)\, dx + 9 \int \frac{dx}{x - 2}$$

$$= \frac{x^3}{3} + x^2 + 4x + 9 \ln |x - 2|.$$

After we have performed any necessary long division, we are left with the rational expression $\frac{R(x)}{D(x)}$ to decompose. The degree of $R(x)$ is less than the degree of $D(x)$. Now we factor the denominator $D(x)$ into a product of real factors. These factors can all be reduced to one of two forms, either $x - a$ or $x^2 + bx + c$, where $b^2 - 4c < 0$. (If $b^2 - 4c \geq 0$, we can factor $x^2 + bx + c$ into two real factors.) Some of the factors may be repeated, so our denominator will be a product of powers of such factors. [The so-called Fundamental Theorem of Algebra guarantees that such a factorization is (theoretically) possible.] For example, the denominator of the rational Expression 58-3 is the product

$$x(x - 1)^2(x^2 - 2x + 2)^2.$$

Each factor $(x - a)^r$ *in the denominator leads to a sum of the form*

$$\frac{A_1}{x - a} + \frac{A_2}{(x - a)^2} + \cdots + \frac{A_r}{(x - a)^r}$$

in the decomposition of $F(x)$. For example, the factor $(x - 1)^2$ in the denominator of Expression 58-3 led to the sum $\frac{2}{x - 1} - \frac{1}{(x - 1)^2}$ in its decomposition. An example will show us how we find such sums.

Example 58-2.   Decompose the rational expression

$$\frac{x^2 - 7x + 8}{(x - 2)(x - 3)^2}.$$

Solution.   We notice first that the degree of the numerator (2) is less than the degree of the denominator (3), so we can omit the long division. The factor $x - 2$ in the denominator leads to a term $\frac{A}{x - 2}$ and the factor $(x - 3)^2$ leads to a sum $\frac{B}{x - 3} + \frac{C}{(x - 3)^2}$ in the decomposition. In other words,

(58-5) $$\frac{x^2 - 7x + 8}{(x - 2)(x - 3)^2} = \frac{A}{x - 2} + \frac{B}{x - 3} + \frac{C}{(x - 3)^2},$$

and now we have to determine the numbers A, B, and C. To do so we multiply both sides of Equation 58-5 by $(x - 2)(x - 3)^2$ and obtain the equation

(58-6) $x^2 - 7x + 8 = A(x - 3)^2 + B(x - 2)(x - 3) + C(x - 2).$

There are now two ways to proceed. We could multiply out the terms on the right in Equation 58-6 and obtain the equation

$$x^2 - 7x + 8 = (A + B)x^2 + (-6A - 5B + C)x + 9A + 6B - 2C.$$

Now when we equate the coefficients of corresponding powers of x, we obtain the following system of equations

$$A + B = 1$$
$$-6A - 5B + C = -7$$
$$9A + 6B - 2C = 8.$$

We find that the solution to this system of algebraic equations is $A = -2$, $B = 3$, and $C = -4$.

We can arrive at the same numbers by means of a somewhat simpler calculation. Equation 58-6 is to be valid for each real number x. If we set, in turn, $x = 2, 3$ and 0, we get the three equations

$$A = -2$$
$$C = -4$$
$$9A + 6B - 2C = 8.$$

The first two equations give us A and C, and then the third equation tells us that $B = 3$. Thus both methods give us the decomposition

$$\frac{x^2 - 7x + 8}{(x - 2)(x - 3)^2} = \frac{-2}{x - 2} + \frac{3}{x - 3} - \frac{4}{(x - 3)^2}.$$

If a factor of the form $(x^2 + bx + c)^r$ appears in the denominator of our rational expression, then in its decomposition we will have a sum of terms of the form

$$\frac{B_1 x + C_1}{(x^2 + bx + c)} + \frac{B_2 x + C_2}{(x^2 + bx + c)^2} + \cdots + \frac{B_r x + C_r}{(x^2 + bx + c)^r}.$$

For example, the decomposition shown in Equation 58-3 contains the sum

$$\frac{1}{(x^2 - 2x + 2)} + \frac{-8x + 11}{(x^2 - 2x + 2)^2}.$$

Again, an example will show us how we find such sums.

Example 58-3.   Decompose the rational expression

$$\frac{2x^2 + 1}{(x^2 - x + 1)^2}.$$

Solution.   We must find numbers A, B, C, and D such that

$$\frac{2x^2 + 1}{(x^2 - x + 1)^2} = \frac{Ax + B}{(x^2 - x + 1)} + \frac{Cx + D}{(x^2 - x + 1)^2}.$$

We multiply both sides of this equation by $(x^2 - x + 1)^2$ and obtain the equation

$$2x^2 + 1 = (Ax + B)(x^2 - x + 1) + Cx + D$$
$$= Ax^3 + (-A + B)x^2 + (A - B + C)x + (B + D).$$

Now we equate the coefficients of corresponding powers of x:

$$A = 0,$$
$$-A + B = 2,$$
$$A - B + C = 0,$$
$$B + D = 1.$$

When we solve this system of equations, we find $B = 2$, $C = 2$, and $D = -1$, and we have

$$\frac{2x^2 + 1}{(x^2 - x + 1)^2} = \frac{2}{x^2 - x + 1} + \frac{2x - 1}{(x^2 - x + 1)^2}.$$

Example 58-4.   Find

$$\int \frac{6x^3 + 5x^2 + 21x + 12}{x(x + 1)(x^2 + 4)} \, dx.$$

Solution.   We first write

$$\frac{6x^3 + 5x^2 + 21x + 12}{x(x + 1)(x^2 + 4)} = \frac{A}{x} + \frac{B}{x + 1} + \frac{Cx + D}{x^2 + 4}.$$

When we clear of fractions, we obtain the equation

$$6x^3 + 5x^2 + 21x + 12 = A(x + 1)(x^2 + 4) + Bx(x^2 + 4)$$
$$+ (Cx + D)x(x + 1)$$
$$= (A + B + C)x^3 + (A + D + C)x^2$$
$$+ (4A + 4B + D)x + 4A.$$

Therefore,

$$A + B + C = 6,$$

$$A + C + D = 5,$$

$$4A + 4B + D = 21,$$

$$4A = 12.$$

Now we solve this system of equations and find $A = 3$, $B = 2$, $C = 1$, $D = 1$, and so

$$\int \frac{6x^3 + 5x^2 + 21x + 12}{x(x + 1)(x^2 + 4)}\, dx = \int \frac{3}{x}\, dx + \int \frac{2}{x + 1}\, dx + \int \frac{x + 1}{x^2 + 4}\, dx.$$

We will leave it to you to show that we can use our integration formulas to write

$$\int \frac{6x^3 + 5x^2 + 21x + 12}{x(x + 1)(x^2 + 4)}\, dx = 3 \ln |x| + 2 \ln |x + 1| + \frac{1}{2} \ln (x^2 + 4)$$

$$+ \frac{1}{2} \operatorname{Arctan} \frac{x}{2} = \ln |x^3(x + 1)^2 \sqrt{x^2 + 4}| + \frac{1}{2} \operatorname{Arctan} \frac{x}{2}.$$

P R O B L E M S   5 8

1. Decompose the following rational expressions.

(a) $\dfrac{x^3}{x + 1}$

(b) $\dfrac{x}{x^2 + x}$

(c) $\dfrac{5x + 2}{x^2 - 4}$

(d) $\dfrac{x^2}{x^2 - x}$

(e) $\dfrac{5x + 2}{x^2 + 4}$

(f) $\dfrac{1}{x^2(x + 1)}$

2. Find an antiderivative of each of the expressions in the preceding problem.

3. Use the method of this section to find:

(a) $\displaystyle\int \frac{3x^2 + 4x + 4}{x(x + 1)(x + 2)}\, dx$

(b) $\displaystyle\int \frac{5x^2 - 3}{x^3 - x}\, dx$

(c) $\displaystyle\int \frac{x^3}{(x + 1)^2}\, dx$

(d) $\displaystyle\int \frac{dx}{x^3 + 4x}$

(e) $\displaystyle\int \frac{(x + 1)^2}{x^3}\, dx$

(f) $\displaystyle\int \frac{x^3 + 1}{x(x - 1)^3}\, dx$

(g) $\displaystyle\int \frac{t^4 - 8}{t^3 + 2t^2}\, dt$

(h) $\displaystyle\int \frac{x^3 + 3x}{x^4 + 2x^2 + 1}\, dx$

4. Use the method of this section to "derive" the following formulas.

(a) V-27   (b) V-29

5. Use the method of this section to "derive" the formula

$$\int \frac{du}{u^2 - a^2} = \frac{1}{2a} \ln \left| \frac{u - a}{u + a} \right|.$$

(See Formulas V-22 and V-23.)

6. Find:

(a) $\displaystyle\int \frac{3x^2 + 2x + 1}{(x + 1)(x^2 + x + 1)} \, dx$

(b) $\displaystyle\int \frac{(x + 1)^2 \, dx}{(x^2 + 1)^2}$

(c) $\displaystyle\int \frac{(x^2 + x) \, dx}{(x - 1)(x^2 + 1)}$

(d) $\displaystyle\int \frac{dt}{t^4 + t^2}$

(e) $\displaystyle\int \frac{2 \, dz}{z^4 - 1}$

(f) $\displaystyle\int \frac{x^5 \, dx}{(x^2 + 4)^2}$

7. Evaluate:

(a) $\displaystyle\int_1^2 \frac{(x - 3) \, dx}{x^3 + x^2}$

(b) $\displaystyle\int_1^3 \frac{(2 - t^2) \, dt}{t^3 + 3t^2 + 2t}$

(c) $\displaystyle\int_0^1 \frac{dx}{x^3 + 1}$

(d) $\displaystyle\int_0^1 \frac{z \, dz}{(z + 2)(z^2 + 1)}$

(e) $\displaystyle\int_3^4 \frac{5x^3 - 4x}{x^4 - 16} \, dx$

(f) $\displaystyle\int_0^1 \frac{x \, dx}{x^3 + 1}$

8. One method of "deriving" the formula for $\int \csc u \, du$ is to proceed as follows. Let $u = 2v$ so that

$$\int \csc u \, du = \int \frac{du}{\sin u} = \int \frac{dv}{\sin v \cos v} = \int \frac{\cos v \, dv}{\sin v \cos^2 v}$$

$$= \int \frac{\cos v \, dv}{\sin v (1 - \sin^2 v)}.$$

Now make the substitution $x = \sin v$, and use the method of this section to obtain Formula V-36.

9. If we want to find $\int R(\cos x, \sin x) \, dx$, where $R(\cos x, \sin x)$ is made up of sums, products, and quotients of numbers and $\cos x$ and $\sin x$, we can use the substitution $u = \tan \frac{1}{2}x$ and then the methods described in this section. With this substitution, $du = \frac{1}{2} \sec^2 \frac{1}{2}x \, dx = \dfrac{dx}{2 \cos^2 \frac{1}{2}x} = \dfrac{dx}{1 + \cos x}$, and now we must find a way of expressing $\cos x$ and $\sin x$ in terms of u. From Equation A-5 (Appendix A), with $t = \frac{1}{2}x$, we see that $\tan^2 \frac{1}{2}x = \dfrac{1 - \cos x}{1 + \cos x}$. Thus $u^2 = \dfrac{1 - \cos x}{1 + \cos x}$, from which we find that $\cos x = \dfrac{1 - u^2}{1 + u^2}$. From the third of equations A-4, with $t = \frac{1}{2}x$, we have $\tan x = \dfrac{2 \tan \frac{1}{2}x}{1 - \tan^2 \frac{1}{2}x}$; that is, $\dfrac{\sin x}{\cos x} = \dfrac{2u}{1 - u^2}$. Since we already know $\cos x$, it is a simple matter to solve this equation for $\sin x$. In summary, then,

$$\cos x = \frac{1 - u^2}{1 + u^2}, \ \sin x = \frac{2u}{1 + u^2}, \text{ and } dx = \frac{2}{1 + u^2}\, du.$$

Use this substitution procedure to find the following

(a) $\displaystyle\int \frac{dx}{1 + \sin x}$ (b) $\displaystyle\int \frac{dx}{3 + 5 \sin x}$ (c) $\displaystyle\int \frac{dx}{5 + 3 \sin x}$ (d) $\displaystyle\int \frac{dx}{3 \sin x + 4 \cos x}$

59 INTEGRATION BY PARTS

Our method of substitution is a device for utilizing the Chain Rule to calculate integrals and find antiderivatives. Now we are going to put another general differentiation formula to work. The Product Rule of differentiation states that if the functions f and g are differentiable in an interval I, then

$$D_x[f(x)g(x)] = f(x)g'(x) + g(x)f'(x)$$

for each $x \in I$. In other words, $f(x)g(x)$ is an antiderivative of $f(x)g'(x) + g(x)f'(x)$. Therefore (if f' and g' are integrable), the Fundamental Theorem of Calculus tells us that

$$\int_a^b [f(x)g'(x) + g(x)f'(x)]\, dx = f(x)g(x) \Big|_a^b$$

for an arbitrary pair of points a and b of I. We may rewrite this equation in the form

(59-1) $$\int_a^b f(x)g'(x)\, dx = f(x)g(x) \Big|_a^b - \int_a^b g(x)f'(x)\, dx.$$

In our abbreviated notation, we drop the limits of integration and simply write

(59-2) $$\int f(x)g'(x)\, dx = f(x)g(x) - \int g(x)f'(x)\, dx.$$

We will change the appearance, but not the content, of this last integration formula if we set $u = f(x)$ and $v = g(x)$. Then $f'(x) = D_x u$ and $g'(x) = D_x v$, and our formula becomes

$$\int u\, D_x v\, dx = uv - \int v\, D_x u\, dx.$$

Now if we replace $D_x v\, dx$ with dv and $D_x u\, dx$ with du, as we do when we use our method of substitution, this last formula becomes

(59-3) $$\int u\, dv = uv - \int v\, du.$$

When using Formula 59-3, we keep the substitution equations $u = f(x)$ and $v = g(x)$ in mind; the formula is really just a notational simplification of Formula 59-2.

The rule that is expressed by Equation 59-1 and Formulas 59-2 and 59-3 is known as the process of **integration by parts.** We can use it to find antiderivatives and integrals that would otherwise be difficult to obtain. Basically, the rule replaces the problem of finding $\int u\, dv$ with the problem of finding $\int v\, du$, and sometimes the second problem is easier to deal with than the first. For example, suppose we let $u = x$ and $v = \sin x$ in Formula 59-3. Then $du = dx$ and $dv = \cos x\, dx$, and our formula becomes

$$\int x \cos x\, dx = x \sin x - \int \sin x\, dx$$

$$= x \sin x + \cos x.$$

These formulas show that we transformed the problem of finding $\int x \cos dx$ into the easier problem of finding $\int \sin x\, dx$. The key step in applying the integration by parts technique is to choose u and v properly. Sometimes a little experimentation is necessary.

Example 59-1.   Find $\int x \ln x\, dx$.

Solution.   Here we let $u = \ln x$, and we will choose v so that $dv = x\, dx$. The simplest choice is $v = \dfrac{x^2}{2}$. We see that $du = \dfrac{1}{x}\, dx$, and so Formula 59-3 reads

$$\int x \ln x\, dx = \frac{x^2}{2} \ln x - \int \frac{x^2}{2} \cdot \frac{1}{x}\, dx$$

$$= \frac{x^2 \ln x}{2} - \int \frac{1}{2} x\, dx$$

$$= \frac{x^2 \ln x}{2} - \frac{x^2}{4}.$$

It is easy to verify this result by differentiation.

In our usual applications, of course, we are not told what substitutions u and v to make. We are presented with an expression of the form $\int F(x)\, dx$, and it is then up to us to write $F(x)\, dx$ as $u\, dv$. We are free to chose u arbitrarily. This choice determines dv, and then to finish filling out the formula, we must compute $du = D_x u\, dx$ and find v such that $D_x v\, dx$ is our chosen dv. There is no set procedure for making the proper choice of u, but once we make our choice, the rest of the calculation is straightforward.

Example 59-2.   Find $\int x(x-3)^5\, dx$.

Solution.   In this case we will choose $u = x$, and so $dv = (x-3)^5\, dx$. It follows immediately that $du = dx$, and now we must find v such that $dv = D_x v\, dx = (x-3)^5\, dx$. Thus we will want $D_x v = (x-3)^5$; in other words, v must be an antiderivative of $(x-3)^5$. In symbols, we have

$$v = \int (x-3)^5\, dx,$$

from which you can find, by substitution if necessary, that $v = \dfrac{(x-3)^6}{6}$ is a suitable choice for v. Now Formula 59-3 becomes

$$\int x(x-3)^5\, dx = \frac{x(x-3)^6}{6} - \frac{1}{6}\int (x-3)^6\, dx$$

$$= \frac{x(x-3)^6}{6} - \frac{(x-3)^7}{42}.$$

Example 59-3.   Find $\int x^2 e^x\, dx$.

Solution.   We let $u = x^2$ and hence $dv = e^x\, dx$. Then $du = 2x\, dx$, and $v = \int e^x\, dx = e^x$, so Formula 59-3 reads

(59-4)
$$\int x^2 e^x\, dx = x^2 e^x - 2 \int x e^x\, dx.$$

To finish our problem, we must find $\int x e^x\, dx$. What we have done so far is to reduce the problem of finding $\int x^2 e^x\, dx$ to the simpler problem of finding $\int x e^x\, dx$. We find $\int x e^x\, dx$ by using the integration by parts procedure a second time. Here we set $u = x$, and again take $v = e^x$. Then $du = dx$, and we have

$$\int x e^x\, dx = x e^x - \int e^x\, dx = x e^x - e^x.$$

When this result is substituted in Formula 59-4 we get

$$\int x^2 e^x\, dx = x^2 e^x - 2x e^x + 2 e^x.$$

Before we leave this problem, let us see how we could have gone wrong in our choice of u. Suppose we had originally let $u = e^x$ and $dv = x^2\, dx$. Then $du = e^x\, dx$, $v = \int x^2\, dx = \dfrac{x^3}{3}$, and Formula 59-3 becomes

$$\int x^2 e^x\, dx = \frac{x^3 e^x}{3} - \frac{1}{3} \int x^3 e^x\, dx.$$

Although this equation is correct, it leaves us with the problem of finding $\int x^3 e^x\, dx$, which is at least as difficult as the original problem. It is quite common to make such a false start, and when we do we just have to go back and start over.

Example 59-4. Find $\displaystyle\int_0^1 \operatorname{Tan}^{-1} x\, dx$.

Solution. Here let us set $f(x) = \operatorname{Tan}^{-1} x$ and $g'(x) = 1$. Then $f'(x) = \dfrac{1}{1+x^2}$, and we can take $g(x) = x$. Thus Equation 59-1 becomes

$$\int_0^1 \operatorname{Tan}^{-1} x\, dx = x \operatorname{Tan}^{-1} x \Big|_0^1 - \int_0^1 \frac{x}{1+x^2}\, dx$$

$$= x \operatorname{Tan}^{-1} x \Big|_0^1 - \tfrac{1}{2} \ln (1 + x^2) \Big|_0^1$$

$$= \operatorname{Tan}^{-1} 1 - \tfrac{1}{2} \ln 2 \approx .44.$$

If you study mathematics further, or go on in fields in which mathematics is used, you will find that integration by parts is an important tool in theoretical investigations. The following example is a simplified version of a problem that arises in the study of differential equations.

Example 59-5. Suppose that u is a function such that $u(a) = u(b) = 0$. Show that

$$\int_a^b u(x) u''(x)\, dx = -\int_a^b [u'(x)]^2\, dx.$$

Solution. We will let $f(x) = u(x)$ and $g(x) = u'(x)$ in Equation 59-1. Then

$$\int_a^b u(x) u''(x)\, dx = u(x) u'(x) \Big|_a^b - \int_a^b u'(x) u'(x)\, dx$$

$$= 0 - \int_a^b [u'(x)]^2\, dx.$$

Our final example emphasizes once more that Integration Formula 59-3 is an abbreviation; the basic rule is Equation 59-1. We must insert the limits of integration to get the basic equation.

Example 59-6.   Apply the integration by parts technique to $\int \dfrac{1}{x}\, dx$.

Solution.   We will set $u = 1/x$, and so $dv = dx$. Then $du = -\dfrac{1}{x^2}\, dx$, and we may take $v = x$. Therefore, Formula 59-3 becomes

$$\int \frac{1}{x}\, dx = 1 + \int \frac{1}{x}\, dx,$$

and it would seem to follow that $1 = 0$. Actually, however, our last formula is an abbreviation for the equation

$$\int_a^b \frac{1}{x}\, dx = 1 \bigg|_a^b + \int_a^b \frac{1}{x}\, dx,$$

and $1 \bigg|_a^b$ *is* 0, so there is no contradiction.

P R O B L E M S   5 9

1. Use integration by parts to find:
  (a) $\int x \sin x\, dx$ (b) $\int x \cos 2x\, dx$
  (c) $\int x e^{2x}\, dx$ (d) $\int t \sec^2 2t\, dt$
  (e) $\int x^5 \ln x\, dx$ (f) $\int \mathrm{Tan}^{-1} 2x\, dx$
  (g) $\int \mathrm{Sin}^{-1} x\, dx$ (h) $\int \mathrm{Cosh}^{-1} x\, dx$
  (i) $\int x(x + 25)^{100}\, dx$ (j) $\int x a^x\, dx$

2. Use integration by parts to evaluate the following integrals.

  (a) $\displaystyle\int_0^2 x(x - 2)^4\, dx$ (b) $\displaystyle\int_0^1 x e^{3x}\, dx$

  (c) $\displaystyle\int_0^{\pi/2} x \cos x\, dx$ (d) $\displaystyle\int_0^1 \mathrm{Cos}^{-1} x\, dx$

  (e) $\displaystyle\int_1^2 (\ln x)^2\, dx$ (f) $\displaystyle\int_0^1 x \,\mathrm{Tan}^{-1} x\, dx$

3. It may be necessary to apply the integration by parts procedure more than once to find the following.

  (a) $\displaystyle\int x^2 \cos x\, dx$ (b) $\displaystyle\int x^4 (\ln x)^2\, dx$

  (c) $\displaystyle\int x^3 \,\mathrm{Tan}^{-1} x\, dx$ (d) $\displaystyle\int_1^2 (x - 1)^2 (x - 2)^{10}\, dx$

  (e) $\displaystyle\int_0^{\pi/2} x^2 \sin x\, dx$ (f) $\displaystyle\int_0^1 x \,\mathrm{Sin}^{-1} x\, dx$

4. Find $\int \ln x \, dx$ by taking $u = \ln x$ and $dv = dx$ and using integration by parts.

5. Find $\int_a^b e^{-x} \cos 2x \, dx$ by the following procedure. First, take $u = e^{-x}$ and $dv = \cos 2x \, dx$. In the new integral that results from using the integration by parts procedure take $u = e^{-x}$ and $dv = \sin 2x \, dx$ to obtain the equation

$$\int_a^b e^{-x} \cos 2x \, dx = \tfrac{1}{2} e^{-x} \sin 2x \Big|_a^b - \tfrac{1}{4} e^{-x} \cos 2x \Big|_a^b - \tfrac{1}{4} \int_a^b e^{-x} \cos 2x \, dx.$$

Find $\int_a^b e^{-x} \cos 2x \, dx$ from this equation.

6. Find: (a) $\int x^3 \cos x^2 \, dx$ (b) $\int x^5 e^{x^2} \, dx$

7. Verify the formula

$$\int x f'(x) \, dx = x f(x) - \int f(x) \, dx.$$

What specific formulas do you obtain by replacing $f(x)$ with $\csc^2 x$, $\cosh x$, and e^x?

8. Find the volume of the solid obtained by rotating about the X-axis the region bounded by the X-axis and the graph of the equation $y = \sqrt[4]{x^2(1-x)}$.

9. (a) Suppose that m is a positive integer and take $u = \sin^{m-1} x$ and $dv = \sin x \, dx$ in the formula for integration by parts to obtain the equation

(i) $\displaystyle\int_0^{\pi/2} \sin^m x \, dx = -\cos x \sin^{m-1} x \Big|_0^{\pi/2} + (m-1) \int_0^{\pi/2} \sin^{m-2} x \cos^2 x \, dx.$

(b) In Equation (i) replace $\cos^2 x$ by $1 - \sin^2 x$ and solve the resulting equation for $\displaystyle\int_0^{\pi/2} \sin^m x \, dx$.

(c) Use the formula you obtained in part (b) to evaluate the integrals $\displaystyle\int_0^{\pi/2} \sin^5 x \, dx$ and $\displaystyle\int_0^{\pi/2} \sin^6 x \, dx$.

10. Use integration by parts to obtain the following formulas.

(a) $\displaystyle\int_0^a x^2 f'''(x) \, dx = a^2 f''(a) - 2a f'(a) + 2f(a) - 2f(0).$

(b) $\displaystyle\int_a^b f(x) g''(x) \, dx = [f(x)g'(x) - f'(x)g(x)] \Big|_a^b + \int_a^b f''(x)g(x) \, dx.$

11. Suppose we apply the integration by parts technique to find $\int \cos x \csc x \, dx$. We will let $u = \csc x$, and so $dv = \cos x \, dx$. Therefore, $du = -\csc x \cot x \, dx$, and we can take $v = \sin x$. Hence formula 59-3 becomes

$$\int \cos x \csc x \, dx = 1 + \int \sin x \csc x \cot x \, dx.$$

It is easy to see that both integrands in the formula above are $\cot x$, so it looks as if we have demonstrated that $1 = 0$. Did we?

12. We can use the integration by parts technique to find the integral $\int_0^a (a^2 - t^2)^{3/2} \, dt$

as follows. First write $\int_0^a (a^2 - t^2)^{3/2} \, dx = a^2 \int_0^a \sqrt{a^2 - t^2} \, dt - \int_0^a t^2 \sqrt{a^2 - t^2} \, dt.$
We know that the first integral on the right-hand side of this equation is $\dfrac{\pi a^2}{4}$.
Apply the integration by parts formula, with $u = t$, $dv = t \sqrt{a^2 - t} \, dt$, to the
second integral, and obtain an equation that you can solve for $\int_0^a (a^2 - t^2)^{3/2} \, dt.$

60 DIFFERENTIAL PROBLEMS

To say that $F(x)$ is an antiderivative of $f(x)$ means that $y = F(x)$ satisfies the differential equation

(60-1) $y' = f(x).$

We solve this differential equation when we use the Fundamental Theorem of Calculus to evaluate the integral $\int_a^b f(x) \, dx$ as the difference $F(b) - F(a)$. For this purpose, any solution of Equation 60-1 will do. For example, to evaluate the integral $\int_1^2 3x^2 \, dx$, we could take $F(x)$ to be x^3, $x^3 + \pi$, $x^3 - 6$, and so on, since $y = x^3$, $y = x^3 + \pi$, $y = x^3 - 6$, and so on, all satisfy the differential equation

(60-2) $y' = 3x^2.$

In most applications of differential equations, however, it is not true that just any solution will do. Only a particular solution, one that also satisfies some given "initial conditions," will solve our problem. Thus in addition to Equation 60-1 we might be given two numbers a and c and be asked to find $F(x)$ such that $y = F(x)$ satisfies the differential equation *and* the initial condition $y = c$ when $x = a$. For example, $y = x^3 + 3$ satisfies Equation 60-2 and the initial condition $y = 3$ when $x = 0$. When we add an initial condition to the Differential Equation 60-1, we obtain the **differential problem**

(60-3) $y' = f(x), \quad y = c \text{ when } x = a.$

When we meet a differential problem, we ask two questions:
(i) Does the problem have a solution? (Existence question)
(ii) If so, is there only one solution? (Uniqueness question)
For Differential Problem 60-3, the answer is "yes" to both questions. Let us consider the uniqueness question first. Suppose that $y = F(x)$ and $y = G(x)$ both satisfy our differential problem in some interval I. Then $F'(x) = G'(x)$, so according

to Theorem 19-3, there is a number C such that $F(x) = G(x) + C$ for each $x \in I$. In particular, this equation holds when x is replaced by a. But our initial condition tells us that $F(a) = c$ and $G(a) = c$, so we have $c = c + C$. It therefore follows that $C = 0$, and the equation $F(x) = G(x) + C$ reduces to $F(x) = G(x)$. In other words, F and G are the same; Problem 60-3 can have only one solution. The next theorem answers the existence question; it tells us that the problem does have a solution. In fact, it tells us what the solution is.

Theorem 60-1.   *If f is continuous in an interval I that contains the point a, then*

$$y = \int_a^x f(t)\, dt + c$$

satisfies Differential Problem 60-3.

Proof. The proof is simply a matter of verification. From Theorem 43-2 we see that $y' = f(x)$, so y satisfies the given differential equation. Furthermore, when we set $x = a$, we obtain $y = c$, and hence our initial condition is also satisfied.

Example 60-1.   At each point (x, y) of a certain graph, the slope is $\sec^2 x$. Furthermore, the graph contains the point $\left(\dfrac{\pi}{4}, 3\right)$. Find the equation of the graph.

Solution.   Since the slope of the graph is y', we see that y must satisfy the differential equation $y' = \sec^2 x$. In addition, we are told that $y = 3$ when $x = \dfrac{\pi}{4}$. Therefore, we are to solve the differential problem

$$y' = \sec^2 x, \quad y = 3 \text{ when } x = \frac{\pi}{4}.$$

According to Theorem 60-1, the solution to this problem is

$$y = \int_{\pi/4}^x \sec^2 t\, dt + 3 = \tan t \Big|_{\pi/4}^x + 3 = \tan x + 2.$$

Example 60-2.   The graph of a function f is shown in Fig. 60-1. Let y satisfy the differential problem $y' = f(x)$, $y = 3$ when $x = 0$. Find y when $x = 2, 3$, and 6.

Solution.   According to Theorem 60-1, our solution is

$$y = \int_0^x f(t)\, dt + 3.$$

Thus when $x = 2$, $y = \displaystyle\int_0^2 f(t)\, dt + 3$. To evaluate the integral $\displaystyle\int_0^2 f(t)\, dt$, we notice that it is simply the area of the triangle based on the interval $[0, 2]$ and with vertex

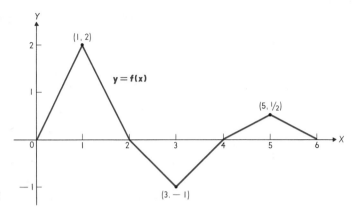

Figure 60-1

(1, 2). The base of this triangle is 2 units long, and its altitude is 2, so its area is 2 square units. Thus $\int_0^2 f(t)\,dt = 2$, so $y = 2 + 3 = 5$ when $x = 2$.

When $x = 3$,

$$y = \int_0^3 f(t)\,dt + 3 = \int_0^2 f(t)\,dt + \int_2^3 f(t)\,dt + 3$$

$$= 2 + \int_2^3 f(t)\,dt + 3 = 5 + \int_2^3 f(t)\,dt.$$

To evaluate the integral $\int_2^3 f(t)\,dt$, we see from Fig. 60-1 that it is simply the negative of the area of a triangle whose base and altitude are both 1. Therefore, $\int_2^3 f(t)\,dt = -\frac{1}{2}$, so $y = 5 - \frac{1}{2} = \frac{9}{2}$ when $x = 3$. When $x = 6$,

$$y = \int_0^6 f(t)\,dt + 3 = \int_0^2 f(t)\,dt + \int_2^4 f(t)\,dt + \int_4^6 f(t)\,dt + 3.$$

We again evaluate our integrals by interpreting them as areas and get

$$y = 2 - 1 + \frac{1}{2} + 3 = \frac{9}{2}.$$

The following table lists the answers to our problem

x	y
2	5
3	$\frac{9}{2}$
6	$\frac{9}{2}$

Recall that if a body is displaced s feet from some initial position t seconds after some initial instant, then the numbers $s' = v$ and $s'' = v' = a$ represent its velocity and acceleration. It is a physical fact that the acceleration of an un-supported body in a vacuum near the surface of the earth is approximately -32 feet per second per second, so its displacement s satisfies the differential equation $s'' = -32$. (Here we are measuring distance on a number scale that is perpendicular to the surface of the earth; the minus sign indicates that this number scale is pointed upwards. Let us suppose that the origin of our number scale is on the surface of the earth so that the displacement s is the number of feet the body is above the surface.) If our body has a velocity of v_0 feet per second when $t = 0$ and is s_0 feet above the surface of the earth at that instant, we have two initial conditions to add to our differential equation to produce the differential problem

(60-4) $\qquad\qquad s'' = -32, \quad s = s_0 \text{ and } s' = v_0 \text{ when } t = 0.$

(Because the highest derivative of s that appears in our differential equation is the second, the differential equation is said to be of the *second order*. As this problem illustrates, when we deal with a differential equation of the second order, we need two initial conditions to determine our solution; when our differential equation is of the third order, we need three initial conditions, and so on.) If we write $v = s'$, we can replace Differential Problem 60-4 with the two problems

(60-5) $\qquad\qquad\qquad\qquad v' = -32, \quad v = v_0 \text{ when } t = 0$

and

(60-6) $\qquad\qquad\qquad\qquad s' = v, \quad s = s_0 \text{ when } t = 0.$

These problems are in the form of Problem 60-3, so we can solve them successively by means of Theorem 60-1. Thus

$$v = \int_0^t (-32) \, dz + v_0 = -32t + v_0.$$

Now we substitute this expression for v in Differential Problem 60-6 and use Theorem 60-1 to solve it:

(60-7) $\qquad s = \int_0^t (-32z + v_0) \, dz + s_0 = -16t^2 + v_0 t + s_0.$

You probably recognize this equation from elementary physics.

> *Example 60-3.* You are at a hotel window 100 feet up with a paper bag full of water. A man is walking toward the spot directly under your window at the rate of 10 feet per second. If you throw the bag straight down when he is 20 feet from the spot, how fast should you throw it to hit him?

Solution. We may use Equation 60-7 to find the initial velocity v_0. We are told that the initial height is $s_0 = 100$. Furthermore, since the target will be in position when $t = 2$, we see that we want $s = 0$ at that time (humanely, we aim the bag at the victim's feet). Therefore, Equation 60-7 becomes

$$0 = -16 \cdot 2^2 + 2v_0 + 100.$$

From this equation we find that $v_0 = -18$. We must throw the bag with a speed of 18 feet per second (the minus sign indicates that we are to throw the bag downward).

Theorem 60-1 tells us how to solve differential equations of the simple form $y' = f(x)$, and in the problems we will show you how to solve differential equations of the form $y' + p(x)y = q(x)$. Our next theorem supplies the procedure for solving still another type of differential equation of the first order (there is no simple rule that will work for all types).

Theorem 60-2. *If f and g are continuous, and $g(y) \neq 0$ for y in some neighborhood $N_p c$ then we can find the solution of the differential problem*

(60-8) $$y' = \frac{f(x)}{g(y)}, \qquad y = c \quad when \quad x = a,$$

in some neighborhood $N_r a$ by solving the equation

(60-9) $$\int_c^y g(t)\, dt = \int_a^x f(t)\, dt$$

for y.

Proof. We will define a function G by means of the equation $G(y) = \int_c^y g(t)\, dt$. Then Equation 60-9 becomes $G(y) = \int_a^x f(t)\, dt$, and we can solve it for y if G has an inverse. Theorem 45-1 tells us that G has an inverse, for $G'(y) = g(y)$, which is not 0 by hypothesis. Notice, too, that $G(c) = 0$, so $c = G^{-1}(0)$. Therefore, if $y = G^{-1}\left(\int_a^x f(t)\, dt \right)$, then $y = c$ when $x = a$. Thus y satisfies the given initial condition, and the easiest way to verify that it also satisfies the given differential equation is to differentiate both sides of Equation 60-9 with respect to x. We obtain $g(y)y' = f(x)$, which is equivalent to the Differential Equation 60-8.

Example 60-4.   A projectile is fired straight up from the surface of the earth. What must its initial velocity be so that it never comes back down?

Solution.   We will first express the given physical problem as a differential problem. To obtain our differential equation, we equate two expressions for the acceleration of the projectile. First we use the Chain Rule to write the acceleration $D_t v$ as $D_t v = D_s v \, D_t s = v \, D_s v$. Our second expression for the acceleration comes from Newton's Inverse Square Law of Gravitation, the physical law that tells how gravitational force varies with distance. In terms of the units we are using, Newton's Law states that when the projectile is s miles from the center of the earth, its acceleration is about $-95,000 s^{-2}$ miles per second per second. We equate our two expressions for acceleration, add the initial condition that $v = v_0$ when $s = 3960$ (the radius of the earth is about 3960 miles), and we obtain the differential problem

$$D_s v = -\frac{95,000}{s^2 v}, \quad v = v_0 \text{ when } s = 3960.$$

Here, in the notation of Equation 60-8, we have $g(v) = v$ and $f(s) = -95,000 s^{-2}$. Therefore, according to Theorem 60-2, we find the solution to our differential problem by solving the equation

$$\int_{v_0}^{v} t \, dt = -95,000 \int_{3960}^{s} t^{-2} \, dt$$

for v. After we integrate and simplify, this equation reduces to

$$v^2 = \frac{190,000}{s} + v_0^2 - \frac{4750}{99}.$$

We have expressed the square of our projectile's velocity in terms of its distance s from the center of the earth and its initial velocity v_0. If the projectile is to escape from the earth, its velocity can never become 0 (if it ever stops, it will fall back). Therefore, no matter how large s gets, we must have $v^2 > 0$, and so we must choose v_0 so that $v_0^2 - \frac{4750}{99} \geq 0$. The smallest possible such number is $v_0 = \sqrt{\frac{4750}{99}} \approx 7$. Therefore, we must fire our projectile with a speed of at least 7 miles per second, or it will fall back.

P R O B L E M S   6 0

1. Use Theorem 60-1 or 60-2 to find the equation of the graph containing the given point and having the given slope m.

(a) $m = x \sin x^2$, $(\sqrt{\pi}, 2)$

(b) $m = e^{2x}$, $(\ln 2, 5)$

(c) $m = \dfrac{\sin x}{\cos y}$, $(0, 0)$

(d) $m = \dfrac{1 + y^2}{1 + x^2}$, $(0, 0)$

2. Use Theorem 60-1 or 60-2 to find the formula for $f(x)$ if:

(a) $f'(x) = \dfrac{\cos(\ln x)}{x}$, $f(1) = 2$ (b) $f'(x) = 2|x|, f(-1) = 3$

(c) $f'(x) = \dfrac{x}{|f(x)|}$, $f(-1) = 3$ (d) $f'(x) = \exp(x + f(x)), f(\ln 3) = \ln \frac{1}{2}$

3. Solve the following differential problems.
(a) $y'' = 3 \sin x + 2 \cos x$, $y = 1$ and $y' = -1$ when $x = 0$.
(b) $y'' = 6x^2 - 2$, $y = 1$ and $y' = 5$ when $x = 0$.

4. Use Simpson's Parabolic Rule with 4 subdivisions to compute y when $x = 2$ if y satisfies the following differential problems.
(a) $y' = \sqrt{1 + x^3}$, $y = 0$ when $x = 0$.   (b) $y' = e^{-y}\sqrt{1 + x^3}, y = 0$ when $x = 0$.

5. Show that Theorem 60-1 is a "special case" of Theorem 60-2.

6. At every point of a certain curve, the tangent line is perpendicular to the segment that joins the point to the origin. The curve contains the point $(2, 3)$. What is its equation?

7. Refer to Problem 46-12, and write a formula for the solution of the differential problem $y' + p(x)y = q(x)$, $y = c$ when $x = a$.

8. Find the equation of the curve that contains the points $(0, 4)$ and $(1, 8)$ and whose slope satisfies the following conditions. The slope of the curve at a point is proportional to (a) the X-coordinate of the point, (b) the Y-coordinate of the point, (c) the product of the X- and Y-coordinates of the point.

9. A ball is thrown directly upward with an initial velocity of v_0. One second later a second ball is thrown directly upward along the path of the first ball and with an initial velocity of $2v_0$. The second ball collides with the first ball just as the first ball reaches the top of its upward flight. Find v_0. (Neglect the radii of the balls.)

10. A ball is thrown directly upward with an initial velocity of v_0, and t_0 seconds later a second ball is thrown directly upward along the path of the first ball and with an initial velocity of w_0. Is it possible to choose t_0 and w_0 in such a way that the two balls collide just as both of them reach the top of their upward flight? (Neglect the radii of the balls.)

11. At lift-off, a certain small rocket weighs 1500 pounds, of which 1000 pounds are fuel. The fuel burns at the rate of 10 pounds per second, producing a thrust of 2000 pounds. Show that at the end of t seconds the rocket is acted on by an upward force of 2000 pounds and a downward force of $1500 - 10t$ pounds. What is the resultant of these forces? According to Newton's Second Law of Motion, this force equals the product of the mass, $\dfrac{1500 - 10t}{32}$, and the acceleration, v', of the rocket. Thus we have the differential problem

$$v' = -32 \,\frac{t + 50}{t - 150}, \quad v = 0 \text{ when } t = 0.$$

What is the velocity of the rocket at burn-out? How high is it then? How high does it finally go?

61 THE DIFFERENTIAL NOTATION

We have said that the only role played by the symbol dx in the integral $\int_a^b f(x)\,dx$ is to identify the variable of integration. Thus

$$\int_0^2 6tx^2\,dx = 2tx^3 \Big|_{x=0}^{x=2} = 16t$$

and

$$\int_0^2 6tx^2\,dt = 3t^2x^2 \Big|_{t=0}^{t=2} = 12x^2.$$

When we make the substitution that replaces the variable of integration x with the variable of integration u, we find it convenient to assume that the "indicators" dx and du are related by the equation

(61-1) $$du = D_x u\,dx.$$

Since we have not interpreted dx and du as numbers, we cannot think of this equation in the usual way—as a relation among numbers. For us, Equation 61-1 means that when making a substitution under an integral sign, we get the correct result if we replace $D_x u\,dx$ with du. But as we have already indicated, we won't go wrong if we do treat this equation as if du and dx were numbers.

There are many instances in mathematics in which we find it convenient to perform such purely formal manipulations with dx and du. For example, suppose we divide both sides of Equation 61-1 by dx. Then we obtain the equation

(61-2) $$\frac{du}{dx} = D_x u.$$

We take this equation as the *definition* of the symbol $\dfrac{du}{dx}$. Notice that since $D_x u$ is a well-defined number, we have a perfectly good definition of the "quotient" $\dfrac{du}{dx}$ even though we haven't defined the numerator and denominator individually. This **differential notation** for the derivative is widely used in mathematics. For example, if $y = \sin x$, then we write $\dfrac{dy}{dx} = \cos x$, or even $\dfrac{d(\sin x)}{dx} = \cos x$. We have used various notations for the derivative, $f'(x)$, $D_x y$, y', and $D_x f(x)$ throughout this book so that you would get experience using the different notations. From now on, we will also use the differential notation $\dfrac{dy}{dx}$. In the differential notation, second and third derivatives are written as $\dfrac{d^2 y}{dx^2}$ and $\dfrac{d^3 y}{dx^3}$, and higher derivatives are treated in a similar manner. Thus $\dfrac{d^4y}{dx^4}$ represents the fourth derivative of y, whereas $\left(\dfrac{dy}{dx}\right)^4$ is the fourth power of the first derivative. Of course, these numbers are *not* always equal, as you can see by setting $y = e^x$, for example. It might help you to remember this new symbolism for higher derivatives if you think of the symbol $\dfrac{d}{dx}$ as replacing the symbol D_x. Then $D_x^2 y = \left(\dfrac{d}{dx}\right)^2 y = \dfrac{d^2y}{dx^2}$, and so on.

The differential notation makes a number of formulas easy to remember. But it is misleading, too, for it makes certain basic theorems of calculus look like trivial algebraic identities, which they are not. For example, if we replace $D_x y$, $D_u y$, and $D_x u$ with $\dfrac{dy}{dx}$, $\dfrac{dy}{du}$, and $\dfrac{du}{dx}$ in the Chain Rule Equation $D_x y = D_u y D_x u$, we obtain the equation

$$(61\text{-}3) \qquad\qquad \frac{dy}{dx} = \frac{dy}{du}\frac{du}{dx}.$$

In like manner, the equation connecting derivatives of inverse functions, $D_y x = 1/D_x y$, becomes

$$(61\text{-}4) \qquad\qquad \frac{dx}{dy} = 1 \Big/ \frac{dy}{dx}.$$

Written this way, these formulas are very attractive; anyone who can perform the simplest arithmetic with fractions can "see" that they are true. The only drawback is that the symbols dx, dy, and du alone don't have any meaning for us; only *quotients* of these symbols have been defined (Equation 61-2). Nevertheless, Equations 61-3 and 61-4 are correct, as we have shown earlier.

Authors who use the differential notation for the derivative may also use a somewhat different notation for a difference quotient from the one we have been using. Let us recall the definition of the derivative of $f(x)$. If f is a given function and x is a point in its domain, then we choose a number h and form the difference quotient

$$(61\text{-}5) \qquad\qquad \frac{f(x + h) - f(x)}{h}.$$

Figure 61-1 shows the geometric significance of the Difference Quotient 61-5. This quotient is the slope of the chord joining the points $(x, f(x))$ and $(x + h, f(x + h))$ of the graph of the equation $y = f(x)$. The numerator of the difference quotient is the difference of the Y-coordinates of the two points, and the denominator is the difference of the X-coordinates. Another common notation used in labeling the same picture is illustrated in Fig. 61-2. Here the difference between the

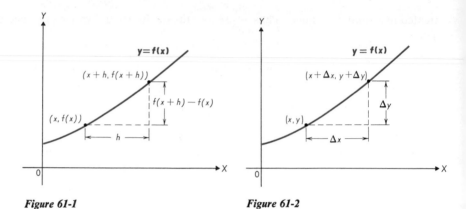

Figure 61-1   **Figure 61-2**

X-coordinates is denoted by Δx, and the difference between the Y-coordinates is Δy. Thus in this notation, $\Delta x = h$ and $\Delta y = f(x + h) - f(x)$. Then the Difference Quotient 61-5 becomes

$$\frac{\Delta y}{\Delta x}.$$

The derivative is the limit of the difference quotient as h approaches zero; that is, as Δx approaches 0. So in the differential notation we have

$$\frac{dy}{dx} = \lim_{\Delta x \to 0} \frac{\Delta y}{\Delta x}.$$

Example 61-1. If $y = x^3$, express $\dfrac{\Delta y}{\Delta x}$ in terms of Δx and compute $\lim\limits_{\Delta x \to 0} \dfrac{\Delta y}{\Delta x}$ to find $\dfrac{dy}{dx}$.

Solution. By definition,

$$y + \Delta y = (x + \Delta x)^3,$$

$$\Delta y = (x + \Delta x)^3 - x^3,$$

and so

$$\frac{\Delta y}{\Delta x} = \frac{(x + \Delta x)^3 - x^3}{\Delta x} = 3x^2 + 3x\,\Delta x + (\Delta x)^2.$$

Since

$$\frac{dy}{dx} = \lim_{\Delta x \to 0} \frac{\Delta y}{\Delta x}, \text{ we see that } \frac{dy}{dx} = 3x^2.$$

Example 61-2. Compute $\dfrac{dy}{dx}$ if $y = e^{\sin x}$.

Solution. We write $y = e^u$ with $u = \sin x$. Then $\dfrac{dy}{du} = e^u$, $\dfrac{du}{dx} = \cos x$, and the Chain Rule Equation

$$\frac{dy}{dx} = \frac{dy}{du}\frac{du}{dx}$$

becomes

$$\frac{dy}{dx} = e^u \cos x = e^{\sin x} \cos x.$$

Example 61-3. Solve the differential problem $x\dfrac{dy}{dx} = 1$, $y = 1$ when $x = 2$.

Solution. According to Theorem 60-1, the solution to our differential problem is

$$y = \int_2^x \frac{dt}{t} + 1 = \ln|x| - \ln 2 + 1 = \ln\left|\frac{ex}{2}\right|.$$

P R O B L E M S   6 1

1. Find $\dfrac{dy}{dx}$.

(a) $y = x^{-3} + 3^{-x}$

(b) $y = \tan \ln x + \ln|\tan x|$

(c) $y = |\text{Arctan }|x||$

(d) $y = \log_{|\cos x|} |\sin x|$

2. Find $\dfrac{d^3y}{dx^3}$ from the following equations.

(a) $y = \displaystyle\int_0^x e^{-t^2}\, dt$

(b) $\displaystyle\int_0^y e^{-t^2}\, dt = \int_0^x e^{-t^2}\, dt.$

3. Which of the following equations are valid if $u = f(x)$ and $v = g(x)$, where f and g are any pair of differentiable functions?

(a) $\dfrac{d}{dx}(u + v) = \dfrac{du}{dx} + \dfrac{dv}{dx}$

(b) $\dfrac{d}{dx}(3u) = 3\dfrac{du}{dx}$

(c) $\dfrac{d}{dx}\left(\dfrac{3}{u}\right) = \dfrac{3}{du/dx}$

(d) $\dfrac{d}{dx}|u| = \left|\dfrac{du}{dx}\right|.$

4. Show that if $y = -\ln|x|$, then $\dfrac{d^2y}{dx^2} = \left(\dfrac{dy}{dx}\right)^2.$

5. Express $\dfrac{\Delta y}{\Delta x}$ in terms of Δx. Use your knowledge of differentiation to evaluate $\displaystyle\lim_{\Delta x \to 0} \dfrac{\Delta y}{\Delta x}$.

(a) $y = (x + 1)^2$ (b) $y = \sin x^2$ (c) $y = \ln x$ (d) $y = |x|^3$

6. Find $\dfrac{dx}{dy}$ if y is given by the equations in the preceding problem.

7. Use implicit differentiation to find $\dfrac{d^2y}{dx^2}$ if:

(a) $x^2 + y^2 = 4$ (b) $xy - y^2 = 1$

(c) $xy + \sin y = 1$ (d) $\sin x + \cos y = 1$

8. Let $y = e^{-x} \displaystyle\int_1^x t^{-1} e^t\, dt$ and compute $\dfrac{dy}{dx} + y - \dfrac{1}{x}$.

9. Explain why the equation $\displaystyle\lim_{\Delta x \to 0} \Delta y = 0$ means that f is continuous at x.

10. Suppose that y satisfies the differential problem

$$\frac{d^2y}{dx^2} = \left(\frac{dy}{dx}\right)^2, y = r \text{ and } \frac{dy}{dx} = s \text{ when } x = a.$$

(a) Let $u = \dfrac{dy}{dx}$ and show that u satisfies the differential problem

$$u' = u^2, u = s \text{ when } x = a.$$

(b) Solve the differential problem in Part (a) to obtain $u = \left(\dfrac{1}{s} + a - x\right)^{-1}$

(c) Use the result of Part (b) to write a differential problem with a differential equation of the first order that is satisfied by y, and solve it.

(d) Compare your result with Number 4 of these problems.

REVIEW PROBLEMS—CHAPTER SEVEN

You can use these problems to test yourself on the material in this chapter.

1. Find the following.

(a) $\displaystyle\int x^2 e^{x^3}\, dx$ (b) $\displaystyle\int x^3 e^{x^2}\, dx$ (c) $\displaystyle\int \frac{x^3 - 8}{2x - 1}\, dx$ (d) $\displaystyle\int \frac{2x - 1}{x^3 - 8}\, dx$

(e) $\displaystyle\int x^2 \sqrt{x^3 + 1}\, dx$ (f) $\displaystyle\int x^3 \sqrt{x^2 + 1}\, dx$ (g) $\displaystyle\int x \cos^2 x^2\, dx$ (h) $\displaystyle\int x^2 \cos x\, dx$

2. Evaluate the integral $\displaystyle\int_0^1 \frac{dx}{\sqrt{x^2 + x + 1}}$ in two ways. (a) Complete the square in the radicand of the denominator and make a suitable trigonometric substitution. (b) Use the substitution $u = 2x + 1 + 2\sqrt{x^2 + x + 1}$.

3. Evaluate the following integrals.

(a) $\displaystyle\int_0^{2\pi} |\sin x \cos x \cos 2x|\, dx$ (b) $\displaystyle\int_0^{2\pi} |\sin x \cos x \sin 2x|\, dx$

(c) $\displaystyle\int_0^{\pi/6} \cos x \sec 2x\, dx$ (d) $\displaystyle\int_2^{\pi} \cos [\![x]\!]\, x\, dx$

4. Show that $\int_a^{a+2\pi} f(\cos x)\,dx = \int_0^{2\pi} f(\cos x)\,dx$ for every number a and continuous function f.

5. If f is continuous in an interval I, use integration by parts to show that for each pair of points a and b of I,

$$\int_a^b xf(x)\,dx = b\int_a^b f(x)\,dx - \int_a^b \left(\int_a^x f(t)\,dt \right)dx.$$

(Hint: If $v = \int_a^x f(t)\,dt$, then $dv = f(x)\,dx$.)

6. Suppose that f is continuous in an interval I and that f^{-1} exists. Show that for each pair of points a and b of I,

$$\int_a^b f^{-1}(x)\,dx = xf^{-1}(x)\Big|_a^b - \int_{f^{-1}(a)}^{f^{-1}(b)} f(x)\,dx.$$

Apply this equation in case $f(x) = \text{Sin } x$ to obtain an integration formula for $\int \text{Sin}^{-1} x\,dx$.

7. Consider the differential problem $y' = \dfrac{x}{|x|}$, $y = 2$ when $x = -1$. What is the largest interval in which we can apply Theorem 60-1 to this problem? What happens if we try to apply the theorem beyond this interval?

8. Suppose that f is continuous in an interval that contains a point a. Let c be a number, and define the function F by the equation $F(x) = \int_a^x f(t)\,dt + c$.

(a) Show that if f is an odd function, then F is an even function.
(b) Show that if f is an even function, then F is an odd function, provided that

$$c = \tfrac{1}{2}\int_0^a f(t)\,dt.$$

POLAR COORDINATES.

VECTORS IN THE PLANE

E I G H T

We will now return to the subject of analytic geometry. This chapter has a twofold purpose. First of all, we will get a new look at the problem of representing points in the plane by means of pairs of numbers. Later it will turn out that some of the tools that we use in taking this new look—vector methods—are also useful in the study of three-dimensional space. So a second objective of this chapter is to lay the groundwork for the study of analytic geometry of three-dimensional space that we will take up in Chapter Nine.

62 POLAR COORDINATES

By introducing a pair of perpendicular lines and a unit of distance, we are able to assign to each point in the plane a pair of real numbers called the rectangular **cartesian coordinates** of the point. There are other ways to associate pairs of numbers with points, and now we are going to study one of the most important of these other ways. Let P be a point in a plane in which we have a system of cartesian coordinates (Fig. 62-1) and let r be the length of the segment OP. Suppose that the X-axis is the initial side and the segment OP is part of the terminal side of an angle of θ, as shown in the figure.

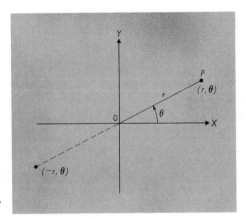

Figure 62-1

Then we can associate the numbers r and θ with the point P; we say that P has **polar coordinates** (r, θ). If we write just a number in place of the angular measure θ (for example $\theta = \pi/4$), we shall suppose that our angle is measured in radians. To indicate degree measure, we use the symbol °—for example, $\theta = 45°$. We refer to the point O (the origin in Fig. 62-1) as the **pole** of our polar coordinate system, and the initial side of the polar angle (here the positive X-axis) is called the **polar axis** of the system. Clearly, it is possible to introduce a polar coordinate system without reference to a cartesian coordinate system. We simply choose a point in the plane to be the pole of our system and choose any half-line emanating from the pole to be the polar axis.

We will allow the use of angles greater than one revolution, and we will also allow negative angles, those angles formed by rotating the initial side in a clockwise direction. We therefore see that a given point P always has infinitely many pairs of polar coordinates. For example, the pairs $(2, 30°)$, $(2, 390°)$, and $(2, -330°)$ all represent the same point. We also occasionally find it convenient to use a negative number for the radial polar coordinate of a point. To plot the point (r, θ) with $r > 0$, we proceed r units from the point O along the terminal side of the polar angle. To plot the point $(-r, \theta)$, we proceed r units from the pole along the extension of the terminal side through the origin (Fig. 62-1). Thus (r, θ) and $(-r, \theta + \pi)$ are polar coordinates of the same point. The coordinates $(0, \theta)$ represent the pole for every θ.

Example 62-1. Plot the points $(2, \pi/2)$, $(3, -225°)$, $(-3, 225°)$, and $(0, 17°)$.

Solution. The listed points are shown in Fig. 62-2.

When a polar coordinate system is superimposed on a given cartesian coordinate system, each point in the plane can be represented either by its cartesian

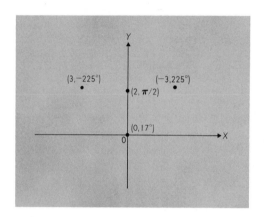

Figure 62-2 **Figure 62-3**

coordinates (x, y) or by polar coordinates (r, θ) (Fig. 62-3). If $r > 0$, the basic Equations 6-2 concerning trigonometric functions of angles tell us the fundamental relations between the cartesian and polar coordinates of a point:

$$(62\text{-}1) \qquad \begin{aligned} x &= r \cos \theta \\ y &= r \sin \theta. \end{aligned}$$

We will leave it to you to verify that these equations are also valid if the polar coordinates of the point are such that $r < 0$. It is obvious how to use Equations 62-1 to find the XY-coordinates of a point if we know a pair of polar coordinates (r, θ). We will use an example to illustrate how we use Equations 62-1 to calculate a pair of polar coordinates of a point when we are given its cartesian coordinates.

Example 62-2. Find a pair of polar coordinates of the point whose cartesian coordinates are $(-1, \sqrt{3})$.

Solution. Figure 62-4 shows the point $(-1, \sqrt{3})$; we have labeled the distance r and the angle of θ that we are to determine. According to Equations 62-1, we must pick r and θ so that

$$(62\text{-}2) \qquad \begin{aligned} -1 &= r \cos \theta \\ \sqrt{3} &= r \sin \theta. \end{aligned}$$

If we square both of these equations and add, we see that

$$4 = r^2(\cos^2 \theta + \sin^2 \theta) = r^2.$$

Thus we can choose either $r = 2$ or $r = -2$. Let us take $r = 2$. Then Equations 62-2 tell us that we must choose θ so that $\cos \theta = -\frac{1}{2}$ and $\sin \theta = \sqrt{3}/2$. From trigonometry we know that the reference angle (the angle of θ_1 in Fig. 62-4) is the acute angle whose cosine is $\frac{1}{2}$. Therefore, $\theta_1 = \pi/3$, and we may take $\theta = \pi - \theta_1 = 2\pi/3$. Thus a pair of polar coordinates of our point is $(2, 2\pi/3)$. Examples of other pairs of polar coordinates of this point are $(2, 8\pi/3)$, $(2, -4\pi/3)$, and $(-2, -\pi/3)$. You might check to see that each of these pairs satisfies Equations 62-2.

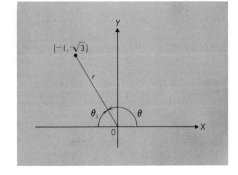

Figure 62-4

In the preceding example we found it convenient to square both sides of Equations 62-2 and add the resulting equations. If we square both sides of Equations 62-1 and add, we obtain the following useful formula that relates the XY-coordinates of a point and its radial polar coordinate r:

(62-3) $$x^2 + y^2 = r^2.$$

The graph of an equation in x and y is the set of points whose XY-coordinates satisfy the equation. Similarly, the graph of an equation in the polar coordinates r and θ is the set of those points that have polar coordinates that satisfy the equation. Thus, for example, the graph of the equation $2x - 3y + 5 = 0$ is a straight line. If we replace x with $r \cos \theta$ and y with $r \sin \theta$, we obtain the equation of the same line in polar coordinates:

$$2r \cos \theta - 3r \sin \theta + 5 = 0.$$

The straightforward way to plot the graph of any equation is to begin with a table of values, plot the points whose coordinates are contained in the table, and fill in the curve suggested by the plotted points. We use the following example to illustrate this procedure in the case of polar coordinates.

Example 62-3. Sketch the graph of the equation

$$r = 2(1 - \cos \theta).$$

Solution.   In this example we can lighten our labor by noting that, since $\cos(-\theta) = \cos\theta$, the point $(r, -\theta)$ belongs to the graph if the point (r, θ) does. Therefore, our graph is symmetric about the line lying along the polar axis. We can sketch the graph by plotting points whose angular coordinates lie between $0°$ and $180°$ and then reflect this portion about the line of symmetry. The table accompanying Fig. 62-5 lists the coordinates we used to sketch the curve. This heart-shaped curve is called a **cardioid**.

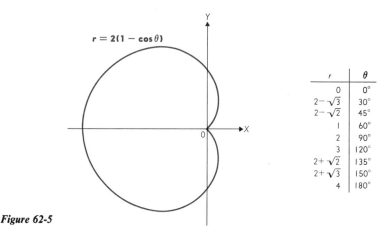

r	θ
0	0°
$2-\sqrt{3}$	30°
$2-\sqrt{2}$	45°
1	60°
2	90°
3	120°
$2+\sqrt{2}$	135°
$2+\sqrt{3}$	150°
4	180°

$r = 2(1 - \cos\theta)$

Figure 62-5

Frequently our knowledge of cartesian equations of curves helps us when we deal with polar equations.

Example 62-4.   Discuss the graph of the equation

$$r = 4\cos\theta - 2\sin\theta.$$

Solution.   We could plot the graph of this equation as we did in the preceding example, but instead we will transform the equation to an equation involving cartesian coordinates x and y. First, we multiply both sides of the given equation by r to obtain the equation

$$r^2 = 4r\cos\theta - 2r\sin\theta.$$

Now we use Equations 62-1 and 62-3 to write our equation in cartesian coordinates:

$$x^2 + y^2 = 4x - 2y.$$

We then complete the square to obtain

$$(x^2 - 4x + 4) + (y^2 + 2y + 1) = 4 + 1,$$
$$(x - 2)^2 + (y + 1)^2 = 5,$$

and we find that our equation represents the circle whose center is the point $(2, -1)$ and whose radius is $\sqrt{5}$.

We have said that a point belongs to the graph of an equation in r and θ if it has a pair of polar coordinates that satisfy the equation. Since each point has infinitely many pairs of polar coordinates, it may be true that some of these pairs satisfy the equation while others don't. For example, the pair of coordinates $(1, 0)$ satisfies the equation $r = e^{2\theta}$, so the point with polar coordinates $(1, 0)$ belongs to the graph of the equation. But the same point has polar coordinates $(-1, \pi)$ and $(1, 2\pi)$, and neither of these pairs satisfies the equation. Similarly, the graph of the equation $r = -6 \cos \theta$ contains the pole since the coordinates $(0, \pi/2)$ satisfy the equation, but other coordinates of the pole (for example, $(0, \pi/7)$) do not satisfy the equation.

It is also true that different polar equations may have the same graph. For example, you can easily see that the graphs of the equations $r = 5$, $r = -5$, and $r^2 = 25$ are all the same circle. You can also verify that the graph of the equation $r = -2(1 + \cos \theta)$ is the cardioid of Example 62-3 (see Problem 62-5). We make these remarks to warn you that you must keep your eyes open when using polar coordinates. In the following example we will illustrate one type of pitfall to avoid.

Example 62-5. Find the points of intersection of the cardioid $r = 2(1 - \cos \theta)$ and the circle $r = -6 \cos \theta$.

Solution. Figure 62-6 shows our two curves. We will attempt to find their points of intersection by finding simultaneous solutions to their equations. We equate the two expressions for r and get the trigonometric equation

$$2(1 - \cos \theta) = -6 \cos \theta,$$

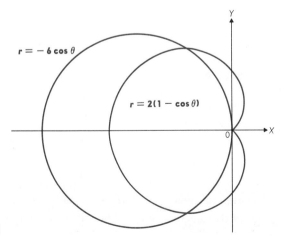

Figure 62-6

from which we see that $\cos \theta = -\frac{1}{2}$. Two choices of θ that satisfy this last equation are $\theta = 2\pi/3$ and $\theta = 4\pi/3$. We see that $r = 3$, no matter which solution for θ is chosen, so we have found two points of intersection, $(3, 2\pi/3)$ and $(3, 4\pi/3)$. However, when we examine our graphs in Fig. 62-6, we see that there are actually three points of intersection. The pole is a point of intersection that we cannot find by solving the equations simultaneously. No pair of coordinates of the pole satisfies both equations. For example, the coordinates $(0, \pi/2)$ satisfy the equation of the circle but not of the cardioid; and the coordinates $(0, 0)$ satisfy the equation of the cardioid, but not of the circle. Nevertheless, the pole certainly does belong to both curves and is therefore a point of intersection.

P R O B L E M S   6 2

1. Find the cartesian coordinates of the points with polar coordinates:
  (a) $(4, 30°)$ (b) $(8, -420°)$
  (c) $(-6, 3\pi/4)$ (d) (π, π)
  (e) $(90, 90°)$ (f) $(-1, 13\pi/6)$

2. Find a set of polar coordinates of the points whose cartesian coordinates are:
  (a) $(-4, 0)$ (b) $(-3\sqrt{3}, -3)$
  (c) $(-6, 6\sqrt{3})$ (d) (π, π)
  (e) $(0, -270)$ (f) $(-4, 3)$

3. Does it follow from Equations 62-1 that $r = \sqrt{x^2 + y^2}$ and $\theta = \text{Tan}^{-1}(y/x)$? (Consider the point whose cartesian coordinates are $(-1, 1)$.)

4. Transform the following equations to cartesian coordinates and graph.
  (a) $r = 2 \cos \theta$ (b) $r = 3 \sec \theta$ (c) $\tan \theta = 5$ (d) $r \sin \theta \tan \theta = 1$

5. Show that the equations $r = 2(1 - \cos \theta)$ and $r = -2(1 + \cos \theta)$ have the same graph.

6. Sketch the graphs of the following equations.
  (a) $r = 4 \cos 2\theta$ (b) $r = 3 \cos 3\theta$
  (c) $r = 2 - \cos \theta$ (d) $r = 1 - 2 \cos \theta$

7. Sketch the graph of the equation $r = 2\sqrt{\cos \theta}$. Is the graph a circle?

8. Find a polar equation of the line that contains the points whose polar coordinates are $(1, \pi)$ and $(2, \pi/2)$. (*Hint:* You can write the cartesian coordinate equation first and then change to polar coordinates.)

9. Discuss the symmetry of the graph of a polar coordinate equation if it can be written in the form:
  (a) $r^2 = f(\theta)$ (b) $r = f(\cos \theta)$
  (c) $r = f(\sin \theta)$ (d) $r = f(\theta)$, f an odd function
  (e) $r = f(\theta)$, f an even function   (f) $r^2 = f(\theta)$, f an even function

10. Sketch the graph of the equation $r\theta = 1$. Show that as θ approaches zero the Y-coordinate of a point (r, θ) of this graph approaches 1.

11. Find the points of intersection of the graphs of the following pairs of equations (draw a sketch).

(a) $r = 4 \cos 2\theta$, $r = 2$ (b) $r = 4 \cos 2\theta$, $r = 4 \cos \theta$

(c) $r^2 = \sin^2 2\theta$, $\tan \theta = 1$ (d) $r = 1 - \cos \theta$, $r = \sin \frac{1}{2}\theta$

12. Sketch the graphs of the following equations.

(a) $r = [\![\theta]\!]$ (b) $[\![r]\!] = \theta$ (c) $[\![r]\!] = [\![\theta]\!]$

13. If we sketch the graph of a certain equation $r = f(\theta)$ in a rectangular coordinate system in which the θ-axis is the horizontal axis and the R-axis is the vertical axis, we can describe the result as follows. In the interval $[0, 2\pi]$, our graph consists of the line segments successively joining the points $(0, 1)$, $(\frac{1}{2}\pi, 0)$, $(\pi, 2)$, $(\frac{3}{2}\pi, 0)$, and $(2\pi, 1)$. This part of the graph is then repeated in the intervals $[2\pi, 4\pi]$, $[-2\pi, 0]$, and so on. Sketch the graph of the equation $r = f(\theta)$ in polar coordinates.

14. Show that the distance between the points (r_1, θ_1) and (r_2, θ_2) is given by the formula

$$d = \sqrt{r_1^2 + r_2^2 - 2r_1r_2 \cos(\theta_2 - \theta_1)}.$$

63 LINES, CIRCLES, AND CONICS IN POLAR COORDINATES

In earlier sections we discussed the cartesian equations of certain common curves—lines, circles, and conics. Now we will consider the representation of these particular curves in polar coordinates. It helps tie our work with polar coordinates to our previous work with rectangular coordinates if we suppose that our polar coordinate system is superimposed on a cartesian system, as it was in the preceding section.

If α is a given number, then it is clear that every point that has polar coordinates (r, θ) such that

(63-1) $\theta = \alpha$

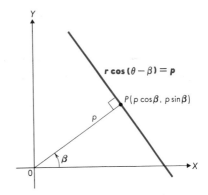

Figure 63-1

belongs to the line that contains the pole and makes an angle of α with the polar axis, and conversely. Thus the graph of Equation 63-1 is a line that contains the pole.

Now let us look at lines that do not contain the pole O (Fig. 63-1). Suppose that P is a point with polar coordinates (p, β), where $p \neq 0$. Then the segment OP has slope $\tan \beta$, and the cartesian equation of any line perpendicular to OP has the form $(\cos \beta)x + (\sin \beta)y = c$. Such a line contains the point P if, and only if, $(\cos \beta)(p \cos \beta) + (\sin \beta)(p \sin \beta) = c$; that is, $p = c$. Thus

(63-2) $x \cos \beta + y \sin \beta = p$

is the cartesian equation of the line that contains the point P with polar coordinates (p, β) and is perpendicular to OP. By replacing x with $r \cos \theta$ and y with $r \sin \theta$ and simplifying, we obtain

(63-3) $$r \cos (\theta - \beta) = p$$

as the polar equation of our line.

Example 63-1. Find the distance between the origin and the line $2x - 3y + 7 = 0$.

Solution. We write

$$-2x + 3y = 7$$

and divide both sides of this equation by

$$\sqrt{(-2)^2 + 3^2} = \sqrt{13}$$

to obtain

$$-\frac{2}{\sqrt{13}} x + \frac{3}{\sqrt{13}} y = \frac{7}{\sqrt{13}}.$$

This last equation is in the form of Equation 63-2, with $p = 7/\sqrt{13}$, $\cos \beta = -2/\sqrt{13}$, and $\sin \beta = 3/\sqrt{13}$. Thus the distance between the origin and the line is $7/\sqrt{13}$, and one possible choice for β is (approximately) $\beta = 2.16$. This problem is illustrated in Fig. 63-2.

The cartesian equation of a circle with a radius of a and whose center is a point with polar coordinates (c, α) is

$$(x - c \cos \alpha)^2 + (y - c \sin \alpha)^2 = a^2.$$

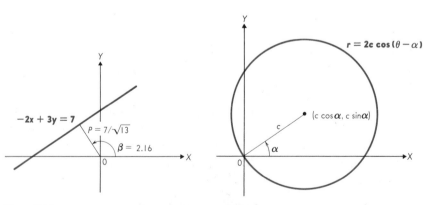

Figure 63-2   **Figure 63-3**

If we replace x with $r \cos \theta$ and y with $r \sin \theta$ and simplify, we obtain the polar equation of our circle—namely,

$$(63\text{-}4) \qquad r^2 - 2rc \cos (\theta - \alpha) + c^2 = a^2.$$

If the center of the circle is the pole O, then $c = 0$ and Equation 63-4 reduces to $r^2 = a^2$, which is equivalent to the polar equation

$$(63\text{-}5) \qquad r = a.$$

If the circle contains the origin (see Figure 63-3), then $c^2 = a^2$ and Equation 63-4 is then equivalent to the equation

$$(63\text{-}6) \qquad r = 2c \cos (\theta - \alpha).$$

In particular, if we set $\alpha = 0$, we obtain the equation

$$(63\text{-}7) \qquad r = 2c \cos \theta$$

that represents a circle with a radius of $|c|$ and whose center is the point of the X-axis with cartesian coordinates $(c, 0)$. Similarly, if we set $\alpha = \pi/2$, we get the equation of a circle with a radius of $|c|$ and whose center is the point of the Y-axis with cartesian coordinates $(0, c)$:

$$(63\text{-}8) \qquad r = 2c \sin \theta.$$

Polar coordinates are particularly well suited for representing conics. In Section 31 we found how a conic is determined by a point called a *focus*, a line called a *directrix*, and a positive number called the *eccentricity* of the conic. A point belongs to the conic if, and only if, the ratio of the distance between the point and the focus to the distance between the point and the directrix is the eccentricity. Suppose we know the focus F, the corresponding directrix d, located p units from F, and the eccentricity e of a certain conic. Let us introduce polar coordinates so that the pole is the focus F and so that the directrix is perpendicular to the polar axis at the point with polar coordinates (p, π), where $p > 0$. We have sketched an arc of our conic in Fig. 63-4. If our conic is a hyperbola $(e > 1)$, it will also have a branch lying to the left of d, but in the case of an ellipse $(e < 1)$ or a parabola $(e = 1)$, the entire conic lies to the right of the directrix. Suppose that P is a point of our conic, and let (r, θ) be polar coordinates of P. The cartesian equation of the directrix is $x = -p$, so the distance between P and d is $|p + r \cos \theta|$. Thus the definition of a conic tells us that

$$\frac{|r|}{|p + r \cos \theta|} = e,$$

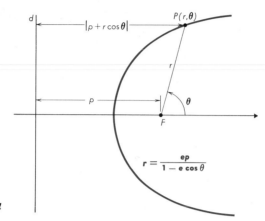

Figure 63-4

so that either

(63-9) $\dfrac{r}{p + r \cos \theta} = e$ or $\dfrac{r}{-(p + r \cos \theta)} = e.$

Now it is easy to show (we ask you to in Problem 63-4) that if the coordinates (r, θ) of a certain point satisfy either one of these equations, then the coordinates $(-r, \theta + \pi)$ *of the same point* satisfy the other equation. It follows that we do not need both equations to describe our conic; either one will do. We will take the equation that is obtained by solving the first of Equations 63-9 for r to be the standard form of the polar equation of our conic:

(63-10) $r = \dfrac{ep}{1 - e \cos \theta}.$

By reasoning as we did above, you can find that if the focus is the pole, and if the directrix is to the right of the pole (see Fig. 63-5), then we can take the standard form of the equation of our conic to be

(63-11) $r = \dfrac{ep}{1 + e \cos \theta}.$

If the directrix is parallel to the polar axis, we take the standard polar equation of the conic to be

(63-12) $r = \dfrac{ep}{1 + e \sin \theta}$

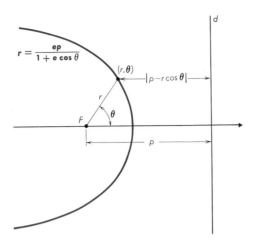

Figure 63-5

if the directrix is above the focus, and

(63-13) $$r = \frac{ep}{1 - e \sin \theta}$$

if the directrix is below the focus (see Fig. 63-6).

In each case the focus is the pole of our coordinate system, and the directrix that corresponds to this focus is p units away from it.

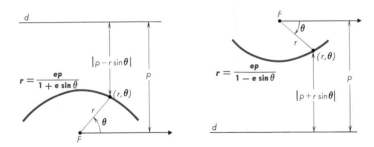

Figure 63-6

Example 63-2. Write a polar equation of the parabola whose focus is the pole, whose axis lies along the polar axis, which opens to the right, and which contains the point $(2, \pi/3)$.

Solution. Since our parabola opens to the right, its directrix lies to the left of the focus (the pole), and hence Equation 63-10 is the equation we want. We are dealing with a parabola, so $e = 1$, and our equation is

$$r = \frac{p}{1 - \cos \theta}.$$

We determine p by setting $r = 2$ and $\theta = \pi/3$, since the point $(2, \pi/3)$ belongs to the parabola. Thus

$$2 = \frac{p}{1 - \cos \pi/3} = \frac{p}{1 - \frac{1}{2}} = 2p,$$

and hence $p = 1$. Therefore, the equation of our parabola is

$$r = \frac{1}{1 - \cos \theta}.$$

Example 63-3. Discuss the graph of the equation

$$(63\text{-}14) \qquad\qquad r = \frac{16}{5 + 3 \sin \theta}.$$

Solution. If we divide the numerator and the denominator of our fraction by 5, we can write Equation 63-14 in the form of Equation 63-12:

$$r = \frac{\frac{16}{5}}{1 + \frac{3}{5} \sin \theta} = \frac{\frac{3}{5} \cdot \frac{16}{3}}{1 + \frac{3}{5} \sin \theta}.$$

Here $e = \frac{3}{5}$ and $p = \frac{16}{3}$. Our curve is an ellipse, since $e < 1$, and its major diameter contains the pole and is perpendicular to the polar axis. Thus we find the vertices of the ellipse by setting $\theta = \pi/2$ and $\theta = 3\pi/2$ in Equation 63-14. We obtain

$$r = \frac{16}{5 + 3 \cdot 1} = 2 \quad \text{when} \quad \theta = \frac{\pi}{2},$$

and

$$r = \frac{16}{5 + 3 \cdot (-1)} = 8$$

when

$$\theta = \frac{3\pi}{2}.$$

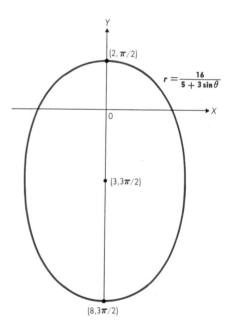

Figure 63-7

Therefore, the vertices are the points with polar coordinates $(2, \pi/2)$ and $(8, 3\pi/2)$. The major diameter is $8 + 2 = 10$ units long. In Section 31 we saw that the eccentricity of an ellipse is the ratio of the distance between its foci to the length of its major diameter. The major diameter of our present ellipse is $2b = 10$ units long, and if its foci are $2c$ units apart, we have the equation $e = 2c/10$; that is $\frac{3}{5} = 2c/10$. Hence $c = 3$. Finally, if the minor diameter of our ellipse is $2a$ units long, then $a = \sqrt{b^2 - c^2} = \sqrt{25 - 9} = 4$. Our ellipse is shown in Fig. 63-7. You may readily verify that its cartesian equation is

$$\frac{x^2}{16} + \frac{(y + 3)^2}{25} = 1.$$

P R O B L E M S   6 3

1. Find the distance between the line $3x + 4y = 30$ and the origin.

2. Find a polar equation of the line of which the point $(3, 27°)$ is the point nearest to the origin.

3. Find a polar equation of the circle whose center has rectangular coordinates $(-1, 1)$ and which contains the pole.

4. Show that if the coordinates (r, θ) of a certain point satisfy one of the Equations 63-9, then the coordinates $(-r, \theta + \pi)$ of the same point satisfy the other equation.

5. Sketch the graphs of the following polar equations. In each case label the vertices (or vertex) and the foci (or focus) of the conic.

(a) $r = \dfrac{16}{3 + 5 \sin \theta}$

(b) $r = \dfrac{16}{5 - 3 \cos \theta}$

(c) $r = \dfrac{4}{1 + \sin \theta}$

(d) $r = \dfrac{16}{5 + 3 \cos \theta}$

(e) $r \sin \theta = 1 - r$

(f) $3r \sin \theta = 5r - 16$

6. A conic has the origin of a cartesian coordinate system as a focus and a corresponding directrix whose equation is $x = -4$. Identify the conic and find a polar equation for it if the conic contains the point whose cartesian coordinates are:

(a) $(5, 12)$ (b) $(5, 2\sqrt{14})$ (c) $(5, 5)$

7. Show that the graph of the equation $r \sin (\theta - \alpha) = q \sin (\beta - \alpha)$ is the line that contains the point with polar coordinates (q, β) and has a slope of $m = \tan \alpha$.

8. Express Equation 63-10 in cartesian coordinates.

9. Describe the conic for which $p = 5,000,000$ and $e = 1/1,000,000$.

10. Show that the standard form of the polar equation of a parabola can be written as

$$r = \frac{p}{2} \csc^2 \frac{\theta}{2}.$$

11. A chord that contains a focus of a conic is divided into two segments by the focus. Prove that the sum of the reciprocals of the lengths of these two segments is the same no matter what chord is chosen.

12. Suppose $e < 1$ in Equation 63-10 and let $2a$ denote the length of the major diameter of the ellipse represented by that equation. Show that

$$a = \frac{ep}{1 - e^2}.$$

13. Suppose $e < 1$ in Equation 63-10 and let $2c$ denote the distance between the foci of the ellipse represented by that equation. Show that $c = e^2p/(1 - e^2)$.

64 TANGENTS TO POLAR CURVES

In the preceding two sections, we have considered the elementary notion of the graph of a polar equation, and now we are ready to apply some of our knowledge of calculus to find out more about such graphs. In this section we will discuss tangent lines, and in the next section we will take up the area problem for curves whose equations are given in polar coordinates.

Suppose that the tangent line to the graph of the equation $r = f(\theta)$ at the point (r, θ) makes an angle of α with the polar axis. If we introduce XY-coordinates in the usual way, so that the positive X-axis is the polar axis, and transform our polar equation into an equation in x and y, then we know that

(64-1) $$\tan \alpha = D_x y.$$

Since we wish to compute $\tan \alpha$ directly from our polar equation $r = f(\theta)$, we will express the derivative $D_x y$ in terms of polar coordinates. We combine the Chain Rule Equation

$$D_x y = D_\theta y \, D_x \theta$$

and the formula for the derivative of an inverse

$$D_x \theta = \frac{1}{D_\theta x}$$

to obtain the equation

(64-2) $$D_x y = \frac{D_\theta y}{D_\theta x}.$$

Now let us calculate $D_\theta y$ and $D_\theta x$. Since $y = r \sin \theta$, and for our curve $r = f(\theta)$, we have $y = f(\theta) \sin \theta$. Thus

$$D_\theta y = f'(\theta) \sin \theta + f(\theta) \cos \theta.$$

Similarly, $x = r \cos \theta = f(\theta) \cos \theta$, and hence

$$D_\theta x = f'(\theta) \cos \theta - f(\theta) \sin \theta.$$

When we substitute these values in Equation 64-2 to find $D_x y$, Equation 64-1 becomes

(64-3) $$\tan \alpha = \frac{f'(\theta) \sin \theta + f(\theta) \cos \theta}{f'(\theta) \cos \theta - f(\theta) \sin \theta}.$$

Notice that the slope of the tangent line to the graph of a polar equation $r = f(\theta)$ at a point is *not* simply $D_\theta r$.

Example 64-1.   Find the angle that the tangent line to the cardioid $r = 2(1 - \cos \theta)$ at the point $(2, \pi/2)$ makes with the polar axis.

Solution.   Here we have $f(\theta) = 2(1 - \cos \theta)$, so $f'(\theta) = 2 \sin \theta$. Hence Equation 64-3 gives us

$$\tan \alpha = \frac{(2 \sin \theta) \sin \theta + 2(1 - \cos \theta) \cos \theta}{(2 \sin \theta) \cos \theta - 2(1 - \cos \theta) \sin \theta}$$

$$= \frac{\cos \theta - \cos 2\theta}{\sin 2\theta - \sin \theta}.$$

Thus at the point $(2, \pi/2)$ we find that $\tan \alpha = -1$. It follows that $\alpha = \dfrac{3\pi}{4}$. You should check this result with Fig. 62-5.

If the pole belongs to the graph of the equation $r = f(\theta)$, it is particularly easy to find the tangent lines there. Suppose that the coordinates $(0, \theta_1)$ of the pole satisfy our equation; that is, suppose that $f(\theta_1) = 0$. Furthermore, suppose that $f'(\theta_1) \neq 0$. Then Equation 64-3 reduces to $\tan \alpha = \tan \theta_1$. From this equation we can conclude that a tangent line at the point $(0, \theta_1)$ makes an angle of θ_1 with the polar axis. Therefore, it has the equation $\theta = \theta_1$, so we find the tangents to the graph of the equation $r = f(\theta)$ at the pole by solving the equation $f(\theta) = 0$.

Example 64-2.   Find the tangents to the graph of the equation $r = 2 \cos 3\theta$ at the pole.

Solution.   Here $f(\theta) = 2 \cos 3\theta$, so we must solve the equation $2 \cos 3\theta = 0$. From this equation it follows that $3\theta = \dfrac{\pi}{2} + n\pi$; that is, $\theta = \dfrac{\pi}{6} + \dfrac{n\pi}{3}$. There are three tangents at the pole, the lines $\theta = \pi/6$, $\theta = \pi/2$, and $\theta = 5\pi/6$. The graph of our equation, showing the tangent lines at the pole, appears in Fig. 64-1.

Equation 64-3 enables us to find the tangent of the angle that the tangent line to the graph of the equation $r = f(\theta)$ at the point (r, θ) makes with the polar

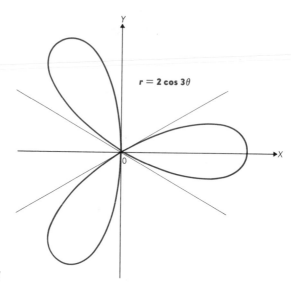

Figure 64-1

axis. In many cases we are interested in the angle of ψ, whose vertex is the point (r, θ), whose initial side is the radial line that contains this point, whose terminal side is the tangent line, and which is such that $0 \leq \psi < \pi$ (Fig. 64-2). The angles of ψ, α, and θ are not independent of each other. At each point of the graph there is an integer n such that ψ is related to α and θ by the equation

$$\psi = \alpha - \theta + n\pi.$$

For example, in the configuration on the left in Fig. 64-2 we have $\psi = \alpha - \theta$, and in the configuration on the right we have $\psi = \alpha - \theta + \pi$. But in any case,

$$\tan \psi = \tan [(\alpha - \theta) + n\pi] = \tan (\alpha - \theta).$$

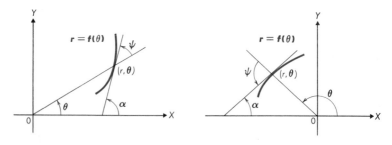

Figure 64-2

From trigonometry we have the formula

$$\tan(\alpha - \theta) = \frac{\tan\alpha - \tan\theta}{1 + \tan\alpha\tan\theta},$$

and if we replace $\tan\alpha$ in this quotient with the right-hand side of Equation 64-3, we will have an expression for $\tan(\alpha - \theta) = \tan\psi$ in terms of θ. In the problems we ask you to make the substitution and show that

(64-4)
$$\tan\psi = \frac{f(\theta)}{f'(\theta)} = \frac{r}{D_\theta r}.$$

Example 64-3.   Find the points of the graph of the equation $r = 2\cos 3\theta$ at which the tangent line is perpendicular to the radial line.

Solution.   The tangent line is perpendicular to the radial line at points where $\psi = \pi/2$; that is, at points where $\tan\psi$ is not defined. From Equation 64-4 we see that $\tan\psi$ is not defined at those points for which $D_\theta r = 0$. Since $D_\theta r = -6\sin 3\theta$, we must solve the equation

$$-6\sin 3\theta = 0.$$

From this equation we find that $3\theta = n\pi$; that is, $\theta = \dfrac{n\pi}{3}$. With the aid of the graph in Fig. 64-1, we see that we need only take the solutions $\theta = 0$, $\pi/3$, and $2\pi/3$ to obtain the three points at which the tangent lines are perpendicular to the radial lines.

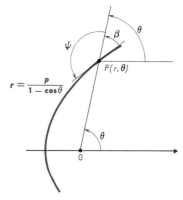

$r = \dfrac{p}{1-\cos\theta}$

Figure 64-3

Example 64-4.   Find the tangent of the angle that the tangent line to a parabola at a point P makes with the line that contains P and the focus.

Solution.   In Fig. 64-3 we have shown a parabola whose polar equation is (Equation 63-10 with $e = 1$)

(64-5)
$$r = \frac{p}{1-\cos\theta}.$$

We are looking for $\tan\beta$. From Fig. 64-3 and Equation 64-4 we see that

$$\tan\beta = -\tan\psi = -\frac{r}{D_\theta r}.$$

From Equation 64-5 we have

$$D_\theta r = D_\theta\left(\frac{p}{1-\cos\theta}\right) = \frac{-p\sin\theta}{(1-\cos\theta)^2},$$

and hence

$$\tan \beta = \frac{1 - \cos \theta}{\sin \theta}.$$

This equation gives us the answer to the question we originally asked, and from it we obtain some interesting information. There is a formula in trigonometry that says

$$\frac{1 - \cos \theta}{\sin \theta} = \tan \frac{\theta}{2}.$$

Thus

$$\tan \beta = \tan \frac{\theta}{2}.$$

This equation tells us that the horizontal line through P in Fig. 64-3 makes the same angle with the tangent line that the radial line through the focus and P does. Therefore, we have another demonstration of the focusing property of the parabola that we discussed in Section 31.

P R O B L E M S   6 4

1. Find ψ at the point $(4\pi, 2\pi)$ of the graph of the equation $r = 2\theta$.

2. Find the slope of the tangent to the graph of the equation $r = 2 \cos 3\theta$ at the point at which:
   (a) $\theta = 0$ (b) $\theta = 2\pi/3$ (c) $\theta = 4\pi/3$ (d) $\theta = -\pi/4$

3. Find polar equations of the lines tangent at the origin to the graphs of the following equations.
   (a) $r = 4 \cos 2\theta$ (b) $r = \sin 3\theta$
   (c) $r^2 = \cos 2\theta$ (d) $r = 1 - 3 \cos \theta$

4. Find the slope of the tangent to the graph of the given equation at the point with indicated angular coordinate.
   (a) $r = 1 - 2 \cos \theta,\ \theta = \pi/2$ (b) $r = \sec^2 \theta,\ \theta = \pi/3$
   (c) $r = 1 + 2\sqrt{\theta},\ \theta = \pi$ (d) $r = (1 + 2 \cos \theta)^{-1},\ \theta = 0$

5. Show that the angular coordinate of a point of the graph of the equation $r = 2 \cos 3\theta$ at which the tangent line is parallel to the polar axis satisfies the equation $3 \tan^4 \theta - 12 \tan^2 \theta + 1 = 0$.

6. Find the points of the cardioid $r = 2(1 - \cos \theta)$ at which the tangent line is perpendicular to the polar axis.

7. Find the polar coordinates of the "highest" point of the cardioid $r = 2(1 - \cos \theta)$.

8. What can you say about the angle between the radial line and the tangent line at a point of the graph of the equation $r = f(\theta)$ that is a maximum distance from the pole?

9. Sketch the curve $r = e^\theta$, and show that at any point of this curve the tangent line makes an angle of 45° with the radial line.

10. Are there any points of the spiral $r\theta = 1$ at which $\psi = \pi/2$? Examine ψ for very large θ.

11. Show that $\tan \psi = \tan \frac{1}{2}\theta$ at points of the cardioid $r = 2(1 - \cos \theta)$.

12. Derive Equation 64-4 by making the substitution suggested in the paragraph preceding that equation.

13. Use the formula for $\tan (\psi_2 - \psi_1)$ to find the angle between the tangents at the points of intersection of the graphs of the given equations.

    (a) $r = 2(1 - \cos \theta)$ (b) $r = \sin \theta$

        $r = -6 \cos \theta$ $r = \cos 2\theta$

14. Show that the curves whose equations are $r = 3\theta$ and $r\theta = 3$ intersect at right angles.

15. Let P be a point of the ellipse $r = \dfrac{ep}{1 - e \cos \theta}$.

    (a) Show that

$$\tan \psi = \frac{-p}{r \sin \theta} = \frac{-p}{y}.$$

    (b) Let F be the focus of the ellipse that is not the pole of the coordinate system chosen for part (a). Choose a new polar coordinate system whose pole is F so that if P has coordinates $(\bar{r}, \bar{\theta})$ in this new system, then

$$\bar{r} = \frac{ep}{1 + e \cos \bar{\theta}}.$$

Show that

$$\tan \bar{\psi} = \frac{p}{y} = -\tan \psi, \text{ and conclude that } \bar{\psi} = \pi - \psi.$$

    (c) Draw a figure to help you deduce that the equation $\bar{\psi} = \pi - \psi$ means that the tangent line to the ellipse at a point P bisects the angle between the two lines that join P to the foci of the ellipse. (The focusing property of the ellipse can now be easily deduced.)

65 AREAS IN POLAR COORDINATES

In this section we consider the problem of finding the area A of the region that is bounded by the graph of a polar equation $r = f(\theta)$ and radial lines $\theta = \alpha$ and $\theta = \beta$, as shown in Fig. 65-1. Let us suppose that $\alpha < \beta$ and that we use radian measure for our angles. It will be easier to solve this area problem if we word it as follows. Let θ be a number such that $\alpha \leq \theta \leq \beta$ and denote by $S(\theta)$ the area of the part of our given region that lies between the radial lines making angles of α and θ with the polar axis. We have shaded this subregion whose area is $S(\theta)$ in Fig. 65-1. Thus we see that $S(\alpha)$ is 0, and the area A of the entire region— the number we are looking for—is $S(\beta)$.

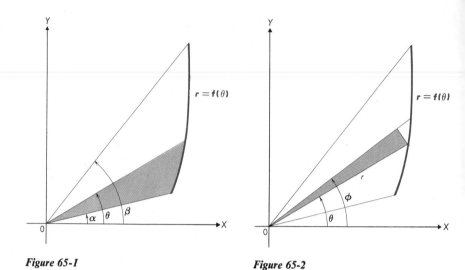

Figure 65-1   **Figure 65-2**

Since a formula for $S(\theta)$ is not immediately available, we will proceed indirectly. According to the Fundamental Theorem of Calculus, $\int_{\alpha}^{\beta} S'(\theta)\, d\theta = S(\beta) - S(\alpha)$. We have just pointed out that $S(\alpha) = 0$ and $S(\beta) = A$, and so our desired area is given by the equation

(65-1) $$A = \int_{\alpha}^{\beta} S'(\theta)\, d\theta.$$

Therefore, to find A we must develop a formula for $S'(\theta)$. Let θ be a number in the interval $[\alpha, \beta]$ and ϕ be a number between θ and β (see Fig. 65-2). Then $S(\phi) - S(\theta)$ is the area of the wedge that lies between the radial lines that make angles of θ and ϕ with the polar axis. If the wedge is narrow, its area is approximately the same as the area of the circular sector with a radius of $r = f(\theta)$ and a central angle of $\phi - \theta$ that we have shaded in Fig. 65-2. The area of this sector (see Appendix A) is $\frac{1}{2}r^2(\phi - \theta)$, and so we have

that is,
$$S(\phi) - S(\theta) \approx \tfrac{1}{2}r^2(\phi - \theta);$$

$$\frac{S(\phi) - S(\theta)}{\phi - \theta} \approx \tfrac{1}{2}r^2.$$

(In our argument we have assumed that $\phi > \theta$, but we would arrive at the same formula if $\phi < \theta$.) From the figure it appears that the closer ϕ is to θ the better this approximation is, and hence it seems reasonable to suppose that

$$\lim_{\phi \to \theta} \frac{S(\phi) - S(\theta)}{\phi - \theta} = \tfrac{1}{2}r^2.$$

The limit of this difference quotient is $S'(\theta)$, so our geometric argument suggests that $S'(\theta) = \tfrac{1}{2}r^2$. Now we replace $S'(\theta)$ with $\tfrac{1}{2}r^2$ in Equation 65-1 and we obtain the equation

(65-2) $$A = \tfrac{1}{2}\int_{\alpha}^{\beta} r^2 \, d\theta = \tfrac{1}{2}\int_{\alpha}^{\beta} f(\theta)^2 \, d\theta.$$

Example 65-1. Find the area of the region that is bounded by the cardioid $r = 2(1 - \cos \theta)$.

Solution. Because of the symmetry of the cardioid (see Fig. 62-5) we see that we may calculate the area of the part of the region for which $\theta \in [0, \pi]$ and multiply it by 2. Thus our desired area A is

$$A = 2 \cdot \tfrac{1}{2} \int_0^{\pi} r^2 \, d\theta = 4 \int_0^{\pi} (1 - \cos \theta)^2 \, d\theta$$

$$= 4 \int_0^{\pi} (1 - 2 \cos \theta + \cos^2 \theta) \, d\theta$$

$$= 6\pi.$$

The area represented by the integral in Equation 65-2 should be thought of as the area of the region that is "swept out" by the radial line segment joining the pole to the point (r, θ) as this point moves along the curve for $\theta \in [\alpha, \beta]$. Thus, for example, if we consider the circle $r = 5$, and let $\alpha = 0$, $\beta = 3\pi$, then the number

$$A = \tfrac{1}{2} \int_0^{3\pi} 25 \, d\theta = \frac{75\pi}{2}$$

is one and one-half times the area of the circle. You should make a sketch showing the region whose area you intend to find and carefully determine α and β so that this region is swept out once, and only once, by the radial line segment to the point (r, θ) for $\theta \in [\alpha, \beta]$. If you study the following example carefully, it will help you avoid a common error in determining α and β.

Example 65-2. Find the area of the region that is cut out of the first quadrant by the curve $r = 2 \cos 3\theta$.

Solution. We are interested in the shaded region shown in Fig. 65-3. The proper numbers α and β are *not* 0 *and* $\pi/2$. You can easily convince yourself that the

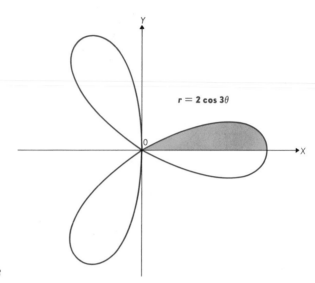

$r = 2 \cos 3\theta$

Figure 65-3

portion of the curve in the first quadrant is obtained by choosing θ from the interval $[0, \frac{1}{6}\pi]$. Thus the area we want is

$$A = \frac{1}{2} \int_0^{\pi/6} 4 \cos^2 3\theta = 2 \int_0^{\pi/6} \cos^2 3\theta \; d\theta = \pi/6.$$

Equation 65-2 can be used to find areas of regions bounded by two polar curves. An example will show us how.

Example 65-3. Find the area of the region that is outside the cardioid $r = 2(1 - \cos \theta)$ and inside the circle $r = -6 \cos \theta$.

Solution. In Fig. 65-4 we have sketched the curves involved and have shaded the region whose area we seek. We found in Example 62-5 that our curves intersect at the points $(3, 2\pi/3)$ and $(3, 4\pi/3)$. So we see that the desired area is obtained by subtracting the area of the region swept out by the radial line of the cardioid from the area of the region swept out by the radial line of the circle as θ goes from $2\pi/3$ to $4\pi/3$. Making use of the symmetry of our region,

$$A = 2 \left[\frac{1}{2} \int_{2\pi/3}^{\pi} 36 \cos^2 \theta \; d\theta - \frac{1}{2} \int_{2\pi/3}^{\pi} 4(1 - \cos \theta)^2 \; d\theta \right]$$

$$= \int_{2\pi/3}^{\pi} [36 \cos^2 \theta - 4(1 - 2 \cos \theta + \cos^2 \theta)] \; d\theta$$

$$= 4 \int_{2\pi/3}^{\pi} (4 \cos 2\theta + 2 \cos \theta + 3) \; d\theta = 4\pi.$$

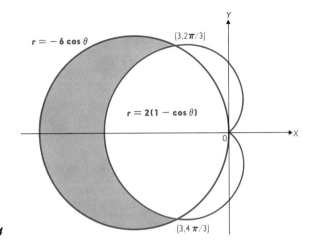

$r = -6 \cos \theta$

$(3, 2\pi/3)$

$r = 2(1 - \cos \theta)$

$(3, 4\pi/3)$

Figure 65-4

P R O B L E M S   6 5

1. Find the area of the region bounded by one loop of the graph of the equation $r = 2 \cos 2\theta$.

2. Find the area of the region bounded by the "first" turn of a spiral ($0 \le \theta \le 2\pi$) and the polar axis if the equation of the spiral is:
(a) $r = \theta$ (b) $r = e^\theta$ (c) $r = \cosh \theta$

3. Find the area of the region bounded by the circle $r = 6 \cos \theta + 8 \sin \theta$.

4. Find the area of the region enclosed by the graph of the polar equation $r = \sin \theta \cos^2 \theta$.

5. Show that the area of the region bounded by two radial lines and the spiral $r\theta = k$ is directly proportional to the difference of the lengths of the two radial segments.

6. Find the area of the region bounded by the inside loop of the graph of the equation $r = 1 - 2 \cos \theta$.

7. Find the area of the region bounded by the curve $r = 3 + 2 \cos \theta$.

8. How much material is needed to cover the face of a bow tie whose outline is the curve $r^2 = 8 \cos 2\theta$?

9. Find the area of the region outside the circle $r = -6 \cos \theta$ and inside the cardioid $r = 2(1 - \cos \theta)$ (see Fig. 65-4).

10. Show that the area of the region enclosed by the rose curve $r = a \cos n\theta$ is one-half the area of the circular disk in which the rose is inscribed if n is an even positive integer and one-fourth the area of the disk if n is an odd positive integer.

11. Find the area of the region that is enclosed by the graph of the equation $r^2 \cos^4 \theta - 5 \cos^2 \theta + 1 = 0$.

12. Interpret the following integral as the area of a region enclosed by a certain ellipse and thereby find the value of the integral: $\displaystyle\int_0^{2\pi} \frac{2\, d\theta}{(2 - \cos \theta)^2}$.

66 ROTATION OF AXES

We now return to the problem of changing from one cartesian coordinate system to another. In Section 27 we found that we can often simplify the form of certain equations by translating the axes. For example, we saw that a proper translation puts the equation of a circle in the form $\bar{x}^2 + \bar{y}^2 = r^2$. At that time we only considered new coordinate systems whose axes were parallel to the original axes. Now we are ready to take up more complicated transformations of axes.

In Fig. 66-1 we show two cartesian coordinate systems—an XY-system and an $\bar{X}\bar{Y}$-system, with the same origin, but such that the $\bar{X}$ axis makes an angle of

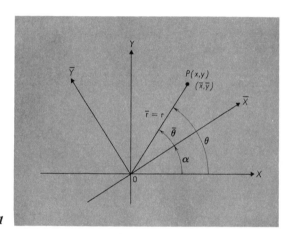

Figure 66-1

α with the X-axis. We say that the $\bar{X}\bar{Y}$-system is obtained from the XY-system by a **rotation** through α. Each point P will have two sets of coordinates, (x, y) and $(\bar{x}, \bar{y})$; we will now find the equations that relate these coordinates.

We introduce two polar coordinate systems, both systems having the origin O as the pole. In one system the positive X-axis is the polar axis, and in the other system the positive $\bar{X}$-axis is the polar axis. Then our point P will have polar coordinates (r, θ) and $(\bar{r}, \bar{\theta})$ in addition to its two pairs of cartesian coordinates. It is easy to see that

$$\bar{r} = r, \quad \text{and} \quad \bar{\theta} = \theta - \alpha.$$

Therefore, the equations

$$\bar{x} = \bar{r} \cos \bar{\theta} \quad \text{and} \quad \bar{y} = \bar{r} \sin \bar{\theta}$$

give us

(66-1) $\bar{x} = r \cos (\theta - \alpha) \quad \text{and} \quad \bar{y} = r \sin (\theta - \alpha).$

Using the trigonometric identities

$$\cos(\theta - \alpha) = \cos\theta\cos\alpha + \sin\theta\sin\alpha$$

and

$$\sin(\theta - \alpha) = \sin\theta\cos\alpha - \cos\theta\sin\alpha,$$

we can write Equations 66-1 as

(66-2)
$$\bar{x} = r\cos\theta\cos\alpha + r\sin\theta\sin\alpha$$
$$\bar{y} = r\sin\theta\cos\alpha - r\cos\theta\sin\alpha.$$

Now we replace $r\cos\theta$ with x and $r\sin\theta$ with y in Equations 66-2, and we obtain our transformation equations

(66-3)
$$\bar{x} = x\cos\alpha + y\sin\alpha$$
$$\bar{y} = -x\sin\alpha + y\cos\alpha.$$

In Problem 66-1 we ask you to solve these equations for x and y and thus obtain the inverse transformation equations

(66-4)
$$x = \bar{x}\cos\alpha - \bar{y}\sin\alpha,$$
$$y = \bar{x}\sin\alpha + \bar{y}\cos\alpha.$$

Example 66-1. Suppose the $\bar{X}\bar{Y}$-axes are obtained by rotating the XY-axes through an angle of $45°$. To what does the equation $xy = 1$ transform?

Solution. Here $\alpha = 45°$, so Equations 66-4 become

$$x = \frac{\bar{x}}{\sqrt{2}} - \frac{\bar{y}}{\sqrt{2}},$$

$$y = \frac{\bar{x}}{\sqrt{2}} + \frac{\bar{y}}{\sqrt{2}}.$$

Hence

$$xy = \frac{(\bar{x} - \bar{y})(\bar{x} + \bar{y})}{2} = \frac{(\bar{x}^2 - \bar{y}^2)}{2}.$$

Thus the equation $xy = 1$ is transformed into the equation

$$\frac{\bar{x}^2}{2} - \frac{\bar{y}^2}{2} = 1.$$

This equation is the standard form for an equilateral hyperbola whose asymptotes bisect the quadrants in the $\bar{X}\bar{Y}$-coordinate system. Thus the equation $xy = 1$

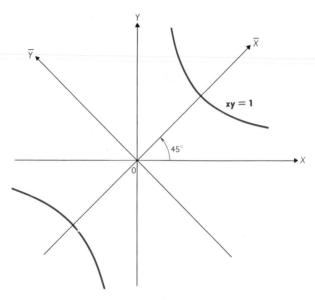

Figure 66-2

represents an equilateral hyperbola whose asymptotes are the *X*- and *Y*-axes (see Fig. 66-2).

Example 66-2.   Find the distance between the point $P(1, 4)$ and the line $2y - x = 2$.

Solution.   Figure 66-3 shows the given point and line. The slope of the line is $\tan \alpha = \frac{1}{2}$, where α is the measure of the angle of inclination. Now let us introduce an $\bar{X}\bar{Y}$-coordinate system in such a way that the $\bar{X}$-axis is parallel to our given line. We can obtain such an $\bar{X}\bar{Y}$-system by a rotation of axes through α. Since $\tan \alpha = \frac{1}{2}$, we see that $\sin \alpha = 1/\sqrt{5}$ and $\cos \alpha = 2/\sqrt{5}$. Thus the Transformation Equations

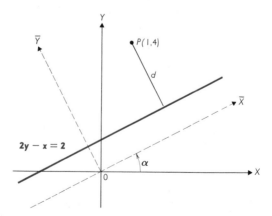

Figure 66-3

66-3 and 66-4 become

$$\bar{x} = \frac{2x}{\sqrt{5}} + \frac{y}{\sqrt{5}}, \quad \bar{y} = \frac{-x}{\sqrt{5}} + \frac{2y}{\sqrt{5}}$$

$$x = \frac{2\bar{x}}{\sqrt{5}} - \frac{\bar{y}}{\sqrt{5}}, \quad y = \frac{\bar{x}}{\sqrt{5}} + \frac{2\bar{y}}{\sqrt{5}}.$$

When we substitute these expressions for x and y in the equation of our line, it becomes $\bar{y} = \dfrac{2}{\sqrt{5}}$. Furthermore, these transformation equations tell us that the $\bar{Y}$-coordinate of the point P is $\dfrac{7}{\sqrt{5}}$. Since the line is parallel to the $\bar{X}$-axis, we find the distance d between it and P by subtraction:

$$d = \frac{7}{\sqrt{5}} - \frac{2}{\sqrt{5}} = \frac{5}{\sqrt{5}} = \sqrt{5}.$$

The **general rigid transformation** equations

(66-5)
$$\bar{x} = x \cos \alpha + y \sin \alpha - h$$
$$\bar{y} = -x \sin \alpha + y \cos \alpha - k$$

are the transformation equations that result from a rotation through α *followed* by a translation.

Example 66-3. Sketch the two cartesian coordinate systems that are related by the equations

(66-6)
$$\bar{x} = \tfrac{3}{5}x + \tfrac{4}{5}y - 3$$
$$\bar{y} = -\tfrac{4}{5}x + \tfrac{3}{5}y - 1.$$

Draw the XY-system in the "usual" position.

Solution. The points whose $\bar{X}\bar{Y}$-coordinates are $(0, 0)$ and $(1, 0)$ determine the $\bar{X}$-axis, and the points whose $\bar{X}\bar{Y}$-coordinates are $(0, 0)$ and $(0, 1)$ determine the $\bar{Y}$-axis. We will locate these points by finding their XY-coordinates from Equations 66-6 and then plotting them in the XY-coordinate system of Fig. 66-4. The XY-coordinates of the point whose $\bar{X}\bar{Y}$-coordinates are $(0, 0)$ are given by the equations

$$0 = \tfrac{3}{5}x + \tfrac{4}{5}y - 3$$

and

$$0 = -\tfrac{4}{5}x + \tfrac{3}{5}y - 1.$$

When we solve these equations, we obtain $x = 1$ and $y = 3$. Similarly, we find that the point whose $\bar{X}\bar{Y}$-coordinates are $(1, 0)$ has XY-coordinates $(\tfrac{8}{5}, \tfrac{19}{5})$. The

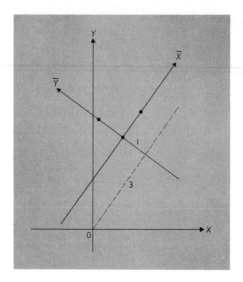

Figure 66-4

point whose $\overline{X}\overline{Y}$-coordinates are $(0, 1)$ has XY-coordinates $(\frac{1}{5}, \frac{18}{5})$. Now we plot these points and draw in the $\overline{X}\overline{Y}$-axes (Fig. 66-4). We see that the $\overline{X}\overline{Y}$-axes are obtained by first rotating the axes through an angle of α, where $\cos \alpha = \frac{3}{5}$ and $\sin \alpha = \frac{4}{5}$, and then translating the origin 3 units in the "new X direction" and 1 unit in the "new Y direction."

PROBLEMS 66

1. Solve Equations 66-3 to obtain Equations 66-4.

2. Find the $\overline{X}\overline{Y}$-coordinates of the point $(-2, 4)$ after a rotation through:
   (a) 30°   (b) 135°   (c) 240°   (d) −180°
   (e) π (f) $-\pi/2$ (g) 2π (h) $-\pi/4$

3. Suppose the $\overline{X}\overline{Y}$-coordinate system is obtained by a rotation through 60°. Find the XY-coordinates of the point whose $\overline{X}\overline{Y}$-coordinates are:
   (a) $(1, 0)$ (b) $(0, 1)$
   (c) $(1, 1)$ (d) $(-2, \sqrt{3})$

4. Suppose we are given the transformation equations
$$\bar{x} = 0.8x + 0.6y$$
$$\bar{y} = -0.6x + 0.8y.$$
What angle does the $\overline{X}$-axis make with the X-axis? Sketch the XY- and the $\overline{X}\overline{Y}$-coordinate axes.

5. Suppose that we rotate our axes through an angle of α, where $0 \leq \alpha < \pi/2$. Let the slope of the $\overline{X}$-axis relative to the X-axis be m. What is the slope of the X-axis relative to the $\bar{X}$-axis? Show that the transformation equations can be written

$$\bar{x} = \frac{x + my}{\sqrt{1 + m^2}}, \quad \bar{y} = \frac{-mx + y}{\sqrt{1 + m^2}}.$$

6. To what equation does the given equation transform under a rotation through 45°?
Describe the graph of the equation.
(a) $x^{1/2} + y^{1/2} = 1$ (b) $y + |y| = x + |x|$

(c) $[\![x + y]\!] = 0$ (d) $y = x + \sqrt{2}\sin\left(\dfrac{x + y}{\sqrt{2}}\right)$

7. Find the distance between the given point and the given line.
(a) $(6, -2)$ and $3x - 4y + 4 = 0$ (b) $(-1, 7)$ and $x + 3y - 6 = 0$
(c) $(4, 3)$ and $x + y + 1 = 0$ (d) $(-2, -3)$ and $2x - y - 4 = 0$

8. Find the distance between the parallel lines $x + y - 2 = 0$ and $2x + 2y - 1 = 0$.

9. What are the transformation equations that relate the XY-coordinates and the $\bar{X}\bar{Y}$-coordinates if we first translate the origin to the point (h, k) and then rotate through an angle of α?

10. Plot the graph of the equation $2x^3 - 6x^2y + 6xy^2 - 2y^3 - x - y = 0$ by first performing a rotation through $-45°$.

11. Is it possible to rotate the axes so that the positive $\bar{X}$-axis lies along the positive Y-axis and the positive $\bar{Y}$-axis lies along the positive X-axis?

12. Give a geometric description of the transformation that is determined by the equations $\bar{x} = hx$ and $\bar{y} = ky$, where h and k are given positive numbers.

67 THE GENERAL QUADRATIC EQUATION

For certain choices of the numbers A, B, C, D, E, and F we already know that the graph of the quadratic equation

$$(67\text{-}1) \qquad Ax^2 + Bxy + Cy^2 + Dx + Ey + F = 0$$

is a circle, a conic, or a line. For example, if we choose $A = 1$, $B = 0$, $C = -1$, $D = 0$, $E = 0$, and $F = -1$, then Equation 67-1 becomes

$$x^2 - y^2 = 1,$$

which we recognize as the equation of an equilateral hyperbola. But other choices of A, B, C, D, E, and F lead to equations that we have not yet studied—for example, the equation

$$(67\text{-}2) \qquad 6x^2 + 24xy - y^2 - 12x + 26y + 11 = 0.$$

In this section we shall see that the graph of a quadratic equation is always a familiar figure. In particular, it will turn out that the graph of Equation 67-2 is a hyperbola.

To find the graph of a quadratic equation we will first make a transformation of axes that reduces the equation to one of the standard forms that we have already studied. Thus in Example 66-1 we saw that a rotation of axes through 45° transforms the equation $xy = 1$ into the standard equation of an equilateral hyperbola

$$\frac{\bar{x}^2}{2} - \frac{\bar{y}^2}{2} = 1.$$

The question that naturally comes to mind is, "How did we decide to rotate through 45°?" The following example shows how we pick our angle of rotation.

Example 67-1.   By a suitable rotation of axes, reduce the equation

(67-3) $8x^2 - 4xy + 5y^2 = 36$

to a standard form.

Solution.   When we make the rotation given by Equations 66-4, our equation becomes

$8(\bar{x} \cos \alpha - \bar{y} \sin \alpha)^2 - 4(\bar{x} \cos \alpha - \bar{y} \sin \alpha) \cdot (\bar{x} \sin \alpha + \bar{y} \cos \alpha)$
$$+ 5(\bar{x} \sin \alpha + \bar{y} \cos \alpha)^2 = 36.$$

Now we expand and collect terms:

(67-4) $(8 \cos^2 \alpha - 4 \sin \alpha \cos \alpha + 5 \sin^2 \alpha)\bar{x}^2$
$$+ (4 \sin^2 \alpha - 6 \sin \alpha \cos \alpha - 4 \cos^2 \alpha)\bar{x}\bar{y}$$
$$+ (8 \sin^2 \alpha + 4 \sin \alpha \cos \alpha + 5 \cos^2 \alpha)\bar{y}^2 = 36.$$

This last equation has the form

(67-5) $\bar{A}\bar{x}^2 + \bar{B}\bar{x}\bar{y} + \bar{C}\bar{y}^2 = 36,$

where the numbers $\bar{A}$, $\bar{B}$, and $\bar{C}$ depend on α. If $\bar{B} = 0$, we would recognize the type of curve we are dealing with, so let us choose α so that $\bar{B} = 0$; that is, so that

$$4 \sin^2 \alpha - 6 \sin \alpha \cos \alpha - 4 \cos^2 \alpha = 0.$$

Since $\cos^2 \alpha - \sin^2 \alpha = \cos 2\alpha$ and $\sin \alpha \cos \alpha = \frac{1}{2} \sin 2\alpha$, this equation can be written as

$$-3 \sin 2\alpha - 4 \cos 2\alpha = 0,$$

from which we see that

$$\cot 2\alpha = -\tfrac{3}{4}.$$

We can select an angle of 2α in the range $0° < 2\alpha < 180°$ that satisfies this equation, and thus $0° < \alpha < 90°$. To find the coefficients of $\bar{x}^2$ and $\bar{y}^2$ we find the numbers $\cos \alpha$ and $\sin \alpha$ from the trigonometric identities

$$\cos \alpha = \sqrt{\frac{1 + \cos 2\alpha}{2}} \quad \text{and} \quad \sin \alpha = \sqrt{\frac{1 - \cos 2\alpha}{2}}.$$

Since $\cot 2\alpha = -\frac{3}{4}$, it follows that the radial line through the point $(-3, 4)$ makes an angle of 2α with the positive X-axis. Hence $\cos 2\alpha = -\frac{3}{5}$, and we have

$$\cos \alpha = \sqrt{\frac{1 - \frac{3}{5}}{2}} = \sqrt{\frac{1}{5}}$$

and

$$\sin \alpha = \sqrt{\frac{1 + \frac{3}{5}}{2}} = \sqrt{\frac{4}{5}}.$$

When we substitute these numbers in Equation 67-4, the equation becomes

$$4\bar{x}^2 + 9\bar{y}^2 = 36.$$

In other words,

$$\frac{\bar{x}^2}{9} + \frac{\bar{y}^2}{4} = 1.$$

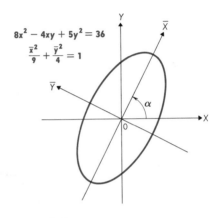

$$8x^2 - 4xy + 5y^2 = 36$$
$$\frac{\bar{x}^2}{9} + \frac{\bar{y}^2}{4} = 1$$

Figure 67-1

So we see that the graph of Equation 67-3 is an ellipse whose major diameter is 6 units long and whose minor diameter is 4 units long. We have shown our ellipse together with the rotated axes in Fig. 67-1.

We can employ the procedure used in the preceding example to reduce any quadratic expression

$$Ax^2 + Bxy + Cy^2$$

in which $B \neq 0$ to the form

$$\bar{A}\bar{x}^2 + \bar{C}\bar{y}^2.$$

We simply replace x and y in terms of $\bar{x}$ and $\bar{y}$ according to the rotation Equations 66-4 and obtain the expression $A(\bar{x} \cos \alpha - \bar{y} \sin \alpha)^2 + B(\bar{x} \cos \alpha - \bar{y} \sin \alpha) \times (\bar{x} \sin \alpha + \bar{y} \cos \alpha) + C(\bar{x} \sin \alpha + \bar{y} \cos \alpha)^2$. When we multiply out and collect the coefficients of $\bar{x}^2$, $\bar{x}\bar{y}$, and $\bar{y}^2$, we find that

$$Ax^2 + Bxy + Cy^2 = \bar{A}\bar{x}^2 + \bar{B}\bar{x}\bar{y} + \bar{C}\bar{y}^2,$$

where

$$\bar{A} = A \cos^2 \alpha + B \sin \alpha \cos \alpha + C \sin^2 \alpha,$$

(67-6) $$\bar{B} = (C - A) \sin 2\alpha + B \cos 2\alpha,$$

$$\bar{C} = A \sin^2 \alpha - B \sin \alpha \cos \alpha + C \cos^2 \alpha.$$

We see from the second of Equations 67-6 that $\bar{B}$ will be 0 if we choose α so that

(67-7) $$\cot 2\alpha = \frac{A - C}{B}.$$

Clearly, we can always choose α so that $0° < 2\alpha < 180°$. We sum up our results as a theorem.

Theorem 67-1.   *Every quadratic expression $Ax^2 + Bxy + Cy^2$ in which $B \neq 0$ can be reduced to the form $\bar{A}\bar{x}^2 + \bar{C}\bar{y}^2$ by rotating axes through an angle of α, where $0° < \alpha < 90°$, and $\cot 2\alpha = (A - C)/B$.*

By rotating axes through the angle of α, as described in Theorem 67-1, we can reduce any quadratic equation of the form of Equation 67-1 in which $B \neq 0$ to a quadratic equation of the form

$$\bar{A}\bar{x}^2 + \bar{C}\bar{y}^2 + \bar{D}\bar{x} + \bar{E}\bar{y} + F = 0.$$

If we don't recognize the graph of this equation, a suitable translation will bring it to a form that we do recognize. We will illustrate the entire procedure by an example. It will pay you to review our work on translation in Chapter 4.

Example 67-2.   Describe the graph of Equation 67-2.

Solution.   Here $A = 6$, $B = 24$, and $C = -1$. So we first rotate the axes through the acute angle of α such that

$$\cot 2\alpha = \tfrac{7}{24}.$$

It is easy to see that $\cos 2\alpha = \tfrac{7}{25}$, and hence

$$\cos \alpha = \sqrt{\frac{1 + \cos 2\alpha}{2}} = \frac{4}{5}$$

and

$$\sin \alpha = \sqrt{\frac{1 - \cos 2\alpha}{2}} = \frac{3}{5}.$$

Therefore, our rotation equations are

$$x = \frac{4\bar{x}}{5} - \frac{3\bar{y}}{5} \quad \text{and} \quad y = \frac{3\bar{x}}{5} + \frac{4\bar{y}}{5}.$$

When we substitute these quantities in Equation 67-2 we obtain the equation

(67-8) $15\bar{x}^2 - 10\bar{y}^2 + 6\bar{x} + 28\bar{y} + 11 = 0.$

Now we will translate the axes by means of the equations (see Section 27),

$$\bar{x} = \bar{\bar{x}} + h \quad \text{and} \quad \bar{y} = \bar{\bar{y}} + k,$$

where h and k are to be determined so as to make our resulting equation "simpler" than Equation 67-8. In terms of $\bar{\bar{x}}$ and $\bar{\bar{y}}$, Equation 67-8 reads

(67-9) $15\bar{\bar{x}}^2 - 10\bar{\bar{y}}^2 + (30h + 6)\bar{\bar{x}} + (-20k + 28)\bar{\bar{y}} + 15h^2$
$$- 10k^2 + 6h + 28k + 11 = 0.$$

Now we select h and k so that $30h + 6 = 0$ and $-20k + 28 = 0$; that is, $h = -\frac{1}{5}$ and $k = \frac{7}{5}$. Then Equation 67-9 becomes

$$15\bar{\bar{x}}^2 - 10\bar{\bar{y}}^2 + 30 = 0.$$

Finally, we write this equation in the standard form

$$\frac{\bar{\bar{y}}^2}{3} - \frac{\bar{\bar{x}}^2}{2} = 1,$$

and we see that our graph is a hyperbola. The "specifications"—diameter, length of latus rectum, focal length, and so on—of our hyperbola can be read from this equation. The graph of our equation is shown in Fig. 67-2 together with the three different coordinate axes involved.

In the preceding example we began with a quadratic equation

(67-10) $Ax^2 + Bxy + Cy^2 + Dx + Ey + F = 0,$

and rotated axes to obtain an equation of the form

(67-11) $\bar{A}\bar{x}^2 + \bar{C}\bar{y}^2 + \bar{D}\bar{x} + \bar{E}\bar{y} + \bar{F} = 0.$

It is easy to verify, by using the proper translation, that if $\bar{A}$ and $\bar{C}$ have opposite signs ($\bar{A}\bar{C} < 0$), then the graph of Equation 67-11 is a hyperbola. If $\bar{A}$ and $\bar{C}$ have the same signs ($\bar{A}\bar{C} > 0$), our curve is an ellipse or a circle. And if one of the numbers $\bar{A}$ or $\bar{C}$ is 0 ($\bar{A}\bar{C} = 0$), we are dealing with a parabola. Here we are allowing for *degenerate* conics, such as the "hyperbola" $x^2 - 4y^2 = 0$, or the "ellipse" $\dfrac{x^2}{4} + \dfrac{y^2}{9} + 1 = 0.$

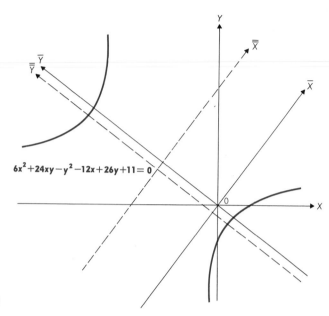

Figure 67-2

In Problem 67-4 we will ask you to verify that

$$\bar{B}^2 - 4\bar{A}\bar{C} = B^2 - 4AC,$$

regardless of the angle of rotation. In particular, if we choose α so that $\bar{B} = 0$, then we find that

$$-4\bar{A}\bar{C} = B^2 - 4AC.$$

Therefore, the sign of $\bar{A}\bar{C}$ is determined by the sign of $B^2 - 4AC$. Thus from our remarks concerning the graph of Equation 67-11, we can conclude that *the graph of Equation* 67-10 *is*
    (i)   *a parabola if* $B^2 - 4AC = 0$,
    (ii) *an ellipse if* $B^2 - 4AC < 0$,
    (iii) *a hyperbola if* $B^2 - 4AC > 0$,
with the understanding that degenerate cases may occur.

    The number $B^2 - 4AC$ is called the *discriminant* of the quadratic Equation 67-10. Notice that the discriminant of Equation 67-2 is $(24)^2 - 4 \cdot 6 \cdot (-1) = 600$, and we found that the graph of this equation is a hyperbola. The discriminant of Equation 67-3 is $(-4)^2 - 4 \cdot 8 \cdot 5 = -144$, and we found that the graph of this equation is an ellipse.

P R O B L E M S   6 7

1. Reduce the following quadratic expressions to the form $\bar{A}\bar{x}^2 + \bar{C}\bar{y}^2$:
(a) $x^2 + 4xy + y^2$ (b) $4x^2 + 15xy - 4y^2$
(c) $x^2 + 4xy + 4y^2$ (d) $x^2 - 9xy + y^2$

2. Rotate the axes so that the following equations take the form $\bar{A}\bar{x}^2 + \bar{C}\bar{y}^2 = \bar{F}$. Sketch the graphs of these equations. Find the algebraic sign of the discriminant of each equation, and use the result to check the form of your graph.
(a) $11x^2 + 24xy + 4y^2 = 20$
(b) $25x^2 + 14xy + 25y^2 = 288$
(c) $3x^2 + 4xy = 4$
(d) $9x^2 - 24xy + 16y^2 - 400x - 300y = 0$

3. Use translations and rotations to help you sketch the graphs of the following equations. Find the algebraic sign of the discriminant of each equation, and use the result to check the form of your graph.
(a) $5x^2 + 6xy + 5y^2 - 32x - 32y + 32 = 0$
(b) $x^2 - 4xy + 4y^2 + 5y - 9 = 0$
(c) $9x^2 - 24xy + 16y^2 - 56x - 92y + 688 = 0$
(d) $x^2 + 2xy + y^2 - 2x - 2y - 3 = 0$

4. Use Equations 67-6 to show that $\bar{A} + \bar{C} = A + C$, and $\bar{B}^2 - 4\bar{A}\bar{C} = B^2 - 4AC$.

5. Find the XY-coordinate equation of the set of points the sum of whose distances from the points $(1, 1)$ and $(-1, -1)$ is 4 by first writing the equation in a rotated system, and then using the rotation Equations 66-3 to obtain the equation in x and y.

6. A parabola has the origin as its vertex, and its directrix is the line $y + x + 1 = 0$. What is the equation of the parabola in a coordinate system whose $\bar{X}$-axis is obtained by rotating the X-axis through $45°$? Find the equation of the parabola in XY-coordinates.

7. Solve the equation $2x^2 + 2xy + y^2 = 9$ for y to obtain $y = -x + \sqrt{9 - x^2}$ or $y = -x - \sqrt{9 - x^2}$. Sketch the graphs of the equations $y = -x$ and $y = \sqrt{9 - x^2}$, and use these graphs to sketch the graph of the given equation by addition or subtraction of Y-coordinates. Use the algebraic sign of the discriminant of the equation to check the form of your graph.

8. Use the method of the preceding question to sketch the graph of the equation $y^2 - 2xy + 2x - 2y + 2 = 0$.

9. Identify the conic that contains the following points:
(a) $(-3, -2), (2, -2), (2, 1), (0, -5), (3, 0)$
(b) $(1, 2), (1, 8), (-1, 6), (-1, 0), (-5, 0)$
(c) $(3, 4), (-3, -2), (-3, 0), (-2, 0), (2, 4)$

10. How must A, B, and C be related algebraically for the graph of the equation $Ax^2 + Bxy + Cy^2 + Dx + Ey + F = 0$ to be a circle (or a degenerate circle).

11. Use the discriminant to identify the "conic" whose equation is $2x^2 + xy - y^2 + 6y - 8 = 0$. Write the equation in factored form, $(x + y - 2)(2x - y + 4) = 0$, and describe the graph of this "conic."

12. Show that if we pick α to satisfy Equation 67-7, then

$$\bar{A} = \frac{|B|\,(A + C) + B\sqrt{(A - C)^2 + B^2}}{2\,|B|}$$

$$\text{and} \quad \bar{C} = \frac{|B|\,(A + C) - B\sqrt{(A - C)^2 + B^2}}{2\,|B|}.$$

68 VECTORS IN THE PLANE

Physicists and engineers talk and think a great deal in terms of **vectors**. These scientists describe a vector quantity as one that has both magnitude and direction; they use vectors to represent such things as velocity, force, and the like. Geometrically, a vector is represented as an arrow in space, the length of the arrow being the magnitude of the vector and the direction of the arrow being the assigned direction of the vector. For the present we shall confine ourselves to vectors that lie in a plane, but in the next chapter we shall study vectors in three-dimensional space.

A vector is determined by an ordered pair of points in the plane—the **initial point** and the **terminal point** of the vector (Fig. 68-1). We use boldface type to denote vectors. For instance, we have labeled the vector on the left in Fig. 68-1

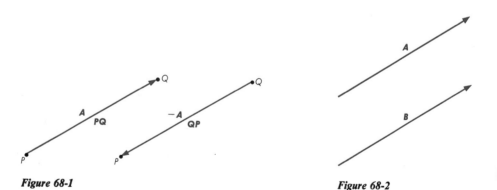

Figure 68-1   **Figure 68-2**

as *A*, and we might also call it *PQ* if we want to emphasize that it is the vector from *P* to *Q*. We denote the magnitude of the vector *A* by the symbol $|A|$. We often refer to this number as the **absolute value** of *A*. If *A* is the vector *PQ*, then the vector *QP* is denoted by $-A$ (see Fig. 68-1).

Two vectors are considered equal if, and only if, they have the same magnitude and the same direction. Thus for the vectors *A* and *B* in Fig. 68-2 we have *A* = *B*. Notice that we do not require that equal vectors coincide, but they must be parallel, have the same length, and point in the same direction.

If we have two vectors A and B as shown on the left in Fig. 68-3, then we obtain the vector sum $A + B$ by making the initial point of B coincide with the terminal point of A and joining the initial point of A to the terminal point of B as

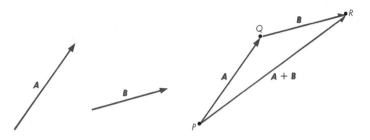

Figure 68-3

shown on the right in Fig. 68-3. Thus, if P, Q, and R are points such that $A = PQ$ and $B = QR$, then $A + B = PR$; that is,

$$PQ + QR = PR.$$

We get the sum $B + A$ by making the initial point of A coincide with the terminal point of B and joining the initial point of B to the terminal point of A. Figure 68-4 shows how we construct $A + B$ and $B + A$, and it is apparent that the **commutative law** of addition,

(68-1) $$A + B = B + A,$$

holds for vector addition. Figure 68-4 suggests the name *parallelogram rule* that is often used to describe the method of adding vectors.

If $A = PQ$, $B = QR$, and $C = RS$ (see Fig. 68-5), then

$$(A + B) + C = (PQ + QR) + RS = PR + RS = PS,$$

and

$$A + (B + C) = PQ + (QR + RS) = PQ + QS = PS.$$

Thus the **associative law** of addition,

(68-2) $$(A + B) + C = A + (B + C),$$

is valid for vectors, and we write $A + B + C$ for this sum.

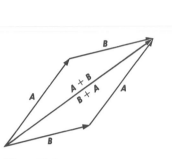

Figure 68-4

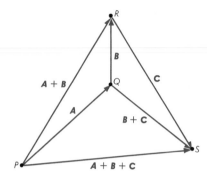

Figure 68-5

We find it convenient to introduce the **zero vector 0**, which can be represented as PP, where P is any point. The magnitude of 0 is 0, and its direction is unspecified. If A is any vector, then

(68-3) $$A + 0 = 0 + A = A.$$

Furthermore, our rules of vector addition tell us that

(68-4) $$A + (-A) = (-A) + A = 0.$$

We define the difference $A - B$ by means of the equation

$$A - B = A + (-B).$$

Then it follows that

$$(A - B) + B = A + [(-B) + B] = A + 0 = A;$$

that is, the difference $A - B$ is the vector that must be added to B to obtain A. If $A = PQ$ and $B = PR$, then

$$A - B = PQ - PR = PQ + RP = RP + PQ = RQ.$$

Figure 68-6 shows the graphical relation among the vectors A, B, and $A - B$.

Some physical quantities, such as temperature and density, are not described by vectors, but rather by numbers. Because he can measure these quantities by means of a number scale, the scientist calls them **scalar quantities** and the numbers that measure them, **scalars**. So, in the context of our vector analysis, the word *scalar* simply means *real number*. Notice that the absolute value $|A|$ of the vector A is a scalar.

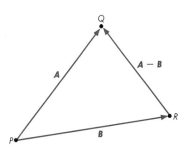

Figure 68-6

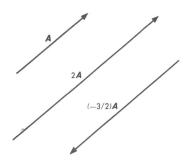

Figure 68-7

If a is a scalar (real number) and A is a vector, then we denote by aA or by Aa *the vector that is* $|a|$ *times as long as* A *and in the direction of* A *if* a *is positive and in the opposite direction if* a *is negative* (see Fig. 68-7). When we think of vectors as geometric arrows, it is easy for us to convince ourselves that the following "natural" rules of arithmetic are valid:

$$1A = A$$

$$(a + b)A = aA + bA$$

(68-5)

$$a(A + B) = aA + aB$$

$$(ab)A = a(bA).$$

Notice that our rules for operating with vectors, Equations 68-1 to 68-5, are like the usual rules of arithmetic, so you should have no trouble in performing the various operations that we have introduced. In a formal development of the theory of vectors, we take these equations as the axioms that define a **vector space**.

The following example shows how we can use vectors to prove theorems of plane geometry.

Example 68-1. Show that the diagonals of a parallelogram bisect each other.

Solution. Figure 68-8 shows a parallelogram $OPQR$. We have labeled the midpoint of PR as M and the midpoint of OQ as N; we are to show that M and N are the same point. To prove that these points coincide, we will show that $ON = OM$. Since N is the midpoint of OQ,

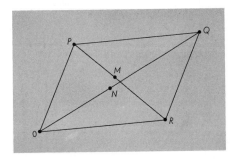

Figure 68-8

we see that $ON = \frac{1}{2}OQ$. But $OQ = OR + RQ$, so we have

(68-6) $$ON = \tfrac{1}{2}OQ = \tfrac{1}{2}(OR + RQ).$$

On the other hand, $OM = OP + PM$. Since M is the midpoint of PR, $PM = \frac{1}{2}PR$. But $PR = OR - OP$, so $PM = \frac{1}{2}(OR - OP)$, and hence

(68-7) $$OM = OP + \tfrac{1}{2}(OR - OP) = \tfrac{1}{2}(OR + OP) = \tfrac{1}{2}(OR + RQ).$$

When we compare Equations 68-6 and 68-7, we see that $OM = ON$, and our assertion is proved.

Two vectors A and B are parallel if they have the same or opposite directions. For convenience, we say that the zero vector $\mathbf{0}$ is parallel to every vector. If A and B are parallel vectors, then one is a scalar multiple of the other. On the other hand, if A and B are not parallel, then one cannot be represented as a scalar multiple of the other and it follows that the *single* vector equation

$$xA + yB = \mathbf{0}$$

is equivalent to the *two* scalar equations

$$x = 0 \quad \text{and} \quad y = 0.$$

In this case the vectors A and B are said to be **linearly independent**.

Example 68-2.   Show that two medians of a triangle intersect at the point of each median that is $\frac{2}{3}$ of the way from the vertex at which the median terminates.

Solution.   A triangle OAB is determined by two non-parallel vectors A and B as shown in Fig. 68-9. We will denote by M and N the midpoints of sides OA and OB and let P denote the intersection of the medians drawn to these midpoints. You can readily see that the medians terminating at M and N can be expressed as the vectors $\frac{1}{2}A - B$ and $\frac{1}{2}B - A$. Now the vector OP can be thought of either as the sum of A and a multiple $x(\frac{1}{2}B - A)$ of the median terminating at N or as the sum of B and a multiple $y(\frac{1}{2}A - B)$ of the median terminating at M. Therefore we have the equation

(68-8)

$$A + x(\tfrac{1}{2}B - A) = B + y(\tfrac{1}{2}A - B),$$

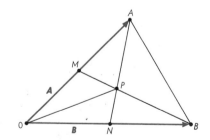

Figure 68-9

and we are to show that $x = y = \frac{2}{3}$. Simple algebraic manipulation of Equation 68-8 gives us the vector equation

$$(1 - x - \tfrac{1}{2}y)A + (\tfrac{1}{2}x + y - 1)B = 0.$$

Since A and B are not parallel, their coefficients must both be zero, so we have the two equations

$$x + \tfrac{1}{2}y = 1 \quad \text{and} \quad \tfrac{1}{2}x + y = 1.$$

When we solve these equations, we find that $x = y = \frac{2}{3}$, as we were to prove.

P R O B L E M S   6 8

1. Let $OP = OA + OB$. Find the coordinates of P if O is the origin and A and B are the points whose coordinates are:
(a) $(1, 0)$ and $(0, 2)$ (b) $(1, 1)$ and $(0, 3)$
(c) $(-1, 0)$ and $(2, 3)$ (d) $(-1, 2)$ and $(3, -1)$

2. Compute $|OP + OQ|$ and $|OP - OQ|$ if O is the origin and the coordinates of P and Q are:
(a) $(-2, -1)$ and $(2, 1)$ (b) $(1, 1)$ and $(-1, 3)$

3. Suppose that the vectors A and B are perpendicular. Express the following quantities in terms of the lengths $|A|$ and $|B|$.
(a) $|A + B|$ (b) $|A - B|$
(c) $|3A + 4B|$ (d) $|A/|A||$
(e) $||A| B + |B| A|$ (f) $||A| B - |B| A|$

4. Let A, B, and C be three points in the plane. Find:
(a) $2AB + 2BC + CA$ (b) $3AB - 3CB$
(c) $-AC - CB$ (d) $6AB + 4CA + 6BC$

5. One diagonal of the parallelogram with sides A and B is $A + B$ (see Fig. 68-4). What is the other diagonal?

6. Suppose that the three points P, Q, and R of the circle of unit radius whose center is the origin O divide the circumference into three equal parts. Find $OP + OQ + OR$.

7. Suppose that A and B are linearly independent vectors. Solve the following equations for t (if possible).
(a) $(t^2 - 4)A + (2t - 4)B = 0.$
(b) $\cos t\, A + \sin t\, B = 0.$

8. Suppose that A and B are linearly independent vectors. Is there a number t such that the vector $(1 - t)A + tB$ is parallel to the vector $A + B$?, $A - B$?

9. Draw a sketch and interpret geometrically the inequalities:
(a) $|A + B| \le |A| + |B|$.
(b) $|A - B| \ge |A| - |B|$.

10. The initial point of a unit vector N (a "unit vector" is a vector that is 1 unit long) is the point $(1, 1)$ of the parabola $y = x^2$ and N is perpendicular to the tangent line to this parabola at the point $(1, 1)$. Find the coordinates of the possible terminal points of N.

11. In each case determine the conditions under which the statement is true

(a) $|aA| = a\,|A|$ (b) $|A + B| = |A| + |B|$

(c) $|A - B| = |A| - |B|$ (d) $|aA + bB| = a\,|A| + b\,|B|$

12. Find a necessary and sufficient condition that $|A + B| = |A - B|$ if A and B are non-zero vectors.

69 BASIS VECTORS AND THE DOT PRODUCT

Now let us introduce a coordinate system into the plane. If we place a given vector R so that its initial point is the origin O of this coordinate system (Fig. 69-1), then its terminal point P will determine a pair of numbers (x, y). Conversely, a point P with coordinates (x, y) determines the vector $R = OP$. We shall refer to a vector whose initial point is the origin as a **radius vector**, or **position vector**.

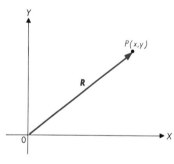

Figure 69-1

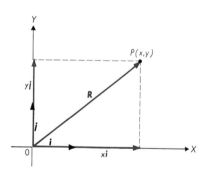

Figure 69-2

Thus we see that, with reference to a particular coordinate system, a pair of numbers determines a position vector, and a position vector determines a pair of numbers.

If we let i and j be vectors in the directions of the positive X- and Y-axes and be 1 unit long, then (see Fig. 69-2)

(69-1) $$R = xi + yj.$$

The vectors xi and yj are called the **projections** of R along i and j. The unit vectors i and j form a **basis** for our system of vectors in the plane. Every vector in the plane can be written as a **linear combination** of i and j, as in Equation 69-1. The coefficients of i and j are the **components** of the vector (relative to the given coordinate system).

If $A = P_1P_2$, where P_1 is the point (x_1, y_1) and P_2 is the point (x_2, y_2) as shown in Fig. 69-3, we can determine the components of A very simply. We observe that $A = OP_2 - OP_1 = (x_2i + y_2j) - (x_1i + y_1j)$. Now we use the rules of arithmetic that we introduced in the last section, and we find that

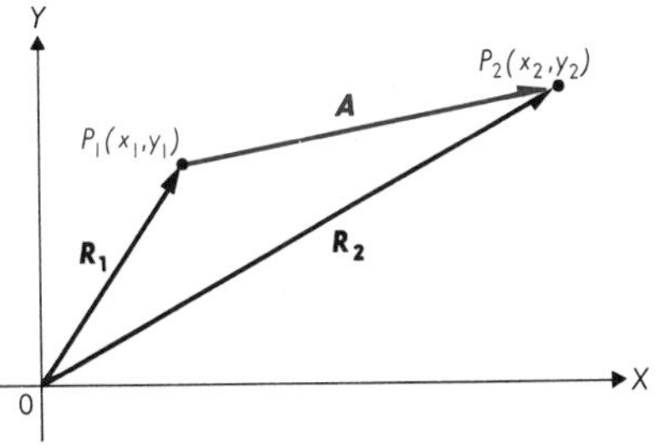

(69-2)

$$A = (x_2 - x_1)i + (y_2 - y_1)j.$$

We will denote the components of the vector A by A_x and A_y, and so we see from Equation 69-2 that

Figure 69-3

$$A_x = x_2 - x_1 \quad \text{and} \quad A_y = y_2 - y_1.$$

The distance between the points P_1 and P_2 is the magnitude of A, so the distance formula allows us to express the magnitude of a vector in terms of its components:

(69-3) $$|A| = \sqrt{(x_2 - x_1)^2 + (y_2 - y_1)^2} = \sqrt{A_x^2 + A_y^2}.$$

Notice that i and j are linearly independent vectors, so the vector equation $A_xi + A_yj = B_xi + B_yj$ is equivalent to the two scalar equations $A_x = B_x$ and $A_y = B_y$.

Example 69-1. What are the coordinates of the point Q that is $\frac{2}{3}$ of the way from the point $P(4, -2)$ to the point $R(7, 10)$?

Solution. Our problem is illustrated in Fig. 69-4; we must find the numbers x and y. We are told that $PQ = \frac{2}{3}PR$, and our first step is to express this vector equation in terms of components. According to Equation 69-2, $PQ = (x - 4)i + (y + 2)j$ and $PR = 3i + 12j$. Therefore, our vector equation is

$$(x - 4)i + (y + 2)j = \tfrac{2}{3}(3i + 12j) = 2i + 8j.$$

This vector equation is equivalent to the two scalar equations $x - 4 = 2$ and $y + 2 = 8$, from which we find that $x = 6$ and $y = 6$. Thus the desired point Q is $(6, 6)$.

We know how to associate with two given vectors a third *vector* called their sum. Now we are going to associate a *number* with a pair of vectors. Two vectors

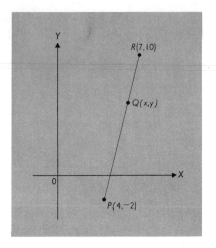

Figure 69-4   **Figure 69-5**

A and *B* determine an angle of θ, where $0 \le \theta \le \pi$, as shown in Fig. 69-5. We define the **dot product** of *A* and *B* by the equation

(69-4) $A \cdot B = |A|\,|B|\cos\theta.$

Thus since the vectors *i* and *j* are each 1 unit long and meet at right angles, we have $i \cdot j = 1 \cdot 1 \cos \dfrac{\pi}{2} = 1 \cdot 1 \cdot 0 = 0.$ Similarly, $i \cdot i = 1 \cdot 1 \cos 0 = 1 \cdot 1 \cdot 1 = 1.$ The dot product is a scalar, so it is sometimes called the **scalar product** of the two vectors.

From the defining Equation 69-4, we see that the dot product of a vector *A* with itself is given by the formula

$$A \cdot A = |A|^2 \cos 0 = |A|^2;$$

that is, the dot product of a vector with itself is the square of its magnitude. Some authors use the abbreviation $A^2 = A \cdot A$. It also follows directly from the definition of the dot product that $A \cdot B = 0$ if, and only if, at least one of the following equations holds: $A = 0$, $B = 0$ or $\theta = \dfrac{\pi}{2}$. Two vectors *A* and *B* are perpendicular, $A \perp B$, if $\theta = \dfrac{\pi}{2}$; and if we agree that the **0** vector is perpendicular to every vector, we see that

$$A \perp B \text{ if, and only if, } A \cdot B = 0.$$

Our definition of the dot product is geometric; we have worded it in terms of the lengths of two line segments and the angle they determine. We also want an algebraic expression for the dot product of two vectors $A = A_x i + A_y j$ and $B = B_x i + B_y j$ in terms of their components. Therefore, we apply the Law of Cosines to the triangle in Fig. 69-5 to obtain the equation

$$(69\text{-}5) \qquad |A - B|^2 = |A|^2 + |B|^2 - 2|A||B| \cos \theta.$$

The numbers $|A - B|^2$, $|A|^2$, and $|B|^2$ are the squares of the sidelengths of our triangle; if we use Equation 69-3 to express these lengths in terms of the components of the vectors involved, we have $|A - B|^2 = (A_x - B_x)^2 + (A_y - B_y)^2$, $|A|^2 = A_x^2 + A_y^2$, and $|B|^2 = B_x^2 + B_y^2$. Furthermore, $|A||B| \cos \theta = A \cdot B$, and when we make these substitutions in Equation 69-5 and simplify, we obtain the following expression for the dot product:

$$(69\text{-}6) \qquad A \cdot B = A_x B_x + A_y B_y.$$

Example 69-2. What is the angle between the position vectors to the points $(-1, 2)$ and $(3, 4)$?

Solution. Our two position vectors can be written as $R_1 = -i + 2j$ and $R_2 = 3i + 4j$; let us suppose that they determine an angle of θ. From Equation 69-4 we see that

$$\cos \theta = \frac{R_1 \cdot R_2}{|R_1||R_2|}.$$

Now we use Equation 69-6 to calculate $R_1 \cdot R_2 = (-1)3 + 2 \cdot 4 = -3 + 8 = 5$, and we readily find that $|R_1| = \sqrt{5}$ and $|R_2| = 5$. Hence

$$\cos \theta = \frac{5}{5\sqrt{5}} = 5^{-1/2},$$

and so

$$\theta = \text{Arccos } 5^{-1/2} \approx 1.11 \text{ radians.}$$

Example 69-3. Verify the following case of the **Cauchy-Schwarz Inequality**: If a_1, a_2, b_1, and b_2 are any four real numbers, then

$$(69\text{-}7) \qquad (a_1 b_1 + a_2 b_2)^2 \leq (a_1^2 + a_2^2)(b_1^2 + b_2^2).$$

In words, we can read this inequality as, "The square of the sum of the products is not greater than the product of the sum of the squares." Corresponding inequalities hold with sums of more than two terms.

Solution. If we set $A = a_1 i + a_2 j$ and $B = b_1 i + b_2 j$, then Inequality 69-7 can be written as

$$(A \cdot B)^2 \leq |A|^2 |B|^2.$$

Since $A \cdot B = |A| \, |B| \cos \theta$, this last inequality is $|A|^2 \, |B|^2 \cos^2 \theta \leq |A|^2 \, |B|^2$, which is obviously true because $\cos^2 \theta \leq 1$. Notice that the symbol $\leq$ can be replaced by $=$ in case $\cos^2 \theta = 1$; that is, when the vectors A and B are parallel. How can this condition be expressed in terms of the original numbers a_1, a_2, b_1 and b_2?

Finally, let us remark that we can use Equation 69-6 and elementary algebra to show that the dot product obeys the following fundamental laws of arithmetic:

$$A \cdot B = B \cdot A \quad \text{(The Commutative Law)}$$

(69-8) $\quad (A + B) \cdot C = A \cdot C + B \cdot C \quad \text{(The Distributive Law)}$

$$(rA \cdot B) = r(A \cdot B).$$

In these equations, A, B, and C are any vectors, and r is an arbitrary scalar.

Example 69-4. Express the components of the vector $A = A_x i + A_y j$ in terms of the dot product

Solution. We leave it to you to find the rule that justifies each step in the following calculation:

$$A \cdot i = (A_x i + A_y j) \cdot i = (A_x i) \cdot i + (A_y j) \cdot i$$

$$= A_x(i \cdot i) + A_y(j \cdot i) = A_x.$$

A similar calculation shows that $A_y = A \cdot j$.

P R O B L E M S   6 9

1. Write A in the form $A = A_x i + A_y j$ and find $|A|$ if A is the vector whose initial point is the first and whose terminal point is the second of the following points.
(a) $(-1, 3), (2, 7)$ (b) $(3, 5), (-3, -3)$
(c) $(0, 3), (0, -2)$ (d) $(2, -1), (-1, -2)$

2. Let $A = 2i - 3j$ and $B = 4i + j$. Find the components of the following vectors.
(a) $2A$ (b) $-3B$ (c) $A + B$
(d) $A - B$ (e) $2A + 3B$ (f) $A - 2B$

3. Find the midpoint of the segment joining the terminal points of the position vectors $R_1 = x_1 i + y_1 j$ and $R_2 = x_2 i + y_2 j$.

4. Let P be the point $(-5, -9)$ and Q be the point $(7, 7)$.
(a) Find the point that is $\frac{3}{4}$ of the way from P to Q.
(b) Find the point that is 5 units from P along the line from P to Q.
(c) Find the point that is as far beyond Q as Q is from P.

5. Find the angles of the triangle whose vertices are the points $(-2, -1), (2, 2)$, and $(-1, 6)$.

6. (a) Show that $|A + B|^2 + |A - B|^2 = 2\,|A|^2 + 2\,|B|^2$.

(b) Prove that the sum of the squares of the lengths of the diagonals of a parallelogram is equal to the sum of the squares of the lengths of its four sides.

7. Find the equation that must be satisfied by the coordinates (x, y) of a point P such that OP is perpendicular to $2i + 3j$. Find a unit vector perpendicular to $2i + 3j$. Illustrate this problem with a sketch.

8. Let A and B be unit position vectors that make angles of α and β with i. Write A and B in component form. Compute $A \cdot B$ to obtain a formula for $\cos(\alpha - \beta)$.

9. Let R_1 and R_2 be unit position vectors that determine an angle of θ, where $0 \le \theta \le \pi$. Show that

$$\sin \frac{\theta}{2} = \frac{1}{2}\,|R_2 - R_1|.$$

10. Let $A = 3i + j$. Let B be the unit vector that is perpendicular to A and has a positive component along i. Let $C = -i + 2j$. Find a and b such that $C = aA + bB$.

11. Let P and R be the endpoints of a diameter of a circle and Q be a third point of the circle. Show that PQR is a right triangle in which Q is the vertex of the right angle.

12. Let R be the position vector whose terminal point has coordinates (x, y) and let $A = 3i + 4j$. Give a geometric description of the set of all terminal points for which R satisfies the following relations.

    (a) $R \cdot A = 12$ (b) $|R| + |A| = 12$ (c) $|R + A| = 12$ (d) $R \cdot A = \frac{1}{2}\,|R|\,|A|$

13. Suppose an $\overline{X}\overline{Y}$-coordinate system is obtained from an XY-system by rotation through an angle of α. Show that the unit vectors $\overline{i}$ and $\overline{j}$ along the $\overline{X}$- and $\overline{Y}$-axes can be written as $\overline{i} = \cos \alpha\, i + \sin \alpha\, j$ and $\overline{j} = -\sin \alpha\, i + \cos \alpha\, j$. Use these equations to express the position vector $\overline{x}\overline{i} + \overline{y}\overline{j}$ of a point relative to the $\overline{X}\overline{Y}$-system in terms of i and j. Now equate this expression to the position vector $xi + yj$ of the same point relative to the XY-system, thereby obtaining Equations 66-4.

70 VECTOR-VALUED FUNCTIONS AND PARAMETRIC EQUATIONS

In this section we will consider functions whose domains are sets of *numbers* and whose ranges are sets of *vectors*; that is, **vector-valued functions.** We will denote a vector-valued function by a boldfaced letter. An example is the function F whose domain is the interval $[0, 2\pi]$ and whose rule of correspondence is the equation

$$F(t) = \cos t\, i + \sin t\, j.$$

Here, corresponding to the *number* $t = 0$ we have the *vector* $F(0) = \cos 0\, i + \sin 0\, j = i$; corresponding to the *number* $t = \pi/4$ we have the *vector*

$$F\left(\frac{\pi}{4}\right) = \left(\frac{\sqrt{2}}{2}\right)i + \left(\frac{\sqrt{2}}{2}\right)j,$$

and so on.

We plot the graph of a vector-valued function F with domain D as follows. For each number $t \in D$ we plot the terminal point of the position vector $R = F(t)$ (Fig. 70-1). The graph of F is the set of all such terminal points:

$$\{(x, y) \mid x\boldsymbol{i} + y\boldsymbol{j} = F(t), \, t \in D\}.$$

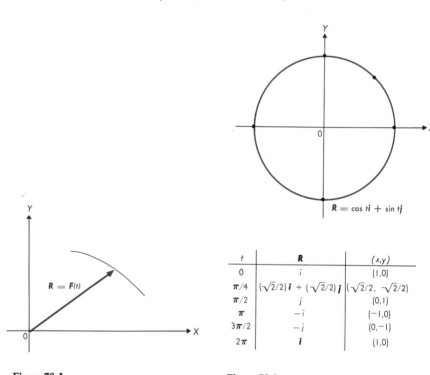

t	R	(x,y)
0	$\boldsymbol{i}$	$(1,0)$
$\pi/4$	$(\sqrt{2}/2)\boldsymbol{i} + (\sqrt{2}/2)\boldsymbol{j}$	$(\sqrt{2}/2, \ \sqrt{2}/2)$
$\pi/2$	$\boldsymbol{j}$	$(0,1)$
π	$-\boldsymbol{i}$	$(-1,0)$
$3\pi/2$	$-\boldsymbol{j}$	$(0,-1)$
2π	$\boldsymbol{i}$	$(1,0)$

Figure 70-1   **Figure 70-2**

Example 70-1. Sketch the graph of the vector equation

$$R = \cos t \, \boldsymbol{i} + \sin t \, \boldsymbol{j}, \quad t \in [0, 2\pi].$$

Solution. We have tabulated some of our vectors and their terminal points and plotted these points in Fig. 70-2. If we plot enough points, they will form a good outline of the graph of our vector equation. But even without plotting points we can see what the graph is. For each number t,

$$|R| = \sqrt{\cos^2 t + \sin^2 t} = 1.$$

Thus each of our position vectors is 1 unit long, and hence its terminal point will be 1 unit from the origin. It is easy to see that since t can be chosen as any point of the interval $[0, 2\pi]$, the graph of our vector equation is the circle whose radius is 1 and whose center is the origin. If we had written $t \in [0, \pi]$ in place of $t \in [0, 2\pi]$, the graph would have formed only the upper semi-circle in Fig. 70-2. On the other hand, if we had written $t \in [0, 4\pi]$ instead of $t \in [0, 2\pi]$, the graph would again be the entire circle. In this case, we might say that the curve is traced out twice.

If we write the vector equation

(70-1) $$\boldsymbol{R} = \boldsymbol{F}(t)$$

in terms of the components of the vectors $\boldsymbol{R} = x\boldsymbol{i} + y\boldsymbol{j}$ and $\boldsymbol{F}(t) = F_x(t)\boldsymbol{i} + F_y(t)\boldsymbol{j}$, we have

$$x\boldsymbol{i} + y\boldsymbol{j} = F_x(t)\boldsymbol{i} + F_y(t)\boldsymbol{j}.$$

Thus the Vector Equation 70-1 is equivalent to the *two* scalar equations:

(70-2) $$x = F_x(t) \quad \text{and} \quad y = F_y(t).$$

These equations assign a point (x, y) to each number t in the domain of $\boldsymbol{F}$. The set of these points is the graph of $\boldsymbol{F}$. Equations 70-2 are referred to as **parametric equations** of this graph, and t is called a **parameter**. Thus the equations

$$x = \cos t \quad \text{and} \quad y = \sin t, \quad t \in [0, 2\pi],$$

are parametric equations of the circle whose "non-parametric" equation is $x^2 + y^2 = 1$.

We frequently change parametric equations to non-parametric form in order to use our knowledge of the graphs of equations in x and y.

Example 70-2. Suppose that a and b are two positive numbers. What is the graph of the equation $\boldsymbol{R} = a \cosh t\, \boldsymbol{i} + b \sinh t\, \boldsymbol{j}, \, t \in (-\infty, \infty)$?

Solution. Parametric equations of our graph are

$$x = a \cosh t \quad \text{and} \quad y = b \sinh t.$$

We must eliminate t from these equations to find a relation between x and y. A direct way to eliminate t would be to solve the second equation for t and substitute in the first. Thus $t = \sinh^{-1} \dfrac{y}{b}$, and so we have $x = a \cosh \sinh^{-1} \dfrac{y}{b}$. This form of the equation tells us no more about the graph than the original vector equation did. However, if we write the parametric equations as $\dfrac{x}{a} = \cosh t$ and $\dfrac{y}{b} = \sinh t$, and substitute in the identity $\cosh^2 t - \sinh^2 t = 1$, we see that

$$\frac{x^2}{a^2} - \frac{y^2}{b^2} = 1.$$

Thus the graph of our equation is a part of a hyperbola. Since $\dfrac{x}{a} = \cosh t > 0$, you can convince yourself that our graph consists of only one branch of the hyperbola.

Sometimes we wish to transform a non-parametric equation in x and y to a pair of parametric equations that have the same graph. The non-parametric equation

(70-3) $y = f(x),$

for example, can always be replaced by the parametric equations

(70-4) $x = t \quad \text{and} \quad y = f(t).$

A given curve can be the graph of many different pairs of parametric equations. The choice of which pair to use is dictated by convenience more than anything else.

Example 70-3. Find a system of parametric equations whose graph is the graph of the equation $x^{2/3} + y^{2/3} = a^{2/3}$.

Solution. We might set $x = t$ and then solve the equation $t^{2/3} + y^{2/3} = a^{2/3}$ for y to obtain the pair of parametric equations

$$x = t \quad \text{and} \quad y = (a^{2/3} - t^{2/3})^{3/2}.$$

These equations represent (for $t \in [-a, a]$) the portion of the graph of our given equation that lies above the X-axis. Because the given curve is symmetric about the X-axis, we can obtain the remainder of the graph by reflecting the upper half about the X-axis. But we can find a more "symmetric" pair of parametric equations as follows. Suppose we divide both sides of the given equation by $a^{2/3}$ to obtain the equation

$$\left(\frac{x^{1/3}}{a^{1/3}}\right)^2 + \left(\frac{y^{1/3}}{a^{1/3}}\right)^2 = 1.$$

Here we have a sum of two squares that equals 1, and this equation suggests that we set

$$\frac{x^{1/3}}{a^{1/3}} = \sin t \quad \text{and} \quad \frac{y^{1/3}}{a^{1/3}} = \cos t.$$

Hence we see that another pair of parametric equations of our curve is the pair

$$x = a \sin^3 t \quad \text{and} \quad y = a \cos^3 t.$$

This pair gives us (for $t \in [0, 2\pi]$) the entire curve.

Let us now consider the problem of finding a **vector equation of a line**. A scalar equation of a line takes the form $y = mx + b$, where the number m determines the direction (slope) of the line, and the number b determines a point (the Y-intercept) of the line. Now we will show that the similar-looking vector equation

(70-5) $\boldsymbol{R} = \boldsymbol{M}t + \boldsymbol{B}, \quad t \in (-\infty, \infty) \quad \text{and} \quad \boldsymbol{M} \neq \boldsymbol{0},$

is also the equation of a line. Not only does this equation resemble the scalar equation $y = mx + b$ in form, but the vector $\boldsymbol{M}$ determines the direction of the line and the position vector $\boldsymbol{B}$ determines a point of the line. Equation 70-5 states that the position vector $\boldsymbol{R}$ is obtained by adding the multiple $\boldsymbol{M}t$ of the vector $\boldsymbol{M}$ to the vector $\boldsymbol{B}$. Figure 70-3 shows how this statement implies that our line is the line that contains the terminal point of $\boldsymbol{B}$ and is in the direction of $\boldsymbol{M}$. Thus Equation 70-5 is a vector equation of a line. We see that if $\boldsymbol{M} = M_x \boldsymbol{i} + M_y \boldsymbol{j}$ and $\boldsymbol{B} = B_x \boldsymbol{i} + B_y \boldsymbol{j}$, then parametric equations of the line are

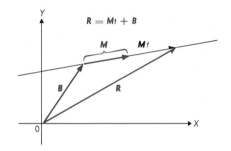

(70-6) $x = M_x t + B_x \quad \text{and}$

$\qquad y = M_y t + B_y, \quad t \in (-\infty, \infty).$

Figure 70-3

Now let us write vector and parametric equations of the line that contains two given points $P_1(x_1, y_1)$ and $P_2(x_2, y_2)$. To use Equation 70-5 we must find a vector $\boldsymbol{M}$ that gives the direction of the line and a vector $\boldsymbol{B}$, the position vector of a point of the line. Since P_1 is a point of the line, we may take the position vector $\boldsymbol{OP_1}$ as $\boldsymbol{B}$ (we could have equally well have chosen $\boldsymbol{OP_2}$). The vector $\boldsymbol{P_1P_2}$ determines the direction of our line, so we take $\boldsymbol{M} = \boldsymbol{P_1P_2}$, and Equation 70-5 becomes

(70-7) $\qquad \boldsymbol{R} = \boldsymbol{P_1P_2}t + \boldsymbol{OP_1}, \quad t \in (-\infty, \infty).$

To obtain parametric equations of our line, we equate the components of the vectors in Equation 70-7, and we obtain the two scalar equations

$\qquad x = (x_2 - x_1)t + x_1 \quad \text{and} \quad y = (y_2 - y_1)t + y_1.$

We can write these parametric equations of our line as

(70-8) $x = tx_2 + (1 - t)x_1 \quad \text{and} \quad y = ty_2 + (1 - t)y_1, \quad t \in (-\infty, \infty).$

You can easily verify (refer to Equation 70-7) that if we take $t \in (0, 1)$, then Equations 70-8 are parametric equations of the line segment *between* the points (x_1, y_1) and (x_2, y_2).

Example 70-4. Find parametric equations of the line that contains the points $(-1, 2)$ and $(2, 3)$.

Solution. If we take as P_1 the point $(-1, 2)$ and as P_2 the point $(2, 3)$ and use Equations 70-8, we obtain the parametric equations

$$x = 2t + (1 - t)(-1) = 3t - 1,$$

$$y = 3t + (1 - t)2 = t + 2,$$

$$t \in (-\infty, \infty).$$

Many times a curve that is defined in terms of a physical motion is most naturally described by means of parametric equations. We conclude this section with an example of a famous curve of this type.

Example 70-5. A circular hoop with a radius of a rolls along a straight line. Find parametric equations of the curve that is traced out by a given point of the hoop.

Solution. Let us suppose that our given point P originally is the origin of a cartesian coordinate system, and that the hoop rolls along the X-axis. In Fig. 70-4 we have pictured the hoop after it has rolled through an angle of t radians. We must find an expression for the position vector OP in terms of t. From Fig. 70-4 we see that

$$\boldsymbol{OP} = \boldsymbol{OT} + \boldsymbol{TS} + \boldsymbol{SP}.$$

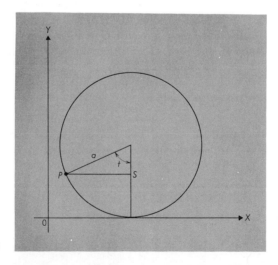

Figure 70-4

Because $|OT| = $ arc $TP = at$, it follows that $OT = ati$. Furthermore, simple trigonometry shows us that

$$TS = (a - a \cos t)j = a(1 - \cos t)j$$

and

$$SP = -PS = -a \sin t \, i.$$

Hence

$$OP = ati + a(1 - \cos t)j - a \sin t \, i$$
$$= a(t - \sin t)i + a(1 - \cos t)j.$$

From this vector equation we obtain the following pair of parametric equations for the coordinates (x, y) of the point P of our curve:

$$x = a(t - \sin t) \quad \text{and} \quad y = a(1 - \cos t), \quad t \in [0, \infty].$$

This curve is called a **cycloid**; we have sketched part of its graph in Fig. 70-5.

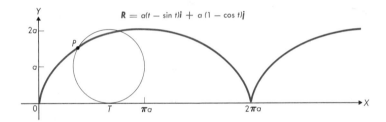

Figure 70-5

P R O B L E M S 7 0

1. Describe the graphs of the following vector equations.
(a) $R = 3 \cos 2t \, i + 3 \sin 2t \, j, \ t \in [0, \frac{1}{2}\pi]$
(b) $R = ti + t^2 j, \ t \in [-1, 1]$
(c) $R = \sin t \, i + \sin t \, j, \ t \in [0, \frac{1}{2}\pi]$
(d) $R = ti + 2tj, \ t \in [0, 1]$
(e) $R = e^t i + e^{-t} j, \ t \in (-\infty, \infty)$
(f) $R = 5 \sin t \, i + \cos t \, j, \ t \in [-\pi, \pi]$

2. Sketch the graph of the equation in Example 70-3.

3. Show that the following scalar and vector equations have the same graph.
(a) $2x - 3y + 4 = 0, \ R = (3t + 4)i + (2t + 4)j, \ t \in (-\infty, \infty)$
(b) $y = 2 \cosh x, \ R = \ln t \, i + (t + 1/t)j, \ t \in (0, \infty)$
(c) $y^2 = x^3, \ R = t^2 i + t^3 j, \ t \in (-\infty, \infty)$

4. Explain why both vector equations have the same graph. (In each case $t \in (-\infty, \infty)$.)

   (a) $R = \pi^t i + \pi^{-t} j$ and $R = e^t i + e^{-t} j$

   (b) $R = \cos 2t\, i + \sin 2t\, j$ and $R = \sin t\, i + \cos t\, j$

   (c) $R = (t^3 + 2t + 3)i + (t^6 + 4t^4 + 6t^3 + 4t^2 + 12t + 9)j$ and $R = ti + t^2 j$

5. Find parametric equations for each of the following lines.

   (a) $y = 3x + 7$ (b) $2x - 4y + 5 = 0$

   (c) $x = 5$ (d) $y = -1$

6. Find two pairs of parametric equations corresponding to each of the following cartesian equations.

   (a) $y^2 = x^3$ (b) $\dfrac{x^2}{4} + y^2 = 1$

   (c) $y^2 + 1 = x^2$ (d) $y = 2x^2 - 1$

7. Find vector equations of the following lines.

   (a) The line containing the points $(2, 3)$ and $(-1, 4)$.

   (b) The line $3x + 2y + 6 = 0$.

   (c) The line of slope 3 that contains the point $(-1, 1)$.

   (d) The line of slope 0 that contains the point $(1, 3)$.

8. Find the slope and Y-intercept of the line $R = (3t - 1)i + (1 - 5t)j$.

9. Show that the spiral $r\theta = 1$ is the graph of the vector equation

$$R = \frac{\cos t}{t} i + \frac{\sin t}{t} j.$$

10. Describe the graph of the parametric equations

$$x = a \sin^2 t + b \cos^2 t, \quad y = c \sin^2 t + d \cos^2 t, \quad t \in (0, \pi/2).$$

What if we replace $t \in (0, \pi/2)$ with $t \in (0, \pi)$?

11. Sketch the graph of the equation $R = (3i - 4j)[\![t]\!] + (2i + 3j)$, $t \in (-\infty, \infty)$.

12. Under what conditions are $R = Mt + B$ and $R = Nt + C$ equations of the same line?

13. Find vectors M and B (expressed in terms of a, b, and c) so that the graph of the vector equation $R = Mt + B$ is the line $ax + by + c = 0$.

71 **DERIVATIVES OF VECTORS. ARCLENGTH**

Now let us use some calculus in our discussion of a vector-valued function F. Using the definition of the derivative in the case of a scalar-valued function as a guide, we define the derivative $F'(t)$ by the equation

(71-1) $F'(t) = \lim_{s \to t} \dfrac{F(s) - F(t)}{s - t}.$

This vector equation means the same thing as the scalar equation

(71-2)
$$\lim_{s \to t} \left| \frac{F(s) - F(t)}{s - t} - F'(t) \right| = 0.$$

Notice that $F'(t)$ is a vector; we now use a geometric argument to convince ourselves that it is tangent to the graph of F. We have sketched this graph in Fig. 71-1, which also shows the vectors $F(t)$, $F(s)$, and $F(s) - F(t)$. The vector $F(s) - F(t)$ lies along a chord of the curve, and since the difference quotient $\dfrac{F(s) - F(t)}{s - t}$ is a scalar multiple of this vector, it lies along the same chord. When s is close to t, this chord approximates the tangent to the graph, so the difference quotient is a vector that is approximately tangent to the curve when s is near t. Since the limit of the difference quotient as s approaches t is the vector $F'(t)$, it appears that *the vector $F'(t)$ is tangent to the graph of the equation $R = F(t)$ at the terminal point of $F(t)$.*

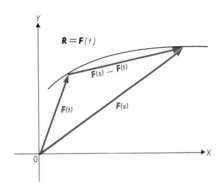

Figure 71-1

The following theorem tells us that we can follow the usual rules of differentiation when we calculate derivatives of vector-valued functions.

Theorem 71-1. *If F_x and F_y are differentiable functions and $F(t) = F_x(t)i + F_y(t)j$ then*

(71-3)
$$F'(t) = F'_x(t)i + F'_y(t)j.$$

Proof. If we write the difference quotient that appears in Equation 71-2 in terms of its components, and replace $F'(t)$ with $F'_x(t)i + F'_y(t)j$, we must show that

$$\left| \left(\frac{F_x(s) - F_x(t)}{s - t} - F'_x(t) \right) i + \left(\frac{F_y(s) - F_y(t)}{s - t} - F'_y(t) \right) j \right|$$

approaches 0 as s approaches t. This number is not greater than the sum

$$\left| \frac{F_x(s) - F_x(t)}{s - t} - F'_x(t) \right| + \left| \frac{F_y(s) - F_y(t)}{s - t} - F'_y(t) \right|.$$

Since F_x and F_y are assumed to be differentiable, each term of this sum approaches 0, and our theorem is proved.

We use our other notations for the derivative, too. Thus, if $R = F(t)$, we write R', $D_t R$ and $\dfrac{dR}{dt}$ for the derivative $F'(t)$. Also, since $R = xi + yj$, where $x = F_x(t)$ and $y = F_y(t)$, we can write Equation 71-3 as

$$R' = x'i + y'j,$$

or

$$D_t R = D_t xi + D_t yj,$$

and so on.

Example 71-1. David whirls a stone in a counter-clockwise direction around the circle whose vector equation is $R = \cos t\, i + \sin t\, j$. When $t = \pi/6$, he releases the stone and it flies off on a tangent. Does it hit Goliath, who is standing at the point $(-1, \sqrt{3})$?

Solution. We first find a vector that is tangent to the circle at the point that corresponds to $t = \pi/6$. According to Equation 71-3, $R' = -\sin t\, i + \cos t\, j$. Thus, if $t = \pi/6$,

$$R = \frac{\sqrt{3}}{2} i + \frac{1}{2} j,$$

and

$$R' = -\frac{1}{2} i + \frac{\sqrt{3}}{2} j.$$

Therefore, the stone is at the point $(\tfrac{1}{2}\sqrt{3}, \tfrac{1}{2})$ of the circle when it is released, and it flies along a line parallel to the vector $-\dfrac{1}{2} i + \dfrac{\sqrt{3}}{2} j$. We leave it to you to show that the vector joining the point $(\tfrac{1}{2}\sqrt{3}, \tfrac{1}{2})$ of the circle to the point in question, $(-1, \sqrt{3})$, is not parallel to the tangent vector $-\dfrac{1}{2} i + \dfrac{\sqrt{3}}{2} j$, so this time Goliath is spared. You should draw a sketch illustrating this problem, and you might try to solve it graphically.

It is not hard to show, using Equation 71-3, that the usual product rule is valid when we compute the derivative of a scalar times a vector; that is,

$$(71\text{-}4) \qquad D_t[f(t)F(t)] = f(t)F'(t) + f'(t)F(t).$$

The product rule also applies to the dot product. Thus

$$(71\text{-}5) \qquad D_t[F(t) \cdot G(t)] = F(t) \cdot G'(t) + F'(t) \cdot G(t).$$

As a final rule of differentiation, let us write the Chain Rule as it applies to vector-valued functions. If $R = F(t)$, where $t = g(s)$, then

$$(71\text{-}6) \qquad D_s F(t) = D_t F(t) D_s t.$$

Example 71-2. Let F be a vector-valued function such that $|F(t)| = c$, where c is a number that is independent of t in an interval $[a, b]$. Show that $F'(t)$ and $F(t)$ are perpendicular vectors for each t in $[a, b]$.

Solution. Since $|F(t)| = c$,

$$F(t) \cdot F(t) = c^2.$$

Now we use Equation 71-5 and we find that

$$F(t) \cdot F'(t) + F'(t) \cdot F(t) = 0,$$

and so

$$F(t) \cdot F'(t) = 0.$$

This equation is equivalent to saying that $F(t)$ and $F'(t)$ are perpendicular.

The graph of a vector equation $R = F(t)$, for t in an interval $[a, b]$ in which $|F'(t)| > 0$, is a curve in the plane. We will now find a formula for the length of such a curve, and in later sections we will discuss its "curvature" and the area of the surface that is generated when the graph is rotated about one of the coordinate axes. In these discussions we shall suppose that $F''(t)$ exists for each t in $[a, b]$. The graph of such a function F is called a **smooth arc**.

We will develop our formula for the length of a smooth arc in much the same way that we earlier developed formulas for area, work, and so on. Thus, to begin with, we won't be too precise about what we mean by arclength; we will just assume that we know what it is and what properties it possesses. On the basis of these assumptions, we will develop a formula for arclength, and after we have the formula we can look at the question of definition in more detail.

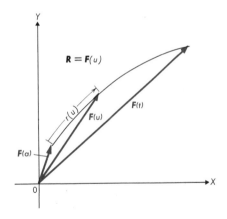

Figure 71-2

So let us suppose that for u in an interval $[a, t]$, the graph of the equation $R = F(u)$ is a smooth arc, as shown in Fig. 71-2, and see if we can find its length. If we had an arclength function r such that the number $r(u)$ is the length of the arc from the terminal point of $F(a)$ to the terminal point of $F(u)$, then our desired number would be $r(t)$. We don't yet have such a function, of course; it is precisely our goal to develop one. Nevertheless, let us assume that such a differentiable arclength function r exists and see what form $r(t)$ must take. Let u and v be two points of the interval $[a, t]$. If $v > u$, the terminal point of $F(v)$ is "beyond" the terminal point of $F(u)$, and hence $r(v) > r(u)$. If $v < u$, then $r(v) < r(u)$, and so the numbers $r(v) - r(u)$ and $v - u$ always have the same sign. The arc that joins the terminal points of $F(u)$ and $F(v)$ is $|r(v) - r(u)|$ units long (Fig. 71-3). It seems natural to require that the ratio of the length of the arc joining two points of our curve to the length of the line segment, or chord, that joins these points should approach 1 as one point approaches the other. The chord that joins the terminal points of the vectors $F(v)$ and $F(u)$ is $|F(v) - F(u)|$ units long, so we will suppose that

$$\lim_{v \to u} \frac{|r(v) - r(u)|}{|F(v) - F(u)|} = 1.$$

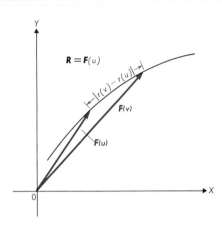

Figure 71-3

From this basic assumption, we can determine what the arclength function r must be.

Because $r(v) - r(u)$ and $v - u$ have the same sign, the difference quotient $\dfrac{r(v) - r(u)}{v - u}$ is always positive, so we can write

$$\frac{r(v) - r(u)}{v - u} = \left| \frac{r(v) - r(u)}{v - u} \right| = \frac{|r(v) - r(u)|}{|F(v) - F(u)|} \cdot \frac{|F(v) - F(u)|}{|v - u|}.$$

Hence

$$r'(u) = \lim_{v \to u} \frac{r(v) - r(u)}{v - u} = \lim_{v \to u} \frac{|r(v) - r(u)|}{|F(v) - F(u)|} \cdot \lim_{v \to u} \frac{|F(v) - F(u)|}{|v - u|}$$

$$= 1 \cdot |F'(u)| .$$

Therefore, the arclength function r must be a function such that $r'(u) = |F'(u)|$. To find the formula for $r(t)$ from this equation, we integrate from a to t and obtain the equation $\displaystyle\int_a^t r'(u)\, du = \int_a^t |F'(u)|\, du$. The Fundamental Theorem of Calculus tells us that $\displaystyle\int_a^t r'(u)\, du = r(t) - r(a)$, and this expression simplifies to $r(t)$, since $r(a) = 0$ (it is the length of the "arc" that joins the terminal point of $F(a)$ to the terminal point of $F(a)$). Therefore, our arclength function r must be the function that is defined by the equation

$$(71\text{-}7) \qquad\qquad r(t) = \int_a^t |F'(u)|\, du.$$

At this stage, we should regard the expression we have just derived as a formula for *graph*length, rather than *arc*length. We think of an arc as a set of points in the plane, such as the part of the parabola $y = x^2$ that joins the points $(0, 0)$ and $(1, 1)$, and this arc is the graph of any number of vector equations, $R = ti + t^2j$, $t \in [0, 1]$, $R = \sin t\, i + \sin^2 t\, j$, $t \in [0, \frac{1}{2}\pi]$, and so on. Since our formula for $r(t)$ is expressed in terms of a particular vector-valued function of which the given arc is the graph, we might expect to obtain different lengths for different functions. It is quite easy to show, however, that if a certain smooth arc is the graph of two different vector-valued functions, our formula gives the same value for its length when we use either function in the computation. We also get the same value if we change our coordinate system by a general rigid transformation. It would therefore be perfectly proper to regard our formula as the definition of the length of a smooth arc. Many mathematicians, however, start with a somewhat more general definition of arclength, from which they then derive our formula. In either case, the distance s from the terminal point of the vector $F(a)$ to the terminal point of $F(t)$ along our smooth arc is given by the equation

$$(71\text{-}8) \qquad\qquad s = \int_a^t |F'(u)|\, du.$$

Notice that this distance is a directed distance; if $t > a$, then s is positive, and if $t < a$, then s is negative. To obtain the number of units of arclength between two points, we can compute s from Equation 71-8 and take the absolute value of the result.

Let us show that our definition of arclength gives us the right answer when we use it to find the length of a line segment.

Example 71-3. Show that Equation 71-8 gives the correct length of the line segment whose equation is $R = Mt + B, t \in [a, b]$.

Solution. The vectors $Ma + B$ and $Mb + B$ are position vectors of the endpoints of our segment, and its length is the number

$$s = |(Mb + B) - (Ma + B)| = |Mb - Ma| = |M|\, (b - a).$$

We are to show that Equation 71-8 also gives us this number. In our present example, $F(u) = Mu + B$. Therefore, $F'(u) = M$, and so Equation 71-8 tells us that

$$s = \int_a^b |M|\, du = |M|\, (b - a), \text{ as it should be.}$$

Example 71-4. Show that if we view Equation 71-7 as the *definition* of an arclength function for a smooth arc, then the ratio of arclength to chordlength does approach 1.

Solution.   If z and t are two points of our parameter interval, then the ratio of the length of the arc that joins the corresponding points of the curve to the length of the chord that joins them is

$$\frac{|r(z) - r(t)|}{|F(z) - F(t)|} = \frac{\left| \displaystyle\int_a^z |F'(u)|\, du - \int_a^t |F'(u)|\, du \right|}{|F(z) - F(t)|}$$

$$= \frac{1}{\left| \dfrac{F(z) - F(t)}{z - t} \right|} \cdot \left| \frac{\displaystyle\int_a^z |F'(u)|\, du - \int_a^t |F'(u)|\, du}{z - t} \right|.$$

As z approaches t, the first factor approaches $1/|F'(t)|$, and the second factor $\left(\text{write out the definition of } D_t \displaystyle\int_a^t |F'(u)|\, du\right)$ approaches $|F'(t)|$. Therefore, our ratio of arclength to chordlength approaches 1.

Equation 71-8 gives us the length s of the arc that is traversed in moving along the curve from the terminal point of $F(a)$ to the terminal point of $F(t)$. From this equation we see that the length L of the arc that is traversed in moving along the curve from the terminal point of $F(a)$ to the terminal point of $F(b)$ is $L = \displaystyle\int_a^b |F'(t)|\, dt$. This equation, of course, is nothing but Equation 71-8 with a slight change of letters. If we set $F'(t) = R' = x'i + y'j$, then $|F'(t)| = \sqrt{x'^2 + y'^2}$, and our expression for arclength takes the form

(71-9) $$L = \int_a^b \sqrt{x'^2 + y'^2}\, dt.$$

Example 71-5.   Show that the length of the graph of the equation $y = f(x)$ for $x \in [a, b]$ is given by the formula

(71-10) $$L = \int_a^b \sqrt{1 + f'(x)^2}\, dx.$$

Solution.   Parametric equations of our given arc are

$$x = t \quad \text{and} \quad y = f(t), \quad t \in [a, b].$$

Thus $x' = 1$ and $y' = f'(t)$, and so Equation 71-10 follows immediately from Equation 71-9.

Example 71-6.   Find the length of the arc whose equation is $y = \cosh x$ and that joins the points $(0, 1)$ and $(1, \cosh 1)$. (This curve is called a **catenary**.)

Solution. We use Equation 71-10 with $a = 0$, $b = 1$, and $f(x) = \cosh x$. Then $f'(x) = \sinh x$, and $1 + f'(x)^2 = 1 + \sinh^2 x = \cosh^2 x$. Thus

$$L = \int_0^1 \cosh x \, dx = \sinh x \Big|_0^1 = \sinh 1 \approx 1.2.$$

From Equation 71-8 we see that

(71-11) $$D_t s = |F'(t)|,$$

and for a smooth arc, $|F'(t)| > 0$. Therefore, Equation 71-8 defines an increasing function, and hence one that has an inverse. In other words, we can solve (theoretically) Equation 71-8 for t in terms of s and so express the radius vector $R = F(t)$ in terms of s. The rule for differentiating an inverse says that $D_s t = \dfrac{1}{D_t s}$, so in view of Equation 71-11 we have $D_s t = \dfrac{1}{|F'(t)|}$. Now we substitute in the Chain Rule Equation 71-6, and we have

$$D_s R = D_s F(t) = \frac{F'(t)}{|F'(t)|}.$$

The vector $F'(t)$ is tangent to our graph, and when we divide this vector by its length we obtain a unit tangent vector which we shall call T. Thus

(71-12) $$T = D_s R = \frac{F'(t)}{|F'(t)|}.$$

P R O B L E M S   7 1

1. Find $F'(1)$ if $F(t) = F_x(t)i + F_y(t)j$ and
(a) $F_x(t) = \ln t$, $F_y(t) = t$
(b) $F_x(t) = e^t$, $F_y(t) = t^2 - 1$
(c) $F_x(t) = \cos^2 t$, $F_y(t) = \sin^2 t$
(d) $F_x(t) = \cosh t$, $F_y(t) = \sinh (1 - t^2)$

2. Find a tangent vector to the curve $R = e^t \sin t \, i + e^{-t} \cos t \, j$ at the point corresponding to $t = 0$. What is the slope of the tangent line to the curve at the point corresponding to $t = 1$?

3. Find unit vectors tangent to the graphs of the following equations at the point corresponding to the given parameter value.
(a) $R = t^3 i + t^4 j$, $t = 1$
(b) $R = 3 \cos 2t \, i + 3 \sin 2t \, j$, $t = 5$
(c) $R = e^t i + \ln t \, j$, $t = 1$
(d) $R = Mt + B$, $t = 0$
(e) $R = t \sin t \, i + \cos t \, j$, $t = \pi/2$

4. The equation $R = \cos t\, i + \sin t\, j$, with t in the interval $[0, 2\pi]$, and the equation $R = \cos t^2\, i + \sin t^2\, j$, with t in the interval $[\sqrt{2\pi}, \sqrt{4\pi}]$, both represent the unit circle. Show that Equation 71-8 yields the circumference of this circle when we use either of these vector representations.

5. Find a vector equation of the line that is tangent to the graph of the equation $R = e^t i + \ln t\, j$ at the point at which $t = 1$.

6. With the aid of Equation 71-3:
(a) Prove that Equation 71-4 is valid.   (b) Prove that Equation 71-5 is valid.

7. Find the length of one arch of the cycloid that we discussed in Example 70-5.

8. Let s denote the length of the arc of the parabola $y = x^2$ from the origin to the point where $x = c$. Express s in terms of c. Find the length of the arc from the origin to the point $(1, 1)$.

9. Find the total length of the curve with parametric equations $x = \cos^3 t$, $y = \sin^3 t$, $t \in [0, 2\pi]$.

10. Find the "circumference" of the *hypocycloid* $x^{2/3} + y^{2/3} = a^{2/3}$.

11. Find the length of the arc with parametric equations $x = t^3$, $y = 2t^2$, t in the interval $[0, 1]$.

12. Find the length of the part of the graph of the equation $y = x^{3/2}$ for x in the interval $[0, \frac{4}{3}]$.

13. Find the length of the graph of the equation $y = \dfrac{x^3}{6} + \dfrac{1}{2x}$ for x in the interval $[1, 2]$.

14. In Section 6 we defined the trigonometric functions in terms of arclength along the unit circle, and in Section 18 we derived the basic equation $\lim\limits_{t \to 0} \dfrac{\sin t}{t} = 1$ on the assumption that the limit of the ratio of arclength to chordlength is 1. Thus we assumed that we knew what arclength along a circle is and what properties it possesses. On the basis of what we have said in this section, can you formulate an appropriate definition of arclength along the unit circle?

72   CURVATURE, VELOCITY, AND ACCELERATION

In this section we will use calculus to go more deeply into the geometry of plane curves and then apply our knowledge to describe the path of a particle moving in the plane. As in the preceding section, we will assume that we are dealing with a vector-valued function F such that the graph of the equation $R = F(t)$, $t \in [a, b]$, is a smooth arc.

Let $T = \dfrac{R'}{|R'|}$ be a unit tangent vector to this curve. Suppose that the angle whose initial side contains the vector i and whose terminal side contains the vector T is an angle of α (Fig. 72-1). Because T is a unit vector, its components are cos α and sin α, so

(72-1) $T = \cos \alpha\, i + \sin \alpha\, j.$

Therefore,

(72-2) $D_s T = (-\sin \alpha\, i + \cos \alpha\, j)D_s\alpha.$

For short, let us write $U = -\sin \alpha\, i + \cos \alpha\, j$. This vector U is a unit vector Furthermore, $T \cdot U = 0$; that is, U is perpendicular to the tangent vector T. Thus $D_s T$ is a vector that is perpendicular to the tangent vector T, and $|D_s T| = |D_s\alpha|$.

We will denote the number $|D_s\alpha|$ by the Greek letter κ; that is,

(72-3) $\kappa = |D_s\alpha|.$

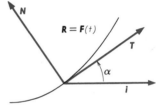

Figure 72-1

We see that the number κ measures the absolute value of the rate of change of α with respect to s. Since it is the tangent vector T that makes the angle of α with i, we often say that κ measures the absolute value of the "arc rate at which the tangent vector turns." We call κ the **curvature** of our curve at a point. From Equation 72-2 we see that the vector $D_s T$ can be written as the product of the curvature κ and a vector N that is perpendicular to the tangent vector:

(72-4) $D_s T = \kappa N.$

This unit normal vector N is either the vector U or the vector $-U$, depending on the sign of $D_s\alpha$. You might try to convince yourself, by means of examples, that the vector $D_s T$ (and hence N) is always directed, as shown in Fig. 72-1, into the convex region between an arc of the curve and its chord.

According to Equation 72-3, if we want to determine the curvature κ of a curve, we should express α in terms of s and then differentiate. That is easier said than done, so we will find a formula for κ that looks more complicated than Equation 72-3 but which is considerably easier to apply.

We can write the equation $T = \dfrac{R'}{|R'|}$ as $R' = |R'|\, T$. In the right-hand side of this equation, we substitute the expression for T given by Equation 72-1, and we replace the left-hand side with $x'i + y'j$ to obtain the equation

$$x'i + y'j = |R'|\,(\cos \alpha\, i + \sin \alpha\, j).$$

This vector equation is equivalent to the two scalar equations

(72-5) $$x' = |\mathbf{R}'| \cos \alpha \quad \text{and} \quad y' = |\mathbf{R}'| \sin \alpha.$$

Now we differentiate both sides of these equations with respect to t:

$$x'' = |\mathbf{R}'|' \cos \alpha - |\mathbf{R}'| \sin \alpha \, D_t \alpha,$$
$$y'' = |\mathbf{R}'|' \sin \alpha + |\mathbf{R}'| \cos \alpha \, D_t \alpha.$$

If we multiply the first of these equations by $\sin \alpha$, subtract the result from $\cos \alpha$ times the second, and use the identity $\sin^2 \alpha + \cos^2 \alpha = 1$, we obtain the equation

$$\cos \alpha \, y'' - \sin \alpha \, x'' = |\mathbf{R}'| \, D_t \alpha.$$

Equations 72-5 allow us to replace $\cos \alpha$ and $\sin \alpha$ with $\dfrac{x'}{|\mathbf{R}'|}$ and $\dfrac{y'}{|\mathbf{R}'|}$, so we see that

$$\frac{x'y'' - y'x''}{|\mathbf{R}'|} = |\mathbf{R}'| \, D_t \alpha,$$

from which

$$D_t \alpha = \frac{x'y'' - y'x''}{|\mathbf{R}'|^2}.$$

This equation gives us $D_t \alpha$, rather than the number $D_s \alpha$ that we want. However, according to the Chain Rule, these derivatives are related by the equation $D_t \alpha = D_s \alpha D_t s$, and since (see Equation 71-11) $D_t s = |\mathbf{R}'|$, we have $D_t \alpha = D_s \alpha |\mathbf{R}'|$. When we substitute this result into our expression for $D_t \alpha$, we find that

$$D_s \alpha = \frac{x'y'' - y'x''}{|\mathbf{R}'|^3}.$$

Now $|\mathbf{R}'| = \sqrt{x'^2 + y'^2}$, so our final equation for $\kappa = |D_s \alpha|$ is

(72-6) $$\kappa = \frac{|x'y'' - y'x''|}{(x'^2 + y'^2)^{3/2}}.$$

Example 72-1. Find the curvature of the circle of radius a that has the parametric equations $x = a \cos t$ and $y = a \sin t$, $t \in [0, 2\pi]$.

Solution. When we substitute in Equation 72-6, we find that

$$\kappa = \frac{|(-a \sin t)(-a \sin t) - (a \cos t)(-a \cos t)|}{[(-a \sin t)^2 + (a \cos t)^2]^{3/2}}$$

$$= \frac{a^2}{a^3} = \frac{1}{a}.$$

From the preceding example we see that the reciprocal of the curvature of a circle is the radius of the circle. In general, we define the number

$$r = \frac{1}{\kappa}$$

to be the **radius of curvature** of the graph of the equation $R = F(t)$ at the terminal point of R. If you construct a circle whose radius is r and whose center is r units from the terminal point of R along the normal vector N, then you obtain what is called the **circle of curvature** at the point. This circle is the circle that "best fits" the curve in the neighborhood of the given point.

Example 72-2. Find the formula for the curvature of the graph of the equation $y = f(x)$.

Solution. One pair of parametric equations for our curve is

$$x = t \quad \text{and} \quad y = f(t).$$

Then $x' = 1$ and $x'' = 0$, and Equation 72-6 becomes

(72-7)
$$\kappa = \frac{|y''|}{(1 + y'^2)^{3/2}}.$$

Example 72-3. Find the curvature of the parabola $y = x^2$ at the point $(1, 1)$. Show that this parabola is nearly a straight line at points far distant from the origin.

Solution. Using Equation 72-7 with $y' = 2x$ and $y'' = 2$, we have

(72-8)
$$\kappa = \frac{2}{(1 + 4x^2)^{3/2}}.$$

Thus the curvature of our parabola at the point $(1, 1)$ is

$$\kappa = \frac{2}{5^{3/2}} \approx .18.$$

If a point is very far from the origin, then the square of its X-coordinate is very large. And if x^2 is a large number, then the number κ given by Equation 72-8 is nearly zero. Thus at points far from the origin, the curvature of the parabola is nearly zero; that is, the parabola is almost a straight line.

We often apply our theory of curves to describe the path of a particle moving in a plane. Usually in such cases the parameter t measures time. Thus if the graph of the equation $R = F(t)$ represents the path of some particle moving on a smooth arc in the plane, then t time units (seconds, for example) after we start to measure time, the particle is at the terminal point of $F(t)$ (Fig. 72-2).

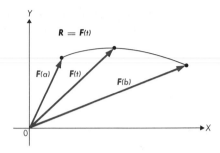

Suppose that $[a, t]$ is a given time interval. According to Equation 71-8, the distance the particle has moved in this time interval is

$$(72\text{-}9) \quad s = \int_a^t |F'(u)| \, du.$$

Figure 72-2

The derivative of s with respect to t (that is, the number $D_t s$) measures the rate of change of distance along our smooth arc with respect to time. It is natural to call this *number $D_t s$* the **speed** of our moving particle. The *vector $F'(t)$* is called the **velocity** V of the particle; thus

$$(72\text{-}10) \qquad\qquad V = F'(t).$$

Furthermore, since $D_t s = |F'(t)|$, we see that

$$(72\text{-}11) \qquad\qquad |V| = |F'(t)| = D_t s.$$

Thus the velocity of our particle is given by a *vector*, and the length of the velocity vector is the *scalar* called the speed of the particle. We can also express the velocity vector V by the equation

$$(72\text{-}12) \qquad\qquad V = D_s R \, D_t s = T D_t s$$

where $T = D_s R$ is the unit tangent vector.

The derivative of V with respect to t measures the rate of change of velocity; we call it the **acceleration** A of the moving particle. Thus

$$(72\text{-}13) \qquad\qquad A = D_t V = D_t^2 R.$$

Notice that acceleration is measured by a *vector*. The length of the velocity vector V is the speed of our moving particle, but the length of the acceleration vector is not, in general, the rate of change of the speed of the particle (we ask you to explain why not in Problem 72-8).

> *Example 72-4.* A projectile is fired at an angle of 30° with the horizontal at a speed of 1000 feet per second. Describe its path.
>
> *Solution.* In Fig. 72-3 we have introduced a coordinate system and have drawn in our initial velocity vector V_0. We know that $|V_0| = 1000$, and that V_0 makes an

angle of 30° with the positive X-axis, so

$$V_0 = 1000(\cos 30° \, i + \sin 30° \, j)$$
$$= 500\sqrt{3}i + 500j.$$

We will assume that the only force acting on the projectile in flight is the force of gravity and that this force is constant. Thus if we measure distance in feet and time in seconds, then the gravitational acceleration is $G = -32j$. Since acceleration is the derivative of velocity, $D_t V = G$. In addition, $V = V_0$ when $t = 0$, so the velocity vector V is the solution of the differential problem

$$D_t V = G, \quad V = V_0 \quad \text{when} \quad t = 0.$$

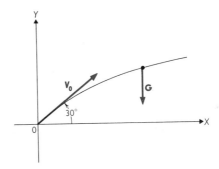

Figure 72-3

In Theorem 60-1 we saw that the solution of this differential problem is

$$V = V_0 + \int_0^t G \, ds = Gt + V_0.$$

But V is the derivative of R, so $D_t R = Gt + V_0$. Furthermore, $R = 0$ when $t = 0$, so R is the solution of the differential problem

$$D_t R = Gt + V_0, \quad R = 0 \quad \text{when} \quad t = 0.$$

The solution of this differential problem is

$$R = 0 + \int_0^t (Gs + V_0) \, ds$$
$$= \tfrac{1}{2}Gt^2 + V_0 t$$
$$= 500\sqrt{3}ti + (500t - 16t^2)j.$$

From this vector equation we see that parametric equations of our projectile's path are

$$x = 500\sqrt{3}t \quad \text{and} \quad y = 500t - 16t^2.$$

To obtain a non-parametric equation of the path, we can solve the first of these parametric equations for t in terms of x and substitute the result in the second, thus giving us

$$y = \frac{x}{\sqrt{3}} - \frac{16x^2}{3(500)^2}.$$

You should recognize this equation as the equation of a parabola.

Let us denote the speed of a moving particle by v; that is, $v = D_t s$. Then Equation 72-12 becomes

$$V = vT,$$

and we can find the acceleration of the particle from this equation. Thus

$$A = D_t(vT) = D_t vT + vD_t T.$$

We use the Chain Rule to write

$$D_t T = D_s T D_t s = vD_s T,$$

and hence our formula for the acceleration becomes

$$A = D_t vT + v^2 D_s T.$$

Finally, since $D_s T = \kappa N$ (Equation 72-4), we see that

$$A = D_t vT + \kappa v^2 N.$$

Thus the acceleration can be considered as the sum of the **tangential acceleration** $D_t vT$ and the **normal acceleration** $\kappa v^2 N$. The normal acceleration is also called the **centripetal acceleration.**

Example 72-5. A rocket plane makes a circular turn at a constant speed of 2400 miles per hour. If the radius of the turn is 10 miles, determine the magnitude of the centripetal acceleration. How many "G's" is the pilot subjected to?

Solution. The centripetal acceleration has a magnitude of κv^2. If we convert our units to feet and seconds and utilize the fact that the curvature of a circle is the reciprocal of its radius (see Example 72-1), then we find that the magnitude of the centripetal acceleration is

$$\kappa v^2 = \frac{1}{52,800} \left(\frac{2400 \cdot 5280}{60 \cdot 60} \right)^2 \approx 235 \text{ feet per second per second.}$$

Since 1 "G" is about 32 feet per second per second, we see that the pilot is subjected to slightly more than 7 G's as he makes his turn.

Example 72-6. Find differential equations satisfied by polar coordinates of a body moving in space if the only force acting upon it is the gravitational attraction of the earth. (We will assume—it can be shown to be true—that the path of the body is a plane curve.)

Solution. In the plane of motion of the body, we set up a polar coordinate system whose pole is the center of the earth. We suppose that t hours after some initial instant the body is at the point (r, θ), where $r = f(t)$ and $\theta = g(t)$. Thus the body is at the terminal point of the position vector $\boldsymbol{R} = r \cos \theta \, \boldsymbol{i} + r \sin \theta \, \boldsymbol{j} = r\boldsymbol{u}$, where $\boldsymbol{u}$ is the unit vector $\cos \theta \, \boldsymbol{i} + \sin \theta \, \boldsymbol{j}$.

The differential equation we seek is a numerical expression of Newton's Second Law of Motion, "Force equals mass times acceleration." The acceleration of our body is $\boldsymbol{R}''$, and it is acted upon by the force of gravity. This force, according to the Law of Gravitation, is directed along the radius vector and has a magnitude which is directly proportional to the mass m of the body and inversely proportional to the square of its distance from the center of the earth. Thus the force vector is $-\dfrac{km}{r^2} \boldsymbol{u}$ for some number k, and the equation mass $\times$ acceleration $=$ force becomes

$$(72\text{-}14) \qquad\qquad m\boldsymbol{R}'' = -\frac{km}{r^2} \boldsymbol{u}.$$

Since $\boldsymbol{R} = r\boldsymbol{u}$, we have $\boldsymbol{R}' = r'\boldsymbol{u} + r\boldsymbol{u}'$. We see that $\boldsymbol{u}' = \theta'(-\sin \theta \, \boldsymbol{i} + \cos \theta \, \boldsymbol{j}) = \theta'\boldsymbol{v}$, where $\boldsymbol{v}$ is the unit vector $-\sin \theta \, \boldsymbol{i} + \cos \theta \, \boldsymbol{j}$, and therefore

$$\boldsymbol{R}' = r'\boldsymbol{u} + r\theta'\boldsymbol{v}.$$

Furthermore, $\boldsymbol{R}'' = r''\boldsymbol{u} + r'\boldsymbol{u}' + (r\theta')'\boldsymbol{v} + r\theta'\boldsymbol{v}'$, and since $\boldsymbol{v}' = -\theta'\boldsymbol{u}$, we obtain the equation

$$\boldsymbol{R}'' = r''\boldsymbol{u} + r'\theta'\boldsymbol{v} + (r\theta')'\boldsymbol{v} - r\theta'^2\boldsymbol{u}$$

$$= (r'' - r\theta'^2)\boldsymbol{u} + [r'\theta' + (r\theta')']\boldsymbol{v}.$$

Thus Equation 72-14 can be written as

$$(r'' - r\theta'^2)\boldsymbol{u} + [r'\theta' + (r\theta')']\boldsymbol{v} = -\frac{k}{r^2} \boldsymbol{u},$$

and this vector equation is equivalent to two scalar equations satisfied by the coordinates (r, θ) of our moving body:

$$(72\text{-}15) \qquad\qquad r'' = r\theta'^2 - \frac{k}{r^2},$$

and

$$(72\text{-}16) \qquad\qquad (r\theta')' + r'\theta' = 0.$$

Example 72-7. Use the equations we derived in the preceding example to discuss the motion of a body in space.

Solution. Equation 72-16 can be written as $r\theta'' + 2r'\theta' = 0$. Let us multiply the left-hand side of this equation by r to obtain the expression $r^2\theta'' + 2rr'\theta'$. This expression is the derivative $D_t(r^2\theta')$, so Equation 72-16 is equivalent to the equation

$D_t(r^2\theta') = 0$. Thus $r^2\theta'$ is independent of time. The quantity $l = mr^2\theta'$ is the *angular momentum* of the body; we have just seen that it is constant in our problem. This fact has an interesting geometric interpretation. Suppose that when $t = a$ our body has polar coordinates (r_a, α) and when $t = b$ it has reached the point (r_b, β). Then the area of the region that is swept out by the radius vector is (Equation 65-1) the number $A = \frac{1}{2} \int_\alpha^\beta r^2 \, d\theta = \frac{1}{2} \int_a^b r^2\theta' \, dt$. Since $r^2\theta' = \dfrac{l}{m}$, we therefore have

$$A = \frac{1}{2} \int_a^b \frac{l}{m} \, dt = \frac{l}{2m}(b - a).$$

This equation says that the area of the region that is swept out by the radius vector during any time interval is proportional to the length of that time interval. This statement is called Kepler's First Law of Planetary Motion; it is usually phrased by saying that "equal areas are swept out in equal times."

We have pointed out that $r^2\theta'$ is a number $\dfrac{l}{m}$. If the number l is 0, then $\theta' = 0$, and our body moves in a line that is an extension of a radius of the earth. The case in which $l \neq 0$ is more difficult, and more interesting. Let us show that then the path of our body is a conic. It is easy to show, using Equation 72-15 and the equation $r^2\theta' = l/m$, that

$$D_t\left[\left(\frac{1}{r} - km^2l^{-2}\right)\cos\theta + \frac{mr'}{l}\sin\theta\right] = 0$$

and

$$D_t\left[\left(\frac{1}{r} - km^2l^{-2}\right)\sin\theta - \frac{mr'}{l}\cos\theta\right] = 0.$$

Thus the expressions in brackets are numbers P and Q that are independent of t:

$$\left(\frac{1}{r} - km^2l^{-2}\right)\cos\theta + \frac{mr'}{l}\sin\theta = P \quad \text{and} \quad \left(\frac{1}{r} - km^2l^{-2}\right)\sin\theta - \frac{mr'}{l}\cos\theta = Q.$$

Now we multiply the first of these equations by $\cos\theta$ and the second by $\sin\theta$ and add, and we find that

$$\frac{1}{r} - km^2l^{-2} = P\cos\theta + Q\sin\theta.$$

When we solve this equation for r, we obtain the equation

$$r = \frac{1}{km^2l^{-2} + P\cos\theta + Q\sin\theta}.$$

We leave it to you to write this equation in the form

$$r = \frac{ep}{1 + e \cos (\theta - \phi)},$$

the polar equation of a conic whose focus is the pole and whose axis makes an angle of ϕ with the polar axis.

Can you now discuss the problem of firing a satellite into orbit about the earth?

P R O B L E M S   7 2

1. Show that the curvature of a straight line is zero at every point. Can you show the converse?

2. Find κ at the point corresponding to the given t.
(a) $R = \sin t\, i + 2 \cos t\, j, t = 0$ (b) $R = (t^2 - 2t)i + 3tj, t = 1$
(c) $R = e^t i + e^{-t} j, t = 0$
(d) $R = 2(t - \sin t)i + 2(1 - \cos t)j, t = \pi/3$

3. Find κ at the point indicated.
(a) $y = x^2 - 2x + 3, (1, 2)$.   (b) $y = e^{3x/4}, (0, 1)$
(c) $y = \cos x, (\pi/2, 0)$ (d) $y^2 = x + 3, (6, 3)$

4. At what points of the graph of the equation $y = x^3$ is the radius of curvature a minimum? At what points is the curvature a minimum?

5. Draw the parabola whose equation is $y^2 = 6x$, and also draw its circle of curvature at the point at which $y = 4$.

6. If the tangent to the graph of the equation $y = f(x)$ is nearly parallel to the X-axis, engineers regard the number $|y''|$ as an approximation of κ. Why?

7. Let a and b be positive numbers with $a > b$. A point moves in an elliptical path whose vector equation is $R = a \cos t\, i + b \sin t\, j$. Sketch the path.
(a) What is the velocity of the point when $t = 0$?
(b) What is its maximum speed? Its minimum speed?
(c) Find the acceleration vector A. Describe its direction.

8. Show that the length of the acceleration vector is not in general equal to the rate of change of speed of a moving particle. When is it equal?

9. Find the magnitudes of the centripetal acceleration and tangential acceleration at the indicated point.
(a) $R = 3ti + 3 \ln t\, j, t = 3$ (b) $R = 2 \tan t\, i + 2 \cot t\, j, t = \pi/4$

10. A bug sits on a hoop of radius 2 feet that rolls along a straight line and makes 1 revolution per second. Find the velocity and acceleration of the bug: (a) at the instant the bug is at the top of the hoop (b) at the instant the bug is at the bottom of the hoop (see Example 70-5).

11. Use the equation $r^2\theta' = l/m$ to eliminate θ from Equation 72-15, and show that the resulting equation is equivalent to the equation

$$D_t\left(\frac{mr'^2}{2}\right) = -D_t\left(\frac{l^2}{2mr^2} - \frac{km}{r}\right).$$

This equation says that there is a number E such that $\dfrac{mr'^2}{2} + \dfrac{l^2}{2mr^2} - \dfrac{km}{r} = E.$

73 THE AREA OF A SURFACE OF REVOLUTION

Suppose the graph of the vector equation $\boldsymbol{R} = \boldsymbol{F}(t) = F_x(t)\boldsymbol{i} + F_y(t)\boldsymbol{j}$, $t \in [a, b]$, is a smooth arc such as the one shown in Fig. 73-1. If this arc is rotated about the X-axis, we will obtain a surface of revolution, and we will now find a formula for the area A of this surface.

You will recall that when we discussed the area of plane figures in Section 33 we avoided a precise definition of what this concept means. Since the question of defining the area of a two-dimensional figure in three-dimensional space is even more complicated, we will also omit a definition of this concept. As before, we hope that your intuitive notion of what area should be will make our remarks seem reasonable.

Let us therefore simply assume that there is a formula for the area of our surface of revolution and find it. Specifically, we will assume that there is a differentiable function r such that for each point $t \in [a, b]$ the number $r(t)$ is the area of the surface that is obtained by rotating about the X-axis the

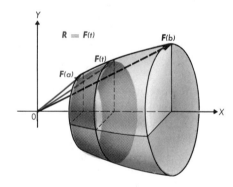

Figure 73-1

arc that joins the terminal point of $\boldsymbol{F}(a)$ to the terminal point of $\boldsymbol{F}(t)$ (the colored region in Fig. 73-1). The area of the surface of revolution we want to measure is therefore $r(b)$, and according to the Fundamental Theorem of Calculus,

$$(73\text{-}1) \qquad\qquad r(b) - r(a) = \int_a^b r'(t)\,dt.$$

Since $r(a)$ is the area of the surface that is generated by rotating the arc that joins the terminal point of $\boldsymbol{F}(a)$ to itself, we see that $r(a) = 0$, and so the right-hand side of Equation 73-1 will give us our desired area. Therefore, we must develop a formula for $r'(t)$.

Our derivation of the corresponding formula in the case of arclength was based on the fact that the ratio of arclength to chordlength approaches 1 as chordlength approaches 0. Thus the ratio of the length of the arc that joins the terminal points of two position vectors $F(s)$ and $F(t)$ to the length of the chord that joins these points approaches 1 as s approaches t. When we rotate our curve about the X-axis, the arc generates one surface and the chord generates another; we will base the derivation of our area formula on the assumption that the ratio of the areas of these surfaces approaches 1 as s approaches t. Let us express this statement in analytic form and so arrive at a formula for $r'(t)$.

From our description of the area function r, it is clear that the area of the surface that is generated by the arc we have just been talking about is $|r(s) - r(t)|$. (The absolute value signs take care of the possibility that the terminal point of $F(t)$ may be "beyond" the terminal point of $F(s)$.) Our chord is shown in Fig. 73-2, and as the figure shows, when we rotate this chord we obtain a frustum (slice) of a cone. In Problem 73-1 we will help you to show that the area of this frustum is 2π times the product of its slant height $|F(s) - F(t)|$ and its mean radius, the number $|y*|$ in Fig. 73-2; that is, area $= 2\pi |y*| |F(s) - F(t)|$. Our

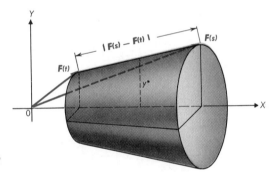

Figure 73-2

basic assumption about the limit of the ratio of our two areas can therefore be written as

$$\lim_{s \to t} \frac{|r(s) - r(t)|}{2\pi |y*| |F(s) - F(t)|} = 1.$$

Because $\lim_{s \to t} |y*| = |y| = |F_y(t)|$, we can also express this assumption in the form

(73-2) $$\lim_{s \to t} \frac{|r(s) - r(t)|}{|F(s) - F(t)|} = 2\pi |y|.$$

Now we can find $r'(t)$. We first observe that the difference quotient $\dfrac{r(s) - r(t)}{s - t}$ is always positive, and then we write it in a form that enables us to make use of

Equation 73-2:

$$\frac{r(s) - r(t)}{s - t} = \left| \frac{r(s) - r(t)}{s - t} \right| = \frac{|r(s) - r(t)|}{|F(s) - F(t)|} \left| \frac{F(s) - F(t)}{s - t} \right|.$$

Now we apply Equation 73-2, and we see that

$$r'(t) = \lim_{s \to t} \frac{r(s) - r(t)}{s - t} = 2\pi \, |y| \, |F'(t)| \,.$$

We have pointed out that the area A that we seek is given by the integral on the right-hand side of Equation 73-1, and when we substitute our expression for $r'(t)$ in that integral, we have the formula

$$(73\text{-}3) \qquad A = 2\pi \int_a^b |y| \, |F'(t)| \, dt = 2\pi \int_a^b |F_y(t)| \, |F'(t)| \, dt.$$

Our derivation of Equation 73-3 rests on the unproved assumption that there exists a differentiable area function r that satisfies Equation 73-2. While this assumption may seem reasonable, it is by no means obvious. We will just have to accept it without proof.

Since $F'(t) = R' = x'i + y'j$, we have $|F'(t)| = \sqrt{x'^2 + y'^2}$, and so we often write Formula 73-3 as

$$(73\text{-}4) \qquad A = 2\pi \int_a^b |y| \sqrt{x'^2 + y'^2} \, dt.$$

In particular, if our arc is the graph of the equation $y = f(x)$, we can regard $x = t$ and $y = f(t)$ as parametric equations of the arc, and then Equation 73-4 becomes

$$(73\text{-}5) \qquad A = 2\pi \int_a^b |y| \sqrt{1 + y'^2} \, dx.$$

Example 73-1.   Use Equation 73-4 to find the area of the surface of a sphere whose radius is a.

Solution.   A sphere with radius a is obtained by rotating about the X-axis the arc with parametric equations

$$x = a \cos t, \quad y = a \sin t, \quad t \in [0, \pi].$$

Here $x' = -a \sin t$ and $y' = a \cos t$. When we substitute these numbers in Equation 73-4 we get

$$A = 2\pi \int_0^\pi a \sin t \sqrt{(-a \sin t)^2 + (a \cos t)^2} \, dt$$

$$= 2\pi a^2 \int_0^\pi \sin t \, dt = 4\pi a^2.$$

If we rotate an arc about the Y-axis instead of the X-axis, the area of the resulting surface can be found by interchanging x and y in the above formulas.

Example 73-2. Find the area of the surface obtained by rotating the arc of the parabola with parametric equations $x = t$, $y = t^2$, $t \in [0, 1]$, about the Y-axis.

Solution. We use the formula

$$A = 2\pi \int_0^1 |x| \sqrt{x'^2 + y'^2} \, dt$$

$$= 2\pi \int_0^1 t \sqrt{1 + 4t^2} \, dt.$$

Now we change the variable of integration by the substitution $u = 1 + 4t^2$ to obtain

$$A = \frac{2\pi}{8} \int_1^5 \sqrt{u} \, du = \frac{\pi}{4} \frac{2}{3} u^{3/2} \Big|_1^5$$

$$= \frac{\pi}{6} (5^{3/2} - 1) \approx 5.33.$$

Example 73-3. The upper half of the cardioid $r = 2(1 - \cos \theta)$ (see Fig. 62-5) is rotated about the X-axis. Find the area of this surface of revolution.

Solution. We recall that the cartesian coordinates (x, y) of a point are related to polar coordinates (r, θ) of the same point by the equations

$$x = r \cos \theta$$

$$y = r \sin \theta.$$

If we replace r with $2(1 - \cos \theta)$ in these equations, we obtain parametric equations for our cardioid;

$$x = 2(1 - \cos \theta) \cos \theta = 2(\cos \theta - \cos^2 \theta),$$

$$y = 2(1 - \cos \theta) \sin \theta = 2(\sin \theta - \cos \theta \sin \theta),$$

where θ is the parameter, and the parameter interval for the upper half of our cardioid is $[0, \pi]$. If we use primes to denote differentiation with respect to the parameter θ, we have

$$x' = 2(-\sin \theta + 2 \cos \theta \sin \theta) = 2(-\sin \theta + \sin 2\theta),$$
$$y' = 2(\cos \theta - \cos^2 \theta + \sin^2 \theta) = 2(\cos \theta - \cos 2\theta).$$

We then find that

$$\begin{aligned} x'^2 + y'^2 &= 4(2 - 2 \sin \theta \sin 2\theta - 2 \cos \theta \cos 2\theta) \\ &= 8[1 - (\cos 2\theta \cos \theta + \sin 2\theta \sin \theta)] \\ &= 8(1 - \cos \theta). \end{aligned}$$

Thus Formula 73-4 becomes

$$\begin{aligned} A &= 2\pi \int_0^\pi 2(1 - \cos \theta) \sin \theta \sqrt{8(1 - \cos \theta)} \, d\theta \\ &= 8\sqrt{2}\pi \int_0^\pi (1 - \cos \theta)^{3/2} \sin \theta \, d\theta. \end{aligned}$$

To evaluate this integral, we change the variable of integration, letting

$$u = 1 - \cos \theta.$$

Then $du = \sin \theta \, d\theta$ and

$$A = 8\sqrt{2}\pi \int_0^2 u^{3/2} \, du = \frac{128\pi}{5}.$$

P R O B L E M S   7 3

1. If a right circular cone is "slit and unrolled," it will form a sector of a circle as shown on the left side of Fig. 73-3; the right side of the figure shows a vertical

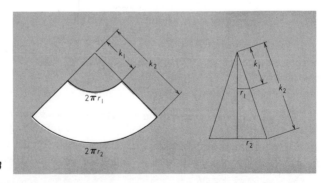

Figure 73-3

cross-section of the cone. We are interested in a formula for the area of a frustum of the cone; that is, the area A of the white region in our figure.

(a) Use the formula for the area of a circular sector (Appendix A) to show that
$A = \pi(r_2 k_2 - r_1 k_1)$.

(b) From the similar triangles in the right side of our figure, show that

$$\frac{r_1}{k_1} = \frac{r_2}{k_2} = \frac{r_1 + r_2}{k_1 + k_2}.$$

(c) Use the equation you verified in part (b) to replace r_1 and r_2 in the equation for A with $\dfrac{r_1 + r_2}{k_1 + k_2} k_1$ and $\dfrac{r_1 + r_2}{k_1 + k_2} k_2$, and obtain (after a certain amount of algebraic simplification) the equation $A = \pi(r_1 + r_2)(k_2 - k_1)$.

(d) The number $k_2 - k_1$ is the slant height s of our frustum, and if we write r for its mean radius $\dfrac{r_1 + r_2}{2}$, we see that $A = 2\pi rs$.

2. Show that Equation 73-5 gives the correct surface area of the cone that is generated by rotating about the X-axis the line segment that joins the origin to the point (h, r).

3. Find the area of the surfaces that are obtained by rotating the graphs of the following equations about the X-axis.
   (a) $R = (2t^2 + 1)i + 3tj$, $t \in [0, 1]$.
   (b) $R = (3e^t + 2)i + (4e^t - 1)j$, $t \in [0, \ln 3]$

4. Find the area of the surface of the ellipsoid that is generated by rotating about the X-axis the curve with parametric equations $x = a \cos t$ and $y = b \sin t$. (Do the cases $a > b$, $a = b$, and $a < b$ separately.)

5. Find the area of the surface that is generated by rotating about the X-axis the arc with parametric equations $x = e^{-t} \cos t$ and $y = e^{-t} \sin t$ for $t \in \left[0, \dfrac{\pi}{2}\right]$.

6. Find the areas of the surfaces that are obtained by rotating the graphs of the following equations about the X-axis.

   (a) $y = 2\sqrt{x}$, $x \in [0, 8]$ (b) $y = \dfrac{x^3}{3}$, $x \in [0, 2]$

   (c) $y = \cosh x$, $x \in [0, 1]$ (d) $y = \dfrac{x^2}{6} + \dfrac{1}{2x}$, $x \in [1, 3]$

7. Find the area of the surface that is generated by rotating about the Y-axis the arc with parametric equations $x = t^2$ and $y = t^3$, $t \in [0, 2]$.

8. Find the area of the surface that is generated by rotating about the Y-axis the arc of the parabola $y = x^2$ that joins the point $(\sqrt{2}, 2)$ to the origin.

9. One arch of the cycloid (Example 70-5) with parametric equations $x = a(t - \sin t)$, $y = a(1 - \cos t)$ is rotated about the X-axis. Find the area of the surface that is generated.

10. If the arc of the circle $x^2 + y^2 = a^2$ that lies above the interval $[x_1,\ x_1 + h]$ is rotated about the X-axis, a surface called a **spherical zone of altitude h** is generated. Show that the area of such a surface is $2\pi ah$.

11. Find the area of the surface that is generated by rotating about the X-axis the curve whose polar equation is $r^2 = a^2 \cos 2\theta$.

REVIEW PROBLEMS—CHAPTER EIGHT

You can use these questions to test yourself on the material covered in this chapter.

1. Suppose that P, Q, R, and S are points in the plane such that P and Q are symmetric with respect to the Y-axis, P and R are symmetric with respect to the origin, and P and S are symmetric with respect to the X-axis. If $(r,\ \theta)$ are polar coordinates of P, find polar coordinates of Q, R, and S.

2. Find a polar equation of the parabola whose focus is the origin and whose vertex is the point $\left(-2, \dfrac{\pi}{4}\right)$.

3. At a maximum or minimum point of the graph of an equation $y = f(x)$ in cartesian coordinates, $D_x y = 0$. At what points of the graph of an equation $r = f(\theta)$ in polar coordinates is $D_\theta r = 0$?

4. The area of the region that is bounded by the polar axis, a radial line making a positive acute angle of θ with the polar axis, and the graph of an equation $r = f(\theta)$ is given by the formula $A(\theta) = 2(e^{2\theta} - 1)$. Find the formula for $f(\theta)$.

5. If we rotate our cartesian axes through any angle of θ, the expression $x^2 + y^2$ is transformed into the expression $\bar{x}^2 + \bar{y}^2$. Through what angles of rotation of the axes is the expression $x^4 + y^4$ transformed into $\bar{x}^4 + \bar{y}^4$?

6. Find the equations of the asymptotes of the hyperbola
$$x^2 - 24xy - 6y^2 - 26x + 12y - 11 = 0.$$

7. Let A and B be two vectors, with $B \neq 0$. For what number x is the number $|A - xB|$ a minimum?

8. Show that two vectors A and B are parallel if, and only if, $|A|^2 |B|^2 - (A \cdot B)^2 = 0$.

9. Find a vector equation of equation of the tangent line to the graph of the equation $R = F(t)$ at the point at which $t = a$.

10. Suppose that A and B are mutually perpendicular unit vectors, and consider the arc whose equation is $R = tA + t^2B$ for $t \in [0, 1]$.
(a) What is the length of this arc?
(b) Find the formula for the curvature at a point of this arc.
(c) What is the area of the surface that is formed when this arc is rotated about a line that contains the origin and is parallel to the vector B?

11. Show that $D_t\,|F(t)| = \dfrac{F(t) \cdot F'(t)}{|F(t)|}$. Explain why it follows that
$$D_t\,|F(t)| \le |D_t F(t)|.$$

ANALYTIC GEOMETRY

IN THREE-DIMENSIONAL

SPACE

N I N E

Because we live in a three-dimensional world, many practical problems that we want to solve mathematically must be stated in terms of solid, rather than plane, geometry. Thus we need to know the language of solid analytic geometry—the subject of this chapter. In later chapters we will see how calculus applies to certain problems in three-dimensional space.

74 COORDINATES AND VECTORS IN THREE DIMENSIONS

A **cartesian coordinate system** in three-dimensional space is formed by three mutually perpendicular number scales that have a common unit of length and a common origin, as shown in Fig. 74-1. These number scales are customarily labeled as the X-, Y-, and Z-axes as shown. The illustrated system is a **right-handed coordinate system.** A right-handed screw pointed along the Z-axis would advance if the

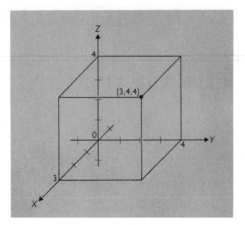

Figure 74-1

positive *X*-axis were rotated 90° into the position of the positive *Y*-axis. If we were to interchange the labels on any two axes—for example, the *X*- and *Y*-axes— we would obtain a **left-handed coordinate system**. Most books on applied mathematics use right-handed coordinate systems; we shall use only such systems in this book.

The three planes that contain the various pairs of axes are known as the **coordinate planes**. They are called the **XY-plane**, the **YZ-plane**, and the **XZ-plane**. To each point *P* we assign coordinates (x, y, z) as follows. The plane that contains the point *P* and is parallel to the *YZ*-plane intersects the *X*-axis in a point. Since the *X*-axis is a number scale, this point represents a number, the *X*-coordinate of *P*. The *Y*- and *Z*-coordinates of *P* are assigned in a similar manner. Figure 74-1 shows the point whose coordinates are (3, 4, 4). You should draw similar figures for other points, including points with one or more negative coordinates, in order to familiarize yourself with the cartesian coordinate system in three-dimensional space.

In Section 68 we introduced the vector concept to help us in our study of the geometry of the plane. Vectors are also very convenient tools to use in dealing with geometry in space. As before, we consider a vector to be an arrow. The concept of equality, the definitions of addition and subtraction of vectors and of multiplication of vectors by scalars, as discussed in Section 68, carry over without change to the three-dimensional situation. In particular, the rules governing vector algebra in three-space are exactly the same as before; that is, Equations 68-1 to 68-5 remain valid.

Example 74-1. Let *ABCD* be a quadrilateral in space (notice that the points *A*, *B*, *C*, and *D* need not lie in the same plane), and denote by *P*, *Q*, *R*, and *S* the midpoints of the sides *AB*, *BC*, *CD*, and *AD*. Show that *PQRS* is a parallelogram.

Solution. Figure 74-2 shows the original quadrilateral, as well as the quadrilateral whose vertices are the midpoints P, Q, R, and S. To show that this latter quadrilateral is a parallelogram, we need only show that the sides RS and QP are parallel and of equal length, which will be true if $RS = QP$. We have $RS = DS - DR = \frac{1}{2}DA - \frac{1}{2}DC = \frac{1}{2}(DA - DC) = \frac{1}{2}CA$. Similarly, $QP = BP - BQ = \frac{1}{2}BA - \frac{1}{2}BC = \frac{1}{2}(BA - BC) = \frac{1}{2}CA$. Therefore, $RS = QP$, as was to be shown.

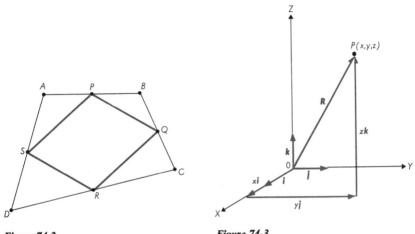

Figure 74-2   **Figure 74-3**

As in the plane, we introduce unit basis vectors parallel to the coordinate axes. The vectors i, j, and k are in the direction of the positive X-, Y-, and Z-axes, respectively, and they are 1 unit long. A point P with coordinates (x, y, z) determines (see Fig. 74-3) the **position vector** $R = OP$ with components x, y, and z. Thus

(74-1) $$R = xi + yj + z\mathbf{k}.$$

In the next section we will be concerned with the concept of the orientation of three vectors relative to our coordinate system. Think of three vectors A, B, and C with the origin as their common initial point. If we can continuously vary the directions of these vectors so as to make the first vector point in the direction of the basis vector i, the second point in the direction of the basis vector j, and the third point in the direction of the basis vector k, and if the vectors never become coplanar during the course of this deformation, then we say that the triple of vectors A, B, C (in that order) is a **right-handed triple**. Of course, i, j, k is a right-handed triple. So is j, k, i, but i, k, j is not. The triple i, j, R shown in Fig. 74-3 is right-handed. Speaking informally, the vectors of a right-handed triple more nearly point in the directions of the basis vectors of our right-handed coordinate system than they point in the directions of the basis vectors of a left-handed system. Formally, the triple A, B, C is right-handed if there are three continuous vector-valued functions F, G, and H whose domains contain the interval $[0, 1]$ and are such that $F(0) = A$, $G(0) = B$, $H(0) = C$, $F(1) = i$, $G(1) = j$, $H(1) = k$, and for no number t in the interval $[0, 1]$ are the vectors $F(t)$, $G(t)$, and $H(t)$ coplanar.

If A is a vector with initial point $P_1(x_1, y_1, z_1)$ and terminal point $P_2(x_2, y_2, z_2)$, then

$$A = OP_2 - OP_1 = x_2 i + y_2 j + z_2 k - (x_1 i + y_1 j + z_1 k)$$
$$= (x_2 - x_1)i + (y_2 - y_1)j + (z_2 - z_1)k.$$

Thus if

$$A = A_x i + A_y j + A_z k,$$

its components are given by the equations

(74-2) $A_x = x_2 - x_1,$ $A_y = y_2 - y_1,$ and $A_z = z_2 - z_1.$

Example 74-2. Find the coordinates of the midpoint of the segment PQ, where P is the point $(-1, 2, 5)$ and Q is the point $(3, 0, -1)$.

Solution. Figure 74-4 shows the points P and Q and also the midpoint M, whose coordinates (x, y, z) we are to find. If we write the vector equation $QM = \frac{1}{2}QP$ in terms of the basis vectors $i, j,$ and k, using Equation 74-2 to calculate the components, we obtain the equation

$$(x - 3)i + yj + (z + 1)k = \tfrac{1}{2}(-4i + 2j + 6k).$$

This single vector equation is equivalent to the three scalar equations

$$x - 3 = -2, \quad y = 1, \quad \text{and} \quad z + 1 = 3,$$

from which we find that the coordinates of the midpoint M are $(1, 1, 2)$.

To help us find a formula for the length $|A|$ of a vector $A = A_x i + A_y j + A_z k$, we first draw it as a position vector (Fig. 74-5). The three planes that contain the terminal point (A_x, A_y, A_z) and are parallel to the coordinate planes, together with the coordinate planes themselves, determine a rectangular parallelepiped (box). We have labeled three vertices of the box P, Q, and R. Since ORP is a right triangle, the length of A is given by the equation

$$|A|^2 = \overline{OP}^2 = \overline{OR}^2 + \overline{RP}^2.$$

We see that OQR is a right triangle and hence $\overline{OR}^2 = \overline{OQ}^2 + \overline{QR}^2$. Thus $\overline{OP}^2 = \overline{OQ}^2 + \overline{QR}^2 + \overline{RP}^2$. Since $\overline{OP}^2 = |A|^2$, $\overline{OQ}^2 = A_x^2$, $\overline{QR}^2 = A_y^2$, and $\overline{RP}^2 = A_z^2$, we

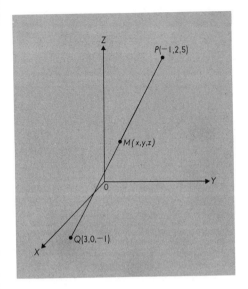

Figure 74-4

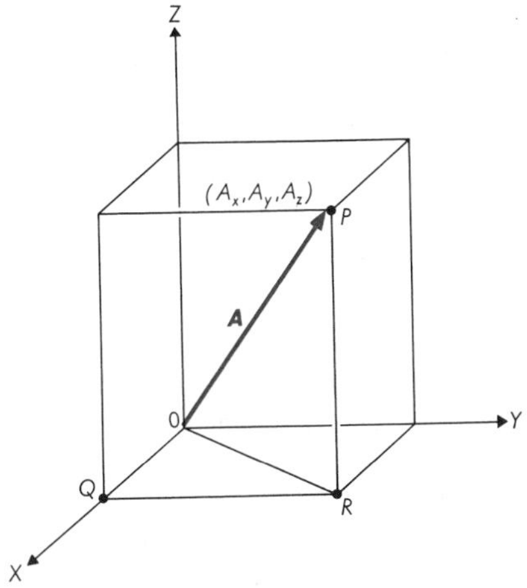

Figure 74-5

can write this last equation as

$$|A|^2 = A_x^2 + A_y^2 + A_z^2;$$

in other words, *the length of the vector **A** is given by the equation*

(74-3) $$|A| = \sqrt{A_x^2 + A_y^2 + A_z^2}.$$

Now suppose that **A** is the vector P_1P_2, where P_1 and P_2 are two points in space. Since the components of **A** are expressed in terms of its endpoints by Equations 74-2, we can word our formula for the length of **A** as follows. *The distance between two points $P_1(x_1, y_1, z_1)$ and $P_2(x_2, y_2, z_2)$ of three-dimensional space is given by the formula*

(74-4) $$\overline{P_1P_2} = \sqrt{(x_2 - x_1)^2 + (y_2 - y_1)^2 + (z_2 - z_1)^2}.$$

Example 74-3. What points of the XY-plane are less than 5 units distant from the point (1, 2, 3)?

Solution. A point that belongs to the XY-plane has coordinates $(x, y, 0)$. According to Equation 74-4, the distance between this point and the point (1, 2, 3) is the number $\sqrt{(x - 1)^2 + (y - 2)^2 + 3^2}$, and this number is to be less than 5. Therefore, we have $\sqrt{(x - 1)^2 + (y - 2)^2 + 3^2} < 5$. When we write this inequality as $(x - 1)^2 + (y - 2)^2 < 16$, we see that our point must be a point of the circular disk in the XY-plane whose center is the point (1, 2) and whose radius is 4.

P R O B L E M S   7 4

I. In a three-dimensional cartesian coordinate system, locate the points whose co-ordinates satisfy the following relations.
(a) $|x| + |y| + |z| = x + y + z$ (b) $|xyz| = xyz$
(c) $[\![z]\!] = 2$ (d) $(x - 2)^2 + (y + 1)^2 + z^2 \leq 16$
(e) $x + y = 1$ (f) $x^2 + y^2 = 1$

2. Let A, B, C, and D be position vectors to the points $(2, -1, 2)$, $(0, 3, 0)$, $(1, 0, -1)$, and $(4 \cos 1, 3, 4 \sin 1)$.
(a) Which of the following triples are right-handed:

$$(i, j, A), \quad (j, k, A), \quad (A, B, C), \quad (A, C, B)?$$

(b) Sketch the vectors A, B, and $\frac{5}{2}(A + B)$.
(c) Give a geometric explanation of why vectors B and C are perpendicular.
(d) Use the Theorem of Pythagoras to show that A and C are perpendicular.
(e) Compare the numbers $|B - D|$ and $|B| - |D|$.
(f) Find scalars a, b, and c such that $aA + bB + cC = D$.

3. Let P and Q have coordinates $(-1, 2, -3)$ and $(11, 11, 3)$, respectively.
(a) Express the vector PQ in terms of the basis vectors i, j, and k.
(b) Find the point that is one-third of the way from P to Q.
(c) What is the distance between P and Q?
(d) Find the point R such that $PR = 2PQ$.
(e) Find a point R such that $\angle PRQ$ is a right angle. What is the set of all such points.

4. Let $A = i + 3j - k$, $B = 2i + 4j - 2k$, and $C = -i + 2j + 4k$. Determine c so that $V = A + B + cC$ is parallel to the YZ-plane. Is A, B, V a right-handed triple? Can you determine c so that V is perpendicular to the YZ-plane?

5. Suppose that P, Q, R, and S are points in space such that $OP - OQ = OS - OR$. Show that $PQRS$ is a parallelogram.

6. Let P, Q, R, and S be the points $(1, 1, 1)$, $(2, 3, 0)$, $(3, 5, -2)$, and $(0, -1, 1)$, respectively. Show that the segments PQ and RS are parallel and find the ratio of their lengths.

7. Two position vectors A and B are non-parallel sides of a parallelogram. Find the position vectors whose terminal points are the vertex opposite the origin and the center of the parallelogram.

8. Prove that the line segment joining the midpoints of two sides of a triangle is parallel to the third side and is half as long as the third side.

9. Suppose we have a vector A and a positive number x. Describe the vector X if $|X| = x$ and $|A + X|$ is a maximum. A minimum. What is the maximum value of $|A + X|$? (Express your answer in the form of an inequality.)

10. Let A, B, and C be position vectors. Use a geometric argument to show that A, B, and C are in the same plane if, and only if, there exist numbers x, y, and z (not all zero) such that $xA + yB + zC = 0$.

II. Do Problem 9-15 by vectors.

75 PRODUCTS OF VECTORS

The dot product of two vectors A and B is defined just as it was in the plane case:

(75-1) $$A \cdot B = |A| \, |B| \cos \theta,$$

where again we are supposing that our two vectors determine an angle of θ, with $0° \le \theta \le 180°$. As before, we see that $A \cdot A = |A|^2$, and $A \cdot B = 0$ if, and only if, A and B are perpendicular.

We apply the Law of Cosines as we did when we derived Equation 69-6, and we find that the dot product of the vectors $A = A_x i + A_y j + A_z k$ and $B = B_x i + B_y j + B_z k$ is expressed in terms of their components by the formula

(75-2) $$A \cdot B = A_x B_x + A_y B_y + A_z B_z.$$

We can use this formula to verify that the following rules of algebra hold for arbitrary vectors A, B, C and scalar r:

$$A \cdot B = B \cdot A \quad \text{(The Commutative Law)}$$
(75-3) $\quad A \cdot (B + C) = A \cdot B + A \cdot C \quad$ (The Distributive Law)
$$(rA) \cdot B = r(A \cdot B).$$

Example 75-1. The vectors $A = 2i - j + k$ and $B = i + j + 2k$ determine an angle of θ. Find it.

Solution. From Equation 75-1 we see that

$$\cos \theta = \frac{A \cdot B}{|A| \, |B|}.$$

Now we use Equation 75-2 to write $A \cdot B = 2 \cdot 1 + (-1) \cdot 1 + 1 \cdot 2 = 3$, and we readily see that $|A| = |B| = \sqrt{6}$. Hence $\cos \theta = \dfrac{3}{\sqrt{6} \, \sqrt{6}} = \frac{1}{2}$, and so $\theta = 60°$.

The dot product of two vectors is a scalar (a number). Now we are going to introduce a product of two vectors that is a vector. This vector is written $A \times B$ and is called the **cross product**, or **vector product**, of A **by** B. We define this cross product by the equation

$$A \times B = |A| \, |B| \sin \theta \, u,$$

where u is a unit vector that is perpendicular to the plane of A and B and is directed so that the triple A, B, u is right-handed. This statement does not determine the vector u if A and B are parallel or if one of them is the zero vector. But then we must have $\theta = 0°$, $\theta = 180°$, $|A| = 0$, or $|B| = 0$, and since any one of these equations tells us that $|A|\,|B| \sin \theta = 0$, we take $A \times B$ to be $\mathbf{0}$ in these cases. The vector u, and hence $A \times B$, points in the direction that a right-handed screw would advance if A were rotated into B through an angle of θ.

You can use the definition of the cross product to check the following multiplication table for the unit basis vectors.

$$i \times j = k \qquad j \times k = i \qquad k \times i = j$$
(75-4) $\qquad j \times i = -k \qquad k \times j = -i \qquad i \times k = -j$
$$i \times i = 0 \qquad j \times j = 0 \qquad k \times k = 0$$

We have already seen that if A and B are parallel, then $A \times B = \mathbf{0}$. Conversely, if $A \times B = \mathbf{0}$, then either $\sin \theta = 0$ and the vectors are parallel, or one of the vectors is the vector $\mathbf{0}$. Let us agree that the vector $\mathbf{0}$ is parallel to every vector. Then we can make the following statement: *The vectors A and B are parallel if, and only if, $A \times B = \mathbf{0}$.* Even when the number $|A \times B|$ is not 0, we can give it a simple geometric interpretation. From Fig. 75-1 you can see that $|B| \sin \theta$ is the

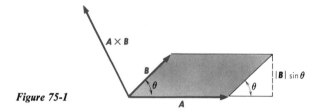

Figure 75-1

altitude of the parallelogram that is determined by the vectors A and B and that $|A|$ is its base length. Hence $|A|\,|B| \sin \theta$ is its area. Since $|A \times B| = |A|\,|B| \sin \theta$, we can therefore interpret the number $|A \times B|$ as the area of the parallelogram that is determined by A and B.

We have seen that we can use the usual rules of arithmetic when operating with the dot product; some of these rules *do not apply* to the cross product. For example, in Equations 75-4 we see that $i \times j = k$, whereas $j \times i = -k$. Since the cross products $i \times j$ and $j \times i$ are not the same, the commutative law is not valid for cross products. You can easily see that for each pair of vectors A and B we have, in fact, the "anti-commutative" rule

$$B \times A = -(A \times B).$$

The associative law of multiplication does not hold either; that is, the products $(A \times B) \times C$ and $A \times (B \times C)$ are not necessarily the same vector. (In Problem 75-1 we furnish an example of the failure of the associative law.)

The following laws of arithmetic, however, are valid for the cross product. If *A*, *B*, and *C* are any vectors, and if *r* is a scalar, then

(75-5) $$A \times (B + C) = A \times B + A \times C$$

and

(75-6) $$(rA) \times B = A \times (rB) = r(A \times B).$$

It is not hard to convince yourself, by a geometric argument based on the definition of the cross product, that the second set of equations is valid. It is harder to see why the first equation is true; we need some preliminary discussion first.

Figure 75-2 shows three vectors *A*, *B*, and *C* and the parallelepiped (squashed brick) that they determine. We wish to give a geometric interpretation of the

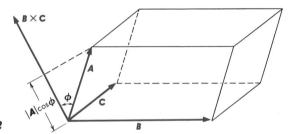

Figure 75-2

number $A \cdot (B \times C)$, the **scalar triple product** of *A*, *B*, and *C*. The definition of the dot product tells us that this number is the number $|A| \, |B \times C| \cos \phi$, where the vectors *A* and *B × C* determine an angle of ϕ. From our figure we see that $0° \leq \phi < 90°$; the fact that *A* and *B × C* determine an acute angle is equivalent to the statement that the triple *A*, *B*, *C* is right-handed. Therefore $\cos \phi > 0$, and the number $|A| \cos \phi$ is the altitude of our parallelepiped. Since $|B \times C|$ is the area of the parallelogram that forms its base, the number

$$A \cdot (B \times C) = |A| \, |B \times C| \cos \phi$$

is the volume of the parallelepiped that is determined by the right-handed triple *A*, *B*, *C*. If our triple *A*, *B*, *C* had not been right-handed, we would have had $90° < \phi \leq 180°$, the number $\cos \phi$ would be negative, and then the scalar triple product $A \cdot (B \times C)$ is the *negative* of the volume of the parallelepiped determined by *A*, *B*, and *C*. Notice that the triple *A*, *B*, *C* is right-handed if, and only if, $A \cdot (B \times C) > 0$, so we can determine the orientation of a triple by determining the sign of a scalar triple product.

Now let *A*, *B*, and *C* be any three vectors. You can easily convince yourself that the triples *A*, *B*, *C* and *C*, *A*, *B* have the same orientation; either both are right-handed or neither is. Thus both the scalar triple products $A \cdot (B \times C)$ and $C \cdot (A \times B)$ equal the volume of the parallelepiped determined by our three vectors, or both equal the negative of this volume. In any case, we see that these products are equal. Since the dot product is commutative, we have

$$C \cdot (A \times B) = (A \times B) \cdot C,$$

and hence we see that *for any three vectors A, B, and C,*

$$(75\text{-}7) \qquad\qquad A \cdot (B \times C) = (A \times B) \cdot C.$$

It is easy to remember this identity because it says that *one may interchange the dot and the cross in a scalar triple product.*

Now let us return to the distributive law, Equation 75-5. Let A, B, and C be arbitrary vectors, and set $V = A \times (B + C) - A \times B - A \times C$. To verify the distributive law we must show that $V = 0$, which is equivalent to the equation $|V|^2 = 0$. We have

$$|V|^2 = V \cdot V = V \cdot [A \times (B + C)] - V \cdot (A \times B) - V \cdot (A \times C).$$

We now interchange the dot and cross in these scalar triple products:

$$V \cdot V = (V \times A) \cdot (B + C) - (V \times A) \cdot B - (V \times A) \cdot C.$$

Since the dot product obeys the distributive law, it is easy to see that this last expression is 0. Therefore, we have shown that $V = 0$, and the distributive law is verified for the cross product.

The general Equations 75-5 and 75-6 and the specific multiplication Formulas 75-4 enable us to express the cross product of $A = A_x i + A_y j + A_z k$ by $B = B_x i + B_y j + B_z k$ in terms of the components of these vectors. Thus when we use these equations to expand the product

$$A \times B = (A_x i + A_y j + A_z k) \times (B_x i + B_y j + B_z k),$$

we will obtain the formula

$$(75\text{-}8) \qquad A \times B = (A_y B_z - A_z B_y)i - (A_x B_z - A_z B_x)j + (A_x B_y - A_y B_x)k.$$

A determinant of the second order is defined by the equation

$$\begin{vmatrix} m & n \\ p & q \end{vmatrix} = mq - np.$$

In this notation

$$(A_yB_z - A_zB_y) = \begin{vmatrix} A_y & A_z \\ B_y & B_z \end{vmatrix},$$

and so on, and hence we can write our cross product in the form

(75-9) $\quad A \times B = \begin{vmatrix} A_y & A_z \\ B_y & B_z \end{vmatrix} i$

$$- \begin{vmatrix} A_x & A_z \\ B_x & B_z \end{vmatrix} j + \begin{vmatrix} A_x & A_y \\ B_x & B_y \end{vmatrix} k.$$

This last equation is sometimes symbolically expressed as

(75-10) $\quad A \times B = \begin{vmatrix} i & j & k \\ A_x & A_y & A_z \\ B_x & B_y & B_z \end{vmatrix}.$

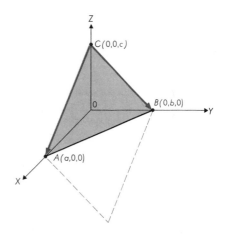

Figure 75-3

Example 75-2. Find the area of the triangle whose vertices are the points $A(a, 0, 0)$, $B(0, b, 0)$, and $C(0, 0, c)$.

Solution. The length of the vector $CA \times CB$ is the area of the parallelogram with CA and CB as two sides. The area of our triangle is one-half of this area (see Fig. 75-3). We see that

$$CA = ai - ck \quad \text{and} \quad CB = bj - ck.$$

Thus

$$CA \times CB = \begin{vmatrix} 0 & -c \\ b & -c \end{vmatrix} i - \begin{vmatrix} a & -c \\ 0 & -c \end{vmatrix} j + \begin{vmatrix} a & 0 \\ 0 & b \end{vmatrix} k$$

$$= bci + acj + abk.$$

Therefore, $|CA \times CB|^2 = b^2c^2 + a^2c^2 + a^2b^2$, and hence the area of our triangle is

$$\tfrac{1}{2} |CA \times CB| = \tfrac{1}{2}\sqrt{b^2c^2 + a^2c^2 + a^2b^2}.$$

Now that we have a formula (Equation 75-8) for the cross product of two vectors in terms of their components, we can express the scalar triple product

$A \cdot (B \times C)$ in terms of the components of A, B, and C as follows:

$$A \cdot (B \times C) = (A_x i + A_y j + A_z k) \cdot \left\{ \begin{vmatrix} B_y & B_z \\ C_y & C_z \end{vmatrix} i - \begin{vmatrix} B_x & B_z \\ C_x & C_z \end{vmatrix} j + \begin{vmatrix} B_x & B_y \\ C_x & C_y \end{vmatrix} k \right\};$$

that is,

$$(75\text{-}11) \quad A \cdot (B \times C) = A_x \begin{vmatrix} B_y & B_z \\ C_y & C_z \end{vmatrix} - A_y \begin{vmatrix} B_x & B_z \\ C_x & C_z \end{vmatrix} + A_z \begin{vmatrix} B_x & B_y \\ C_x & C_y \end{vmatrix}.$$

If you are familiar with determinants of the third order (we will discuss them in Section 86), you will realize that we can write this result as

$$(75\text{-}12) \qquad A \cdot (B \times C) = \begin{vmatrix} A_x & A_y & A_z \\ B_x & B_y & B_z \\ C_x & C_y & C_z \end{vmatrix}.$$

Example 75-3. Show that the area of the triangle in the plane whose vertices are the points (x_1, y_1), (x_2, y_2), and (x_3, y_3) is given by the absolute value of the number

$$(75\text{-}13) \quad \tfrac{1}{2} \begin{vmatrix} 1 & 1 & 1 \\ x_1 & x_2 & x_3 \\ y_1 & y_2 & y_3 \end{vmatrix} = \tfrac{1}{2}[(x_2 y_3 - x_3 y_2) - (x_1 y_3 - x_3 y_1) + (x_1 y_2 - x_2 y_1)].$$

Solution. Let us consider the plane in which our given triangle lies to be the XY-plane of a three-dimensional space so that the vertices of the triangle are the points $A(x_1, y_1, 0)$, $B(x_2, y_2, 0)$, and $C(x_3, y_3, 0)$. The area of our triangle is (see Example 75-2) $\tfrac{1}{2}|CA \times CB|$. Since the vectors CA and CB lie in the XY-plane, we see that the vector $CA \times CB$ is parallel to the Z-axis. Therefore, the absolute value of the dot product of the vector $CA \times CB$ and the unit vector k is the product of the lengths $|CA \times CB|$ and $|k| = 1$. Thus our desired area is simply the absolute value of the number $\tfrac{1}{2} k \cdot (CA \times CB)$. Now

$$CA = (x_1 - x_3)i + (y_1 - y_3)j$$

and

$$CB = (x_2 - x_3)i + (y_2 - y_3)j,$$

so when we substitute in Equation 75-11, we get

$$\tfrac{1}{2} k \cdot (CA \times CB) = \tfrac{1}{2} \cdot 1 \cdot \begin{vmatrix} x_1 - x_3 & y_1 - y_3 \\ x_2 - x_3 & y_2 - y_3 \end{vmatrix}.$$

We now expand this second order determinant and simplify, and we obtain the expression on the right-hand side of Equation 75-13.

P R O B L E M S   7 5

1. By computing the cross products $(i \times i) \times j$ and $i \times (i \times j)$, show that the associative law does not hold for cross products.

2. Let $A = 2i + 2j - k$, $B = i - 2j + 2k$, and $C = i - j + k$.
   (a) Find the cosine of the angle determined by A and B.
   (b) Find the sine of the angle determined by A and B.
   (c) Find the volume of the parallelepiped determined by A, B, and C.
   (d) Is A, B, C a right-handed triple?
   (e) Find a unit vector u that is perpendicular to A and to B and is such that A, B, u is a right-handed triple.
   (f) Find a vector that is parallel to the plane determined by A and B and perpendicular to C.
   (g) Suppose we think of the vectors A, B, and C as position vectors. What is the area of the triangle whose vertices are the terminal points of these vectors?

3. By writing both sides of the equation in terms of the components of the vectors involved, one can show that for any three vectors A, B, and C,

$$A \times (B \times C) = (A \cdot C)B - (A \cdot B)C.$$

   (a) Verify this equation for the vectors of the preceding question.
   (b) Show that in general the vectors on both sides of the equation are perpendicular to A.
   (c) Use the above equation to find a similar equation for $(A \times B) \times C$.

4. Find a number x such that the vectors $A = i + 4j + 3k$ and $B = 4i + 2j + xk$ are perpendicular. Can you find a number x such that the vectors are parallel? Can you find numbers x and y such that $C = 4i + xj + yk$ is parallel to A?

5. Suppose that A and B are two vectors that determine an angle of θ. We say that the number $|A| \cos \theta$ is the **component of A along B**.
   (a) Show that the component of A along B is $\dfrac{A \cdot B}{|B|}$.
   (b) Under what circumstances is the component of B along A equal to the component of A along B?
   (c) Find the component of $A = 3i - j + 2k$ along $B = i + 2j - k$.
   (d) Give a geometric interpretation of the component of A along B.

6. Find the area of the triangle whose vertices in an XY-plane are $(1, 1)$, $(5, 4)$, and $(-1, 5)$.

7. Find $A \times B$ if $A = \cos \alpha\, i + \cos \beta\, j + \cos \gamma\, k$, and $B = \sin \alpha\, i + \sin \beta\, j + \sin \gamma\, k$.

8. Show that the vector $(B \cdot B)A - (A \cdot B)B$ is perpendicular to B.

9. Show that

$$(A \times B) \cdot (A \times B) = \begin{vmatrix} A \cdot A & A \cdot B \\ A \cdot B & B \cdot B \end{vmatrix}$$

10. Let P, Q, and R be position vectors to points P, Q, and R. Show that the vector $(P \times Q) + (Q \times R) + (R \times P)$ is perpendicular to the plane PQR.

76 PLANES

Graphs of equations in x and y, such as $3x + 2y = 5$ and $x^2 - 7y^2 = 3x$, are curves in the coordinate plane. Now we are going to see that graphs of equations in x, y, and z, such as $3x - 2y + 4z = 7$ and $x^2 + y^2 - z^2 = 16$, are surfaces in three-dimensional space. In this section we will take up the simplest kind of surfaces—namely, planes.

In plane analytic geometry we determine a line by assigning its direction and specifying one of its points. Similarly, in solid analytic geometry we determine a plane by giving its orientation and specifying one of its points. Thus in Fig. 76-1 we

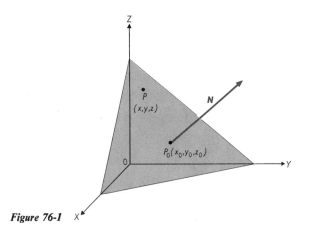

Figure 76-1

have shown a point P_0 and a vector N. These quantities determine the plane consisting of those points P for which the vector P_0P is perpendicular to N. The vector N is called a **normal** to the plane. For two vectors to be perpendicular, their dot product must be 0, so

(76-1) $$N \cdot P_0P = 0.$$

This equation is one form of the equation of the plane. Now suppose that the coordinates of P_0 are (x_0, y_0, z_0), the coordinates of P are (x, y, z), and $N = ai + bj + ck$. Then

$$P_0P = (x - x_0)i + (y - y_0)j + (z - z_0)k,$$

and Equation 76-1 becomes

(76-2) $$a(x - x_0) + b(y - y_0) + c(z - z_0) = 0.$$

This form of the equation of our plane corresponds to the point-slope form of the equation of a line.

Example 76-1. Find the equation of the plane that contains the point $(1, 2, 3)$ and has the vector $N = 2i - j + 3k$ as a normal.

Solution. Here we have $x_0 = 1$, $y_0 = 2$, $z_0 = 3$, $a = 2$, $b = -1$, and $c = 3$. Hence Equation 76-2 becomes $2(x - 1) - (y - 2) + 3(z - 3) = 0$, which simplifies to

$$2x - y + 3z - 9 = 0.$$

We can expand Equation 76-2 and write it in the form

(76-3) $$ax + by + cz + d = 0,$$

where $d = -ax_0 - by_0 - cz_0$. Notice the similarity between Equation 76-3 and the equation $ax + by + c = 0$ of a line in plane analytic geometry. We can easily determine the slope of such a line from the coefficients of x and y. Similarly, the coefficients of x, y, and z in Equation 76-3 are the components of a vector normal to the plane; that is, the vector $N = ai + bj + ck$ is normal to the plane $ax + by + cz + d = 0$.

Example 76-2. Discuss the plane $2x + y + 3z = 6$.

Solution. A plane is determined by 3 points, and we can find points of a surface by choosing 2 coordinates and solving for the third. Thus if we let $x = 0$ and $y = 0$,

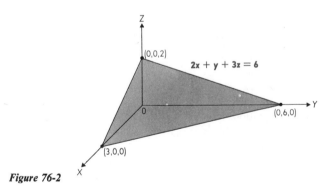

Figure 76-2

we find $z = 2$, and hence the point $(0, 0, 2)$ is one of the points of our plane. In like manner, we find that two other points are $(3, 0, 0)$ and $(0, 6, 0)$. These points are the points in which the plane intersects the axes, and Fig. 76-2 shows how they determine the plane. The coefficients of x, y, and z give us a vector that is normal to the plane: $N = 2i + j + 3k$.

Example 76-3. Find the equation of the plane that contains the points $A(1, -1, 2)$, $B(3, 2, 1)$, and $C(2, 1, 3)$.

Solution. Figure 76-3 shows our three points A, B, and C; we have also drawn the vectors CA and CB. The vector $CA \times CB$ is a vector that is normal to our plane. Since

$$CA = -i - 2j - k \quad \text{and} \quad CB = i + j - 2k,$$

we readily find (with the aid of Equation 75-8) that

$$CA \times CB = 5i - 3j + k.$$

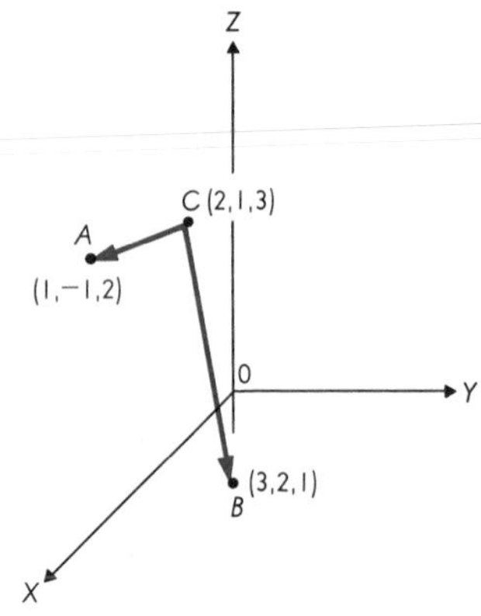

If we let the point $A(1, -1, 2)$ play the role of P_0 in Equation 76-1 (either of the points B or C would do as well), and let $N = CA \times CB$, we obtain the equation of our plane in the form of Equation 76-2:

$$5(x - 1) - 3(y + 1) + (z - 2) = 0.$$

We can rewrite this equation in the form of Equation 76-3 as

$$5x - 3y + z = 10.$$

Example 76-4. Find the distance d between the point $(2, 3, 4)$ and the plane $2x + y + 2z = 2$.

Solution. Our point and plane are shown in Fig. 76-4. We sketched the plane by finding its intercepts $(1, 0, 0)$, $(0, 2, 0)$, and $(0, 0, 1)$. We know that the vector $N = 2i + j + 2k$ is perpendicular to this plane. Therefore, the line with vector equation $R = Nt + B$, where $B = 2i + 3j + 4k$, is a normal line. Now let A be a vector from our given point to a point of the plane—for example, the point $(0, 0, 1)$. If the smaller angle between A and the normal line is an angle of ϕ, the distance we want is given by the equation $d = |A| \cos \phi$. Since $\cos(\pi - \phi) = -\cos \phi$, we see that we can also write

$$d = |A| |\cos(\pi - \phi)|.$$

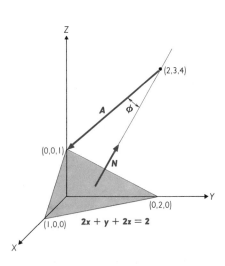

Figure 76-3

Figure 76-4

Thus we have found that $d = |A| |\cos \theta|$, where the angle of θ is either the smaller or the larger angle between A and our normal line. We can consider this number to be the absolute value of the dot product of A and a unit vector in the direction of the normal line. Such a unit vector is $\dfrac{N}{|N|}$, so we have

$$d = \frac{|A \cdot N|}{|N|} = \frac{|(-2i - 3j - 3k) \cdot (2i + j + 2k)|}{\sqrt{4 + 1 + 4}} = \frac{13}{3}.$$

P R O B L E M S   7 6

1. Find unit vectors normal to the following planes. Sketch the graphs of the planes.
(a) $2x + y - 2z = 5$ (b) $3x - 4y = 12$
(c) $x + y + z = 0$ (d) $y - z - 4x - 7 = 0$

2. Find an equation of the plane for which the given vector is a normal vector and which contains the given point.
(a) $N = 2i - 3j + k$, $(1, 2, 3)$ (b) $N = 3i - k$, $(-1, -2, -3)$
(c) $N = i$, $(0, 0, 0)$ (d) $N = j + k$, $(0, 1, 0)$

3. Describe the set of planes such that each plane in the set is the graph of the equation $2x - 3y + 4z + d = 0$ for some number d.

4. Find an equation of the plane that contains the points $(1, 0, -1)$, $(2, 3, 1)$, and $(-2, 1, 1)$.

5. Find an equation of the plane that contains the points $(1, 2, 3)$ and $(-2, 1, 1)$ and which does not intersect the Y-axis.

6. Find a vector that is parallel to the line of intersection of the planes $2x - y + 3z + 12 = 0$ and $x + 2y - z - 17 = 0$.

7. Find an equation of the plane that contains the point $(-1, 7, 9)$ and is parallel to the plane $3x + 4y - z + 6 = 0$.

8. Find the cosine of the angle between the (normals to the) planes $x - 2y + z + 4 = 0$ and $2x - 3y - z + 1 = 0$.

9. Find the distance between the two parallel planes $2x - y + 2z + 3 = 0$ and $2x - y + 2z - 6 = 0$.

10. Find the coordinates of the point P of the plane $2x + y + 2z + 10 = 0$ such that the position vector OP is parallel to the vector $i + j + k$.

11. Find an equation of the plane that is perpendicular to the plane $14x + 2y + 7 = 0$, that contains the origin, and whose normal makes a $45°$ angle with the Z-axis.

12. Find an equation of the plane that is the set of all points equidistant from the two points $(2, 5, -1)$ and $(5, -2, -4)$.

13. Show that the distance between the plane $ax + by + cz + d = 0$ and the point (x_0, y_0, z_0) is the number

$$\frac{|ax_0 + by_0 + cz_0 + d|}{\sqrt{a^2 + b^2 + c^2}}.$$

14. Sketch the graphs of the following equations.

(a) $|x + y + z| = 1$ (b) $|x| + |y| + |z| = 1$

(c) $[x + y + z] = 1$ (d) $[x] + [y] + [z] = 1$

77 · CYLINDERS. SURFACES OF REVOLUTION

The **cylinders** are among the simpler types of surfaces. We will consider cylinders which are generated by moving a line that is perpendicular to a given plane along a curve in that plane. Thus, for example, an ordinary right-circular cylinder (stovepipe) is generated by moving a line that is perpendicular to the plane of a circle around the circle; a parabolic cylinder is generated by moving a line that is perpendicular to the plane of a parabola along the parabola, and so on. The lines are the **generators** of the cylinder.

When the generators are parallel to one of the coordinate axes, the equation of the surface does not involve the corresponding coordinate. Thus let us show that in space the graph of the equation $x^2 + z^2 = 4$ is the right circular cylinder whose generators are parallel to the Y-axis that is shown in Fig. 77-1. We first choose a pair of numbers that satisfy our equation; to be specific, we will take $x = 1$ and $z = \sqrt{3}$. Then for every number y the point $(1, y, \sqrt{3})$ belongs to our graph. The set of points $\{(1, y, \sqrt{3}) \mid y \in (-\infty, \infty)\}$ is a line parallel to the Y-axis; it is one of the generators of the cylinder. We obtain the other generators by starting with other values of x and z. It is clear that we can think of our cylinder as the surface that is generated by moving

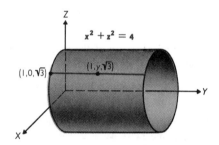

Figure 77-1

any one of these lines around the circle $x^2 + z^2 = 4$ in the XZ-plane, keeping the line parallel to the Y-axis during the motion. We say that the graph of the equation $x^2 + z^2 = 4$ *in space* is the cylinder whose base curve is the graph of the equation $x^2 + z^2 = 4$ *in the XZ-plane*.

To plot the graph of a cylinder whose equation does not involve a particular coordinate, we simply plot the base curve in the coordinate plane that is perpendicular to the axis of the missing coordinate and then "slide" the base curve parallel to this axis.

Example 77-1. Sketch the graph of the equation $y^2 = x$ in space.

Solution. Our equation does not involve z, so its graph is a cylinder whose generators are parallel to the Z-axis. We plot the base curve—the parabola $y^2 = x$ in the XY-plane (Fig. 77-2). Then we obtain the cylinder by sliding this parabola parallel to the Z-axis.

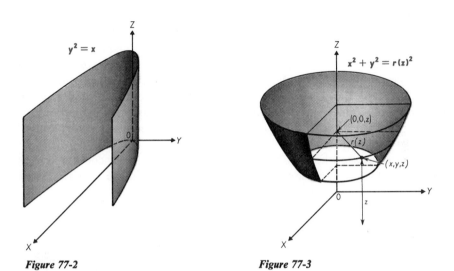

Figure 77-2   **Figure 77-3**

Another simple type of surface is formed when we rotate a plane curve about a line. The equation of such a **surface of revolution** is easy to recognize if the axis of rotation is one of the coordinate axes. For example, in Fig. 77-3 we show a surface that is obtained by rotating a plane curve about the Z-axis. From the figure, we see that planes parallel to the XY-plane intersect the surface in circles. Suppose such a plane is z units from the XY-plane, and let $r(z)$ be the radius of the circle of intersection. Therefore, if (x, y, z) is a point of our surface, we see that

(77-1) $$x^2 + y^2 = r(z)^2.$$

The graph of Equation 77-1 is a surface of revolution about the Z-axis. The plane curve in which this surface intersects the YZ-plane is the set of points

$$\{(x, y, z) \mid x^2 + y^2 = r(z)^2\} \cap \{(x, y, z) \mid x = 0\} = \{(0, y, z) \mid y^2 = r(z)^2\}.$$

Thus the equation of our plane curve of intersection is $y^2 = r(z)^2$, which is obtained by setting $x = 0$ in Equation 77-1. Similarly, when we set $y = 0$ in Equation 77-1, we get the equation of the curve in which our surface intersects the *XZ*-plane: $x^2 = r(z)^2$. In this paragraph we showed how to find the equation of a plane curve that generates a given surface of revolution; now let us start with the equation of a plane curve and find the equation of the surface that results when we rotate it about one of the coordinate axes.

The surface of revolution that results from rotating a plane curve $y = r(z)$ about the *Z*-axis is a set of points whose distance from the *Z*-axis depends only on their *Z*-coordinates. Specifically, the condition that a point (x, y, z) be a point of the surface is that its distance to the *Z*-axis; that is, to the point $(0, 0, z)$, be $|r(z)|$. Thus we must have $x^2 + y^2 = r(z)^2$, and so our surface of revolution is the set $\{(x, y, z) \mid x^2 + y^2 = r(z)^2\}$. We therefore obtain the equation of our surface of revolution from the equation $y = r(z)$ by squaring both sides and replacing y^2 with $x^2 + y^2$. Similarly, the equation of the surface that is obtained by rotating the graph of the equation $x = r(z)$ about the *Z*-axis is found by squaring both sides and replacing x^2 with $x^2 + y^2$.

For a surface whose axis of rotation is one of the other coordinate axes, we make the obvious interchanges of the letters x, y, z in the remarks above. In particular, we must replace z with the co-ordinate of the axis of rotation. Thus, sur-faces of revolution about the *X*-axis and the *Y*-axis have equations of the form $y^2 + z^2 = r(x)^2$ and $x^2 + z^2 = r(y)^2$, respectively.

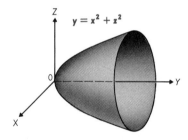

Figure 77-4

Example 77-2. Describe the surface whose equation is $y = x^2 + z^2$.

Solution. This equation has the form $x^2 + z^2 = r(y)^2$, with $r(y) = \sqrt{y}$, and so its graph is a surface that is obtained by rotat-ing a plane curve about the *Y*-axis. We obtain the equation of this curve in the *XY*-plane by replacing z with 0 in our original equation, thus obtaining the parabola $y = x^2$. Our surface, which may also be obtained by rotating the parabola $y = z^2$ about the *Y*-axis, is shown in Fig. 77-4.

Example 77-3. Describe the surface whose equation is $z^2 = x^2 + y^2$.

Solution. The graph of this equation is a surface of revolution whose axis is the *Z*-axis. If we set $x = 0$, we obtain the equation of the intersection of the surface and the *YZ*-plane. Thus, the surface intersects the *YZ*-plane in the curve whose equation is $z^2 = y^2$. The graph of the equation $z^2 = y^2$ consists of two lines in the *YZ*-plane—one bisecting the first quadrant and one bisecting the second quad-rant. When we rotate these lines about the *Z*-axis, we get the cone shown in Fig. 77-5.

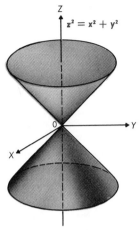

Figure 77-5

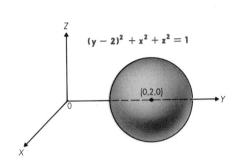

Figure 77-6

Example 77-4. Find the equation of the surface that is generated by rotating the circle $(y - 2)^2 + z^2 = 1$ about the Y-axis. What if we rotate it about the Z-axis?

Solution. In the first case, we simply replace z^2 with $x^2 + z^2$ to obtain the equation $(y - 2)^2 + x^2 + z^2 = 1$. The graph of this equation is the sphere shown in Fig. 77-6.

It is harder to find the equation of the surface we get when we rotate about the Z-axis. According to the procedure outlined above, we should write the equation of the plane curve we are to rotate in the form $y^2 = r(z)^2$ and then replace y^2 with $x^2 + y^2$. When we solve the equation of our given circle for y, we get two solutions:

$$y = 2 + \sqrt{1 - z^2} \quad \text{and} \quad y = 2 - \sqrt{1 - z^2}.$$

Our surface of revolution is the union of the surfaces that are obtained when we rotate the graphs of these equations about the Z-axis. The equations of these surfaces are $x^2 + y^2 = (2 + \sqrt{1 - z^2})^2$ and $x^2 + y^2 = (2 - \sqrt{1 - z^2})^2$; that is,

$$x^2 + y^2 + z^2 - 5 = 4\sqrt{1 - z^2} \quad \text{and} \quad x^2 + y^2 + z^2 - 5 = -4\sqrt{1 - z^2}.$$

A point belongs to the union of the graphs of these two equations if its coordinates satisfy one or the other of them, and this statement is equivalent to the statement that the coordinates satisfy the equation

$$(x^2 + y^2 + z^2 - 5)^2 = 16(1 - z^2).$$

We take this last equation to be the equation of the desired surface; we leave it to you to sketch it. Such a doughnut-shaped surface is called a **torus**. These surfaces have certain interesting properties that make them play a more prominent role in mathematics than you might expect.

P R O B L E M S   7 7

1. Sketch the following cylinders.

(a) $3y + 2z = 6$ (b) $z = 4 - y^2$ (c) $z = |x|$

(d) $\dfrac{x^2}{4} + \dfrac{z^2}{9} = 1$ (e) $z = \cos y$ (f) $y = \cos \dfrac{\pi}{[\![x]\!]}$, $x \in [1, 5)$

(g) $[\![y]\!] + [\![2z]\!] = 0$ (h) $[\![x^2 + y^2]\!] = 0$

2. What are the equations of the surfaces of revolution that are obtained when the plane curves of the preceding question are rotated about the coordinate axes of the planes in which they lie? (There will be two surfaces for each curve.)

3. Sketch the graphs of the following equations.

(a) $4x^2 - y^2 - z^2 = 4$ (b) $9x^2 + 4y^2 + 9z^2 = 36$ (c) $x^2 + z^2 = \sin^2 \pi y$

(d) $y^2 = \sin^2 \pi \sqrt{x^2 + z^2}$ (e) $x^2 + z^2 = e^{2y}$ (f) $z = [\![x^2 + y^2]\!]$

(g) $|z| = x^2 + y^2$ (h) $|x^2 + y^2 + z| = 1$

4. Describe the surface whose equation is $9(x - 1)^2 + 9(y + 1)^2 + 4(z - 3)^2 = 36$.

5. Find an equation of the torus (see Example 77-4) that is obtained by rotating a circle of radius r about a line that is b units from its center. (We assume, of course, that $0 < r < b$.)

6. The cardioid in the XY-plane whose polar coordinate equation in the XY-plane is $r = 2(1 - \cos \theta)$ is rotated about the X-axis. Find the equation of the resulting surface.

7. Describe the surface that is the set of all points that are equidistant from the Y-axis and the plane $x = 4$.

8. Use the methods we discussed in Section 73 to find the area of the surface whose equation is $9x^2 + 9y^2 + 25z^2 = 225$.

9. Show that if we rotate the graph of the equation $z = f(y)$ in the YZ-plane about the line $z = a$, then the equation of the resulting surface is $(z - a)^2 + x^2 = (f(y) - a)^2$.

10. Show that a surface that is obtained by rotating a curve in the YZ-plane about the line $z = (\tan \alpha)y$ has an equation of the form

$$(y \sin \alpha - z \sin \alpha)^2 + x^2 = [r(y \cos \alpha + z \sin \alpha)]^2.$$

78 QUADRIC SURFACES

In our study of plane analytic geometry we considered the graphs of quadratic equations; that is, equations of the form $Ax^2 + Bxy + Cy^2 + Dx + Ey + F = 0$. We found that by suitably translating and rotating axes we could reduce our study to equations in certain "standard" forms, and we are able to recognize the standard forms of the equations of ellipses, hyperbolas, and so on. In this section we will briefly discuss the standard forms for analogous figures in space.

These figures, the graphs of quadratic equations in x, y, and z, are called **quadric surfaces**. In Chapter 10 we will take up the problem of rotating and translating the axes so as to put general quadratic equations in standard form.

The graph of an equation of the form

(78-1) $$\frac{x^2}{a^2} + \frac{y^2}{b^2} + \frac{z^2}{c^2} = 1$$

is called an **ellipsoid**. We obtain the curves of intersection of this figure with the coordinate planes by setting x, y, and z equal to 0, one at a time. These curves of intersection are ellipses. In fact, it is not hard to see that every plane that is parallel to one of the coordinate planes, and that intersects our ellipsoid, intersects it in an ellipse. Figure 78-1 shows the graph of Equation 78-1. You will notice that if $a = b = c$, the graph is just the sphere of radius a whose center is the origin.

The graph of Equation 78-1 intersects all three coordinate planes in ellipses. The graph of an equation of the form

(78-2) $$\frac{x^2}{a^2} + \frac{y^2}{b^2} - \frac{z^2}{c^2} = 1$$

intersects the XY-plane in an ellipse, but it intersects the other two coordinate planes in hyperbolas. Such a surface is called a **hyperboloid of one sheet**, and it is shown in Fig. 78-2. If x and z (or y and z) are interchanged in Equation 78-2, we still obtain a hyperboloid of one sheet but its axis is then the X-axis (or the Y-axis).

The graph of an equation of the form

(78-3) $$\frac{x^2}{a^2} - \frac{y^2}{b^2} - \frac{z^2}{c^2} = 1$$

intersects the XY- and XZ-planes in hyperbolas, but it doesn't intersect the

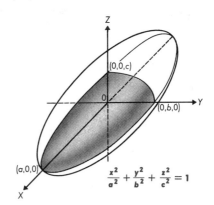

Figure 78-1

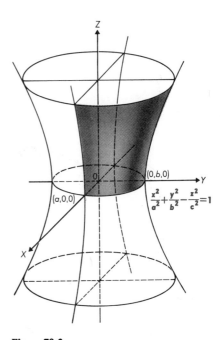

Figure 78-2

YZ-plane at all (for no point with coordinates $(0, y, z)$ can satisfy Equation 78-3). However, a plane $x = k$, where $k^2 > a^2$, intersects the surface in an ellipse. For if (k, y, z) is a point of such a plane, then y and z satisfy the equation

$$\frac{k^2}{a^2} - \frac{y^2}{b^2} - \frac{z^2}{c^2} = 1,$$

which can be written in the standard form of the equation of an ellipse:

$$\frac{y^2}{b^2(k^2 - a^2)/a^2} + \frac{z^2}{c^2(k^2 - a^2)/a^2} = 1.$$

The graph of Equation 78-3 is called a **hyperboloid of two sheets,** and Fig. 78-3 shows what such a surface looks like.

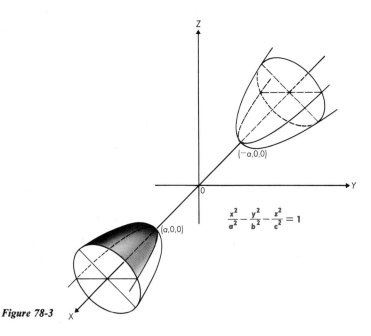

Figure 78-3

Corresponding to the parabola in two dimensions we have the **elliptic paraboloid** in three dimensions. The graph of the equation

(78-4)
$$z = \frac{x^2}{a^2} + \frac{y^2}{b^2}$$

is such a surface. We notice that the *XZ*-plane cuts the surface in the parabola whose equation is $z = x^2/a^2$, and the *YZ*-plane cuts it in the parabola whose equation is $z = y^2/b^2$. Each plane $z = k$, where $k > 0$, cuts the surface in an ellipse. In Fig. 78-4 we have drawn the graph of Equation 78-4.

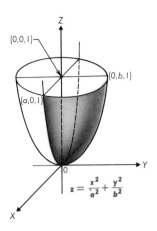

   If the elliptical cross sections of an ellipsoid, hyperboloid, or elliptical paraboloid are circles, the surface is merely a surface of revolution. Our next surface does not resemble a surface of revolution in any way. The graph of the equation

$$(78\text{-}5) \quad z + \frac{x^2}{a^2} - \frac{y^2}{b^2} = 0$$

Figure 78-4

is a **hyperbolic paraboloid.** This surface intersects the *YZ*-plane in the parabola $z = y^2/b^2$ and the *XZ*-plane in the parabola $z = -x^2/a^2$. It intersects planes parallel to the *XY*-plane in hyperbolas, as shown in Fig. 78-5.

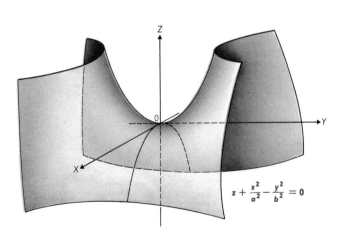

Figure 78-5

   As a final quadratic surface, we consider the **elliptical cone**, the graph of the equation

$$(78\text{-}6) \qquad \frac{x^2}{a^2} + \frac{y^2}{b^2} = \frac{z^2}{c^2}.$$

If $x = 0$, we see that either $z = cy/b$ or $z = -cy/b$. Thus the surface intersects the YZ-plane in the two lines represented by the last equations. Similarly, the surface intersects the XZ-plane in the lines $z = cx/a$ and $z = -cx/a$. Planes parallel to the XY-plane cut the surface in ellipses. Figure 78-6 shows the graph of Equation 78-6. If $a = b$, the surface is a **right circular cone**.

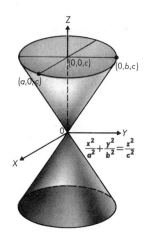

Example 78-1. Discuss the graph of the equation
$$\frac{x^2}{25} + \frac{y^2}{16} - \frac{z\,|z|}{9} = 1.$$

Solution. If $z \leq 0$, we have $|z| = -z$, and so part of our graph is the bottom half of the ellipsoid
$$\frac{x^2}{25} + \frac{y^2}{16} + \frac{z^2}{9} = 1.$$ When $z > 0$, we have $|z| = z$, and then we have the upper half of the hyperboloid
$$\frac{x^2}{25} + \frac{y^2}{16} - \frac{z^2}{9} = 1.$$ You might try to sketch part of our figure, say for $z \leq 5$. It looks like a squashed badminton bird.

Example 78-2. The plane $z = 1$ intersects the hyperbolic paraboloid $x = 6y^2 - 4z^2$ in a parabola. What is the focus of this parabola?

Figure 78-6

Solution. When $z = 1$, we have $x = 6y^2 - 4$. The equation of this parabola can be written as $x + 4 = 4 \cdot \frac{3}{2}y^2$, so we know from our work with the parabola in Section 30 that its focus is $\frac{3}{2}$ units from the vertex. The vertex is the point $(-4, 0, 1)$, and thus the X-coordinate of the focus is $-4 + \frac{3}{2} = -\frac{5}{2}$. The Y-coordinate is 0, and of course the Z-coordinate is 1. Therefore, the point we were asked to find is the point $(-\frac{5}{2}, 0, 1)$.

P R O B L E M S   7 8

1. Describe the graphs of the following equations, and sketch that part of each surface that lies in the first octant.

(a) $x^2 + 2y^2 + 3z^2 = 6$ (b) $9y^2 - 36z\,|z| = 36 + 4x^2$

(c) $\dfrac{x^2}{9} + \dfrac{z^2}{16} = 1 + \dfrac{y^2}{25}$ (d) $4\,|x| = 4y^2 + z^2$

(e) $4y^2 = x^2 + 4z^2$ (f) $x + z^2 = y\,|y|$

2. When the hyperbolic paraboloid $z = \dfrac{x^2}{4} - \dfrac{y^2}{9}$ is intersected by the following planes, we obtain familiar plane curves. Name these curves, find the coordinates of their

vertices, and use the resulting information to sketch the hyperbolic paraboloid.
(a) the YZ-plane
(b) the XY-plane
(c) the plane parallel to the XZ-plane and 3 units to its right
(d) the plane parallel to the XY-plane and 1 unit below it
(e) the plane parallel to the YZ-plane and 4 units in front of it

3. Find numbers A, B, C, and D such that the quadric surface

$$Ax^2 + By^2 + Cz^2 + D = 0$$

contains the following points. Name the surface.
(a) $(1, 1, -1)$, $(2, 1, 0)$, $(5, -5, 3)$
(b) $(2, -1, 1)$, $(-3, 0, 0)$, $(1, -1, -2)$
(c) $(1, 2, -1)$, $(0, 1, 0)$, $(3, 1, -2)$

4. Find the center and radius of the sphere.
(a) $x^2 + y^2 + z^2 - 2x + 2y - 2 = 0$
(b) $x^2 + y^2 + z^2 - x - 2y - 4z + 3 = 0.$

5. Find the equation of the plane that is tangent to the given sphere at the given point.
(a) $x^2 + y^2 + z^2 = 9$, $(1, 2, 2)$
(b) $x^2 + y^2 + z^2 - 10x + 4y - 6z - 187 = 0$, $(-9, 3, 1)$

6. Discuss the graphs of the following equations. (*Hint:* First complete the square.)
(a) $x^2 + 4y^2 - 9z^2 - 2x - 16y - 19 = 0$
(b) $x^2 + z^2 + 2x - 4y - 2z + 6 = 0$
(c) $x^2 - y^2 - z^2 - 2|x| + 2|y| + 2|z| - 2 = 0$

7. Let the point (x, y, z) be at a distance r_1 from the point $(0, 2, 0)$ and at a distance r_2 from the plane $y = -2$. Find the equation of the surface that contains the point (x, y, z) in the following cases. Describe the surface.

(a) $r_1 = r_2$ (b) $r_1 = 2r_2$ (c) $r_2 = 2r_1$

8. Find the equation of the surface that contains the point (x, y, z) and describe the surface if:
(a) the square of the distance from the point to the Y-axis is $\frac{2}{5}$ the distance from the point to the XZ-plane.
(b) the distance from the point to the origin is $\frac{3}{2}$ its distance from the Z-axis.

9. Prove that a point, the sum of whose distances from two fixed points is a given number, belongs to an ellipsoid of revolution.

10. Prove that a point, the difference of whose distances from two fixed points is a given number, belongs to a hyperboloid of revolution.

79 SPACE CURVES

The graph of a function F whose values are vectors in three-dimensional space is obtained in exactly the same way that we found the graphs of vector-valued functions in two dimensions in Section 70. Thus for each number t in the domain D of F, we plot the terminal point of the position vector $R = F(t)$, and the set of all such points is the graph of F. If we write the vector equation $R = F(t)$ in terms of the components of the vectors involved, then

$$xi + yj + zk = F_x(t)i + F_y(t)j + F_z(t)k.$$

The graph of F is the set of points

$$\{(x, y, z) \mid x = F_x(t), \quad y = F_y(t),$$
$$z = F_z(t), \quad t \in D\}.$$

The three scalar equations

$$x = F_x(t), \quad y = F_y(t), \quad z = F_z(t)$$

are called **parametric equations** of the graph.

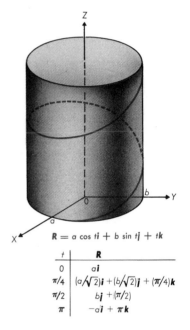

$$R = a \cos t\, i + b \sin t\, j + t k$$

t	R
0	ai
$\pi/4$	$(a/\sqrt{2})i + (b/\sqrt{2})j + (\pi/4)k$
$\pi/2$	$bj + (\pi/2)$
π	$-ai + \pi k$

Figure 79-1

Example 79-1. Sketch the graph of the vector equation $R = a \cos t\, i + b \sin t\, j + tk$.

Solution. We construct the table of values shown in Fig. 79-1, plot the terminal points of these vectors and join the plotted points to form the curve shown in the figure. This curve is called a **helix**. Parametric equations of our helix are

$$x = a \cos t, \quad y = b \sin t, \quad z = t.$$

If (x, y, z) is any point of the helix, we see that $\dfrac{x^2}{a^2} + \dfrac{y^2}{b^2} = 1$, and so our helix lies in an elliptical cylinder whose generators are parallel to the Z-axis. The helix forms a "barber's pole stripe" in this cylinder. In particular, if $b = a$ the helix is called a *circular helix*; it lies in the right-circular cylinder $x^2 + y^2 = a^2$.

As in the case of vectors in the plane, we define the derivative $F'(t)$ by means of the equation (see Equation 71-1)

$$(79\text{-}1) \qquad\qquad F'(t) = \lim_{s \to t} \frac{F(s) - F(t)}{s - t}.$$

By a proof similar to that of Theorem 71-1, it can be shown that

$$(79\text{-}2) \qquad\qquad F'(t) = F_x'(t)i + F_y'(t)j + F_z'(t)k.$$

Again we find that the usual rules concerning sums and products, and the chain rule, are valid (see Equations 71-4, 71-5, 71-6). In particular, the usual product rules apply when we differentiate the cross product and the scalar triple product:

$$(79\text{-}3) \qquad D_t(F(t) \times G(t)) = F(t) \times G'(t) + F'(t) \times G(t),$$

$$(79\text{-}4) \quad D_t[F(t) \cdot (G(t) \times H(t))] = F'(t) \cdot (G(t) \times H(t))$$
$$+ F(t) \cdot (G'(t) \times H(t)) + F(t) \cdot (G(t) \times H'(t)).$$

The vector $F'(t)$ plays the same role relative to space curves that it does relative to plane curves. Thus $F'(t)$ *is a vector tangent to the graph of F.* If the parameter t measures time and we consider our space curve to be the path of a moving particle, then the number $|F'(t)|$ is the *speed* of the particle. The vector $V = F'(t)$ is the *velocity* of the particle, and the vector $A = F''(t)$ is the *acceleration* of the particle. If $F''(t)$ exists for each $t \in D$ and $|F'(t)| \neq 0$, we will again call the graph of F a **smooth arc**. We restrict our attention to smooth arcs.

Exactly as in the two-dimensional case, the length of the arc that corresponds to a parameter interval $[a, b]$ is given by the formula

$$(79\text{-}5) \qquad L = \int_a^b |F'(t)| \, dt = \int_a^b \sqrt{x'^2 + y'^2 + z'^2} \, dt.$$

Example 79-2. The portion of the circular helix $R = \cos t\, i + \sin t\, j + t k$ that corresponds to the T-interval $[0, 2\pi]$ makes one complete circuit about the Z-axis. How long is this arc?

Solution. Here $F'(t) = -\sin t\, i + \cos t\, j + k.$ Hence

$$|F'(t)| = \sqrt{\sin^2 t + \cos^2 t + 1} = \sqrt{2},$$

and Equation 79-5 gives us

$$L = \int_0^{2\pi} \sqrt{2} \, dt = \sqrt{2}\, 2\pi \approx 8.9.$$

If we let s be the distance from the terminal point of the vector $F(a)$ to the terminal point of the vector $F(t)$ along our smooth arc, then (see Equation 71-8)

$$s = \int_a^t |F'(u)| \, du,$$

and

$$D_t s = |F'(t)| = \sqrt{x'^2 + y'^2 + z'^2}.$$

The vector T defined by the equation

$$(79\text{-}6) \qquad\qquad T = \frac{F'(t)}{|F'(t)|} = D_s R$$

is called the **unit tangent** to the graph of the equation $R = F(t)$.

As in the two-dimensional case, if a vector has the same length at each point of an interval, it is perpendicular to its derivative. In particular, since the length of the vector T is always 1, $D_s T$ is perpendicular to T. Using the two-dimensional case (Section 72) as a model, we define the **unit normal** N and the **curvature** κ of a space curve so that they satisfy the equation

$$(79\text{-}7) \qquad\qquad D_s T = \kappa N.$$

In order to determine completely the direction of N, we arbitrarily specify that the curvature κ shall be non-negative; that is, $\kappa \geq 0$. Then

$$(79\text{-}8) \qquad\qquad \kappa = |D_s T| = |D_t T D_s t| = \frac{|D_t T|}{|D_t R|}.$$

Since N is perpendicular to T, we see that $|T \times N| = |T| |N| \sin 90° = 1 \cdot 1 \cdot 1 = 1$. Therefore, the equation

$$(79\text{-}9) \qquad\qquad B = T \times N$$

defines a unit vector, called the **unit binormal** to the curve. The three unit vectors T, N, and B are basic vectors that are used to study space curves. In addition to Equation 79-9, it is easy to see that $N = B \times T$ and $T = N \times B$.

Example 79-3. Find the three basic vectors T, N, and B associated with the circular helix of Example 79-2 and find the curvature of that helix.

Solution. We use primes to denote differentiation with respect to our parameter t. Then

$$R' = -\sin t\, i + \cos t\, j + k, \quad \text{and} \quad |R'| = \sqrt{2}.$$

Thus

$$T = \frac{R'}{|R'|} = \frac{1}{\sqrt{2}}(-\sin t\, i + \cos t\, j + k).$$

Hence

$$T' = \frac{1}{\sqrt{2}}(-\cos t\, i - \sin t\, j),$$

and so

$$|T'| = \frac{1}{\sqrt{2}}.$$

We see from Equation 79-8 that

$$\kappa = \frac{|T'|}{|R'|} = \frac{1/\sqrt{2}}{\sqrt{2}} = \tfrac{1}{2}.$$

Now

$$\frac{T'}{|R'|} = \tfrac{1}{2}(-\cos t\,i - \sin t\,j) = \kappa N,$$

so

$$N = -\cos t\,i - \sin t\,j.$$

It then follows that

$$B = T \times N = \begin{vmatrix} \dfrac{\cos t}{\sqrt{2}} & \dfrac{1}{\sqrt{2}} \\ -\sin t & 0 \end{vmatrix} i - \begin{vmatrix} -\dfrac{\sin t}{\sqrt{2}} & \dfrac{1}{\sqrt{2}} \\ -\cos t & 0 \end{vmatrix} j + \begin{vmatrix} -\dfrac{\sin t}{\sqrt{2}} & \dfrac{\cos t}{\sqrt{2}} \\ -\cos t & -\sin t \end{vmatrix} k$$

$$= \frac{1}{\sqrt{2}}(\sin t\,i - \cos t\,j + k).$$

Example 79-4.   We know that $D_sT = \kappa N$. Find expressions for D_sN and D_sB.

Solution.   Since $B \cdot B = 1$, we can differentiate both sides of this equation to find that D_sB is perpendicular to B. Also, $T \cdot B = 0$, and when we differentiate this equation we obtain the equation $T \cdot D_sB + \kappa N \cdot B = 0$. Thus, since $N \cdot B = 0$, we have $T \cdot D_sB = 0$. So we see that D_sB is perpendicular to both B and T; it must therefore lie along the line determined by the vector N. Thus, D_sB is a scalar multiple of N. The negative of the scalar by which we multiply N to obtain D_sB is called the **torsion** of the curve, and it is denoted by the greek letter τ. Thus we write

(79-10) $$D_sB = -\tau N.$$

Then

$$D_sN = D_s(B \times T) = B \times \kappa N + (-\tau N) \times T$$
$$= \tau B - \kappa T.$$

The three formulas

$$D_sT = \kappa N, \quad D_sN = \tau B - \kappa T, \quad \text{and} \quad D_sB = -\tau N$$

are called the **Frenet Formulas**. They are of fundamental importance in the study of curves in space.

P R O B L E M S   7 9

1. Find the unit tangent vector T at the point corresponding to $t = \pi/2$. Also find the length of the arc corresponding to the T-interval $[0, \pi]$.
  (a) $R = e^t \cos t\,i + e^t \sin t\,j + e^t k$
  (b) $R = \cos 2t\,i + \sin 2t\,j + 3t k$
  (c) $R = 3t \cos t\,i + 3t \sin t\,j + 4t k$
  (d) $R = \cos \tfrac{1}{4}t\,i + \sin \tfrac{1}{4}t\,j + \ln(\cos \tfrac{1}{4}t)\,k$

2. The helix $R = \cos t\, i + \sin t\, j + tk$ intersects the graph of the equation
$$R = (1 - 2t)i - (t^2 - 2t)j + (t^3 + t)k$$
at the point $(1, 0, 0)$. What is the angle between the tangents at this point?

3. Find a unit vector that is tangent to the graph of the equation $R = (t - 1)i + (t^2 + t)j + t^4k$ at the point where the curve intersects the YZ-plane.

4. The graphs of the equations $y = \sin x$ and $z = \cos x$ in three-dimensional space are cylinders. Write a vector equation of the curve of intersection of these cylinders.

5. Find the length of the graph of the equation $R = ti + \dfrac{t^2}{\sqrt{2}}j + \dfrac{t^3}{3}k$ for t in the interval $[0, 2]$.

6. The position vector of a particle moving in space is $R = \cos t\, i + \sin t\, j + tk$, where we measure time in seconds and distance in feet. When $t = \pi/4$, we release the particle and it flies off on a tangent. Where is it when $t = \pi/2$?

7. Let C be a given vector, independent of t; for example, $C = 3i + 4j + k$. Describe the relation between the graphs of the equations $R = F(t)$ and $R = F(t) + C$.

8. Show that the curvature is equal to the torsion at all points of the graph of the equation $R = (3t - t^3)i + 3t^2j + (3t + t^3)k$. What is the curvature at the origin?

9. Find the 3 basic vectors T, N, and B, associated with the graph of the equation $R = \cosh t\, i + \sinh t\, j + tk$.

10. Find

(a) $D_t(F(t) \times F'(t))$ (b) $D_t[F(t) \cdot (F'(t) \times F''(t))]$

(c) $D_t |F(t)|$ (d) $D_t[(F(t) \times F'(t)) \cdot F'(t)]$

11. Find the torsion of the helix of Example 79-2.

12. What can you conclude if you know that the torsion of a curve is zero at all points of the curve?

13. The number $|D_sN|$ is called the **screw curvature**. Express the screw curvature in terms of the curvature and torsion.

14. Express D_s^3R in terms of T, N, and B.

15. Compute the following numbers if primes denote differentiation with respect to s.

(a) $T' \cdot B'$ (b) $R' \cdot R''$ (c) $R' \cdot R'''$

(d) $R'' \cdot R''$ (e) $(R' \times R'') \cdot R'''$

80 LINES IN SPACE

In Section 70 we found that a line in the plane is the graph of a vector equation of the form

(80-1) $R = Mt + B, \quad M \neq 0, \quad t \in (-\infty, \infty)$.

When the vectors R, M, and B belong to three-dimensional space, the graph of Equation 80-1 is a line in space. If the initial point of B is the origin, its terminal point is a point of the line. The vector M gives the direction of the line (Fig. 80-1).

Example 80-1. Find an equation of the line that contains the points $P(-1, 2, 3)$ and $Q(2, 1, -3)$.

Solution. Our answer will be an equation of the form $R = Mt + B$, so our problem amounts to finding the direction vector M and the position vector B. As the direction vector M, we can take the vector $M = PQ = 3i - j - 6k$. Since the point P belongs to the line, we can take the position vector B to be $B = OP = -i + 2j + 3k$. Thus an equation of our line is

$$R = (3i - j - 6k)t + (-i + 2j + 3k)$$
$$= (3t - 1)i - (t - 2)j - (6t - 3)k.$$

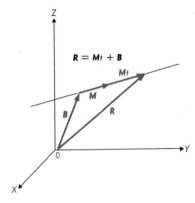

We could also have chosen the position vector B to be the vector $B = OQ = 2i + j - 3k$, which would have given us the equation

$$R = (3t + 2)i - (t - 1)j - (6t + 3)k.$$

Figure 80-1

Although our two vector equations are different, you can readily check to see that the graph of each is the line that contains the points P and Q, and hence either equation will serve as a solution to our problem.

Example 80-2. Find the equation of the line that contains the point $(2, -1, 3)$ and meets the plane $x + 2y - 4z + 12 = 0$ at right angles.

Solution. Our line will be the graph of an equation of the form $R = Mt + B$, where B is the position vector to a point of the line and M determines the direction of the line. The point $(2, -1, 3)$ belongs to our line, so we can take

$$B = 2i - j + 3k.$$

The direction of our line is that of a normal to the given plane. Since the vector $i + 2j - 4k$ is normal to the plane, we can take it to be our direction vector M. Hence an equation of our line is

$$R = (i + 2j - 4k)t + (2i - j + 3k)$$
$$= (t + 2)i + (2t - 1)j - (4t - 3)k.$$

Example 80-3. Under what conditions do two lines $R = Mt + B$ and $R = Nt + C$ intersect? When do these two equations represent the same line?

Solution. The condition that the two lines have a common point is that there be numbers r and s such that $Mr + B = Ns + C$; that is, $B - C = Ns - Mr$. If the two lines are not parallel, this equation says that $B - C$ is a linear combination of the non-parallel vectors M and N. This condition is equivalent to the statement that the three vectors $B - C$, M, and N are parallel to the same plane. We can express this geometric statement as the equation $(B - C) \cdot (M \times N) = 0$.

For the two equations to represent the same line, M and N must be parallel vectors; that is, $N = kM$ for some number k. But then the equation $B - C = Ns - Mr = (ks - r)M$ tells us that $B - C$ is also a multiple of M; in other words, the vectors $B - C$, M, and N are all parallel.

If the direction vector of a line is $M = li + mj + nk$ and the position vector to a point of the line is $B = ai + bj + ck$, then the vector equation $R = Mt + B$ becomes

$$xi + yj + zk = (lt + a)i + (mt + b)j + (nt + c)k.$$

Thus

$$x = lt + a, \quad y = mt + b, \quad z = nt + c, \quad t \in (-\infty, \infty),$$

are parametric equations of our line. If the numbers l, m, and n are not 0, we can solve for t:

$$t = \frac{x - a}{l}, \quad t = \frac{y - s}{m}, \quad \text{and} \quad t = \frac{z - c}{n}.$$

You will frequently see these equations of the line that has the **direction numbers** l, m, and n, and that contains the point (a, b, c), combined and written as

$$\frac{x - a}{l} = \frac{y - b}{m} = \frac{z - c}{n}.$$

These equations can be interpreted as saying that our line is the line of intersection of any pair of the planes

$$\frac{x - a}{l} = \frac{y - b}{m}, \quad \frac{x - a}{l} = \frac{z - c}{n},$$

and

$$\frac{y - b}{m} = \frac{z - c}{n}.$$

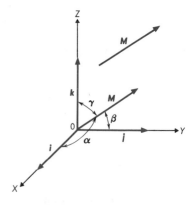

Figure 80-2

In case the direction vector M of our line is a unit vector that makes angles of α, β, and γ with i, j, and k (see Fig. 80-2), the components M_x, M_y, and M_z of M are given by the equations

$$M_x = M \cdot i = \cos \alpha, \quad M_y = M \cdot j = \cos \beta,$$
$$M_z = M \cdot k = \cos \gamma.$$

The numbers $\cos \alpha$, $\cos \beta$, and $\cos \gamma$ are called **direction cosines** of the line represented by the equation $R = Mt + B$. Since we are assuming here that M is a unit vector, $M_x^2 + M_y^2 + M_z^2 = 1$, and so the direction cosines of a line satisfy the equation

$$\cos^2 \alpha + \cos^2 \beta + \cos^2 \gamma = 1.$$

Example 80-4. Find direction cosines of the line of intersection of the two planes $2x - 3y + z = 4$ and $x + 4y - 2z = 6$.

Solution. The vector $N_1 = 2i - 3j + k$ is a normal vector to the plane $2x - 3y + z = 4$, and the vector $N_2 = i + 4j - 2k$ is a normal vector to the plane $x + 4y - 2z = 6$. The vector $(N_1 \times N_2)/|N_1 \times N_2|$ is a unit vector along the line of intersection of the two planes (why?). We find that

$$N_1 \times N_2 = \begin{vmatrix} -3 & 1 \\ 4 & -2 \end{vmatrix} i - \begin{vmatrix} 2 & 1 \\ 1 & -2 \end{vmatrix} j + \begin{vmatrix} 2 & -3 \\ 1 & 4 \end{vmatrix} k$$

$$= 2i + 5j + 11k.$$

Thus

$$|N_1 \times N_2| = \sqrt{150} = 5\sqrt{6},$$

and so the vector

$$\frac{2}{5\sqrt{6}} i + \frac{1}{\sqrt{6}} j + \frac{11}{5\sqrt{6}} k$$

is a unit vector along our line. Therefore, its components are direction cosines of the line. Using four-place decimal approximations, we find

$$\cos \alpha = .1633, \quad \cos \beta = .4082, \quad \cos \gamma = .8981,$$

and so

$$\alpha \approx 81°, \quad \beta \approx 66°, \quad \gamma \approx 26°.$$

P R O B L E M S   8 0

1. Find vector equations of the lines that contain the following pairs of points.
  (a) $(-1, 2, -4)$ and $(2, 0, 3)$ (b) $(0, 0, 0)$ and $(0, 1, 0)$
  (c) $(1, 2, 3)$ and $(-1, -3, 2)$ (d) $(\ln 8, \ln 25, \ln 3)$ and $(\ln 4, \ln 5, \ln 6)$

2. Show that the following vector equations all represent the same line.
  $R = (3t - 1)i + (1 - 2t)j + 4tk$
  $R = (3t + 2)i - (2t + 1)j + (4t + 4)k$
  $R = (6t - 10)i + (7 - 4t)j + (8t - 12)k$

3. (a) Find an equation of the line that contains the point $(2, -1, 3)$ and is parallel to the line $R = (3t - 2)i + 2tj + (4 - t)k$.
  (b) Find the equation of the plane that contains the given point and is perpendicular to the given line.

4. Find vector equations of the following lines.

(a) $\dfrac{x+2}{2} = \dfrac{y-1}{1} = \dfrac{z-2}{2}$ 　　　(b) $\dfrac{x-2}{3} = \dfrac{y}{2} = \dfrac{z-4}{1}$

5. Do the lines in the preceding problem intersect?

6. Find a vector equation of the line of intersection of the planes $2x - 3y + z = 5$ and $x + 2z = 7$.

7. Let A and B be given position vectors. Describe the graph of the equation

$$R = (1 - t)A + tB, \quad t \in [0, 1].$$

8. For a given pair of vectors M and B, and $t \in (-\infty, \infty)$, describe the graph of the equation.

(a) $R = M[\![t]\!] + B$ 　　　　　(b) $R = M|t| + B$
(c) $R = M \sin t + B$ 　　　　　(d) $R = Me^t + B$

9. Find an equation of the line that contains the point of intersection of the lines $R = (3t - 1)i + (2t + 2)j + (1 - t)k$ and $R = (t - 3)i + (8 - 3t)j + (2t - 3)k$ and is perpendicular to both lines.

10. Does the line that is tangent to the graph of the equation $R = ti + t^2j + t^3k$ at the point at which $t = 2$ contain the point $(1, 0, -4)$?

11. (a) Find the direction cosines of the lines

$$\frac{x-2}{-1} = \frac{y+1}{3} = z \quad \text{and} \quad \frac{x+1}{7} = \frac{y-8}{-3} = z - 3.$$

(b) Do the lines in Part (a) intersect?

12. Find the measure of the smaller angle between the normal to the plane

$$2x + y + z = 7 \quad \text{and the line} \quad x - 3 = \frac{y+1}{2} = \frac{z-4}{-1}.$$

13. The position vector of a particle in space t seconds after some initial instant is given by the equation $R = F(t)$. When $t = a$, the particle flies off on a tangent. Express the position vector R in terms of t for $t \geq a$.

81 CYLINDRICAL COORDINATES. SPHERICAL COORDINATES

Cartesian coordinates do not provide the only method of associating numbers with points in space. In this section we discuss two other useful coordinate systems— cylindrical coordinates and spherical coordinates.

Let P be a point in space, and suppose that its cartesian coordinates are (x, y, z). Let r and θ be polar coordinates of the point $(x, y, 0)$ in the XY-plane (see Fig. 81-1), Then we say that (r, θ, z) are **cylindrical coordinates** of P. From our knowledge of polar coordinates (Section 62), we know that $x = r \cos \theta$ and $y = r \sin \theta$. Thus the cartesian coordinates of P are related to the cylindrical coordinates of P by the equations

(81-1) $$x = r \cos \theta, \quad y = r \sin \theta, \quad z = z.$$

A **coordinate surface** in a given coordinate system is a surface that is obtained by "fixing" one of the coordinates. For example, in a cartesian coordinate system the coordinate surface $\{(x, y, z) \mid y = 2\}$ is a plane, and in fact, you can readily see that every coordinate surface in a cartesian coordinate system is a plane. There are two kinds of coordinate surfaces in a cylindrical coordinate system. The coordinate surface $\{(r, \theta, z) \mid z = a\}$ is a plane that is parallel to the XY-plane, and the coordinate surface $\{(r, \theta, z) \mid \theta = b\}$ is a plane that contains the Z-axis. But the coordinate surface $\{(r, \theta, z) \mid r = c\}$ is a right-circular cylinder; it is from this fact that the name cylindrical coordinates is derived.

The graph of an equation in r, θ, and z is, of course, the set of points that have cylindrical coordinates that satisfy the equation.

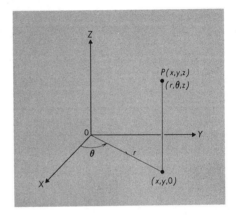

Figure 81-1

Example 81-1. Describe the graph of the equation $\theta = z$.

Solution. Let us find some points of our graph. If we let $\theta = 0$, then $z = 0$, and any point $(r, 0, 0)$ belongs to our graph, no matter what number r is. The set of all these points forms the X-axis. Similarly, if we let $\theta = \pi/4$, so that $z = \pi/4$ also, we see that all points of the set $\{(r, \pi/4, \pi/4) \mid r \in (-\infty, \infty)\}$ belong to our graph. This set is the line that is parallel to the XY-plane, is $\pi/4$ units above it, and is directed so that it bisects the angle between the XZ-plane and the YZ-plane. For other choices of θ we obtain similar lines. In fact, our surface is generated by a moving line that is kept parallel to the XY-plane while it is simultaneously moved along the Z-axis and twisted about it. A surface that is generated by a moving line is called a **ruled surface**, and our surface here is a particular ruled surface called a **helicoid**. (The cylinders we discussed in Section 77 are also ruled surfaces.) In Fig. 81-2 we have shown part of our helicoid.

Just as a curve in space can be represented by three parametric equations for the cartesian coordinates x, y, and z, so we can also represent the equation of a space curve by giving three parametric equations for the cylindrical coordinates r,

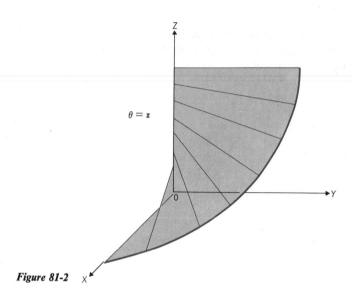

Figure 81-2

θ, and z. For example, the curve represented by the parametric equations

$$r = 1, \quad \theta = t, \quad z = t, \quad t \in (-\infty, \infty),$$

is the circular helix of Example 79-1.

The length of an arc in space is given by the formula

$$(81\text{-}2) \qquad L = \int_a^b \sqrt{x'^2 + y'^2 + z'^2}\, dt.$$

In order to use this formula to find the length of the arc with parametric equations

$$r = f(t), \quad \theta = g(t), \quad z = h(t) \quad \text{for} \quad t \in [a, b],$$

we must express the derivatives x' and y' in terms of r' and θ'. We therefore differentiate both sides of the first two of Equations 81-1 to obtain

$$x' = r' \cos \theta - r\theta' \sin \theta \quad \text{and} \quad y' = r' \sin \theta + r\theta' \cos \theta.$$

Then you can easily check to see that

$$x'^2 + y'^2 + z'^2 = r'^2 + r^2\theta'^2 + z'^2,$$

and therefore Equation 81-2 becomes

(81-3)
$$L = \int_a^b \sqrt{r'^2 + r^2\theta'^2 + z'^2}\, dt.$$

Example 81-2. Find the length of the arc with parametric equations $r = 2e^t$, $\theta = t$, $z = e^t$, $t \in [0, 1]$.

Solution. Here we have

$$r'^2 = 4e^{2t}, \quad r^2 = 4e^{2t}, \quad \theta'^2 = 1, \quad \text{and} \quad z'^2 = e^{2t}.$$

Thus Formula 81-3 tells us that the length of our arc is

$$L = \int_0^1 \sqrt{4e^{2t} + 4e^{2t} + e^{2t}}\, dt$$

$$= \int_0^1 3e^t\, dt = 3(e - 1).$$

Again let (x, y, z) be the cartesian coordinates of a point P and let r and θ, $r \geq 0$, be polar coordinates of the point $(x, y, 0)$ in the XY-plane. Suppose the position vector OP and k make an angle of ϕ, where $0 \leq \phi \leq \pi$, and let $|OP| = \rho$ (see Fig. 81-3). Then the numbers (ρ, θ, ϕ) are called **spherical coordinates** of P. We see that $z = OP \cdot k = \rho \cos \phi$. Furthermore, $k \times OP = k \times (xi + yj + zk) = xj - yi$, so

$$\rho \sin \phi = |k \times OP| = \sqrt{x^2 + y^2} = r.$$

When we substitute this result in the equations $x = r \cos \theta$ and $y = r \sin \theta$, we obtain the first two of the following relations between our spherical coordinates and the cartesian coordinates of the point P:

(81-4)
$$x = \rho \cos \theta \sin \phi,$$
$$y = \rho \sin \theta \sin \phi,$$
$$z = \rho \cos \phi.$$

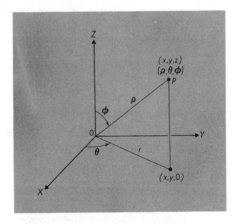

Figure 81-3

In our spherical coordinate system, the coordinate surface $\{(\rho, \theta, \phi) \mid \theta = a\}$ is a plane that contains the Z-axis. The coordinate surface $\{(\rho, \theta, \phi) \mid \phi = b\}$ is a cone whose vertex is the origin (unless $b = 0$, $b = \pi$ or $b = \pi/2$, in which case the cone "degenerates"). The coordinate surface $\{(\rho, \theta, \phi) \mid \rho = c$, where $c > 0\}$ is a sphere; it is from this fact that the name spherical coordinates is derived.

Of course, a space curve may be represented by parametric equations in spherical coordinates. For example, the parametric equations

$$(81\text{-}5) \qquad \rho = t, \quad \theta = t, \quad \phi = \frac{\pi}{4}, \qquad t \in [0, \infty],$$

represent a curve that lies in the cone $\phi = \pi/4$ and winds around this cone in much the same manner that a helix winds around a cylinder (see Example 79-1).

To find a formula for the length of the arc with parametric equations

$$\rho = f(t), \quad \theta = g(t), \quad \phi = h(t), \quad t \in [a, b],$$

we must express x', y', and z' in terms of ρ', θ', and ϕ' and then substitute these expressions in Equation 81-2. When we differentiate both sides of each of Equations 81-4, we obtain

$$x' = \rho' \cos \theta \sin \phi - \rho\theta' \sin \theta \sin \phi + \rho\phi' \cos \theta \cos \phi,$$
$$y' = \rho' \sin \theta \sin \phi + \rho\theta' \cos \theta \sin \phi + \rho\phi' \sin \theta \cos \phi,$$
$$z' = \rho' \cos \phi - \rho\phi' \sin \phi.$$

It is now a simple matter of elementary trigonometry and algebra to show that

$$x'^2 + y'^2 + z'^2 = \rho'^2 + (\rho^2 \sin^2 \phi)\theta'^2 + \rho^2\phi'^2.$$

We substitute this result in Equation 81-2 to obtain the arclength formula

$$(81\text{-}6) \qquad L = \int_a^b \sqrt{\rho'^2 + (\rho^2 \sin^2 \phi)\theta'^2 + \rho^2\phi'^2}\ dt.$$

Example 81-3. Find the length of the first winding of the conical helix given by Equations 81-5; that is, find the length of the arc that corresponds to the parameter interval $[0, 2\pi]$.

Solution. Here we have

$$\phi' = 0, \quad \rho' = \theta' = 1, \quad \sin^2 \phi = \tfrac{1}{2}, \quad \text{and} \quad \rho = t.$$

Therefore, Formula 81-6 becomes

$$L = \int_0^{2\pi} \sqrt{1 + \tfrac{1}{2}t^2}\ dt$$

$$= \frac{1}{\sqrt{2}} \int_0^{2\pi} \sqrt{t^2 + 2}\ dt.$$

We use Integration Formula V-31 to evaluate this integral, and we find that

$$L = \pi\sqrt{2\pi^2 + 1} + \frac{1}{\sqrt{2}}\ln(\pi\sqrt{2} + \sqrt{2\pi^2 + 1}) \approx 16.$$

P R O B L E M S   8 1

1. Plot the points with the given cylindrical coordinates. Find their cartesian coordinates, find another set of cylindrical coordinates, and find a set of spherical coordinates.
   (a) $(2, 30°, -2)$ (b) $(0, 90°, 5)$ (c) (π, π, π) (d) $(-3, 45°, -3)$

2. (a) Find the formula for the distance between two points with cylindrical coordinates (r_1, θ_1, z_1) and (r_2, θ_2, z_2).
   (b) Find the formula for the distance between two points with spherical coordinates $(\rho_1, \theta_1, \phi_1)$ and $(\rho_2, \theta_2, \phi_2)$.

3. The following equations are written in terms of cylindrical coordinates. Describe their graphs. In some cases you may want to write an equivalent equation in cartesian coordinates to make use of your previous knowledge of graphs.
   (a) $z = 2r^2$ (b) $\dfrac{r^2}{4} + \dfrac{z^2}{9} = 1$ (c) $3r\cos\theta + r\sin\theta + z = 2$
   (d) $z = \sin r$ (e) $z = [\![r]\!]$ (f) $r = [\![z]\!]$

4. The following equations are written in terms of spherical coordinates. Describe their graphs.
   (a) $\rho = 3$ (b) $[\![\rho]\!] = 3$ (c) $\rho\cos\phi = 5$ (d) $\rho\sin\phi = 5$
   (e) $\rho = 2\cos\phi$ (f) $\rho = 2\sin\phi$ (g) $\rho = [\![\sin\phi]\!]$ (h) $[\![\rho]\!] = \sin\phi$

5. What can you say about the graph of an equation in cylindrical or spherical coordinates that does not contain θ (as in Numbers 3(a) and 4)?

6. Express the following equations in cylindrical and in spherical coordinates.
   (a) $x^2 + y^2 = z$ (b) $3x + 4y + 5z = 6$
   (c) $x^2 + y^2 + z^2 - 4z = 0$ (d) $(x^2 + y^2 + z^2)^2 = 4(1 - z^2)$

7. Verify the equations that we used in the derivations of Equations 81-3 and 81-6:
   (a) $x'^2 + y'^2 + z'^2 = r'^2 + r^2\theta'^2 + z'^2$ (cylindrical coordinates)
   (b) $x'^2 + y'^2 + z'^2 = \rho'^2 + \rho^2\theta'^2\sin^2\phi + \rho^2\phi'^2$ (spherical coordinates)

8. Find the lengths of the curves with the following parametric equations in cylindrical coordinates.
   (a) $r = 5\cos t, \ \theta = \sec t, \ z = 5\sin t, \ t \in [0, \pi/6]$
   (b) $r = \cos t, \ \theta = \sqrt{2}\sec t, \ z = \sec t, \ t \in [0, \pi/4]$

9. Find parametric equations in cylindrical coordinates that represent the curve of intersection of the surfaces $\rho = 2$ and $\rho\sin^2\phi = 3\cos\phi$. How long is this curve?

10. Find the length of the curve with parametric equations in spherical coordinates of $\rho = 1, \ \theta = k\ln(\sec t + \tan t), \ \phi = \tfrac{1}{2}\pi - t, \ t \in [0, \tfrac{1}{2}\pi)$. Describe this curve.

REVIEW PROBLEMS—CHAPTER NINE

You can use these questions to test yourself on the material covered in this chapter.

1. Suppose that the coordinates of point P are (3, 4, 5). What are the coordinates of the points Q, R, S, and T, where Q is symmetric to P with respect to the plane $z = 1$, R is symmetric to P with respect to the plane $x = -2$, S is symmetric to P with respect to the point (1, 2, 3), and T is symmetric to P with respect to the plane $x + y = 0$?

2. Let $P(-1, -2, -3)$, $Q(-3, 2, 4)$, and $R(2, -1, 0)$ be three points in space. Find the point S such that $PQRS$ is the parallelogram in which Q and S are opposite vertices.

3. Suppose that A and B are non-parallel vectors. Find a number t such that the vectors $(1 - t)A + tB$ and $3A + 4B$ are parallel.

4. Convince yourself that the equation $(A \times B) \times (C \times D) = 0$ means that the vectors A, B, C, and D are parallel to the same plane (or that $A \parallel B$ or $C \parallel D$).

5. What is the equation of the plane that intersects the coordinate axes in the points $(a, 0, 0)$, $(0, b, 0)$, and $(0, 0, c)$?

6. Suppose that along the line $x + y = 1$ in the XY-plane we move a line that is parallel to the vector $i + j + k$. What is the equation of the plane that the moving line generates?

7. Show that if a certain surface is a surface of revolution about *both* the X-axis and the Y-axis, then it must be a sphere whose center is the origin.

8. At what point of the graph of the vector equation

$$R = (3t + 1)i + 2t^2j + (6t - 1)k$$

is the tangent vector parallel to the vector $i + 4j + 2k$?

9. Find a vector equation of the line that is tangent to the space curve whose equation is $R = F(t)$ at the point at which $t = a$. Find the equation of the plane that is perpendicular to the line at this point.

10. Let $P(a, \theta, \phi)$ be a point of the sphere $\rho = a$, and extend the segment OP until it intersects the cylinder $r = a$. What are the cylindrical coordinates of the point of intersection?

11. What is the distance between two parallel planes $ax + by + cz + d = 0$ and $ax + by + cz + e = 0$?

12. Sketch the graphs of the following equations.

(a) $\left[\dfrac{x^2}{25} + \dfrac{y^2}{16} + \dfrac{z^2}{5}\right] = 1$

(b) $\left[\dfrac{x^2}{25} + \dfrac{y^2}{16} - \dfrac{z^2}{9}\right] = 1$

(c) $\dfrac{x\,|x|}{25} + \dfrac{y\,|y|}{16} + \dfrac{z\,|z|}{9} = 1$

(d) $[x^2 + y^2 - z^2] = 0$

13. Show that if $R = F(t)$ and $R = G(t)$ are two solutions of the differential equation $R' = A \times R$, where A is a given constant vector, then $D_t[F(t) \cdot G(t)] = 0$.

14. Consider the vector equation $A \times X = B$, where A and B are given vectors (with $A \neq 0$), and we are to solve for X. Show that this equation does not have a solution if $A \cdot B \neq 0$. If $A \cdot B = 0$, show that $X = \dfrac{B \times A}{|A|^2}$ is a solution (use the formula of Problem 75-3). Explain why we can add a scalar multiple of A to a solution and obtain another solution. Can every solution be written as $X = rA + \dfrac{B \times A}{|A|^2}$ for some scalar r?

LINEAR SYSTEMS

AND MATRICES

T E N

In the preceding two chapters, we considered the vectors we were dealing with to be "arrows" in the plane or in space. As we pointed out in Section 68, when we introduce the idea of adding such vectors and multiplying them by scalars we obtain a **vector space**, a mathematical system in which the rules of arithmetic represented by Equations 68-1 to 68-5 are valid. In this chapter we are going to introduce arithmetic operations into our sets R^2, R^3, and so on, that turn these sets into vector spaces. Then we will use these spaces to help us in our study of analytic geometry. We will start with a study of systems of linear equations, where the idea of turning R^2 and R^3 into vector spaces arises in a natural way.

494

82 SYSTEMS OF LINEAR EQUATIONS. TRIANGULAR FORM

A **linear equation** in n unknowns $x_1, \ldots, x_n$ has the form

$$a_1 x_1 + \cdots + a_n x_n = b$$

where $a_1, \ldots, a_n$ and b are given numbers. For example,

$$3x - 4y = 5,$$

$$5s - 46t + 7u = 9,$$

and
$$43x_1 - 57x_2 + 4x_3 - x_4 = 29$$

are linear equations in two, three, and four unknowns, respectively. In this section we will be concerned with methods by which we can solve a system of n linear equations in n unknowns. A **solution** of a system of equations in n unknowns consists of a set of n numbers that satisfy all the equations of the system. For example, you can readily verify by substitution that the three numbers $x_1 = 1$, $x_2 = 0$, and $x_3 = 2$ satisfy each of the equations of the system

$$
\begin{aligned}
3x_1 - 4x_2 + x_3 &= 5 \\
6x_1 - 8x_2 - 2x_3 &= 2 \\
x_1 + 3x_2 - x_3 &= -1.
\end{aligned}
$$

(82-1)

We shall often write our solution as $(x_1, x_2, x_3) = (1, 0, 2)$; that is, we consider the solution to be an element of R^3.

Definition 82-1. *Two systems of linear equations are* **equivalent** *if every solution of one system is also a solution of the other.*

The systems
$$
\begin{aligned}
7x + 3y &= 4 \\
x + y &= 0,
\end{aligned}
$$

and
$$
\begin{aligned}
x &= 1 \\
x + y &= 0,
\end{aligned}
$$

for example, are equivalent, since the only solution of each system is the number pair $(x, y) = (1, -1)$.

When confronted with a system of linear equations, we shall try to replace it with an equivalent system that is easier to solve. Any time we perform one of the following operations on a system of linear equations to obtain a new system of equations we obtain a system that is equivalent to the original system.

Operation 82-1. Interchange the position of two equations.

Operation 82-2. Replace an equation with a non-zero multiple of itself. (A multiple of an equation is the equation that results when we multiply both sides of the equation by the same number.)

Operation 82-3. Replace an equation with the sum of a non-zero multiple of itself and a multiple of another equation of the system. (Adding two equations means, of course, adding the corresponding sides of the equations.)

Let us illustrate these three operations by applying each to System 82-1. As an example of Operation 82-1, we will interchange the positions of the first and third equations of System 82-1 to obtain the system

$$
\begin{aligned}
x_1 + 3x_2 - x_3 &= -1 \\
6x_1 - 8x_2 - 2x_3 &= 2 \\
3x_1 - 4x_2 + x_3 &= 5.
\end{aligned}
$$

(82-2)

As an example of Operation 82-2, let us replace the second equation of System 82-1 with the equation that results from multiplying the second equation by $\frac{1}{2}$ to obtain the system

$$
\begin{aligned}
3x_1 - 4x_2 + x_3 &= 5 \\
3x_1 - 4x_2 - x_3 &= 1 \\
x_1 + 3x_2 - x_3 &= -1.
\end{aligned}
$$

(82-3)

As an example of Operation 82-3, let us replace the second equation of System 82-1 with the sum of three times the second equation and eight times the third equation to obtain the system

$$
\begin{aligned}
3x_1 - 4x_2 + x_3 &= 5 \\
26x_1 - 14x_3 &= -2 \\
x_1 + 3x_2 - x_3 &= -1.
\end{aligned}
$$

(82-4)

Each of the Systems 82-2, 82-3, and 82-4 is equivalent to System 82-1.

In elementary algebra we solved two linear equations in two unknowns by first eliminating one of the unknowns. This method is basically a scheme for replacing one system of two linear equations with an equivalent system of equations that is easier to solve. To illustrate, let us consider an example.

Example 82-1. Solve the system of equations

$$
\begin{aligned}
2x + 3y &= 4 \\
3x - y &= -5.
\end{aligned}
$$

(82-5)

Solution. If we multiply the second equation by 3 and add it to the first, we obtain an equation in x alone. We can replace the first equation of our system with this equation in x alone and obtain the equivalent system

(82-6)
$$11x = -11$$
$$3x - y = -5.$$

System 82-6 is easy to solve; we find $x = -1$ from the first equation and then substitute $x = -1$ in the second equation to find $y = 2$. Since System 82-6 is equivalent to System 82-5, we conclude that the solution of System 82-5 is $(x, y) = (-1, 2)$.

System 82-6 is in what is called *triangular* form. A system of n linear equations in n unknowns is said to be in **triangular form** if the first equation involves only x_1; the second equation involves x_2 and perhaps x_1, but not x_3, x_4, ..., and x_n; the third equation involves x_3 and perhaps x_1 and x_2, but not x_4, ..., x_n; and so on. The following system, for example, is in triangular form:

(82-7)
$$2x = 4$$
$$3x - 2y = 8$$
$$x + y - 4z = 1.$$

From the first equation of this system it is apparent that $x = 2$. Once we know that $x = 2$, it is clear from the second equation that $y = -1$, and then we can solve the third equation to find $z = 0$. Thus the solution of System 82-7 is $(x, y, z) = (2, -1, 0)$.

It is easy to solve a system of equations that is in triangular form, so we adopt the following method of solving a system of linear equations. *By using Operations 82-1, 82-2, and 82-3, we try to replace a given system of linear equations with an equivalent system that is in triangular form.* "Most" systems can be reduced to triangular form in this way, and, as we shall see in the next section, our efforts will not be wasted if we attempt the reduction on a system that is not equivalent to a system in triangular form. We can best describe the procedure by applying it to some typical examples.

Example 82-2. Solve the system of equations

(82-8)
$$\tfrac{1}{2}x - \tfrac{2}{3}y + z = \tfrac{8}{3}$$
$$2x - y + z = 6$$
$$3x + 2y = 4.$$

Solution. To simplify things, we multiply the first equation by 6 and interchange the order of the equations to obtain

$$3x + 2y \qquad = 4$$
$$3x - 4y + 6z = 16$$
$$2x - y \ + z \ = 6.$$

Now we multiply the third equation by 6 and subtract it from the second to obtain a system in which z is missing from the second equation:

$$3x + 2y \qquad = 4$$
(82-9) $\qquad -9x + 2y \qquad = -20$
$$2x - y + z = 6.$$

Next we get an equivalent system in triangular form by subtracting the second of Equations 82-9 from the first:

$$12x \qquad\qquad = 24$$
(82-10) $\qquad -9x + 2y \qquad = -20$
$$2x - y + z = 6.$$

System 82-10 easily yields the solution $(x, y, z) = (2, -1, 1)$.

Example 82-3. Solve the system

$$x - 6y + 2z = 5$$
$$2x - 3y + z \ = 4$$
$$3x + 4y - z \ = -2.$$

Solution. When we add the third equation to the second, and twice the third equation to the first, we get the equivalent system

$$7x + 2y \qquad = 1$$
(82-11) $\qquad 5x + y \qquad = 2$
$$3x + 4y - z = -2.$$

Next we subtract twice the second of Equations 82-11 from the first to obtain the equivalent system in triangular form

$$-3x \qquad\qquad = -3$$
(82-12) $\qquad 5x + y \qquad = 2$
$$3x + 4y - z = -2.$$

We can then easily find that the solution of this system is $(x, y, z) = (1, -3, -7)$.

Notice that the last equation was used to eliminate one of the unknowns from all the other equations; then the next to the last equation was used to eliminate another unknown from the equation above it. Although this procedure stops after two steps in our example, it is clear that it is a direct method that can be used to reduce a system consisting of more linear equations in more unknowns to triangular form.

All the operations used in solving a system of linear equations are the simplest possible—multiplication, division, addition, and subtraction. But there are a lot of operations involved. In the next section we will introduce some notation that simplifies writing out the method of solution that we have introduced here.

P R O B L E M S   8 2

1. Solve the following systems of equations.

(a)
$$2x + 4y = 0$$
$$3x - 2y = 8$$

(b)
$$2x + 4y = 6$$
$$3x - 2y = -7$$

(c)
$$x - 5y = -5$$
$$2x + y = 1$$

(d)
$$x - 5y = 2$$
$$2x + y = 4$$

(e)
$$\frac{x}{3} + y = 1$$
$$x - \frac{y}{4} = \frac{2}{5}$$

(f)
$$\frac{x}{3} + y = \frac{4}{3}$$
$$x - \frac{y}{4} = \frac{3}{4}$$

2. Solve the following systems of equations.

(a)
$$x + 2y = 5$$
$$x - 2y = -3$$
$$2x + 4y - 2z = 12$$

(b)
$$x + 2y = 4$$
$$x - 2y = 0$$
$$2x + 4y - 2z = 6$$

(c)
$$x + 3y - 4z = -2$$
$$2x - y + 2z = 6$$
$$4x - 6y + z = 9$$

(d)
$$x + 3y - 4z = 2$$
$$2x - y + 2z = 1$$
$$4x - 6y + z = 9$$

(e)
$$3x - 4y + 2w = 11$$
$$2x - y + w = 5$$
$$x + 5y - z = -4$$
$$y - 3z + w = 1$$

(f)
$$3x - 4y + 2w = -7$$
$$2x - y + w = -1$$
$$x + 5y - z = 13$$
$$y - 3z + w = 7$$

3. Express x and y in terms of a, b, c, d, u, and v if

$$ax + by = u$$
$$cx + dy = v.$$

4. Solve the following "homogeneous" systems.

(a)
$$x + 3y - 4z = 0$$
$$2x - y + 2z = 0$$
$$4x - 6y + z = 0$$

(b)
$$x + 2y - 2z = 0$$
$$2x - y + z = 0$$
$$4x + y - 3z = 0$$

5. (a) Show that both $(1, 2, -1)$ and $(6, 5, -8)$ are solutions of the following system:

$$2x - y + z = -1$$
$$x + 3y + 2z = 5$$
$$x - 4y - z = -6.$$

(b) In fact, show that $(1 + 5t, 2 + 3t, -1 - 7t)$ is a solution of this system for each number t.

(c) Show that if (x, y, z) and (u, v, w) are solutions of our system, then $(x - u, y - v, z - w)$ is a solution of the system we get when we replace each of the numbers on the right-hand sides of our equations with zero.

6. Let A, B, and C denote the degree measures of the angles of a triangle. One angle is $20°$ less than the sum of the other two, and $10°$ more than the positive difference of the other two. Find the measures of the angles.

7. Show that the three lines $x - 2y - 3 = 0$, $2x + y + 1 = 0$, and $3x + 4y + 5 = 0$ intersect in a point.

8. Solve for x and y.

(a) $3[\![x]\!] - 2[\![y]\!] = -7$
     $2[\![x]\!] + 5[\![y]\!] = 8$

(b) $3|x| - 2|y| = -7$
     $2|x| + 5|y| = 8$

(c) $\log \dfrac{x^3}{y^2} = -7$
     $\log x^2 y^5 = 8$

(d) $3D_t x - 2D_t y = -7$
     $2D_t x + 5D_t y = 8$

9. To what extent can you use Operations 82-1, 82-2, and 82-3 to solve the system of inequalities

$$3x - 2y < -7$$
$$2x + 5y < 8?$$

83 MATRICES. DETERMINATIVE SYSTEMS

The process of solving a system of linear equations by reducing it to triangular form requires us to write a number of equivalent systems. We can cut down the amount of labor involved in this process by using a notation in which the symbols for the unknowns need not be copied down every time we write out a new equivalent system.

To illustrate this notation, consider the system

$$\tfrac{1}{2}x - 3y + z = 5$$

(83-1) $$x + 4y - 3z = 2$$

$$2x \qquad + \tfrac{1}{4}z = -1.$$

The coefficients of the unknowns can be exhibited as an array of numbers:

(83-2)
$$\begin{bmatrix} \frac{1}{2} & -3 & 1 \\ 1 & 4 & -3 \\ 2 & 0 & \frac{1}{4} \end{bmatrix}.$$

An array of numbers such as this one is called a **matrix**. In particular, if there are the same number of rows and columns in the array, the matrix is called a **square matrix**. The square Matrix 83-2 is the **coefficient matrix** of System 83-1. The numbers on the right-hand sides of the equations in System 83-1 can be displayed as a matrix with three rows and one column:

(83-3)
$$\begin{bmatrix} 5 \\ 2 \\ -1 \end{bmatrix}.$$

We combine the coefficient matrix with the one-column matrix of the numbers on the right-hand sides of the equations to get the **augmented matrix** of a system. The matrix

$$\left[\begin{array}{ccc|c} \frac{1}{2} & -3 & 1 & 5 \\ 1 & 4 & -3 & 2 \\ 2 & 0 & \frac{1}{4} & -1 \end{array}\right]$$

is the augmented matrix of System 83-1. (The vertical bar between the third and fourth colums is not really a part of matrix notation; we use it here to remind us that part of our matrix represents one side of a system of equations and part the other.)

We can translate the operations that we used to obtain equivalent systems of equations from a given system into operations to be performed on the rows of numbers in the augmented matrix of the system. These operations always produce a matrix of an equivalent system of equations. They can be summarized as follows.

Operation 83-1. Interchange two rows in a matrix.

Operation 83-2. Multiply all the elements of some row by the same non-zero number. (We say that we *multiply the row* by the number.)

Operation 83-3. Replace a row with the sum of a non-zero multiple of itself and a multiple of another row. (Adding two rows means, of course, adding corresponding elements.)

Example 83-1.   Use matrix notation to solve the system in Example 82-3.

Solution.   The augmented matrix of the system in Example 82-3 is

$$\left[\begin{array}{ccc|c} 1 & -6 & 2 & 5 \\ 2 & -3 & 1 & 4 \\ 3 & 4 & -1 & -2 \end{array}\right].$$

If we add the last row to the second row, and add twice the last row to the first, we obtain the matrix (of System 82-11)

$$\left[\begin{array}{ccc|c} 7 & 2 & 0 & 1 \\ 5 & 1 & 0 & 2 \\ 3 & 4 & -1 & -2 \end{array}\right].$$

Now subtracting twice the second row from the first produces the matrix

$$\left[\begin{array}{ccc|c} -3 & 0 & 0 & -3 \\ 5 & 1 & 0 & 2 \\ 3 & 4 & -1 & -2 \end{array}\right]$$

of the triangular System 82-12, from which we easily obtained the solution of the original system.

Example 83-2.   Solve the system of equations that corresponds to the matrix

(83-4)
$$\left[\begin{array}{cccc|c} 2 & -1 & 1 & -1 & -1 \\ 1 & 3 & -2 & 0 & -5 \\ 3 & -2 & 0 & 4 & 1 \\ -1 & 1 & -3 & -1 & -6 \end{array}\right].$$

Solution.   First, we multiply the last row by 4 and add to the third; then we subtract the last row from the first to produce the matrix

$$\left[\begin{array}{cccc|c} 3 & -2 & 4 & 0 & 5 \\ 1 & 3 & -2 & 0 & -5 \\ -1 & 2 & -12 & 0 & -23 \\ -1 & 1 & -3 & -1 & -6 \end{array}\right].$$

The fourth column is now in satisfactory form, so we concentrate on the first three rows and work to make the first two elements in the third column 0. We multiply the second row by 6 and subtract the third row from this new second row. Then we multiply the first row by 3 and add the third row to this new first row. These operations yield the matrix

$$\begin{bmatrix} 8 & -4 & 0 & 0 & | & -8 \\ 7 & 16 & 0 & 0 & | & -7 \\ -1 & 2 & -12 & 0 & | & -23 \\ -1 & 1 & -3 & -1 & | & -6 \end{bmatrix}.$$

Now we add the second row to 4 times the first and obtain the matrix

$$\begin{bmatrix} 39 & 0 & 0 & 0 & | & -39 \\ 7 & 16 & 0 & 0 & | & -7 \\ -1 & 2 & -12 & 0 & | & -23 \\ -1 & 1 & -3 & -1 & | & -6 \end{bmatrix}.$$

This matrix is the matrix of the system of equations in triangular form

(83-5)
$$\begin{aligned} 39x_1 &= -39 \\ 7x_1 + 16x_2 &= -7 \\ -x_1 + 2x_2 - 12x_3 &= -23 \\ -x_1 + x_2 - 3x_3 - x_4 &= -6. \end{aligned}$$

From System 83-5 we readily find that the solution is $(x_1, x_2, x_3, x_4) = (-1, 0, 2, 1)$.

For most systems of linear equations that we have seen thus far, there has been exactly one set of numbers that satisfies all the equations—that is, the system has just one solution. We will call a system of linear equations with exactly one solution a **determinative system**. Not all systems are determinative. A system may have no solution, in which case we say that the system is **inconsistent**. On the other hand, a system of n linear equations in n unknowns may have more than one solution, in which case the system is called **dependent**. The method of solving systems of linear equations by trying to reduce them to triangular form is still applicable to inconsistent and dependent systems. In fact, this method will enable us to tell when we are dealing with an inconsistent or a dependent system. The following two examples illustrate how we can detect these situations.

Example 83-3. Solve the system of equations

(83-6)
$$\begin{aligned} 2x - y + z &= 1 \\ x + 2y - z &= 3 \\ x + 7y - 4z &= 2. \end{aligned}$$

Solution. In matrix notation the steps used to reduce the system to triangular form appear as

$$
\begin{bmatrix}
2 & -1 & 1 & | & 1 \\
1 & 2 & -1 & | & 3 \\
1 & 7 & -4 & | & 2
\end{bmatrix}
\rightarrow
\begin{bmatrix}
9 & 3 & 0 & | & 6 \\
3 & 1 & 0 & | & 10 \\
1 & 7 & -4 & | & 2
\end{bmatrix}
\rightarrow
\begin{bmatrix}
0 & 0 & 0 & | & -24 \\
3 & 1 & 0 & | & 10 \\
1 & 7 & -4 & | & 2
\end{bmatrix}.
$$

The third matrix results from subtracting 3 times the second row from the first row of the second matrix. We performed this operation to remove the 3 in the first row, but in the process it also removed the 9. The final matrix can be considered as the matrix of the system

$$
\begin{aligned}
0 &= 24 \\
3x + y &= 10 \\
x + 7y - 4z &= 2.
\end{aligned}
$$

We must now interpret the presence of the false statement $0 = 24$. Logically, our argument runs as follows. *If* there is a solution of System 83-6, *then* $0 = 24$. Since $0 \neq 24$, we conclude that there simply cannot be a solution of System 83-6. The system is therefore *inconsistent*.

Example 83-4. Solve the system of equations

$$
\begin{aligned}
2x - y + z &= 1 \\
x + 2y - z &= 3 \\
x + 7y - 4z &= 8.
\end{aligned}
\tag{83-7}
$$

Solution. In this case the matrix reduction is as follows:

$$
\begin{bmatrix}
2 & -1 & 1 & | & 1 \\
1 & 2 & -1 & | & 3 \\
1 & 7 & -4 & | & 8
\end{bmatrix}
\rightarrow
\begin{bmatrix}
9 & 3 & 0 & | & 12 \\
3 & 1 & 0 & | & 4 \\
1 & 7 & -4 & | & 8
\end{bmatrix}
\rightarrow
\begin{bmatrix}
0 & 0 & 0 & | & 0 \\
3 & 1 & 0 & | & 4 \\
1 & 7 & -4 & | & 8
\end{bmatrix}.
$$

This last matrix is the matrix of the system

$$
\begin{aligned}
0 &= 0 \\
3x + y &= 4 \\
x + 7y - 4z &= 8.
\end{aligned}
\tag{83-8}
$$

Unlike Example 83-3 (which yielded $0 = 24$), the first equation here is of absolutely no help. There is nothing false about the statement that $0 = 0$, but it doesn't tell us anything we didn't already know. There are many solutions of System 83-8, and hence of System 83-7. For instance, we could take $x = 1$; then $y = 1$ and $z = 0$. Or if $x = 0$, then $y = 4$ and $z = 5$. Indeed, if t is any number, then a solution of System 83-7 is $x = t$, $y = 4 - 3t$, and $z = 5 - 5t$. System 83-7 is dependent.

If a system consists of two linear equations in two unknowns, or three linear equations in three unknowns, and if all the given numbers are real, then there is a simple way of interpreting geometrically what it means for the system to be determinative. Since a linear equation $ax + by = c$, where a, b, and c are real numbers, is the equation of a line in a plane, the *pair* of equations

$$ax + by = c$$
(83-9)
$$dx + ey = f$$

represents *two* lines in a plane. A solution of System 83-9 is a pair of real numbers, and we can interpret these numbers as the coordinates of a point that belongs to both the lines represented by System 83-9. Thus *System 83-9 is determinative if, and only if, the lines represented by that system are distinct and non-parallel and hence intersect in one point.*

A linear equation $ax + by + cz = d$, where a, b, c, and d are real numbers, is the equation of a plane in space. Thus a system of three linear equations in three unknowns represents three planes in space. The solution of such a system is a triple of real numbers, and we can interpret these numbers as the coordinates of a point in space that lies in all three of the planes represented by the system. Thus *a system of three linear equations in three unknowns is determinative if, and only if, the planes represented by that system have exactly one point in common.*

PROBLEMS 83

1. Use matrix notation to solve the following systems of equations.

(a) $2x + 3y = 7$
$\quad\ 3x - y = 5$

(b) $2x + 3y = 1$
$\quad\ 3x - y = -4$

(c) $2x + 3y = 1$
$\quad\ x + 2y = 1$

(d) $2x + 3y = -1$
$\quad\ x + 2y = -1$

(e) $\quad 2y = 6$
$\quad x - y = 1$

(f) $\quad 2y = 2$
$\quad x - y = 3$

2. Use matrix notation to solve the following systems of equations.

(a) $2x + 3y - z = -2$
$\quad x - y + 2z = 4$
$\quad x + 2y + z = 0$

(b) $2x + 3y - z = 0$
$\quad x - y + 2z = 0$
$\quad x + 2y + z = 0$

(c) $\quad x + 4y - 2z = 0$
$\quad -2x + y = 0$
$\quad\quad x - y + z = 0$

(d) $\quad x + 4y - 2z = -1$
$\quad -2x + y = 3$
$\quad\quad x - y + z = 0$

(e) $x + y = 2$
$\quad y + z = -1$
$\quad\quad z + w = 0$
$\quad x - y + z - w = 0$

(f) $x + y = 3$
$\quad y + z = 5$
$\quad\quad z + w = 7$
$\quad x - y + z - w = -2$

3. Use matrix notation to solve the following "homogeneous" systems.

(a) $\begin{aligned} 2x - y + z &= 0 \\ x + 3y + 2z &= 0 \\ x - 4y - z &= 0 \end{aligned}$ (b) $\begin{aligned} 2x - y + z &= 0 \\ x + 3y + 2z &= 0 \\ 3x + 2y + 3z &= 0 \end{aligned}$

4. The augmented matrix of a system of equations is

$$\left[\begin{array}{ccc|c} 24 & 0 & 0 & 0 \\ 1 & 2 & 0 & 2 \\ 3 & 4 & 1 & 5 \end{array} \right].$$

Is the system determinative?

5. Solve, if possible, the following systems.

(a) $\begin{aligned} 2x - 3y + z &= -4 \\ x - 4y - z &= -3 \\ x - 9y - 4z &= -5 \end{aligned}$ (b) $\begin{aligned} 2x - 3y + z &= 4 \\ x - 4y - z &= 3 \\ x - 9y - 4z &= 5 \end{aligned}$

(c) $\begin{aligned} 2x - 3y + z &= 3 \\ x - 4y - z &= 4 \\ x - 9y - 4z &= 5 \end{aligned}$ (d) $\begin{aligned} 2x - 3y + z &= 0 \\ x - 4y - z &= 0 \\ x - 9y - 4z &= 0 \end{aligned}$

6. The sum of the digits of a three-digit number is 14 and the middle digit is the sum of the other two digits. If the last two digits are interchanged, the number obtained is 27 less than the original number. Find the number. Can you solve the problem if the number obtained when the last two digits are interchanged is 72 less than the original number?

7. Consider how three planes in space can intersect (or fail to intersect). From these geometric considerations, what can you conclude about the possible solutions of a system of three linear equations in three unknowns?

8. For simplicity, we have confined our attention to systems of equations with the same number of unknowns as equations. Nothing we have done so far requires us to make this restriction. If we have a different number of equations and unknowns, our reduction technique leads to "echelon form," rather than triangular form, but there is no real conceptual difference. Solve the following systems of equations.

(a) $\begin{aligned} 3x - 2y + z &= 2 \\ x + 3y - 2z &= 2 \end{aligned}$ (b) $\begin{aligned} 3x + y &= 4 \\ 2x - 3y &= -1 \\ x - 2y &= -1 \end{aligned}$ (c) $\begin{aligned} 3x + y &= -1 \\ 2x - 3y &= 4 \\ x - 2y &= -1 \end{aligned}$

(d) $\begin{aligned} x_1 + x_2 + x_3 + x_4 + x_5 + x_6 + x_7 + x_8 &= 2 \\ x_1 - x_2 + x_3 - x_4 + x_5 - x_6 + x_7 - x_8 &= 0 \end{aligned}$

9. Can you convince yourself that a system of two linear equations in three unknowns always has either infinitely many solutions or no solutions? Can you convince yourself that a system of two homogeneous (right-hand side is 0) linear equations in three unknowns always has solutions in addition to the "trivial" solution $(0, 0, 0)$?

10. Discuss the problem of finding the coefficients a, b, and c so that the graph of the polynomial equation $y = ax^2 + bx + c$ contains three given points (x_1, y_1), (x_2, y_2) and (x_3, y_3).

11. Find a simple function f such that $f(1) = 1$, $f'(1) = 2$, $f''(1) = 3$, and $f'''(1) = 4$.

12. Discuss the solution of the equation $A \times X = P$, where $A = a\mathbf{i} + b\mathbf{j} + c\mathbf{k}$ and $P = p\mathbf{i} + q\mathbf{j} + r\mathbf{k}$ are given vectors, and $X = x\mathbf{i} + y\mathbf{j} + z\mathbf{k}$ is the vector we are to find. See Number 15 of the Review Problems for Chapter 9.

84 VECTORS AND MATRICES

An element of R^3 is a triple of real numbers; for example, $(1, -3, \pi)$ and $(0, 0, -2)$ are elements of R^3. We will sometimes find it a notational convenience to write these triples as columns, $\begin{pmatrix} 1 \\ -3 \\ \pi \end{pmatrix}$ and $\begin{pmatrix} 0 \\ 0 \\ -2 \end{pmatrix}$, instead of rows. This variation in notation represents no conceptual change. We still are dealing with triples of numbers and hence elements of R^3. The column notation merely helps us perform more easily some of the rules of calculating with vectors and matrices that we will introduce later in the section.

From our present point of view, R^3 is just a set. It has no arithmetic or other mathematical structure. We now introduce arithmetic into R^3 by means of the following definition. Because we are here thinking of elements of R^3 as individual entities, we use a single boldface letter, rather than a triple, to represent an element of R^3. We use the same notation for elements of R^2, R^4, and so on; you can tell from the context whether a stands for (a_1, a_2, a_3), (a_1, a_2), or whatever. The numbers a_1, a_2, and a_3 are the **components** of the element (a_1, a_2, a_3) of R^3.

Definition 84-1. *If $a = (a_1, a_2, a_3)$ and $b = (b_1, b_2, b_3)$ are two elements of R^3 and r is a real number, then*

$$a + b = (a_1 + b_1, a_2 + b_2, a_3 + b_3) \text{ and } ra = (ra_1, ra_2, ra_3).$$

It is a simple matter to show that $a + b = b + a$, and, for any elements a, b, and c, $(a + b) + c = a + (b + c)$. The element $0 = (0, 0, 0)$ plays the role of 0; that is, for any element a, we have $a + 0 = 0 + a = a$. The negative of an element $a = (a_1, a_2, a_3)$ is the element $-a = (-a_1, -a_2, -a_3)$, and we see that $a + (-a) = (-a) + a = 0$. Finally, there is no difficulty in verifying that Equations 68-5 are valid. Thus, when we introduce the arithmetic operations of Definition 84-1, our *set R^3* becomes a *vector space*, and when we have these operations in mind, we speak of the elements of R^3 as vectors.

While our definition is written in terms of R^3, it is perfectly clear that the same sort of thing could be done to make a vector space out of R^2, R^4, R^{1492}, and so on. In this chapter we are going to write our formulas in terms of vectors from

R^2 or R^3 because we are mainly interested in the applications of our theory to problems in the geometry of two- or three-dimensional space. In addition, formulas that involve only two or three components are easier to write out explicitly than those which contain a larger number of components. But all our work can also be carried out in higher dimensions.

In addition to the arithmetic operations of Definition 84-1, we want to introduce, in an abstract sense, the idea of distance and direction into our vector space R^3. The dot product of two geometric vectors $A = A_x i + A_y j + A_z k$ and $B = B_x i + B_y j + B_z k$ is the number

$$A \cdot B = |A| \, |B| \cos \theta = A_x B_x + A_y B_y + A_z B_z,$$

where the geometric vectors A and B determine the angle of θ. We use this product as a model to define the **dot product** of the vectors $a = (a_1, a_2, a_3)$ and $b = (b_1, b_2, b_3)$ of R^3 by means of the equation

$$(84\text{-}1) \qquad\qquad a \cdot b = a_1 b_1 + a_2 b_2 + a_3 b_3.$$

The dot product of two elements of R^n is defined similarly when n is different from 3. As the geometric case suggests, if the dot product $a \cdot b$ is 0, we say that the vectors a and b are **perpendicular** or **orthogonal**. We speak of the number $|a| = \sqrt{a \cdot a}$ as the **length** of the vector a. It is easy to verify the following rules of arithmetic for the dot product. Here we assume that a, b, and c are elements of R^n for some positive integer n, and r is a number:

$$b \cdot a = a \cdot b,$$

$$a \cdot (b + c) = a \cdot b + a \cdot c,$$

$$(84\text{-}2)$$

$$(ra) \cdot b = r(a \cdot b),$$

$$a \cdot a > 0 \text{ if } a \neq 0 \quad \text{and} \quad 0 \cdot 0 = 0.$$

Example 84-1. Verify the second of Equations 84-2 in case $a = (2, -3)$, $b = (0, 1)$, and $c = (-1, -1)$.

Solution. Here we are dealing with the vector space R^2. Since $b + c = (-1, 0)$, we see that $a \cdot (b + c) = 2(-1) + (-3) \cdot 0 = -2$. On the other hand, $a \cdot b = -3$ and $a \cdot c = 1$, so $a \cdot b + a \cdot c = -3 + 1 = -2$, and our equation is checked.

Example 84-2. Show that, for any three vectors a, b, and c, the vector $(a \cdot c)b - (a \cdot b)c$ is orthogonal to a. (Of course, we define the difference of two vectors, $u - v$, as $u + (-v)$.)

Solution. We leave it to you to decide which of Equations 84-2 and our other rules of arithmetic we use as we go through the following steps:

$$[(a \cdot c)b - (a \cdot b)c] \cdot a = (a \cdot c)(b \cdot a) - (a \cdot b)(c \cdot a)$$
$$= (a \cdot c)(a \cdot b) - (a \cdot c)(a \cdot b)$$
$$= 0.$$

Thus the dot product of our given vectors is 0, and so, by definition, the vectors are orthogonal.

A capital letter, such as A, will denote a square matrix. Because we will be working in 2 or 3 dimensions, we will mostly consider only 2 by 2 or 3 by 3 matrices; that is, matrices of *order* 2 or *order* 3. The number in row i and column j of the matrix A will be denoted by a_{ij}. Thus, for example, we write

$$A = \begin{bmatrix} a_{11} & a_{12} & a_{13} \\ a_{21} & a_{22} & a_{23} \\ a_{31} & a_{32} & a_{33} \end{bmatrix}.$$

The rows and columns of a matrix can be regarded as vectors. Thus we can write our matrix A as

$$A = \begin{bmatrix} r_1 \\ r_2 \\ r_3 \end{bmatrix} = [c_1, c_2, c_3],$$

where

$$r_1 = (a_{11}, a_{12}, a_{13}), r_2 = (a_{21}, a_{22}, a_{23}), \text{ and } r_3 = (a_{31}, a_{32}, a_{33})$$

are the row vectors of A, and

$$c_1 = \begin{pmatrix} a_{11} \\ a_{21} \\ a_{31} \end{pmatrix}, \quad c_2 = \begin{pmatrix} a_{12} \\ a_{22} \\ a_{32} \end{pmatrix}, \quad \text{and} \quad c_3 = \begin{pmatrix} a_{13} \\ a_{23} \\ a_{33} \end{pmatrix}$$

are the column vectors of A.

Example 84-3. Compute the dot product of the first row vector and the second column vector of the matrix $\begin{bmatrix} 2 & -1 \\ 3 & 2 \end{bmatrix}$.

Solution. Here $r_1 = (2, -1)$ and $c_2 = \begin{pmatrix} -1 \\ 2 \end{pmatrix}$. Thus, $r_1 \cdot c_2 = -2 - 2 = -4$.

We will now define the product of a vector by a matrix. As usual, we will confine ourselves to three dimensions; the extension to other dimensions is self-evident. So suppose we are given a 3 by 3 matrix A and a vector $x \in R^3$. The product Ax will be a vector; that is, an element of R^3, so we must give the rule that assigns its three components. It is customary in this situation to write our vectors as columns, and we make the following definition of the product Ax:

$$(84\text{-}3) \qquad \begin{bmatrix} a_{11} & a_{12} & a_{13} \\ a_{21} & a_{22} & a_{23} \\ a_{31} & a_{32} & a_{33} \end{bmatrix} \begin{pmatrix} x_1 \\ x_2 \\ x_3 \end{pmatrix} = \begin{pmatrix} a_{11}x_1 + a_{12}x_2 + a_{13}x_3 \\ a_{21}x_1 + a_{22}x_2 + a_{23}x_3 \\ a_{31}x_1 + a_{32}x_2 + a_{33}x_3 \end{pmatrix}.$$

Example 84-4. Find Ax, when A is the matrix of Example 84-3 and $x = (3, -2)$.

Solution. Here we have

$$\begin{bmatrix} 2 & -1 \\ 3 & 2 \end{bmatrix} \begin{pmatrix} 3 \\ -2 \end{pmatrix} = \begin{pmatrix} 2 \cdot 3 + (-1)(-2) \\ 3 \cdot 3 + 2(-2) \end{pmatrix} = \begin{pmatrix} 8 \\ 5 \end{pmatrix}.$$

It is not difficult to show that for any vectors u and v and any numbers p and q, we have the "general distribution law"

$$(84\text{-}4) \qquad A(pu + qv) = pAu + qAv.$$

Notice that we have not defined (and we will not define) the symbol xA.

The concept of the product of a vector by a matrix provides us with an especially simple and useful notation for a system of linear equations. Thus suppose that we are given a matrix A and a vector $b = (b_1, b_2, b_3)$, and we seek a vector x that satisfies the matrix-vector equation

$$Ax = b.$$

This single equation between two vectors is equivalent to three equations between their components; that is (see Equation 84-3 for the components of the vector on the left-hand side), our matrix-vector equation is equivalent to the system of linear equations

$$a_{11}x_1 + a_{12}x_2 + a_{13}x_3 = b_1$$
$$a_{21}x_1 + a_{22}x_2 + a_{23}x_3 = b_2$$
$$a_{31}x_1 + a_{32}x_2 + a_{33}x_3 = b_3.$$

Clearly, we can use this scheme with matrices of arbitrary order n and vectors from R^n to represent a system of n linear equations in n unknowns as a single matrix-vector equation.

Earlier in the section we introduced algebraic operations into our set R^3; now we will take up the algebra of square matrices. To be concrete, we frame the following definitions in terms of 3 by 3 matrices, but they extend to matrices of other orders in an obvious manner.

Definition 84-2. *If* $A = \begin{bmatrix} a_{11} & a_{12} & a_{13} \\ a_{21} & a_{22} & a_{23} \\ a_{31} & a_{32} & a_{33} \end{bmatrix}$ *and* $B = \begin{bmatrix} b_{11} & b_{12} & b_{13} \\ b_{21} & b_{22} & b_{23} \\ b_{31} & b_{32} & b_{33} \end{bmatrix}$ *are 3 by 3*

matrices and r is a number, then

$$A + B = \begin{bmatrix} a_{11} + b_{11} & a_{12} + b_{12} & a_{13} + b_{13} \\ a_{21} + b_{21} & a_{22} + b_{22} & a_{23} + b_{23} \\ a_{31} + b_{31} & a_{32} + b_{32} & a_{33} + b_{33} \end{bmatrix} \quad and \quad rA = \begin{bmatrix} ra_{11} & ra_{12} & ra_{13} \\ ra_{21} & ra_{22} & ra_{23} \\ ra_{31} & ra_{32} & ra_{33} \end{bmatrix}.$$

The matrix 0, called the **zero matrix** and defined by the equation

$$0 = \begin{bmatrix} 0 & 0 & 0 \\ 0 & 0 & 0 \\ 0 & 0 & 0 \end{bmatrix},$$

plays the role of zero in our algebra. Thus $0 + A = A + 0 = A$. If we define $-A = (-1)A$, and $A - B = A + (-B)$, then $A - A = 0$. It is not hard to show that the "natural" rules of arithmetic hold, so that, for example,

$$A + B = B + A, \; A + (B + C) = (A + B) + C,$$
$$r(A + B) = rA + rB, \quad and \quad (p + q)A = pA + qA.$$

Multiplication of matrices is more complicated. We define the product AB as the matrix whose column vectors are obtained by multiplying the column vectors of B by the matrix A. Thus if c_1, c_2, and c_3 are the column vectors of B, we define the product AB by the equation

$$AB = [Ac_1, Ac_2, Ac_3].$$

We use Equation 84-3 to compute the components of these column vectors. For example, in the case of 2 by 2 matrices, our multiplication rule reads

$$(84\text{-}5) \qquad \begin{bmatrix} a_{11} & a_{12} \\ a_{21} & a_{22} \end{bmatrix} \begin{bmatrix} b_{11} & b_{12} \\ b_{21} & b_{22} \end{bmatrix} = \begin{bmatrix} a_{11}b_{11} + a_{12}b_{21} & a_{11}b_{12} + a_{12}b_{22} \\ a_{21}b_{11} + a_{22}b_{21} & a_{21}b_{12} + a_{22}b_{22} \end{bmatrix}.$$

Example 84-5.   Compute both AB and BA if

$$A = \begin{bmatrix} 2 & -1 \\ -4 & 2 \end{bmatrix} \quad \text{and} \quad B = \begin{bmatrix} 1 & 5 \\ 2 & 10 \end{bmatrix}.$$

Solution.   According to Equation 84-5, we have

$$AB = \begin{bmatrix} 2 & -1 \\ -4 & 2 \end{bmatrix} \begin{bmatrix} 1 & 5 \\ 2 & 10 \end{bmatrix} = \begin{bmatrix} 2 \cdot 1 + (-1)2 & 2 \cdot 5 + (-1)10 \\ (-4)1 + 2 \cdot 2 & (-4)5 + 2 \cdot 10 \end{bmatrix} = \begin{bmatrix} 0 & 0 \\ 0 & 0 \end{bmatrix}$$

and

$$BA = \begin{bmatrix} 1 & 5 \\ 2 & 10 \end{bmatrix} \begin{bmatrix} 2 & -1 \\ -4 & 2 \end{bmatrix} = \begin{bmatrix} 1 \cdot 2 + 5(-4) & 1(-1) + 5 \cdot 2 \\ 2 \cdot 2 + 10(-4) & 2(-1) + 10 \cdot 2 \end{bmatrix}$$

$$= \begin{bmatrix} -18 & 9 \\ -36 & 18 \end{bmatrix}.$$

The preceding example shows that *it is not always true that AB and BA are equal.* Moreover, it is possible that $AB = 0$ without either A or B being the 0 matrix. Most of the other rules of the arithmetic of multiplication, however, are valid for matrices. Thus, for example,

$$A(BC) = (AB)C \quad \text{and} \quad A(B + C) = AB + BC.$$

Furthermore,

$$(AB)x = A(Bx) \quad \text{and} \quad (A + B)x = Ax + Bx.$$

These statements can be proved by writing the various expressions in terms of the components of the vectors and matrices involved.

The matrix I that is defined by the equation

$$I = \begin{bmatrix} 1 & 0 & 0 \\ 0 & 1 & 0 \\ 0 & 0 & 1 \end{bmatrix}$$

acts like the number 1 of our real number system. Thus

$$IA = AI = A \quad \text{and} \quad Ix = x.$$

This matrix I is called the **identity matrix.**

P R O B L E M S   8 4

1. If $a = (2, -1, 2)$ and $b = (4, 0, 3)$, calculate the following quantities.
(a) $2a - 3b$ (b) $(a - b) \cdot (a + b)$ (c) $|a| |b| - a \cdot b$ (d) $(3a) \cdot (3b) - 3(a \cdot b)$

2. Compute the following products.

(a) $\begin{bmatrix} 1 & 2 \\ -1 & 3 \end{bmatrix} \begin{pmatrix} 2 \\ 0 \end{pmatrix}$

(b) $\begin{bmatrix} 1 & 7 \\ 6 & 4 \end{bmatrix} \begin{bmatrix} -1 & 0 \\ 2 & 0 \end{bmatrix}$

(c) $\begin{bmatrix} 2 & 5 & -1 \\ 6 & 0 & 2 \\ 1 & 3 & 4 \end{bmatrix} \begin{pmatrix} 1 \\ -1 \\ 2 \end{pmatrix}$

(d) $\begin{bmatrix} -1 & 0 & 1 \\ 2 & 5 & -3 \\ 4 & 1 & -1 \end{bmatrix} \begin{bmatrix} 0 & 2 & 6 \\ 4 & -1 & 0 \\ 2 & 2 & 1 \end{bmatrix}$

3. Let $A = \begin{bmatrix} 1 & -2 \\ 3 & 4 \end{bmatrix}$, $x = (2, 1)$, $y = (1, 1)$, and calculate the following numbers.

(a) $Ax \cdot y$ (b) $Ay \cdot x$ (c) $Ax \cdot Ay$ (d) $A^2 x \cdot y$

4. Find a vector that is orthogonal to the vector $(2, 1)$.
(b) Find a unit vector (one that is 1 unit long) that is orthogonal to the vector $(2, 1)$. How many such unit vectors are there?
(c) Find a unit vector that is orthogonal to the vectors $(2, -1, 1)$ and $(1, 0, 3)$.

5. (a) Show that any two row vectors or any two column vectors of the following matrix are orthogonal:

$$A = \begin{bmatrix} 0 & 1 & 0 \\ 0 & 0 & 1 \\ 1 & 0 & 0 \end{bmatrix}.$$

(b) Find A^2 and A^3. What is A^{4321}?

6. (a) A matrix of the form $\begin{bmatrix} a_{11} & a_{12} & a_{13} \\ 0 & a_{22} & a_{23} \\ 0 & 0 & a_{33} \end{bmatrix}$, with 0's below the "main diagonal," is

an "upper triangular" matrix. Show that the product of two upper triangular matrices is an upper triangular matrix.

(b) Find A^3 if $A = \begin{bmatrix} 0 & 1 & 2 \\ 0 & 0 & 3 \\ 0 & 0 & 0 \end{bmatrix}.$

7. Suppose that $a \in R^3$ and b and c are numbers. Show that $b(ca) = (bc)a$ and $(b + c)a = ba + ca$.

8. Suppose $S = \begin{bmatrix} 1 & 1 & 1 \\ 1 & 1 & 1 \\ 1 & 1 & 1 \end{bmatrix}.$

(a) Find S^{10}.
(b) Describe the most general matrix A such that $AS = SA$.

9. Let S be the matrix of the preceding problem, and let $x = (1, 1, 1)$, $y = (2, -1, -1)$, and $z = (0, 1, -1)$. Show that $Sx = 3x$, $Sy = 0y$, and $Sz = 0z$. Show also that $x \cdot y = 0$, $x \cdot z = 0$, and $y \cdot z = 0$.

10. Let $J = \begin{bmatrix} 0 & 1 \\ -1 & 0 \end{bmatrix}$.

    (a) Show that $J^2 = -I$.

    (b) Show that $X = 3I - 2J$ satisfies the equation $X^2 - 6X + 13I = 0$.

11. Suppose that each of the vectors u and v satisfies the equation $Ax = b$. Show that the vector $u - v$ satisfies the equation $Ax = 0$. If w satisfies the equation $Ax = 0$, show that tw satisfies the same equation for any number t. Illustrate these remarks by considering the system of equations of Problem 82-5.

12. To see one reason why matrix multiplication is defined as it is, consider the two-dimensional case. Let A and B be square matrices of order 2, and let x be a vector with two components. Show that the Associative Law $A(Bx) = (AB)x$ holds. Now, conversely, show that if C is a matrix such that $A(Bx) = Cx$ for every x, then $C = AB$.

13. A set of vectors $\{a, b, c\}$ is **linearly independent** if the equation $xa + yb + zc = 0$ holds only when $x = 0$, $y = 0$, and $z = 0$. Suppose our set is linearly independent, and let u be the vector that is obtained when we divide a by its length, v be the vector that is obtained when we divide $b - (b \cdot u)u$ by its length, and w be the vector that is obtained when we divide $c - (c \cdot u)u - (c \cdot v)v$ by its length. Show that each of the vectors u, v, and w is 1 unit long and is perpendicular to the other two.

14. Show that the set of all 2 by 2 matrices is a vector space. Find a set of four linearly independent "vectors" in this space (see the preceding problem).

85 THE INVERSE OF A MATRIX

In the preceding section we saw how to express a system of three linear equations in three unknowns in matrix-vector form

$$(85\text{-}1) \qquad\qquad Ax = b.$$

We are supposing that the coefficient matrix A and the vector b are given and the unknowns of our system are the components of x. The natural way to solve Equation 85-1 for x is to "divide" both sides by the matrix A; that is, to multiply both sides by the "reciprocal of A." So we shall use this problem to introduce the idea of the *reciprocal*, or *inverse*, of a matrix. We start with the following definition.

Definition 85-1. *The matrix A^{-1} is the **inverse** of the matrix A if*

$$(85\text{-}2) \qquad\qquad AA^{-1} = A^{-1}A = I.$$

This definition tells us that $X = A^{-1}$ satisfies the two equations $AX = I$ and $XA = I$. In Problem 85-11 we ask you to show that these equations cannot have two different solutions; in other words, if a matrix has an inverse it has only one. Therefore, in Definition 85-1 it is proper to speak of *the* inverse of a matrix, rather than *an* inverse. Furthermore, in the next section (Theorem 86-3) we will show that we need only solve the single equation $AX = I$ to find the inverse of A; the equation $XA = I$ will automatically be satisfied. From the symmetry of the definition of the inverse, it is clear that A is the inverse of A^{-1}; that is, $(A^{-1})^{-1} = A$.

Example 85-1. If $A = \begin{bmatrix} 2 & 1 \\ 1 & 1 \end{bmatrix}$, show that $A^{-1} = \begin{bmatrix} 1 & -1 \\ -1 & 2 \end{bmatrix}$.

Solution. We need only verify that

$$\begin{bmatrix} 2 & 1 \\ 1 & 1 \end{bmatrix} \begin{bmatrix} 1 & -1 \\ -1 & 2 \end{bmatrix} = \begin{bmatrix} 1 & -1 \\ -1 & 2 \end{bmatrix} \begin{bmatrix} 2 & 1 \\ 1 & 1 \end{bmatrix} = \begin{bmatrix} 1 & 0 \\ 0 & 1 \end{bmatrix}.$$

Example 85-2. Show that the matrix $A = \begin{bmatrix} 1 & 1 \\ 1 & 1 \end{bmatrix}$ does not have an inverse.

Solution. Let us take an arbitrary matrix $X = \begin{bmatrix} a & b \\ c & d \end{bmatrix}$ and consider the product AX. We have

$$AX = \begin{bmatrix} 1 & 1 \\ 1 & 1 \end{bmatrix} \begin{bmatrix} a & b \\ c & d \end{bmatrix} = \begin{bmatrix} a+c & b+d \\ a+c & b+d \end{bmatrix}.$$

It is clear that no choice of a, b, c, and d will make this product the identity matrix I. We simply cannot, for example, choose a and c so that $a + c = 1$ *and* $a + c = 0$. Therefore, we cannot solve the equation $AX = I$, and so we cannot hope to satisfy Equations 85-2.

If the matrix A has an inverse, the solution of Equation 85-1 can be expressed in terms of the inverse matrix and the given vector b. We simply multiply both sides of Equation 85-1 by A^{-1} to obtain

$$A^{-1}Ax = A^{-1}b,$$

$$Ix = A^{-1}b,$$

$$x = A^{-1}b.$$

Example 85-3. Solve the system of equations

$$2x + y = 3$$
$$x + y = -4.$$

Solution. If we express this system in the form of the matrix-vector Equation 85-1, we will have

$$A = \begin{bmatrix} 2 & 1 \\ 1 & 1 \end{bmatrix}, \quad b = \begin{pmatrix} 3 \\ -4 \end{pmatrix}, \quad \text{and} \quad x = \begin{pmatrix} x \\ y \end{pmatrix}.$$

We are given A^{-1} in Example 85-1, and therefore

$$x = A^{-1}b = \begin{bmatrix} 1 & -1 \\ -1 & 2 \end{bmatrix} \begin{pmatrix} 3 \\ -4 \end{pmatrix} = \begin{pmatrix} 7 \\ -11 \end{pmatrix}.$$

You may verify this solution by substituting $(x, y) = (7, -11)$ in the original system of equations.

Let us put aside the question of the existence of the inverse of a given matrix for the moment and turn to the question of calculating the inverse, supposing that there is one. We have seen that if a matrix A has an inverse A^{-1}, then $X = A^{-1}$ is a solution of the equation

(85-3) $AX = I.$

Suppose we denote the column vectors of the matrix X by x_1, x_2, and x_3. Then the column vectors of the matrix AX are Ax_1, Ax_2, and Ax_3, so Equation 85-3 is equivalent to the three matrix-vector equations

(85-4) $Ax_1 = \begin{pmatrix} 1 \\ 0 \\ 0 \end{pmatrix}, \quad Ax_2 = \begin{pmatrix} 0 \\ 1 \\ 0 \end{pmatrix}, \quad Ax_3 = \begin{pmatrix} 0 \\ 0 \\ 1 \end{pmatrix}.$

Each of these three matrix-vector equations is, in turn, equivalent to a system of three linear equations in three unknowns, and we can solve such systems by the methods we discussed in Section 83. In this way we can find the solution $X = A^{-1}$ of Equation 85-3.

Let us use an example to show how we actually proceed. Suppose that A is the matrix

$$A = \begin{bmatrix} 2 & 1 & 2 \\ 2 & -4 & 1 \\ 1 & 1 & 1 \end{bmatrix}.$$

Then to solve Equations 85-4 by the methods of Section 83 we "manipulate" the augmented matrices

$$
\begin{bmatrix}
2 & 1 & 2 & | & 1 \\
2 & -4 & 1 & | & 0 \\
1 & 1 & 1 & | & 0
\end{bmatrix},
\begin{bmatrix}
2 & 1 & 2 & | & 0 \\
2 & -4 & 1 & | & 1 \\
1 & 1 & 1 & | & 0
\end{bmatrix},
\quad \text{and} \quad
\begin{bmatrix}
2 & 1 & 2 & | & 0 \\
2 & -4 & 1 & | & 0 \\
1 & 1 & 1 & | & 1
\end{bmatrix}.
$$

The operations we perform on these augmented matrices are determined by the square matrix on the left of the vertical line. Since this square matrix is the same in each of the three cases, we won't treat them separately but will lump them together in the single augmented matrix

$$
\begin{bmatrix}
2 & 1 & 2 & | & 1 & 0 & 0 \\
2 & -4 & 1 & | & 0 & 1 & 0 \\
1 & 1 & 1 & | & 0 & 0 & 1
\end{bmatrix}.
$$

We treat this matrix just as we treated the augmented matrices of Section 83. By various row operations we try to reduce the matrix on the left of the vertical line to triangular form. The matrix on the right will be changed in the process, but we pay no attention to that. Thus we have

$$
\begin{bmatrix}
2 & 1 & 2 & | & 1 & 0 & 0 \\
2 & -4 & 1 & | & 0 & 1 & 0 \\
1 & 1 & 1 & | & 0 & 0 & 1
\end{bmatrix}
\rightarrow
\begin{bmatrix}
0 & -1 & 0 & | & 1 & 0 & -2 \\
1 & -5 & 0 & | & 0 & 1 & -1 \\
1 & 1 & 1 & | & 0 & 0 & 1
\end{bmatrix}
$$

(85-5)

$$
\rightarrow
\begin{bmatrix}
0 & -5 & 0 & | & 5 & 0 & -10 \\
1 & -5 & 0 & | & 0 & 1 & -1 \\
1 & 1 & 1 & | & 0 & 0 & 1
\end{bmatrix}
\rightarrow
\begin{bmatrix}
-1 & 0 & 0 & | & 5 & -1 & -9 \\
1 & -5 & 0 & | & 0 & 1 & -1 \\
1 & 1 & 1 & | & 0 & 0 & 1
\end{bmatrix}.
$$

Now we can stop and solve for the vectors x_1, x_2, and x_3. For example, if $x_1 = (u, v, w)$ the components u, v, and w satisfy the system of equations

$$
\begin{aligned}
-u &&&= 5 \\
u - 5v &&&= 0 \\
u + v + w &&&= 0,
\end{aligned}
$$

and so $x_1 = (-5, -1, 6)$. Similar calculations show that $x_2 = (1, 0, -1)$ and $x_3 = (9, 2, -10)$. It follows that the matrix

$$X = [x_1, x_2, x_3] = \begin{bmatrix} -5 & 1 & 9 \\ -1 & 0 & 2 \\ 6 & -1 & -10 \end{bmatrix}$$

satisfies the equation $AX = I$ and we have found A^{-1}.

A more elegant way to proceed is to continue Chain 85-5 until the matrix on the left of the vertical line becomes the identity matrix. To accomplish this result, we apply row operations to make the elements below the main diagonal zero, and then we multiply as necessary to make the elements that remain in the diagonal 1:

$$\left[\begin{array}{ccc|ccc} -1 & 0 & 0 & 5 & -1 & -9 \\ 1 & -5 & 0 & 0 & 1 & -1 \\ 1 & 1 & 1 & 0 & 0 & 1 \end{array}\right] \rightarrow \left[\begin{array}{ccc|ccc} -1 & 0 & 0 & 5 & -1 & -9 \\ 0 & -5 & 0 & 5 & 0 & -10 \\ 0 & 1 & 1 & 5 & -1 & -8 \end{array}\right]$$

$$\rightarrow \left[\begin{array}{ccc|ccc} -1 & 0 & 0 & 5 & -1 & -9 \\ 0 & -1 & 0 & 1 & 0 & -2 \\ 0 & 1 & 1 & 5 & -1 & -8 \end{array}\right] \rightarrow \left[\begin{array}{ccc|ccc} -1 & 0 & 0 & 5 & -1 & -9 \\ 0 & -1 & 0 & 1 & 0 & -2 \\ 0 & 0 & 1 & 6 & -1 & -10 \end{array}\right]$$

$$\rightarrow \left[\begin{array}{ccc|ccc} 1 & 0 & 0 & -5 & 1 & 9 \\ 0 & 1 & 0 & -1 & 0 & 2 \\ 0 & 0 & 1 & 6 & -1 & -10 \end{array}\right].$$

Now we see that the matrix to the right of the vertical line is A^{-1}.

We can sum up the procedure for finding the inverse of a matrix A as follows. First, form the augmented matrix

$$[A \mid I].$$

Then apply Operations 83-1, 83-2, and 83-3 until this augmented matrix takes the form

$$[I \mid A^{-1}].$$

As we indicated in our example, a systematic way to proceed is first to reduce the matrix on the left of the vertical line to triangular form. At that point our augmented matrix will look like this

$$\left[\begin{array}{ccc|ccc} d_1 & 0 & 0 & * & * & * \\ * & d_2 & 0 & * & * & * \\ * & * & d_3 & * & * & * \end{array}\right].$$

Now whether or not we can continue to reduce the matrix on the left to the identity depends on the diagonal numbers d_1, d_2, and d_3. If none of these numbers is zero, we can reduce the matrix on the left to the identity matrix; otherwise not. Thus the question of whether or not the equation $AX = I$ has a solution becomes the question of whether or not the three numbers d_1, d_2, and d_3 are all different from zero.

Let us put this criterion into different words. If we were to attempt to solve the homogeneous (we use the word "homogeneous" when the vector on the right side of the equation is the vector $\mathbf{0}$) matrix-vector equation

$$Ax = 0$$

by the methods we used in Section 83, we would set up the augmented matrix

$$[A \mid 0]$$

and reduce to triangular form

$$\begin{bmatrix} d_1 & 0 & 0 & \Big| & 0 \\ * & d_2 & 0 & \Big| & 0 \\ * & * & d_3 & \Big| & 0 \end{bmatrix}.$$

If all the numbers d_1, d_2, and d_3 are different from zero, the equation $Ax = 0$ has only the solution $x = 0$; otherwise it also has non-zero solutions. Since the numbers d_1, d_2, and d_3 are the same as those in the preceding paragraph, it follows that the matrix equation $AX = I$ has a solution if, and only if, the homogeneous matrix-vector equation $Ax = 0$ has only the "trivial" solution $x = 0$. Therefore we can state the following theorem.

Theorem 85-1. *The matrix A has an inverse if, and only if, the homogeneous matrix-vector equation $Ax = 0$ has only the "trivial" solution $x = 0$.*

Example 85-4. Show that the homogeneous system

$$\begin{aligned} 2x - y + z &= 0 \\ x - 2y + 3z &= 0 \\ 3x \quad\quad - z &= 0 \end{aligned}$$

has non-trivial solutions. What can you conclude about the existence of the inverse of the coefficient matrix?

Solution. Using matrix notation to reduce to triangular form, we have

$$\begin{bmatrix} 2 & -1 & 1 & \Big| & 0 \\ 1 & -2 & 3 & \Big| & 0 \\ 3 & 0 & -1 & \Big| & 0 \end{bmatrix} \rightarrow \begin{bmatrix} 5 & -1 & 0 & \Big| & 0 \\ 10 & -2 & 0 & \Big| & 0 \\ 3 & 0 & -1 & \Big| & 0 \end{bmatrix} \rightarrow \begin{bmatrix} 0 & 0 & 0 & \Big| & 0 \\ 10 & -2 & 0 & \Big| & 0 \\ 3 & 0 & -1 & \Big| & 0 \end{bmatrix}.$$

Thus we obtain the equivalent system

$$10x - 2y = 0$$
$$3x - z = 0.$$

These equations tell us that $y = 5x$ and $z = 3x$. We may choose x to be any number we please, and we will obtain the solution $(x, 5x, 3x)$. For example, $(1, 5, 3)$ is a non-trivial solution to our system. It follows from Theorem 85-1 that the matrix

$$\begin{bmatrix} 2 & -1 & 1 \\ 1 & -2 & 3 \\ 3 & 0 & -1 \end{bmatrix}$$

does not have an inverse.

P R O B L E M S   8 5

1. Verify that the members of the following pairs of matrices are inverses of each other.

(a) $\begin{bmatrix} 2 & 1 \\ 5 & 3 \end{bmatrix}, \begin{bmatrix} 3 & -1 \\ -5 & 2 \end{bmatrix}$

(b) $\begin{bmatrix} 1 & 0 & 0 \\ 0 & -2 & 0 \\ 0 & 0 & 3 \end{bmatrix}, \begin{bmatrix} 1 & 0 & 0 \\ 0 & -\frac{1}{2} & 0 \\ 0 & 0 & \frac{1}{3} \end{bmatrix}$

(c) $\begin{bmatrix} 0 & 0 & 1 \\ 0 & 1 & 0 \\ 1 & 0 & 0 \end{bmatrix}, \begin{bmatrix} 0 & 0 & 1 \\ 0 & 1 & 0 \\ 1 & 0 & 0 \end{bmatrix}$

(d) $\begin{bmatrix} 1 & 0 & 0 \\ 2 & 1 & 0 \\ 3 & 2 & 1 \end{bmatrix}, \begin{bmatrix} 1 & 0 & 0 \\ -2 & 1 & 0 \\ 1 & -2 & 1 \end{bmatrix}$

2. Which of the following statements are true and which false for arbitrary matrices A and B that have inverses? (To test whether a matrix X is the inverse of a matrix Y, we simply multiply them and see if we get the identity matrix I.)
(a) $(A^{-1})^{-1} = A$ (b) $(AB)^{-1} = A^{-1}B^{-1}$ (c) $(AB)^{-1} = B^{-1}A^{-1}$
(d) $(A + B)^{-1} = A^{-1} + B^{-1}$ (e) $(3A)^{-1} = 3A^{-1}$ (f) $(A^3)^{-1} = (A^{-1})^3$

3. Find the inverse of each of the following matrices.

(a) $\begin{bmatrix} \frac{2}{3} & 0 & 0 \\ 0 & -1 & 0 \\ 0 & 0 & \frac{3}{5} \end{bmatrix}$

(b) $\begin{bmatrix} 0 & 0 & 1 \\ 0 & 2 & 0 \\ 3 & 0 & 0 \end{bmatrix}$

(c) $\begin{bmatrix} 2 & 2 & 1 \\ 1 & -4 & 1 \\ 2 & 1 & 1 \end{bmatrix}$

(d) $\begin{bmatrix} 1 & 2 & 2 \\ 1 & 1 & 2 \\ 1 & -4 & 1 \end{bmatrix}$

(e) $\begin{bmatrix} 1 & 2 & 0 & 0 \\ 4 & 9 & 0 & 0 \\ 0 & 0 & -3 & 1 \\ 0 & 0 & -8 & 3 \end{bmatrix}$

(f) $\begin{bmatrix} 13 & 4 & 0 & 0 \\ 3 & 1 & 0 & 0 \\ 0 & 0 & -2 & 3 \\ 0 & 0 & -1 & 2 \end{bmatrix}$

4. Use the result of Number 3(c) to express x, y, and z in terms of u, v, and w if

$$2x + 2y + z = u$$
$$x - 4y + z = v$$
$$2x + y + z = w$$

5. (a) Find a formula for A^{-1} if $A = \begin{bmatrix} a & b \\ c & d \end{bmatrix}$.

(b) Use this formula to find the inverse of the matrices $\begin{bmatrix} 4 & 1 \\ 7 & 2 \end{bmatrix}$ and $\begin{bmatrix} 1 & 2 \\ 3 & 4 \end{bmatrix}$.

(c) Under what conditions is $A^{-1} = A$?

(d) Can you show that A has an inverse if, and only if, $ad \neq bc$?

6. Find the inverses of the following matrices.

(a) $\begin{bmatrix} 2 & 3 & -1 \\ 1 & -1 & 2 \\ 1 & 2 & 1 \end{bmatrix}$ (b) $\begin{bmatrix} -1 & 2 & 1 \\ 3 & -1 & 2 \\ 2 & 1 & 1 \end{bmatrix}$

(c) $\begin{bmatrix} 1 & 2 & -1 \\ 3 & 0 & 2 \\ 1 & 1 & 1 \end{bmatrix}$ (d) $\begin{bmatrix} 1 & 3 & 1 \\ 1 & 0 & 2 \\ 1 & 2 & -1 \end{bmatrix}$

7. Suppose that A is a matrix such that $A^4 = 0$. Show that $(I - A)^{-1} = I + A + A^2 + A^3$.

8. Suppose we are given two square matrices A and B of the same order and form the augmented matrix $[A \mid B]$. Furthermore, suppose that by applying our row operations we can reduce this matrix to the form $[I \mid C]$. What is the matrix C?

9. If $ABC = I$, is it true that $CAB = BCA$?

10. Make up an example (see Example 84-5) to show that the equation $AB = AC$ does not necessarily imply that $B = C$. What if A^{-1} exists?

11. Show that the equations $AX = XA = I$ have only one solution, if they have any.

86 THE DETERMINANT OF A MATRIX

To find the inverse of the 2 by 2 matrix

$$A = \begin{bmatrix} a_{11} & a_{12} \\ a_{21} & a_{22} \end{bmatrix}$$

we must solve the matrix equation $AX = I$. The solution

$$X = \begin{bmatrix} x_{11} & x_{12} \\ x_{21} & x_{22} \end{bmatrix}$$

will be our inverse. The single matrix equation $AX = I$ is equivalent to 4 linear equations in x_{11}, x_{12}, x_{21} and x_{22}. These equations are easily solved (Problem 85-5), and yield

$$x_{11} = \frac{a_{22}}{|A|}, \quad x_{12} = -\frac{a_{12}}{|A|}, \quad x_{21} = -\frac{a_{21}}{|A|}, \quad \text{and} \quad x_{22} = \frac{a_{11}}{|A|},$$

where we have introduced the abbreviation

$$|A| = a_{11}a_{22} - a_{12}a_{21}.$$

Thus we can write the matrix $X = A^{-1}$ in the form

$$A^{-1} = \frac{1}{|A|} \mathcal{A},$$

where $\mathcal{A}$ is the matrix

$$\mathcal{A} = \begin{bmatrix} a_{22} & -a_{12} \\ -a_{21} & a_{11} \end{bmatrix}.$$

Of course, our formula for A^{-1} makes sense only if $|A| \neq 0$. However, if we multiply A by $\mathcal{A}$ we find that

(86-1) $$A\mathcal{A} = \mathcal{A}A = |A|\, I$$

whether $|A| = 0$ or not.

The number $|A|$ is called the **determinant** of the matrix A. We denote the determinant of a matrix by vertical bars. Thus the symbols $|A|$ and $\begin{vmatrix} a_{11} & a_{12} \\ a_{21} & a_{22} \end{vmatrix}$ stand for the determinant of the matrix

$$A = \begin{bmatrix} a_{11} & a_{12} \\ a_{21} & a_{22} \end{bmatrix}.$$

In this notation

(86-2) $$|A| = \begin{vmatrix} a_{11} & a_{12} \\ a_{21} & a_{22} \end{vmatrix} = a_{11}a_{22} - a_{12}a_{21}.$$

Example 86-1. Find $\begin{vmatrix} 7 & 2 \\ 1 & -3 \end{vmatrix}$.

Solution. According to Equation 86-2,

$$\begin{vmatrix} 7 & 2 \\ 1 & -3 \end{vmatrix} = 7(-3) - 2 \cdot 1 = -21 - 2 = -23.$$

With each square matrix A, of any order, we can associate a matrix $\mathcal{A}$ and a number $|A|$ such that Equation 86-1 is valid. The details of this association are somewhat complicated, however, and we shall restrict our attention to the case of a 3 by 3 matrix

$$A = \begin{bmatrix} a_{11} & a_{12} & a_{13} \\ a_{21} & a_{22} & a_{23} \\ a_{31} & a_{32} & a_{33} \end{bmatrix}.$$

We first construct nine 2 by 2 submatrices of A as follows. *We define A_{ij} as the 2 by 2 matrix that is obtained by striking out the ith row and the jth column of the matrix A.* Thus, for example, we obtain the submatrix A_{21} by striking out the second row and the first column of A:

$$A_{21} = \begin{bmatrix} a_{12} & a_{13} \\ a_{32} & a_{33} \end{bmatrix}.$$

Now we compute the determinants of these submatrices and use these nine numbers to form our matrix $\mathcal{A}$. This matrix is defined by the equation

$$\mathcal{A} = \begin{bmatrix} |A_{11}| & -|A_{21}| & |A_{31}| \\ -|A_{12}| & |A_{22}| & -|A_{32}| \\ |A_{13}| & -|A_{23}| & |A_{33}| \end{bmatrix}.$$

This definition of $\mathcal{A}$ is completely analogous to the definition of $\mathcal{A}$ in the 2 by 2 case. By striking out rows and columns of our 2 by 2 matrix, we obtain the four submatrices $A_{11} = [a_{22}]$, $A_{12} = [a_{21}]$, $A_{21} = [a_{12}]$, and $A_{22} = [a_{11}]$. Then we define

$$\mathcal{A} = \begin{bmatrix} |A_{11}| & -|A_{21}| \\ -|A_{12}| & |A_{22}| \end{bmatrix},$$

where by the determinant of a matrix consisting of just one number we mean the number itself. Thus $|A_{11}| = a_{22}$, $|A_{12}| = a_{21}$, and so on, and we see that this formula for $\mathcal{A}$ coincides with our previous formula.

Now we return to the formula for $\mathcal{A}$ in the 3 by 3 case. If we replace $|A_{11}|$ with

$$\begin{vmatrix} a_{22} & a_{23} \\ a_{32} & a_{33} \end{vmatrix} = a_{22}a_{33} - a_{23}a_{32},$$

$|A_{12}|$ with

$$\begin{vmatrix} a_{21} & a_{23} \\ a_{31} & a_{33} \end{vmatrix} = a_{21}a_{33} - a_{23}a_{31},$$

and so on, in our expression for $\mathcal{A}$ and then multiply by the matrix A, we will obtain Equation 86-1 with

$$|A| = a_{11}a_{22}a_{33} + a_{12}a_{23}a_{31} + a_{13}a_{21}a_{32} - a_{13}a_{22}a_{31} - a_{11}a_{23}a_{32} - a_{12}a_{21}a_{33}.$$

Thus the determinant of a 3 by 3 matrix is given by the equation

$$(86\text{-}3) \quad \begin{vmatrix} a_{11} & a_{12} & a_{13} \\ a_{21} & a_{22} & a_{23} \\ a_{31} & a_{32} & a_{33} \end{vmatrix} = a_{11}a_{22}a_{33} + a_{12}a_{23}a_{31} + a_{13}a_{21}a_{32} - a_{13}a_{22}a_{31} \\ - a_{11}a_{23}a_{32} - a_{12}a_{21}a_{33}.$$

Example 86-2. Show that, in the case of our 3 by 3 matrix,

$$(86\text{-}4) \qquad\qquad |A| = a_{11}|A_{11}| - a_{12}|A_{12}| + a_{13}|A_{13}|.$$

Solution. According to Equation 86-1, the number $|A|$ appears in the first row and first column of the product $A\mathcal{A}$. But the definition of matrix multiplication tells us that this number is the first component of the product of the matrix A and the first column vector of $\mathcal{A}$. If you refer to Equation 84-3, which defines matrix-vector multiplication, you will see that this component is simply the right-hand side of Equation 86-4.

Example 86-3. Evaluate the determinant $\begin{vmatrix} 1 & 2 & 0 \\ 3 & -2 & 1 \\ -4 & 3 & 2 \end{vmatrix}$.

Solution. We use Equations 86-4 and 86-2:

$$\begin{vmatrix} 1 & 2 & 0 \\ 3 & -2 & 1 \\ -4 & 3 & 2 \end{vmatrix} = 1\begin{vmatrix} -2 & 1 \\ 3 & 2 \end{vmatrix} - 2\begin{vmatrix} 3 & 1 \\ -4 & 2 \end{vmatrix} + 0\begin{vmatrix} 3 & -2 \\ -4 & 3 \end{vmatrix}$$

$$= 1(-4 - 3) - 2(6 + 4) + 0 = -27.$$

You might use Equation 86-3 to check this result.

If A and B are square matrices of the same order, it can be shown that

$$(86\text{-}5) \qquad\qquad |AB| = |A|\,|B|.$$

Thus if we multiply the matrices A and B and then calculate the determinant of the product matrix, we get the same number that we would obtain by first calculating the determinants of A and B individually and then multiplying these numbers. In the problems at the end of the section, we will ask you to verify Equation 86-5 for 2 by 2 matrices. The verification for matrices of higher order is also perfectly straightforward but quite tedious.

From Equation 86-1 we see that if $|A| \neq 0$, then

$$A\left(\frac{1}{|A|}\mathcal{A}\right) = \frac{1}{|A|}A\mathcal{A} = I \quad \text{and} \quad \left(\frac{1}{|A|}\mathcal{A}\right)A = \frac{1}{|A|}\mathcal{A}A = I.$$

In other words, $X = (1/|A|)\mathcal{A}$ satisfies the equations $AX = I$ and $XA = I$. So *if* the determinant of a matrix is not 0, *then* the matrix has an inverse. Conversely, suppose that A^{-1} exists. Then $AA^{-1} = I$, and Equation 86-5 tells us that $|A|\,|A^{-1}| = |I|$. It is easy to see that $|I| = 1$, and so we have $|A|\,|A^{-1}| = 1$. Therefore, $|A| \neq 0$, and we have the following theorem.

Theorem 86-1.   *The matrix A has an inverse if, and only if, $|A| \neq 0$.*

This theorem enables us to prove a theorem that is basic to the study of systems of linear equations.

Theorem 86-2.   *The homogeneous matrix-vector equation $Ax = 0$ has a non-trivial solution if, and only if, $|A| = 0$.*

Proof. According to Theorem 85-1, the equation $Ax = 0$ has a non-trivial solution if, and only if, the matrix A *does not* have an inverse. But now Theorem 86-1 tells us that this condition is equivalent to the equation $|A| = 0$. Hence the equation $Ax = 0$ has a non-trivial solution if, and only if, $|A| = 0$.

Another consequence of Theorem 86-1 is the theorem that allows us to calculate an inverse by solving one, rather than two, equations.

Theorem 86-3.   *If $AX = I$, then $XA = I$.*

Proof. We use Equation 86-5 and the equation $|I| = 1$ to see that $|A| \neq 0$. Therefore, Theorem 86-1 tells us that A^{-1} exists. Now we multiply both sides of the equation $AX = I$ by A^{-1}:

$$A^{-1}(AX) = A^{-1}I,$$
$$(A^{-1}A)X = A^{-1},$$
$$X = A^{-1}.$$

Since $X = A^{-1}$, we have $XA = I$, and our proof is complete.

P R O B L E M S   8 6

1. Evaluate the following determinants.

(a) $\begin{vmatrix} 2 & 3 \\ 4 & 5 \end{vmatrix}$
(b) $\begin{vmatrix} a & 0 \\ b & c \end{vmatrix}$
(c) $\begin{vmatrix} 2 & 4 \\ -4 & -8 \end{vmatrix}$
(d) $\begin{vmatrix} \cos\theta & \sin\theta \\ -\sin\theta & \cos\theta \end{vmatrix}$

2. Verify the following equations.

(a) $\begin{vmatrix} a & b \\ c & d \end{vmatrix} = \begin{vmatrix} a & c \\ b & d \end{vmatrix}$
(b) $\begin{vmatrix} ka & kb \\ kc & kd \end{vmatrix} = k^2 \begin{vmatrix} a & b \\ c & d \end{vmatrix}$

(c) $\begin{vmatrix} a & b \\ c & d \end{vmatrix} = - \begin{vmatrix} c & d \\ a & b \end{vmatrix}$
(d) $\begin{vmatrix} ka & b \\ kc & d \end{vmatrix} = k \begin{vmatrix} a & b \\ c & d \end{vmatrix}$

(e) $\begin{vmatrix} a + tc & b + td \\ c & d \end{vmatrix} = \begin{vmatrix} a & b \\ c & d \end{vmatrix}$

3. Let $A = \begin{bmatrix} a_{11} & a_{12} \\ a_{21} & a_{22} \end{bmatrix}$ and $B = \begin{bmatrix} b_{11} & b_{12} \\ b_{21} & b_{22} \end{bmatrix}$. Show that $|AB| = |A|\,|B|$.

4. Evaluate the following determinants.

(a) $\begin{vmatrix} 1 & 2 & -1 \\ 3 & 0 & 2 \\ 1 & 1 & 1 \end{vmatrix}$
(b) $\begin{vmatrix} 2 & 0 & 0 \\ 5 & 3 & 0 \\ -2 & 1 & 7 \end{vmatrix}$
(c) $\begin{vmatrix} 1 & 1 & 1 \\ 1 & 1 & 1 \\ 1 & 1 & 1 \end{vmatrix}$

(d) $\begin{vmatrix} 1 & 0 & 0 \\ 0 & 1 & 0 \\ 0 & 0 & 1 \end{vmatrix}$
(e) $\begin{vmatrix} 2 & 1 & 0 \\ -1 & 1 & 2 \\ 3 & 6 & -2 \end{vmatrix}$
(f) $\begin{vmatrix} 1 & 2 & 0 \\ 3 & 0 & 0 \\ -1 & 5 & 2 \end{vmatrix}$

5. Show that (if A is a 3 by 3 matrix):

(a) $|A| = a_{11}\,|A_{11}| - a_{21}\,|A_{21}| + a_{31}\,|A_{31}|$
(b) $|A| = -a_{12}\,|A_{12}| + a_{22}\,|A_{22}| - a_{32}\,|A_{32}|$
(c) $0 = -a_{11}\,|A_{21}| + a_{12}\,|A_{22}| - a_{13}\,|A_{23}|$

6. Let $A = \begin{bmatrix} 2 & -1 & 1 \\ 1 & 3 & 2 \\ 1 & -4 & -1 \end{bmatrix}$. Does the equation $Ax = 0$ have a non-trivial solution?

7. Solve for x: $\begin{vmatrix} 2-x & 1 \\ 4 & 5-x \end{vmatrix} = 0.$

8. For what values of k does the following system have non-trivial solutions?

$$(6 - k)x - 2y = 0$$
$$-2x + (3 - k)y = 0.$$

9. From a 3 by 3 matrix A form the matrix A^* whose rows are the columns of A (in the same order). Show that then the columns of A^* are the rows of A and that $|A^*| = |A|$.

10. Compare Equation 86-4 with Equation 75-11 for the scalar triple product $A \cdot (B \times C)$.

11. (a) Show that $|A^{-1}| = |A|^{-1}$.

(b) Show that for a 2 by 2 matrix, $|-A| = |A|$, and for a 3 by 3 matrix, $|-A| = -|A|$.

(c) Use the results of parts (a) and (b) to show that there is no 3 by 3 matrix A (of real numbers) such that $A^{-1} = -A$.

(d) Can you find a 2 by 2 matrix of real numbers such that $A^{-1} = -A$?

87 THE TRANSPOSE OF A MATRIX

Suppose we have a matrix

$$A = \begin{bmatrix} a_{11} & a_{12} & a_{13} \\ a_{21} & a_{22} & a_{23} \\ a_{31} & a_{32} & a_{33} \end{bmatrix}$$

and two vectors

$$x = (x_1, x_2, x_3), \; y = (y_1, y_2, y_3).$$

Since the product Ax is a vector, we can compute its dot product with the vector y. You can easily verify the following expression of the number $Ax \cdot y$ in terms of the elements of A, x, and y:

$$Ax \cdot y = (a_{11}x_1 + a_{12}x_2 + a_{13}x_3)y_1$$
$$+ (a_{21}x_1 + a_{22}x_2 + a_{23}x_3)y_2$$
$$+ (a_{31}x_1 + a_{32}x_2 + a_{33}x_3)y_3.$$

Now let us regroup the terms in this sum, factoring out the numbers x_1, x_2, and x_3. Thus

(87-1)
$$Ax \cdot y = (a_{11}y_1 + a_{21}y_2 + a_{31}y_3)x_1$$
$$+ (a_{12}y_1 + a_{22}y_2 + a_{32}y_3)x_2$$
$$+ (a_{13}y_1 + a_{23}y_2 + a_{33}y_3)x_3.$$

From this last equation we see that we can obtain the dot product $Ax \cdot y$ by first multiplying y by a suitable matrix and then dotting the resulting vector with x. We denote the "suitable" matrix by A^* and call it the **transpose** of A. Thus the basic relation between a matrix A and its transpose A^* is the following equation, valid for every pair of vectors x and y,

(87-2)
$$Ax \cdot y = x \cdot A^*y.$$

It is clear from Equation 87-1 that

(87-3)
$$A^* = \begin{bmatrix} a_{11} & a_{21} & a_{31} \\ a_{12} & a_{22} & a_{32} \\ a_{13} & a_{23} & a_{33} \end{bmatrix};$$

that is, the rows of A become the columns of A^*, and the columns of A become the rows of A^*. Thus we also have $(A^*)^* = A$.

Example 87-1. Let $A = \begin{bmatrix} 1 & 2 \\ 3 & 4 \end{bmatrix}$, $x = (1, 1)$, and $y = (1, -1)$; verify Equation 87-2.

Solution. We have $Ax = (3, 7)$, and so $Ax \cdot y = -4$. To get A^* we replace the rows of A with its columns. Thus

$$A^* = \begin{bmatrix} 1 & 3 \\ 2 & 4 \end{bmatrix}.$$

Now $A^*y = (-2, -2)$, and hence $x \cdot A^*y = -4$, the same number we had formerly found for $Ax \cdot y$. Equation 87-2 tells us that "when we transfer A across the dot, it becomes A^*."

Example 87-2. Show that $x \cdot A^*Ax \geq 0$ regardless of the vector x or matrix A.

Solution. When we transfer A across the dot in the product $Ax \cdot Ax$, we obtain the equation

$$Ax \cdot Ax = x \cdot A^*Ax.$$

The right-hand side of this equation is the number we are considering. The left side is the dot product of a vector by itself (the square of its length) and hence is greater than or equal to zero.

In the example above, we noted that for any matrix A and vector x, $Ax \cdot Ax = x \cdot A^*Ax$. More generally, we see that if x and y are arbitrary vectors, then $Ax \cdot Ay = x \cdot A^*Ay$. If A is a matrix such that $A^*A = I$, our equation reduces to $Ax \cdot Ay = x \cdot y$. Thus, if we multiply x and y by our matrix A and compute the dot product of the resulting vectors, we get the same number we obtain by computing the dot product of x and y directly. A matrix with this property is called an **orthogonal** matrix, and we say that an orthogonal matrix "preserves" dot products. In Section 89 we will discuss the geometric role played by orthogonal matrices; here we will only look at some of their algebraic features.

Let us think of a matrix A, not necessarily orthogonal, as expressed in terms of its row vectors:

$$A = \begin{bmatrix} r_1 \\ r_2 \\ r_3 \end{bmatrix}.$$

The columns of the transpose A^* are the rows of A, so, in terms of its column vectors, we have

$$A^* = [r_1, r_2, r_3].$$

Thus we see that the product AA^* can be written as $AA^* = [Ar_1, Ar_2, Ar_3]$. Let us take a closer look at the column vector Ar_1. A careful study of the rule for multiplying a vector by a matrix (Equation 84-3) shows us that the first component of Ar_1 is the dot product $r_1 \cdot r_1$, the second component is the number $r_2 \cdot r_1$, and the third component is $r_3 \cdot r_1$. Thus $Ar_1 = \begin{pmatrix} r_1 \cdot r_1 \\ r_2 \cdot r_1 \\ r_3 \cdot r_1 \end{pmatrix}$. There are similar expressions for the column vectors Ar_2 and Ar_3, and so we see that if A is a 3 by 3 matrix, then

(87-4)
$$AA^* = \begin{bmatrix} r_1 \cdot r_1 & r_1 \cdot r_2 & r_1 \cdot r_3 \\ r_2 \cdot r_1 & r_2 \cdot r_2 & r_2 \cdot r_3 \\ r_3 \cdot r_1 & r_3 \cdot r_2 & r_3 \cdot r_3 \end{bmatrix}.$$

Now suppose that R is an orthogonal matrix; that is, a matrix such that

(87-5)
$$RR^* = R^*R = I.$$

Since, according to Equation 87-4, the elements of RR^* are dot products of row vectors of R, the equation $RR^* = I$ says that the dot product of each row vector with itself is 1 and with each other row vector is 0. Thus we see that *each row vector of an orthogonal matrix is a unit vector and is orthogonal to the other row vectors*. Since $(R^*)^* = R$, Equations 87-5 tell us that the transpose of R^* is the inverse of R^*; in other words, R^* is an orthogonal matrix. Therefore, its row vectors are unit vectors and each is orthogonal to the others. These *row* vectors of R^* are the *column* vectors of R, so we see that the column vectors share with the row vectors the property of being unit vectors that are orthogonal in pairs. Conversely, if each of the row vectors of a matrix A is 1 unit long and is orthogonal to the other row vectors, then Equation 87-4 shows that $AA^* = I$. Hence $A^* = A^{-1}$, and so A is orthogonal. The same conclusion follows, of course, if we consider column, rather than row, vectors.

Example 87-3. Show that the matrix

$$R = \begin{bmatrix} \cos \theta & \sin \theta \\ -\sin \theta & \cos \theta \end{bmatrix}$$

is orthogonal, regardless of the choice of θ.

Solution. We must show that $R^* = R^{-1}$; that is, that $RR^* = I$:

$$\begin{bmatrix} \cos \theta & \sin \theta \\ -\sin \theta & \cos \theta \end{bmatrix} \begin{bmatrix} \cos \theta & -\sin \theta \\ \sin \theta & \cos \theta \end{bmatrix} = \begin{bmatrix} 1 & 0 \\ 0 & 1 \end{bmatrix}.$$

Example 87-4. Solve the system of equations

$$\bar{x} = x \cos \theta + y \sin \theta$$
$$\bar{y} = -x \sin \theta + y \cos \theta$$

for x and y in terms of $\bar{x}$ and $\bar{y}$.

Solution. If we set $v = (x, y)$ and $\bar{v} = (\bar{x}, \bar{y})$, we can write this system of equations in matrix-vector form

$$\bar{v} = Rv,$$

where R is the matrix of the preceding example. Now we multiply both sides of this equation by R^* and use the fact that $R^*R = I$ to see that

$$v = R^*\bar{v}.$$

This matrix-vector equation is equivalent to the system

$$x = \bar{x} \cos \theta - \bar{y} \sin \theta$$
$$y = \bar{x} \sin \theta + \bar{y} \cos \theta.$$

If A is a 2 by 2 or a 3 by 3 matrix, it is easy to verify (see Problems 86-2(a) and 86-9) that $|A^*| = |A|$. When we apply this result, together with the equation $|RR^*| = |R| |R^*|$, to the equation $I = RR^*$, we see that

$$1 = |R| |R^*| = |R|^2.$$

It follows that $|R| = 1$ or -1; that is, *the determinant of an orthogonal matrix is either 1 or −1.*

P R O B L E M S   8 7

1. Verify the equation $Ax \cdot y = x \cdot A^*y$ in the following cases.

(a) $A = \begin{bmatrix} 2 & -1 \\ -3 & 5 \end{bmatrix}$, $x = (3, 2), y = (-1, 4)$

(b) $A = \begin{bmatrix} 2 & 1 \\ 1 & 0 \end{bmatrix}$, $x = (1, 3), y = (-2, 2)$

(c) $A = \begin{bmatrix} 2 & -1 & 1 \\ 3 & 0 & 2 \\ 1 & 2 & -1 \end{bmatrix}$, $x = (2, -1, 1), y = (1, 0, 2)$

(d) $A = \begin{bmatrix} 2 & -1 & 3 \\ -1 & 0 & 1 \\ 3 & 1 & 2 \end{bmatrix}$, $x = (2, 1, 0), y = (0, 1, 2)$

2. The following equations are true for any matrices. Verify their validity for the choices

$$A = \begin{bmatrix} 2 & 1 \\ 1 & 1 \end{bmatrix} \quad \text{and} \quad B = \begin{bmatrix} 1 & 2 \\ -1 & 0 \end{bmatrix}.$$

(a) $(A^*)^* = A$ (b) $|B^*| = |B|$ (c) $(A + B)^* = A^* + B^*$
(d) $(A^{-1})^* = (A^*)^{-1}$ (e) $(AB)^* = B^*A^*$

3. Show that $(A + B)^* = A^* + B^*$.

4. Show that $x \cdot A^*By = B^*Ax \cdot y$.

5. Show that $Ax \cdot x = A^*x \cdot x$.

6. Verify that the following matrices are orthogonal.

(a) $\begin{bmatrix} 0 & 1 & 0 \\ 1 & 0 & 0 \\ 0 & 0 & 1 \end{bmatrix}$

(b) $\begin{bmatrix} 1 & 0 & 0 \\ 0 & -1 & 0 \\ 0 & 0 & -1 \end{bmatrix}$

(c) $\begin{bmatrix} \cos\theta & 0 & \sin\theta \\ 0 & 1 & 0 \\ -\sin\theta & 0 & \cos\theta \end{bmatrix}$

(d) $\begin{bmatrix} \frac{2}{3} & \frac{1}{3} & -\frac{2}{3} \\ \frac{1}{3} & \frac{2}{3} & \frac{2}{3} \\ \frac{2}{3} & -\frac{2}{3} & \frac{1}{3} \end{bmatrix}$

(e) $\begin{bmatrix} \frac{1}{\sqrt{3}} & \frac{2}{\sqrt{6}} & 0 \\ \frac{1}{\sqrt{3}} & \frac{-1}{\sqrt{6}} & \frac{1}{\sqrt{2}} \\ \frac{1}{\sqrt{3}} & \frac{-1}{\sqrt{6}} & \frac{-1}{\sqrt{2}} \end{bmatrix}$

(f) $\begin{bmatrix} \frac{3}{5} & \frac{4}{5} \\ \frac{4}{5} & -\frac{3}{5} \end{bmatrix}$

7. Is there a number t such that $\begin{bmatrix} 1 & 0 \\ 4 & t \end{bmatrix}$ is an orthogonal matrix?

8. Determine numbers u, v, w, x, y, and z so that the matrix $\begin{bmatrix} u & 0 & 0 \\ v & w & 0 \\ x & y & z \end{bmatrix}$ is an orthogonal matrix.

9. Regardless of the numbers θ and ϕ, the matrices

$$A = \begin{bmatrix} \cos\theta & \sin\theta \\ -\sin\theta & \cos\theta \end{bmatrix} \quad \text{and} \quad B = \begin{bmatrix} \cos\phi & \sin\phi \\ -\sin\phi & \cos\phi \end{bmatrix}$$

are orthogonal. Show that AB is also orthogonal.

10. (a) By writing each side of the equation in terms of the elements of the matrices that appear, show that $(AB)^* = B^*A^*$ for 2 by 2 matrices A and B.

(b) Suppose that A and B are square matrices of the same order (not necessarily 2 by 2). Show that $x \cdot (AB)^*y = x \cdot B^*A^*y$ for arbitrary vectors x and y. Can you show that this identity implies that $(AB)^* = B^*A^*$?

(c) Use the equation $(AB)^* = B^*A^*$ to show that the product of two orthogonal matrices is an orthogonal matrix.

88 CHARACTERISTIC VALUES AND THE DIAGONALIZATION OF A MATRIX

A matrix A transforms a vector x into another vector Ax. A question that frequently arises is the following. Under what circumstances is the transformed vector simply a scalar multiple of the original vector? Thus, when is $Ax = 5x$, or $Ax = \pi x$, or $Ax = 0x$? In general, we ask, "Is there a scalar multiplier λ such that the equation

$$(88\text{-}1) \qquad\qquad Ax = \lambda x$$

holds for some vector x." If A is any matrix and λ is any number, then the vector $x = 0$ will satisfy Equation 88-1. This solution is called the **trivial solution**, and we hereby rule out the trivial solution when we ask our question.

We can write Equation 88-1 as $Ax = \lambda Ix$, and so we have

$$(88\text{-}2) \qquad\qquad (A - \lambda I)x = 0.$$

Now we can apply the results of Section 86. Theorem 86-2 says that a homogeneous matrix-vector equation possesses a non-trivial solution if, and only if, the determinant of the coefficient matrix is 0. Therefore, Equation 88-1 has a solution $x \neq 0$ if, and only if, λ is a number that satisfies the **characteristic equation**

$$(88\text{-}3) \qquad\qquad |A - \lambda I| = 0.$$

Example 88-1. Solve Equation 88-1 if A is replaced by the matrix

$$S = \begin{bmatrix} 3 & 2 \\ 2 & 0 \end{bmatrix}.$$

Solution. In this case our characteristic Equation 88-3 is

$$\begin{vmatrix} 3 - \lambda & 2 \\ 2 & -\lambda \end{vmatrix} = (3 - \lambda)(-\lambda) - 4 = (\lambda - 4)(\lambda + 1) = 0.$$

Its solutions are the numbers $\lambda = 4$ and $\lambda = -1$. Corresponding to each of these numbers is a solution $x = (x_1, x_2) \neq (0, 0)$ of Equation 88-1 (or the equivalent Equation 88-2). Let us choose $\lambda = 4$. Then the coefficient matrix of Equation 88-2 becomes

$$S - 4I = \begin{bmatrix} 3 - 4 & 2 \\ 2 & -4 \end{bmatrix} = \begin{bmatrix} -1 & 2 \\ 2 & -4 \end{bmatrix}.$$

Thus to find a vector x that corresponds to the number 4, we must find a solution of the homogeneous system

$$-x_1 + 2x_2 = 0$$
$$2x_1 - 4x_2 = 0.$$

We see that the vector $x = (2, 1)$ is one solution of this system. Therefore, for this vector x,

$$Sx = 4x.$$

If we set $\lambda = -1$, we can take $x = (1, -2)$, and then $Sx = (-1)x$, as you can easily verify.

The preceding example illustrates the following facts about Equation 88-1. The characteristic equation is an algebraic equation whose degree is the order of the matrix A. Thus the matrix of our example was a 2 by 2 matrix, and λ satisfied a quadratic equation. Therefore, the number of different possible choices for λ is at most the order of A. These numbers λ are called the **characteristic values** of the matrix A. Corresponding to each characteristic value there is a **characteristic vector** x, that is, a vector $x \neq 0$ that satisfies Equation 88-1. If x is a characteristic vector, so is any non-zero multiple of x, for example $3x$, $5x$, and so on. Frequently we multiply a characteristic vector by the reciprocal of its length to get a **unit characteristic vector**. For example, the vector $x = (2/\sqrt{5}, 1/\sqrt{5})$ is a characteristic vector of the matrix S of Example 88-1, and it is 1 unit long. The vector $x = (-2/\sqrt{5}, -1/\sqrt{5})$ is another unit characteristic vector that corresponds to the characteristic value 4.

The matrix of Example 88-1 is of a special form that appears often in mathematical applications. A matrix S is said to be **symmetric** if $S^* = S$; you will notice that our matrix S of Example 88-1 is a symmetric matrix. The characteristic vectors $(2, 1)$ and $(1, -2)$ of the symmetric matrix of Example 88-1 are orthogonal, and the next theorem shows that this fact is no accident.

Theorem 88-1. *If x and y are characteristic vectors of a symmetric matrix S that correspond to different characteristic values λ and μ, then $x \cdot y = 0$.*

Proof. We are supposing that

$$Sx = \lambda x \quad \text{and} \quad Sy = \mu y.$$

If we dot the first of these equations with y and the second with x and subtract, we obtain the equation

$$Sx \cdot y - x \cdot Sy = (\lambda - \mu)x \cdot y.$$

Because S is symmetric, $x \cdot Sy = S^*x \cdot y = Sx \cdot y$, and so the left side of this equation is 0. Furthermore, we are assuming that $\lambda - \mu \neq 0$, and hence we see that $x \cdot y = 0$.

Although we shall not give the simple proof of this fact, even if the characteristic values of a real symmetric n by n matrix are not all different, we can find n mutually orthogonal characteristic vectors.

To see the implications of the fact that we can choose the characteristic vectors of a symmetric matrix to be pairwise orthogonal, let us return to our matrix of Example 88-1. The vectors $x_1 = (2/\sqrt{5}, 1/\sqrt{5})$ and $x_2 = (1/\sqrt{5}, -2/\sqrt{5})$ are characteristic vectors of the matrix S. Each is 1 unit long, and their dot product is 0. Now we form the matrix whose column vectors are these vectors:

$$P = \begin{bmatrix} 2/\sqrt{5} & 1/\sqrt{5} \\ 1/\sqrt{5} & -2/\sqrt{5} \end{bmatrix}.$$

Because its columns are orthogonal and each is 1 unit long, this matrix is an orthogonal matrix. Furthermore, as you can easily check,

$$P^*SP = \begin{bmatrix} 4 & 0 \\ 0 & -1 \end{bmatrix}.$$

Thus we have "transformed" S into a diagonal matrix by means of the orthogonal matrix P. The diagonal elements of the resulting matrix are the characteristic values of S.

Here is the general situation in the three-dimensional case. Suppose that S is a symmetric matrix with characteristic values λ_1, λ_2, and λ_3 and corresponding characteristic vectors x_1, x_2, and x_3, each of which is 1 unit long and orthogonal to the other two. We use these vectors as columns and construct the matrix

$$P = [x_1, x_2, x_3].$$

Because the vectors x_1, x_2, and x_3 are pairwise orthogonal and of unit length, this matrix P is an orthogonal matrix. Now

$$SP = [Sx_1, Sx_2, Sx_3] = [\lambda_1 x_1, \lambda_2 x_2, \lambda_3 x_3],$$

and you may readily verify that this product may be written as PD, where

(88-4)
$$D = \begin{bmatrix} \lambda_1 & 0 & 0 \\ 0 & \lambda_2 & 0 \\ 0 & 0 & \lambda_3 \end{bmatrix}.$$

Thus $SP = PD$, and since $P*P = I$, we have

$$P*SP = D.$$

In this way we can transform any symmetric matrix to diagonal form by means of an orthogonal matrix, as stated in the following theorem.

Theorem 88-2.   *If S is a symmetric matrix with characteristic values λ_1, λ_2, and λ_3, then there exists an orthogonal matrix P such that $P*SP = D$, where the matrix D is given by Equation 88-4.*

Example 88-2.   Diagonalize the symmetric matrix

$$S = \begin{bmatrix} 1 & 1 & 1 \\ 1 & 1 & 1 \\ 1 & 1 & 1 \end{bmatrix}.$$

Solution.   In Problem 84-9 you were asked to verify that the characteristic values of S are the numbers 3, 0, 0 and that corresponding mutually orthogonal characteristic vectors are $(1, 1, 1)$, $(2, -1, -1)$, and $(0, 1, -1)$. Now we divide each of these vectors by its length and use the resulting unit vectors as the columns of an orthogonal matrix P:

$$P = \begin{bmatrix} 1/\sqrt{3} & 2/\sqrt{6} & 0 \\ 1/\sqrt{3} & -1/\sqrt{6} & 1/\sqrt{2} \\ 1/\sqrt{3} & -1/\sqrt{6} & -1/\sqrt{2} \end{bmatrix}.$$

Our theory says, and you may confirm, that

$$P*SP = \begin{bmatrix} 3 & 0 & 0 \\ 0 & 0 & 0 \\ 0 & 0 & 0 \end{bmatrix}.$$

P R O B L E M S   8 8

1. Let S be the matrix $S = \begin{bmatrix} 2 & 1 \\ 1 & 2 \end{bmatrix}$.

    (a) What is the characteristic equation of S?

    (b) What are the characteristic values of S?

    (c) Find characteristic vectors that correspond to the characteristic values.

    (d) Construct an orthogonal matrix P whose column vectors are characteristic vectors of S.

    (e) Show that $P*SP = D$, where D is a diagonal matrix.

2. Answer the questions in Number 1 if $S = \begin{bmatrix} 1 & -2 \\ -2 & 1 \end{bmatrix}$.

3. For each of the following symmetric matrices S we can find an orthogonal matrix P such that $P*SP = D$, a diagonal matrix. Find D in each case.

    (a) $\begin{bmatrix} 4 & 1 \\ 1 & 4 \end{bmatrix}$
    (b) $\begin{bmatrix} 4 & 2 \\ 2 & 1 \end{bmatrix}$
    (c) $\begin{bmatrix} 0 & 1 \\ 1 & 0 \end{bmatrix}$

    (d) $\begin{bmatrix} 1 & 2 \\ 2 & 3 \end{bmatrix}$
    (e) $\begin{bmatrix} 2 & 3 \\ 3 & -2 \end{bmatrix}$

4. If a, b, and c are real numbers, show that the characteristic values of the matrix $\begin{bmatrix} a & b \\ b & c \end{bmatrix}$ are real numbers. (It can be shown that the characteristic values of any real symmetric matrix are real.)

5. Let S be the matrix $S = \begin{bmatrix} 1 & 1 & 1 \\ 1 & 2 & 0 \\ 1 & 0 & 2 \end{bmatrix}$.

    (a) What is the characteristic equation of S?

    (b) What are the characteristic values of S?

    (c) Find characteristic vectors that correspond to the characteristic values.

    (d) Construct an orthogonal matrix P whose column vectors are characteristic vectors of S.

    (e) Show that $P*SP = D$, a diagonal matrix.

6. Answer the questions in Number 5 if $S = \begin{bmatrix} 2 & -2 & -2 \\ -2 & 1 & -1 \\ -2 & -1 & 1 \end{bmatrix}$.

7. For each of the following symmetric matrices S we can find an orthogonal matrix P such that $P*SP = D$ is a diagonal matrix. Find D in each case.

(a) $\begin{bmatrix} 0 & 0 & 2 \\ 0 & 1 & 0 \\ 2 & 0 & 0 \end{bmatrix}$
    (b) $\begin{bmatrix} 4 & 1 & 0 \\ 1 & 4 & 0 \\ 0 & 0 & 2 \end{bmatrix}$
    (c) $\begin{bmatrix} 2 & 0 & 1 \\ 0 & 1 & 0 \\ 1 & 0 & 2 \end{bmatrix}$

(d) $\begin{bmatrix} 0 & 1 & 0 \\ 1 & 0 & 1 \\ 0 & 1 & 0 \end{bmatrix}$
    (e) $\begin{bmatrix} 5 & -1 & -1 \\ -1 & 3 & 1 \\ -1 & 1 & 3 \end{bmatrix}$

8. What can you conclude about a symmetric matrix if all of its characteristic values are equal?

9. Suppose that λ is the smallest and μ is the largest characteristic value of a symmetric matrix S. Show that for each vector x, $\lambda x \cdot x \leq x \cdot Sx \leq \mu x \cdot x$.

10. Find characteristic values and characteristic vectors for the following non-symmetric matrices. It is clear that symmetric matrices are much nicer to deal with.

(a) $\begin{bmatrix} 0 & 1 \\ -1 & 0 \end{bmatrix}$
    (b) $\begin{bmatrix} 5 & 1 \\ 0 & 5 \end{bmatrix}$
    (c) $\begin{bmatrix} 0 & 2 & 1 \\ -2 & 0 & 2 \\ -1 & -2 & 0 \end{bmatrix}$

89 ROTATION OF AXES

A cartesian coordinate system is a device that enables us to identify the vector space of arrows in three-dimensional space with the vector space R^3 of triples of numbers. In different coordinate systems, a given geometric vector (arrow) will be expressed as different elements of R^3. We are now going to study how these different elements are related if one of the coordinate systems can be obtained from the other by a rotation of axes.

Suppose we have introduced a cartesian coordinate system into three-dimensional space, and let us as usual denote by i, j, and k the unit vectors in the direction of the X-, Y-, and Z-axes. Then each geometric vector V can be expressed as a combination

(89-1) $$V = xi + yj + zk$$

of these unit basis vectors. Equation 89-1 associates with the geometric vector V the element $v = (x, y, z)$ of R^3. The numbers x, y, and z are the components of V relative to the given coordinate system, so we shall use the term "component vector" when we refer to the element v.

Now let us introduce a new cartesian coordinate system, determined by an orthogonal matrix

$$R = \begin{bmatrix} r_{11} & r_{12} & r_{13} \\ r_{21} & r_{22} & r_{23} \\ r_{31} & r_{32} & r_{33} \end{bmatrix}.$$

We shall take the origin of this new system to be the origin of the original system and its unit basis vectors to be the vectors $\bar{i}, \bar{j},$ and $\bar{k}$ that are defined by the following equations:

(89-2)
$$\begin{aligned} \bar{i} &= r_{11}i + r_{12}j + r_{13}k \\ \bar{j} &= r_{21}i + r_{22}j + r_{23}k \\ \bar{k} &= r_{31}i + r_{32}j + r_{33}k. \end{aligned}$$

Our first task is to verify that these vectors really do form a basis for a cartesian system; that is, that each is 1 unit long and is perpendicular to the other two. This fact follows from the orthogonality of R. Let us look, for example, at the "typical" dot products

$$\bar{i} \cdot \bar{i} = (r_{11}i + r_{12}j + r_{13}k) \cdot (r_{11}i + r_{12}j + r_{13}k)$$

and

$$\bar{i} \cdot \bar{j} = (r_{11}i + r_{12}j + r_{13}k) \cdot (r_{21}i + r_{22}j + r_{23}k).$$

When we use the rules of vector algebra to expand the dot products on the right-hand sides of these equations, we find that

$$\bar{i} \cdot \bar{i} = r_{11}^2 + r_{12}^2 + r_{13}^2 \quad \text{and} \quad \bar{i} \cdot \bar{j} = r_{11}r_{21} + r_{12}r_{22} + r_{13}r_{23}.$$

From these equations we see that the numbers $\bar{i} \cdot \bar{i}$ and $\bar{i} \cdot \bar{j}$ are dot products of vectors of R^3, $\bar{i} \cdot \bar{i}$ is the dot product of the first row vector of the matrix R with itself, and $\bar{i} \cdot \bar{j}$ is the dot product of the first and second row vectors of R. Since R is an orthogonal matrix, each of these row vectors is 1 unit long, and they are orthogonal. Therefore, $\bar{i} \cdot \bar{i} = 1$ and $\bar{i} \cdot \bar{j} = 0$. Similar calculations show that $\bar{i} \cdot \bar{k} = 0, \bar{j} \cdot \bar{j} = 1$, and so on.

Thus, given a cartesian coordinate system, an orthogonal matrix determines a set of three mutually perpendicular vectors, each 1 unit long, which will serve as a basis for a new cartesian coordinate system. Conversely, a second cartesian coordinate system based on three mutually perpendicular unit vectors $\bar{i}, \bar{j},$ and $\bar{k}$ determines an orthogonal matrix. For the vectors $\bar{i}, \bar{j},$ and $\bar{k}$ can be expressed in terms of the original basis vectors $i, j,$ and k. Therefore, we will have a system of equations, System 89-2, in which the coefficients $r_{11}, r_{12}, \ldots, r_{33}$ are the components of $\bar{i}, \bar{j}$, and $\bar{k}$ relative to the original coordinate system. Since we are assuming that $\bar{i} \cdot \bar{i} = 1$ and $\bar{i} \cdot \bar{j} = 0$, we find that

$$r_{11}^2 + r_{12}^2 + r_{13}^2 = 1 \quad \text{and} \quad r_{11}r_{21} + r_{12}r_{22} + r_{13}r_{23} = 0,$$

and so on. These equations say that each of the row vectors of the matrix of coefficients of System 89-2 is 1 unit long and is orthogonal to the other row vectors. In other words, the matrix is an orthogonal matrix.

We can express a given geometric vector V either in terms of the basis vectors i, j, and k, as in Equation 89-1, or in terms of the basis vectors $\bar{i}, \bar{j}$, and $\bar{k}$:

(89-3) $$V = \bar{x}\bar{i} + \bar{y}\bar{j} + \bar{z}\bar{k}.$$

Therefore, relative to our second coordinate system, we see that the geometric vector V corresponds to the component vector $\bar{v} = (\bar{x}, \bar{y}, \bar{z})$. Let us find the relation between the component vectors v and $\bar{v}$. From Equations 89-1 and 89-3 we see that

$$xi + yj + zk = \bar{x}\bar{i} + \bar{y}\bar{i} + \bar{z}\bar{k}.$$

In this equation we may replace $\bar{i}, \bar{j}$, and $\bar{k}$ in terms of i, j, and k according to Equations 89-2:

$$xi + yj + zk = \bar{x}(r_{11}i + r_{12}j + r_{13}k)$$
$$+ \bar{y}(r_{21}i + r_{22}j + r_{23}k)$$
$$+ \bar{z}(r_{31}i + r_{32}j + r_{33}k).$$

Now we collect terms and equate the coefficients of i, j, and k to obtain the system of equations

(89-4)
$$x = r_{11}\bar{x} + r_{21}\bar{y} + r_{31}\bar{z}$$
$$y = r_{12}\bar{x} + r_{22}\bar{y} + r_{32}\bar{z}$$
$$z = r_{13}\bar{x} + r_{23}\bar{y} + r_{33}\bar{z}.$$

In matrix-vector form, this system of equations is simply

(89-5) $$v = R^*\bar{v}.$$

If we multiply both sides of Equation 89-5 by R and take into account the fact that $RR^* = I$, we can rewrite this relation between v and $\bar{v}$ as

(89-6) $$\bar{v} = Rv.$$

If we think of our geometric vector V as the position vector of a point P, the component vectors $v = (x, y, z)$ and $\bar{v} = (\bar{x}, \bar{y}, \bar{z})$ give us the coordinates of P relative to our two coordinate systems. Equations 89-5 and 89-6 are therefore the transformation of coordinates equations for the two cartesian systems.

Example 89-1. Discuss the transformation of coordinates that is determined by the orthogonal matrix

$$R = \begin{bmatrix} \cos \theta & \sin \theta \\ -\sin \theta & \cos \theta \end{bmatrix}.$$

Solution. In this case the matrix-vector Equation 89-6 is equivalent to the system of equations

$$\bar{x} = x \cos \theta + y \sin \theta$$

$$\bar{y} = -x \sin \theta + y \cos \theta.$$

We recognize (see Section 66) these equations as the transformation equations for a rotation of axes through an angle of θ. In this case our orthogonal matrix determines a rotation.

It is "almost" true that the transformation determined by every orthogonal matrix is a rotation. The facts are these. In Section 87 we learned that the determinant of an orthogonal matrix R is either $+1$ or -1. We can show, by using

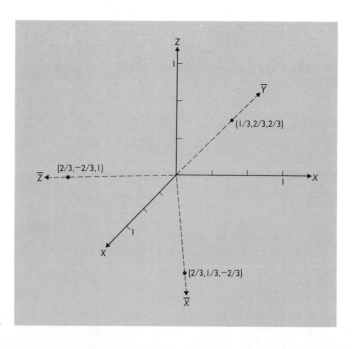

Figure 89-1.

Equations 89-2 to compute $\bar{i} \times \bar{j}$ and taking into account the fact that R is orthogonal, that $\bar{i} \times \bar{j} = |R| \, \bar{k}$. If $|R| = 1$, the basis vectors $\bar{i}, \bar{j},$ and $\bar{k}$ have the same orientation (right-handed or left-handed) as the vectors $i, j,$ and k. In that case, the two sets of coordinate axes can be brought into coincidence by ordinary Euclidean rotations. If $|R| = -1$, then $\bar{i} \times \bar{j} = -\bar{k}$, and to bring the two axis systems into coincidence we must perform Euclidean rotations *and* reflect along one of the coordinate axes.

Example 89-2. Discuss the transformation determined by the orthogonal matrix

$$R = \begin{bmatrix} \frac{2}{3} & \frac{1}{3} & -\frac{2}{3} \\ \frac{1}{3} & \frac{2}{3} & \frac{2}{3} \\ \frac{2}{3} & -\frac{2}{3} & \frac{1}{3} \end{bmatrix}.$$

Solution. You can easily verify that $|R| = 1$, so the transformation determined by this matrix is a rotation. To locate the $\bar{X}$-, $\bar{Y}$- and $\bar{Z}$-axes relative to the X-, Y-, and Z-axes, we recall that the rows of R are the components of the basis vectors $\bar{i}, \bar{j},$ and $\bar{k}$ relative to the XYZ-axes. In other words, the points $(\frac{2}{3}, \frac{1}{3}, -\frac{2}{3})$, $(\frac{1}{3}, \frac{2}{3}, \frac{2}{3})$, and $(\frac{2}{3}, -\frac{2}{3}, \frac{1}{3})$ are the terminal points of the vectors $\bar{i}, \bar{j},$ and $\bar{k}$, and so they determine the $\bar{X}$-, $\bar{Y}$-, and $\bar{Z}$-axes, as shown in Fig. 89-1.

Example 89-3. Discuss the transformation determined by the orthogonal matrix

$$R = \begin{bmatrix} 0 & 0 & 1 \\ 0 & 1 & 0 \\ 1 & 0 & 0 \end{bmatrix}.$$

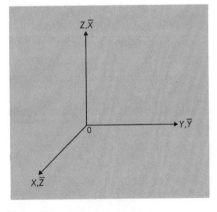

Figure 89-2

Solution. The terminal points of the vectors $\bar{i}, \bar{j},$ and $\bar{k}$ are the points $(0, 0, 1)$, $(0, 1, 0)$, and $(1, 0, 0)$. Hence the $\bar{X}$-axis is the Z-axis, the $\bar{Y}$-axis is the Y-axis, and the $\bar{Z}$-axis is the X-axis. Notice that $R = -1$ and that no rotation will bring the $\bar{X}\bar{Y}\bar{Z}$- and XYZ-axes into coincidence (see Fig. 89-2).

P R O B L E M S 8 9

I. Let $v = (x, y)$ and $\bar{v} = (\bar{x}, \bar{y})$, the coordinates of a point relative to an XY- and an $\bar{X}\bar{Y}$-coordinate system, be related by the equation $\bar{v} = Rv$. Draw the XY-axes in "standard position" and sketch the $\bar{X}\bar{Y}$-axes for the following choices of R.

(a) $\begin{bmatrix} \frac{3}{5} & \frac{4}{5} \\ -\frac{4}{5} & \frac{3}{5} \end{bmatrix}$ (b) $\begin{bmatrix} 0 & 1 \\ 1 & 0 \end{bmatrix}$ (c) $\begin{bmatrix} 1 & 0 \\ 0 & -1 \end{bmatrix}$ (d) $\begin{bmatrix} 0 & 1 \\ -1 & 0 \end{bmatrix}$

(e) $\begin{bmatrix} 1/\sqrt{2} & 1/\sqrt{2} \\ -1/\sqrt{2} & 1/\sqrt{2} \end{bmatrix}$.

2. Let $\begin{bmatrix} a & b \\ c & d \end{bmatrix}$ be an orthogonal matrix. Show that there is an angle of θ such that $a = \cos\theta$ and $b = \sin\theta$. Then show that either $c = -\sin\theta$ and $d = \cos\theta$, or $c = \sin\theta$ and $d = -\cos\theta$. It follows that every 2 by 2 orthogonal matrix must either be a rotation matrix $\begin{bmatrix} \cos\theta & \sin\theta \\ -\sin\theta & \cos\theta \end{bmatrix}$ or a matrix $\begin{bmatrix} \cos\theta & \sin\theta \\ \sin\theta & -\cos\theta \end{bmatrix}$ that represents a rotation and a reflection.

3. The matrix $\begin{bmatrix} \frac{1}{2}\sqrt{3} & \frac{1}{2} \\ -\frac{1}{2} & \frac{1}{2}\sqrt{3} \end{bmatrix}$ represents a rotation of axes through an acute angle; find it.

4. Let the coordinates $v = (x, y, z)$ and $\bar{v} = (\bar{x}, \bar{y}, \bar{z})$ of a point relative to an XYZ- and an $\bar{X}\bar{Y}\bar{Z}$-coordinate system be related by the equation $\bar{v} = Rv$. Draw the XYZ-axes in "standard position" and sketch the $\bar{X}\bar{Y}\bar{Z}$-axes for the following choices of R.

(a) $\begin{bmatrix} 0 & 1 & 0 \\ 1 & 0 & 0 \\ 0 & 0 & 1 \end{bmatrix}$ (b) $\begin{bmatrix} 1 & 0 & 0 \\ 0 & -1 & 0 \\ 0 & 0 & -1 \end{bmatrix}$ (c) $\begin{bmatrix} \frac{1}{3} & -\frac{2}{3} & \frac{2}{3} \\ \frac{2}{3} & \frac{2}{3} & \frac{1}{3} \\ -\frac{2}{3} & \frac{1}{3} & \frac{2}{3} \end{bmatrix}$

(d) $\begin{bmatrix} \frac{3}{5} & 0 & \frac{4}{5} \\ 0 & 1 & 0 \\ -\frac{4}{5} & 0 & \frac{3}{5} \end{bmatrix}$ (e) $\begin{bmatrix} 1/\sqrt{3} & 2/\sqrt{6} & 0 \\ 1/\sqrt{3} & -1/\sqrt{6} & 1/\sqrt{2} \\ 1/\sqrt{3} & -1/\sqrt{6} & -1/\sqrt{2} \end{bmatrix}$

5. What is the matrix of an orthogonal transformation such that the $\bar{X}$-axis is the Y-axis, the $\bar{Y}$-axis is the negative of the Z-axis, and the $\bar{Z}$-axis is the X-axis? Is this transformation a rotation?

6. Let the coordinates $v = (x, y, z)$ and $\bar{v} = (\bar{x}, \bar{y}, \bar{z})$ of a point relative to an XYZ- and an $\bar{X}\bar{Y}\bar{Z}$-coordinate system be related by the equation $\bar{v} = Rv$,

where $$R = \begin{bmatrix} \frac{2}{3} & \frac{1}{3} & -\frac{2}{3} \\ \frac{1}{3} & \frac{2}{3} & \frac{2}{3} \\ \frac{2}{3} & -\frac{2}{3} & \frac{1}{3} \end{bmatrix}.$$

(a) Find the $\bar{X}\bar{Y}\bar{Z}$-coordinates of the point whose XYZ-coordinates are $(3, -6, 9)$.
(b) Find the XYZ-coordinates of the point whose $\bar{X}\bar{Y}\bar{Z}$-coordinates are $(3, -6, 9)$.
(c) The plane whose XYZ-coordinate equation is $6x - 9y + 3z + 1 = 0$ has a similar equation in terms of $\bar{x}$, $\bar{y}$, and $\bar{z}$. What is it?
(d) The plane whose $\bar{X}\bar{Y}\bar{Z}$-coordinate equation is $6\bar{x} - 9\bar{y} + 3\bar{z} + 1 = 0$ has a similar equation in terms of x, y, and z. What is it?

(e) What is the equation of the XY-plane in terms of $\bar{x}$, $\bar{y}$, and $\bar{z}$?

(f) Show that $\bar{x}^2 + \bar{y}^2 + \bar{z}^2 = x^2 + y^2 + z^2$.

7. It can be shown that every 3 by 3 rotation matrix R (an orthogonal matrix with determinant 1) leaves at least one vector fixed; that is, the equation $Rx = x$ has a solution in addition to the "trivial" solution $x = 0$. Solve this equation for the matrix R of Number 6.

8. The equation of a plane $ax + by + cz = d$ can be written as $n \cdot v = d$, where n is the normal vector (a, b, c) and v is the position vector (x, y, z). Under the transformation of coordinates equation $\bar{v} = Rv$, where R is a given orthogonal matrix, the equation of this plane becomes $\bar{a}\bar{x} + \bar{b}\bar{y} + \bar{c}\bar{z} = d$. What is the new normal vector $(\bar{a}, \bar{b}, \bar{c})$ in the $\bar{X}\bar{Y}\bar{Z}$-coordinate system?

9. Explain why the elements of an orthogonal matrix R are the cosines of the angles between the X and $\bar{X}$-, X and $\bar{Y}$-, and so on, axes.

10. What are the transformation of coordinates equations for a translation of axes in three-dimensions? For a rotation followed by a translation? For a translation followed by a rotation?

90 GRAPHS OF QUADRATIC EQUATIONS

The graph of a quadratic equation (in the plane) is a conic, as we know. To find out more about the conic, we may want to rotate axes to reduce the given equation to "standard form." Similarly, we shall now show that a rotation of axes in three dimensions will reduce a general quadratic equation such as

$$(90\text{-}1) \qquad 5x^2 + 2y^2 + 11z^2 + 20xy - 16xz + 4yz = 9$$

to the standard form of the equation of a quadric surface.

We shall use vector-matrix notation. Let us introduce the symmetric matrix

$$(90\text{-}2) \qquad S = \begin{bmatrix} a & d & e \\ d & b & f \\ e & f & c \end{bmatrix}$$

and the vector $v = (x, y, z)$. You may readily verify the equation

$$(90\text{-}3) \qquad Sv \cdot v = ax^2 + by^2 + cz^2 + 2dxy + 2exz + 2fyz.$$

If we compare the right-hand side of Equation 90-3 with the left-hand side of Equation 90-1, we see that Equation 90-1 can be written as

$$(90\text{-}4) \qquad Sv \cdot v = 9,$$

where

$$S = \begin{bmatrix} 5 & 10 & -8 \\ 10 & 2 & 2 \\ -8 & 2 & 11 \end{bmatrix}.$$

Let us sketch our line of attack on Equation 90-4, and then we will come back later and fill in the details. According to Theorem 88-2, there is an orthogonal matrix P such that $P*SP = D$, where D is a diagonal matrix,

$$(90\text{-}5) \qquad\qquad D = \begin{bmatrix} \lambda_1 & 0 & 0 \\ 0 & \lambda_2 & 0 \\ 0 & 0 & \lambda_3 \end{bmatrix}.$$

Now we set $R = P*$ and introduce new coordinates $\bar{v} = (\bar{x}, \bar{y}, \bar{z})$ by means of the equation $\bar{v} = Rv$ (see Equation 89-6). Therefore, $v = R*\bar{v} = P\bar{v}$, and Equation 90-4 becomes $SP\bar{v} \cdot P\bar{v} = 9$. When we transfer P across the dot, it becomes $P*$, and hence this last equation is

$$P*SP\bar{v} \cdot \bar{v} = D\bar{v} \cdot \bar{v} = 9.$$

Now if we calculate the product $D\bar{v} \cdot \bar{v}$, we obtain the sum $\lambda_1\bar{x}^2 + \lambda_2\bar{y}^2 + \lambda_3\bar{z}^2$, and so, in terms of $\bar{x}$, $\bar{y}$, and $\bar{z}$, our original Equation 90-1 reads

$$(90\text{-}6) \qquad\qquad \lambda_1\bar{x}^2 + \lambda_2\bar{y}^2 + \lambda_3\bar{z}^2 = 9.$$

This equation is the standard form of the equation of a quadric surface. Since we studied such standard forms in Section 78, we are now on familiar ground.

So let us turn to the task of finding the numbers λ_1, λ_2, and λ_3, and the matrix R. The numbers λ_1, λ_2, and λ_3 are the characteristic values of the matrix S; hence we find them by solving the characteristic equation

$$\begin{vmatrix} 5 - \lambda & 10 & -8 \\ 10 & 2 - \lambda & 2 \\ -8 & 2 & 11 - \lambda \end{vmatrix} = 0.$$

When we expand the determinant, this equation becomes

$$\lambda^3 - 18\lambda^2 - 81\lambda + 1458 = 0.$$

Its solutions are $\lambda_1 = 18$, $\lambda_2 = 9$, and $\lambda_3 = -9$. Therefore, Equation 90-6 is

$$2\bar{x}^2 + \bar{y}^2 - \bar{z}^2 = 1.$$

We know that the graph of this equation is a hyperboloid of one sheet in standard form relative to the $\overline{X}\,\overline{Y}\overline{Z}$-coordinate system. Thus the graph of Equation 90-1 is a hyperboloid. If we were merely interested in the form of the graph, we could stop now. However, if we actually want to sketch the graph, we must find how the $\overline{X}$-, $\overline{Y}$-, and $\overline{Z}$-axes are related to the X-, Y-, and Z-axes. To this end, we must find the transformation matrix R.

The columns of $P = R^*$ are unit characteristic vectors of S, so they are solutions of the equations obtained from the equation

$$(S - \lambda I)x = 0$$

by setting $\lambda = 18$, 9, and -9. The first such equation is

$$\begin{bmatrix} -13 & 10 & -8 \\ 10 & -16 & 2 \\ -8 & 2 & -7 \end{bmatrix} x = 0.$$

We leave it to you to show that $x = (2, 1, -2)$ is a solution, and when we divide this vector by its length, 3, we obtain the unit characteristic vector $x_1 = (\frac{2}{3}, \frac{1}{3}, -\frac{2}{3})$ that corresponds to the characteristic value $\lambda_1 = 18$. Unit characteristic vectors that correspond to the characteristic values $\lambda_2 = 9$ and $\lambda_3 = -9$ are $x_2 = (\frac{1}{3}, \frac{2}{3}, \frac{2}{3})$ and $x_3 = (\frac{2}{3}, -\frac{2}{3}, \frac{1}{3})$. These vectors form the columns of our matrix P and therefore the rows of the transformation matrix $R = P^*$. Thus

$$R = \begin{bmatrix} \frac{2}{3} & \frac{1}{3} & -\frac{2}{3} \\ \frac{1}{3} & \frac{2}{3} & \frac{2}{3} \\ \frac{2}{3} & -\frac{2}{3} & \frac{1}{3} \end{bmatrix}.$$

This matrix is the transformation matrix we studied in Example 89-2, and the relation of the $\overline{X}$-, $\overline{Y}$-, and $\overline{Z}$-axes to the X-, Y-, and Z-axes is shown in Fig. 89-1. Our study of the graph of Equation 90-1 is therefore complete.

We proceed in the same way with any quadratic equation of the form

$$(90\text{-}7) \qquad ax^2 + by^2 + cz^2 + 2dxy + 2exz + 2fyz = g.$$

According to Equation 90-3, this equation is equivalent to the equation

$$(90\text{-}8) \qquad Sv \cdot v = g,$$

where S is the symmetric matrix defined by Equation 90-2, and v is the vector $v = (x, y, z)$. We know that there is an orthogonal matrix P such that $P^*SP = D$, where D is the diagonal matrix of Equation 90-5. So we set $R = P*$ and introduce new coordinates $\bar{v} = (\bar{x}, \bar{y}, \bar{z})$ by means of the equation $\bar{v} = Rv$. Thus $v = R*\bar{v} = P\bar{v}$, and therefore Equation 90-8 becomes

$$Sv \cdot v = SP\bar{v} \cdot P\bar{v} = P*SP\bar{v} \cdot \bar{v} = D\bar{v} \cdot \bar{v} = g.$$

But $D\bar{v} \cdot \bar{v} = \lambda_1\bar{x}^2 + \lambda_2\bar{y}^2 + \lambda_3\bar{z}^2$, so we see that there is an orthogonal transformation of axes (in the problems we ask you to show that it can always be chosen to be a rotation) under which Equation 90-7 is reduced to the form

(90-9) $$\lambda_1\bar{x}^2 + \lambda_2\bar{y}^2 + \lambda_3\bar{z}^2 = g.$$

This equation tells us the form of the graph of Equation 90-7. If we want to sketch the graph, we must go on to calculate the transformation matrix R.

Example 90-1. Discuss the graph of the quadratic equation

$$2x^2 + 5y^2 + 3z^2 + 4xy = 3.$$

Solution. The symmetric matrix S associated with this equation is

$$S = \begin{bmatrix} 2 & 2 & 0 \\ 2 & 5 & 0 \\ 0 & 0 & 3 \end{bmatrix}.$$

Its characteristic values are solutions of the equation

$$\begin{vmatrix} 2 - \lambda & 2 & 0 \\ 2 & 5 - \lambda & 0 \\ 0 & 0 & 3 - \lambda \end{vmatrix} = (3 - \lambda)[(2 - \lambda)(5 - \lambda) - 4]$$
$$= (3 - \lambda)(\lambda - 6)(\lambda - 1) = 0.$$

Hence $\lambda_1 = 6$, $\lambda_2 = 3$, and $\lambda_3 = 1$. There is a coordinate system, a rotation of the XYZ-system, in which our surface is the graph of the equation $6\bar{x}^2 + 3\bar{y}^2 + \bar{z}^2 = 3$. This graph, we know, is an ellipsoid.

Example 90-2. What is the plane graph of the equation $x^2 - 4xy - 2y^2 = 3$?

Solution. In this case our matrix S is the 2 by 2 matrix

$$S = \begin{bmatrix} 1 & -2 \\ -2 & -2 \end{bmatrix}.$$

Its characteristic values are the solutions of the equation

$$\begin{vmatrix} 1 - \lambda & -2 \\ -2 & -2 - \lambda \end{vmatrix} = \lambda^2 + \lambda - 6 = (\lambda + 3)(\lambda - 2) = 0.$$

Therefore, $\lambda_1 = 2$ and $\lambda_2 = -3$. There is a rotation of axes under which our equation becomes

$$2\bar{x}^2 - 3\bar{y}^2 = 3,$$

which we recognize as the equation of a hyperbola.

In Section 67 we found that the graph of the quadratic equation

(90-10) $$ax^2 + bxy + cy^2 + dx + ey + f = 0$$

is a conic; we can tell which conic by examining the *discriminant* $b^2 - 4ac$. In accordance with the ideas we have been developing in this chapter, we would treat Equation 90-10 as follows. The matrix associated with the quadratic form $ax^2 + bxy + cy^2$ is

$$S = \begin{bmatrix} a & \frac{1}{2}b \\ \frac{1}{2}b & c \end{bmatrix},$$

and we find its characteristic values λ_1 and λ_2 by solving the characteristic equation

(90-11) $$\begin{vmatrix} a - \lambda & \dfrac{b}{2} \\ \dfrac{b}{2} & c - \lambda \end{vmatrix} = \lambda^2 - (a + c)\lambda + \frac{4ac - b^2}{4} = 0.$$

After a suitable translation and rotation of axes, Equation 90-10 reduces to the form

$$\lambda_1 \bar{\bar{x}}^2 + \lambda_2 \bar{\bar{y}}^2 = k$$

(or $\bar{\bar{x}}^2 = k\bar{\bar{y}}$ if one of the characteristic values is 0). Thus, except for "degenerate cases," Equation 90-10 represents an ellipse if λ_1 and λ_2 have the same sign, a hyperbola if they have opposite signs, and a parabola if one of them is 0. Since the term $\dfrac{4ac - b^2}{4}$ in the quadratic Equation 90-11 is the product of the roots λ_1 and λ_2, we see that λ_1 and λ_2 have the same sign if $4ac - b^2$ is positive, have opposite signs if $4ac - b^2$ is negative, and one of the characteristic values is 0 if $4ac - b^2$ is 0. Therefore, as before, we find that the graph of Equation 90-10 is (taking degenerate cases into account)

(i) an ellipse if $4ac - b^2 > 0$,
(ii) a hyperbola if $4ac - b^2 < 0$,
(iii) a parabola if $4ac - b^2 = 0$.

P R O B L E M S   9 0

1. Consider the quadratic equation $2x^2 + 2xy + 2y^2 = 1$. (See Problem 88-1.)
   (a) Under a suitable rotation of axes, the equation is reduced to what standard form?
   (b) Find a rotation matrix that produces this transformation.
   (c) Through what angle are the axes rotated?

2. Answer the questions in Number 1 for the quadratic equation $x^2 - 4xy + y^2 = 1$.

3. Express the following quadratic equations in standard form.
   (a) $4x^2 + 2xy + 4y^2 = 3$ (b) $2x^2 + 6xy - 2y^2 = 13$
   (c) $2xy = 1$ (d) $x^2 + 4xy + 3y^2 = 1$
   (e) $4x^2 + 4xy + y^2 = 5$ (f) $x^2 + 2xy + y^2 + x - y = 0$

4. Consider the equation $x^2 + 2y^2 + 2z^2 + 2xy + 2xz = 1$. (See Problem 88-4.)
   (a) Under a suitable rotation of axes, this equation is reduced to what standard form?
   (b) Find a rotation matrix that produces this transformation.
   (c) Sketch the graph of our equation.

5. Answer the questions in Number 4 for the equation $2x^2 + y^2 + z^2 - 4xy - 4xz - 2yz = 1$.

6. Express the following quadratic equations in standard form.
   (a) $4x^2 + 4y^2 + 2z^2 + 2xy = 2$ (b) $2x^2 + y^2 + 2z^2 + 2xz = 5$
   (c) $2xy + 2yz = 2$ (d) $y^2 + 4xz = 3$
   (e) $5x^2 + 3y^2 + 3z^2 - 2xy - 2xz + 2yz = 6$
   (f) $-x^2 - y^2 - 7z^2 + 16xy + 8xz + 8yz = 9$

7. Explain why we can always take our orthogonal matrix R to be a rotation matrix.

8. Suppose the graph of Equation 90-7 is an ellipsoid. Express the lengths of its longest and shortest diameters in terms of characteristic values of S. Do characteristic vectors point along these diameters?

9. Show that if the matrix S has two equal characteristic values, then the graph of Equation 90-7 is a surface revolution. What if S has three equal characteristic values?

10. What is the graph of Equation 90-7 if one of the characteristic values of S is 0?

REVIEW PROBLEMS—CHAPTER TEN

   You can use the following problems to test yourself on the material of this chapter.

1. Suppose you have a combination of ten coins consisting of nickels, dimes, and quarters whose total value is $1.25. How many of each coin do you have?

2. Show that the following system is inconsistent unless $2r - s - 3t = 0$:

$$x + 3y = r$$
$$2x - 3z = s$$
$$2y + z = t.$$

Give a geometric description of the solution of this system in case $r = 2$, $s = -2$, and $t = 2$.

3. Show that $\begin{vmatrix} x & y & 1 \\ x_1 & y_1 & 1 \\ x_2 & y_2 & 1 \end{vmatrix} = 0$ is the equation of the line that contains the points (x_1, y_1) and (x_2, y_2).

4. Let $S = \begin{bmatrix} \cos^2 x & \sin x \cos x \\ \sin x \cos x & \sin^2 x \end{bmatrix}$, and let S' be the matrix whose elements are the derivatives of the elements of S. Show that (a) $S^2 = S$ and (b) $SS'S = 0$.

5. Suppose that $A = \begin{bmatrix} a & b \\ c & d \end{bmatrix}$. What are the relations among the numbers a, b, c, and d if $AA^* = A^*A$?

6. It is a fact that the determinant of a matrix is the product of its characteristic values. Prove this result for symmetric matrices.

7. Discuss the graph of the equation

$$5y^2 + 4z^2 + 4xy + 8xz + 12yz + 12y - 12z = 0.$$

8. Find the characteristic values and corresponding characteristic vectors for the matrix $S = \begin{bmatrix} 0 & 1 & 1 \\ 1 & 0 & 1 \\ 1 & 1 & 0 \end{bmatrix}$. Now find an orthogonal matrix P such that P^*SP is a diagonal matrix. Use this result to discuss the graph of the equation $xy + yz + zx - 2x - 5y - z + 1 = 0$.

9. We have only multiplied square matrices, but our rule for multiplication may also be applied to matrices with more rows than columns or more columns than rows. Compute the following products. Can you reverse the order of multiplication in these examples?

(a) $\begin{bmatrix} 1 & 2 & 3 \\ -1 & 1 & 2 \end{bmatrix} \begin{bmatrix} 1 & -1 \\ 0 & 2 \\ 3 & 1 \end{bmatrix}$
(b) $\begin{bmatrix} 1 & -1 \\ 0 & 2 \end{bmatrix} \begin{bmatrix} 1 & 2 & 3 \\ -1 & 1 & 2 \end{bmatrix}$

(c) $\begin{bmatrix} 1 & 2 & 3 \end{bmatrix} \begin{bmatrix} 4 \\ 5 \\ 6 \end{bmatrix}$

10. The equation of a plane, $ax + by + cz = d$, can be written as $n \cdot v = d$, where $n = (a, b, c)$ and $v = (x, y, z)$. Discuss the problem of choosing a rotation matrix R so that the transformation of coordinates equation $v = R^*\bar{v}$ reduces the equation of our plane to the simple form $e\bar{z} = d$. In other words, how do we rotate the axes so that our plane is parallel to the $\bar{X}\bar{Y}$-plane?

PARTIAL

DERIVATIVES

E L E V E N

The law of a falling body, $s = 16t^2$, defines a simple function. With each number t there is associated a number s; if the body falls for t seconds, it will travel s feet. Many physical situations cannot be described by such simple functions, however. For example, to compute the pressure of a certain quantity of gas in a cylinder, we must prescribe not one but two numbers—namely, numbers that measure volume and temperature. In this chapter we will extend our notion of function to cover such cases and extend our knowledge of calculus to deal with such functions.

91 FUNCTIONS ON R^n

We determine a function by prescribing its domain D, its range R, and the rule of correspondence that assigns to each element of D an element of R. In most of our examples so far, the sets D and R

have been sets of numbers (subsets of R^1), but we have seen examples in which D is a set of angles, R is a set of vectors, and so on. In this chapter we will be dealing with functions with domains or ranges that are subsets of R^1, R^2, or R^3. The topics we will take up are natural extensions of ideas we have already studied, but there are certain notational complications as we go from 1 to higher dimensions. Therefore, as in Chapter 10, we will only explicitly mention R^n with $n \leq 3$, even though our theory applies to higher dimensional spaces.

Once we have chosen a cartesian coordinate system in three-dimensional space, an element of R^3 corresponds to a point in space, and conversely. Therefore, we are accustomed to using geometric language to refer to elements of R^3; we speak of the point (x, y, z), and so on. In Chapter 10 we saw how R^3 can be thought of as a vector space. Relative to our given coordinate system, the elements of this vector space are in 1-to-1 correspondence with the geometric vectors in three-dimensional space. Thus we can represent a component vector (x, y, z) of R^3 as the geometric vector $x\boldsymbol{i} + y\boldsymbol{j} + z\boldsymbol{k}$ in space. We will freely use this interchangeability of triples of numbers with points in space and geometric vectors in space. For example, if we are working in three-dimensional space, we may use the letter $\boldsymbol{i}$ to denote the unit vector along the positive X-axis or the element $(1, 0, 0)$ of R^3. If we are in two-dimensional space, we may interpret $x\boldsymbol{i} + y\boldsymbol{j}$ as a geometric vector in the coordinate plane or as the element (x, y) of R^2, and so on. We will use bold-face letters to denote elements of R^2 and R^3 and also functions whose values belong to one of these spaces. We often follow the convention of assigning as the name of a vector in R^n its first component written in boldface type. Thus we will write $\boldsymbol{x} = (x, y)$, $\boldsymbol{u} = (u, v, w)$ and the like.

To show this notation in action, we now consider an example. Let $\boldsymbol{m} = (2, -2, 1)$, and define a function f by the equation $f(\boldsymbol{x}) = \boldsymbol{m} \cdot \boldsymbol{x}$. Since $\boldsymbol{m} \in R^3$, it is clear that we are to consider $\boldsymbol{x}$ as an element of R^3. As with any function defined by a formula, the domain of our function f consists of all the elements of R^3 for which the formula $\boldsymbol{m} \cdot \boldsymbol{x}$ makes sense. We can replace $\boldsymbol{x}$ in this formula with any element of R^3, so we see that the domain of f is R^3. For each $\boldsymbol{x} \in R^3$, $f(\boldsymbol{x})$ is a *number*, so the range of f is a subset of R^1 (in fact, the range of f is the entire set R^1). If $\boldsymbol{x}$ is the vector (x, y, z), we will often write $f(x, y, z)$ in place of $f(\boldsymbol{x})$, and we could express $\boldsymbol{m} \cdot \boldsymbol{x}$ as $2x - 2y + z$. Therefore, our function f is also defined by the equation $f(x, y, z) = 2x - 2y + z$. All these notational devices are simply ways of saying that, "To the triple of numbers $(1, 2, 3)$ corresponds the number 1, to the triple $(-1, 0, 2)$ corresponds the number 0, and so on."

If the domain of a function f is a subset of R^n, we say that f is a **function on** R^n. Thus the function of the last paragraph is a function on R^3. The usual functions we have dealt with up to now—for example, the trigonometric functions—are functions on R^1. If the range of a function is a subset of R^1, we will say that the function is **scalar-valued**; if the range of f is a subset of R^n, where $n > 1$, then f is **vector-valued**.

In principle, there is nothing difficult about the idea of a vector-valued function on R^n, but in practice such a function may be rather complicated to describe and work with. Again let us look at an example. The equation

$$f(x, y, z) = (\ln z, x + y)$$

defines a vector-valued function f on R^3 whose range is a subset of R^2. Because we consider only logarithms of positive numbers, we see that (x, y, z) belongs to the domain of f if, and only if, $z > 0$. We leave it to you to show that the range of f is all of R^2. We could write $(u, v) = f(x, y, z)$, and then we would say that our function is given by the **component equations** $u = \ln z$, $v = x + y$. We could also write $\mathbf{u} = f(\mathbf{x})$, where $\mathbf{u} = (u, v)$ and $\mathbf{x} = (x, y, z)$. For example, in our present function we have $f(\mathbf{k}) = \mathbf{0}$. One has to read such an equation in context, of course. Because we know that the range of our function is a subset of R^2 and its domain is a subset of R^3, we know that here $\mathbf{0} = (0, 0)$ and $\mathbf{k} = (0, 0, 1)$.

Because we live in a three-dimensional world and write on two-dimensional paper, we encounter certain obvious technical problems when we try to graph functions on R^n if $n > 1$. The case of scalar-valued functions on R^2, however, is one that we can handle. Here we proceed just as we do with scalar-valued functions on R^1. The graph of a scalar-valued function f with domain $D \subseteq R^2$ is a subset of three-dimensional space; a point (x, y, z) belongs to the graph of f provided that $(x, y) \in D$ and $z = f(x, y)$. Thus the graph of f is simply the graph of the equation $z = f(x, y)$, and we discussed such graphs in Chapter 9. The graphs of most of the scalar valued functions on R^2 that we will consider are surfaces in space.

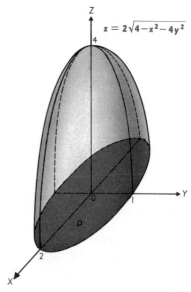

Example 91-1. Sketch the graph of the function that is defined by the equation $f(x, y) = 2\sqrt{4 - x^2 - 4y^2}$.

Solution. The domain D of this function is the subset of R^2 for which our defining formula makes sense; that is, the set $\{(x, y) \mid 4 - x^2 - 4y^2 \geqslant 0\}$. When we write this inequality in the form $\dfrac{x^2}{4} + y^2 \leq 1$, we see that our domain D is the elliptical region shown in the XY-plane in Fig. 91-1. The graph of our function f is the graph of the equation $z = 2\sqrt{4 - x^2 - 4y^2}$, and so the resulting surface is the upper half of the ellipsoid $\dfrac{x^2}{4} + y^2 + \dfrac{z^2}{16} = 1$, which we have sketched.

$z = 2\sqrt{4 - x^2 - 4y^2}$

Figure 91-1

Our Definition 10-2 of what we mean when we say that a number A is the limit of a scalar-valued function on R^1 at a point a is expressed in terms of neighborhoods of the points A and a. Therefore, as we now turn to the limit concept in higher dimensions, our first task is to define a neighborhood of a point of R^n. If r is a positive number, then the **neighborhood $N_r a$ of radius r** about the point $a \in R^n$ is the set

$$N_r a = \{x \mid x \in R^n, |x - a| < r\}.$$

Since $|x - a|$ stands for the distance between the points x and a, $N_r a$ is the set of points of R^n that are less than r units from a; that is, the interior of an "n-dimensional ball." This definition corresponds exactly to the definition of a neighborhood of radius r of a point $a \in R^1$ as the interval $(a - r, a + r)$, which is the interior of a "one-dimensional ball." We obtain the **punctured neighborhood $N_r^* a$** by deleting the point a from the set $N_r a$. Now our definition of limit applies to vector- or scalar-valued functions on R^n for any positive integer n. We rewrite it here.

Definition 91-1. *The equation $\lim_{x \to a} f(x) = A$ means that for each neighborhood $N_p A$ there exists a punctured neighborhood $N_r^* a$ such that $f(N_r^* a) \subseteq N_p A$.*

As before, f is continuous at a if its limit at a is its value at a. Formally, f is con-continuous at a if to each $N_p f(a)$ there corresponds an $N_r a$ such that $f(N_r a) \subseteq N_p f(a)$.

Example 91-2. Show that the function f that is defined by the equation $f(x) = m \cdot x$, where m is a given vector, is continuous at each point of R^3.

Solution. We must show that if a is a given point of R^3, then $\lim_{x \to a} m \cdot x = m \cdot a$. In informal terms, this equation says that $m \cdot x$ is close to $m \cdot a$ when x is close to a. Since $m \cdot x - m \cdot a = m \cdot (x - a) = |m| |x - a| \cos \theta$ (where we are supposing that the vectors m and $x - a$ determine an angle of θ), we see that $|m \cdot x - m \cdot a| \leq |m| |x - a|$. This inequality clearly shows that $m \cdot x$ is close to $m \cdot a$ if x is close to a. We leave to you the task of putting the proof of this obvious statement into the formal language of limits.

The general limit theorems that we proved in Section 11 for scalar-valued functions on R^1 can be extended to apply to the functions on R^n that we consider in this chapter. Thus, limits of sums are sums of limits; theorems analogous to Theorem 11-3 on composite functions are true, and so on. In the sections that follow, we will use without proof certain natural extensions of the theorems of Section 11.

P R O B L E M S   9 1

1. In this question, f is the function that is defined by the statement, "To each point $(x, y, z) \in R^3$ let there correspond the number xy^2z^3."
   (a) What is the formula for $f(x, y, z)$?
   (b) Show that $f(x, y, z)^2 = f(x^2, y^2, z^2)$ for every point $(x, y, z) \in R^3$. Is this statement true for every scalar-valued function on R^3?
   (c) Is the equation $[f(x, y, z)] = f([x], [y], [z])$ true for every point of R^3? Any point?
   (d) Compare the numbers $f(x)$ and $f(-x)$, where x is an arbitrary point of R^3.
   (e) Express the product $f(x, y, z)f(y, z, x)f(z, x, y)$ in terms of x, y, and z.
   (f) Let $x = (3, 2, 1)$ and, as usual, $j = (0, 1, 0)$, and define the quotient function q on R^1 by means of the equation

   $$q(h) = \frac{f(x + hj) - f(x)}{h}.$$

   What is the domain of q? What is $\lim_{h \to 0} q(h)$?

2. Examine $\lim_{h \to 0} q(h)$, where $q(h) = \dfrac{f(2 + h, 3) - f(2, 3)}{h}$, and f is given by the formula listed below. When convenient, you might sketch the graph of the equation $y = q(h)$ in an HY-coordinate system.
   (a) $f(x, y) = x^2 \ln y$ (b) $f(x, y) = y^2 \ln x$ (c) $f(x, y) = x^y$
   (d) $f(x, y) = y^x$ (e) $f(x, y) = [x] + [y]$ (f) $f(x, y) = [x + y]$

3. Sketch the graph of f and state its domain and range. At what points of its domain is f continuous?
   (a) $f(x, y) = 4x^2 + 9y^2$ (b) $f(x, y) = \text{Arcsin } x + 1$
   (c) $f(x, y) = [x] + [y]$ (d) $f(x) = |x|^2 + 2i \cdot x - 4j \cdot x + 3$, $x \in R^2$

4. Each of the following equations defines a function on R^3. What is the domain of the function? What is its range? At what points is f continuous?
   (a) $f(x, y, z) = \sqrt{x} - y \ln z$ (b) $f(x, y, z) = [x][y][z]$
   (c) $f(x) = \tan |x|$ (d) $f(x) = i \times x$

5. Let f be the function that makes correspond to a point $(x, y) \in R^2$ the slope (if any) of the line joining (x, y) and $(0, 0)$. What is the formula that defines f? Graph f. Is f continuous at each point of its domain?

6. Let f be the function on R^2 defined as follows: $f(x, y) = \dfrac{|y| - |x|}{||y| - |x||}$ if (x, y) is a point for which the formula makes sense, and $f(x, y) = 0$ if (x, y) is a point at which we cannot apply the formula. Describe the graph of f. Is f continuous at each point of R^2? What is the range of f?

7. The resistance of a piece of wire is directly proportional to its length and inversely proportional to the square of its radius. If a wire 10 centimeters long with a radius

of 2 millimeters has a resistance of .1 ohms, what is the formula expressing the resistance in terms of the length and radius? In what units should the various quantities in your formula be expressed?

8. Let

$$f(x, y, z) = \begin{vmatrix} 1 & 1 & 1 \\ x & y & z \\ x^2 & y^2 & z^2 \end{vmatrix}.$$

Describe the set of points in space for which $f(x, y, z) = 0$.

9. Let $m = 2i - 3j + 4k$.
  (a) If $f(x) = m \cdot x$, describe the set of points in R^3 such that $f(x) = 7$.
  (b) If $f(x) = m \times x$, describe the set of points in R^3 such that $f(x) = 7i - 2j - 5k$.

10. Show that if $f(x, y) \geq f(y, x)$ for each point $(x, y) \in R^2$, then $f(x, y) = f(y, x)$. What can you conclude if you know that $f(x, y, z) \geq f(y, z, x)$ for each point $(x, y, z) \in R^3$?

92 PARTIAL DERIVATIVES

Now let us introduce some of the ideas of calculus into our study of functions on R^n. From a given scalar-valued function f on R^1, we construct a derived function f' by means of the equation $f'(x) = \lim\limits_{h \to 0} \dfrac{f(x + h) - f(x)}{h}$. In a similar manner we will now construct derived functions from a given function on R^n. Most of our discussion will be about scalar-valued functions on R^2, but the concepts can be extended to functions on R^n for any n.

If f is a scalar-valued function on R^2, we define two **derived functions** f_1 and f_2 by means of the equations

(92-1) $$f_1(x, y) = \lim\limits_{h \to 0} \frac{f(x + h, y) - f(x, y)}{h}$$

and

(92-2) $$f_2(x, y) = \lim\limits_{h \to 0} \frac{f(x, y + h) - f(x, y)}{h}.$$

The numbers $f_1(x, y)$ and $f_2(x, y)$ are called the **(first) partial derivatives** of $f(x, y)$. Although the idea of partial derivatives is new to us, the process of computing them is just our usual process of differentiation, as the next example shows.

Example 92-1.   Find $f_1(2, 3)$ if $f(x, y) = 2y^3 \sin x$.

Solution.   According to Equation 92-1,

$$(92\text{-}3) \qquad f_1(2, 3) = \lim_{h \to 0} \frac{f(2 + h, 3) - f(2, 3)}{h}$$

$$= \lim_{h \to 0} \frac{2 \cdot 3^3 \sin (2 + h) - 2 \cdot 3^3 \sin 2}{h}$$

$$= \lim_{h \to 0} \frac{54 \sin (2 + h) - 54 \sin 2}{h} \, .$$

We use our knowledge of ordinary differentiation to find this limit. Let us define the function g on R^1 by means of the equation $g(x) = f(x, 3) = 2 \cdot 3^3 \sin x = 54 \sin x$. Then Equation 92-3 can be written as

$$f_1(2, 3) = \lim_{h \to 0} \frac{g(2 + h) - g(2)}{h} \, .$$

But this last limit is the number $g'(2)$, so we see that $f_1(2, 3) = g'(2)$. Since $g'(x) = D_x 54 \sin x = 54 \cos x$, we have $g'(2) = 54 \cos 2$, and therefore $f_1(2, 3) = 54 \cos 2$.

We found the derivative in our example above by "fixing" the value of y in the formula $2y^3 \sin x$ at 3 and then applying the differential operator D_x. In general, the definition of $f_1(x, y)$ tells us that when we find this derivative we are to treat y as a "fixed" number and differentiate $f(x, y)$ with respect to x. For example, if $f(x, y) = 2y^3 \sin x$, then $f_1(x, y) = D_x 2y^3 \sin x = 2y^3 \cos x$. Here we have an equation that is valid for any x and y; if we want $f_1(2, 3)$, we replace x with 2 and y with 3. Similarly, to find $f_2(x, y)$, we apply the differential operator D_y, which tells us to differentiate with respect to y and keep x "fixed." In our present example, we find that $f_2(x, y) = D_y 2y^3 \sin x = 6y^2 \sin x$. The derivative $f_1(x, y)$ is the result of differentiating $f(x, y)$ with respect to the first component of the element (x, y) of R^2; we obtain $f_2(x, y)$ by differentiating $f(x, y)$ with respect to the second component.

The symbol $\dfrac{d}{dx}$ is another name for the differential operator D_x as applied in R^1. When we deal with partial derivatives, it is customary to replace the "straight" d with the "curved d" symbol ∂ and so obtain the differential operator $\dfrac{\partial}{\partial x}$. Because it is a little simpler to write, most of the time we will use the symbol D_x to denote differentiation with respect to x, both in R^1 and in R^n when $n > 1$. If f is a function on R^1 and $w = f(x)$, we write $w' = D_x w = f'(x)$. The corresponding notation in case $w = f(x, y)$, where f is a function on R^2, is $w_x = D_x w = \dfrac{\partial w}{\partial x} = f_1(x, y)$ and $w_y = D_y w = \dfrac{\partial w}{\partial y} = f_2(x, y)$. We might mention that some authors also write $f_x(x, y)$ and $f_y(x, y)$ where we have written $f_1(x, y)$ and $f_2(x, y)$.

The derivative $D_x^2 f(x, y) = D_x(D_x f(x, y))$ is a second partial derivative of $f(x, y)$. We denote it by the symbol $f_{11}(x, y)$. (The symbol f_{11} can be read as "f sub one, one." If f were a function on R^n with $n \geq 11$, we might have to write $f_{1,1}$ to distinguish it from "f sub eleven," but we omit the comma when no confusion can arise.) The derivative $D_y D_x f(x, y) = D_y(D_x f(x, y))$ is a "mixed" second partial derivative that we denote by $f_{12}(x, y)$, and so on. Other symbols for second derivatives, if $w = f(x, y)$, are

$$D_x^2 w = \frac{\partial^2 w}{\partial x^2} = w_{xx} = f_{11}(x, y),$$

$$D_y D_x w = \frac{\partial^2 w}{\partial y\, \partial x} = w_{xy} = f_{12}(x, y),$$

$$D_x D_y w = \frac{\partial^2 w}{\partial x\, \partial y} = w_{yx} = f_{21}(x, y),$$

$$D_y^2 w = \frac{\partial^2 w}{\partial y^2} = w_{yy} = f_{22}(x, y).$$

Of course, we also talk about derivatives of order higher than the second; the notation will be clear to you when you meet it.

Example 92-2. Find all the second derivatives of w if $w = (x + y) \sin x$.

Solution. The first derivatives of w are

$$D_x w = \sin x + (x + y) \cos x \quad \text{and} \quad D_y w = \sin x.$$

Therefore,

$$D_x^2 w = D_x[\sin x + (x + y) \cos x] = 2 \cos x - (x + y) \sin x,$$
$$D_y^2 w = D_y \sin x = 0,$$
$$D_y D_x w = D_y[\sin x + (x + y) \cos x] = \cos x,$$
$$D_x D_y w = D_x \sin x = \cos x.$$

You may have difficulty in remembering that $f_{12}(x, y)$ means $D_y D_x f(x, y)$ and not $D_x D_y f(x, y)$. In example 92-2 we see that it does not matter, the two numbers are the same, anyway. In fact, the two numbers $f_{12}(x, y)$ and $f_{21}(x, y)$ are equal for almost every function f you are likely to encounter for a while. The following theorem is proved in advanced calculus.

Theorem 92-1. *If the derived functions f_{12} and f_{21} are continuous at a point (x, y), then $f_{12}(x, y) = f_{21}(x, y)$.*

Theorem 92-1 tells us that mixed partial derivatives of the second order are equal (under suitable conditions of continuity). In fact, this theorem can be used to show that mixed derivatives of higher order with the same set of subscripts are also equal (under suitable conditions of continuity). And, as before, our results can be extended to functions on R^n with $n > 2$.

Example 92-3.   If $f(x, y) = e^{xy}$, show that $f_{112}(x, y) = f_{121}(x, y) = f_{211}(x, y)$.

Solution.   We have

$$f_1(x, y) = ye^{xy} \quad \text{and} \quad f_2(x, y) = xe^{xy}.$$

Hence

$$f_{11}(x, y) = y^2e^{xy}, f_{12}(x, y) = f_{21}(x, y) = (1 + xy)e^{xy}.$$

Thus

$$f_{112}(x, y) = (2y + xy^2)e^{xy},$$

and

$$f_{121}(x, y) = f_{211}(x, y) = ye^{xy} + (1 + xy)ye^{xy} = (2y + xy^2)e^{xy}.$$

Recall that $D_x y$ is interpreted geometrically as the slope of the tangent line to the graph of the equation $y = f(x)$ at the point (x, y). Now we shall take up the geometric meaning of partial derivatives. If the graph of a scalar-valued function f on R^2 is a surface, the intersection of this surface with the plane $y = b$ is a curve. We can obtain a picture of this curve of intersection by sketching the graph of the equation $z = f(x, b)$ in an XZ-plane. The number $f_1(a, b)$—which is a value of $D_x z$—is the slope of the graph at the point where $x = a$ (see Fig. 92-1). Similarly, the intersection of the graph of f with the plane $x = a$ produces the curve whose equation is $z = f(a, y)$. Since $D_y z = f_2(a, y)$, we see that the number $f_2(a, b)$ is the slope of this curve at the point where $y = b$. Thus we may interpret the numbers $f_1(a, b)$ and $f_2(a, b)$ as the slopes of the profile curves obtained by cutting the graph

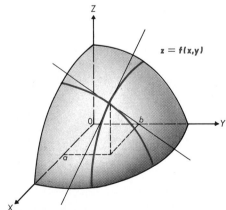

Figure 92-1

of f with planes that contain the point $(a, b, f(a, b))$ and are parallel to the XZ-plane and the YZ-plane.

One of the most-used theorems in the calculus of functions on R^1 is the Chain Rule. You will recall that if f and g are scalar-valued differentiable functions on R^1, and if $u = g(x)$, then the Chain Rule Equation reads

$$(92\text{-}4) \qquad\qquad D_x f(u) = f'(u) D_x u.$$

Precisely the same formula holds if g is a function on R^n, where $n > 1$. Thus if $n = 2$, we have $u = g(x, y)$. We calculate $D_x f(u)$ by differentiating with respect to x, keeping y "fixed." In this differentiation process, we use the ordinary Chain Rule, and we obtain Equation 92-4. For example, $D_x \sin x^2 y = (\cos x^2 y) D_x(x^2 y) = 2xy \cos x^2 y$. Similarly, we have the Chain Rule equation.

$$(92\text{-}5) \qquad\qquad D_y f(u) = f'(u) D_y u.$$

Example 92-4. Show that if f is any differentiable function on R^1, then $w = f(3x + 4y)$ satisfies the *partial differential equation*

$$4w_x - 3w_y = 0.$$

Solution. Since $w = f(3x + 4y)$, $w_x = D_x f(3x + 4y)$ and $w_y = D_y f(3x + 4y)$. We calculate these derivatives by replacing u with $3x + 4y$ in Equations 92-4 and 92-5, and we obtain

$$w_x = f'(3x + 4y) D_x(3x + 4y) = 3f'(3x + 4y)$$

and

$$w_y = f'(3x + 4y) D_y(3x + 4y) = 4f'(3x + 4y).$$

Therefore

$$4w_x - 3w_y = 12f'(3x + 4y) - 12f'(3x + 4y) = 0.$$

P R O B L E M S   9 2

1. Find $f_1(3, -2)$ if:

(a) $f(x, y) = x^2 e^y$

(b) $f(x, y) = e^x y^2$

(c) $f(x, y) = \operatorname{Sin}^{-1} \dfrac{x}{y}$

(d) $f(x, y) = \operatorname{Sin}^{-1} \dfrac{y}{x}$

(e) $f(x, y) = x^{-y}$

(f) $f(x, y) = (-y)^x$

(g) $f(x, y) = \ln x^y$

(h) $f(x, y) = (\ln x)^y$

(i) $f(x, y) = \displaystyle\int_y^x \cos \pi t^2 \, dt$

(j) $f(x, y) = \displaystyle\int_x^y \cos \pi t^2 \, dt$

2. Calculate $f_{12}(x, y)$ and $f_{21}(x, y)$ and show that they are equal for each function f in the preceding question.

3. Determine from Fig. 92-1 whether the numbers $f_1(a, b)$ and $f_2(a, b)$ are positive or negative. What does the figure tell us about the signs of the numbers $f_{11}(a, b)$ and $f_{22}(a, b)$?

4. Show that the following equations define solutions of the partial differential equation $w_{xx} + w_{yy} = 0$ (Laplace's Equation).

(a) $w = 2x + 3y - 1$ (b) $w = e^x \cos y$ (c) $w = x^2 - y^2$

(d) $w = \ln (x^2 + y^2)$ (e) $w = \text{Tan}^{-1} \dfrac{y}{x}$ (f) $w = \cos x \cosh y$

5. The point $(1, 2, 3)$ is on the surface of a mountain whose equation is $z = 17 - 2x^2 - 3y^2$. Is the path down from the point steeper in the positive X-direction or in the positive Y-direction?

6. Let $w = f(u)$ and $u = g(x, y)$. Show that $w_{xx} = f'(u)u_{xx} + f''(u)u_x^2$ Verify this equation if $w = u^2$ and $u = \sin xy$.

7. If h is a function on R^2 and $w = h(x, y)$, we define $\Delta w = w_{xx} + w_{yy}$. Show that if $w = r^{2m}$, where $r^2 = x^2 + y^2$, then $\Delta w = 4m^2 r^{2m-2}$. (You may want to use the formula in the preceding problem.)

8. Let $w = \cos (3x - 4y + 5z)$ and form the vector $V = D_x w i + D_y w j + D_z w k$. Show that V is perpendicular to the vector $8i + j - 4k$.

9. Evaluate the determinant $\begin{vmatrix} u_x & v_x \\ u_y & v_y \end{vmatrix}$ if:

(a) $u = x \cos y, v = x \sin y$ (b) $u = x \cosh y, v = x \sinh y$

(c) $u = \displaystyle\int_x^y \cos t^2 \, dt, v = \int_x^y \sin t^2 \, dt$ (d) $u = f(x, y), v = g(u)$.

10. Evaluate the determinant $\begin{vmatrix} z_{xx} & z_{xy} \\ z_{yx} & z_{yy} \end{vmatrix}$ if:

(a) $z = ax^2 + 2bxy + cy^2$ (b) $z = \displaystyle\int_3^{x^2-2y} e^{-t^2} \, dt$.

11. Is the equation $D_x f(x^2, y^2) = f_1(x^2, y^2)$ true for *every* function f on R^2? For *any* function f on R^2?

12. The gas in a certain cylinder is at a pressure of P pounds when its volume is V cubic centimeters and its temperature is T degrees; the numbers P, T, and V are related by the equation $P = 10T/V$. How much does the pressure change if we change T from 100 to 101, keeping $V = 200$? Again let us start with $T = 100$ and $V = 200$, and this time hold T at 100. Approximately what change in volume will produce the same pressure change as before?

13. Suppose $f(x, y) = \dfrac{xy}{x^2 + y^2}$ if $(x, y) \neq (0, 0)$, and $f(0, 0) = 0$. Use Equations 92-1 and 92-2 with $(x, y) = (0, 0)$ to find $f_1(0, 0)$ and $f_2(0, 0)$. What happens if you first find $D_x f(x, y)$ and $D_y f(x, y)$ and then replace (x, y) with $(0, 0)$?

93 CHAIN RULES

Using vector-valued functions on R^n as building blocks, we can construct quite complicated composite functions. To find the derivatives of these functions, we must develop the proper chain rules. In the preceding section, we stated the Chain Rule that gives us derivatives of the composition of a scalar-valued function g on R^n by a function f on R^1. This rule is a simple consequence of the ordinary Chain Rule that we introduced in Section 16. However, if f is a function on some R^n and g is a function that takes values in R^n, where $n > 1$, then we must develop a new chain rule to deal with the composition of g by f. That is our goal in this section.

As the first step in our development of this new chain rule, we derive a kind of mean value theorem for scalar-valued functions on R^2.

Theorem 93-1. *If the partial derivatives $f_1(x, y)$ and $f_2(x, y)$ exist for each point of the right-angle path joining the points (a, b) and (c, d) shown in Fig. 93-1, then*

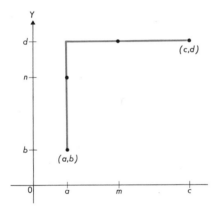

Figure 93-1

there is a number m between a and c and a number n between b and d such that

(93-1) $f(c, d) - f(a, b) = f_1(m, d)(c - a) + f_2(a, n)(d - b).$

Proof. First we write

(93-2) $f(c, d) - f(a, b) = f(c, d) - f(a, d) + f(a, d) - f(a, b)$

and look at the differences $f(c, d) - f(a, d)$ and $f(a, d) - f(a, b)$ separately. We can consider the number $f(c, d) - f(a, d)$ as the difference of two values of the function on R^1 that is defined by the equation $z = f(x, d)$. According to the Theorem of the Mean (Theorem 19-5), there is a point m between a and c at which the derivative of z equals the quotient $\dfrac{f(c, d) - f(a, d)}{c - a}$. Since $D_x z = f_1(x, d)$, this statement tells us that there is a number m between a and c such that

$$(93\text{-}3) \qquad\qquad f(c, d) - f(a, d) = f_1(m, d)(c - a).$$

In the same way we show that there is a number n between b and d such that

$$(93\text{-}4) \qquad\qquad f(a, d) - f(a, b) = f_2(a, n)(d - b).$$

When we substitute the results of Equations 93-3 and 93-4 in Equation 93-2, we obtain Equation 93-1.

In Section 95 we will derive a somewhat more elegant Mean Value Theorem for functions on R^n, but Equation 93-1 will serve our present purposes.

Example 93-1. Show that if $f_1(x, y) = 0$ and $f_2(x, y) = 0$ at each point $(x, y) \in R^2$, then f is a constant function on R^2.

Solution. We must show that the value of f at any point (a, b) is the same as its value at any other point (c, d). Since we are assuming that all first partial derivatives are 0, the numbers $f_1(m, d)$ and $f_2(a, n)$ in Equation 93-1 are 0. Therefore, that equation reduces to the equation $f(c, d) - f(a, b) = 0$; that is, $f(c, d) = f(a, b)$.

Now we develop our chain rules. To begin, suppose that f is a scalar-valued function on R^2 whose domain is contained in the range of a vector-valued function g on R^1. The function g can be defined in terms of a vector equation $u = g(x)$, or it can be defined in terms of scalar-valued functions g and h by means of the component equations $u = g(x)$, $v = h(x)$. We will assume that the derived functions f_1 and f_2 are continuous and that g and h are differentiable functions. Although we won't specifically mention these hypotheses again, similar assumptions underlie all the differentiation rules that we will use in the remainder of this chapter. If F is the composite function defined by the equation $F(x) = f(u)$, where $u = (u, v) = (g(x), h(x))$, we can write

$$F(x) = f(u, v) = f(g(x), h(x)).$$

Our task is to find a formula for $F'(x)$. According to the definition of the derivative,

$$F'(x) = \lim_{z \to x} \frac{F(z) - F(x)}{z - x}.$$

Thus $F'(x)$ is the limit of the difference quotient

$$\frac{f(g(z), h(z)) - f(g(x), h(x))}{z - x}.$$

We can use Equation 93-1 with $c = g(z)$, $d = h(z)$, $a = g(x)$, and $b = h(x)$ to rewrite this difference quotient in the form

(93-5) $\quad \dfrac{F(z) - F(x)}{z - x} = f_1(m, h(z)) \dfrac{g(z) - g(x)}{z - x} + f_2(g(x), n) \dfrac{h(z) - h(x)}{z - x},$

where m is a number between $g(x)$ and $g(z)$, and n is a number between $h(x)$ and $h(z)$. We have assumed that g and h are differentiable functions, so they are continuous; that is, $\lim_{z \to x} g(z) = g(x)$ and $\lim_{z \to x} h(z) = h(x)$. Since m is trapped between $g(z)$ and $g(x)$, and n is trapped between $h(z)$ and $h(x)$, and since we are assuming that f_1 and f_2 are continuous functions, we have

(93-6) $\qquad\qquad \lim_{z \to x} f_1(m, h(z)) = f_1(g(x), h(x))$

and

(93-7) $\qquad\qquad \lim_{z \to x} f_2(g(x), n) = f_2(g(x), h(x)).$

Finally, the definition of the derivative gives us the equations

(93-8) $\quad \lim_{z \to x} \dfrac{g(z) - g(x)}{z - x} = g'(x)$ and $\lim_{z \to x} \dfrac{h(z) - h(x)}{z - x} = h'(x).$

Now we use Equations 93-5, 93-6, 93-7, and 93-8 to calculate $F'(x)$, and we find that

(93-9) $\qquad F'(x) = f_1(g(x), h(x))g'(x) + f_2(g(x), h(x))h'(x).$

We have just derived the following Chain Rule: *If $u = g(x)$ and $v = h(x)$, then*

(93-10) $\qquad\qquad D_x f(u, v) = f_1(u, v) D_x u + f_2(u, v) D_x v.$

Notice how this equation compares with the Chain Rule Equation for a function f on R^1: $D_x f(u) = f'(u) D_x u$. If $w = f(u, v)$, we can also write our Chain Rule Equation 93-10 as

(93-11) $\qquad\qquad D_x w = D_u w \, D_x u + D_v w \, D_x v,$

or, in the curved ∂ notation, as

$$\frac{dw}{dx} = \frac{\partial w}{\partial u} \frac{du}{dx} + \frac{\partial w}{\partial v} \frac{dv}{dx}.$$

Example 93-2. Show that Equation 93-11 gives the correct value of $D_x w$ if $w = u^2 + v^2$ and $u = x$, $v = e^x$.

Solution. We see that $w = x^2 + (e^x)^2 = x^2 + e^{2x}$. Hence

$$D_x w = 2x + 2e^{2x}.$$

Now we will obtain the same result from Equation 93-11. We have

$$D_u w = 2u, \qquad D_v w = 2v, \qquad D_x u = 1, \quad \text{and} \quad D_x v = e^x.$$

When we substitute these numbers in Equation 93-11, we get

$$D_x w = 2u \cdot 1 + 2v \cdot e^x = 2x + 2e^x e^x = 2x + 2e^{2x},$$

the correct result.

Equation 93-10 was derived on the assumption that $u = g(x)$ and $v = h(x)$, where g and h are differentiable functions on R^1. But when we compute a partial derivative, we differentiate as if we were dealing with a function on R^1, and so Equation 93-10 remains valid when g and h are functions on R^2 (or on any R^n). In that case, of course, one considers $D_x f(u, v)$, $D_x u$, and $D_x v$ as partial derivatives. Thus to express Equation 93-11 in differential notation, we use the curved ∂ symbol in each term:

$$\frac{\partial w}{\partial x} = \frac{\partial w}{\partial u}\frac{\partial u}{\partial x} + \frac{\partial w}{\partial v}\frac{\partial v}{\partial x}.$$

Example 93-3. Use a chain rule to compute $D_y(x + y)^{xy}$.

Solution. We can think of the desired derivative as $D_y u^v$, where $u = x + y$ and $v = xy$. Then the Chain Rule Equation 93-11 (with D_y in place of D_x, of course) gives us

$$D_y u^v = D_u u^v D_y u + D_v u^v D_y v$$
$$= (vu^{v-1}) \cdot 1 + u^v(\ln u)x.$$

Now we replace u and v in terms of x and y, simplify, and we have our answer:

$$D_y(x + y)^{xy} = x(x + y)^{xy} \left[\frac{y}{x + y} + \ln (x + y)\right].$$

Our Chain Rule is related to the process of implicit differentiation that we discussed in Section 26. Thus suppose that the graph of the equation $y = h(x)$ is a subset of the graph of the equation $f(x, y) = 0$. Then we can think of x and y as playing the roles of u and v in Equation 93-10, and we have

$$D_x f(x, y) = f_1(x, y)D_x x + f_2(x, y)D_x y.$$

Of course $D_x x = 1$, and since $f(x, y) = 0$, we have $D_x f(x, y) = 0$. Therefore we find that

(93-12)
$$D_x y = -\frac{f_1(x, y)}{f_2(x, y)}.$$

Example 93-4. Suppose that u and v are functions on R^2 that satisfy the **Cauchy-Riemann partial differential equations:**

$$u_1(x, y) = v_2(x, y) \quad \text{and} \quad u_2(x, y) = -v_1(x, y).$$

Show that the graphs of the equations $u(x, y) = a$ and $v(x, y) = b$, where a and b are given numbers, meet at right angles.

Solution. First we let $u(x, y) - a$ play the role of $f(x, y)$ in Equation 93-12, and we see that the slope of the graph of the equation $u(x, y) = a$ is

$$m_1 = -\frac{u_1(x, y)}{u_2(x, y)}.$$

Then we set $f(x, y) = v(x, y) - b$ in Equation 93-12, and we find that the slope of the graph of the equation $v(x, y) = b$ is

$$m_2 = -\frac{v_1(x, y)}{v_2(x, y)}.$$

In this last equation we replace $v_1(x, y)$ with $-u_2(x, y)$ and $v_2(x, y)$ with $u_1(x, y)$ in accordance with the Cauchy-Riemann equations, and we obtain the equation

$$m_2 = \frac{u_2(x, y)}{u_1(x, y)}.$$

Therefore, the product of the slopes of our graphs is the number $m_1 m_2 = -1$; that is, the graphs meet at right angles. This property of the graphs of solutions of the Cauchy-Riemann equations is very useful in the study of electric fields, fluid flow, and in many other important physical situations.

Although we have written our Chain Rule in terms of scalar-valued functions, it applies to vector-valued functions, too. In that case, we simply remember that the derivative of a component vector is obtained by differentiating, its components; for instance, $D_x \mathbf{r} = D_x(r, s) = (D_x r, D_x s)$. Let us look at an example.

Example 93-5. The transformation equations

$$x = r \cos \theta, \quad y = r \sin \theta,$$

can be used to express r and θ in terms of x and y. Find $D_x r$ and $D_x \theta$ without first expressing r and θ in terms of x and y.

Solution. Suppose we think of our given equations as component equations that define a vector-valued function F on R^2. Thus we have

$$(x, y) = F(r, \theta) = (r \cos \theta, r \sin \theta).$$

When we apply the Chain Rule Equation 93-10 to our vector-valued function F, we have

(93-13) $$D_x F(r, \theta) = F_1(r, \theta)D_x r + F_2(r, \theta)D_x \theta.$$

Since $F(r, \theta) = (r \cos \theta, r \sin \theta)$, a simple computation shows us that

$$F_1(r, \theta) = (\cos \theta, \sin \theta) \quad \text{and} \quad F_2(r, \theta) = (-r \sin \theta, r \cos \theta).$$

From the equation $F(r, \theta) = (x, y)$ we have $D_x F(r, \theta) = D_x(x, y) = (D_x x, D_x y) = (1, D_x y)$. We keep y "fixed" when we differentiate with respect to x, so $D_x y = 0$, and hence $D_x F(r, \theta) = (1, 0)$.

Therefore, we can write Equation 93-13 as the vector equation

$$(1, 0) = (\cos \theta, \sin \theta)D_x r + (-r \sin \theta, r \cos \theta)D_x \theta,$$

or the equivalent pair of scalar equations

$$1 = \cos \theta \, D_x r - r \sin \theta \, D_x \theta$$
$$0 = \sin \theta \, D_x r + r \cos \theta \, D_x \theta.$$

These scalar equations are simply a pair of linear equations in the two unknowns $D_x r$ and $D_x \theta$. We solve them by the usual algebraic methods and find

$$D_x r = \cos \theta \quad \text{and} \quad D_x \theta = \frac{-\sin \theta}{r}.$$

PROBLEMS 93

1. Find $D_x w$ in two ways; first, use the Chain Rule, and second, replace u and v in terms of x and y before differentiating.

(a) $w = e^v \ln u; u = e^x, v = \ln x$ (b) $w = \displaystyle\int_u^v \sin t^2 \, dt; u = \sqrt{x}, v = x^{3/2}$

(c) $w = e^{uv}; u = x + y, v = x - y$

(d) $w = \sin (u + v); u = x + y, v = x - y.$

2. Suppose $w = x^{y^x}$. Make the substitution $u = y^x$ and $v = x$ and then use the Chain Rule to calculate $D_x w$ and $D_y w$.

3. Suppose that $f(x, y) = e^{xy}$ and that g and h are functions such that $g(2) = 3$, $g'(2) = 4$, $h(2) = 5$, and $h'(2) = 6$. Find $F'(2)$ if $F(t) = f(g(t), h(t))$.

4. It is the form of a chain rule, not the letters we use, that is important. In the following examples we use different letters from those we used in Equation 93-10, but we are still talking about the same chain rule. Complete the statement of it.
(a) If $x = g(u)$ and $y = h(u)$, then $D_u f(x, y) =$ —————.
(b) If $x = u(g)$ and $f = y(g)$, then $D_g h(x, f) =$ —————.
(c) If $p = x(s, t)$, $q = y(s, t)$, and $r = z(s, t)$, then $D_t F(p, q, r) =$ —————.
(d) If $a = b(c, d)$, $e = f(c, d)$, and $g = h(c, d)$, then $D_c i(a, e, g) =$ —————.

5. Let f be a function on R^2 with the property that $f_1(x, x) = f_2(x, x)$. Find the slope of the tangent to the graph of the equation $y = f(\cos x, \sin x)$ at the point whose X-coordinate is $\pi/4$.

6. Show that if $f_{11}(x, y) = f_{12}(x, y) = f_{22}(x, y) = 0$ at every point $(x, y) \in R^2$, then there are numbers a, b, and c such that $f(x, y) = ax + by + c$.

7. Let F be the vector-valued function defined by the equation $F(x, y) = x^y i + y^x j$. Show that if $x = g(t)$ and $y = h(t)$, then

$$D_t F(x, y) = x^y \left[\frac{y}{x} D_t x + (\ln x) D_t y \right] i + y^x \left[(\ln y) D_t x + \frac{x}{y} D_t y \right] j.$$

8. Show that the tangent lines to the graph of the equation $f(x, y) = 0$ are horizontal at points where $f_1(x, y) = 0$ and $f_2(x, y) \neq 0$, and are vertical at points where $f_2(x, y) = 0$ and $f_1(x, y) \neq 0$. What can you say about tangent lines at points where $f_1(x, y) = f_2(x, y) \neq 0$?

9. (a) Differentiate both sides of Equation 93-11 to show that

$$D_x^2 w = f_1(u, v) D_x^2 u + f_2(u, v) D_x^2 v + f_{11}(u, v)(D_x u)^2$$
$$+ 2f_{12}(u, v) D_x u D_x v + f_{22}(u, v)(D_x v)^2.$$

(b) Use the formula of Part (a) to find $D_x w$ if $w = u^2 + v$; $u = e^x$, $v = \ln x$.
(c) Check your answer to Part (b) by first expressing w in terms of x and then differentiating.
(d) Suppose that $F(x) = f(mx + a, nx + b)$. Show that $F''(0) = f_{11}(a, b)m^2 + 2f_{12}(a, b)mn + f_{22}(a, b)n^2$.
(e) Explain why the sign of $F''(0)$ is the same as the sign of $f_{11}(a, b)$ for every choice of m and n if $\begin{vmatrix} f_{11}(a, b) & f_{12}(a, b) \\ f_{21}(a, b) & f_{22}(a, b) \end{vmatrix} > 0$.

10. Use the technique of Example 93-5 to find $D_x u$, $D_x v$, $D_y u$, and $D_y v$ if $x = e^u \cos v$ and $y = e^u \sin v$. Find $D_y D_x u$. To check your results, solve the original equations for u and v in terms of x and y and then differentiate.

11. In this problem we ask you to apply the technique of Example 93-5 to the general transformation equations $x = f(u, v)$, $y = g(u, v)$.
(a) Write $(x, y) = (f(u, v), g(u, v))$ and differentiate both sides with respect to x to obtain the equation $(1, 0) = (f_1(u, v) D_x u + f_2(u, v) D_x v, g_1(u, v) D_x u + g_2(u, v) D_x v)$.

(b) Solve the preceding vector equation for $D_x u$ and $D_x v$. Use the abbreviation

$$J(u, v) = \begin{vmatrix} f_1(u, v) & f_2(u, v) \\ g_1(u, v) & g_2(u, v) \end{vmatrix}.$$

(c) Find $D_y u$ and $D_y v$.

(d) Use your results to check Example 93-5 and the preceding problem.

12. Suppose f is a function such that

(i) $$f(tx, ty) = t^3 f(x, y)$$

for every point $(x, y) \in D \subseteq R^2$, and for every positive number t. Differentiate both sides of this equation with respect to t and then set $t = 1$ to obtain the equation

(ii) $$x f_1(x, y) + y f_2(x, y) = 3 f(x, y).$$

13. Suppose we are told that f is a function that satisfies equation (ii) of the preceding problem. Show that f must also satisfy equation (i) of that problem. (Hint: At a particular point (x, y) set $g(t) = t^{-3} f(tx, ty)$, and find $g'(t)$. Conclude that $g'(t) = 0$ from equation (ii) with x and y replaced with tx and ty. It then follows that $g(t) = g(1)$ for each positive number t.)

14. A function that satisfies equation (i) of Problem 12 is said to be **homogeneous of degree 3**. An example is the function defined by the equation $f(x, y) = x^3 \sin \dfrac{x}{y} + xy^2$. Show that the partial derivatives of $f(x, y)$ are homogeneous of degree 2. Show that if a function is homogeneous of degree k, then its partial derivatives are homogeneous of degree $k - 1$.

94 THE GRADIENT

In the preceding section, we saw how to find derivatives of $f(u, v)$ when $u = g(x)$ and $v = h(x)$. Here f is a function on R^2, and the equations $u = g(x)$ and $v = h(x)$ define a vector-valued function g whose range is a subset of R^2. Our Chain Rule gives us derivatives of the composition of g by f. We don't have to specify the dimension of the domain of g, but in order to talk about the composition of g by f, the domain of f and the range of g must have the same dimension. Otherwise the symbol $f(g(x))$ would be meaningless.

The Chain Rule Equation 93-10 says that

(94-1) $$D_x f(u, v) = f_1(u, v) D_x u + f_2(u, v) D_x v.$$

We can view this expression as the dot product of the component vectors $(f_1(u, v), f_2(u, v))$ and $(D_x u, D_x v)$. This second vector can be written as $D_x \mathbf{u}$, where $\mathbf{u} = (u, v)$; now we will introduce a concise notation for the vector $(f_1(u, v), f_2(u, v))$. We define a vector-valued function ∇f, called the **gradient** function of f, by means of the equation

(94-2)
$$\nabla f(u) = (f_1(u), f_2(u)).$$

Then our Chain Rule Equation 94-1 takes the compact form

(94-3)
$$D_x f(u) = \nabla f(u) \cdot D_x u.$$

(Strictly speaking, our gradient probably should be regarded as a 1 by 2 matrix, rather than as a vector. The distinction is a rather subtle one, however, and since we get the same results in either case, we will use our familiar language of vectors instead of introducing and using non-square matrices.)

There are some obvious variations of the gradient notation. For example, if $w = f(u, v)$, we may write $\nabla w = (w_u, w_v)$, or we might write $\nabla f(u) = f_1(u)i + f_2(u)j$. If f is a function on R^3, the values of the vector-valued function ∇f are elements of R^3. In this case, we have $\nabla f(u) = (f_1(u), f_2(u), f_3(u))$, and so on. The symbol ∇ is called "del," and some authors write **grad** f in place of our ∇f.

> *Example 94-1.* Suppose that the temperature w at each point (x, y, z) in space is given by the equation $w = f(x, y, z)$, and suppose that a rocket travels along a path whose vector equation is $R = F(t)$. Show that at the coldest point through which the rocket passes the path of the rocket is perpendicular to the gradient of the temperature.
>
> *Solution.* The temperature encountered by the rocket at the point whose position vector is R is $f(R)$. We know that at a minimum point the derivative of the temperature is 0, and so $D_t f(R) = 0$. According to Equation 94-3, this derivative is $D_t f(R) = \nabla f(R) \cdot D_t R$, and so we have $\nabla f(R) \cdot D_t R = 0$. This equation says that the gradient of the temperature is perpendicular to the tangent vector $D_t R$ to the rocket's path, as we were to show.
>
> *Example 94-2.* Suppose that u and v are functions on R^2 that satisfy the Cauchy-Riemann partial differential equations (Example 93-4). Show that at each point $(x, y) \in R^2$, $\nabla u(x, y) \cdot \nabla v(x, y) = 0$.
>
> *Solution.* Equation 94-2 expresses a gradient in terms of derivatives with respect to the first and second components of the vector $u = (u, v)$. In our present case, the letters x and y play the roles of u and v in that equation, so we have
>
> $$\nabla u(x, y) = (u_1(x, y), u_2(x, y)) \quad \text{and} \quad \nabla v(x, y) = (v_1(x, y), v_2(x, y)).$$
>
> Therefore, $\nabla u(x, y) \cdot \nabla v(x, y) = u_1(x, y)v_1(x, y) + u_2(x, y)v_2(x, y)$. When we use the Cauchy-Riemann equations to replace $v_1(x, y)$ with $-u_2(x, y)$ and $v_2(x, y)$ with $u_1(x, y)$, we see that this dot product is 0, as we were to show.

The many symbols that appear in certain computations with partial derivatives can make a problem seem more difficult than it really is. Our next example shows how the gradient notation can be used to help minimize this symbolic confusion.

Example 94-3. Suppose that $w = f(\boldsymbol{u})$, where $\boldsymbol{u} = (u, v) = (x - ct, x + ct)$. Express the difference $w_{tt} - c^2 w_{xx}$ in terms of derivatives of w with respect to u and v.

Solution. The chain Rule Equation 94-3 tells us that

$$w_t = D_t w = \nabla w \cdot D_t \boldsymbol{u} \quad \text{and} \quad w_x = D_x w = \nabla w \cdot D_x \boldsymbol{u}.$$

Here $D_t \boldsymbol{u} = (-c, c)$ and $D_x \boldsymbol{u} = (1, 1)$, so we have

(94-4) $$w_t = (w_u, w_v) \cdot (-c, c) = -cw_u + cw_v$$

and

$$w_x = (w_u, w_v) \cdot (1, 1) = w_u + w_v.$$

By definition, $w_{tt} = D_t w_t$, and we use our Chain Rule to find this derivative: $D_t w_t = \nabla w_t \cdot D_t \boldsymbol{u}$. From the Equations 94-4 we obtain

$$\nabla w_t = \nabla(-cw_u + cw_v) = (-cw_{uu} + cw_{vu}, -cw_{uv} + cw_{vv}).$$

Hence

$$w_{tt} = (-cw_{uu} + cw_{vu}, -cw_{uv} + cw_{vv}) \cdot (-c, c) = c^2(w_{uu} - 2w_{uv} + w_{vv}).$$

(Notice that we have assumed that $w_{uv} = w_{vu}$.) Exactly the same sort of calculation shows us that $w_{xx} = w_{uu} + 2w_{uv} + w_{vv}$. Therefore,

(94-5) $$w_{tt} - c^2 w_{xx} = -4c^2 w_{uv}.$$

The result of the preceding example is important in the applications of mathematics to certain physical problems involving vibrations. In these problems, we must solve the **wave equation** $w_{tt} = c^2 w_{xx}$, and Equation 94-5 shows us that this equation is equivalent to the equation $w_{uv} = 0$. In our next example, we investigate solutions of this equation.

Example 94-4. Show that solutions of the equation $w_{uv} = 0$ have the form $w = f(u) + g(v)$, where f and g are arbitrary differentiable functions on R^1.

Solution. It is easy to verify that if $w = f(u) + g(v)$, then $w_{uv} = 0$. The converse is more difficult. Suppose that F is a function with continuous mixed partial derivatives and such that $w = F(u, v)$ satisfies the partial differential equation $w_{uv} = 0$. We are to show that there are functions f and g on R^1 such that for each point (u, v) in the region of R^2 in which we are working, $F(u, v) = f(u) + g(v)$.

Suppose (a, b) is a point of our region, and let $G(u, v) = F(u, v) - F(u, b) - F(a, v)$. Then $G_1(u, v) = F_1(u, v) - F_1(u, b)$. According to the Theorem of the Mean (Theorem 19-5), there is a point n between v and b such that this difference is equal to $F_{12}(u, n)(v - b)$. Since $w = F(u, v)$ satisfies the partial differential equation $w_{uv} = 0$, however, we see that the mixed derivative $F_{12}(u, n)$ is 0. Thus $G_1(u, v) = 0$. In exactly the same way we find that $G_2(u, v) = 0$. Therefore, as we saw in Example 93-1, G is a constant function; that is, for each point (u, v), $G(u, v) = G(a, b)$. In terms of values of F, this equation can be written as

$$F(u, v) = F(u, b) + F(a, v) - F(a, b).$$

Therefore, if we let the equations $f(u) = F(u, b)$ and $g(v) = F(a, v) - F(a, b)$ define functions on R^1, we see that we have expressed $F(u, v)$ in the desired form.

The preceding two examples tell us that solutions of the wave equation take the form $w = f(x - ct) + g(x + ct)$. For example, particular solutions of the wave equation are $w = \sin(x - ct) + \ln(x + ct)$, $w = e^x e^{ct}$, and so on.

PROBLEMS 94

1. Find $\nabla f(2, -3)$ for the following functions.

(a) $f(u, v) = |uv|$

(b) $f(u, v) = \displaystyle\int_u^v \sec \pi t \, dt$

(c) $f(u, v) = \log_u |v|$

(d) $f(u, v) = u^{[\![\sin v]\!]}$

2. It is the idea, not the letters we use to express it, that is important. We have completed the first of the following equations; you complete the rest.

(a) $\nabla f(u, v) = (f_1(u, v), f_2(u, v))$.

(b) $\nabla f(g, h) = $ _____

(c) $\nabla a(b, c, d) = $ _____

(d) $\nabla x(f, g, h) = $ _____

(e) $\nabla f(g, g, g) = $ _____

(f) $\nabla p(q, r, s, t) = $ _____

3. Let a be a given vector of R^3 and define the functions f and g on R^3 by means of the equations $f(x) = a \cdot x$ and $g(x) = |x|$.

(a) Show that $\nabla f(x) = a$

(b) Show that $\nabla g(x) = \dfrac{1}{|x|} x$

(c) What are the corresponding facts if we replace R^3 with a general R^n?

4. If $w = f(u)$, where $u = g(x)$, show that $\nabla w = f'(u)\nabla u$.

5. Use the results of the preceding two problems to find ∇w if:

(a) $w = |x|^2$

(b) $w = e^{a \cdot x}$

(c) $w = \cos |x|^4$

(d) $w = |a + x|^2$

6. Show that if $\nabla f(x) = 0$ at each point of the domain of f, then f is a constant function.

7. Let $u = f(x, y)$ and $v = g(x, y)$. Show that $\nabla(uv) = u\nabla v + v\nabla u$.

8. If $w = f(u)$, where $u = g(t)$, then our Chain Rule Equation 94-3 can be written as $D_t w = \nabla w \cdot D_t u$. Show that $D_t^2 w = \nabla w \cdot D_t^2 u + (D_t \nabla w) \cdot D_t u$.

9. Suppose that $w = F(\boldsymbol{u})$, where $\boldsymbol{u} = (u, v) = (x, x - y)$, satisfies the partial differential equation $w_{xx} + 2w_{xy} + w_{yy} = 0$. Use the technique of Example 94-3 to show that $w_{uu} = 0$. Show that this equation implies that $w = f(v)u + g(v)$, where f and g are arbitrary differentiable functions on R^1. Conclude that solutions of the equation $w_{xx} + 2w_{xy} + w_{yy} = 0$ must have the form $w = f(x - y)x + g(x - y)$. Show that if w does have this form, then w satisfies the given partial differential equation.

10. Our Chain Rule applies to vector-valued functions as well as to scalar-valued ones, but we can't use Equation 94-3 to express the Chain Rule for vector-valued functions until we define the symbol $\nabla f(\boldsymbol{u})$. As we said in the text, a gradient is really a matrix-valued function. For example, if $\boldsymbol{f}(u, v) = (f(u, v), g(u, v))$, we define

$$\nabla \boldsymbol{f}(u, v) = \begin{bmatrix} f_1(u, v) & f_2(u, v) \\ g_1(u, v) & g_2(u, v) \end{bmatrix}.$$

Show that with this definition, $D_t \boldsymbol{f}(\boldsymbol{u}) = \nabla \boldsymbol{f}(\boldsymbol{u}) \, D_t \boldsymbol{u}$, where $\boldsymbol{u} = (u, v)$; $u = r(t)$ and $v = s(t)$ (or r and s could be functions on a general R^n).

95 DIRECTIONAL DERIVATIVES. THE THEOREM OF THE MEAN

Suppose that f is a function on R^3 and that (x, y, z) is a point of its domain. If $w = f(x, y, z)$, the numbers

$$D_x w = f_1(x, y, z), \ D_y w = f_2(x, y, z), \quad \text{and} \quad D_z w = f_3(x, y, z)$$

measure the (instantaneous) rate of change of the functional values of f with respect to distance. These numbers are computed *at the point* (x, y, z), and they give us rates of change *in the directions* of the positive X-, Y-, and Z-axes. Now we want to calculate rates of change in other directions as well. Our first task is to decide what we mean by this concept. Thus suppose we are given a function f on R^n and a point $\boldsymbol{x}$ of its domain. What do we mean by the rate of change of the values of f at the point $\boldsymbol{x}$ and in a particular direction? We will specify the direction by prescribing a unit vector $\boldsymbol{u}$. Then for each number s, the point $\boldsymbol{x} + s\boldsymbol{u}$ is a point of the line that contains the point $\boldsymbol{x}$ and has the direction of $\boldsymbol{u}$. Furthermore, the point $\boldsymbol{x} + s\boldsymbol{u}$ is $|s|$ units from the point $\boldsymbol{x}$ (see Fig. 95-1 that illustrates the situation in R^3).

Thus the quotient $\dfrac{f(\boldsymbol{x} + s\boldsymbol{u}) - f(\boldsymbol{x})}{s}$ represents the average rate of change (with respect

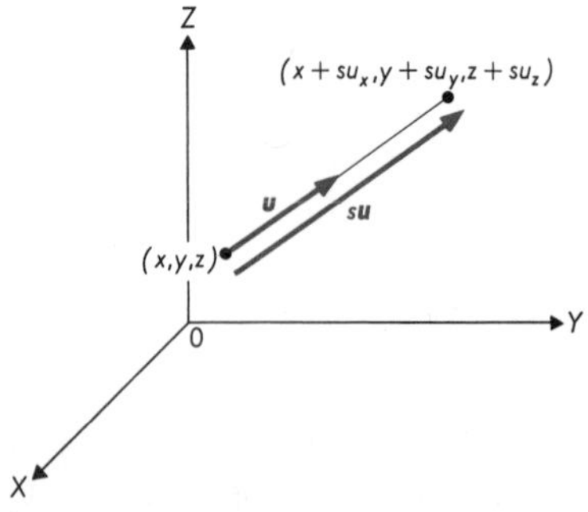

Figure 95-1

to distance) of the values of f in the direction of u. It is natural to take the limit of this quotient to be the (instantaneous) rate of change of the values of f, and that is what we do. This limit is called the **directional derivative** of $f(x)$ *at the point x* and *in the direction of u*; we denote it by the symbol $D_u f(x)$. Thus we have

$$(95\text{-}1) \qquad D_u f(x) = \lim_{s \to 0} \frac{f(x + su) - f(x)}{s}.$$

Example 95-1. Find the formula for the directional derivatives of the function that is defined by the equation $f(x) = |x|^2$.

Solution. For a given point x and directional unit vector u, our difference quotient is

$$\frac{f(x + su) - f(x)}{s} = \frac{|x + su|^2 - |x|^2}{s}.$$

Since

$$|x + su|^2 = (x + su) \cdot (x + su) = |x|^2 + 2sx \cdot u + s^2 |u|^2 = |x|^2 + 2sx \cdot u + s^2,$$

we have

$$\frac{f(x + su) - f(x)}{s} = 2x \cdot u + s.$$

From this expression, it is clear that the limit of our difference quotient is $2x \cdot u$, so we have derived the formula $D_u |x|^2 = 2x \cdot u$.

The concept of the directional derivative is a generalization of the idea of partial derivatives. For example, if in the defining Equation 95-1 we take as our unit directional vector u the basis vector i, it is easy to see that the resulting directional derivative $D_i f(x)$ is simply the partial derivative $D_x f(x)$, and so on.

Everything we have said so far about the idea of the directional derivative applies both to scalar- and to vector-valued functions. Now, however, we want to take up a technique of *calculating* directional derivatives that applies only to scalar-valued functions. To generalize this technique and make it apply to vector-valued functions requires the introduction of still more notation, so we leave that problem to a course in advanced calculus. Thus let us suppose that f is a scalar-valued function on R^n, that x is a point of the domain of f and u is a given unit vector, and let us find the number $D_u f(x)$. This number is the limit of the difference quotient $\dfrac{f(x + su) - f(x)}{s}$. Now we set $g(s) = f(x + su)$, and our difference quotient simplifies to $\dfrac{g(s) - g(0)}{s}$. The ordinary definition of the derivative tells us that the limit of this difference quotient as s approaches 0 is the number $g'(0)$. Therefore, the number $D_u f(x)$ that we are seeking is the number $g'(0)$. Now we use the Chain Rule Equation 94-3 to find $g'(s)$:

$$g'(s) = D_s g(s) = \nabla f(x + su) \cdot D_s(x + su) = \nabla f(x + su) \cdot u.$$

From this equation we see that $g'(0) = \nabla f(x) \cdot u$, and hence

(95-2) $$D_u f(x) = \nabla f(x) \cdot u.$$

Example 95-2. Find $D_u f(1, 2)$ if $f(x, y) = x^2 + y^2$, and u makes an angle of $60°$ with the positive X-axis.

Solution. Figure 95-2 shows the point $(1, 2)$ and the vector u. Since u is 1 unit long, we see that $u = (\cos 60°, \sin 60°) = (\frac{1}{2}, \frac{1}{2}\sqrt{3})$. Furthermore, $f_1(1, 2) = 2$ and $f_2(1, 2) = 4$, so $\nabla f(1, 2) = (2, 4)$. Therefore,

$$D_u f(1, 2) = (2, 4) \cdot (\tfrac{1}{2}, \tfrac{1}{2}\sqrt{3}) = 1 + 2\sqrt{3}.$$

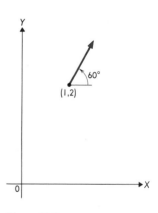

Example 95-3. Find $D_u w$ at the point $(2, -1, 2)$ and in the direction from this point to the origin, if $w = 2x^2 y + 3z$.

Solution. We must find the vectors ∇w and u and then compute their dot product. First, we see that

$$\nabla w = D_x w\, i + D_y w\, j + D_z w\, k = 4xy i + 2x^2 j + 3k.$$

Therefore, at the point $(2, -1, 2)$ we have

$$\nabla w = -8i + 8j + 3k.$$

Figure 95-2

The vector u is 1 unit long and its direction is that of the vector $v = -2i + j - 2k$ whose initial point is the point $(2, -1, 2)$ and whose terminal point is the origin. Hence

$$u = \frac{v}{|v|} = \frac{-2i + j - 2k}{3} = -\frac{2}{3}i + \frac{1}{3}j - \frac{2}{3}k.$$

Thus we finally have

$$D_u w = (-8i + 8j + 3k) \cdot (-\tfrac{2}{3}i + \tfrac{1}{3}j - \tfrac{2}{3}k)$$
$$= \tfrac{16}{3} + \tfrac{8}{3} - \tfrac{6}{3} = 6.$$

When we calculate the directional derivatives of w at a point x by means of the formula $D_u w = \nabla w \cdot u$, we use the same vector ∇w for each direction vector u. For different direction vectors this formula yields different directional derivatives, and it is natural to ask which direction gives us the *greatest* directional derivative.

To answer this question, we write $\nabla w \cdot u = |\nabla w| \, |u| \cos \theta$ (we suppose that the vectors ∇w and u determine an angle of θ). Since $|u| = 1$, this formula for the directional derivative reduces to

$$(95\text{-}3) \qquad\qquad D_u w = |\nabla w| \cos \theta.$$

Figure 95-3 shows a geometric interpretation of the directional derivative $D_u w$ in terms of the vectors ∇w and u. Since the number $\cos \theta$ is a maximum when $\theta = 0$, we see that the number $D_u w$ is largest when u is selected as the unit vector in the direction of ∇w; that is, $u = \dfrac{1}{|\nabla w|} \nabla w$. Then the maximum directional derivative is the number $(D_u w)_{\max} = |\nabla w| \cos 0 = |\nabla w|$. Thus we see that *the maximum rate of change of w at a point occurs in the direction of the gradient vector calculated at that point, and the magnitude of the gradient of w is the maximum value of the rate of change of w with respect to distance.* Equation 95-3 also tells us that the rate of change of w with respect to distance

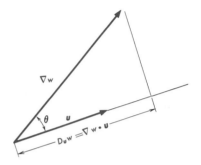

Figure 95-3

is 0 in directions perpendicular to the gradient, and that w decreases with distance most rapidly along the vector $-\nabla w$.

Example 95-4. The electric potential (voltage) at a point (x, y, z) of a certain region in space is given by the formula $V = x^2 - y^2 + 2xz$. If we put a unit positive charge at the point $(1, 2, 3)$, which way will it start to move?

Solution. It is a fact from electric field theory that the charge will start to move in the direction of the greatest potential drop; that is, in the direction in which V decreases most rapidly. Therefore, the charge will move in the direction of $-\nabla V$. At the point $(1, 2, 3)$, $\nabla V = 8i - 4j + 2k$, and hence the charge will start to move in the direction of the vector $-8i + 4j - 2k$.

We close this section with the statement of the Theorem of the Mean for a scalar-valued function f on R^n. Suppose that a and b are two points of its domain, and define the function g on R^1 by means of the equation $g(t) = f(a + t(b - a))$. According to the ordinary Theorem of the Mean (Theorem 19-5), there is a point $m \in (0, 1)$ such that

$$(95\text{-}4) \qquad\qquad g(1) - g(0) = g'(m),$$

and when we express this equation in terms of our original function f, we will obtain the result we seek. In the first place, we have $g(0) = f(a)$ and $g(1) = f(b)$, and so the left-hand side of Equation 95-4 is the number $f(b) - f(a)$. According to the Chain Rule,

$$g'(t) = D_t f(a + t(b - a)) = \nabla f(a + t(b - a)) \cdot (b - a),$$

so $g'(m) = \nabla f(a + m(b - a)) \cdot (b - a)$. Since m is a number between 0 and 1, it follows that the point $a + m(b - a)$ is a point m of the line segment joining the points a and b, so the right-hand side of Equation 95-4 is the number $\nabla f(m) \cdot (b - a)$. Thus we have shown that *there is a point* m *of the line segment between the points* a *and* b *such that*

(95-5) $$f(b) - f(a) = \nabla f(m) \cdot (b - a).$$

We call this statement the **Theorem of the Mean** for scalar-valued functions on R^n, and you can see that it is a generalization of the Theorem of the Mean for functions on R^1.

P R O B L E M S   9 5

1. Find the directional derivative of w at the given point and in the given direction.
   (a) $w = e^{2x+3y}$, $(0, 0)$, direction: $u = \frac{3}{5}i - \frac{4}{5}j$
   (b) $w = 2xy^2$, $(-1, 2)$, direction: $v = i - 2j$
   (c) $w = e^x \sin(y + z)$, $(0, 0, 0)$, in the direction of the line from the origin to the point $(-1, 2, -2)$.
   (d) $w = x^2 + y^2$, $(2, 1)$, in the direction of a vector that makes a positive angle of $60°$ with the positive X-axis.
   (e) $w = (y + x)/(y - x)$, $(1, 2)$, direction: normal to the line $3x + 4y = 11$.
   (f) $w = \ln xyz^2$, $(1, 2, 1)$, direction: $\frac{1}{3}i - \frac{2}{3}j + \frac{2}{3}k$.

2. Suppose you are standing at the point $(-1, 5, 8)$ on a hill whose equation is $z = 74 - x^2 - 7xy - 4y^2$. The Y-axis points north and the X-axis east, and distances are measured in meters.
   (a) If you move to the south, are you ascending or descending? At what rate?
   (b) If you move to the northwest, are you ascending or descending? At what rate?
   (c) In what direction is the steepest downward path?
   (d) In what directions is the path level?

3. Find a unit vector in the direction in which the maximum rate of change of w at the given point occurs if $w = \text{Tan}^{-1} xy + z$.
   (a) $(0, 0, 0)$ (b) $(1, 0, 0)$ (c) $(0, 1, 0)$ (d) $(0, 0, 1)$

4. Suppose a is a given vector, x is a position vector, and define a function f by means of the equation $f(x) = a \cdot x$. Use the definition of the directional derivative to find $D_u f(x)$ for an arbitrary unit vector u.

5. Suppose that the temperature at a point (x, y, z) in a region in space is given by the formula $w = e^{-x^2-y^2-z^2}$. Find the rate of change of temperature at the point $(1, 2, 3)$ and in the direction from that point to the origin.

6. Explain why $D_i f(x, y, z) = D_x f(x, y, z)$.

7. Suppose that a and b are points of the domain of a function f such that $f(a) = f(b)$. Show that there is a point m of the line segment between a and b such that the vectors $\nabla f(m)$ and $b - a$ are perpendicular.

8. Suppose that F is the vector-valued function defined by the equation $F(x, y, z) = (2x^2 - 3xyz, x + y + z)$. Find $D_u F(1, -2, 2)$, where u is in the direction from the given point toward the origin. (Hint: Formula 95-2 applies only to scalar-valued functions; however, $D_u(f(x), g(x)) = (D_u f(x), D_u g(x))$, so we can find directional derivatives of $F(x, y, z)$ by finding the directional derivatives of its components.)

9. Suppose that f and g are given functions on R^n. Compare the directional derivative of $f(x)$ in the direction of the gradient of g at x with the directional derivative of $g(x)$ in the direction of the gradient of f at x.

10. Suppose that $w = f(z)$, where $z = g(x)$. Show that for an arbitrary unit vector u, $D_u w = f'(z) D_u g(x)$. (Hint: See Problem 94-4.)

11. Suppose that $r = f(x)$ and $s = g(x)$, and that u is a unit vector. Show that the following equations are correct.

(a) $D_u(r + s) = D_u r + D_u s$ (b) $D_u rs = r D_u s + s D_u r$

(c) $D_u \dfrac{r}{s} = \dfrac{s D_u r - r D_u s}{s^2}$

96 NORMALS TO CURVES AND SURFACES

Suppose that c is a number in the range of a function f on R^2 and that the graph of the equation $f(x, y) = c$ is a curve in the plane. Then this curve is called a **level curve** of the function f. At all points of a given level curve, the function f has the same value. For example, if a geographical map is considered as a region in the XY-plane and if $f(x, y)$ is the altitude of the point (x, y) of the map, then the level curves of f are the contour lines of the map. If f measures temperature or voltage, the level curves are "isotherms" or "equipotential lines," and so on.

Example 96-1. Let $f(x, y) = 9x^2 + 16y^2$. Sketch the level curves that correspond to the functional values 12, 36, and 48.

Solution. The level curves are ellipses whose equations are $9x^2 + 16y^2 = c$, where c is replaced by 12, 36, and 48. They are shown in Fig. 96-1.

The situation in three dimensions is analogous to the two-dimensional case. If c is a number in the range of a function f on R^3 and the graph of the equation $f(x, y, z) = c$ is a surface in space, then this surface is called a **level surface** of f. Every surface in space can be regarded as a level surface of some function on R^3.

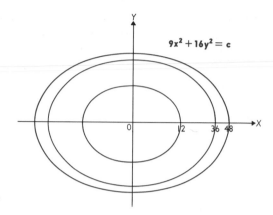

$$9x^2 + 16y^2 = c$$

Figure 96-1

Example 96-2. Find a function f for which the paraboloid of revolution $z + 4 = x^2 + y^2$ is a level surface.

Solution. Since our given equation is equivalent to the equation $z - x^2 - y^2 + 4 = 0$, we see that its graph is a level surface (corresponding to the choice $c = 0$) of the function defined by the equation $f(x, y, z) = z - x^2 - y^2 + 4$. Or we might define the function g by means of the equation $g(x, y, z) = x^2 + y^2 - z$, and then the graph of our given equation is the level surface $g(x, y, z) = 4$. There is no end to the number of functions for which our given surface is a level surface.

Let f be a function on R^3 and let us consider a curve in the level surface $f(x, y, z) = c$. A curve in space is given by a vector equation $R = F(t)$, and to say that the curve lies in the given level surface is to say that R satisfies the equation $f(R) = c$ for each t (see Fig. 96-2). Now we will differentiate both sides of this equation with respect to t. Equation 94-3 tells us that the derivative of the left-hand side is $\nabla f(R) \cdot D_t R$, and the derivative of the right-hand side is 0. Thus, we have

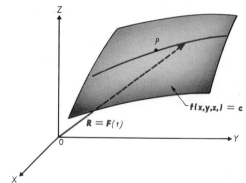

$$R = F(t)$$

$$f(x,y,z,) = c$$

Figure 96-2

the equation

(96-1) $$\nabla f(R) \cdot D_t R = 0.$$

The vector $D_t R$ is tangent to the graph of the vector equation $R = F(t)$. Therefore, the geometric interpretation of Equation 96-1 is as follows: *If P is any point of our level surface, then the gradient of f at P is perpendicular to the tangent line (at P) to any curve that lies in the surface and contains P.* Of course, there are infinitely many curves that lie in the surface and contain P, but Equation 96-1 says that their tangents at P all lie in the same plane, the plane that contains P and has the vector $\nabla f(R)$ as a normal. This plane is called the **tangent plane** to our surface at the point P. A vector that is normal to this plane is said to be **normal** to the surface at P. Thus *the vector $\nabla f(x, y, z)$ is normal to the surface $f(x, y, z) = c$.*

> **Example 96-3.** Show that the position vector to a point (x, y, z) of the sphere $x^2 + y^2 + z^2 = 4$ is normal to the sphere.
>
> **Solution.** Let $f(x, y, z) = x^2 + y^2 + z^2$; then our sphere is the level surface $f(x, y, z) = 4$. As we have just said, the vector $\nabla f(x, y, z)$ is normal to this surface. Since $\nabla f(x, y, z) = 2xi + 2yj + 2zk = 2R$, where R is the position vector to (x, y, z), we see that R is also normal to our sphere. Thus we see that our definition of a normal vector to a surface leads to the natural result that a radius is normal to a sphere.
>
> **Example 96-4.** The graph of a function f on R^2 is the surface whose equation is $z = f(x, y)$. Find a vector normal to this surface.
>
> **Solution.** If we write the equation of our surface as $f(x, y) - z = 0$, we see that it is a level surface of the function F that is defined by the equation $F(x, y, z) = f(x, y) - z$. Therefore, a vector that is normal to our surface is the gradient $\nabla F(x, y, z) = f_1(x, y)i + f_2(x, y)j - k$.

Now we will find the equation of the tangent plane to a surface in space. Suppose the point (x_0, y_0, z_0) belongs to the graph of the equation $f(x, y, z) = c$. When we studied planes in Section 76, we found that a plane that has the vector $ai + bj + ck$ as a normal, and that contains the point (x_0, y_0, z_0), has the equation $a(x - x_0) + b(y - y_0) + c(z - z_0) = 0$. We have just seen that our tangent plane has the gradient vector $f_1(x_0, y_0, z_0)i + f_2(x_0, y_0, z_0)j + f_3(x_0, y_0, z_0)k$ as a normal, and so we see that *the tangent plane has the equation*

(96-2) $$f_1(x_0, y_0, z_0)(x - x_0) + f_2(x_0, y_0, z_0)(y - y_0)$$
$$+ f_3(x_0, y_0, z_0)(z - z_0) = 0.$$

> **Example 96-5.** Find the equation of the plane that is tangent, at the point $(1, 1, 5)$, to the graph of the equation $x^2 y^3 z = 4 + x$.

Solution.   Before we use Equation 96-2, we must write our equation as the equation of a level surface; for example, as $x^2y^3z - x = 4$. Then we use Equation 96-2 with $f(x, y, z) = x^2y^3z - x$ and $(x_0, y_0, z_0) = (1, 1, 5)$. We find that $f_1(x, y, z) = 2xy^3z - 1$, and so $f_1(1, 1, 5) = 9$. Similarly, $f_2(1, 1, 5) = 15$, and $f_3(1, 1, 5) = 1$, and therefore the desired tangent plane has the equation $9(x - 1) + 15(y - 1) + (z - 5) = 0$, or in simplified form,

$$9x + 15y + z = 29.$$

Our remarks concerning surfaces in space can be modified so as to apply to curves in a plane. For example, suppose that the graph of the equation $f(x, y) = c$ is a level curve of a function f on R^2. Then the gradient vector $\nabla f(x, y)$ is perpendicular to this level curve at the point (x, y) (that is, the gradient vector is perpendicular to the tangent to the level curve at the point).

Example 96-6.   Find the equation of the tangent line to the level curve $f(x, y) = c$ at the point (x_0, y_0).

Solution.   The tangent line plays the same role in the plane that the tangent plane plays in space. To obtain the equation of the desired tangent, we simply drop the last term on the left-hand side of Equation 96-2:

$$f_1(x_0, y_0)(x - x_0) + f_2(x_0, y_0)(y - y_0) = 0.$$

Notice that the slope of this tangent line is $-\dfrac{f_1(x_0, y_0)}{f_2(x_0, y_0)}$, which agrees with Equation 93-12 for the slope of the graph of the equation $f(x, y) - c = 0$.

P R O B L E M S   9 6

1. Describe the level curves of the function f; in particular, sketch the level curve that contains the point $(1, 1)$. Sketch the gradient vector at the point $(1, 1)$.
   (a) $f(x, y) = x^2 + y^2 - 1$ (b) $f(x, y) = 4x^2 - y^2 - 8x + 4y$
   (c) $f(x, y) = y - \cos x$ (d) $f(x, y) = e^y - e^x$

2. Describe the level surface of the function f that contains the given point, and find a normal vector to the level surface at that point.
   (a) $f(x, y, z) = 2x - 3y + 4z$, $(1, 1, 1)$
   (b) $f(x, y, z) = 4x^2 + y^2 + z^2$, $(1, 1, 1)$
   (c) $f(x, y, z) = x^2 + y^2$, $(1, 2, 3)$
   (d) $f(x, y, z) = \ln(x^2 + y^2 - z)$, $(1, 1, 2)$

3. Find the equation of the tangent plane at the given point.
   (a) $2x^2 - 3xy + 4y^2 = z$, $(-1, 1, 9)$.
   (b) $x^2y + y^2z + z^2x + 4 = 0$, $(2, -1, 0)$.
   (c) $e^{xy} - 2\sin z = 1$, $(0, 0, 0)$.
   (d) $4\operatorname{Tan}^{-1}\dfrac{y}{x} = \pi \ln xyz$, $(1, 1, e)$

4. At what point is the normal to the surface $z = 3x^2 - 2y^2$ parallel to the vector $2i + 4j + \frac{1}{3}k$?

5. Find M and B such that the vector equation of the line that is perpendicular to the surface $3x^2 - 4yz + xz^2 = 12$ at the point $(1, -2, 1)$ is $R = Mt + B$.

6. At what points of the graph of the equation $x^2 + 4y^2 + 16z^2 - 2xy = 12$ are the tangent planes parallel to the XZ-plane?

7. Find the directional derivative of $w = 3x^2yz + 2yz^2$ at the point $(1, 1, 1)$ and in a direction normal to the surface $x^2 - y + z^2 = 1$ at $(1, 1, 1)$.

8. Find a vector tangent to the curve of intersection of the surfaces $x^2 - 2xz + y^2z = 1$ and $3xy + 2yz + 6 = 0$ at the point $(1, -2, 0)$. (*Hint:* This vector must be perpendicular to normals to both surfaces.)

9. Show that the line that is normal at the point (x_0, y_0, z_0) to the surface given by the equation $f(x, y, z) = c$ has parametric equations

$$x = f_1(x_0, y_0, z_0)t + x_0, \quad y = f_2(x_0, y_0, z_0)t + y_0, \quad z = f_3(x_0, y_0, z_0)t + z_0.$$

10. (a) Let f and g be functions on R^2, and suppose that they have the same level curves. Show that at each point x,

$$\begin{vmatrix} f_1(x) & f_2(x) \\ g_1(x) & g_2(x) \end{vmatrix} = 0.$$

(b) Let f and g be functions on R^3, and suppose that they have the same level surfaces. Show that at each point x.

$$\begin{vmatrix} f_1(x) & f_2(x) \\ g_1(x) & g_2(x) \end{vmatrix} = \begin{vmatrix} f_2(x) & f_3(x) \\ g_2(x) & g_3(x) \end{vmatrix} = \begin{vmatrix} f_1(x) & f_3(x) \\ g_1(x) & g_3(x) \end{vmatrix} = 0.$$

97 MAXIMA AND MINIMA OF FUNCTIONS ON R^n

If a differentiable function f on R^1 has a maximum (or a minimum) value at an interior point a of its domain, then we know that

$$(97\text{-}1) \qquad\qquad f'(a) = 0.$$

Now we will find the analogous equations for functions on a general R^n.

We can get a feeling for maximum and minimum problems when we look at the situation geometrically. From this point of view, Equation 97-1 states that the tangent line to the graph of f at the point $(a, f(a))$ is parallel to the X-axis. Now let us interpret the corresponding situation if our given function f is a function on R^2. Figure 97-1 illustrates the case in which f takes a maximum value at the point (a, b). Thus for each point (x, y) in some neighborhood of (a, b) we have $f(x, y) < f(a, b)$. At this maximum point (and the same remarks would apply to a minimum point) the tangent plane is parallel to the XY-plane. In other words,

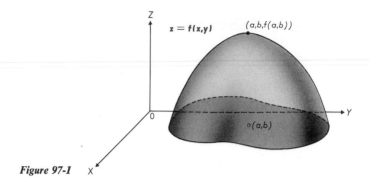

Figure 97-1

normals to the graph of f at the point $(a, b, f(a, b))$ are parallel to the Z-axis. In Example 96-4 we showed that the vector $f_1(a, b)\boldsymbol{i} + f_2(a, b)\boldsymbol{j} - \boldsymbol{k}$ is such a normal vector, and the condition that this vector be parallel to the Z-axis is that

$$(97\text{-}2) \qquad f_1(a, b) = 0 \quad \text{and} \quad f_2(a, b) = 0.$$

We can combine this pair of scalar equations into the vector equation

$$(97\text{-}3) \qquad \nabla f(a, b) = \boldsymbol{0}.$$

Equations 97-1 and 97-3 (or 97-2) are completely analogous. *If* the given function has a maximum or a minimum value at the given point, then the equation holds.

We cannot draw pictures for functions on R^n if $n > 2$, but the results are the same, as the following informal argument suggests. Suppose that a function f takes a maximum value at a point $\boldsymbol{a}$. Then as we move away from the point $\boldsymbol{a}$, the values of f cannot increase; that is, the rate of change of the values of f with respect to distance cannot be positive. In other words, at the point $\boldsymbol{a}$ no directional derivative of $f(\boldsymbol{x})$ is positive. In particular, the maximum directional derivative, which we know to be the number $|\nabla f(\boldsymbol{a})|$, cannot be positive. But this number cannot be negative, either, and so we must have

$$(97\text{-}4) \qquad \nabla f(\boldsymbol{a}) = \boldsymbol{0}.$$

Similar remarks lead to the same conclusion if $\boldsymbol{a}$ is a minimum point. Notice that the vector Equation 97-4 tells us that *all the first partial derivatives of f are zero at the point $\boldsymbol{a}$.* Thus, if f is a function on R^n, Equation 97-4 is equivalent to n scalar equations.

You must keep clearly in mind that the conditions we have mentioned are *necessary* in order that a differentiable function f should take a maximum or a minimum value at an interior point $\boldsymbol{a}$ of its domain. *If* the function takes a maximum or a minimum value, then the appropriate one of our equations holds. But the conditions are not *sufficient*; that is, the fact that one of our conditions holds at a point does not guarantee that f takes a maximum or a minimum value there. For example, if $f(x) = x^3$, then $f'(0) = 0$, but $f(0) = 0$ is neither a maximum nor a minimum value of f. And similar remarks hold for functions on R^n if $n > 1$.

Example 97-1. Show that there are no maximum or minimum points of the hyperbolic paraboloid $z = y^2 - \frac{1}{4}x^2$. In other words, show that the function f defined by the equation $f(x, y) = y^2 - \frac{1}{4}x^2$ has no maximum or minimum values.

Solution. At a maximum or a minimum point, $D_x z$ must equal 0 and $D_y z$ must equal 0. Since $D_x z = -\frac{1}{2}x$ and $D_y z = 2y$, we see that $x = 0$ and $y = 0$ at a maximum or a minimum point. Hence $(0, 0, 0)$ is the only possible maximum or minimum point of our surface. But Fig. 97-2 makes it clear that the point $(0, 0, 0)$ is neither a maximum nor a minimum point, and therefore our surface has no such points.

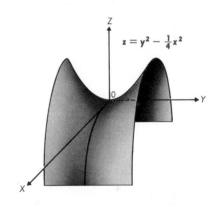

$z = y^2 - \frac{1}{4}x^2$

Figure 97-2

There are analytic tests, analogous to the Second Derivative Test that we used in the case of functions on R^1, for selecting maximum and minimum points from among the points at which the first partial derivatives of a function are 0. We will leave the discussion of these tests to a course in advanced calculus. In our examples, we can use geometric or physical reasoning to decide when we have maxima or minima. It will pay you to proceed by the following sequence of steps as you solve the "word problems" of this section:

(i) Decide what quantity is to be maximized (or minimized).

(ii) Express this quantity as the value of a function on R^n; choose n as small as you can.

(iii) Find the points at which the first partial derivatives of the function are zero and determine whether or not the corresponding functional value is a maximum or a minimum.

(iv) Re-read the question, and use the information from Step (iii) to answer it.

Example 97-2. Find the point of the plane $3x + 2y + z = 14$ that is nearest the origin.

Solution. The quantity that must be minimized is the distance d between the origin and a point (x, y, z) of the plane. According to the distance formula, we see that

$d = \sqrt{x^2 + y^2 + z^2}$. Since our point (x, y, z) belongs to the given plane, $z = 14 - 3x - 2y$, and therefore we can express d in terms of x and y only:

$$d = \sqrt{x^2 + y^2 + (14 - 3x - 2y)^2}.$$

Since our problem is to locate the point at which the function defined by this equation takes its minimum value, we might now take partial derivatives, find where they are 0, and so on. Actually, it will simplify our differentiation if we recognize that d is a minimum where d^2 is a minimum, and hence we will try to find the point at which the function defined by the equation

$$f(x, y) = x^2 + y^2 + (14 - 3x - 2y)^2$$

takes its minimum value. Here

$$f_1(x, y) = 2x - 6(14 - 3x - 2y),$$
$$f_2(x, y) = 2y - 4(14 - 3x - 2y).$$

After a little simplification, the equations $f_1(x, y) = 0$ and $f_2(x, y) = 0$ become

$$5x + 3y = 21$$
$$6x + 5y = 28.$$

We solve this system of linear equations and find that $x = 3$ and $y = 2$. Since the equations $f_1(x, y) = 0$ and $f_2(x, y) = 0$ have the single solution $(x, y) = (3, 2)$, it follows that *if* our function f has a minimum value, *then* that value must be the number $f(3, 2) = 14$. The geometry of the situation makes it clear that there *is* a point of the plane that is nearest the origin, and hence the point $(3, 2)$ *does* give a minimum value for f. Therefore, the X- and Y-coordinates of the nearest point are $x = 3$ and $y = 2$. We obtain the Z-coordinate from the equation of the plane, $z = 14 - 3 \cdot 3 - 2 \cdot 2 = 1$, and so we have found that the point $(3, 2, 1)$ is the point of the given plane that is nearest the origin.

Example 97-3.   A rectangular box without a top is to be constructed from 900 square feet of material. What should its dimensions be in order that its volume be a maximum?

Solution.   We must maximize the volume V of the box. If the base of the box is x feet by y feet and it is h feet high, then

$$V = xyh.$$

Since we may use only 900 square feet of material, we can express one of the quantities x, y, or h in terms of the other two. For it requires $xy + 2xh + 2yh$ square feet of material to construct an x by y by h box without a top, and therefore

$$xy + 2xh + 2yh = 900.$$

From this equation we find that

(97-5) $$h = \frac{900 - xy}{2(x + y)},$$

and hence

$$V = \frac{xy(900 - xy)}{2(x + y)}.$$

Now we must find the points at which $D_xV = 0$ and $D_yV = 0$. After differentiating and simplifying, we have

$$D_xV = \frac{900y^2 - 2xy^3 - x^2y^2}{2(x + y)^2}$$

and

$$D_yV = \frac{900x^2 - 2x^3y - x^2y^2}{2(x + y)^2}.$$

When we equate these derivatives to 0 and simplify, we arrive at the system of equations

$$900 - 2xy - x^2 = 0$$
$$900 - 2xy - y^2 = 0.$$

From these equations we see at once that $x^2 = y^2$, and therefore that $x = y$, since both these numbers must be positive. So we can replace y with x in the first equation and find that $x^2 = 300$. Therefore, $x = 10\sqrt{3}$ and $y = 10\sqrt{3}$. From Equation 97-5 we find that $h = 5\sqrt{3}$. Thus the box with the largest volume has a square base measuring $10\sqrt{3}$ by $10\sqrt{3}$ feet, and it is $5\sqrt{3}$ feet high.

P R O B L E M S   9 7

1. Find the point of the plane $2x + y + z = 6$ that has positive coordinates and is such that:
(a) The product of the coordinates is a maximum.
(b) The sum of the squares of the coordinates is a minimum.

2. Find the lowest point of the surface whose equation is:
(a) $z = 5x^2 - 6xy + 2y^2 - 8x - 32$
(b) $9x^2 + 36y^2 + 4z^2 - 18x + 144y + 99 = 0.$

3. Find the highest point of the surface whose equation is:
(a) $z = 6y - 2x - x^2 - y^2.$
(b) $9x^2 + 36y^2 + 4z^2 - 18x + 144y + 99 = 0.$

4. Use calculus to find the distance between the point $(2, -1, 3)$ and the plane $2x - y + 2z = 5$. (Find the point of the plane that is nearest the point $(2, -1, 3)$.) Use a geometric argument to check your result.

5. Find the distance between the lines with parametric equations $x = t$, $y = 2t$, $z = t + 1$, and $x = s$, $y = s + 3$, $z = s$.

6. Find a point of the surface $z^2 = xy - 3x + 9$ that is closest to the origin.

7. One end of a house is to be built of glass in the shape of a rectangle surmounted by an isosceles triangle and is to have a given perimeter p. Find the slope of the roof if the house is constructed to admit a maximum amount of light.

8. Show that a rectangular box (with a top) made out of S square feet of material has a maximum volume if it is a cube.

9. Find the equation of the plane that contains the point $(1, 2, 1)$ and cuts off the least volume from the first octant.

10. Show that a rectangular box (without a top) made out of S square feet of material has a maximum volume if it has a square base and an altitude that is one-half the length of one side of the base.

11. Let f be the function whose domain is the unit sphere $x^2 + y^2 + z^2 = 1$, and whose rule of correspondence is $f(x, y, z) = x^2 y^2 z^2$. What are the maximum and minimum values of f?

12. Show that the product of the sines of the angles of a triangle is a maximum when the triangle is equilateral.

13. Suppose that we wish to make a rectangular box to hold 20 cubic feet of gold dust. The material used for the sides costs \$1 per square foot, the material used for the bottom costs \$2 per square foot, and the material used for the top costs \$3 per square foot. What are the dimensions of the cheapest box?

14. A long piece of tin 12 inches wide is to be made into a trough by bending up strips of equal width along the edges at equal angles with the horizontal. How wide should these strips be, and what angle must they make with the horizontal if the trough is to have a maximum carrying capacity?

15. Three points of the unit circle form the vertices of a triangle. Use calculus to determine how these points should be located so that we obtain a triangle with a maximum perimeter. Is there a triangle with minimum perimeter? What if we have more than three points?

REVIEW PROBLEMS—CHAPTER ELEVEN

You can use the following problems to test yourself on the material of this chapter.

1. Suppose that u and v satisfy the Cauchy-Riemann partial differential equations (see Example 93-4). Show that they also satisfy Laplace's differential equation $w_{xx} + w_{yy} = 0$.

2. Explain why Examples 93-4 and 94-2 are merely two different wordings of the same problem.

3. If f is a function on R^2 such that $f_1(0, 0) = 5$ and $f_2(0, 0) = 8$ and we write $F(x, y) = f(x - y, y - x)$, find the number $F_2(3, 3)$.

4. If $R = x i + y j + z k$ and $w = |R|^n$, where n is a given number, show that $\nabla w = n |R|^{n-2} R$.

5. Suppose that $F(x) = f(3x, 4x)$, where f is a function on R^2 such that $f_1(u, v) = u$ and $f_2(u, v) = 3v$. Find $F'(2)$, $F''(2)$, and $F'''(2)$.

6. What is the relation between two functions f and g if for each x, $\nabla f(x) = \nabla g(x)$?

7. Show that for every set of four positive numbers w, x, y, and z, we have

$$\sqrt[4]{wxyz} \leq \frac{w + x + y + z}{4}.$$

(Hint: Find the maximum value of the quotient $\sqrt[4]{wxyz}/(w + x + y + z)$.)
This inequality says that the geometric mean of four numbers is not greater than their arithmetic mean. Is the same statement true when we are dealing with n positive real numbers, $n \neq 4$?

8. The equation $f(x, y, z) = \text{Arcsin} \left(\dfrac{x^2}{6} + \dfrac{3y^2}{2} + \dfrac{z^2}{24} - \dfrac{1}{2} \right)$ defines a scalar-valued function on R^3.
(a) What is the domain of f?   (b) What is the range of f?

(c) Sketch the level surface $f(x, y, z) = \dfrac{\pi}{6}$.

(d) Find the equation of the tangent plane to this level surface at the point $(1, \frac{1}{3}, -4)$.
(e) At what rate do the functional values change as we start to move from the point $(1, \frac{1}{3}, -4)$ toward the point $(2, -\frac{5}{3}, -2)$?

9. Suppose that $w = F(x, y)$ satisfies the partial differential equation
(i) $aw_x + bw_y + cw = d$, where $abc \neq 0$.

If $w = e^u + \dfrac{d}{c}$, where $u = g(x, y)$, show that u satisfies the equation $au_x + bu_y + c = 0$. Now suppose that $u = v - \dfrac{cy}{b}$, where $v = h(x, y)$, and show that $av_x + bv_y = 0$. Set $s = bx - ay$ and $t = bx + ay$, and show that $v_t = 0$. Therefore, $v = f(s)$ for some function f on R^1. Conclude that the solution of (i) has the form

$$w = G(bx - ay)e^{-cy/b} + \dfrac{d}{c}.$$

10. It is frequently convenient to think of ∇ as a *vector differential operator*. Thus in R^3 we write $\nabla = (D_x, D_y, D_z)$, and if $w = f(x, y, z)$ we operate on w with the vector operator ∇ to obtain the gradient vector $\nabla w = (D_x w, D_y w, D_z w)$. We compute dot and cross products in the natural way; that is, we use our usual rules of computation but we interpret $D_x w$ as a derivative, not a product. For example, if $R = (x, y, z)$, $\nabla \cdot R = D_x x + D_y y + D_z z = 1 + 1 + 1 = 3$. Find:
(a) $\nabla \times R$ (b) $\nabla \cdot \nabla w$ (c) $\nabla \times \nabla w$ (d) $\nabla(\nabla w)$ in R^2 (see Problem 94-10)

MULTIPLE INTEGRATION

AND LINE INTEGRALS

T W E L V E

The two basic operations in the calculus of scalar-valued functions on R^1 are differentiation and integration. These same operations also play fundamental roles when we come to functions on R^n. In the preceding chapter, we considered some aspects of the differential calculus of functions on R^n, and now we will take up integration of scalar-valued and vector-valued functions on R^2 and R^3.

98 DOUBLE INTEGRALS

Our discussion in Chapter 5 of the integral of a function f on R^1 over an interval of the number scale was designed to answer three questions:

1. What is an integral?
2. What functions are integrable?
3. How do we calculate integrals?

We raise these same questions now as we take up the concept of the integral of a scalar-valued function on R^2 over a region in the plane. Since this new concept is completely analogous to the concept of the integral of a function on R^1 that we met in Chapter 5, a brief review of that situation is in order.

The integral $\int_a^b f(x)\,dx$ of a function f over an interval $[a, b]$ is a *number*, the limit of approximating sums that are formed as follows. The interval of integration $[a, b]$ is first partitioned into a set of n subintervals. Then in each subinterval we select a point, the point in the ith interval being denoted by x_i^*. The value of f at this point x_i^* is multiplied by the length Δx_i of the subinterval to obtain the product $f(x_i^*)\,\Delta x_i$. We now add these numbers to obtain our approximating sum $\sum_{i=1}^n f(x_i^*)\,\Delta x_i$. Graphically, this approximating sum is the area of the region made up of the rectangular strips shown in Fig. 98-1, and the area of the region that is

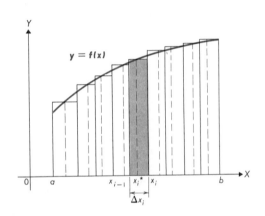

Figure 98-1

bounded by the graph of f, the X-axis, and the lines $x = a$ and $x = b$ is the limit of these sums; that is, the integral $\int_a^b f(x)\,dx$.

We define the integral of a function f on R^2 in a similar manner. Thus suppose that the domain of f contains a rectangular region $R = \{(x, y) \mid a \leq x \leq b, c \leq y \leq d\}$ (Fig. 98-2); let us see what we mean by the integral of f over R. The **region of integration R** corresponds to the interval of integration for a function on R^1, and our first step is to **partition** this region R by drawing lines parallel to the coordinate axes and so forming a network of rectangular subregions that cover R. The **norm** of this partition is the length of the longest of the diagonals of the rectangular subregions of the partition. Now we number the subregions of the partition from 1 to n. For each index i we denote by Δx_i the width of the ith subregion and by Δy_i its height. Thus the product $\Delta x_i\,\Delta y_i$ is the area of the ith

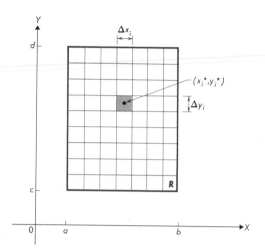

Figure 98-2

rectangular subregion, and we write

$$\Delta A_i = \Delta x_i \, \Delta y_i.$$

Now let us select a point (x_i^*, y_i^*) in the ith subregion, compute the number $f(x_i^*, y_i^*) \, \Delta A_i$, and then add all these products to obtain the sum

(98-1) $$s = \sum_{i=1}^{n} f(x_i^*, y_i^*) \Delta A_i.$$

We can, of course, compute many such sums, depending on how we partition the region R and choose the points (x_i^*, y_i^*). But if the function f is a "reasonable" function, all the sums that we can form when we use partitions with small norms will be close to one particular number, the limit of s as the norm of the partition of R approaches 0. This number is called the **double integral of f over R**, and we will denote it by one of the symbols

$$\iint\limits_{R} f(x, y) \, dA, \; \iint\limits_{R} f(x, y) \, dx \, dy, \; \text{or} \iint\limits_{R} f(x, y) \, dy \, dx.$$

Thus, in rough terms, *the double integral $\iint\limits_{R} f(x, y) \, dA$ is the number that is approximated by every sum s that we can form when we use a partition with a small norm.*

We will now formulate a definition of the double integral of f over R that puts what we have just said in more precise language. This definition is the natural extension of the definition of the (single) integral that we made in Section 33. We first define a set-valued function S as follows. To a positive number u let there correspond the set $S(u)$ of all possible approximating sums that can be based on partitions of R with norm u. Then if $\lim\limits_{u \downarrow 0} S(u)$ exists, we say that f is **integrable** on R and call this limit the **integral** of f over R. Thus

$$\iint\limits_{R} f(x, y)\, dA = \lim_{u \downarrow 0} S(u).$$

In this first course in calculus, we will usually interpret the double integral in the more informal language of the preceding paragraph.

Example 98-1. Let R be the square region $\{(x, y) \mid 0 \le x \le 2, 0 \le y \le 2\}$. Approximate the number $\iint\limits_{R} (8x^2 + 2y)\, dA$.

Solution. In Fig. 98-3, we show our region R partitioned into 4 subregions by the lines $x = 1$ and $y = 1$. Each sub-region is square and measures 1 by 1, so $\Delta A_i = 1$ for each index i. In each square subregion, we have selected the center as our point (x_i^*, y_i^*). Thus, since $f(x, y) = 8x^2 + 2y$, a sum that approximates the desired integral is

$$\begin{aligned} s &= f(\tfrac{1}{2}, \tfrac{1}{2}) \cdot 1 + f(\tfrac{1}{2}, \tfrac{3}{2}) \cdot 1 \\ &\quad + f(\tfrac{3}{2}, \tfrac{3}{2}) \cdot 1 + f(\tfrac{3}{2}, \tfrac{1}{2}) \cdot 1 \\ &= 3 \cdot 1 + 5 \cdot 1 + 21 \cdot 1 + 19 \cdot 1 \\ &= 48. \end{aligned}$$

We therefore have found that

$$\iint\limits_{R} (8x^2 + 2y)\, dA \approx 48.$$

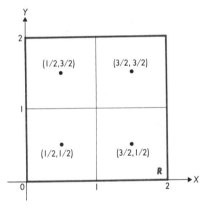

Figure 98-3

We shall see in the next section (Example 99-1) that actually the integral is $\tfrac{152}{3} = 50\tfrac{2}{3}$.

In order that a function f on R^1 should be integrable on a given interval, f must be bounded and the points of the interval at which f is discontinuous must form a set of "measure zero" (see Section 34). The same remarks apply in case f is a function on R^2. As before, we are not going to give a precise definition of the technical term "measure." In one dimension, the measure of a set is a generalization of the idea of the length of an interval; in two dimensions, measure is a generalization of area. If you can find the area of a plane region, you will have its measure. In particular, then, a set that consists of a finite number of line segments, circular arcs, isolated points, and so on, is a set of measure zero.

Example 98-2. Do the integrals $\iint_R ([\![x]\!] + [\![y]\!])\, dA$ and $\iint_R \sec(x+y)\, dA$, where R is the square region shown in Fig. 98-3, exist?

Solution. The function f defined by the equation $f(x, y) = [\![x]\!] + [\![y]\!]$ is bounded in R, and it is continuous at all points of R except for the line segments shown in the figure. Thus the points of discontinuity form a set of measure zero, so f is integrable on R. The function g, where $g(x, y) = \sec(x+y)$, is unbounded in any neighborhood of a point (x, y) of the line $x + y = \tfrac{1}{2}\pi$, so we see that

$$\iint_R \sec(x+y)\, dA \quad \text{does not exist.}$$

We will have more to say about calculating double integrals in the following sections, but let us take up the geometric interpretation of double integrals first. Even when a single integral arises in a non-geometric problem, we know that we can interpret it in terms of the area of some plane region. Now we will see how we can interpret a double integral in terms of volume. Suppose that f is a function on R^2 and that $f(x, y) \geq 0$ for each point (x, y) of a rectangular region R of the XY-

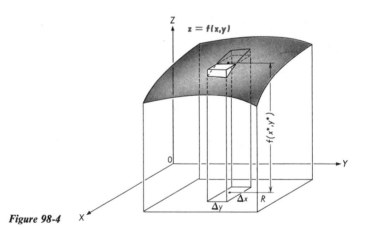

Figure 98-4

plane. Then the graph of the equation $z = f(x, y)$, for $(x, y) \in R$, is a surface that lies above the XY-plane, as shown in Fig. 98-4. In the figure, we have shown one of the sub-regions into which R is partitioned when we form the Approximating Sum 98-1. A typical term of this sum has the form

$$f(x^*, y^*)\, \Delta A = f(x^*, y^*)\, \Delta x\, \Delta y,$$

and this number is the volume of the rectangular block whose base measures Δx by Δy and whose altitude is $f(x^*, y^*)$. Approximating Sum 98-1 is the sum of such volumes, and it appears from the figure that this sum approximates the volume of the three-dimensional region that is bounded by R, planes that contain the boundaries of R, and the graph of f. Since our approximating sum also approximates the number $\iint\limits_R f(x, y)\, dA$, it is natural to expect that the volume of the region under the graph of f is the integral. This expectation is correct. It follows from the mathematical definition of volume that the integral is the volume of the region under the graph. Since our intuitive idea of the properties that volume ought to possess coincides with the properties that volume actually does possess, we can use our ideas about volume to compute double integrals in exactly the same way that we use our ideas about area to compute single integrals.

Example 98-3. Evaluate the integral $\iint\limits_R (\,[\![x]\!] + [\![y]\!]\,)\, dA$, where R is the square region shown in Fig. 98-3.

Solution. In Fig. 98-5, we have shown the part of the graph of the equation $z = [\![x]\!] + [\![y]\!]$ that lies above the region R. The region under this graph can be

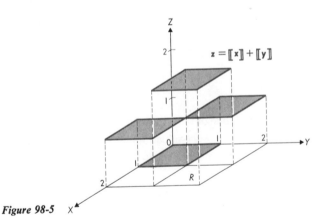

Figure 98-5

considered as two 1 by 1 by 1 blocks and one 1 by 1 by 2 block, so its volume is 4 cubic units. Hence we conclude that $\iint\limits_R (\,[\![x]\!] + [\![y]\!]\,)\, dA = 4$.

Some of the most important properties of single integrals also are possessed by double integrals. Formal proofs of the following formulas follow in a straightforward manner from the rules of limits for set-valued functions. If f and g are integrable on a rectangular region R, and if m and n are any numbers, then

$$(98\text{-}2) \quad \iint_R [mf(x, y) + ng(x, y)]\, dA = m \iint_R f(x, y)\, dA + n \iint_R g(x, y)\, dA.$$

Furthermore, suppose we split a rectangular region R into two non-overlapping subregions R_1 and R_2; that is, suppose $R = R_1 \cup R_2$, where $R_1 \cap R_2$ has zero area. Then

$$(98\text{-}3) \quad \iint_R f(x, y)\, dA = \iint_{R_1} f(x, y)\, dA + \iint_{R_2} f(x, y)\, dA.$$

This last equation corresponds to the equation

$$\int_a^c f(x)\, dx = \int_a^b f(x)\, dx + \int_b^c f(x)\, dx$$

for single integrals.

P R O B L E M S   9 8

1. Let R be the rectangular region $\{(x, y) \mid -1 \le x \le 1, 0 \le y \le 2\}$. The lines $y = 1$ and $x = 0$ partition this region into 4 square subregions in each of which we take the center as our point (x^*, y^*). Based on this partition and choice of points within subregions, form the sums that approximate the following integrals.

(a) $\displaystyle\iint_R (x + y)^2\, dA$ (b) $\displaystyle\iint_R (x^2 + y^2)\, dA$ (c) $\displaystyle\iint_R (|x| + |y|)\, dA$ (d) $\displaystyle\iint_R \cos^2 \pi xy\, dA$

2. In Example 98-1, we found that one of the approximating sums based on a partition of norm $\sqrt{2}$ is 48. Thus, if S is the set-valued function used to define the double integral, $48 \in S(\sqrt{2})$. Find 4 other numbers in $S(\sqrt{2})$. Explain why $[20, 92] \subseteq S(\sqrt{2})$. Is $48 \in S(\frac{1}{2}\sqrt{2})$?

3. Use the volume interpretation of the double integral to evaluate the following integrals over the square region $R = \{(x, y) \mid 0 \le x \le 2, 0 \le y \le 2\}$.

(a) $\displaystyle\iint_R x\, dA$ (b) $\displaystyle\iint_R |y - 1|\, dA$ (c) $\displaystyle\iint_R \sqrt{1 - (x - 1)^2}\, dA$

(d) $\displaystyle\iint_R [\![x + y]\!]\, dA$ (e) $\displaystyle\iint_R \left(1 + \frac{x - y}{|x - y|}\right) dA$ (f) $\displaystyle\iint_R (1 - [\![(x - 1)^2 + (y - 1)^2]\!])\, dA$

4. When you use the volume interpretation to evaluate the following double integrals, notice that the regions whose volumes you are to find are cylindrical solids. You may use single integration to find the areas of the bases of these regions. In each

case, R is the square region $\{(x, y) \mid -1 \leq x \leq 1, -1 \leq y \leq 1\}$.

(a) $\displaystyle\iint\limits_R x^2 \, dA$ (b) $\displaystyle\iint\limits_R \sin y \, dA$ (c) $\displaystyle\iint\limits_R \ln (x + 2) \, dA$ (d) $\displaystyle\iint\limits_R |4y^2 - 1| \, dA$

5. Let R be the rectangular region $\{(x, y) \mid a \leq x \leq b, c \leq y \leq d\}$.

(a) Use the geometric interpretation of the integral to show that

$$\iint\limits_R (x - a) \, dA = \tfrac{1}{2}(b - a)^2(d - c).$$

(b) Now write $x = (x - a) + a$ and use Equation 98-2 to show that $\displaystyle\iint\limits_R x \, dA = \tfrac{1}{2}(b^2 - a^2)(d - c)$.

(c) Show that $\displaystyle\iint\limits_R y \, dA = \tfrac{1}{2}(d^2 - c^2)(b - a)$.

(d) Show that for any three numbers p, q, and r,

$$\iint\limits_R (px + qy + r) \, dA = \left[p\left(\frac{a + b}{2}\right) + q\left(\frac{c + d}{2}\right) + r \right](b - a)(d - c).$$

Interpret this result geometrically.

6. Let $R = \{(x, y) \mid 0 \leq x \leq 1, 0 \leq y \leq 1\}$. Which of the following integrals exist?

(a) $\displaystyle\iint\limits_R \ln x \, dA$ (b) $\displaystyle\iint\limits_R \tan (x + y) \, dA$ (c) $\displaystyle\iint\limits_R e^{[\![3x+2y]\!]} \, dA$ (d) $\displaystyle\iint\limits_R \sin \left(\frac{x}{y} + \frac{y}{x}\right) dA$

7. Explain why $\displaystyle\iint\limits_R f(x, y) \, dA \geq 0$, if $f(x, y) \geq 0$ for each point $(x, y) \in R$. If $f(x, y) \leq g(x, y)$ at each point of R, does it follow that $\displaystyle\iint\limits_R f(x, y) \, dA \leq \iint\limits_R g(x, y) \, dA$?

8. Let $R = \{(x, y) \mid 0 \leq x \leq 1, 0 \leq y \leq 1\}$ and let f be the function that is defined by the equations $f(0, 0) = 1$ and $f(x, y) = 0$ if $(x, y) \neq (0, 0)$. Show that in this case our set-valued function S has as its domain the interval $(0, \sqrt{2}]$ and that for each $u \in (0, \sqrt{2}]$ we have $S(u) = [0, \tfrac{1}{2}u^2]$. Draw the graph of S, and conclude that $\lim\limits_{u \downarrow 0} S(u) = 0$. Does this result agree with our geometric interpretation of the double integral?

99 EVALUATING DOUBLE INTEGRALS

We will now use our geometric interpretation of a double integral as a volume to develop a method of evaluating double integrals by using successive single integrals. This method enables us to find double integrals by using the tricks for evaluating integrals that we developed in earlier chapters. Our arguments in this section will be quite informal; we leave the translation of these arguments into more precise language to a course in advanced calculus.

Let us suppose we are given a function f that is integrable on a rectangular region $R = \{(x, y) \mid a \leq x \leq b, c \leq y \leq d\}$. In order to use our geometric interpretation of the double integral as a volume, we will assume here that $f(x, y) \geq 0$ for each point (x, y) in R; it is easy to extend our results to cover cases in which

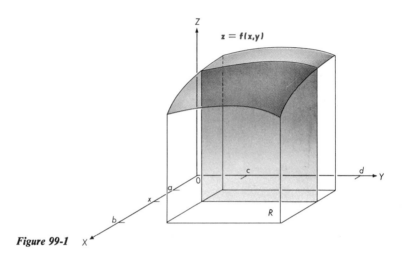

Figure 99-1

$f(x, y)$ is allowed to take negative values. Figure 99-1 shows the graph of the equation $z = f(x, y)$ for $(x, y) \in R$. The number $\displaystyle\iint_R f(x, y)\, dA$ that we seek is the volume of the solid region between this surface and R. We will find this volume by considering our solid as a "union of narrow slices," a technique that we developed in Section 41. Choose $x \in [a, b]$, and consider the plane that contains x and is parallel to the YZ-plane. This plane will intersect our solid in the plane region that is shaded gray in the figure. If the area of this plane region is $A(x)$, the "method of slicing" of Section 41 shows us that the volume of our solid is $\displaystyle\int_a^b A(x)\, dx$. This volume is the double integral we seek, so we have

$$(99\text{-}1) \qquad \iint_R f(x, y)\, dA = \int_a^b A(x)\, dx.$$

Therefore, we can evaluate the double integral of f over R by finding a single integral of $A(x)$. Our problem is now reduced to finding $A(x)$ for a given number x. Since $A(x)$ is the area of a plane region, we find it by integration. Figure 99-1 shows that the upper boundary of this plane region is the graph of the equation $z = f(x, y)$ for $y \in [c, d]$. Hence its area is $A(x) = \int_c^d f(x, y)\, dy$. When we substitute this result in Equation 99-1, we obtain the fundamental formula for evaluating double integrals

(99-2)
$$\iint_R f(x, y)\, dA = \int_a^b \left[\int_c^d f(x, y)\, dy \right] dx.$$

We usually omit the brackets in the **iterated integral** on the right-hand side of Equation 99-2 and write the equation as

(99-3)
$$\iint_R f(x, y)\, dA = \int_a^b \int_c^d f(x, y)\, dy\, dx.$$

When we evaluate the "inner integral" in Equation 99-3, we should remember that y is the variable of integration, not x. In this integration, x is considered "fixed," just as it is considered "fixed" when we apply the differential operator D_y to find the partial derivative $D_y f(x, y)$.

Example 99-1   Evaluate the integral $\iint_R (8x^2 + 2y)\, dA$, where R is the region $\{(x, y) \mid 0 \le x \le 2, 0 \le y \le 2\}$.

Solution.   Here $a = 0$, $b = 2$, $c = 0$, and $d = 2$, so Equation 99-3 becomes

$$\iint_R (8x^2 + 2y)\, dA = \int_0^2 \int_0^2 (8x^2 + 2y)\, dy\, dx$$

$$= \int_0^2 \left[\int_0^2 (8x^2 + 2y)\, dy \right] dx$$

$$= \int_0^2 [8x^2 y + y^2] \Big|_0^2 \, dx$$

$$= \int_0^2 (16x^2 + 4)\, dx = 50\tfrac{2}{3}.$$

So far, we have only talked about double integrals over rectangular regions in the plane; now let us turn to regions of other shapes, such as the region R shown in Fig. 99-2. We will consider a function f whose domain contains R and introduce the idea of the integral of f over R. Our first step is to enclose R in a rectangular region $\bar{R}$, as shown in Fig. 99-2. Now we define a new function $\bar{f}$ whose value at a point (x, y) is $f(x, y)$ if $(x, y) \in R$, and is 0 if $(x, y) \notin R$. Our definition of the double integral over rectangular regions enables us to talk about the integral $\iint_R \bar{f}(x, y)\, dA$, and we therefore *define* the integral of f over R by the equation

(99-4) $$\iint_R f(x, y)\, dA = \iint_{\bar{R}} \bar{f}(x, y)\, dA.$$

Because $\bar{f}$ takes the value 0 outside of R, we can choose as our region $\bar{R}$ *any* rectangular region that contains R, and Equation 99-4 will give us the same value of the integral of f over R.

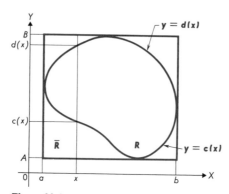

Figure 99-2

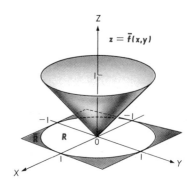

Figure 99-3

Example 99-2. Evaluate the integral $\iint_R \sqrt{x^2 + y^2}\, dA$, where R is the unit disk $x^2 + y^2 \leq 1$.

Solution. We can take $\bar{R}$ to be any rectangular region that contains the unit disk, so let us choose $\bar{R} = \{(x, y) \mid -1 \leq x \leq 1,\ -1 \leq y \leq 1\}$. The graph of the function $\bar{f}$ is shown in Fig. 99-3; it is the union of a cone and the part of the XY-plane that lies outside the unit circle. Our definition of an integral over the region R tells us that we are to evaluate the integral $\iint_{\bar{R}} \bar{f}(x, y)\, dA$. This integral is the volume of the region "between" the graph of $\bar{f}$ and the rectangular region $\bar{R}$. Since the graph of $\bar{f}$ coincides with the XY-plane except in the region R, we see that we are actually to find the volume of the region between the cone and the disk R. When we calculate this volume, we find that

$$\iint_R \sqrt{x^2 + y^2}\, dA = \tfrac{2}{3}\pi.$$

You will notice that unless $f(x, y) = 0$ at a boundary point of R, the function $\bar{f}$ will be discontinuous there, as it is in our example above. Thus $\bar{f}$ is quite likely to be discontinuous on the boundary of R. But we will assume that the boundary of R is a curve whose area (and hence measure) is 0, and so discontinuities at the boundary points will not affect the integrability of $\bar{f}$. Thus f is integrable on R provided that it is bounded and the set of points of R at which f is discontinuous is of measure 0. The General Integration Formulas 98-2 and 98-3 remain valid when R, R_1, and R_2 are non-rectangular regions.

Now let us see how to express a double integral over a region like the one shown in Fig. 99-2 as an iterated integral. Here we have chosen our bounding rectangle $\bar{R}$ to fit the given region R "tightly," and the formula we will develop (Equation 99-7) depends on the fact that vertical lines in $\bar{R}$ intersect the boundary of R in exactly two points. We are often able to express a region that does not have this property as a union of regions that do have it or the analogous property that horizontal lines intersect the boundary exactly twice. Then we can write an integral over such a region as a sum of integrals over regions of our special types and use the integral formulas we will now develop to find the terms of the sum. Since $\bar{R} = \{(x, y) \mid a \leq x \leq b, A \leq y \leq B\}$, we may write the integral on the right-hand side of Equation 99-4 as an iterated integral:

$$(99\text{-}5) \qquad \iint_{\bar{R}} \bar{f}(x, y)\, dA = \int_a^b \int_A^B \bar{f}(x, y)\, dy\, dx.$$

Our figure shows that the region R is the set $\{(x, y) \mid a \leq x \leq b, c(x) \leq y \leq d(x)\}$; that is, the upper and lower boundaries of R are graphs of the equations $y = d(x)$ and $y = c(x)$. Thus, for a given point x, $A \leq c(x) \leq d(x) \leq B$. Now let us write the inner integral of the iterated integral in Equation 99-5 as

$$(99\text{-}6) \qquad \int_A^B \bar{f}(x, y)\, dy = \int_A^{c(x)} \bar{f}(x, y)\, dy + \int_{c(x)}^{d(x)} \bar{f}(x, y)\, dy + \int_{d(x)}^B \bar{f}(x, y)\, dy.$$

According to our definition of $\bar{f}$, we see that $\bar{f}(x, y) = 0$ if $A \leq y < c(x)$ or $d(x) < y \leq B$, and $\bar{f}(x, y) = f(x, y)$ if $c(x) \leq y \leq d(x)$. Thus Equation 99-6 simplifies to

$$\int_A^B \bar{f}(x, y)\, dA = \int_{c(x)}^{d(x)} f(x, y)\, dy.$$

When this result is substituted in Equation 99-5 and then in Equation 99-4, we obtain an integration formula that expresses a double integral over our non-rectangular region R as an iterated integral:

$$(99\text{-}7) \qquad \iint_R f(x, y)\, dA = \int_a^b \int_{c(x)}^{d(x)} f(x, y)\, dy\, dx.$$

Notice how the limits of integration on the iterated integral may be read from the description of our region of integration as the set $R = \{(x, y) \mid a \leq x \leq b, c(x) \leq y \leq d(x)\}$.

Example 99-3. Evaluate $\iint\limits_R x \, dA$, where R is the region that is bounded by the Y-axis and the semi-circle $x = \sqrt{4 - y^2}$.

Solution. The given region (Fig. 99-4) is the set

$$R = \{(x, y) \mid 0 \leq x \leq 2,$$
$$-\sqrt{4 - x^2} \leq y \leq \sqrt{4 - x^2}\}.$$

Thus when we use Equation 99-7 to evaluate our integral we have

$$\iint\limits_R x \, dA = \int_0^2 \int_{-\sqrt{4-x^2}}^{\sqrt{4-x^2}} x \, dy \, dx = \int_0^2 x \left[y \Big|_{-\sqrt{4-x^2}}^{\sqrt{4-x^2}} \right] dx$$

$$= \int_0^2 2x \sqrt{4 - x^2} \, dx = \tfrac{16}{3}.$$

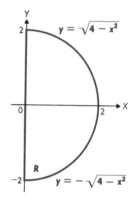

Figure 99-4

According to Equation 99-7, we can express a double integral as an iterated integral in which we first consider y as the variable of integration and then x. Of course, the roles of x and y can be interchanged (if R is of the right shape). Thus if $R = \{(x, y) \mid c \leq y \leq d, a(y) \leq x \leq b(y)\}$, then

(99-8) $$\iint\limits_R f(x, y) \, dA = \int_c^d \int_{a(y)}^{b(y)} f(x, y) \, dx \, dy.$$

Example 99-4. Use Equation 99-8 to evaluate the integral in Example 99-3.

Solution. The left boundary of our region is the line $x = 0$, and the right boundary is the semi-circle $x = \sqrt{4 - y^2}$. Thus

$$R = \{(x, y) \mid -2 \leq y \leq 2, 0 \leq x \leq \sqrt{4 - y^2}\},$$

and Equation 99-8 becomes

$$\iint\limits_R x \, dA = \int_{-2}^2 \int_0^{\sqrt{4-y^2}} x \, dx \, dy = \int_{-2}^2 \frac{x^2}{2} \Big|_0^{\sqrt{4-y^2}} dy$$

$$= \tfrac{1}{2} \int_{-2}^2 (4 - y^2) \, dy = \tfrac{16}{3}.$$

The region of integration R determines the limits of integration on an iterated integral used to evaluate a double integral and, conversely, these limits determine R. Thus if $a < b$ and $c(x) \le d(x)$ for each $x \in [a, b]$, then the iterated integral $\int_a^b \int_{c(x)}^{d(x)} f(x, y) \, dy \, dx$ is the double integral of f over the region

$$R = \{(x, y) \mid a \le x \le b, c(x) \le y \le d(x)\}.$$

Similarly, if $c < d$ and $a(y) \le b(y)$ for each $y \in [c, d]$, then the iterated integral $\int_c^d \int_{a(y)}^{b(y)} f(x, y) \, dx \, dy$ is the double integral of f over the region $R = \{(x, y) \mid c \le y \le d, a(y) \le x \le b(y)\}$. Figure 99-5 shows how the boundary of the

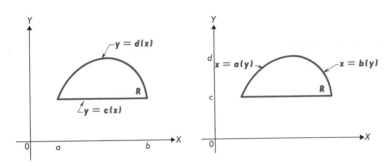

Figure 99-5

same region of integration looks from these two points of view. It may be important to have both pictures in mind because you may want to shift from one iterated integral to the other, as the following example shows.

Example 99-5. Evaluate the iterated integral

$$\int_0^1 \int_y^1 \tan x^2 \, dx \, dy.$$

Solution. In order to evaluate the integral as written, our first task would be to find $\int_y^1 \tan x^2 \, dx$. But none of our integration formulas applies, so let us change the order of integration in our given iterated integral. From its limits of integration, we see that this integral equals the double integral of $\tan x^2$ over the region $R = \{(x, y) \mid 0 \le y \le 1, y \le x \le 1\}$. Figure 99-6 shows us that we can also write $R = \{(x, y) \mid 0 \le x \le 1, 0 \le y \le x\}$,

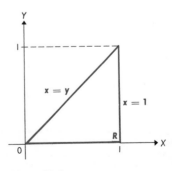

Figure 99-6

and this expression tells how to express our double integral as an iterated integral
in which we first integrate with respect to y:

$$\iint\limits_{R} \tan x^2 \, dA = \int_0^1 \int_0^x \tan x^2 \, dy \, dx.$$

Therefore,

$$\int_0^1 \int_y^1 \tan x^2 \, dx \, dy = \int_0^1 \int_0^x \tan x^2 \, dy \, dx$$

$$= \int_0^1 x \tan x^2 \, dx = \tfrac{1}{2} \ln \sec x^2 \Big|_0^1$$

$$= \tfrac{1}{2} \ln \sec 1 \approx .308.$$

P R O B L E M S 9 9

1. Evaluate $\displaystyle\iint\limits_{R} f(x, y) \, dA$ if $R = \{(x, y) \mid 0 \le x \le 2, 0 \le y \le 1\}$ and:

(a) $f(x, y) = xy^2$ (b) $f(x, y) = x + y^2$

(c) $f(x, y) = e^x(\cos y + \cos e^x)$ (d) $f(x, y) = e^x \cos (y + e^x)$

2. Evaluate the following iterated integrals.

(a) $\displaystyle\int_1^2 \int_0^1 (1 - y)x^2 \, dy \, dx$ (b) $\displaystyle\int_{-1}^1 \int_{-1}^2 x(xy + \sin x) \, dy \, dx$

(c) $\displaystyle\int_0^{\pi/2} \int_0^1 xy \cos x^2 y \, dx \, dy$ (d) $\displaystyle\int_0^{\pi} \int_0^{\pi/2} \sin u \cos (v - \pi) \, du \, dv$

3. Evaluate the following iterated integrals.

(a) $\displaystyle\int_0^4 \int_0^x x \, dy \, dx$ (b) $\displaystyle\int_0^1 \int_0^{x^2} \sin \pi x^3 \, dy \, dx$

(c) $\displaystyle\int_0^1 \int_{2x}^{3x} e^{x+y} \, dy \, dx$ (d) $\displaystyle\int_1^2 \int_0^{\sqrt{x}} y \ln x^2 \, dy \, dx$

(e) $\displaystyle\int_0^2 \int_{\sqrt{4-x^2}}^{3e^{x^2}} x \, dy \, dx$ (f) $\displaystyle\int_0^{\pi/2} \int_0^{\sin y} \frac{dx \, dy}{\sqrt{1 - x^2}}$

4. Use the geometric interpretation of the double integral to evaluate $\displaystyle\iint\limits_{D} f(x, y) \, dA$
if D is the unit disk $x^2 + y^2 \le 1$, and $f(x, y)$ is equal to:

(a) 1 (b) $\sqrt{1 - x^2 - y^2}$ (c) $ax + by + c$ (d) $[\![5(x^2 + y^2)]\!]$

5. Evaluate the integral $\displaystyle\iint\limits_{R} xy \, dA$ if R is the region:

(a) $\{(x, y) \mid 0 \le x \le 4, 0 \le y \le 2\}$ (b) $\{(x, y) \mid 0 \le x \le 2, 0 \le y \le x\}$

(c) $\{(x, y) \mid x \ge 0, y \ge 0, x^2 + y^2 \le 1\}$ (d) $\{(x, y) \mid 0 \le x \le 2, x^2 \le y \le 4\}$

6. Sketch the region of integration R if the double integral $\iint\limits_{R} f(x, y)\, dA$ can be expressed as the iterated integral:

(a) $\int_{0}^{1} \int_{-\sqrt{1-x^2}}^{1-x^2} f(x, y)\, dy\, dx$ (b) $\int_{0}^{1} \int_{\text{Arcsin } x}^{2} f(x, y)\, dy\, dx$

7. Evaluate $\iint\limits_{D} f(x, y)\, dA$ if $f(-x, -y) = -f(x, y)$ and D is the unit disk $x^2 + y^2 \le 1$.

8. Evaluate $\iint\limits_{R} f(x, y)\, dA$ for the following choices of $f(x, y)$ and R.

(a) $f(x, y) = 2x$; R is the region bounded by the parabola $4y = x^2$ and the line $x - 2y + 4 = 0$.

(b) $f(x, y) = x \sin xy$; $R = \{(x, y) \mid 0 \le x \le 1, 0 \le y \le \frac{1}{2}\pi\}$.

(c) $f(x, y) = (1 - x^4)^{-1/2}$; $R = \{(x, y) \mid 0 \le x \le 1/\sqrt{2}, 0 \le y \le x\}$.

(d) $f(x, y) = x$; $R = \{(x, y) \mid 0 \le x \le 1, 0 \le y \le \text{Arccos } x\}$.

(e) $f(x, y) = \dfrac{\sin x}{4 - \sin^2 y}$; $R = \{(x, y) \mid 0 \le x \le \frac{1}{2}\pi, 0 \le y \le x\}$.

(f) $f(x, y) = y^2$; $R = \{(x, y) \mid 1 \le x \le e, -\ln x \le y \le 0\}$.

(g) $f(x, y) = \dfrac{1}{4 - x}$; $R = \{(x, y) \mid 2 \le x \le 3, 0 \le y \le 1/x\}$.

(h) $f(x, y) = \sec y$; $R = \{(x, y) \mid 0 \le x \le 1, \text{Arctan } x \le y \le \frac{1}{4}\pi\}$.

9. Evaluate the following integrals by changing the order of integration.

(a) $\int_{0}^{2} \int_{2y}^{4} e^{x^2}\, dx\, dy$ (b) $\int_{0}^{1} \int_{y}^{1} \sin x^2\, dx\, dy$ (c) $\int_{0}^{1} \int_{0}^{\text{Arccos } x} e^{\sin y}\, dy\, dx$

10. Invert the order of integration in the iterated integral

$$\int_{a}^{b} \int_{0}^{x} f(x, y)\, dy\, dx, \quad (0 < a < b).$$

11. Evaluate: $\int_{-1}^{0} \int_{\text{Arccos } x}^{2\pi} e^{y}\, dy\, dx$.

12. The equation $F(x, y) = \int_{0}^{x} \int_{0}^{y} \sin (u^2 + v^2)\, du\, dv$ defines a function on R^2. What is the domain of this function? Is $F(1, 1)$ positive or negative? Is $F_1(1, 1)$ positive or negative? Calculate $F_{12}(x, y)$ and $F_{21}(x, y)$. Show that $F(y, x) = F(x, y)$.

100 FINDING VOLUMES AND AREAS BY DOUBLE INTEGRATION

Double integrals are widely used in science and engineering to calculate such things as work, force, and so on. Because we do not want to take up the background material that would be necessary to understand these physical applications, we shall restrict our applications of multiple integrals to geometric problems. This restriction is purely a matter of convenience, and you should realize that double integrals are not simply devices for finding volumes, areas, and the like, even though that is the only use we will make of them. These relatively minor applications will, however, give you experience in setting up and evaluating double integrals, and this experience will come in handy when you are faced with a double integral in some other context.

If $f(x, y) > 0$ at each point (x, y) of a region R of the XY-plane, then the region R, the cylinder based on the boundary of R, and the graph of the equation $z = f(x, y)$ bound a region in space. We will speak of this region as the "region under the graph of f and above the plane region R," and our geometric interpretation of the double integral is that the volume of this region is the number

(100-1) $$V = \iint\limits_R f(x, y) \, dA.$$

We will now consider, in some detail, an example of how this formula is used.

Example 100-1. Find the volume of the region that is bounded by the XY-plane, the plane $x + y + z = 2$, and the parabolic cylinder $y = x^2$.

Solution. On the left-hand side of Fig. 100-1 we show the three-dimensional region whose volume we are to find. The parabolic cylinder intersects the XY-plane in the parabola $y = x^2$, and the plane $x + y + z = 2$ intersects the XY-plane in the

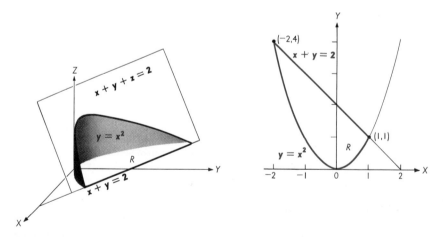

Figure 100-1

line $x + y = 2$. These curves bound the plane region R that is shown on the right-hand side of Fig. 100-1. The solid whose volume we seek is the region under the plane $x + y + z = 2$ (that is, $z = 2 - x - y$) and above R, so Equation 100-1 tells us that we are looking for the number

$$V = \iint\limits_R (2 - x - y)\, dA.$$

We calculate this double integral by replacing it with an iterated integral. Thus, since $R = \{(x, y) \mid -2 \le x \le 1,\ x^2 \le y \le 2 - x\}$, we have

$$V = \int_{-2}^{1} \int_{x^2}^{2-x} (2 - x - y)\, dy\, dx = \int_{-2}^{1} \left(2y - xy - \frac{y^2}{2}\right)\Big|_{x^2}^{2-x} dx$$

$$= \int_{-2}^{1} (2 - 2x - \tfrac{3}{2}x^2 + x^3 + \tfrac{1}{2}x^4)\, dx = \tfrac{81}{20}.$$

If we express our double integral as an iterated integral in which the first integration is with respect to x, we write

(100-2)
$$V = \int_{0}^{4} \int_{a(y)}^{b(y)} (2 - x - y)\, dx\, dy,$$

where $x = a(y)$ and $x = b(y)$ are equations of the left and right boundaries of R. Now $a(y) = -\sqrt{y}$ for each $y \in [0, 4]$, but the formula for $b(y)$ depends on the value of y. Thus we see that $b(y) = \sqrt{y}$ if $y \in [0, 1]$, and $b(y) = 2 - y$ if $y \in [1, 4]$.

To take these different formulas into account, we write our iterated integral over the Y-interval $[0, 4]$ as the sum of integrals over $[0, 1]$ and $[1, 4]$, and Equation 100-2 becomes

(100-3)
$$V = \int_{0}^{1} \int_{a(y)}^{b(y)} (2 - x - y)\, dx\, dy + \int_{1}^{4} \int_{a(y)}^{b(y)} (2 - x - y)\, dx\, dy$$

$$= \int_{0}^{1} \int_{-\sqrt{y}}^{\sqrt{y}} (2 - x - y)\, dx\, dy + \int_{1}^{4} \int_{-\sqrt{y}}^{2-y} (2 - x - y)\, dx\, dy$$

$$= \frac{131}{60} + \frac{28}{15} = \frac{81}{20}.$$

Another way of looking at the problem is to write our region of integration as $R = R_1 \cup R_2$, where

$$R_1 = \{(x, y) \mid 0 \le y \le 1,\ -\sqrt{y} \le x \le \sqrt{y}\}$$

and

$$R_2 = \{(x, y) \mid 1 \le y \le 4,\ -\sqrt{y} \le x \le 2 - y\}.$$

Then we have

$$V = \iint\limits_R (2 - x - y)\, dA = \iint\limits_{R_1} (2 - x - y)\, dA + \iint\limits_{R_2} (2 - x - y)\, dA,$$

which becomes Equation 100-3 when we replace the last two double integrals with iterated integrals.

Our formal definition in Section 99 of the double integral of a function *f* over a plane region *R* can be stated informally as follows. First we cover *R* with a rectangular mesh as shown in Fig. 100-2. We call such a mesh a *covering* of *R*. In each subregion of the covering we choose a point; the figure shows a typical subregion of dimensions Δx by Δy, in which we have chosen the point (x^*, y^*). At this point our function *f* has the value $f(x^*, y^*)$. (For subregions that contain boundary points of *R*, it is possible that our chosen point is not in *R*; then we use 0 in place of $f(x^*, y^*)$.) We multiply this number by the area $\Delta A = \Delta x \, \Delta y$ of the subregion. When we perform this computation for each subregion of our covering and add the resulting products, we obtain a sum of the form

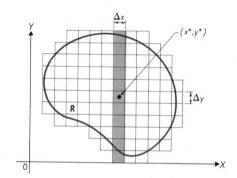

Figure 100-2

$$\sum f(x^*, y^*) \, \Delta A = \sum f(x^*, y^*) \, \Delta x \, \Delta y$$

(for simplicity of notation, we have omitted the index of summation.) The double integral is the limit of such approximating sums.

Although approximating sums and double integrals are not the same thing, we nevertheless frequently find it convenient to think of the process of evaluating the double integral $\iint\limits_R f(x,y) \, dA$ as a matter of addition. We can consider an iterated integral as a device by which this addition is performed systematically. Thus, informally, we can view the iterated integral in which the first integration is with respect to *y* as a method of adding terms that correspond to rectangular subregions that form a strip parallel to the *Y*-axis, such as the one shown in Fig. 100-2. Then our second integration (with respect to *x*) adds up the contributions that correspond to these vertical strips. If we set up our iterated integral so that we first integrate with respect to *x*, we reverse the procedure—we first add terms that correspond to a horizontal strip of rectangular subregions and then we add up the contributions of these strips. Thus we evaluate a double integral by using an iterated integral to "sweep out" the region *R*, first in one direction and then in the other.

If *f* is the constant function with value 1, then for each point (x^*, y^*) we have $f(x^*, y^*) = 1$, and our approximating sums become $\sum \Delta A$. It is apparent that the limit of this sum is the area A of R, and since this limit is also the double integral $\iint\limits_{R} dA$, we have the formula

(100-4)
$$A = \iint\limits_{R} dA.$$

Example 100-2. Find the area of the plane region that lies in the first quadrant and is bounded by the X-axis, the circle $x^2 + y^2 = 18$, and the parabola $y^2 = 3x$.

Solution. In Fig. 100-3 we have shown two drawings of our plane region R covered

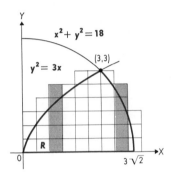 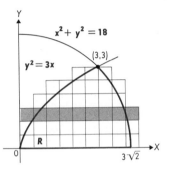

Figure 100-3

with a rectangular mesh. The area we seek is $A = \iint\limits_{R} dA$. If we evaluate this double integral by means of an iterated integral, we must decide whether to use x or y first as the variable of integration. Intuitively, if we first integrate with respect to y, we are first finding the area of a vertical strip (see the picture on the left in Fig. 100-3). The disadvantage of using vertical strips first lies in the fact that two different equations describe the curve that forms the upper boundary of our region. If we first integrate with respect to x, we are first finding the area of a horizontal strip, as in the diagram on the right in Fig. 100-3. In this case the right-boundary curve is given by the equation $x = \sqrt{18 - y^2}$, and the left-boundary curve is given by the equation $x = \frac{1}{3}y^2$. Thus we describe R as $\{(x, y) \mid 0 \leq y \leq 3, \frac{1}{3}y^2 \leq x \leq 18 - y^2\}$, and our iterated integral in this case (which appears to be the simpler case) is

$$A = \int_0^3 \int_{y^2/3}^{\sqrt{18-y^2}} dx \, dy = \int_0^3 (\sqrt{18 - y^2} - \tfrac{1}{3}y^2) \, dy$$

$$= \left[\frac{y\sqrt{18 - y^2}}{2} + 9 \, \mathrm{Sin}^{-1}\left(\frac{y}{3\sqrt{2}}\right) - \frac{y^3}{9} \right]_0^3$$

$$= \frac{6 + 9\pi}{4}.$$

P R O B L E M S   1 0 0

1. Use double integration to find the areas of the following regions:
   (a) The region bounded by the curves $y^2 = x + 1$ and $x + y = 1$.
   (b) The first quadrant region bounded by the curves $x^2 = 4 - 2y$, $x = 0$, $y = 0$.
   (c) The region bounded by the curves $xy = 4$ and $x + y = 5$.
   (d) The region bounded by the curves $y^2 = x^3$ and $y = x$.
   (e) The region bounded by the curves $y = 2x - x^2$ and $y = 2x^3 - x^2$.
   (f) The region bounded by the curves $y^2 = 4x$ and $y^2 = 5 - x$.

2. Use double integration to find the area of the triangular region whose vertices are the points $(0, 0)$, $(6, 4)$, and $(2, 8)$.

3. Use double integration to find the volume of the solid tetrahedron whose vertices are the points $(0, 0, 0)$, $(a, 0, 0)$, $(0, b, 0)$, and $(0, 0, c)$.

4. Use double integration to find the volume of the region in the first octant and bounded by the following surfaces:
   (a) The planes $z = x$, $x = 0$, $x = 1$, $y = 0$, $y = 1$, $z = 0$.
   (b) The planes $x = 0$, $y = 0$, $z = 0$, $z = y$, and the cylinder $x^2 + y^2 = 4$.
   (c) The planes $x = 0$, $y = 0$, $z = 0$, $x + z = 4$, and the cylinder $y = 4 - x^2$.

5. Use double integration to find the volume of one of the wedges bounded by the cylinder $x^2 + y^2 = a^2$, the XY-plane, and the plane $z = mx$.

6. Find the volume of the region bounded by the cylinder $x^2 + z = 1$ and by the planes $x + y = 1$, $y = 0$, and $z = 0$.

7. Find the volume of the wedge that is bounded by the cylinder $y^2 = x$, the XY-plane, and the plane $x + z = 1$.

8. The XY-plane and the surface $y^2 = 16 - 4z$ cut the cylinder $x^2 + y^2 = 4x$. Find the volume of the region bounded by these surfaces.

9. The nose cone of a certain missile has the shape of the region bounded by the XY-plane and the paraboloid $x^2 + y^2 + z = 1$. Use double integration to find the volume of the nose cone.

10. Use double integration to show that the volume of the region bounded by the ellipsoid $\dfrac{x^2}{a^2} + \dfrac{y^2}{b^2} + \dfrac{z^2}{c^2} = 1$ is $\dfrac{4}{3}\pi abc$.

101 MOMENTS AND MOMENTS OF INERTIA OF PLANE REGIONS

Let us consider a rectangular region whose sides are parallel to the coordinate axes (Fig. 101-1). Suppose that the coordinates of its geometric center (the intersection of the diagonals of the rectangle) are (x, y) and that its area is A square units. Then the numbers

$$(101\text{-}1) \qquad\qquad M_X = yA \quad \text{and} \quad M_Y = xA$$

are called the **moments** of the region about the X- and Y-axis, respectively. Notice that we have defined the moment of a rectangular region; that is, of a geometric object. However, if we think of our region as a plate made of some material of uniform density, then its mass will be proportional to its area A. Thus if we suppose that gravity acts in a direction perpendicular to the XY-plane, we can find the moments of the plate in the usual mechanical sense of force times lever arm by multiplying the right-hand sides of Equations 101-1 by a factor of proportionality.

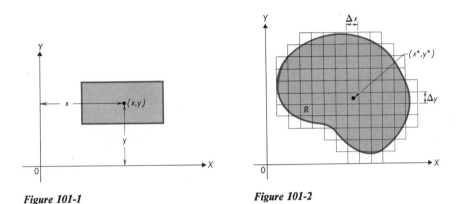

| Figure 101-1 | Figure 101-2 |

In general, we define the moment of a region R such as the one shown in Fig. 101-2 as follows. We first cover R with a rectangular covering as in the figure. In a typical subregion of this covering, with an area of $\Delta A = \Delta x \, \Delta y$, we select the center (x^*, y^*), and so the moment of this subregion about the X-axis is $y^* \, \Delta A$. The sum of these moments, $\Sigma \, y^* \, \Delta A$, is the moment of the covering of R. Now we take the limit of these sums as the norm of our collection of subregions approaches 0 to be the moment of R itself. Since this number is the integral of y over R, we have

$$(101\text{-}2) \qquad M_X = \iint\limits_R y \, dA.$$

Similarly, the moment of R about the Y-axis is defined to be the number

$$(101\text{-}3) \qquad M_Y = \iint\limits_R x \, dA.$$

Example 101-1. Find the moments M_X and M_Y of the region that is bounded by the semi-circle $y = \sqrt{a^2 - x^2}$ and the X-axis.

Solution.   Our region R is shown in Fig. 101-3. According to Equation 101-2,

$$M_X = \iint_R y \, dA = \int_{-a}^{a} \int_{0}^{\sqrt{a^2 - x^2}} y \, dy \, dx$$

$$= \int_{-a}^{a} \frac{a^2 - x^2}{2} \, dx = \frac{2a^3}{3}.$$

We use Equation 101-3 to find M_Y. Thus

$$M_Y = \iint_R x \, dA = \int_{0}^{a} \int_{-\sqrt{a^2 - y^2}}^{\sqrt{a^2 - y^2}} x \, dx \, dy$$

$$= \int_{0}^{a} 0 \, dy = 0.$$

You will notice that, for ease of calculation, we used different orders of integration when we replaced the double integrals for M_X and M_Y with iterated integrals.

Our concept of moment gives us a "net moment" of a region about an axis. If the axis is vertical, for example, the moment of the part of the region to the right

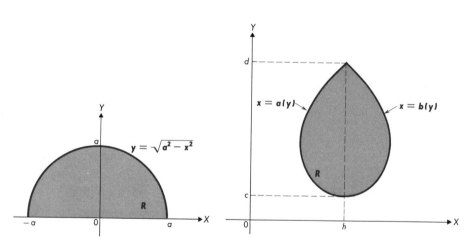

Figure 101-3   **Figure 101-4**

of the axis is positive and the moment of the part to the left is negative. In Example 101-1 we saw how these moments cancelled each other when we calculated the moment about the Y-axis and found that $M_Y = 0$.

If a region is symmetric about a line that is parallel to one of the coordinate axes, it is easy to find its moment about that axis. Thus suppose that we have a region R, such as the one shown in Fig. 101-4, that is symmetric about the line $x = h$. This symmetry means that the average of the X-coordinates of the two boundary points with the same Y-coordinate is always h. Thus if the equations $x = a(y)$ and $x = b(y)$ represent the left and right boundaries of R, we have

$$\frac{a(y) + b(y)}{2} = h$$

for each y. Therefore

$$M_Y = \int_c^d \int_{a(y)}^{b(y)} x \, dx \, dy = \int_c^d \left[\frac{b(y)^2 - a(y)^2}{2} \right] dy$$

$$= \int_c^d \left(\frac{b(y) + a(y)}{2} \right) (b(y) - a(y)) \, dy = h \int_c^d (b(y) - a(y)) \, dy.$$

Now observe that the area A of R is given by the equation

$$A = \int_c^d \int_{a(y)}^{b(y)} dx \, dy = \int_c^d (b(y) - a(y)) \, dy,$$

and so $M_Y = hA$. Similarly, if our region were symmetric with respect to a line $y = k$, we would have $M_X = kA$.

In mechanics we define the **center of gravity** of a body as being "the point at which we can imagine the mass of the body to be concentrated." By this statement we mean that if we replace a given body with a "point mass" at the center of gravity, then the moment of this new system about an axis will be the same as the moment of the original body about that axis. The concept of the centroid of a plane region is similar. The **centroid** of a region R that has an area of A is the point $(\bar{x}, \bar{y})$ such that the "moments" $\bar{y}A$ and $\bar{x}A$ equal the moments of R about the X- and Y-axes. Thus $\bar{x}$ and $\bar{y}$ are numbers such that

(101-4) $$\bar{x}A = M_Y \quad \text{and} \quad \bar{y}A = M_X.$$

With the aid of Equations 101-2 and 101-3, we can rewrite these equations for $\bar{x}$ and $\bar{y}$ in the form

(101-5) $$\bar{x} = \frac{\displaystyle\iint_R x \, dA}{A} \quad \text{and} \quad \bar{y} = \frac{\displaystyle\iint_R y \, dA}{A}.$$

Example 101-2. Find the centroid of the region shown in Fig. 101-3.

Solution.   In Example 101-1 we found that $M_X = 2a^3/3$ and $M_Y = 0$. The area of our semi-circular region whose radius is a is $A = \pi a^2/2$. Therefore, according to Equations 101-4, we have

$$\bar{x} = \frac{0}{A} = 0 \quad \text{and} \quad \bar{y} = \frac{2a^3/3}{\pi a^2/2} = \frac{4a}{3\pi}.$$

Thus the centroid of R is the point $(0, 4a/3\pi)$. If we make a cardboard model of R, it will balance on a pin placed at the point $(0, 4a/3\pi)$.

If a region R with an area of A square units is symmetric with respect to the line $x = h$, we have seen that $M_Y = hA$, and hence, since M_Y is also $\bar{x}A$, $\bar{x}A = hA$. Thus $\bar{x} = h$; that is, the centroid is in the line of symmetry, as illustrated by the preceding example, Similarly, if a region is symmetric with respect to the line $y = k$, then $\bar{y} = k$. You should take advantage of symmetry when you calculate moments and centroids.

Example 101-3.   Find the centroid of the region that is bounded by the X-axis and one arch of the sine curve.

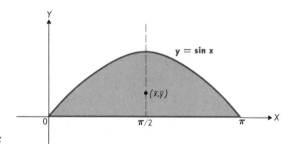

Figure 101-5

Solution.   Since the region (shown in Fig. 101-5) is symmetric about the line $x = \pi/2$, we know immediately that $\bar{x} = \pi/2$. Furthermore,

$$A = \int_0^\pi \sin x \, dx = 2,$$

and

$$M_X = \int_0^\pi \int_0^{\sin x} y \, dy \, dx = \frac{1}{2} \int_0^\pi \sin^2 x \, dx = \frac{\pi}{4}.$$

Thus

$$\bar{y} = \frac{M_X}{A} = \frac{\pi}{8},$$

so our centroid is the point $(\pi/2, \pi/8)$.

We can define moments of a region R about lines other than the coordinate axes. For example, the moment about the line L whose equation is $x = h$ is

$$M_L = \iint_R (x - h)\, dA.$$

Since

$$\iint_R (x - h)\, dA = \iint_R x\, dA - h \iint_R dA = M_Y - hA,$$

we have the equation

(101-6) $$M_L = M_Y - hA.$$

Similarly, the moment M_L of a region R about the line L whose equation is $y = k$ is

(101-7) $$M_L = M_X - kA.$$

Example 101-4. Find the centroid of the region R that consists of a circular disk D whose radius is 1 and a 2 by 2 square region S that touches it, as shown in Fig. 101-6.

Solution. Our figure is symmetric about the Y-axis, so the X-coordinate of its centroid is 0. By definition, $M_X = \iint_R y\, dA$. Since our given region is the union of the disk D and the square region S, we may use Equation 98-3 to write

$$M_X = \iint_R y\, dA = \iint_D y\, dA + \iint_S y\, dA.$$

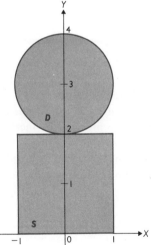

Figure 101-6

The two integrals on the right-hand side of this equation yield the moments M_{DX} and M_{SX} of the disk and the square region about the X-axis, so $M_X = M_{DX} + M_{SX}$. We find these moments by multiplying the areas of D and S by the distances of their lines of symmetry from the X-axis; thus $M_{DX} = 3\pi$, and $M_{SX} = 1 \cdot 4 = 4$. Therefore, $M_X = 3\pi + 4$. The area of R is $A = \pi + 4$, so $\bar{y} = \dfrac{M_X}{A} = \dfrac{3\pi + 4}{\pi + 4} \approx 1.85$. The coordinates of the centroid of our region are therefore approximately $(0, 1.85)$.

Example 101-5.   Find the moment of the region R of the preceding example about the line L whose equation is $y = 1$.

Solution.   In the preceding example we found that $M_X = 3\pi + 4$ and $A = \pi + 4$. Then, according to Equation 101-7 with $k = 1$,

$$M_L = (3\pi + 4) - (\pi + 4) = 2\pi.$$

Another idea that we meet in mechanics is the concept of the **moment of inertia** of a body. The moment of inertia about the X-axis of the rectangular region shown in Fig. 101-1 is the number $y^2 A$, the moment of inertia about the Y-axis is the number $x^2 A$, and the moment of inertia about the origin is the number $(x^2 + y^2)A$. In general, if I_X, I_Y, and I_O are the moments of inertia of the region shown in Fig. 101-2 about the X-axis, the Y-axis, and the origin, then by definition

$$I_X = \iint\limits_{R} y^2 \, dA$$

(101-8)
$$I_Y = \iint\limits_{R} x^2 \, dA$$

$$I_O = \iint\limits_{R} (x^2 + y^2) \, dA.$$

We immediately see that $I_O = I_X + I_Y$. If our region R were a plate made of material of uniform density, then its moments of inertia (as the term is used in mechanics) are obtained by multiplying our numbers I_X, I_Y, and I_O by the density. The moment of inertia of a body plays a role in rotational motion that is analogous to the role played by the mass of the body in linear motion.

Example 101-6.   Find the moment of inertia of the interior of a right triangle about the vertex of the $90°$ angle.

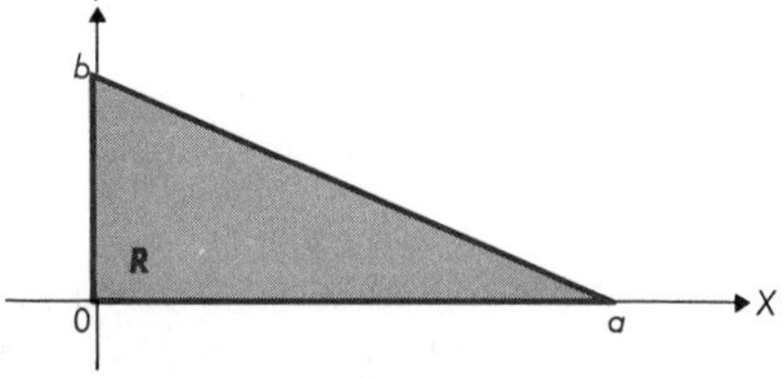

Figure 101-7

Solution.   Suppose that the legs of our triangle are a and b units long and that we place it in a coordinate system as in Fig. 101-7. We must compute I_O, which is given by the formula

$$I_O = \iint\limits_{R} (x^2 + y^2) \, dA.$$

The equation of the hypotenuse of our triangle is $\dfrac{x}{a} + \dfrac{y}{b} = 1$, and therefore,

$$I_O = \iint\limits_R (x^2 + y^2)\, dA = \int_0^b \int_0^{a - \frac{ay}{b}} (x^2 + y^2)\, dx\, dy = \frac{ab}{12}(a^2 + b^2).$$

Example 101-7. Find I_X and I_Y for the region R shown in Fig. 101-3.

Solution. According to Equations 101-8,

$$I_X = \iint\limits_R y^2\, dA = \int_{-a}^{a} \int_0^{\sqrt{a^2 - x^2}} y^2\, dy\, dx$$

$$= \tfrac{1}{3} \int_{-a}^{a} (a^2 - x^2)^{3/2}\, dx$$

$$= \tfrac{1}{3} \int_{-a}^{a} a^2 \sqrt{a^2 - x^2}\, dx - \tfrac{1}{3} \int_{-a}^{a} x^2 \sqrt{a^2 - x^2}\, dx$$

$$= \frac{\pi a^4}{8} \quad \text{(see Integration Formulas V-30 and V-32).}$$

Similarly,

$$I_Y = \iint\limits_R x^2\, dA = \int_0^a \int_{-\sqrt{a^2 - y^2}}^{\sqrt{a^2 - y^2}} x^2\, dx\, dy$$

$$= \frac{2}{3} \int_0^a (a^2 - y^2)^{3/2}\, dy = \frac{\pi a^4}{8}.$$

P R O B L E M S   1 0 1

1. Find the centroids of the following plane regions:
   (a) The first quadrant quarter of the disk $x^2 + y^2 \le a^2$.
   (b) The upper half of the region bounded by the ellipse $4x^2 + 9y^2 = 36$.
   (c) The first quadrant region bounded by the coordinate axes and the parabola $y^2 = 4 - x$.
   (d) The region bounded by the parabola $x^2 = 4y$ and the line $y = 1$.
   (e) The triangular region whose vertices are the points $(0, 0)$, (a, b) and $(c, 0)$, where $b > 0$ and $c > 0$.
   (f) The region bounded by the curves $\sqrt{x} + \sqrt{y} = \sqrt{a}$, $x = 0$, and $y = 0$.
   (g) The region bounded by the parabolas $x^2 = y$ and $y^2 = x$.
   (h) The graph of the equation $[\![x]\!]^2 + [\![y]\!]^2 = 1$.
2. Find the centroid of the region $R = \{(x, y)\,|\, 0 \le x \le \pi/2,\, 0 \le y \le \sin x\}$.

3. Show that the centroid of a triangular region is the intersection of the medians of the triangle that forms its boundary (see Number 1e).

4. Suppose the point $(\bar{x}, \bar{y})$ is the centroid of a certain region R which has an area of A square units. Show that the moment of R about the line $x = h$ is $(\bar{x} - h)A$, and the moment of R about the line $y = k$ is $(\bar{y} - k)A$. Show that if R is symmetric about the line $x = h$ or the line $y = k$, then the moment of R about the line is 0.

5. Use the result of the preceding problem to find the moment of the given region R about the given line L.
(a) R: $x^2 + y^2 \le a^2$, L: $x = 5a$.
(b) R: The region bounded by the ellipse $b^2x^2 + a^2y^2 = a^2b^2$, L: A latus rectum of the ellipse.
(c) R: The region bounded by the parabolas $x^2 = 4y$ and $x^2 = 5 - y$, L: A vertical line containing the right-hand intersection point of the given curves.

6. Find I_X, I_Y, and I_O for the following regions.
(a) The rectangular region $\{(x, y) \mid 0 \le x \le a, 0 \le y \le b\}$.
(b) The region that is bounded by the parabola $y^2 = 8x$ and the line $x = 2$.
(c) The region that is bounded by the graph of the equation $|x| + |y| = 1$.
(d) The graph of the equation $[\![x]\!] + [\![y]\!] = 1$.

7. The moment of inertia of a region R about the line L whose equation is $x = h$ is defined by the equation

$$I_L = \iint\limits_R (x - h)^2 \, dA.$$

(a) Show that $I_L = I_Y - 2hM_Y + h^2A = I_Y + h(h - 2\bar{x})A$, where A is the area of R.
(b) What can you conclude from the equation in Part (a) if the centroid of R is a point of the Y-axis?
(c) What can you conclude from the equation in Part (a) if the centroid of R is a point of L?
(d) If K is the line $x = k$, show that

$$I_K = I_L - 2M_Y(k - h) + (k^2 - h^2)A = I_L + (k + h - 2\bar{x})(k - h)A.$$

8. (a) Find I_Y for the elliptical region $b^2x^2 + a^2y^2 \le a^2b^2$.
(b) Use the result you found in Part (a) to find I_X and I_O.
(c) Find I_Y for the disk $x^2 + y^2 \le a^2$. (Compare your answer with our results in Example 101-7.)
(d) Suppose that $a > b$, and use the formulas of Number 7 to find the moment of inertia about a latus rectum of the ellipse $b^2x^2 + a^2y^2 = a^2b^2$.
(e) Suppose that $a > b$, and use the formulas of Number 7 to find the moment of inertia about a directrix of the ellipse $b^2x^2 + a^2y^2 = a^2b^2$.

9. Let $R = \{(x, y) \mid x^2 + y^2 - 2|x| - 2|y| + 1 \le 0\}$. Refer to Numbers 7 and 8 for the necessary formulas to find I_O and I_L, where L is the line $x = -1$.

10. The moment of a region about a line through its centroid is zero. Can you find a line such that the moment of inertia of the region about the line is zero?

102 DOUBLE INTEGRALS IN POLAR COORDINATES

The double integral of a function f over a plane region R is the limit of sums of the form

(102-1) $$s = \sum f(x^*, y^*) \, \Delta A.$$

Here the number ΔA is the area of a rectangular subregion of a covering of R. It does not matter at what point (x^*, y^*) in this subregion we evaluate f; if the maximum dimension of the subregions is small, then the Sum 102-1 is close to the number $\iint\limits_{R} f(x, y) \, dA$. Even if the subregions of the covering are not rectangular, if they are of reasonably regular shape, it can be shown that the limit of s will still be the integral of f over R. In this section we are going to investigate the non-rectangular covering we get when we use polar coordinates.

Suppose we introduce a polar coordinate system into the coordinate plane, taking as the pole the origin of the cartesian coordinate system and as the polar

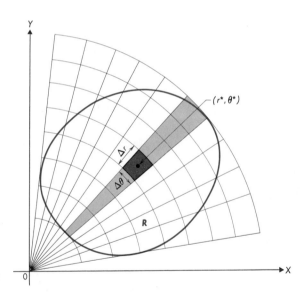

Figure 102-1

axis the positive X-axis. We form a "polar covering" of a region R by drawing a network of radial lines and concentric circles, as shown in Fig. 102-1. The norm of this covering is the longest of the "diagonals" of the "curved rectangles" that make up the covering. We assert that if our covering has a small norm, then when we evaluate f at a point in each subregion of the covering, multiply this value of f by the area of the subregion, and add up the resulting numbers, the sum we obtain will approximate the integral of f over R. Let us see what one such approximating sum looks like. We shall suppose that the two radial lines that form the sides of our typical subregion make an angle of $\Delta\theta$ and that the concentric circles that form its ends are Δr units apart. Now let (r^*, θ^*) be polar coordinates of the point of our subregion that is equidistant from its ends and from its sides. The XY-coordinates of this point are $(r^* \cos \theta^*, r^* \sin \theta^*)$, so the value of f there is $f(r^* \cos \theta^*, r^* \sin \theta^*)$. Our typical subregion can be considered to be the difference of two circular "wedges," both with a central angle of $\Delta\theta$, but one having a radius of $r^* - \dfrac{\Delta r}{2}$ and the other a radius of $r^* + \dfrac{\Delta r}{2}$. The area of a circular wedge is one-half the product of the radian measure of its central angle and the square of its radius (see Appendix A). Therefore, the area of our typical subregion is

$$\Delta A = \frac{1}{2}\left(r^* + \frac{\Delta r}{2}\right)^2 \Delta\theta - \frac{1}{2}\left(r^* - \frac{\Delta r}{2}\right)^2 \Delta\theta.$$

After a little simplification, we find that this formula reduces to

(102-2) $$\Delta A = r^* \, \Delta r \, \Delta\theta.$$

Therefore, there is an approximating sum that is expressed in terms of polar coordinates as

(102-3) $$s = \sum f(r^* \cos \theta^*, r^* \sin \theta^*)r^* \, \Delta r \, \Delta\theta.$$

The limit of such sums is the double integral of f over R, and their form suggests that we write

(102-4) $$\iint\limits_{R} f(x, y) \, dA =$$

$$\iint\limits_{R} f(r \cos \theta, r \sin \theta)r \, dr \, d\theta.$$

It is convenient to think that we obtain the right-hand side of this equation from the left-hand side by replacing x with $r \cos \theta$, y with $r \sin \theta$, and dA with $r \, dr \, d\theta$ (see Equation 102-2).

To evaluate our double integral, we use iterated integrals. Let us first assume

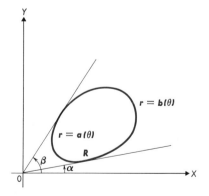

Figure 102-2

that our region R lies between, and is tangent to, two radial lines $\theta = \alpha$ and $\theta = \beta$, as shown in Fig. 102-2. The remainder of the boundary of R consists of the two curves $r = a(\theta)$ and $r = b(\theta)$, $\theta \in [\alpha, \beta]$. Thus $R = \{(r, \theta) \mid \alpha \le \theta \le \beta, a(\theta) \le r \le b(\theta)\}$. Informally, we think of our double integral as a sum, each term of which corresponds to one of the subregions of the covering of R. We may first add the terms that correspond to subregions forming a radial wedge, like the shaded one in Fig. 102-1, and then add the contributions of the wedges. From this point of view, it seems reasonable that our double integral should be given by an iterated integral as follows:

$$(102\text{-}5) \quad \iint_R f(r \cos \theta, r \sin \theta) r \, dr \, d\theta = \int_\alpha^\beta \int_{a(\theta)}^{b(\theta)} f(r \cos \theta, r \sin \theta) r \, dr \, d\theta.$$

Now let us suppose that our region R lies between, and is tangent to, circles of radii a and b whose center is the origin, and that the remainder of the boundary

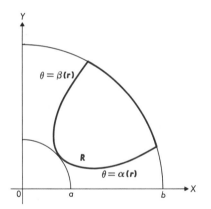

Figure 102-3

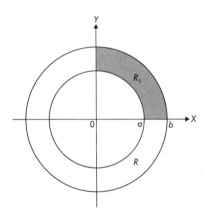

Figure 102-4

of R consists of the curves $\theta = \alpha(r)$ and $\theta = \beta(r)$, $r \in [a, b]$, as shown in Fig. 102-3. Thus $R = \{(r, \theta) \mid a \le r \le b, \alpha(r) \le \theta \le \beta(r)\}$. Now we integrate with respect to θ first, and our double integral is given by another iterated integral:

$$(102\text{-}6) \quad \iint_R f(r \cos \theta, r \sin \theta) r \, dr \, d\theta = \int_a^b \int_{\alpha(r)}^{\beta(r)} f(r \cos \theta, r \sin \theta) r \, d\theta \, dr.$$

Example 102-1. Find the moment of inertia about the origin of the region bounded by two concentric circles of radii a and b, where $a < b$.

Solution. The given region is shown in Fig. 102-4. Using Equations 102-4 and 102-5, we see that the required moment of inertia is

$$I_O = \iint_R (x^2 + y^2) \, dA$$

$$= \iint_R r^2 r \, dr \, d\theta$$

$$= \int_0^{2\pi} \int_a^b r^3 \, dr \, d\theta = \frac{\pi}{2}(b^4 - a^4).$$

Example 102-2. Find the centroid of the part of the "washer" described in the last example that lies in the first quadrant.

Solution. Our region, we will label it R_1 in this example, is the shaded quarter of the region R of Fig. 102-4. If we denote the coordinates of the required centroid by $(\bar{x}, \bar{y})$, considerations of symmetry tell us that $\bar{x} = \bar{y}$. So we need only compute $\bar{y}$. According to Equation 101-5,

(102-7)
$$\bar{y} = \frac{\displaystyle\iint_{R_1} y \, dA}{A}.$$

Now, using Equations 102-4 and 102-5, we have

$$\iint_{R_1} y \, dA = \iint_{R_1} r \sin \theta \, r \, dr \, d\theta = \int_0^{\pi/2} \int_a^b r^2 \sin \theta \, dr \, d\theta$$

$$= \int_0^{\pi/2} \frac{b^3 - a^3}{3} \sin \theta \, d\theta = \frac{b^3 - a^3}{3}.$$

It is a matter of simple geometry to show that the area A of the region R_1 is $\frac{\pi}{4}(b^2 - a^2)$. Hence Equation 102-7 tells us that

$$\bar{y} = \frac{4(b^3 - a^3)}{3\pi(b^2 - a^2)}.$$

P R O B L E M S   1 0 2

1. Use an iterated integral and polar coordinates to find the area of the region that is bounded by the graphs of each of the following equations.
   (a) $r = 2 \cos 3\theta$ (b) $r^2 = \cos 2\theta$ (c) $r = 1 + \sin \theta$ (d) $r = |\cos \theta|$

2. Describe the region of integration R if the double integral $\iint\limits_{R} f(x, y)\, dA$ equals the following iterated integral in polar coordinates.

(a) $\displaystyle\int_{1}^{2}\int_{3}^{4} f(r \cos \theta, r \sin \theta)r\, dr\, d\theta$

(b) $\displaystyle\int_{1}^{2}\int_{3}^{4} f(r \cos \theta, r \sin \theta)r\, d\theta\, dr$

(c) $\displaystyle\int_{0}^{\pi}\int_{0}^{\llbracket\theta\rrbracket} f(r \cos \theta, r \sin \theta)r\, dr\, d\theta$

(d) $\displaystyle\int_{0}^{\pi}\int_{0}^{\llbracket r\rrbracket} f(r \cos \theta, r \sin \theta)r\, d\theta\, dr$

3. Use polar coordinates to evaluate the integral $\iint\limits_{R} \sqrt{x^2 + y^2}\, dA$ over the region R if:

(a) $R = \{(x, y)\,|\, x^2 + y^2 \leq a^2\}$
(b) $R = \{(r, \theta)\,|\, 0 \leq \theta \leq \pi,\, 0 \leq r \leq \sin \theta\}$
(c) $R = \{(r, \theta)\,|\, 0 \leq \theta \leq 2\pi,\, 0 \leq r \leq 1 - \cos \theta\}$
(d) $R = \{(r, \theta)\,|\, 0 \leq \theta \leq \tfrac{1}{2}\pi,\, \sqrt{3} \leq r \leq 2 \sin 2\theta\}$

4. Show how to replace the double integral in the formula $A = \iint\limits_{R} dA$ with an iterated

integral to obtain the polar coordinate area formula $A = \tfrac{1}{2}\displaystyle\int_{\alpha}^{\beta} r^2\, d\theta$.

5. Replace the given iterated integral with an iterated integral in polar coordinates and evaluate.

(a) $\displaystyle\int_{0}^{2}\int_{0}^{\sqrt{4-x^2}} e^{-x^2-y^2}\, dy\, dx$

(b) $\displaystyle\int_{0}^{1}\int_{y}^{\sqrt{2-y^2}} x^4\, dx\, dy$

(c) $\displaystyle\int_{0}^{3}\int_{-\sqrt{18-y^2}}^{-y} \sin (x^2 + y^2)\, dx\, dy$

(d) $\displaystyle\int_{0}^{3}\int_{x/\sqrt{3}}^{\sqrt{12-x^2}} (1 + x^2 + y^2)^{-1}\, dy\, dx$

6. Use polar coordinates to calculate the volume of the region that is cut from the cylindrical region $\{(x, y, z)\,|\, x^2 + y^2 \leq a^2\}$ by the following surfaces.
(a) The sphere $x^2 + y^2 + z^2 = 4a^2$
(b) The half planes $z = mx$ and $z = 0$, with $x \geq 0$. (See Problem 100-5.)

7. Let W be a wedge cut from a circular disk of radius a by an angle whose vertex is the center of the disk and which cuts an arc of length s from the boundary of the disk.
(a) What is the moment of inertia of W about its vertex?
(b) How far from the vertex is the centroid of W?
(c) What is the moment of inertia about one edge of W?

8. Use polar coordinates to evaluate the double integral that gives the volume of a right circular cone of altitude h and base radius a.

9. Find the centroid of the plane region described:
(a) The interior of the cardioid $r = a(1 - \cos \theta)$.
(b) The region in the upper half plane that is bounded by the graph of the equation $r^2 = a \cos \theta$.
(c) The interior of one loop of the graph of the equation $r = 4 \sin 2\theta$.
(d) The region bounded by the rays $\theta = 0$ and $\theta = \dfrac{\pi}{4}$, and the curve $r = \cos 2\theta$.

10. Examine the formula for the coordinates of the centroid of the region R of Example 102-2. (a) Where is the centroid if $a = 0$? (b) What is $\lim_{a \uparrow b} \bar{x}$? (c) Can we choose a so that the centroid of R is a point on the inner boundary of R? outside R?

103 TRIPLE INTEGRALS

The concept of the triple integral of a function on R^3 over a solid region in three-dimensional space is a straightforward generalization of the idea of the double integral of a function on R^2 over a plane region. To start with, we consider a function f whose domain contains a rectangular block R as shown in Fig. 103-1.

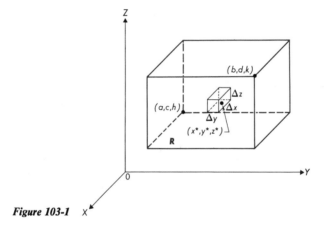

Figure 103-1

As a first step in the definition of the integral of f over R, we use a set of planes parallel to the coordinate planes to partition the block R into smaller blocks that we will call *subblocks* of R. The *norm* of this partition is the longest of the diagonals of these subblocks. We have labeled the dimensions of the typical subblock shown in Fig. 103-1 as Δx, Δy, and Δz, so its volume is $\Delta V = \Delta x \, \Delta y \, \Delta z$. In each subblock of the partition, we pick a point (x^*, y^*, z^*) and consider sums of the form

$$(103\text{-}1) \qquad s = \sum f(x^*, y^*, z^*) \, \Delta V,$$

where the sum has a term for each subblock of the partition of R. Just as in the one- and two-dimensional cases, we use this procedure to define a set-valued function S. With each positive number u we associate the set $S(u)$ of sums that can be obtained from Equation 103-1 when we use a partition of norm u. Then if $\lim_{n \downarrow 0} S(u)$ exists, we say that f is **integrable** over R and the limit is called the **triple**

integral of f over R. We denote this integral by one of the symbols

$$\iiint_R f(x, y, z) \, dV \quad \text{or} \quad \iiint_R f(x, y, z) \, dx \, dy \, dz.$$

The geometric argument that we used to convince ourselves that a double integral can be evaluated as an iterated integral cannot be used for triple integrals, but the result is still true. Thus for the block $R = \{(x, y, z) \mid a \leq x \leq b, c \leq y \leq d, h \leq z \leq k\}$ the counterpart of Equation 99-3 is

$$(103\text{-}2) \qquad \iiint_R f(x, y, z) \, dV = \int_a^b \int_c^d \int_h^k f(x, y, z) \, dz \, dy \, dx.$$

Example 103-1. Evaluate the integral $\iiint_R xy \sin yz \, dV$, if R is the cubical block $\{(x, y, z) \mid 0 \leq x \leq \pi, 0 \leq y \leq \pi, 0 \leq z \leq \pi\}$.

Solution. In this case (if you are in doubt, make a sketch), the numbers a, c, and h in Equation 103-2 are all 0, and the numbers b, d, and k are all π. Thus

$$\iiint_R xy \sin yz \, dV = \int_0^\pi \int_0^\pi \int_0^\pi xy \sin yz \, dz \, dy \, dx$$

$$= \int_0^\pi \int_0^\pi -x \cos yz \Big|_0^\pi dy \, dx$$

$$= \int_0^\pi \int_0^\pi x(1 - \cos \pi y) \, dy \, dx$$

$$= \int_0^\pi x\left(y - \frac{1}{\pi} \sin \pi y\right)\Big|_0^\pi dx$$

$$= \int_0^\pi x\left(\pi - \frac{\sin \pi^2}{\pi}\right) dx = \frac{\pi^3 - \pi \sin \pi^2}{2}.$$

To extend the idea of a triple integral from a block-shaped region to a region of a different shape, such as the region R in Fig. 103-2, we use the same technique that we employed in the two-dimensional case. We put R inside a block $\bar{R}$, "extend" our given function f to a new function $\bar{f}$ that has the values of f at points of R and takes the value 0 outside R, and then integrate $\bar{f}$ over the block $\bar{R}$. We won't go through the details of this extension; we will simply tell how the resulting triple integral can be expressed as an iterated integral. Suppose, as shown in the the figure, that our given region R projects onto a region R_{XY} of the XY-plane,

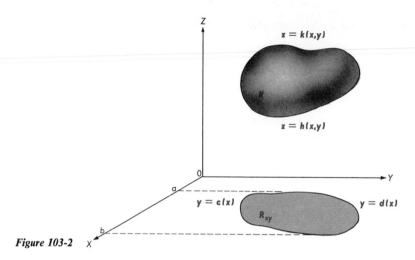

Figure 103-2

and is bounded above and below by the graphs of the equations $z = k(x, y)$ and $z = h(x, y)$. In other words, suppose that

$$R = \{(x, y, z) \mid (x, y) \in R_{XY}, h(x, y) \leq z \leq k(x, y)\}.$$

Then our triple integral is given by the iterated integral

$$(103\text{-}3) \qquad \iiint\limits_{R} f(x, y, z) \, dV = \iint\limits_{R_{XY}} \left[\int_{h(x,y)}^{k(x,y)} f(x, y, z) \, dz \right] dA.$$

This equation says that the triple integral on the left is the double integral over R_{XY} of the function g that is defined by the equation

$$g(x, y) = \int_{h(x,y)}^{k(x,y)} f(x, y, z) \, dz.$$

This double integral over R_{XY} can then be written as an iterated integral. Thus if $R_{XY} = \{(x, y) \mid a \leq x \leq b, c(x) \leq y \leq d(x)\}$, then

$$(103\text{-}4) \qquad \iiint\limits_{R} f(x, y, z) \, dV = \int_{a}^{b} \int_{c(x)}^{d(x)} \int_{h(x,y)}^{k(x,y)} f(x, y, z) \, dz \, dy \, dx.$$

When our region is of suitable shape, we can integrate in some other order, using limits that are appropriate to the order of integration.

Example 103-2. Evaluate the integral $\iiint\limits_{R} e^{x+y+z}\,dV$, where R is the region that is bounded by the plane $2x + y + z = 4$ and the coordinate planes.

Solution. The region R is shown in Fig. 103-3. When we project R onto the XY-plane, we obtain the triangular region R_{XY} that is bounded by the X- and Y-axes and the line $2x + y = 4$. Thus

$$R = \{(x, y, z)\,|\,(x, y) \in R_{XY},$$
$$0 \le z \le 4 - 2x - y\},$$

so Equation 103-3 tells us that

(103-5) $\iiint\limits_{R} e^{x+y+z}\,dV$

$$= \iint\limits_{R_{XY}} \left[\int_{0}^{4-2x-y} e^{x+y+z}\,dz\right] dA.$$

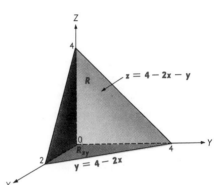

Figure 103-3

Since $R_{XY} = \{(x, y)\,|\,0 \le x \le 2,$ $0 \le y \le 4 - 2x\}$, we can express the double integral in Equation 103-5 as an iterated integral, and we obtain the equation

$$\iiint\limits_{R} e^{x+y+z}\,dV = \int_{0}^{2} \int_{0}^{4-2x} \int_{0}^{4-2x-y} e^{x+y+z}\,dz\,dy\,dx.$$

We leave the evaluation of this integral to you; you should obtain the number $e^4 + 4e^2 - 1$.

We think of a triple integral $\iiint\limits_{R} f(x, y, z)\,dV$ as the limit of sums of the form $\Sigma f(x^*, y^*, z^*)\,\Delta V$, each term in the sum corresponding to one of a set of rectangular blocks that covers R. In particular, then, the integral $\iiint\limits_{R} dV$ is the limit of sums of the form $\Sigma\,\Delta V$, and so this integral appears to be the volume of R; that is,

$$V = \iiint\limits_{R} dV.$$

We define the **centroid** of R to be the point $(\bar{x}, \bar{y}, \bar{z})$, where

$$\bar{x}V = \iiint\limits_{R} x\, dV, \quad \bar{y}V = \iiint\limits_{R} y\, dV, \quad \bar{z}V = \iiint\limits_{R} z\, dV.$$

The **moments of inertia** of a three-dimensional region about the coordinate axes are given by the equations

$$I_X = \iiint\limits_{R} (y^2 + z^2)\, dV, \quad I_Y = \iiint\limits_{R} (x^2 + z^2)\, dV, \quad I_Z = \iiint\limits_{R} (x^2 + y^2)\, dV.$$

Example 103-3. Let R be the "wedge" that is bounded by the cylinder $y = x^2$, the XY-plane, and the plane $y + z = 1$, as shown in Fig. 103-4. Find the moment of inertia of R about the Z-axis.

Solution. We will replace the triple integral

$$I_z = \iiint\limits_{R} (x^2 + y^2)\, dV$$

with an iterated integral in which we first integrate with respect to z and then integrate the result over R_{XY}, the projection of R onto the XY-plane. Thus we write

$$R = \{(x, y, z) \mid (x, y) \in R_{XY},$$
$$0 \le z \le 1 - y\},$$

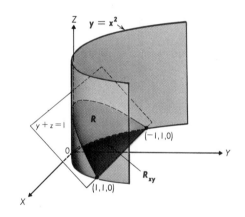

Figure 103-4

so the limits of integration on z are 0 and $1 - y$. Since

$$R_{XY} = \{(x, y) \mid -1 \le x \le 1,\ x^2 \le y \le 1\}$$

we have

$$I_Z = \int_{-1}^{1} \int_{x^2}^{1} \int_{0}^{1-y} (x^2 + y^2)\, dz\, dy\, dx$$

$$= \int_{-1}^{1} \int_{x^2}^{1} (x^2 + y^2 - x^2 y - y^3)\, dy\, dx$$

$$= \int_{-1}^{1} \left(\frac{x^8}{4} + \frac{x^6}{6} - x^4 + \frac{x^2}{2} + \frac{1}{12} \right) dx$$

$$= \frac{64}{315}.$$

P R O B L E M S   1 0 3

1. Evaluate the following iterated integrals.

(a) $\displaystyle\int_{-1}^{0}\int_{e}^{2e}\int_{0}^{\pi/3} x \ln y \tan z \, dz \, dy \, dx$ (b) $\displaystyle\int_{0}^{3}\int_{-\pi/3}^{\pi/6}\int_{-1}^{2} y \sin \left([\![x]\!]yz\right) dz \, dy \, dx$

(c) $\displaystyle\int_{0}^{2}\int_{0}^{\sqrt{4-z^2}}\int_{0}^{2-z} y \, dx \, dy \, dz$ (d) $\displaystyle\int_{-\ln 2}^{\ln 2}\int_{0}^{\sqrt{x}}\int_{0}^{x+y^2} y \, e^{z} \, dz \, dy \, dx$

2. Use a geometric argument to evaluate $\displaystyle\iiint_{R} [\![x^2 + y^2 + z^2]\!] \, dV$ if R is:

(a) The cube whose faces lie in the planes $x^2 = 1$, $y^2 = 1$, and $z^2 = 1$.
(b) The spherical ball $x^2 + y^2 + z^2 \le 4$.
(c) The cube whose faces lie in the planes $x^2 = 4$, $y^2 = 4$, and $z^2 = 4$.

3. Evaluate $\displaystyle\iiint_{R} xy \, dV$ if R is:

(a) The rectangular block whose faces lie in the coordinate planes and the planes $x = 2$, $y = 3$, and $z = 4$.
(b) The prism bounded by the coordinate planes, the plane $z = 2$, and the plane $x + y = 1$.
(c) The first octant region cut from the cylindrical region $\{(x, y, z) \mid x^2 + y^2 \le 1\}$ by the coordinate planes and the plane $z = x$.
(d) The graph of the equation $[\![x]\!]^2 + [\![y]\!]^2 + [\![z]\!]^2 = 1$.

4. Describe the region of integration R if the triple integral $\displaystyle\iiint_{R} f(x, y, z) \, dV$ can be expressed as the given iterated integral.

(a) $\displaystyle\int_{0}^{4}\int_{0}^{3}\int_{0}^{2} f(x, y, z) \, dz \, dy \, dx$ (b) $\displaystyle\int_{0}^{3}\int_{0}^{2}\int_{0}^{x} f(x, y, z) \, dz \, dy \, dx$

(c) $\displaystyle\int_{0}^{2}\int_{0}^{x}\int_{0}^{y} f(x, y, z) \, dz \, dy \, dx$ (d) $\displaystyle\int_{-1}^{1}\int_{0}^{1-x^2}\int_{0}^{y} f(x, y, z) \, dz \, dy \, dx$

5. Find the moment of inertia about the edge of length b of a brick whose dimensions are a units by b units by c units.

6. Find the centroid of the tetrahedron that is bounded by the plane $\dfrac{x}{a} + \dfrac{y}{b} + \dfrac{z}{c} = 1$ and the coordinate planes.

7. Find the centroid of the region bounded by the planes $y + z = 1$, $z = 0$, and the cylinder $x^2 = 4y$.

8. Find I_Z for the tetrahedron that is bounded by the coordinate planes and the plane $x + y + z = 1$.

9. The moment of inertia of a region R about the line formed by the intersection of the planes $x = a$ and $y = b$ is defined to be $I_L = \displaystyle\iiint_{R} [(x - a)^2 + (y - b)^2] \, dV$.

Show that $I_L = I_Z + (a^2 + b^2 - 2a\bar{x} - 2b\bar{y})V$. What is I_L if the centroid of R is a point of the Z-axis? If the centroid of R is a point of L?

10. (a) Show that the moment of inertia of an ellipsoid whose diameters are $2a, 2b$, and $2c$ about the diameter whose length is $2a$ is $\frac{1}{5}(b^2 + c^2)V$.
   (b) Show that the moment of inertia about its axis of a right circular cylinder whose altitude is h and whose base radius is a is $\frac{1}{2}a^2V$.

104 TRIPLE INTEGRALS IN CYLINDRICAL AND SPHERICAL COORDINATES

In Section 102, we considered double integrals in polar coordinates; in this section we will discuss triple integrals in cylindrical and spherical coordinates. We think of the triple integral of a function f on R^3 over a three-dimensional region R as the limit of sums of the form

(104-1) $$s = \sum f(x^*, y^*, z^*)\,\Delta V.$$

The number ΔV is the volume of a typical subblock of a covering of R. These subblocks are formed by slicing R with coordinate surfaces. When we use rectangular coordinates, these coordinate surfaces are simply planes parallel to the XY-plane, the YZ-plane, and the XZ-plane. In other coordinate systems, the coordinate surfaces are not all planes, so when we slice R with coordinate surfaces the resulting subregions are not rectangular blocks. Therefore, we cannot calculate the volume ΔV of a typical one of these subregions by multiplying the lengths of its edges. We must develop, for each coordinate system that we use, an appropriate formula for ΔV. The key to integration in cylindrical or spherical coordinates is the proper formula for ΔV.

Let us introduce a cylindrical coordinate system into our space as we did in Section 81. Now we slice our region R with coordinate surfaces, here cylinders whose common axis is the Z-axis, planes that intersect along the Z-axis, and planes parallel to the XY-plane. A typical subregion that results is shown in Fig. 104-1.

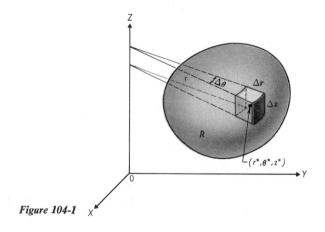

Figure 104-1

Its dimensions are indicated in the figure. Planes parallel to the XY-plane cut this subregion in figures that are congruent to its base. Therefore, the volume of our typical subregion is given by the formula

$$\Delta V = \text{(area of the base)}\ \Delta z.$$

The base of this subregion has the form of one of the polar subregions that are illustrated in Fig. 102-1. In Section 102 we found that the area of such a subregion is $r^* \Delta r\ \Delta \theta$, where r^* is the radial coordinate of a suitably chosen point inside the region. Let us suppose that the coordinates of such a point are (r^*, θ^*, z^*). Then $\Delta V = r^* \Delta r\ \Delta \theta\ \Delta z$, and so one of our approximating sums is

$$\sum f(r^* \cos \theta^*, r^* \sin \theta^*, z^*) r^* \Delta r\ \Delta \theta\ \Delta z.$$

The limit of such sums is the triple integral of f over R, and their form suggests that we write

$$(104\text{-}2) \qquad \iiint\limits_{R} f(x, y, z)\ dV = \iiint\limits_{R} f(r \cos \theta, r \sin \theta, z) r\ dr\ d\theta\ dz.$$

It is convenient to think that we obtain the right-hand side of this equation from the left-hand side by replacing x with $r \cos \theta$, y with $r \sin \theta$, z with z, and dV with $r\ dr\ d\theta\ dz$.

We evaluate such integrals as iterated integrals, as the following examples show.

Example 104-1. Evaluate the integral $\iiint\limits_{R} x^2\ dV$, where R is the region that is bounded by cylinders whose radii are 3 and 4 and the planes $z = 0$ and $z = 3$, as shown in Fig. 104-2.

Solution. In this case the limits of integration on r are 3 and 4, the limits on θ are 0 and 2π, and the limits on z are 0 and 3. Thus

$$\iiint\limits_{R} x^2\ dV = \iiint\limits_{R} r^2 \cos^2 \theta\ r\ dr\ d\theta\ dz$$

$$= \int_0^3 \int_0^{2\pi} \int_3^4 r^3 \cos^2 \theta\ dr\ d\theta\ dz = \frac{525\pi}{4}.$$

Example 104-2. Use cylindrical coordinates to find the moment of inertia about its axis of a solid right-circular cylinder whose altitude is h and whose base radius is a.

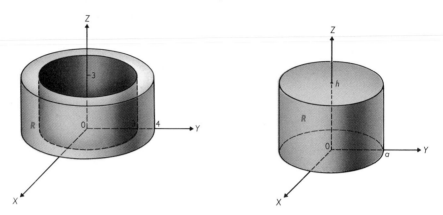

Figure 104-2   **Figure 104-3**

Solution. We introduce a cylindrical coordinate system (Fig. 104-3) so that our cylinder is the region R that is bounded by the planes $z = h$ and $z = 0$ and the surface whose equation in cylindrical coordinates is $r = a$. Then

$$I_Z = \iiint\limits_R (x^2 + y^2) \, dV = \iiint\limits_R r^2 \, dV.$$

Now we express this integral as an iterated integral in cylindrical coordinates:

$$I_Z = \int_0^a \int_0^{2\pi} \int_0^h r^3 \, dz \, d\theta \, dr$$

$$= h \int_0^a \int_0^{2\pi} r^3 \, d\theta \, dr = 2\pi h \int_0^a r^3 \, dr = \frac{\pi h a^4}{2} = \frac{a^2 V}{2}.$$

If you use cartesian coordinates to find this moment of inertia (see Problem 103-10b) you can appreciate how simple the calculations in this example are.

The role of spherical coordinates in the study of triple integrals is similar to the role of cylindrical coordinates. Let us introduce a spherical coordinate system into our space and slice a three-dimensional region R with coordinate surfaces, here concentric spheres whose center is the origin, planes containing the Z-axis, and cones whose axis is the Z-axis and whose vertex is the origin. One of the subregions that results is shown in Fig. 104-4. We have labeled one corner of this region P, and let us suppose that the coordinates of this point P are (ρ, θ, ϕ). The three edges of the subregion that meet at P have lengths $\Delta\rho$, $\rho\,\Delta\phi$, and $\rho \sin \phi \, \Delta\theta$, where the meaning of the symbols $\Delta\rho$, $\Delta\theta$, and $\Delta\phi$ is indicated on the figure. If our region were rectangular, its volume would be the product of the lengths of these edges; that is, the number

$$\rho^2 \sin \phi \; \Delta\rho \; \Delta\theta \; \Delta\phi.$$

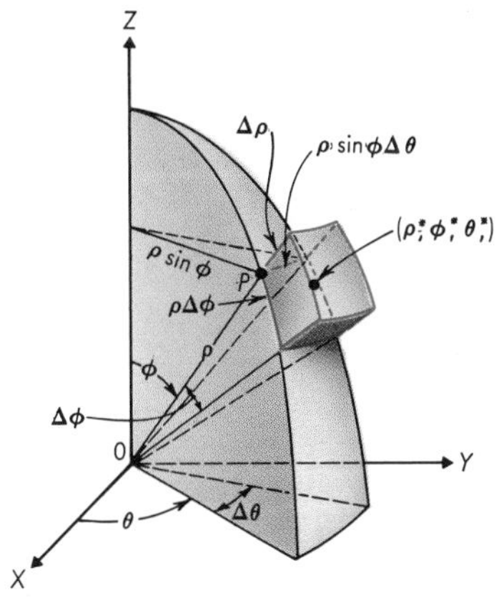

Actually, this number is not quite equal to ΔV, but it can be shown that there is a point $(\rho^*, \theta^*, \phi^*)$ inside our region for which

$$\Delta V = \rho^{*2} \sin \phi^* \; \Delta\rho \; \Delta\theta \; \Delta\phi.$$

Furthermore, we know that

$$x^* = \rho^* \sin \phi^* \cos \theta^*,$$

Figure 104-4

$y^* = \rho^* \sin \phi^* \sin \theta^*$, and $z^* = \rho^* \cos \phi^*$ are the cartesian coordinates of our point $(\rho^*, \theta^*, \phi^*)$. Therefore, one of the sums (Equation 104-1) that approximate the integral of f over R takes the form

$$\sum f(\rho^* \sin \phi^* \cos \theta^*, \; \rho^* \sin \phi^* \sin \theta^*, \; \rho^* \cos \phi^*)\rho^{*2} \sin \phi^* \; \Delta\rho \; \Delta\theta \; \Delta\phi.$$

This sum suggests that we write

$$(104\text{-}3) \quad \iiint\limits_{R} f(x, y, z) \; dV$$

$$= \iiint\limits_{R} f(\rho \sin\phi \cos \theta, \; \rho \sin\phi \sin \theta, \; \rho \cos \phi) \; \rho^2 \sin\phi \; d\rho \; d\theta \; d\phi.$$

It is convenient to think that we obtain the right-hand side of this equation from the left-hand side by replacing x with $\rho \sin \phi \cos \theta$, y with $\rho \sin \phi \sin \theta$, z with $\rho \cos \phi$, and dV with $\rho^2 \sin \phi \; d\rho \; d\theta \; d\phi$.

The following examples show how we evaluate such integrals by replacing them with iterated integrals.

Example 104-3. Find the volume of the "ice cream cone" that is cut from a sphere whose radius is 6 by a cone with a half-angle of 30°, as shown in Fig. 104-5.

Solution. The volume of R is the integral $V = \iiint\limits_{R} dV$. From the figure we see that the limits on the variable of integration ρ are 0 and 6, the limits on θ are 0 and 2π, and the limits on ϕ are 0 and $\pi/6$. Thus

$$V = \int_0^{\pi/6} \int_0^{2\pi} \int_0^6 \rho^2 \sin \phi \, d\rho \, d\theta \, d\phi = 72\pi[2 - \sqrt{3}].$$

Example 104-4. Find the moment of inertia about a diameter of a spherical ball of radius a.

Solution. Let the ball be represented in spherical coordinates by the inequality $\rho \le a$, and let us compute I_Z. Then

$$I_Z = \iiint\limits_R (x^2 + y^2) \, dV$$

$$= \iiint\limits_R \rho^2 \sin^2 \phi \, dV$$

$$= \int_0^\pi \int_0^{2\pi} \int_0^a \rho^4 \sin^3 \phi \, d\rho \, d\theta \, d\phi$$

$$= \frac{a^5}{5} \int_0^\pi \int_0^{2\pi} \sin^3 \phi \, d\theta \, d\phi$$

$$= \frac{2\pi a^5}{5} \int_0^\pi \sin^3 \phi \, d\phi$$

$$= \frac{8\pi a^5}{15}.$$

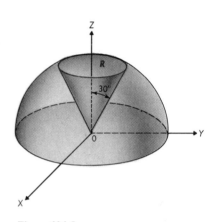

Figure 104-5

To appreciate the simplicity of this calculation, you should use cartesian coordinates to find this moment of inertia.

P R O B L E M S   1 0 4

1. Find the formula for the volume of a spherical ball S of radius a by evaluating the triple integral $\iiint\limits_S dV$ as an iterated integral in rectangular, cylindrical, and spherical coordinates.

2. Use cylindrical coordinates to evaluate $\iiint\limits_R x^4yz^2 \, dV$, where R is the first octant region bounded by the plane $z = 2$ and the cylinder $x^2 + y^2 = 9$. Check your answer by using rectangular coordinates. Can you do the problem in spherical coordinates?

3. Use spherical coordinates to evaluate the integral $\iiint\limits_R xyz \, dV$, where R is the first octant portion of the solid spherical ball $x^2 + y^2 + z^2 \leq 9$. Check your answer by using cylindrical coordinates and rectangular coordinates.

4. Find the moment of inertia of a circular cylindrical shell whose length is L, inside radius is a, and outside radius is b:
   (a) About the longitudinal axis.
   (b) About a line containing its center and perpendicular to its longitudinal axis.
   (c) Find approximations to these moments of inertia if our shell is very thin, with a mean radius of c and thickness $2h$, by setting $b = c + h$ and $a = c - h$ and supposing that h is so small that h^2 can be neglected.

5. Find the moment of inertia about a diameter of a spherical shell bounded by two concentric spheres of radii a and b, where $a < b$. Use your result to check the solution of Example 104-4. Show that there is a number c between a and b such that this moment of inertia is $\dfrac{8\pi}{3} c^4 t$, where t is the thickness of the shell.

6. Let R be the region bounded by the XY-plane, the sphere $x^2 + y^2 + z^2 = 4$, and the cylinder $x^2 + y^2 = 1$. Find I_Z. What is the centroid of R?

7. Use cylindrical coordinates to find the moment of inertia about the axis of a solid right circular cone whose base radius is a and whose altitude is h. How far above the base is the centroid of the cone?

8. The region $R = \{(x, y, z) \,|\, a^2 < x^2 + y^2 + z^2 < b^2, z \geq 0\}$ forms an inverted bowl lying on the XY-plane. Find the Z-coordinate $\bar{z}$ of the centroid of the bowl. What is the Z-coordinate of the centroid of a solid hemisphere? What is $\lim\limits_{a \uparrow b} \bar{z}$? Show that the Z-coordinate of the centroid of our bowl always lies between these two numbers.

105 LINE INTEGRALS

In the preceding sections of this chapter, we have extended the concept of the integral from scalar-valued functions on R^1 to scalar-valued functions on R^2 and R^3. Now we will generalize the notion of the integral in yet another direction; namely, to integrals of vector-valued functions on R^2. Although much of our discussion applies to a general R^n, we limit ourselves to R^2 for the sake of simplicity. Even so, some of the details and proofs are too long or too difficult (or both) to include in a first course in calculus, and we often have to fall back on informal arguments to make our points. If you keep your eyes on our figures, and draw some of your own, you can understand what we are talking about here. The difficulties come when we try to express in words and mathematical symbols things that seem obvious in the pictures.

As one of our notational conventions, we often designate the component vector (x, y) of R^2 by writing its first component in boldface type; thus, $\boldsymbol{x} = (x, y)$. When we picture (x, y) as a point of the coordinate plane, the vector $\boldsymbol{x}$ can be thought of as the position vector to the point. We can also introduce the basis vectors $\boldsymbol{i}$ and $\boldsymbol{j}$ and write $\boldsymbol{x} = x\boldsymbol{i} + y\boldsymbol{j}$.

The semi-circle shown in Fig. 105-1 is the graph of the vector equation $x = 5 \cos t\,\boldsymbol{i} + 5 \sin t\,\boldsymbol{j}$, $t \in [-\frac{1}{2}\pi, \frac{1}{2}\pi]$. We say that this equation "maps" the interval $[-\frac{1}{2}\pi, \frac{1}{2}\pi]$ onto the semi-circle. Since the interval is part of a number scale, it is directed, the positive direction being from the point $-\frac{1}{2}\pi$ toward the point $\frac{1}{2}\pi$. Our equation transfers this direction to the semi-circle; for example, the "first" point of the semi-circle is $(0, -5)$ and the "last" point is $(0, 5)$ in this mapping. We will denote this directed semi-circle by the bold-face letter $\boldsymbol{C}$. Our semi-circle can also be thought of as the image of the interval $[-5, 5]$ under the mapping that is determined by the parametric equations $x = \sqrt{25 - u^2}$ and $y = u$, $u \in [-5, 5]$. We observe that this mapping gives the semi-circle the same direction that our previous one did, so we have different parametric representations of the same directed semi-circle.

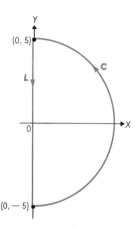

Figure 105-1

The parametric equations $x = \sqrt{25 - v^2}$ and $y = -v$, $v \in [-5, 5]$, also map the interval $[-5, 5]$ onto our semi-circle, but now its direction is reversed. It will be important for us here to distinguish this new directed semi-circle from $\boldsymbol{C}$; we call it $-\boldsymbol{C}$.

In general, a **directed arc** $\boldsymbol{C}$ is the graph of a vector equation $x = \boldsymbol{r}(t)$, $t \in [a, b]$, where $\boldsymbol{r}$ is a differentiable vector-valued function such that $|\boldsymbol{r}'(t)| > 0$ for each $t \in [a, b]$. The direction of $\boldsymbol{C}$ is inherited from the parameter interval $[a, b]$. Suppose we are given such a directed arc $\boldsymbol{C}$ and a vector-valued function $\boldsymbol{f}$ on R^2 whose domain contains the points of $\boldsymbol{C}$. Then we define the **line integral** of $\boldsymbol{f}$ along $\boldsymbol{C}$ to be the number

$$(105\text{-}1) \qquad \int_{\boldsymbol{C}} \boldsymbol{f}(\boldsymbol{x}) \cdot d\boldsymbol{x} = \int_a^b \boldsymbol{f}(\boldsymbol{r}(t)) \cdot \boldsymbol{r}'(t)\, dt.$$

Line integrals can be written in many different notations. Let us suppose that $\boldsymbol{f}(\boldsymbol{x}) = f(x, y)\boldsymbol{i} + g(x, y)\boldsymbol{j}$ and that the vector equation $\boldsymbol{x} = \boldsymbol{r}(t)$ that represents $\boldsymbol{C}$ can be expressed as the parametric scalar equations $x = r(t)$ and $y = s(t)$. Then $\boldsymbol{r}'(t) = (r'(t), s'(t))$, and so the expanded form of Equation 105-1 is

$$(105\text{-}2) \qquad \int_{\boldsymbol{C}} \boldsymbol{f}(\boldsymbol{x}) \cdot d\boldsymbol{x} = \int_a^b [f(r(t), s(t))r'(t) + g(r(t), s(t))s'(t)]\, dt.$$

Since $\boldsymbol{x} = x\,\boldsymbol{i} + y\,\boldsymbol{j}$, it is natural to replace $d\boldsymbol{x}$ with $dx\,\boldsymbol{i} + dy\,\boldsymbol{j}$. Then the dot product $\boldsymbol{f}(\boldsymbol{x}) \cdot d\boldsymbol{x}$ becomes $f(x, y)\, dx + g(x, y)\, dy$, and we write

$$(105\text{-}3) \qquad \int_{\boldsymbol{C}} \boldsymbol{f}(\boldsymbol{x}) \cdot d\boldsymbol{x} = \int_{\boldsymbol{C}} f(x, y)\, dx + g(x, y)\, dy.$$

Of course, when we compute the right-hand side of this equation we must replace x with $r(t)$, y with $s(t)$, dx with $r'(t)\,dt$, dy with $s'(t)\,dt$, and integrate over the parameter interval $[a, b]$.

Example 105-1. Find the line integral of f along the directed arc C of Fig. 105-1 if $f(x) = x^2 i + y^2 j$.

Solution. As we have seen, our directed semi-circle C can be represented in more than one way. If we think of C as the graph of the vector equation $x = r(t) = 5 \cos t\, i + 5 \sin t\, j$ for $t \in [-\frac{1}{2}\pi, \frac{1}{2}\pi]$, then $f(r(t)) = 25 \cos^2 t\, i + 25 \sin^2 t\, j$, and $r'(t) = -5 \sin t\, i + 5 \cos t\, j$. Therefore, our line integral is

$$\int_C f(x) \cdot dx = \int_{-\pi/2}^{\pi/2} (25 \cos^2 t\, i + 25 \sin^2 t\, j) \cdot (-5 \sin t\, i + 5 \cos t\, j)\, dt$$

$$= \int_{-\pi/2}^{\pi/2} (-125 \cos^2 t \sin t + 125 \sin^2 t \cos t)\, dt$$

$$= 125\left(\frac{1}{3} \cos^3 t + \frac{1}{3} \sin^3 t\right)\Big|_{-\pi/2}^{\pi/2} = \frac{250}{3}.$$

Now suppose we think of C as the image of the interval $[-5, 5]$ under the mapping that is determined by the parametric equations $x = \sqrt{25 - u^2}$ and $y = u$. From these equations we see that we should replace dx with $-(25 - u^2)^{-1/2}\, du$ and dy with du when we write our line integral in the form of Equation 104-3:

$$\int_C f(x) \cdot dx = \int_C x^2\, dx + y^2\, dy$$

$$= \int_{-5}^{5} [-u(25 - u^2)^{1/2} + u^2]\, du$$

$$= [\tfrac{1}{3}(25 - u^2)^{3/2} + \tfrac{1}{3}u^3]\big|_{-5}^{5} = \tfrac{250}{3}.$$

Equation 105-1 that defines the line integral of a function f along a directed arc C is expressed in terms of values of a vector-valued function r of which C is the graph. Therefore, it might appear that we would get different values for the line integral, depending on which representation of C we use. That this is not so is illustrated in Example 105-1. There we used two different representations of C to calculate our line integral, and we got the same result each time. We will omit the proof and simply state that the line integral of a function f along a directed arc C depends only on f and C, not on any particular choice of a function r of which C is the graph. It can be shown that reversing the direction of an arc changes the sign of line integrals along the arc; that is,

(105-4) $$\int_{-C} f(x) \cdot dx = -\int_C f(x) \cdot dx.$$

It follows directly from our definition (Equation 105-1) that line integrals possess many of the properties of ordinary integrals. For example, integrals of sums are sums of integrals, and so on. Furthermore, we may join a number of directed arcs to form a **directed path.** The line integral of a vector-valued function along the path is then defined as the sum of its line integrals along the arcs. For example, the line integral of f around a (directed) square is the sum of its integrals along the sides (properly directed) of the square.

Example 105-2.   Find the line integral of the vector-valued function of Example 105-1 along the closed directed path P (shown in Fig. 105-1) that is formed by joining to the directed semi-circle C the directed line segment L from the point $(0, 5)$ to the point $(0, -5)$.

Solution.   We compute the desired number $\int_P f(x) \cdot dx$ by adding to the line integral

of f along $C\left(\text{which we know is } \dfrac{250}{3}\right)$ the number $\int_L f(x) \cdot dx = \int_L x^2 \, dx + y^2 \, dy.$

Parametric equations of L are $x = 0$ and $y = -t, \ t \in [-5, 5]$, so

$$\int_L x^2 \, dx + y^2 \, dy = -\int_{-5}^{5} t^2 \, dt = -\frac{1}{3} t^3 \Big|_{-5}^{5} = -\frac{250}{3}.$$

Usually we don't go through this whole substitution routine. We simply notice that $x = 0$ on L and y varies from 5 to -5. We therefore write

$$\int_L x^2 \, dx + y^2 \, dy = \int_{5}^{-5} y^2 \, dy = \frac{y^3}{3} \Big|_{5}^{-5} = -\frac{250}{3}.$$

Now we add this number to the integral along the semi-circle, and we see that

$$\int_P f(x) \cdot dx = \frac{250}{3} - \frac{250}{3} = 0.$$

Line integrals are frequently used to calculate work. In Section 42, we defined work as the integral of force, under the assumption that the force acts along the line of motion. Now we will drop this restriction. Suppose that at each point (x, y) of the coordinate plane a force vector $f(x, y)$ is defined. For example, if a positive electrical charge of 1 coulomb is placed at the origin, it will exert (according to the Inverse Square Law) a force of

$$(105\text{-}5) \qquad f(x, y) = x(x^2 + y^2)^{-3/2}i + y(x^2 + y^2)^{-3/2}j$$

dynes on a unit charge at the point (x, y) (assuming that distances are measured in centimeters). Thus if a point moves along a directed arc C, then at each point (x, y) it will be subjected to a force of $f(x, y)$, and we say that the equation

$$W = \int_C f(x) \cdot dx$$

gives the work done as C is traversed.

   Example 105-3.   In our electrical example above, how much work is required to move a positive charge of 1 coulomb along the straight path from the point $(-1, 1)$ to the point $(0, 1)$?

   Solution.   Parametric equations of our path are $x = r(t) = t$ and $y = s(t) = 1$, $t \in [-1, 0]$.
      When we substitute these values into Equation 105-2 (we read the components of the force vector from Equation 105-5) we find that

$$W = \int_{-1}^{0} t(t^2 + 1)^{-3/2} \, dt = \frac{1}{\sqrt{2}} - 1 \approx -.3 \text{ ergs.}$$

The negative answer indicates that the net work has been done "against the force."

   Many times we wish to integrate a function f around a *closed* path; that is, one that "begins" and "ends" at the same point, such as the path in Example 105-2. Of course, we must distinguish between the two directions around the path. We will use the symbol

$$\oint_P f(x) \cdot dx$$

to denote the line integral of f around a closed path P in a counter-clockwise direction.

   Example 105-4.   Show that if the force vector is the gradient of a scalar-valued function f, then the work done in traversing a closed directed arc C is zero.

   Solution.   We are to show that if C is the graph of the vector equation $x = r(t)$, then

$$\oint_C \nabla f(x) \cdot dx = \int_a^b \nabla f(r(t)) \cdot r'(t) \, dt = 0.$$

Our Chain Rule Equation 94-3 tells us that $\nabla f(r(t)) \cdot r'(t) = D_t f(r(t))$, and so we have

(105-6) $$\oint_C \nabla f(x) \cdot dx = \int_a^b D_t f(r(t)) \, dt = f(r(b)) - f(r(a)).$$

We are supposing that C is a closed arc, and hence $r(a) = r(b)$. Therefore, our integral has the value 0, as we were to show. It is a simple matter to extend our result to closed *paths* (rather than arcs); we ask you to do so in the problems.

We notice that Equation 105-6 is valid even if C is not a closed arc. If C is a directed arc from the point $a = r(a)$ to the point $b = r(b)$ then we can write Equation 105-6 as

$$(105\text{-}7) \qquad \int_C \nabla f(x) \cdot dx = f(b) - f(a).$$

This equation is sometimes called the Fundamental Theorem of Calculus for line integrals.

P R O B L E M S   1 0 5

1. Let $f(x, y) = 3x^2yi + (2x - y)j$. Find $\displaystyle\int_P f(x) \cdot dx$, where P is the directed path from $(0, 0)$ to $(1, 1)$ described as follows.
(a) The line segment.
(b) The parabolic arc $y = x^2$, $x \in [0, 1]$.

(c) The graph of the vector equation $x = \sin t\, i + \dfrac{2t}{\pi} j$, $t \in [0, \pi/2]$.

(d) The graph of the parametric equations $x = t^2$ and $y = t^3$, $t \in [0, 1]$.
(e) The union of the segment from $(0, 0)$ to $(1, 0)$ and the segment from $(1, 0)$ to $(1, 1)$.

2. Find $\displaystyle\int_P 3x^2y\, dx + (2x - y)\, dy$ if P is the shortest path from $(0, 0)$ to $(2, 2)$ that also contains the points $(1, 0)$, $(1, 1)$, and $(2, 1)$.

3. Find $\displaystyle\int_C y^2\, dx + x^2\, dy$ along each of the following directed arcs.

(a) The arc of the ellipse $\dfrac{x^2}{a^2} + \dfrac{y^2}{b^2} = 1$ from the point $(a, 0)$ to the point $(0, b)$.

(b) The line segment from the point $(a, 0)$ to the point $(0, b)$.

4. Show that no work is done if we move through a force field along a path that is perpendicular to the lines of force—for instance, if we move along circular arcs whose center is the origin in our electrical example.

5. If we view an interval of the X-axis as a small portion of the surface of the earth and the Y-axis as pointing up, then the gravitational force on an object of mass m is expressed by the vector $G = -mg\, j$, where g is a number that depends on the units we use. Show that the work done by gravity as the object is moved from a point (a, b) to a point (c, d) along any path is $mg(d - b)$.

6. Show that $\int_C f(x) \cdot dx$ is the length of C if $f(x)$ is the unit tangent vector in the positive direction at each point x of C.

7. Let $f(x) = x \cdot x$, and let P be the directed path consisting of the union of the directed line segments from $(0, 0)$ to $(1, 0)$ and from $(1, 0)$ to $(1, 1)$. Use Equation 105-3 to compute $\int_P \nabla f(x) \cdot dx$, and use Equation 105-7 to check your result.

8. Let P be the closed path consisting of line segments joining the points $(0, 0)$, $(1, 0)$, $(1, 1)$, $(0, 1)$, $(0, 0)$ in that order. Compute the work done as P is traversed, if the force function is defined by the equation $f(x) = (x^2 - y^2)i + 2xy\,j$. Can you find a function g such that $f = \nabla g$? Do the problem if the defining equation is $f(x) = (x^2 + y^2)i + 2xy\,j$.

9. Show that the line integral of a gradient is 0 if the path of integration is a closed path formed by joining a number of directed arcs.

10. For each number a of the interval $[0, 1]$ we construct the path $P(a)$ from the point $(0, 0)$ to the point $(1, 1)$ by proceeding from $(0, 0)$ along the X-axis to $(a, 0)$, then parallel to the Y-axis to $(a, 1)$, and then parallel to the X-axis to $(1, 1)$. Then we calculate the number $I(a) = \int_{P(a)} x^2(y - 1)\,dx + xy^8\,dy$. For what number a is $I(a)$ a maximum? What is the minimum value of $I(a)$?

11. Let f be a vector-valued function on R^2, and let C be a directed arc in the domain of f. Suppose there is a number M such that for each point $(x, y) \in C$, $|f(x, y)| \leq M$, and let L be the length of C. Show that $|\int_C f(x) \cdot dx| \leq ML$.

106 GREEN'S THEOREM. FUNCTIONS DEFINED BY LINE INTEGRALS

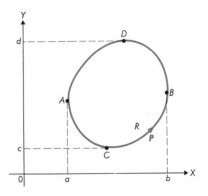

Figure 106-1

We called Equation 105-7 the Fundamental Theorem of Calculus for line integrals. Now we are going to take up the Fundamental Theorem of Calculus for double integrals, which is known as Green's Theorem. A detailed discussion of the most general form of Green's Theorem is both long and difficult, so we will have to be content with an informal presentation of some of the simpler cases. Nevertheless, you will find that our results are sufficient for many applications of mathematics.

Let us start with a vector-valued function f, where $f(x, y) = f(x, y)i + g(x, y)j$, and a closed path P, such as the one shown in Fig. 106-1. We will let R

denote the region that is bounded by P, and take P to be directed in the counter-clockwise sense. This path can be viewed as the union of the directed arcs ACB and BDA, or as the union of the directed arcs CBD and DAC. We wish to find the line integral of f around P:

$$(106\text{-}1) \qquad \oint_P f(x) \cdot dx = \oint_P f(x, y)\, dx + g(x, y)\, dy$$

$$= \oint_P f(x, y)\, dx + \oint_P g(x, y)\, dy.$$

To evaluate each of these last two integrals, we decompose the path P into two directed arcs. For the first integral we think of P as the union of ACB and BDA, and for the second integral we think of P as the union of CBD and DAC, so we have

$$\oint_P f(x, y)\, dx = \int_{ACB} f(x, y)\, dx + \int_{BDA} f(x, y)\, dx$$

and

$$\oint_P g(x, y)\, dy = \int_{CBD} g(x, y)\, dy + \int_{DAC} g(x, y)\, dy.$$

Let us suppose that the lower arc ACB is the graph of the equation $y = r(x)$ and the upper arc ADB is the graph of the equation $y = s(x)$, where the domains of the functions r and s contain the interval $[a, b]$. Then

$$\int_{ACB} f(x, y)\, dx = \int_a^b f(x, r(x))\, dx$$

and

$$\int_{BDA} f(x, y)\, dx = -\int_{ADB} f(x, y)\, dx = -\int_a^b f(x, s(x))\, dx,$$

and hence

$$\oint_P f(x, y)\, dx = -\int_a^b [f(x, s(x)) - f(x, r(x))]\, dx.$$

According to the Fundamental Theorem of Calculus, for each $x \in [a, b]$ we have

$$f(x, s(x)) - f(x, r(x)) = f(x, y) \Big|_{r(x)}^{s(x)} = \int_{r(x)}^{s(x)} f_2(x, y)\, dy,$$

and therefore we can write

$$\oint_P f(x, y)\, dx = -\int_a^b \int_{r(x)}^{s(x)} f_2(x, y)\, dy\, dx.$$

Since the iterated integral in this equation equals the double integral $\iint\limits_{R} f_2(x, y)\, dA$, we finally have

$$\oint_P f(x, y)\, dx = -\iint\limits_{R} f_2(x, y)\, dA.$$

Similarly, if the arcs **CBD** and **CAD** are graphs of the equations $x = p(y)$ and $x = q(y)$, $y \in [c, d]$, then

$$\oint_P g(x, y)\, dy = \int_c^d g(q(y), y)\, dy - \int_c^d g(p(y), y)\, dy$$

$$= \int_c^d [g(q(y), y) - g(p(y), y)]\, dy$$

$$= \int_c^d g(x, y)\,\Big|_{p(y)}^{q(y)}\, dy = \int_c^d \int_{p(y)}^{q(y)} g_1(x, y)\, dy$$

$$= \iint\limits_{R} g_1(x, y)\, dA.$$

Now we substitute the expressions we have just found for $\oint_P f(x, y)\, dx$ and $\oint_P g(x, y)\, dy$ in Equation 106-1, and we obtain the equation

$$(106\text{-}2) \qquad \oint_P f(x) \cdot dx = \iint\limits_{R} [g_1(x, y) - f_2(x, y)]\, dA.$$

This equation is the conclusion of **Green's Theorem** in the plane. We usually read it from right to left. Thus we view Green's Theorem as a rule for expressing a double integral over a region R as a line integral over the boundary P of R. In this sense, Green's Theorem is analogous to the Fundamental Theorem of Calculus; the equation $\int_a^b F'(x)\, dx = F(b) - F(a)$ expresses an integral over an interval $[a, b]$ in terms of values of F at the "boundary points" a and b of $[a, b]$. In developing Green's Theorem we assumed that our boundary path P had an especially simple form. By "patching together" regions of the type we have considered, the range of validity of Equation 106-2 can be greatly extended. In fact, Green's Theorem is true for quite general regions.

> *Example 106-1.* Explain why, if we had known Green's Theorem at that time, we could have anticipated that 0 would be the answer to our problem in Example 105-2.

Solution.   In that example, $f(x, y) = x^2$ and $g(x, y) = y^2$. Therefore, $g_1(x, y) = 0$ and $f_2(x, y) = 0$ at each point (x, y) of the region that is bounded by our path of integration. Hence the right-hand side of Equation 106-2 is 0, and so the left-hand side must also be 0.

When we use integrals to define functions on R^1, we start with a function f defined in an interval I, choose a point $c \in I$, and define a new function F whose domain is I by means of the equation

$$F(x) = \int_c^x f(u)\, du.$$

Because x is the upper limit of integration here, we don't want to use it also as the variable of integration; we use u instead. Thus we can think of the domain I of

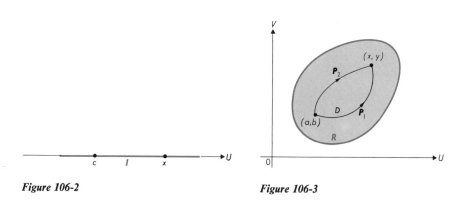

Figure 106-2   Figure 106-3

our function F as an interval of the U-axis, as shown in Fig. 106-2. To evaluate F at a point x of the interval, we integrate f from c to x.

Now we are going to do the analogous thing for functions on R^2. Here we start with two functions, f and g, defined in a region R of the UV-plane like the one shown in Fig. 106-3, and set $\boldsymbol{f}(\boldsymbol{u}) = f(u, v)\boldsymbol{i} + g(u, v)\boldsymbol{j}$. To define a function F, we choose a point $\boldsymbol{a} = (a, b)$ of R and say that at any point $\boldsymbol{x} = (x, y)$ of R,

(106-3) $$F(\boldsymbol{x}) = \int_a^x \boldsymbol{f}(\boldsymbol{u}) \cdot d\boldsymbol{u}.$$

Although this equation looks exactly like the equation we use to define a function on R^1, there is a difficulty here that was not present in the previous case. Equation 106-3 tells us to integrate from the point $\boldsymbol{a} = (a, b)$ to the point $\boldsymbol{x} = (x, y)$, but it doesn't tell us which path to follow. Generally speaking (see Problem 105-1 for an example), if we calculate our integral along different paths joining the points

(a, b) and (x, y), we get different numbers. Because we want to assign just one number $F(x, y)$ to a given point (x, y), we will have to restrict our attention to line integrals whose values depend only on the endpoints, not on the complete path of integration. For example, Equation 105-7 shows us that if our given vector-valued function f is the gradient of some scalar-valued function, then the line integral in Equation 106-3 depends only on the choice of endpoints, so the equation really does define a function. Green's Theorem tells us how to recognize line integrals that are independent of the path of integration. Thus suppose that P_1 and P_2 are two directed paths in R that connect the points (a, b) and (x, y), as shown in Fig. 106-3. We want $F(x, y)$ to be the value of the line integral along either one of these paths, and so we require that

$$\int_{P_1} f(u) \cdot du = \int_{P_2} f(u) \cdot du.$$

This equation is equivalent to the equation $\oint_{P} f(u) \cdot du = 0$, where the path of integration P is the closed path from (a, b) along P_1 to (x, y) and then returning to (a, b) along $-P_2$. Now let us assume that any such closed path P bounds a region D that lies wholly in R. (For a region with holes in it, such as the set H shown in Fig. 106-4, it is possible to join two points with curves that lie in H, but which bound

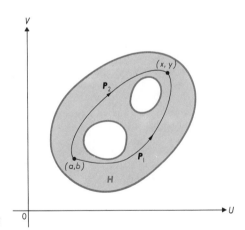

Figure 106-4

a set that is not entirely contained in H. So we will restrict our attention to regions that do not contain holes. Such regions are said to be **simply connected**.) Then according to Green's Theorem,

$$\oint_{P} f(u) \cdot du = \iint_{D} [g_1(u, v) - f_2(u, v)] \, dA.$$

This double integral is zero if, for each point of D, $g_1(u, v) = f_2(u, v)$. Since $D \subseteq R$, this equation will surely hold throughout D if it holds throughout R. Thus we have shown that, *if R is a simply connected region, and*

(106-4) $f_2(x, y) = g_1(x, y)$ *for each point* $(x, y) \in R$,

then Equation 106-3 defines a function F in R; we may use any convenient path to evaluate the integral, because each path gives the same result. We say that the line integral in Equation 106-3 is *independent of path.*

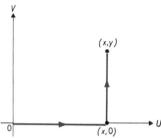

Figure 106-5

Example 106-2.   Discuss the function that is defined by the equation

$$F(x) = \int_0^x 2uv^3 \, du + 3u^2v^2 dv.$$

Solution.   Here $f(u, v) = 2uv^3$ and $g(u, v) = 3u^2v^2$, so $f_2(u, v) = 6uv^2 = g_1(u, v)$. Therefore, Condition 106-4 is satisfied throughout the coordinate plane, so our integral defines a function whose domain is R^2. We can evaluate this integral by using any path from $(0, 0)$ to (x, y); for example, we could proceed from $(0, 0)$ along the U-axis to $(x, 0)$ and then parallel to the V-axis to (x, y) as shown in Fig. 106-5. Then we have

$$F(x, y) = \int_0^x 0 \, du + \int_0^y 3x^2v^2 dv = x^2v^3 \Big|_0^y = x^2y^3.$$

In the problems, we ask you to show that you get the same result by integrating along the directed line segment from the origin to the point (x, y).

P R O B L E M S   1 0 6

1. Use Green's Theorem to show that the area of the region that is bounded by a closed path P is given by the formulas:

$$A = \frac{1}{2} \oint_P x \, dy - y \, dx = \oint_P x \, dy = -\oint_P y \, dx.$$

Check your result if P is the unit circle whose center is the origin.

2. Suppose a unit positive charge is placed at the origin (see Example 105-3). Use Green's Theorem to deduce that no net work is done if another unit positive charge is moved around the square whose vertices are $(1, -1)$, $(1, 1)$, $(3, 1)$ and $(3, -1)$. What if the square is replaced by any closed path that doesn't encircle the origin?

3. Let D be a region in which f has continuous first and second partial derivatives. Use Green's Theorem to show that the line integral of ∇f around the boundary of D is 0, and compare this result with Problem 105-9.

4. Use Green's Theorem to evaluate the line integral of $f(x) = ay\,\boldsymbol{i} - bx\,\boldsymbol{j}$ around the circle $x^2 + y^2 = 1$ in the counter-clockwise direction.

5. Express $F(x, y)$ without using the integral sign.

(a) $$F(x, y) = \int_{(1,0)}^{(x,y)} (1 + uv)\, e^{uv}\, du + u^2 e^{uv}\, dv$$

(b) $$F(x, y) = \int_{(1,1)}^{(x,y)} \ln v\, du + \frac{u}{v}\, dv$$

(c) $$F(x, y) = \int_{(1,1)}^{(x,y)} (3v^2 + 2)\, du + 6uv\, dv$$

(d) $$F(x, y) = \int_{(2,\pi)}^{(x,y)} -2uv^2 \sin u^2v\, du + (\cos u^2v - u^2v \sin u^2v)\, dv$$

6. Let $(\bar{x}, \bar{y})$ be the centroid of a region R that has an area of A square units and is bounded by a closed directed arc C (Equation 101-5). Show that

$$\bar{x} = \frac{1}{2A} \oint_C x^2\, dy \quad \text{and} \quad \bar{y} = \frac{1}{A} \oint_C xy\, dy.$$

107 DERIVATIVES OF FUNCTIONS DEFINED BY INTEGRALS. EXACT DIFFERENTIAL EQUATIONS

Theorem 43-2 tells us that if $F(x) = \int_a^x f(u)\, du$, then at each point at which f is continuous we have $F'(x) = f(x)$. Thus, derivatives of functions defined by integrals are values of the integrands. Now we will find that the same statement is true for a function on R^2 that is defined by an equation of the form $F(x) = \int_a^x f(u) \cdot du$; that is,

(107-1) $$F(x, y) = \int_{(a,b)}^{(x,y)} f(u, v)\, du + g(u, v)\, dv.$$

Of course, we will assume that our line integral is independent of path in some region R; otherwise, Equation 107-1 does not define a function. Furthermore, we will suppose that f and g are continuous in R.

Now let us calculate the first partial derivative $F_1(x, y)$ at an arbitrary point (x, y) of R. When we compute a partial derivative with respect to x, we keep y "fixed"; in geometric language, we confine ourselves to lines parallel to the X-axis. Therefore, let us pick a point (c, y), as shown in Fig. 107-1, such that the horizontal segment joining (c, y) to (x, y) is contained in our basic region R, and write

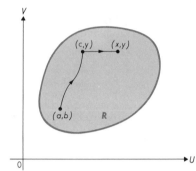

$$F(x, y) = \int_{(a,b)}^{(c,y)} f(u) \cdot du + \int_{(c,y)}^{(x,y)} f(u) \cdot du.$$

Since the first of these integrals is independent of x, we have $D_x \int_{(a,b)}^{(c,y)} f(u) \cdot du = 0$, and so

Figure 107-1

(107-2)

$$F_1(x, y) = D_x \int_{(c,y)}^{(x,y)} f(u, v) \, du + g(u, v) \, dv.$$

We may use any path we please when we evaluate the integral in this equation, and we naturally choose the horizontal segment joining (c, y) to (x, y). Then we have

$$\int_{(c,y)}^{(x,y)} f(u, v) \, du + g(u, v) \, dv = \int_{c}^{x} f(u, y) \, du,$$

and Equation 107-2 becomes $F_1(x, y) = D_x \int_{c}^{x} f(u, y) \, du$. But now we can use our ordinary rule for differentiating integrals (Theorem 43-2), and we see that $D_x \int_{c}^{x} f(u, y) \, du = f(x, y)$. Therefore, we have found that $F_1(x, y) = f(x, y)$. In exactly the same way, we can show that $F_2(x, y) = g(x, y)$, and thus we have the differentiation rules

(107-3) $$D_x \int_{(a,b)}^{(x,y)} f(u, v) \, du + g(u, v) \, dv = f(x, y)$$

and

(107-4) $$D_y \int_{(a,b)}^{(x,y)} f(u, v) \, du + g(u, v) \, dv = g(x, y).$$

To illustrate these rules, let us return to Example 106-2. There we found that if $F(x, y) = \int_{(0,0)}^{(x,y)} 2uv^3 \, du + 3u^2v^2 \, dv$, then $F(x, y) = x^2y^3$. From this last expression, it is clear that $F_1(x, y) = 2xy^3$ and $F_2(x, y) = 3x^2y^2$, which are exactly the formulas we obtain when we replace u and v with x and y in the expressions $f(u, v) = 2uv^3$ and $g(u, v) = 3u^2v^2$ that constitute the integrand of the integral that defines F.

Equation 105-7 tells us that line integrals of a gradient are independent of path. Conversely, we will now show that if line integrals of a continuous function f are independent of path in some region R, then f is the gradient of a scalar-valued function. In fact, we can take as this scalar-valued function the function F defined by Equation 107-1. For we have

$$\nabla F(x) = F_1(x, y)\mathbf{i} + F_2(x, y)\mathbf{j} \qquad \text{(Definition of } \nabla F)$$

$$= f(x, y)\mathbf{i} + g(x, y)\mathbf{j} \qquad \text{(Equations 107-3 and 107-4)}$$

$$= f(x).$$

In physics we call a force **conservative** if the work that is required to move from one point to another in the force field does not depend on the path that is traversed. Our remarks in the preceding paragraph tell us that a conservative force function is the gradient of a scalar-valued function. This scalar-valued function is called a **potential function.**

In Section 106 we saw that if f and g are functions on R^2, and if the equation

$$(107\text{-}5) \qquad\qquad f_2(x, y) = g_1(x, y)$$

holds for each point (x, y) of a simply connected region R, then line integrals of $f(x) = f(x, y)\mathbf{i} + g(x, y)\mathbf{j}$ are independent of path. We have just seen that this condition implies that f is the gradient of a scalar-valued function. Conversely, if f is the gradient of a scalar-valued function F with continuous mixed second derivatives, then Equation 107-5 holds. For we are assuming that $f(x, y) = \nabla F(x, y)$; that is, $f(x, y) = F_1(x, y)$ and $g(x, y) = F_2(x, y)$. Therefore, $f_2(x, y) = F_{12}(x, y)$ and $g_1(x, y) = F_{21}(x, y)$, and Equation 107-5 follows from the identity $F_{12}(x, y) = F_{21}(x, y)$.

Example 107-1. Suppose that $f(x, y) = (xy \cos xy + \sin xy)\mathbf{i} + x^2 \cos xy\ \mathbf{j}$. Find a scalar-valued function F such that $f = \nabla F$.

Solution. You can easily check to see that Equation 107-5 is satisfied at each point of R^2, so our theory tells us that f will be the gradient of F, where

$$F(x, y) = \int_{(0,0)}^{(x,y)} (uv \cos uv + \sin uv)\, du + u^2 \cos uv\, dv.$$

As in Example 106-2, we find it convenient to integrate along the path shown in Fig. 106-5. Thus,

$$F(x, y) = \int_0^x 0 \, du + \int_0^y x^2 \cos xv \, dv = x \sin xv \Big|_0^y = x \sin xy.$$

From this explicit expression for $F(x, y)$, you can readily verify that $\nabla F = f$.

Let f and g be two functions that satisfy Equation 107-5, and let F be the function defined by Equation 107-1. If c is a number in the range of F, then the set of points that satisfy the equation $F(x, y) = c$ constitutes a level curve of F (see Section 96). Suppose that r is a differentiable function whose graph in some interval is a subset of this level curve; that is, suppose that $F(x, r(x)) = c$ for each point x in some interval I. Now let us differentiate with respect to x: $D_x F(x, r(x)) = D_x c = 0$. If we replace u with x, and v with $r(x)$, in the Chain Rule Equation 93-10, and then make use of Equations 107-3 and 107-4, we find that

$$D_x F(x, r(x)) = F_1(x, r(x)) D_x x + F_2(x, r(x)) D_x r(x)$$

$$= f(x, r(x)) + g(x, r(x)) r'(x).$$

Therefore, $f(x, r(x)) + g(x, r(x)) r'(x) = 0$. In other words, we have shown that in the interval I, $y = r(x)$ satisfies the differential equation

$$(107\text{-}6) \qquad\qquad f(x, y) + g(x, y) y' = 0.$$

A differential equation of the form of Equation 107-6, in which f and g satisfy Equation 107-5, is called an **exact differential equation.** We have just seen that level curves of functions defined by line integrals can furnish us with solutions of exact differential equations; here is an example.

Example 107-2. Solve the differential equation $6x + y^3 + 3xy^2 y' = 0$.

Solution. Here $f(x, y) = 6x + y^3$ and $g(x, y) = 3xy^2$. Therefore, $f_2(x, y) = 3y^2 = g_1(x, y)$. We can set

$$F(x, y) = \int_{(0,0)}^{(x,y)} (6u + v^3) \, du + 3uv^2 \, dv,$$

and use the path of integration shown in Fig. 106-5 to find that $F(x, y) = xy^3 + 3x^2$. Level curves of this function are graphs of equations of the form $xy^3 + 3x^2 = c$, so we see that if $y = \left(\dfrac{c - 3x^2}{x} \right)^{1/3}$, where c may be any number, then y satisfies our given differential equation. In practice, we are usually faced with a differential *problem*; that is, in addition to our given differential equation, we have an initial condition, such as the statement that $y = 2$ when $x = 1$. Then we choose the level curve that contains the point with these coordinates. Here our initial point is $(1, 2)$, so the equation of the level curve is $xy^3 + 3x^2 = 11$. Thus the solution of the differential problem $6x + y^3 + 3xy^2y' = 0$, and $y = 2$ when $x = 1$, is given by the equation $y = \left(\dfrac{11 - 3x^2}{x}\right)^{1/3}$.

P R O B L E M S   1 0 7

1. (a) Find F such that $\nabla F(x, y) = (9x^2y^2 + y^{-1})\mathbf{i} + (6x^3y - xy^{-2})\mathbf{j}$. Is there more than one such F?

(b) Find F such that $F_1(x, y) = \cos(x + y^2)$ and $F_2(x, y) = 2y \cos(x + y^2)$. Is there more than one such F?

(c) Can you find F such that $F_1(x, y) = 1$ and $F_2(x, y) = 2y$? Is there more than one such F?

2. Let R^* be the coordinate plane with the origin removed. Let $f(x, y) = \dfrac{y}{x^2 + y^2}$ and $g(x, y) = \dfrac{-x}{x^2 + y^2}$, and let $f(x) = f(x, y)\mathbf{i} + g(x, y)\mathbf{j}$.

(a) Show that $f_2(x, y) = g_1(x, y)$ at each point of R^*.

(b) Compute the line integrals of f from the point $(1, 0)$ to the point $(-1, 0)$ along the upper half and along the lower half of the unit circle. Are line integrals of f independent of path in R^*? In view of Part (a), does your answer violate our statement that contains Equation 107-5?

3. Discuss the equation $\displaystyle\int_{(a,b)}^{(x,y)} f(u)\, du + g(v)\, dv = \int_a^x f(t)\, dt + \int_b^y g(t)\, dt.$

4. Solve the following differential problems.

(a) $e^x y + 1 + e^x y' = 0$, and $y = 0$ when $x = 1$

(b) $2x + e^y + xe^y y' = 0$, and $y = 0$ when $x = 1$

(c) $\mathrm{Tan}^{-1} y - 3x^2 + \dfrac{x}{1 + y^2} y' = 0$, and $y = 1$ when $x = \tfrac{1}{2}\sqrt{\pi}$

(d) $\ln y - \cos x + \dfrac{x}{y} y' = 0$, and $y = 1$ when $x = \pi$

5. If we divide each term of the differential equation in Question 4(a) by e^x, we obtain the equivalent equation $y + e^{-x} + y' = 0$. Is this differential equation exact?

6. The differential equation $y - xy' = 0$ is not exact, but if we multiply it by the "integrating factor" $(x^2 + y^2)^{-1}$, we obtain an equivalent equation that is exact (see Question 2). Show that $(xy)^{-1}$ is also an integrating factor, and use both integrating factors to solve the differential problem that consists of the given differential equation and the initial condition that $y = 2$ when $x = 1$.

7. In Section 93 we met the Cauchy-Riemann partial differential equations $f_1(x, y) = g_2(x, y)$ and $f_2(x, y) = -g_1(x, y)$. If $f(x, y)$ and $g(x, y)$ satisfy these equations, show that

$$F(x, y) = \int_{(a,b)}^{(x,y)} f(u, v) \, du - g(u, v) \, dv \quad \text{and} \quad G(x, y) = \int_{(c,d)}^{(x,y)} g(u, v) \, du + f(u, v) \, dv$$

also satisfy them.

8. Suppose that $w = f(x, y)$ satisfies Laplace's partial differential equation $w_{xx} +$ $w_{yy} = 0$. Let $g(x, y) = \int_{(a,b)}^{(x,y)} -f_2(u, v) \, du + f_1(u, v) \, dv$, and show that $f(x, y)$ and $g(x, y)$ satisfy the Cauchy-Riemann equations.

REVIEW PROBLEMS—CHAPTER TWELVE

You can use the following problems to test yourself on the material of this chapter.

1. Evaluate the integrals $\iint_R (5 \llbracket x \rrbracket + 2 \llbracket y \rrbracket) \, dA$ and $\iint_R (5 \, |x| + 2 \, |y|) \, dA$ for the following regions.
   (a) $R = \{(x, y) \mid -1 \le x \le 2, 0 \le y \le 1\}$
   (b) $R = \{(x, y) \mid |x| + |2y| \le 2\}$
   (c) $R = \{(x, y) \mid (|x| + x)^2 + (|y| + y)^2 \le 4\}$
   $\quad \cap \{(x, y) \mid (|x| - x)^2 + (|y| - y)^2 \le 4\}$
   (d) $R = \{(x, y) \mid -1 \le x \le 1, |y| \le |\sin \pi x| \}$

2. Evaluate the following integrals if $R = \{(r, \theta) \mid 0 \le r \le 3\}$ (a disk of radius 3).
   (a) $\iint_R \llbracket r \rrbracket \, dA$ (b) $\iint_R \llbracket \theta \rrbracket \, dA$ (c) $\iint_R \llbracket x \rrbracket \, dA$

3. Sketch the region R if:
   (a) $R = \{(x, y) \mid -1 \le x \le 1, x + |x| \le y \le x - |x| + 2\}$
   (b) $R = \{(r, \theta) \mid \frac{1}{2}\pi \le \theta \le \frac{3}{2}\pi, \llbracket \cos \theta \rrbracket \le r \le 2 + \llbracket \sin \theta \rrbracket\}$
   (c) $R = \{(x, y, z) \mid 0 \le x \le 3, 0 \le y \le \llbracket x + 1 \rrbracket, 0 \le z \le \llbracket x + 1 \rrbracket\}$
   (d) $R = \{(\rho, \theta, \phi) \mid 0 \le \phi \le \pi, 0 \le \theta \le \frac{1}{2}\pi, 0 \le \rho \le 2 + \llbracket \cos \phi \rrbracket\}$

4. Show that the volume V of the region under the plane $z = ax + by + c$ and above a plane region R is given by the equation $V = aM_Y + bM_X + cA$, where M_X and M_Y are the moments of R about the X- and Y-axes, and A is the area of R.

5. Express the iterated integral $\int_0^\pi \int_0^{\sin x} f(x, y) \, dy \, dx$ as an iterated integral in which we must first integrate with respect to x.

6. Find in two ways the moment about the Y-axis of the region that is bounded by the graph of the equation $y = \sin x$ and the interval $[0, 2\pi]$.

7. If we rotate one arch of the sine curve $y = \sin x$ about the X-axis, we obtain a surface that bounds a spindle-shaped region. What is the moment of inertia of this region about the axis of rotation?

8. Use a geometric argument to show that, for any positive number R,

(i) $$\int_0^{R/\sqrt{2}} \int_0^{R/\sqrt{2}} e^{-x^2-y^2}\, dx\, dy < \int_0^{\pi/2} \int_0^{R} e^{-r^2} r\, dr\, d\theta < \int_0^{R} \int_0^{R} e^{-x^2-y^2} dx\, dy.$$

Now explain why, for any number a, $\displaystyle\int_0^a \int_0^a e^{-x^2-y^2}\, dx\, dy = \left(\int_0^a e^{-u^2}\, du\right)^2.$

Use this result to write (i) as
$$\int_0^{R/\sqrt{2}} e^{-u^2}\, du < \frac{\sqrt{\pi}}{2} \sqrt{1 - e^{-R^2}} < \int_0^{R} e^{-u^2}\, du.$$

Finally, show that

(ii) $$\frac{\sqrt{\pi}}{2} \sqrt{1 - e^{-R^2}} < \int_0^{R} e^{-u^2}\, du < \frac{\sqrt{\pi}}{2}.$$

9. Use the area formula $A = \frac{1}{2} \oint_P x\, dy - y\, dx$ that we introduced in Problem 106-1 to compute the area of the region $R = \{(r,\theta) \mid \alpha \le \theta \le \beta,\, 0 \le r \le f(\theta)\}$, and hence obtain Equation 65-1.

10. Evaluate the integral $\displaystyle\iiint_R \sqrt{x^2 + y^2}\, dV$, where R is the cube
$$\{(x, y, z) \mid 0 \le x \le a,\, 0 \le y \le a,\, 0 \le z \le a\}.$$

11. Explain why the solution to the differential problem
$$f(x, y) + g(x, y)y' = 0, \text{ and } y = b \text{ when } x = a,$$
where the given differential equation is exact, is obtained by solving the equation
$$\int_{(a,b)}^{(x,y)} f(u, v)\, du + g(u, v)\, dv = 0 \text{ for } y.$$

l'HOSPITAL'S RULE.

IMPROPER INTEGRALS.

TAYLOR'S FORMULA

T H I R T E E N

In one way or another, everything in calculus is based on the notion of a limit. The definitions of the derivative and the integral, for example, are stated in terms of limits. In this chapter we will learn a very useful rule for calculating limits, and we shall also use limits to extend the idea of the integral. The techniques we learn here will be used in the next chapter, too.

108 l'HOSPITAL'S RULE

When we introduced the Theorem of the Mean and the Extended Theorem of the Mean in Section 19, we were able to interpret the former geometrically, but we said that a geometric description of the latter theorem would have to wait until we had studied vectors. Since we will want to use the Extended Theorem of the Mean in this section, this is a good time to produce our promised geometric interpretation.

652

The Extended Theorem of the Mean states that if F and G are differentiable in an open interval (a, b), continuous in $[a, b]$, and if G' does not take the value 0 in (a, b), then there is a point $m \in (a, b)$ such that

(108-1)
$$\frac{F(b) - F(a)}{G(b) - G(a)} = \frac{F'(m)}{G'(m)}.$$

To interpret this equation geometrically, let us consider the vector equation $R = F(t)i + G(t)j$ for t in the interval $[a, b]$. The graph of this vector equation is an arc that joins the terminal points of the vectors $F(a)i + G(a)j$ and $F(b)i + G(b)j$.

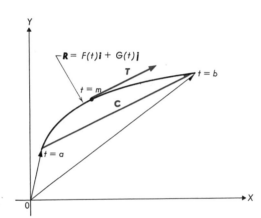

Figure 108-1

If we denote by C the "chord-vector" from the first of these points to the second (Fig. 108-1), then
$$C = [F(b) - F(a)]i + [G(b) - G(a)]j.$$

We recall that the derivative R' is a vector tangent to our arc. Thus, in particular, the vector
$$T = F'(m)i + G'(m)j$$

is tangent to the arc at the point $(F(m), G(m))$. It is easy to see, by using Equation 108-1, that $T = \dfrac{G'(m)}{G(b) - G(a)} C$; that is, T and C are parallel. Thus the geometric interpretation of the Extended Theorem of the Mean is the same as the interpretation of the "ordinary" Theorem of the Mean: *There is a point of the arc at which the tangent is parallel to the chord that joins the endpoints.*

We will need the Extended Theorem of the Mean as we proceed with our next topic, a study of limits of quotients. If f and g are functions with limits at a point a, then Theorem 11-6 tells us that

$$(108\text{-}2) \qquad \lim_{x \to a} \frac{f(x)}{g(x)} = \frac{\lim_{x \to a} f(x)}{\lim_{x \to a} g(x)},$$

provided, of course, that $\lim_{x \to a} g(x) \neq 0$. If $\lim_{x \to a} g(x) = 0$, the right-hand side of Equation 108-2 is meaningless, although the left-hand side may be a perfectly definite number. The prime example of the breakdown of Equation 108-2 is furnished by the limit of the difference quotient used to define a derivative. Thus if f is differentiable at a, then $\lim_{x \to a} \dfrac{f(x) - f(a)}{x - a} = f'(a)$, but we cannot find $f'(a)$ by dividing $\lim_{x \to a} [f(x) - f(a)]$ by $\lim_{x \to a} (x - a)$, since both of these limits are 0. Another simple example is furnished by the quotient

$$\frac{\sin^2 x}{1 - \cos x}.$$

As x approaches 0, both $\sin^2 x$ and $1 - \cos x$ approach 0, and hence we cannot use Equation 108-2 to find the limit of this quotient as x approaches 0. However, if we write the given quotient as

$$\frac{\sin^2 x}{1 - \cos x} = \frac{1 - \cos^2 x}{1 - \cos x} = \frac{(1 - \cos x)(1 + \cos x)}{1 - \cos x} = 1 + \cos x,$$

we see that

$$\lim_{x \to 0} \frac{\sin^2 x}{1 - \cos x} = \lim_{x \to 0} (1 + \cos x) = 1 + 1 = 2.$$

Equation 108-2 fails when $\lim_{x \to a} g(x) = 0$, and then the only possibility that $\lim_{x \to a} \dfrac{f(x)}{g(x)}$ exists is that $\lim_{x \to a} f(x) = 0$, also. The following theorem tells us that we should then look at the limit of the quotient $\dfrac{f'(x)}{g'(x)}$ in order to find the limit of the given quotient $\dfrac{f(x)}{g(x)}$.

Theorem 108-1. l'Hospital's Rule. *Let f and g be differentiable in a punctured neighborhood of the point a, and suppose that $\lim_{x \to a} f(x) = 0$ and $\lim_{x \to a} g(x) = 0$.*

Suppose further that $g'(x) \neq 0$ in this neighborhood. Then

$$(108\text{-}3) \qquad \lim_{x \to a} \frac{f(x)}{g(x)} = \lim_{x \to a} \frac{f'(x)}{g'(x)}$$

if the limit on the right-hand side of this equation exists. The symbols $x \to a$ may be replaced by $x \uparrow a$ or $x \downarrow a$ in the appropriate circumstances.

Proof. Our hypotheses say nothing about the values of the functions f and g at the point a itself, so we will introduce two new functions F and G by means of the equations $F(x) = f(x)$ and $G(x) = g(x)$ if $x \neq a$, and $F(a) = G(a) = 0$. This definition insures that F and G are continuous at a, as well as at the other points of our given neighborhood of a. Because F and G are also differentiable at these other points, we see that if b is a point of our given punctured neighborhood, then F and G satisfy the hypotheses of the Extended Theorem of the Mean on the interval that has a and b as endpoints. The theorem tells us that there is a number m between a and b such that Equation 108-1 holds, and since $F(a) = G(a) = 0$, this equation reduces to

$$\frac{F(b)}{G(b)} = \frac{F'(m)}{G'(m)}.$$

Because $F(x) = f(x)$, $G(x) = g(x)$, $F'(x) = f'(x)$, and $G'(x) = g'(x)$ if $x \neq a$, our equation can also be written

$$\frac{f(b)}{g(b)} = \frac{f'(m)}{g'(m)}.$$

The number m is "trapped" between a and b, so it follows that

$$\lim_{b \to a} \frac{f(b)}{g(b)} = \lim_{m \to a} \frac{f'(m)}{g'(m)},$$

if the limit on the right-hand side of this equation exists. This equation is equivalent to Equation 108-3, and our theorem is proved.

Example 108-1. Use l'Hospital's Rule to find $\displaystyle\lim_{x \to 0} \frac{\sin^2 x}{1 - \cos x}$.

Solution. We notice that $\displaystyle\lim_{x \to 0} \sin^2 x = \lim_{x \to 0} (1 - \cos x) = 0$, so l'Hospital's Rule applies and

$$\lim_{x \to 0} \frac{\sin^2 x}{1 - \cos x} = \lim_{x \to 0} \frac{D_x \sin^2 x}{D_x(1 - \cos x)} = \lim_{x \to 0} \frac{2 \sin x \cos x}{\sin x}$$

$$= \lim_{x \to 0} 2 \cos x = 2,$$

as we found earlier.

Example 108-2. Find $\lim\limits_{x \to \frac{1}{2}\pi} \dfrac{(2x - \pi)(\sin x - 1)}{\cos^2 x}$.

Solution. When we apply l'Hospital's Rule we get

$$\lim_{x \to \frac{1}{2}\pi} \frac{(2x - \pi)(\sin x - 1)}{\cos^2 x} = \lim_{x \to \frac{1}{2}\pi} \frac{(2x - \pi)\cos x + 2(\sin x - 1)}{-2 \cos x \sin x}.$$

Again, both the numerator and denominator have the limit 0 at $\pi/2$, so we apply l'Hospital's Rule once more, and we have

$$\lim_{x \to \frac{1}{2}\pi} \frac{(2x - \pi)\cos x + 2(\sin x - 1)}{-2 \cos x \sin x} = \lim_{x \to \frac{1}{2}\pi} \frac{4 \cos x - (2x - \pi)\sin x}{2(\sin^2 x - \cos^2 x)} = \frac{0}{2} = 0.$$

Since l'Hospital's Rule applies only to quotients, we often have to "rearrange" a given expression into the form of a quotient before we can find its limit, as in the next example.

Example 108-3. Find $\lim\limits_{x \to 0} \left(\csc x - \dfrac{1}{x} \right)$.

Solution. If x is a number that is near 0, both $\csc x$ and $1/x$ have large absolute values. But, as we shall see, their difference is small. To find the required limit, we write

$$\csc x - \frac{1}{x} = \frac{1}{\sin x} - \frac{1}{x} = \frac{x - \sin x}{x \sin x}$$

and apply l'Hospital's Rule twice. Thus we have

$$\lim_{x \to 0} \left(\csc x - \frac{1}{x} \right) = \lim_{x \to 0} \frac{x - \sin x}{x \sin x}$$

$$= \lim_{x \to 0} \frac{1 - \cos x}{\sin x + x \cos x}$$

$$= \lim_{x \to 0} \frac{\sin x}{2 \cos x - x \sin x}$$

$$= \tfrac{0}{2} = 0.$$

We are sometimes called on to evaluate limits of exponential expressions of the form $\lim\limits_{x \to a} f(x)^{g(x)}$, where the "natural" formula $(\lim\limits_{x \to a} f(x))^{\lim\limits_{x \to a} g(x)}$ does not apply. For example, both $f(x)$ and $g(x)$ may approach 0, or $f(x)$ may approach 1 while $g(x)$ gets large. In such cases we set $y = f(x)^{g(x)}$. Therefore, $\ln y = g(x) \ln f(x)$. Then we write $g(x) \ln f(x)$ as a quotient and apply l'Hospital's Rule to find

$$\lim_{x \to a} \ln y = L.$$

Since $y = e^{\ln y}$, and because the exponential function is continuous, we have

$$\lim_{x \to a} y = e^{(\lim_{x \to a} \ln y)} = e^L.$$

Thus the limit of our original exponential expression is e^L.

Example 108-4. Find $\lim\limits_{x \to \frac{1}{2}\pi} (1 + \cos x)^{\sec x}$.

Solution. If x is near $\pi/2$, it is not obvious what number is approximated by the exponential $(1 + \cos x)^{\sec x}$. For example, if $x = 1.57$, then $1 + \cos x = 1.0008$ and $\sec x = 1256$. Are we to conclude that $(1.0008)^{1256}$ is near 1 because 1.0008 is near 1, or is it large because 1256 is large? Perhaps there is some middle ground. To find the required limit, we set

$$y = (1 + \cos x)^{\sec x},$$

and so

$$\ln y = \sec x \ln (1 + \cos x).$$

In order to use l'Hospital's Rule, we must now write this product as a quotient:

$$\ln y = \frac{\ln (1 + \cos x)}{\cos x}.$$

Therefore,

$$\lim_{x \to \frac{1}{2}\pi} \ln y = \lim_{x \to \frac{1}{2}\pi} \frac{\ln (1 + \cos x)}{\cos x}$$

$$= \lim_{x \to \frac{1}{2}\pi} \frac{-\sin x/(1 + \cos x)}{-\sin x}$$

$$= \lim_{x \to \frac{1}{2}\pi} \frac{1}{(1 + \cos x)} = 1.$$

Thus we see that $\lim\limits_{x \to \frac{1}{2}\pi} y = e^1 = e$, and so we have shown that

$$\lim_{x \to \frac{1}{2}\pi} (1 + \cos x)^{\sec x} = e.$$

P R O B L E M S   1 0 8

1. For the following choices of F, G, a, and b, find m in Equation 108-1, and make a sketch that illustrates your result.
(a) $F(t) = 2 \cos t$, $G(t) = \sin t$, $a = 0$, $b = \dfrac{\pi}{2}$

(b) $F(t) = e^{4t}$, $G(t) = e^{2t}$, $a = 0$, $b = \ln 2$

(c) $F(x) = \sin x + 3$, $G(x) = \cos x + 7$, $a = 0$, $b = \dfrac{\pi}{2}$

(d) $F(y) = \sin y + 3$, $G(y) = \cos 2y$, $a = 0$, $b = \dfrac{\pi}{2}$

2. Find the following limits.

(a) $\displaystyle\lim_{x \to 0} \frac{e^{3x} - \cos x}{x}$

(b) $\displaystyle\lim_{x \to 0} \frac{x + \tan x}{\sin 3x}$

(c) $\displaystyle\lim_{x \to \pi} \frac{\ln x - \ln \pi}{\sin 2x}$

(d) $\displaystyle\lim_{x \to 3} \frac{x^3 + x^2 - 7x - 15}{x^3 - 5x^2 + 8x - 6}$

(e) $\displaystyle\lim_{x \to 0} \frac{\tan x - x}{x - \sin x}$

(f) $\displaystyle\lim_{x \to \frac{1}{2}\pi} \frac{\ln (\sin x)}{(\pi - 2x)^2}$

3. Find the following limits.

(a) $\displaystyle\lim_{x \to 0} \left[\frac{1}{x} - \frac{1}{e^x - 1} \right]$

(b) $\displaystyle\lim_{x \to \frac{1}{2}\pi} \left(x - \frac{\pi}{2} \right) \tan x$

(c) $\displaystyle\lim_{\theta \to \frac{1}{2}\pi} (\sec \theta - \tan \theta)$

(d) $\displaystyle\lim_{x \to 0} (x^{-2} - \csc^2 x)$

4. Find the following limits.

(a) $\displaystyle\lim_{x \to 0} \frac{\displaystyle\int_0^x \exp(-t^2)\, dt}{\displaystyle\int_0^x (\cos t^3 + \cos^3 t)\, dt}$

(b) $\displaystyle\lim_{x \to 0} \frac{1}{x^3} \int_0^x \sin t^2\, dt$

5. Find the following limits.

(a) $\displaystyle\lim_{x \to 0} (1 + x^{12})^{1/x}$

(b) $\displaystyle\lim_{x \to 0} (\sec x + \tan x)^{\csc x}$

(c) $\displaystyle\lim_{x \to 0} (1 + \sin x)^{1/x}$

(d) $\displaystyle\lim_{x \to \frac{1}{2}\pi} (\sin x)^{\tan x}$

6. Show that $\lim_{x \downarrow 0}(1 + x^r)^{1/x} = 1$ if $r > 1$. What is the limit if $r = 1$? If $0 \le r < 1$?

7. Find the following limits.

(a) $\displaystyle\lim_{x \to 0} \frac{\sqrt[3]{1 + x} - \sqrt[3]{1 - x}}{\sqrt[5]{1 + x} - \sqrt[5]{1 - x}}$

(b) $\displaystyle\lim_{x \to 0} \frac{\sinh x - \sin x}{\sin^3 x}$

(c) $\displaystyle\lim_{x \to \frac{1}{2}\pi} \frac{1 - \sin x}{1 + \cos 2x}$

(d) $\displaystyle\lim_{x \to 0} \frac{\sec x - 1}{x \sin x}$

8. Let $h(\theta)$ be the vertical distance from the polar axis to a point of the spiral whose polar coordinate equation is $r\sqrt{\theta} = 5$. Find $\lim_{\theta \downarrow 0} h(\theta)$.

9. At a point A of a circle with a radius of a (see Fig. 108-2) we draw a tangent line and a diameter. Next we pick a point P, different from A, of the circle. Then we choose a point Q of the tangent line so that the distance $\overline{AQ}$ equals the length of the arc AP. The line that contains P and Q intersects the diameter at a point R. Find the limiting position of R as P approaches A.

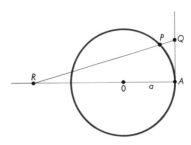

Figure 108-2

10. The current flowing t seconds after a switch is thrown in a series circuit containing a resistor of R ohms resistance and a coil of L henries inductance connected to a battery of E volts is given by the equation $I = (E/R)(1 - e^{-Rt/L})$. Find the limit of I as R approaches zero.

11. Find $\displaystyle\lim_{x \to a} \frac{\displaystyle\int_a^x \sin f(t)\, dt}{\sin \displaystyle\int_a^x f(t)\, dt}$ if f is continuous in some open interval that contains a.

109 EXTENDED LIMITS

When we introduced the symbols ∞ and $-\infty$ in Chapter 1 we were careful to point out that *they do not stand for numbers.* Nevertheless, we find them convenient symbols to use as part of our notation for intervals that do not have one or the other endpoint. Now let us carry that notation one step farther. A finite interval (a, b) is, as we defined the terms in Section 10, a right neighborhood of a and a left neighborhood of b. By extension, let us say that an interval $(-\infty, c)$ is a right neighborhood of $-\infty$, and an interval (c, ∞) is a left neighborhood of ∞. This new terminology still does not make $-\infty$ and ∞ stand for numbers, but we can use it to make useful extensions of the limit concept.

If a and A are numbers and f is a function, the equation $\lim_{x \uparrow a} f(x) = A$ means that to each neighborhood $N_p A$ there corresponds a left neighborhood $L_r a$ such that $f(L_r a) \subseteq N_p A$. It is natural, therefore, to make the following definitions.

Definition 109-1. *The equation $\lim_{x \uparrow \infty} f(x) = A$ means that for each neighborhood $N_p A$ there exists a left neighborhood (c, ∞) of ∞ such that $f((c, \infty)) \subseteq N_p A$, and the equation $\lim_{x \uparrow a} f(x) = \infty$ means that for each neighborhood (c, ∞) of ∞ there exists a left neighborhood $L_r a$ such that $f(L_r a) \subseteq (c, \infty)$.* You can easily make the modifications that are necessary to define $\lim_{x \uparrow \infty} f(x) = \infty$ and to replace $\uparrow$ with $\downarrow$ and ∞ with $-\infty$.

In rough terms, the equation $\lim\limits_{x\uparrow\infty} f(x) = A$ says that $f(x)$ approximates A when x is large. And the equation $\lim\limits_{x\uparrow a} f(x) = \infty$ says that $f(x)$ is large when x is slightly less than a. It is also easy to see that $\lim\limits_{x\uparrow\infty} f(x) = \lim\limits_{x\downarrow 0} f\left(\dfrac{1}{h}\right)$, a fact which is frequently useful when proving limit theorems.

Example 109-1.   Find the following limits: (a) $\lim\limits_{x\uparrow\infty} \dfrac{x^2 + 2x - 1}{3x^2 - 5}$ and (b) $\lim\limits_{x\downarrow 0} e^{1/x}$.

Solution.   (a) If we divide the numerator and the denominator of our given fraction by x^2, we obtain the fraction

$$\frac{1 + \dfrac{2}{x} - \dfrac{1}{x^2}}{3 - \dfrac{5}{x^2}}.$$

You can see that when x is very large, this quotient approximates $\tfrac{1}{3}$ and so we conclude that

$$\lim_{x\uparrow\infty} \frac{x^2 + 2x - 1}{3x^2 - 5} = \frac{1}{3}.$$

(b) When x is close to 0, but positive, $\dfrac{1}{x}$ is very large. So, then, is $e^{1/x}$, and hence we conclude that $\lim\limits_{x\downarrow 0} e^{1/x} = \infty$.

Example 109-2.   Show that $\lim\limits_{x\uparrow\infty} \ln x = \infty$.

Solution.   Suppose we are given a neighborhood (c, ∞) of ∞; we are to find a left neighborhood (d, ∞) of ∞ such that $\ln (d, \infty) \subseteq (c, \infty)$. We can take as this neighborhood (d, ∞) the neighborhood (e^c, ∞). For if $x \in (e^c, \infty)$, then $e^c < x$. Therefore, since ln is an increasing function, $\ln e^c < \ln x$; that is, $c < \ln x$. Thus $\ln x \in (c, \infty)$ for each $x \in (e^c, \infty)$, and we have verified the desired inclusion $\ln (e^c, \infty) \subseteq (c, \infty)$.

This last example illustrates an important property of increasing functions that we wish to discuss further. Actually, we deal with *non-decreasing* functions; a function f is **non-decreasing** in a subset of its domain if $f(u) \leq f(v)$ whenever u and v are points of the subset and $u < v$.

Theorem 109-1.   *Suppose that f is a non-decreasing function in an interval (a, b), where b may be either a number or the symbol ∞. According to the Completeness Property of the real numbers (Property 2-1), the set $f((a, b))$ is contained in a smallest closed interval $[A, B]$. We assert that $\lim\limits_{x\uparrow b} f(x) = B$.*

Proof. We must show that to each neighborhood of B there corresponds a left neighborhood (r, b) of b such that $f((r, b))$ is a subset of the given neighborhood of B. Since any given neighborhood of B contains an interval of the form $(C, B]$, it will be sufficient for us to show that to a given interval $(C, B]$ there corresponds an interval (r, b) such that $f((r, b)) \subseteq (C, B]$. We first observe that there must be a point $r \in (a, b)$ such that $f(r) \in (C, B]$. Otherwise, it would be true that for each $x \in (a, b), f(x) \leq C$. Therefore, we would have $f((a, b)) \subseteq [A, C]$, which contradicts the fact that $[A, B]$ is the *smallest* closed interval that contains $f((a, b))$. Since f is a non-decreasing function, it follows that for each $x \geq r, f(x) \geq f(r)$, and so $f(x) \in (C, B]$. Therefore, we have found an interval (r, b) such that $f(r, b) \subseteq (C, B]$, and the equation $\lim_{x \uparrow b} f(x) = B$ is verified.

We say that a function f is **bounded above** in the interval (a, b) if there is a number M such that $f(x) \leq M$ for each $x \in (a, b)$. If f is bounded above in the interval (a, b), then the letter B in the preceding theorem stands for a number (and not the symbol ∞), and the following theorem follows immediately.

Theorem 109-2. *Let f be a non-decreasing function in an interval (a, b). Then there is a number B such that $\lim_{x \uparrow b} f(x) = B$ if, and only if, f is bounded above in (a, b).*

In the problems at the end of this section, we will give you a hint and ask you to show that l'Hospital's Rule (Theorem 108-1) remains valid when the symbols $x \to a$ are replaced by $x \uparrow \infty$. Our next example illustrates the use of l'Hospital's Rule in that case.

Example 109-3. Find $\lim_{x \uparrow \infty} x\left(\dfrac{\pi}{2} - \text{Arctan } x\right)$.

Solution. We apply l'Hospital's Rule, after first writing our given expression as a quotient:

$$\lim_{x \uparrow \infty} x\left(\frac{\pi}{2} - \text{Arctan } x\right) = \lim_{x \uparrow \infty} \frac{\dfrac{\pi}{2} - \text{Arctan } x}{\dfrac{1}{x}}$$

$$= \lim_{x \uparrow \infty} \frac{D_x\left(\dfrac{\pi}{2} - \text{Arctan } x\right)}{D_x \dfrac{1}{x}} = \lim_{x \uparrow \infty} \frac{-\dfrac{1}{1 + x^2}}{-\dfrac{1}{x^2}}$$

$$= \lim_{x \uparrow \infty} \frac{x^2}{1 + x^2} = 1.$$

l'Hospital's Rule also remains valid when the hypotheses $\lim\limits_{x \to a} f(x) = 0$ and $\lim\limits_{x \to a} g(x) = 0$ are replaced with the assumptions that $\lim\limits_{x \to a} f(x) = \infty$ (or $-\infty$) and $\lim\limits_{x \to a} g(x) = \infty$ (or $-\infty$). This theorem is considerably harder to prove than our original statement of l'Hospital's Rule. We will leave its proof to a course in advanced calculus, and simply state it and show you how it works.

Theorem 109-3.   Second Case of l'Hospital's Rule. *Let f and g be differentiable functions in a punctured neighborhood of some given point a, and suppose that* $\lim\limits_{x \to a} f(x) = \infty$ *(or* $-\infty$*) and* $\lim\limits_{x \to a} g(x) = \infty$ *(or* $-\infty$*). Suppose further that* $g'(x) \neq 0$ *in this neighborhood. Then*

$$\lim_{x \to a} \frac{f(x)}{g(x)} = \lim_{x \to a} \frac{f'(x)}{g'(x)},$$

if the limit on the right-hand side of this equation exists. The symbols $x \to a$ *can be replaced with* $x \uparrow a$, $x \downarrow a$, $x \uparrow \infty$, *or* $x \downarrow -\infty$.

Example 109-4.   Find $\lim\limits_{x \uparrow \infty} x^m e^{-x}$, where m is a positive integer.

Solution.   We write $x^m e^{-x}$ as $\dfrac{x^m}{e^x}$. Since $\lim\limits_{x \uparrow \infty} x^m = \infty$ and $\lim\limits_{x \uparrow \infty} e^x = \infty$, Theorem 109-3 applies, and we have

$$\lim_{x \uparrow \infty} \frac{x^m}{e^x} = \lim_{x \uparrow \infty} \frac{D_x x^m}{D_x e^x} = \lim_{x \uparrow \infty} \frac{m x^{m-1}}{e^x}.$$

If $m = 1$, this limit is clearly 0, but if $m > 1$, $\lim\limits_{x \uparrow \infty} m x^{m-1} = \infty$, and we must apply l'Hospital's Rule again:

$$\lim_{x \uparrow \infty} \frac{m x^{m-1}}{e^x} = \lim_{x \uparrow \infty} \frac{D_x m x^{m-1}}{D_x e^x} = \lim_{x \uparrow \infty} \frac{m(m-1) x^{m-2}}{e^x}.$$

If $m = 2$, this limit (and hence our original limit) is 0, but if $m > 2$,

$$\lim_{x \uparrow \infty} m(m-1) x^{m-2} = \infty,$$

and we must apply l'Hospital's Rule once more. It should now be clear that to solve our problem we must apply l'Hospital's Rule m times in all, and then we have

$$\lim_{x \uparrow \infty} \frac{x^m}{e^x} = \lim_{x \uparrow \infty} \frac{m!}{e^x} = 0.$$

Some limit problems require a little thought, in addition to l'Hospital's Rule.

Example 109-5. Let f be the function that is defined by the equation $f(x) = e^{-1/x^2}$ if $x \neq 0$ and $f(0) = 0$. Find $f'(0)$.

Solution. By definition,

$$f'(0) = \lim_{h \to 0} \frac{f(h) - f(0)}{h} = \lim_{h \to 0} \frac{e^{-1/h^2} - 0}{h}$$

$$= \lim_{h \to 0} \frac{e^{-1/h^2}}{h} .$$

Both the numerator and the denominator of this fraction approach 0 as h approaches 0, so we apply l'Hospital's Rule:

$$\lim_{h \to 0} \frac{e^{-1/h^2}}{h} = \lim_{h \to 0} \frac{(2/h^3)e^{-1/h^2}}{1} = \lim_{h \to 0} \frac{2e^{-1/h^2}}{h^3} .$$

Since this last limit is at least as hard to evaluate as the original, we must change our tactics. We set $x = 1/h$. Then

$$\lim_{h \to 0} \frac{e^{-1/h^2}}{h} = \lim_{|x| \uparrow \infty} xe^{-x^2} = \lim_{|x| \uparrow \infty} \frac{x}{e^{x^2}} .$$

Now we fare better when we apply l'Hospital's Rule:

$$\lim_{|x| \uparrow \infty} \frac{x}{e^{x^2}} = \lim_{|x| \uparrow \infty} \frac{1}{2xe^{x^2}} = 0.$$

Thus we have shown that $f'(0) = 0$.

PROBLEMS 109

1. Find the following limits "by inspection."

(a) $\lim_{x \downarrow 0} \exp \dfrac{1}{x}$

(b) $\lim_{x \uparrow 0} \exp \dfrac{1}{x}$

(c) $\lim_{x \uparrow \infty} \dfrac{3x^3 - 2x^2 + 1}{7x^3 + x - 3}$

(d) $\lim_{x \downarrow -\infty} \text{Arctan } x$

(e) $\lim_{x \uparrow \infty} \tanh x$

(f) $\lim_{x \downarrow -\infty} \tanh x$

2. Show that $\lim_{x \downarrow 0} \ln x = -\infty$. What is $\ln \dfrac{1}{10{,}000{,}000}$?

3. Find the following limits.

(a) $\lim_{x \uparrow \infty} \dfrac{\ln x}{x}$

(b) $\lim_{x \uparrow \infty} \dfrac{\ln x}{\sqrt{x}}$

(c) $\lim_{x \uparrow \infty} \dfrac{x^{234}}{e^x}$

(d) $\lim_{x \uparrow \infty} \dfrac{\sin e^{-x}}{\sin (1/x)}$

(e) $\lim_{x \uparrow \infty} \dfrac{x - \sin x}{2x}$

(f) $\lim_{t \uparrow \infty} \dfrac{\ln(kt + 1)}{\ln t}$

4. Find the following limits.

(a) $\lim\limits_{x \uparrow \infty} \dfrac{\displaystyle\int_0^x \exp t^2\, dt}{\exp x^2}$

(b) $\lim\limits_{x \uparrow \infty} \dfrac{\displaystyle\int_3^x e^t(4t^2 + 3t - 1)\, dt}{\displaystyle\int_5^x e^t(2t^2 + 5t + 6)\, dt}$

(c) $\lim\limits_{x \uparrow \infty} \dfrac{\displaystyle\int_0^{[x]} t\, dt}{x^2}$

(d) $\lim\limits_{x \uparrow \infty} \dfrac{\displaystyle\int_0^x [t]\, dt}{x^2}$

5. Find the following limits.

(a) $\lim\limits_{x \uparrow 0} xe^{1/x}$ (b) $\lim\limits_{x \downarrow 0} xe^{1/x}$ (c) $\lim\limits_{x \uparrow \infty} xe^{1/x}$ (d) $\lim\limits_{x \downarrow \infty} xe^{1/x}$

6. Find the following limits.

(a) $\lim\limits_{x \downarrow 0} x^x$ (b) $\lim\limits_{x \uparrow \infty} x^{1/x}$ (c) $\lim\limits_{x \uparrow \infty} \left(\cos \dfrac{2}{x}\right)^x$ (d) $\lim\limits_{x \uparrow \infty} x^{\cos(2/x)}$

7. Show that $\lim\limits_{x \uparrow \infty} (1 + r^x)^{1/x} = 1$ if $0 \le r \le 1$. What is the limit if $r > 1$?

8. What can you conclude about $\lim\limits_{x \uparrow b} f(x)$ if you are told that f is non-increasing in an interval (a, b)?

9. Find $\lim\limits_{x \uparrow \infty} x^m e^{-x}$ if m is not necessarily a positive integer.

10. Prove l'Hospital's Rule with the symbols $x \to a$ replaced by $x \uparrow \infty$. Hint: set $h = \dfrac{1}{x}$.

11. Show that for each real number a, $\lim\limits_{x \uparrow \infty} [xa] \dfrac{a}{x} = a^2$.

110 IMPROPER INTEGRALS

An integral $\displaystyle\int_a^b f(x)\, dx$ is a *number*, the limit of approximating sums that we form according to the rules laid down in Chapter 5. If these sums do not have a limit, then f is not integrable on $[a, b]$, and we say that $\displaystyle\int_a^b f(x)\, dx$ "does not exist." Now let us look at an example of a different use of the integral sign.

If R is any positive number, then

$$\int_1^R \frac{1}{x^2}\, dx = -\frac{1}{x}\Big|_1^R = 1 - \frac{1}{R}.$$

Thus, since $\lim\limits_{R \uparrow \infty} \left(1 - \dfrac{1}{R}\right) = 1$, we have the equation $\lim\limits_{R \uparrow \infty} \displaystyle\int_1^R \dfrac{1}{x^2}\, dx = 1$. We write this equation in the abbreviated form $\displaystyle\int_1^\infty \dfrac{1}{x^2}\, dx = 1$. Here the number

$\int_1^\infty \dfrac{1}{x^2}\, dx$ is not obtained as the limit of approximating sums as is the case with "proper" integrals (it can't be, because the interval of integration is not a finite interval). Nevertheless, such an "improper integral," if correctly interpreted, can be useful in mathematical applications. For example, suppose that the force between two unit charges x centimeters apart is F dynes, where the relation between force and distance is the inverse square law $F = \dfrac{1}{x^2}$. Then if the charges were initially 1 centimeter apart, our improper integral $\int_1^\infty \dfrac{1}{x^2}\, dx$ represents the amount of work (in ergs) that is necessary to move one of the charges "infinitely" far away from the other.

In general, suppose that a function f is integrable on the interval $[a, R]$ for every number $R > a$. If $\lim\limits_{R\uparrow\infty} \int_a^R f(x)\, dx$ exists, we denote it by the symbol $\int_a^\infty f(x)\, dx$. Thus the **improper integral** $\int_a^\infty f(x)\, dx$ is a number, the limit of proper integrals of the form $\int_a^R f(x)\, dx$. If these proper integrals have a limit, we say that the improper integral $\int_a^\infty f(x)\, dx$ is **convergent**. It is **divergent** if $\lim\limits_{R\uparrow\infty} \int_a^R f(x)\, dx$ does not exist; that is, if there is no number that is the limit of $\int_a^R f(x)\, dx$. (In particular, the equation $\lim\limits_{R\uparrow\infty} \int_a^R f(x)\, dx = \infty$ tells us that the integral $\int_a^\infty f(x)\, dx$ is divergent, since ∞ is not a number.)

Example 110-1.   Test the integrals $\int_0^\infty e^{-x}\, dx$ and $\int_{\pi/2}^\infty \cos x\, dx$ for convergence.

Solution.   We have

$$\int_0^R e^{-x}\, dx = 1 - e^{-R},$$

and so

$$\lim_{R\uparrow\infty} \int_0^R e^{-x}\, dx = \lim_{R\uparrow\infty} (1 - e^{-R}) = 1.$$

Therefore, $\int_0^\infty e^{-x}\, dx = 1$. On the other hand, $\int_{\pi/2}^R \cos x\, dx = \sin R - 1$. Since $\lim\limits_{R\uparrow\infty} (\sin R - 1)$ does not exist, the improper integral $\int_{\pi/2}^\infty \cos x\, dx$ is divergent.

Example 110-2.   For what choices of the number p is the integral $\int_1^\infty \dfrac{dx}{x^p}$ convergent?

Solution.   If $p \neq 1$,

$$\int_1^R \frac{dx}{x^p} = \int_1^R x^{-p}\, dx = \frac{x^{1-p}}{1-p}\bigg|_1^R = \frac{R^{1-p}-1}{1-p}.$$

Therefore, we must investigate

$$\lim_{R \uparrow \infty} \frac{R^{1-p} - 1}{1 - p}.$$

If $p > 1$, then the exponent of R is negative, so $\lim_{R \uparrow \infty} R^{1-p} = 0$, and hence

$$\lim_{R \uparrow \infty} \frac{R^{1-p} - 1}{1 - p} = \frac{-1}{1 - p} = \frac{1}{p - 1}.$$

If $p < 1$, the exponent of R is positive, and $\lim_{R \uparrow \infty} \dfrac{R^{1-p} - 1}{1 - p}$ does not exist. If $p = 1$, we have $\displaystyle\int_1^R \frac{dx}{x} = \ln x \Big|_1^R = \ln R$, and hence $\lim_{R \uparrow \infty} \displaystyle\int_1^R \frac{dx}{x}$ does not exist. Summarizing:

$$\int_1^\infty \frac{dx}{x^p} \begin{cases} = \dfrac{1}{p - 1} & \text{if } p > 1, \\[2mm] \text{diverges} & \text{if } p \leq 1. \end{cases}$$

If f is integrable on each interval $[R, a]$, and if $\lim_{R \downarrow -\infty} \displaystyle\int_R^a f(x)\, dx$ exists, we denote this limit by $\displaystyle\int_{-\infty}^a f(x)\, dx$. It is easy to see that $\displaystyle\int_{-\infty}^a f(x)\, dx = \int_{-a}^\infty f(-x)\, dx$. Also, let us observe that an improper integral $\displaystyle\int_a^\infty f(x)\, dx$ converges if, and only if, the integral $\displaystyle\int_b^\infty f(x)\, dx$ converges for each number $b \geq a$, and then

$$(110\text{-}1) \qquad \int_a^\infty f(x)\, dx = \int_a^b f(x)\, dx + \int_b^\infty f(x)\, dx.$$

The integral $\displaystyle\int_a^\infty f(x)\, dx$ is improper because it does not have a finite interval of integration. We will now give an example of another type of improper integral. If t is any number between 0 and 1, then

$$\int_0^t \frac{dx}{\sqrt{1 - x^2}} = \operatorname{Arcsin} x \Big|_0^t = \operatorname{Arcsin} t.$$

Therefore,

$$\lim_{t \uparrow 1} \int_0^t \frac{dx}{\sqrt{1 - x^2}} = \lim_{t \uparrow 1} \operatorname{Arcsin} t = \frac{\pi}{2}.$$

Because of this limit relation we will write $\displaystyle\int_0^1 \frac{dx}{\sqrt{1 - x^2}} = \frac{\pi}{2}$, but we must note that the "integral" $\displaystyle\int_0^1 \frac{dx}{\sqrt{1 - x^2}}$ is not a proper integral as we defined the term in

Chapter Five. The integrand $\dfrac{1}{\sqrt{1-x^2}}$ is unbounded in our interval of integration, and unbounded functions are not integrable. The integral $\displaystyle\int_0^1 \dfrac{dx}{\sqrt{1-x^2}}$ represents a new type of improper integral. In general, suppose that we have a function f that is integrable on every interval $[a, t]$, where $a < t < b$, but that f is unbounded in the interval $[a, b)$. If $\displaystyle\lim_{t \uparrow b} \int_a^t f(x)\,dx$ exists, we denote it by $\displaystyle\int_a^b f(x)\,dx$, but we again realize that we are dealing with an improper integral. Similarly, if f is integrable on every interval $[t, b]$, where $a < t < b$, but is unbounded in the interval $(a, b]$, then $\displaystyle\int_a^b f(x)\,dx$ stands for the number $\displaystyle\lim_{t \downarrow a} \int_t^b f(x)\,dx$, if this limit exists. If it doesn't, the improper integral $\displaystyle\int_a^b f(x)\,dx$ is divergent.

Example 110-3. Test the integral $\displaystyle\int_0^1 \dfrac{dx}{x}$ for convergence.

Solution. The integrand $\dfrac{1}{x}$ is unbounded in the interval $(0, 1]$, so we must investigate the limit

$$\lim_{t \downarrow 0} \int_t^1 \frac{dx}{x} = \lim_{t \downarrow 0} (-\ln t).$$

Since the limit on the right-hand side of this equation does not exist, we see that the integral $\displaystyle\int_0^1 \dfrac{dx}{x}$ is divergent.

Example 110-4. For what choices of the number p is the integral $\displaystyle\int_0^1 \dfrac{dx}{x^p}$ convergent?

Solution. We have just seen that this integral is divergent for $p = 1$. Further, it is a proper integral for $p \le 0$, and its value is $\dfrac{1}{1 - p}$. Therefore, we need only examine the case in which p is a positive number different from 1. In that case, the integrand is unbounded near 0, so we look at the integral

$$\int_t^1 \frac{dx}{x^p} = \frac{x^{1-p}}{1-p} \Big|_t^1 = \frac{1 - t^{1-p}}{1-p}.$$

If $0 < p < 1$, then the exponent of t is positive, and so t^{1-p} approaches 0. Thus

$$\lim_{t \downarrow 0} \frac{1 - t^{1-p}}{1-p} = \frac{1}{1-p}.$$

But if $p > 1$, the exponent of t is negative, and so $\lim\limits_{t \downarrow 0} \dfrac{1 - t^{1-p}}{1 - p}$ does not exist. Hence we see that

$$\int_0^1 \frac{dx}{x^p} \begin{cases} = \dfrac{1}{1 - p} & \text{if } p < 1 \\[2mm] \text{diverges if } p \geq 1. \end{cases}$$

If a function f is unbounded in a neighborhood of an interior point c of an interval $[a, b]$, we regard the improper integral $\int_a^b f(x)\, dx$ as the sum of two improper integrals, $\int_a^c f(x)\, dx + \int_c^b f(x)\, dx$. If both these integrals converge, we say that our original integral converges; otherwise it diverges. Thus

$$\int_0^\pi \sec^2 x\, dx = \int_0^{\frac{1}{2}\pi} \sec^2 x\, dx + \int_{\frac{1}{2}\pi}^\pi \sec^2 x\, dx.$$

Both of the improper integrals on the right-hand side of this equation diverge; for example,

$$\lim_{t \uparrow \frac{1}{2}\pi} \int_0^t \sec^2 x\, dx = \lim_{t \uparrow \frac{1}{2}\pi} \tan t = \infty.$$

Because both of the integrals into which the original integral was decomposed must converge for the original integral to converge, we see that $\int_0^\pi \sec^2 x\, dx$ is divergent. Notice that if we had ignored the fact that $\sec^2 x$ is not integrable on the interval $[0, \pi]$ and had simply tried to apply the Fundamental Theorem of Calculus, we would have obtained the incorrect result: $\int_0^\pi \sec^2 x\, dx$ is the number $\tan x \big|_0^\pi$.

PROBLEMS 110

1. Evaluate the following improper integrals, or show that they diverge.

(a) $\displaystyle\int_4^\infty x^{-3/2}\, dx$

(b) $\displaystyle\int_5^\infty x \sin x^2\, dx$

(c) $\displaystyle\int_5^\infty x e^{-x^2}\, dx$

(d) $\displaystyle\int_0^\infty (1 + x^2)^{-1}\, dx$

(e) $\displaystyle\int_0^\infty x(1 + x^2)^{-1}\, dx$

(f) $\displaystyle\int_0^\infty x^2(1 + x^2)^{-1}\, dx$

2. Test the following improper integrals for convergence.

(a) $\displaystyle\int_0^1 \frac{\cos \sqrt{x}}{\sqrt{x}}\, dx$

(b) $\displaystyle\int_0^{\pi/2} \sec x\, dx$

(c) $\displaystyle\int_0^{\pi/2} \cot x\, dx$

(d) $\displaystyle\int_0^1 \ln x\, dx$

3. Evaluate the following improper integrals, or show that they diverge.

(a) $\displaystyle\int_0^1 x^{-1/3}\, dx$

(b) $\displaystyle\int_0^1 x^{-2}\, dx$

(c) $\displaystyle\int_0^3 (9 - x^2)^{-1/2}\, dx$

(d) $\displaystyle\int_1^3 (x - 1)^{-3/2}\, dx$

(e) $\displaystyle\int_0^{\pi/2} \tan x\, dx$

(f) $\displaystyle\int_0^4 x(16 - x^2)^{-3/2}\, dx$

4. Evaluate the following improper integrals or show that they diverge. Notice that they are improper at both limits of integration.

(a) $\displaystyle\int_1^\infty (x \ln x)^{-1}\, dx$

(b) $\displaystyle\int_{-1}^1 (1 - x^2)^{-1/2}\, dx$

(c) $\displaystyle\int_{-\infty}^\infty (x^2 + 2x + 2)^{-1}\, dx$

(d) $\displaystyle\int_0^\infty x^{-1/2} e^{-x^{1/2}}\, dx$

5. (a) Explain why the integral $\displaystyle\int_{-1}^1 x^{-2}\, dx$ is improper. Does it converge?

(b) Is the integral $\displaystyle\int_0^{\pi/2} \frac{\sin \sqrt{t}}{\sqrt{t}}\, dt$ improper?

6. If f is a function such that $\displaystyle\lim_{R \uparrow \infty} f(R)e^{-R} = 0$, use integration by parts to derive the formula

$$\int_0^\infty f(x)e^{-x}\, dx = f(0) + \int_0^\infty f'(x)e^{-x}\, dx,$$

provided that the improper integrals converge. Use this formula to show that:

(a) $\displaystyle\int_0^\infty e^{-x} \sin x\, dx = \int_0^\infty e^{-x} \cos x\, dx$

(b) $\displaystyle\int_0^\infty e^{-x} \cos x\, dx = 1 - \int_0^\infty e^{-x} \sin x\, dx$

(c) Use parts (a) and (b) to compute $\displaystyle\int_0^\infty e^{-x} \sin x\, dx$.

(d) Compute $\displaystyle\int_0^\infty x^n e^{-x}\, dx$ (n a positive integer).

7. Use integration by parts to find $\displaystyle\int_1^\infty x^{-2} \ln x\, dx$.

8. Show that $\displaystyle\int_{-\infty}^\infty x(1 + x^2)^{-2}\, dx = 0$, but that $\displaystyle\int_{-\infty}^\infty x(1 + x^2)^{-1}\, dx$ diverges.

9. The gravitational force of attraction between the earth and a body is inversely proportional to the square of the distance between the body and the center of the earth. Assume that the radius of the earth is 4000 miles, and that the nose cone of a rocket weighs 1 ton on the surface of the earth. Find the work required to propel the nose cone out of the earth's gravitational field.

10. The force of repulsion between two positive charges q_1 and q_2 is given by the equation $F = kq_1q_2/d^2$, where d is the distance between the charges and k is a physical constant. The electric potential at a point is frequently defined as the work required to bring a unit charge from "infinity" to the point. Find a formula for the potential V at a point r units away from a charge of q units.

11. (a) Show that $\displaystyle\int_{-\infty}^{a} f(x)\,dx = \int_{-a}^{\infty} f(-x)\,dx.$

(b) Verify Equation 110-1.

12. Suppose that f is integrable (in the ordinary sense) on a finite interval $[a, b]$. Show that $\displaystyle\lim_{t\uparrow b}\int_{a}^{t} f(x)\,dx = \int_{a}^{b} f(x)\,dx.$

III   TESTING THE CONVERGENCE OF IMPROPER INTEGRALS

When we are faced with an improper integral we ask two questions:
(i) Does it converge?
(ii) If so, what is its value?
In this section we will briefly take up some of the techniques that are used to answer the first of these questions. Of course, if we find that the answer to the first question is "no," then there is no need to go on to the second. If the answer to the first question is "yes," we may be able to approximate the value of our integral (as in Example 111-2), or we may turn to some of the elegant methods of evaluating improper integrals that are developed in courses in advanced calculus and complex variable theory. For brevity, we restrict our attention in this section to improper integrals of the form $\displaystyle\int_{a}^{\infty} f(x)\,dx$; it is easy to modify our results to apply to other types of improper integrals.

To verify the convergence of an improper integral $\displaystyle\int_{a}^{\infty} f(x)\,dx$ we must show that $\displaystyle\lim_{R\uparrow\infty} F(R)$ exists, where $F(R) = \displaystyle\int_{a}^{R} f(x)\,dx$. Let us suppose now that $f(x) \geq 0$ for each $x \geq a$. Then it is easy to see that F is non-decreasing in the interval (a, ∞), and so, according to Theorem 109-2, $\displaystyle\lim_{R\uparrow\infty} F(R)$ exists if, and only if, the function F is bounded above. We use this convergence criterion to develop the most widely used test for the convergence of improper integrals. Let g be a function such that $0 \leq g(x) \leq f(x)$ for each $x \geq a$, and write $G(R) = \displaystyle\int_{a}^{R} g(x)\,dx$.

Then $G(R) \leq F(R)$ for each $R \geq a$. If the integral $\int_a^{\infty} f(x)\, dx$ converges, our convergence criterion tells us that the function F is bounded above. Hence, since $G(R) \leq F(R)$, the function G is also bounded above. Therefore, we may apply our convergence criterion again, and we see that the integral $\int_a^{\infty} g(x)\, dx$ converges. This result is the **comparison test** for the convergence of improper integrals.

Theorem 111-1. *Suppose that f and g are integrable functions on the interval $[a, R]$ for each $R > a$ and that $0 \leq g(x) \leq f(x)$ for $x \geq a$. If the improper integral $\int_a^{\infty} f(x)\, dx$ converges, then the improper integral $\int_a^{\infty} g(x)\, dx$ converges. This conclusion also implies that if the integral $\int_a^{\infty} g(x)\, dx$ diverges, then the integral $\int_a^{\infty} f(x)\, dx$ diverges.*

Example 111-1. Test for convergence: $\int_1^{\infty} \dfrac{dx}{\sqrt{x^6 + 8x^4 + 5}}$.

Solution. Since, for $x \geq 1$,

$$0 \leq \frac{1}{\sqrt{x^6 + 8x^4 + 5}} \leq \frac{1}{x^3},$$

and since the improper integral $\int_1^{\infty} \dfrac{dx}{x^3}$ converges (Example 110-2), Theorem 111-1 tells us that the given integral converges.

Example 111-2. Show that the improper integral $\int_0^{\infty} e^{-x^2}\, dx$ converges. Approximate its value.

Solution. As we pointed out in the last section, our given integral converges if, and only if, the integral $\int_1^{\infty} e^{-x^2}\, dx$ converges. We will compare this integral with the convergent (Example 110-1) integral $\int_1^{\infty} e^{-x}\, dx$. Since, for $x \geq 1$, $0 \leq e^{-x^2} \leq e^{-x}$, Theorem 111-1 tells us that convergence of the integral $\int_1^{\infty} e^{-x}\, dx$ implies convergence of $\int_1^{\infty} e^{-x^2}\, dx$.

To approximate the value of the given integral, we notice that e^{-x^2} is extremely small when x is even moderately large. Thus the integral $\int_0^{\infty} e^{-x^2}\, dx$ converges very rapidly; that is, $\int_0^{R} e^{-x^2}\, dx$ approximates its limit $\int_0^{\infty} e^{-x^2}\, dx$ reasonably well even when R is fairly small. For example, according to Equation 110-1,

$$\int_0^\infty e^{-x^2}\, dx = \int_0^3 e^{-x^2}\, dx + \int_3^\infty e^{-x^2}\, dx.$$

If $x \geq 3$, then $e^{-x^2} \leq e^{-3x}$, so

$$\int_3^\infty e^{-x^2}\, dx \leq \int_3^\infty e^{-3x}\, dx \approx .00004.$$

Therefore, you can be sure that the first four decimal places of $\int_0^3 e^{-x^2}\, dx$ and $\int_0^\infty e^{-x^2}\, dx$ differ by no more than one digit in the fourth decimal place. If you use Simpson's Rule with $n = 6$, use six-place tables, and round off your result to four places, you will find that the number .8862 is an approximation of $\int_0^3 e^{-x^2}\, dx$. Actually, it can be shown (see Number 8 of the Review Problems at the end of Chapter 12) that $\int_0^\infty e^{-x^2}\, dx = \dfrac{\sqrt{\pi}}{2}$, and this number is .8862 with four-place accuracy.

Example 111-3. Show that for each integer $n \geq 0$,

(111-1) $$\int_0^\infty x^{n+1}e^{-x}\, dx = (n + 1)\int_0^\infty x^n e^{-x}\, dx.$$

Solution. Our first task is to show that the improper integrals that appear in Equation 111-1 converge, so let us show that for each integer $m \geq 0$ the integral $\int_0^\infty x^m e^{-x}\, dx$ converges. For this purpose, we consider the limit $\lim\limits_{x \uparrow \infty} x^{m+2}e^{-x}$. In Example 109-4 we showed that this limit is 0. The equation $\lim\limits_{x \uparrow \infty} x^{m+2}e^{-x} = 0$ tells us that if we choose the neighborhood $(-1, 1)$ of 0, then there is an interval (c, ∞) such that if $x \in (c, \infty)$, we have $x^{m+2}e^{-x} \in (-1, 1)$. Clearly, we can take $c > 0$, and so $x^{m+2}e^{-x} \in (0, 1)$; that is, $0 < x^{m+2}e^{-x} < 1$. Therefore, for $x > c$, we have $0 < x^m e^{-x} < x^{-2}$, and we can compare the integrals $\int_c^\infty x^m e^{-x}\, dx$ and $\int_c^\infty x^{-2}\, dx$. In the last section, we saw that the latter integral converges, so Theorem 111-1 tells us that the former does, and convergence of the integral $\int_c^\infty x^m e^{-x}\, dx$ implies convergence of the integral $\int_0^\infty x^m e^{-x}\, dx$.

Now we turn to verification of Equation 111-1. Integration by parts yields

$$(111\text{-}2) \qquad \int_0^R x^{n+1}e^{-x}\,dx = -x^{n+1}e^{-x}\Big|_0^R + (n+1)\int_0^R x^n e^{-x}\,dx$$

$$= -R^{n+1}e^{-R} + (n+1)\int_0^R x^n e^{-x}\,dx.$$

We get Equation 111-1 when we take limits in Equation 111-2, referring to Example 109-4 to see that $\lim\limits_{R\uparrow\infty} (-R^{n+1}e^{-R}) = 0$.

Our comparison test applies only to integrals whose integrands do not change sign, and so we cannot apply it directly to an integral $\int_a^\infty f(x)\,dx$ if f takes both positive and negative values. In that case we may be able to apply our test to the integral $\int_a^\infty |f(x)|\,dx$ and use the following theorem.

Theorem 111-2. *If f is integrable on the interval $[a, R]$ for each $R > a$, and if the integral $\int_a^\infty |f(x)|\,dx$ converges, then the integral $\int_a^\infty f(x)\,dx$ converges.*

Proof. For each number x, we have the inequalities

$$0 \le \tfrac{1}{2}[|f(x)| + f(x)] \le |f(x)| \quad \text{and} \quad 0 \le \tfrac{1}{2}[|f(x)| - f(x)] \le |f(x)|.$$

Therefore, since the integral $\int_a^\infty |f(x)|\,dx$ converges, our comparison test tells us that the integrals $\int_a^\infty \tfrac{1}{2}[|f(x)| + f(x)]\,dx$ and $\int_a^\infty \tfrac{1}{2}[|f(x)| - f(x)]\,dx$ converge. For each number R we can write

$$\int_a^R f(x)\,dx = \int_a^R \tfrac{1}{2}[|f(x)| + f(x)]\,dx - \int_a^R \tfrac{1}{2}[|f(x)| - f(x)]\,dx.$$

We have just shown that the limits of the two integrals on the right-hand side of this equation exist, so $\lim\limits_{R\uparrow\infty}\int_a^R f(x)\,dx$ exists; that is, the integral $\int_a^\infty f(x)\,dx$ converges.

Example 111-4. Test the integral $\int_1^\infty \dfrac{\sin x}{x^2}\,dx$ for convergence.

Solution. Since $0 \leq \dfrac{|\sin x|}{x^2} \leq \dfrac{1}{x^2}$, and since $\displaystyle\int_1^\infty \dfrac{dx}{x^2}$ converges, the comparison test tells us that $\displaystyle\int_1^\infty \dfrac{|\sin x|}{x^2}\, dx$ converges. Now we use Theorem 111-2 to see that the integral $\displaystyle\int_1^\infty \dfrac{\sin x}{x^2}\, dx$ converges.

If the integral $\displaystyle\int_a^\infty |f(x)|\, dx$ converges, we say that the improper integral $\displaystyle\int_a^\infty f(x)\, dx$ **converges absolutely.** It is possible that the integral $\displaystyle\int_a^\infty f(x)\, dx$ converges, but that $\displaystyle\int_a^\infty |f(x)|\, dx$ does not. In this case the integral $\displaystyle\int_a^\infty f(x)\, dx$ is said to **converge conditionally.** For example, in Problem 111-4 we will help you show that $\displaystyle\int_0^\infty \dfrac{\sin x}{x}\, dx$ converges, but in Example 117-5 we will show that $\displaystyle\int_0^\infty \dfrac{|\sin x|}{x}\, dx$ diverges. Thus the integral $\displaystyle\int_0^\infty \dfrac{\sin x}{x}\, dx$ converges conditionally. Many of the ideas and techniques of dealing with improper integrals will become clearer after you have studied sequences and infinite series in the next chapter.

P R O B L E M S   I I I

1. Test the following integrals for convergence.

(a) $\displaystyle\int_2^\infty \dfrac{x^2}{x^7 + 3}\, dx$

(b) $\displaystyle\int_4^\infty \dfrac{x}{x^2 - 3}\, dx$

(c) $\displaystyle\int_4^\infty \dfrac{\sqrt[5]{x^3 - 2x}}{\sqrt[3]{2x^5 + 4x + 1}}\, dx$

(d) $\displaystyle\int_1^\infty \dfrac{\coth x}{\sqrt{x}}\, dx$

(e) $\displaystyle\int_0^\infty e^{-\sin x} \sin e^{-x}\, dx$

(f) $\displaystyle\int_2^\infty \dfrac{\ln x}{x^2}\, dx$

(g) $\displaystyle\int_4^\infty \dfrac{dx}{[\![x]\!]!}$

(h) $\displaystyle\int_1^\infty \int_1^x e^{-xy^2}\, dy\, dx.$

2. Use a comparison test that is analogous to Theorem 111-1 to test the following integrals for convergence.

(a) $\displaystyle\int_0^1 x^{-1} e^x\, dx$

(b) $\displaystyle\int_0^1 x^{-1/2} \cos x\, dx$

(c) $\displaystyle\int_5^7 \dfrac{dx}{(x^2 + 3)\sqrt[3]{7 - x}\, \sqrt[5]{x - 5}}$

(d) $\displaystyle\int_{-1}^1 x^{-4/3} \sin x\, dx$

(e) $\displaystyle\int_{-2}^2 x^{-2} \sinh x\, dx$

(f) $\displaystyle\int_0^1 x^{-1/2} \ln x\, dx$

3. Suppose that $f(x)$ and $g(x)$ are both positive for $x \geq a$ and that $\displaystyle\lim_{x \uparrow \infty} \dfrac{f(x)}{g(x)} = L$, where $L > 0$. Show that it therefore follows that there is an interval (c, ∞) such that if $x \in (c, \infty)$, then $\dfrac{f(x)}{g(x)} \in (\tfrac{1}{2}L, \tfrac{3}{2}L)$. From the inequalities $\tfrac{1}{2}Lg(x) \leq f(x) \leq \tfrac{3}{2}Lg(x)$, when $x \geq c$, deduce that $\displaystyle\int_a^\infty f(x)\, dx$ converges if, and only if, $\displaystyle\int_a^\infty g(x)\, dx$ converges. Apply this result to test the following integrals for convergence. (Compare with Number 1.)

(a) $\displaystyle\int_2^\infty \frac{x^2}{x^7 - 3}\, dx$ (b) $\displaystyle\int_4^\infty \frac{x}{x^2 + 3}\, dx$ (c) $\displaystyle\int_4^\infty \frac{\sqrt[5]{x^3 + 2x}}{\sqrt[3]{2x^5 - 4x - 1}}\, dx$

(d) $\displaystyle\int_1^\infty \frac{\tanh x}{\sqrt{x}}\, dx$

4. Use integration by parts to show that

$$\int_{\pi/2}^R \frac{\sin x}{x}\, dx = -\frac{\cos R}{R} - \int_{\pi/2}^R \frac{\cos x}{x^2}\, dx.$$

From this equation infer that $\displaystyle\int_0^\infty \frac{\sin x}{x}\, dx$ converges.

5. From the inequalities $x - 1 < [\![x]\!] \leq x$ deduce that $\displaystyle\int_1^\infty \frac{dx}{[\![x]\!]^p}$ converges if, and only if, $p > 1$. Why is it reasonable to express this integral as the "infinite sum"

$$1 + \frac{1}{2^p} + \frac{1}{3^p} + \frac{1}{4^p} + \cdots\, ?$$

6. Each of the following "infinite" regions has a finite "area." Find the area of the region that lies in the first quadrant and is bounded by the X-axis and:
(a) The Y-axis and the curve $y(x^2 + 4a^2) = 8a^3$.
(b) The line $x = 3$ and the curve $y^2(x^2 - 1)^3 = 4x^2$.
(c) The Y-axis and the curve $xy^2(x + 4)^2 = 1$.
(d) The line $x = 3$ and the curve $yx^2 = 1 + 4y$.

7. Let R be the infinite region bounded by the coordinate axes, the line $x = 1$, and the curve $y = 1/\sqrt{1 - x}$. Express the area of R by means of an integral if you use (a) "vertical strips," and (b) "horizontal strips." Conclude from (a) and (b) that

$$\int_0^1 \frac{dx}{\sqrt{1 - x}} = 1 + \int_1^\infty \frac{dy}{y^2}.$$

Check this equality by actually computing both integrals.

8. Suppose we rotate the region R of the preceding problem about the X-axis to obtain an "infinite" solid. Even though R has a finite area, show that the solid of revolution has an "infinite" volume.

9. As a contrast to the preceding problem, consider the infinite region R that lies in the first quadrant and is bounded by the Y-axis, the line $y = 1$, and the curve

$y = 1/x$. Show that R has an "infinite" area, but that the infinite solid obtained by rotating R about the Y-axis has a finite volume. Does the solid have a finite surface area?

112 TAYLOR'S FORMULA

Let f be a function that is continuous in an interval $[a, b]$ and has continuous derivatives of whatever orders are needed for the following discussion. The Theorem of the Mean tells us that there is a number $m \in (a, b)$ such that

$$(112\text{-}1) \qquad f(b) = f(a) + f'(m)(b - a).$$

We can interpret this equation as saying that $f(a)$ approximates $f(b)$ with an error of $f'(m)(b - a)$.

In Section 25 we went one step farther. We considered the number $f(a) + f'(a)(b - a)$ as an approximation of $f(b)$, and we found that the error of this approximation is $\frac{1}{2}f''(m)(b - a)^2$, where m is a point of (a, b) (not necessarily the same number that appears in Equation 112-1, of course). Thus we have

$$(112\text{-}2) \qquad f(b) = f(a) + f'(a)(b - a) + \tfrac{1}{2}f''(m)(b - a)^2.$$

This equation suggests that as our next approximation to $f(b)$ we take the number $f(a) + f'(a)(b - a) + \tfrac{1}{2}f''(a)(b - a)^2$, and so on. The result of continuing this process is the following theorem.

Theorem 112–1. *Let n be an integer that is greater than or equal to 0, and suppose that f is a function for which the derived function $f^{(n)}$ is continuous in the closed interval $[a, b]$. Furthermore, suppose that $f^{(n+1)}(x)$ exists at each point x in the open interval (a, b). Then there is a number $m \in (a, b)$ such that*

$$(112\text{-}3)$$

$$f(b) = f(a) + f'(a)(b - a) + \cdots + f^{(n)}(a)\frac{(b - a)^n}{n!} + f^{(n+1)}(m)\frac{(b - a)^{n+1}}{(n + 1)!}$$

Equation 112-3 is known as **Taylor's Formula.** We observe that Equations 112-1 and 112-2 represent the cases of Taylor's Formula in which $n = 0$ and $n = 1$. If we know the value of f and some of its derivatives at a point a, we can use Taylor's Formula to calculate approximate values of f at points near a. Since the error term in Taylor's Formula contains $\dfrac{(b - a)^{n+1}}{(n + 1)!}$ as a factor, a number that is small when b is near a and n is large, our approximations are often very accurate. Let us look at some examples of how we use Taylor's Formula before we take up the proof of Theorem 112-1.

Example 112-1. Express the polynomial $f(x) = x^3 + 2x^2 - x + 5$ as a polynomial in $x - 2$.

Solution. We will set $n = 3$, $b = x$, and $a = 2$. Then $f(a) = f(2) = 19$, $f'(a) = f'(2) = 19$, $f''(a) = f''(2) = 16$, $f'''(a) = f'''(2) = 6$, and Taylor's Formula reads

$$f(x) = 19 + 19(x - 2) + 16 \frac{(x-2)^2}{2!} + 6 \frac{(x-2)^3}{3!} + f^{(4)}(m) \frac{(x-2)^4}{4!},$$

where m is some number (Theorem 112-1 doesn't tell us which) between 2 and x. Since our function f is defined by a polynomial of degree 3, its fourth derived function $f^{(4)}$ is the constant function with value 0, and so $f^{(4)}(m) = 0$. Therefore, after some simplification and rearrangement, our expression for $f(x)$ in powers of $(x - 2)$ is

$$f(x) = (x - 2)^3 + 8(x - 2)^2 + 19(x - 2) + 19.$$

Example 112-2. Use Taylor's Formula with $f(x) = e^x$, $a = 0$, $b = 1$, and $n = 5$ to approximate e. How close is this approximation?

Solution. Here $f(a) = e^0 = 1$, $f'(a) = e^0 = 1$, and so on. Therefore, Equation 112-3 is

$$e = 1 + 1 \cdot (1 - 0) + 1 \cdot \frac{(1-0)^2}{2!}$$

$$+ 1 \cdot \frac{(1-0)^3}{3!} + 1 \cdot \frac{(1-0)^4}{4!} + 1 \cdot \frac{(1-0)^5}{5!} + e^m \frac{(1-0)^6}{6!}$$

$$= 1 + 1 + \frac{1}{2!} + \frac{1}{3!} + \frac{1}{4!} + \frac{1}{5!} + \frac{e^m}{6!},$$

where m is a number between 0 and 1. Thus the sum

$$2 + \frac{1}{2!} + \frac{1}{3!} + \frac{1}{4!} + \frac{1}{5!} \approx 2.717$$

approximates e with an error of $\dfrac{e^m}{6!}$. Since $0 < m < 1$, we see that $e^m < e$. The number e, in turn, is less than 3, so our error is less than $\dfrac{3}{6!} = \dfrac{1}{240} < .005$.

Example 112-3. Show how Taylor's Formula could be used to compute the entries in a 5-place table of values of the sine function.

Solution. We set $f(x) = \sin x$, $a = 0$, and $n = 10$ in Taylor's Formula. Then $f(a) = \sin 0 = 0$, $f'(a) = \cos 0 = 1$, $f''(a) = -\sin 0 = 0$, $f'''(a) = -\cos 0 = -1, \ldots, f^{(10)}(a) = -\sin 0 = 0$, and $f^{(11)}(m) = -\cos m$. Thus for any number b,

Taylor's Formula becomes

$$\sin b = 0 + 1(b - 0) + 0\frac{(b-0)^2}{2!} + \cdots + 0\frac{(b-0)^{10}}{10!} + (-\cos m)\frac{(b-0)^{11}}{11!},$$

where m is a number between 0 and b. If we drop the last term and simplify, we obtain the approximation formula

(112-4)
$$\sin b \approx b - \frac{b^3}{3!} + \frac{b^5}{5!} - \frac{b^7}{7!} + \frac{b^9}{9!}.$$

The accuracy of this approximation can be judged by examining the size of the term that we dropped. The error that we make by using the right-hand side of Formula 112-4 as an approximation to the left-hand side is $(-\cos m)\dfrac{b^{11}}{11!}$. All we know about m is that it is a number between 0 and b, but whatever it is, $|\cos m| \leq 1$, and so the absolute error that we make by using Formula 112-4 is certainly no greater than $\dfrac{|b|^{11}}{11!}$. A table of trigonometric values need only contain values of the sine function that correspond to b in the interval $\left(0, \dfrac{\pi}{2}\right)$, and therefore our absolute error will be less than $\dfrac{(\pi/2)^{11}}{11!}$. We will leave it to you to show that this number is less than .000004. Hence Formula 112-4 can be used to compute values of the sine function for a five-place table and the error (from rounding off) in any particular value would be, at worst, .00001.

Now let us prove Theorem 112-1.

Proof. As in the derivation of Equation 112-2, the key ingredient of our proof is the Extended Theorem of the Mean; we apply it to two "properly chosen" functions that we will now define. Our choice of these functions seems arbitrary, but actually it is the result of much experimentation. We let

$$F(x) = f(x) + f'(x)(b-x) + f''(x)\frac{(b-x)^2}{2!} + \cdots + f^{(n)}(x)\frac{(b-x)^n}{n!}$$

and

$$G(x) = (b - x)^{n+1}.$$

According to the Extended Theorem of the Mean, there is a point $m \in (a, b)$ such that

(112-5)
$$\frac{F(b) - F(a)}{G(b) - G(a)} = \frac{F'(m)}{G'(m)}.$$

Before we can apply this equation to our particular functions F and G, we must calculate $F'(x)$ and $G'(x)$. Therefore, we first find that

$$F'(x) = D_x f(x) + D_x[f'(x)(b-x)] + D_x\left[f''(x)\frac{(b-x)^2}{2!}\right]$$

$$+ \cdots + D_x\left[f^{(n)}(x)\frac{(b-x)^n}{n!}\right]$$

$$= f'(x) + [-f'(x) + f''(b-x)]$$

$$+ \left[-f''(x)(b-x) + f'''(x)\frac{(b-x)^2}{2!}\right]$$

$$+ \cdots + \left[-f^{(n)}(x)\frac{(b-x)^{n-1}}{(n-1)!} + f^{(n+1)}(x)\frac{(b-x)^n}{n!}\right].$$

If you study the pattern of this sum (perhaps you will want to put in a few more terms where we have dots), you will see that it "collapses," and we have

$$F'(x) = f^{(n+1)}(x)\frac{(b-x)^n}{n!}.$$

Clearly,

$$G'(x) = -(n+1)(b-x)^n.$$

Now we substitute in Equation 112-5, and we obtain the equation

$$\frac{f(b) - \left[f(a) + f'(a)(b-a) + f''(a)\frac{(b-a)^2}{2!} + \cdots + f^{(n)}(a)\frac{(b-a)^n}{n!}\right]}{-(b-a)^{n+1}}$$

$$= \frac{f^{(n+1)}(m)\frac{(b-m)^n}{n!}}{-(n+1)(b-m)^n}.$$

A little algebra reduces this equation to Equation 112-3, and then our proof is complete.

P R O B L E M S   1 1 2

1. Let $a = 0$, $b = 1$, and $n = 2$ in Taylor's Formula. Find m for the following choices of $f(x)$.

(a) $f(x) = e^x$ (b) $f(x) = \sin x$ (c) $f(x) = \ln(1+x)$ (d) $f(x) = \sinh x$

2. Use $a = 0$ and the given value of n and approximate $f(b)$ by dropping the "error term" in Taylor's Formula.

(a) $f(x) = \ln(1 + x)$, $n = 5$ (b) $f(x) = (1 - x)^{-1/2}$, $n = 3$

(c) $f(x) = (1 + e^x)^{-1}$, $n = 3$ (d) $f(x) = \cos x$, $n = 4$

3. Use the approximation formulas that you found in the preceding question to determine three-place decimal approximations of the following numbers. Compare your results with tabular values where possible.

(a) $\ln 2$ (b) $\ln 1.4$ (c) $\dfrac{1}{\sqrt{2}}$ (d) $\sqrt{2}$ (e) $\dfrac{1}{1 + e}$ (f) $\dfrac{e}{1 + e}$ (g) $\cos .1$ (h) $\cos \frac{1}{2}$

4. Express the polynomial $x^4 + 3x^2 + 2$ as a polynomial in $x - 1$. As a polynomial in $x + 1$.

5. Find an upper bound for the error incurred when using the approximation $\tan x \approx x$ for $x \in [0, .1]$.

6. Use Taylor's Formula with $a = 0$, $b = t$, and $n = 4$ to write

$$e^t = 1 + t + \frac{t^2}{2!} + \frac{t^3}{3!} + \frac{t^4}{4!} + \frac{t^5}{5!} e^m.$$

Use the first five terms as an approximation of e^t and then approximate the integral $\int_0^1 e^{x^2} \, dx$. Show that the error E that you incur satisfies the inequalities

$$\frac{1}{11 \cdot 5!} < E < \frac{3}{11 \cdot 5!}.$$

7. Show that Taylor's Formula can be written as

$$f(a + h) = f(a) + f'(a)h + f''(a)\frac{h^2}{2!} + \cdots + f^{(n)}(a)\frac{h^n}{n!} + f^{(n+1)}(m)\frac{h^{n+1}}{(n + 1)!}$$
$$= \sum_{r=0}^{n} f^{(r)}(a)\frac{h^r}{r!} + f^{(n+1)}(m)\frac{h^{n+1}}{(n + 1)!}.$$

8. Let $f(x) = x^3 |x|$, $a = -1$, $b = 1$, and $n = 2$ in Taylor's Formula. What is m? What if we set $n = 3$?

9. Suppose that $f'(a) = f''(a) = \cdots = f^{(n)}(a) = 0$, and that $f^{(n+1)}(x) > 0$ for x in a neighborhood of a. Then if b is any point of this neighborhood, Taylor's Formula tells us that $f(b) - f(a) = f^{(n+1)}(m)\dfrac{(b - a)^{n+1}}{(n + 1)!}$, where m is a number between a and b. Use this equation to show that $f(a)$ is a minimum value of f if n is odd. Use this result to show that if $f(x) = x^3 \sin x$, then f has a minimum value at 0.

10. It is clear that if $f(x)$ is a polynomial of degree n or less, then $f^{(n+1)}$ is the constant function with value 0. Show that the converse of this statement is also true.

11. Let n be a positive integer such that $f^{(n)} = g^{(n)}$. What is the relation between $f(x)$ and $g(x)$?

REVIEW PROBLEMS—CHAPTER THIRTEEN

You can use these problems to test yourself on the material of this chapter.

1. Suppose the functions f and g are continuous in the finite interval $[a, b]$ and that for each $x \in (a, b)$, $g(x) \neq 0$. Show that there is a point $m \in (a, b)$ such that

$$\frac{\int_a^b f(x)\,dx}{\int_a^b g(x)\,dx} = \frac{f(m)}{g(m)}.$$

2. The Extended Theorem of the Mean says that if C is the chord vector that joins two points of the graph of the vector equation $R = F(t)i + G(t)j$, then there is a point of the graph between them at which the tangent vector is parallel to C. Is this theorem also true for curves in three dimensions?

3. Evaluate the following limits

(a) $\displaystyle\lim_{x \to 0} \frac{\ln(1 + x^2)}{[\ln(1 + x)]^2}$

(b) $\displaystyle\lim_{x \to 0} \frac{\sin 3x^2}{\sin^2 x}$

(c) $\displaystyle\lim_{x \to 0} (1 - \cos x)^{\sin x}$

(d) $\displaystyle\lim_{x \downarrow 0} (\sin x)^{1 - \cos x}$

4. Suppose $\lim_{x \uparrow \infty} f(x) = A$ and $\lim_{x \uparrow \infty} g(x) = B$, where $A \neq 0$ and $B \neq 0$. Show that

$$\lim_{x \uparrow \infty} \frac{\int_a^x f(t)\,dt}{\int_a^x g(t)\,dt} = \frac{A}{B},$$

where a is any number such that f and g are continuous in the interval $[a, \infty)$.

5. When t is very large, the tangent vector to the graph of the equation $R = t \ln t^4\, i + (t^2 + 2)j$ is almost parallel to what unit vector?

6. Evaluate the improper integral $\displaystyle\int_0^\infty [\![3e^{-x}]\!]\,dx$.

7. Show that $\displaystyle\int_0^\infty \frac{\sin ax}{x}\,dx = \frac{a}{|a|} \int_0^\infty \frac{\sin x}{x}\,dx$ if $a \neq 0$. (We showed in Problem 111-4 that this last integral converges.)

8. Do the following integrals converge?

(a) $\displaystyle\int_0^\infty e^{\sin x}\,dx$

(b) $\displaystyle\int_0^\infty \sin e^{\sin x}\,dx$

(c) $\displaystyle\int_0^\infty \sin e^x\,dx$

9. Test the following integrals for convergence.

(a) $\int_1^\infty \dfrac{\cos x}{1 + x^2}\,dx$

(b) $\int_1^\infty \dfrac{x}{1 + x^2}\,dx$

(c) $\int_1^\infty \dfrac{[\![x]\!]}{1 + x^2}\,dx$

(d) $\int_1^\infty \dfrac{x}{1 + [\![x]\!]^2}\,dx$

(e) $\int_{-\infty}^\infty \left[\dfrac{[\![x]\!]}{1 + x^2}\right]dx$

(f) $\int_1^\infty \sin\left(\dfrac{x}{1 + x^2}\right)dx$

10. Set $a = 0$, $b = x$ (a number less than 1), and $f(t) = \dfrac{1}{1 - t}$ in Taylor's Formula for an arbitrary positive integer n. Find the resulting number m in terms of x and n.

SEQUENCES

AND INFINITE SERIES

F O U R T E E N

You know that the number 3.14159 is only an approximation of the number π. Nevertheless, for most practical applications this approximation is close enough, and if it isn't, we can replace the number 3.14159 by a still closer approximation. The number π is the limit of the *sequence* of numbers 3, 3.1, 3.14, 3.141, 3.1415, ... Sometimes we express the terms of such a sequence as a sum; for example, we might write 3, 3 + .1, 3 + .1 + .04, and so on. Here the more numbers we add together, the closer the sum approximates the number π. We are going to study such sequences in this chapter. We will find, for example, that another sequence whose limit is π is the sequence 4, $4 - \frac{4}{3}$, $4 - \frac{4}{3} + \frac{4}{5}$, $4 - \frac{4}{3} + \frac{4}{5} - \frac{4}{7}$, and so on. Thus we can get as accurate an approximation of π as we like by adding together sufficiently many terms in the "sum"

$$4 - \frac{4}{3} + \frac{4}{5} - \frac{4}{7} + \frac{4}{9} - \frac{4}{11} + \cdots .$$

Similar sums will give us such numbers as e, ln 2, sin .7, and so on.

683

113 SEQUENCES AND THEIR LIMITS

A function f with domain D and range R is a set of pairs of the form $(x, f(x))$, where x is a member of D, and $f(x)$ is the corresponding member of R. In most of our work, we have taken the sets D and R to be sets of real numbers, but on occasion we have found it convenient to use sets that consist of other mathematical objects, such as angles, vectors, and so on. In this chapter we will be working with functions whose domains are sets of integers; such functions are called **sequences**. The ranges of our sequences will be sets of real numbers.

Sequences have traditionally played a central role in mathematical analysis, and they have acquired a special notation of their own, which we will now explain. If an integer n is in the domain of a function a, then the corresponding element in the range of a is denoted by $a(n)$. In sequence notation, we denote this element by a_n. Thus a sequence is a set of pairs of the form (n, a_n), where n is an integer. It is customary to abbreviate this notation and to speak of "the sequence $\{a_n\}$." Usually we don't specifically mention the domain of a sequence. Most of our sequences will have the entire set of positive integers as their domains, and if a sequence has some other domain, it will be clear from the context what it is. Another domain that we will often meet is the set of non-negative integers. The numbers $a_1, a_2, a_3, \ldots$ are called the **terms** of the sequence $\{a_n\}$, and because they are paired with the integers $1, 2, 3, \ldots$, we speak of the *first term a_1*, the *second term a_2*, and so on.

Example 113-1. Find the second, fifth, and fourteenth terms of the sequence $\left\{\dfrac{(-1)^n}{(2n-1)!}\right\}$.

Solution. If we denote this sequence by $\{a_n\}$, where $a_n = \dfrac{(-1)^n}{(2n-1)!}$, we see that $a_2 = (-1)^2/3! = \frac{1}{6}$, $a_5 = (-1)^5/9! = -1/9!$ and $a_{14} = 1/27!$.

The terms of a sequence need not be given by a simple arithmetic formula, as in the last example. Any rule that assigns a number a_n to each integer n will define a sequence.

Example 113-2. Let $\{a_n\}$ be the sequence of digits in the decimal representation of $\sin \dfrac{\pi}{3}$. Find the first four terms of the sequence.

Solution. We know that $\sin \dfrac{\pi}{3} = \dfrac{\sqrt{3}}{2} = .866025\ldots$. Thus $a_1 = 8$, $a_2 = 6$, $a_3 = 6$, and $a_4 = 0$. We have no simple algebraic formula to calculate a_n for each n, but the number a_{34}, for example, is completely determined, and we could find it if we cared to.

A sequence may also be given by specifying the first term and then stating a *recursion formula* that tells how to find each remaining term from the term that precedes it.

Example 113-3. Let $\{a_n\}$ be the sequence in which $a_1 = 1$, and $a_n = 3a_{n-1} - 1$ for $n > 1$. Find a_2, a_3, and a_4.

Solution. When we set $n = 2$ in the recursion formula $a_n = 3a_{n-1} - 1$, we see that $a_2 = 3a_1 - 1$. Since $a_1 = 1$, this equation tells us that $a_2 = 3 \cdot 1 - 1 = 2$. Now we set $n = 3$ in the recursion formula to find that $a_3 = 3a_2 - 1$. We have already found that $a_2 = 2$, so now we see that $a_3 = 3 \cdot 2 - 1 = 5$. Similarly, $a_4 = 3a_3 - 1 = 14$. It is clear that we can find any term, for example, a_{1776}, simply by plodding along a step at a time.

Another common way to specify a sequence is to list the first few terms and let the reader use them to infer the general pattern. There is really no logical basis for saying that the fifth term of the sequence $\{1, \frac{1}{2}, \frac{1}{3}, \frac{1}{4}, \ldots\}$ is $\frac{1}{5}$, but that is the number that would come to most people's minds, so a sequence is often specified in this way.

After our experience with limits, we can easily interpret the equation $\lim_{n \uparrow \infty} a_n = A$. Informally, it means that a_n is close to A if n is large. Formally, we have the following minor modification of our earlier Definition 109-1.

Definition 113-1. *The equation* $\lim_{n \uparrow \infty} a_n = A$ *means that for each neighborhood* $N_p A$ *there exists an interval* (K, ∞) *such that for each integer* $n \in (K, \infty)$, *we have* $a_n \in N_p A$. *In other words, to each neighborhood* $N_p A$ *there corresponds a number* K *such that for each index* $n > K$, *we have* $a_n \in N_p A$.

The number A is called the *limit of* a_n, and it is also referred to as the *limit of the sequence* $\{a_n\}$. If a sequence has a limit, we say that it **converges**; otherwise, it **diverges**. The simplest way (when it works) to find limits is by inspection, using our informal definition of limit. Our formal Definition 113-1 can then be used to verify that the number we found by inspection actually is the limit of the sequence.

Example 113-4. Find the limit of the sequence of Example 113-1.

Solution. Here $a_n = (-1)^n/(2n - 1)!$. If n is a large number, the denominator is a large number, but the numerator is not. Hence the given fraction is nearly zero, and we conclude that

$$\lim_{n \uparrow \infty} \frac{(-1)^n}{(2n - 1)!} = 0.$$

To use Definition 113-1 to verify that 0 is the limit of our sequence, we suppose we are given a neighborhood $N_p 0$, and we must tell how to choose K so that for each index $n > K$ we have $\dfrac{(-1)^n}{(2n-1)!} \in N_p 0 = (-p, p)$. Let us choose $K = \frac{1}{2}\left(\dfrac{1}{p}+1\right)$. Then if $n > K$, we see that $p > \dfrac{1}{2n-1}$, and so the interval $\left[-\dfrac{1}{2n-1}, \dfrac{1}{2n-1}\right]$ is a subinterval of the interval $(-p, p)$. Since it is true that $\dfrac{(-1)^n}{(2n-1)!} \in \left[-\dfrac{1}{2n-1}, \dfrac{1}{2n-1}\right]$ for each index n, it follows that $\dfrac{(-1)^n}{(2n-1)!} \in (-p, p)$ for each $n > K$.

Frequently, the terms of a sequence are the values at the positive integers of a function whose domain contains the set of positive real numbers. For example, the terms of the sequence $\left\{ n\left(\dfrac{\pi}{2} - \text{Arctan } n\right)\right\}$ are the numbers $f(1)$, $f(2)$, ..., where $f(x) = x\left(\dfrac{\pi}{2} - \text{Arctan } x\right)$. In such a case it is obvious that the limit of the sequence is the number $\lim\limits_{x \uparrow \infty} f(x)$, if this latter limit exists. Thus in Example 109-3 we used l'Hospital's Rule to find that $\lim\limits_{x \uparrow \infty} x\left(\dfrac{\pi}{2} - \text{Arctan } x\right) = 1$, and so the limit of the sequence $\left\{ n\left(\dfrac{\pi}{2} - \text{Arctan } n\right)\right\}$ is the number 1.

The following theorem is merely a rewording of some of our standard limit theorems in the language of sequences.

Theorem 113-1. *If $\{a_n\}$ and $\{b_n\}$ are convergent sequences, then*

(113-1) $$\lim_{n \uparrow \infty} (a_n + b_n) = \lim_{n \uparrow \infty} a_n + \lim_{n \uparrow \infty} b_n,$$

(113-2) $$\lim_{n \uparrow \infty} (a_n b_n) = \lim_{n \uparrow \infty} a_n \lim_{n \uparrow \infty} b_n,$$

and

(113-3) $$\lim_{n \uparrow \infty} \frac{a_n}{b_n} = \frac{\lim\limits_{n \uparrow \infty} a_n}{\lim\limits_{n \uparrow \infty} b_n} \qquad \left(\text{provided that } \lim_{n \uparrow \infty} b_n \neq 0\right).$$

As a special case of Equation 113-2, *we have*

(113-4) $$\lim_{n \uparrow \infty} c a_n = c \lim_{n \uparrow \infty} a_n,$$

where c may be any number.

If we can see at a glance that the limit of a given sequence $\{a_n\}$ is a number A, we can consider ourselves fortunate. In general, we would not even expect to be able to tell whether or not a sequence converges, much less what its limit is. The sequence $\left\{\left(\dfrac{n+1}{n}\right)^n\right\}$ is an example. Is it obvious that this sequence converges, and if so, that its limit is the number e? If we set $h = \dfrac{1}{n}$ in Equation 48-8, then we see that the sequence does converge to e, but this fact is not apparent from just looking at the sequence. We will now discuss some simple and useful criteria for determining whether or not sequences of certain types converge.

Let $[A, B]$ be the smallest closed interval that contains all the terms of a given sequence $\{a_n\}$. Here the letters A and B stand for numbers, or perhaps A may be the symbol $-\infty$ or B the symbol ∞. For example, the smallest closed intervals that contain the sequences $\{(-1)^n n^2\}$ and $\left\{\dfrac{(-1)^n}{n^2}\right\}$ are $[-\infty, \infty]$ and $[-1, 1]$. If B is a number (that is, not the symbol ∞), then we say that the sequence $\{a_n\}$ is **bounded above**, and we call the number B the **least upper bound** of the sequence. Similarly, if A is a number (that is, not the symbol $-\infty$), then the sequence $\{a_n\}$ is said to be **bounded below**, and A is the **greatest lower bound** of the sequence. If $\{a_n\}$ is bounded above and bounded below, then we say that it is **bounded**. A sequence is bounded if, and only if, there exist *some* numbers C and D such that all the terms of the sequence are contained in the interval $[C, D]$. In that case, the *smallest* closed interval $[A, B]$ that contains all the terms of the sequence will itself be contained in $[C, D]$, and we will have $C \leq A$ and $B \leq D$ The number C is called *a lower bound* of the sequence, and D is *an upper bound*.

Suppose now that our sequence $\{a_n\}$ is convergent; that is, suppose there is a number L such that $\lim\limits_{n \uparrow \infty} a_n = L$. Therefore, to the neighborhood $N_1 L = (L - 1, L + 1)$ there corresponds an integer K such that

$$a_n \in (L - 1, L + 1) \quad \text{if} \quad n > K.$$

The finite set of numbers $\{a_1, a_2, \ldots, a_K, L - 1, L + 1\}$ has a smallest element C and a largest element D. Then the interval $[C, D]$ contains every term of our sequence, so the sequence $\{a_n\}$ is bounded. We state this important result as a theorem.

Theorem 113-2. *If a sequence converges, then it is bounded.*

Theorem 113-2 can also be worded: *If a sequence is not bounded, then it does not converge.* But notice that the converse of this theorem is *not* true. It is possible for a sequence to be bounded yet not be convergent; the sequence $\{(-1)^n\}$ is an example.

A sequence $\{a_n\}$ is **non-decreasing** if $a_1 \leq a_2 \leq \cdots$; that is, if $a_n \leq a_{n+1}$ for each positive integer n. If $a_1 \geq a_2 \geq \cdots$; that is, if $a_n \geq a_{n+1}$ for each positive integer n, then $\{a_n\}$ is a **non-increasing** sequence. Together, these two types of sequences form the class of **monotone** sequences. It is clear that the smallest closed interval that contains the terms of a non-decreasing sequence $\{a_n\}$ will have the form $[a_1, B]$, while the smallest closed interval that contains the terms of a non-increasing sequence $\{a_n\}$ will be of the form $[A, a_1]$. By precisely the same type of argument that we used to prove Theorem 109-1, we see that $\lim\limits_{n \uparrow \infty} a_n = B$ in the first case and $\lim\limits_{n \uparrow \infty} a_n = A$ in the second. The sequences converge if, and only if, A and B are numbers; that is, if the sequences are bounded. Therefore, we have the following theorem.

Theorem 113-3. *A monotone sequence converges if, and only if, it is bounded. The limit of a non-decreasing sequence is its least upper bound, and the limit of a non-increasing sequence is its greatest lower bound.*

Example 113-5. Suppose that $a_1 = \frac{3}{4}$, and $a_n = \dfrac{4n^2 - 1}{4n^2} a_{n-1}$ for $n \geq 2$. Show that the sequence $\{a_n\}$ converges.

Solution. We have

$$a_1 = \tfrac{3}{4}, a_2 = \tfrac{3}{4} \cdot \tfrac{15}{16}, a_3 = \tfrac{3}{4} \cdot \tfrac{15}{16} \cdot \tfrac{35}{36}, \ldots.$$

In this sequence, each term is the product of positive numbers, so each term is positive. Therefore, the sequence is bounded below, and its greatest lower bound is a number $A \geq 0$. We also notice that each term is obtained from the preceding term by multiplying it by a proper fraction. Therefore, each term is smaller than its predecessor, and so the sequence is non-increasing. Thus we have a non-increasing sequence that is bounded below by 0, and so Theorem 113-3 tells us that it converges to its greatest lower bound A. Actually, the limit of this sequence is the number $2/\pi$. You might calculate a_5 to see what kind of an approximation to the limit it gives.

We bring this section to a close by pointing out a self-evident, but useful, fact. Suppose we construct a new sequence $\{b_n\}$ from a given sequence $\{a_n\}$ by choosing a positive integer h and setting $b_n = a_{n+h}$ for $n = 1, 2, \ldots$. For example, we might take $h = 4$, and then $b_1 = a_5$, $b_2 = a_6$, $b_3 = a_7$, and so on. We obtain the sequence $\{b_n\}$ by deleting the *initial segment* $\{a_1, a_2, \ldots, a_h\}$ from $\{a_n\}$, and we usually denote the new sequence as $\{a_{n+h}\}$, rather than as $\{b_n\}$. It is clear that $\{a_{n+h}\}$ converges if, and only if, $\{a_n\}$ converges. If the two sequences converge, they obviously have the same limit. For example, the first few terms of the sequence $\{n^3/n!\}$ are $1, 4, \frac{9}{2}, \frac{8}{3}, \frac{25}{24}, \ldots$. Therefore, the sequence is not monotone. However, if we delete the first two terms, we obtain a non-increasing sequence of positive terms. We can therefore apply Theorem 113-3 to see that the new sequence has a limit, and this limit is also the limit of the original sequence.

P R O B L E M S   1 1 3

1. Find and simplify the fifth term of each of the following sequences. Which of them converge? Can you find the limits of the convergent sequences? Can you find a lower bound and an upper bound for these sequences? Can you find the smallest closed interval that contains all the terms of a sequence?

(a) $\left\{\cos \dfrac{n\pi}{2}\right\}$

(b) $\{1 + (-1)^n\}$

(c) $\left\{\dfrac{k!2^{k+3}}{(k+3)!2^k}\right\}$

(d) $\left\{n \ln\left(1 + \dfrac{2}{n}\right)\right\}$

(e) $\left\{\dfrac{1 \cdot 3 \cdot 5 \cdot \ldots \cdot (2k-1)}{2 \cdot 4 \cdot 6 \cdot \ldots \cdot (2k)}\right\}$

(f) $\left\{\dfrac{(2m)!}{(2^m m!)^2}\right\}$

(g) $\left\{\dfrac{\sin n}{n}\right\}$

(h) $\left\{\dfrac{(4n+1)(5n-2)}{(2n+3)(3n-5)}\right\}$

(i) $\left\{\displaystyle\int_0^n e^{-x^2}\, dx\right\}$

(j) $\left\{\displaystyle\int_0^{2n\pi} |\cos nx|\, dx\right\}$

2. Write the first four terms of the sequence $\{c_n\}$. Can you guess a formula for c_n?

(a) $c_1 = 5,\ c_n = nc_{n-1}$ if $n > 1$

(b) $c_1 = 3,\ c_n = \tfrac{1}{2}c_{n-1}$ if $n > 1$

(c) $c_1 = 15,\ c_2 = 4,\ c_n = [\tfrac{1}{2}(c_{n-1} + c_{n-2})]$ if $n > 2$

(d) $c_1 = 5,\ c_2 = 4,\ c_n = \tfrac{1}{2}(c_{n-1} + c_{n-2})$ if $n > 2$

3. Find a simple formula for a_n such that the first few terms of the sequence $\{a_n\}$ are as follows.

(a) $1, 3, 7, 15, 31, \ldots$

(b) $1, 0, -1, 0, 1, 0, -1, \ldots$

(c) $0, 3, 8, 15, 24, \ldots$

(d) $1, -1, -1, 1, 1, -1, -1, 1, \ldots$

4. (a) Find the formula for the nth term of the sequence of Example 113-3.

(b) Show that a formula for the nth term of the sequence of Example 113-2 is

$$a_n = [\![10^n \sin \tfrac{1}{3}\pi]\!] - 10[\![10^{n-1} \sin \tfrac{1}{3}\pi]\!].$$

5. The first few terms of some sequences are given below. Use Theorem 113-3 to show that they converge.

(a) $\dfrac{3}{1}, \dfrac{3^2}{2!}, \dfrac{3^3}{3!}, \dfrac{3^4}{4!}, \ldots$

(b) $5, \sqrt{5}, \sqrt{\sqrt{5}}, \sqrt{\sqrt{\sqrt{5}}}, \ldots$

(c) $1, 2!/2^2, 3!/3^3, 4!/4^4, \ldots$

(d) $\displaystyle\int_0^1 e^{x^2}\, dx,\ \int_0^1 \int_0^x e^{y^2}\, dy\, dx,\ \int_0^1 \int_0^x \int_0^y e^{z^2}\, dz\, dy\, dx, \ldots$

6. Find an index K beyond which all the terms of the given sequence are contained in

the interval $N_{.1}0 = (-.1, .1)$.

(a) $\left\{\dfrac{\cos n}{n}\right\}$ (b) $\{2^{-n}\}$ (c) $\left\{\dfrac{n^2 + 3n - 2}{n^3}\right\}$ (d) $\left\{\dfrac{n!}{n^n}\right\}$

7. Let a_n be the area of the regular n-sided polygon inscribed in the unit circle. Find a formula for $a_n (n \geq 3)$. What is $\lim_{n \uparrow \infty} a_n$?

8. Let $a_1 = 1$ and $a_n = \dfrac{n^2 - 1}{n^2} a_{n-1}$ for $n \geq 2$. Show that $\{a_n\}$ converges. Find a formula for a_n and show that $\lim_{n \uparrow \infty} a_n = \frac{1}{2}$.

9. Use l'Hospital's Rule to show that the limit of the sequence $\left\{ \left(\dfrac{n+1}{n} \right)^n \right\}$ is e.

10. Carefully explain why the sequence $\{(-1)^n\}$ is divergent.

11. (a) If the domain of the sequence $\{a_n\}$ is the set of positive integers and h is a positive integer, what is the "understood" domain of the sequences $\{a_{n+h}\}$ and $\{a_{n-h}\}$?

(b) If $\lim_{n \uparrow \infty} a_n = A$, show that $\lim_{n \uparrow \infty} a_{n+h} = \lim_{n \uparrow \infty} a_{n-h} = A$.

12. Suppose that r is a number in the interval $(0, 1)$, and let $\{a_n\}$ be the sequence that is defined by the equation $a_n = r^n$. Use Theorem 113-3 to show that this sequence converges. Now take limits of both sides of the equation $a_n = ra_{n-1}$ (using the equation $\lim_{n \uparrow \infty} a_n = \lim_{n \uparrow \infty} a_{n-1}$ that we verified in the last problem) and show that $\lim_{n \uparrow \infty} a_n = 0$.

114 INFINITE SERIES

With each sequence $\{a_n\}$ we can associate a sequence $\{S_n\}$ whose terms are defined by the equation

(114-1) $$S_n = \sum_{k=1}^{n} a_k = a_1 + a_2 + \cdots + a_n.$$

This sequence $\{S_n\}$ is the sequence of **partial sums** of $\{a_n\}$. We have $S_1 = a_1$, $S_2 = a_1 + a_2 = S_1 + a_2$, $S_3 = a_1 + a_2 + a_3 = S_2 + a_3$, and so on. Clearly, for each $n > 1$,

(114-2) $$S_n = S_{n-1} + a_n.$$

Example 114-1. Find the first five terms of the sequence of partial sums of the sequence $\{a_n\} = \{1/n(n + 1)\}$, and also find a formula that gives S_n for each positive integer n.

Solution. We have

$$S_1 = a_1 = \frac{1}{1 \cdot 2} = \frac{1}{2},$$

$$S_2 = S_1 + a_2 = \frac{1}{2} + \frac{1}{2 \cdot 3} = \frac{2}{3},$$

$$S_3 = S_2 + a_3 = \frac{2}{3} + \frac{1}{3 \cdot 4} = \frac{3}{4},$$

$$S_4 = S_3 + a_4 = \frac{3}{4} + \frac{1}{4 \cdot 5} = \frac{4}{5},$$

$$S_5 = S_4 + a_5 = \frac{4}{5} + \frac{1}{5 \cdot 6} = \frac{5}{6}.$$

When we look at these terms, we are strongly tempted to conclude that $S_6 = \frac{6}{7}$, $S_7 = \frac{7}{8}$, and in general that $S_n = \dfrac{n}{n+1}$. This conclusion is correct, for

$$a_k = \frac{1}{k(k+1)} = \frac{1}{k} - \frac{1}{k+1},$$

and therefore

$$S_n = a_1 + a_2 + a_3 + \cdots + a_n$$

$$= \left(1 - \frac{1}{2}\right) + \left(\frac{1}{2} - \frac{1}{3}\right) + \left(\frac{1}{3} - \frac{1}{4}\right) + \cdots + \left(\frac{1}{n} - \frac{1}{n+1}\right).$$

When we remove the parentheses, this sum "collapses" to

$$S_n = 1 - \frac{1}{n+1} = \frac{n}{n+1}.$$

If the partial sums of the sequence $\{a_n\}$ converge to the number S, we express that fact by writing

$$(114\text{-}3) \qquad S = \sum_{k=1}^{\infty} a_k = a_1 + a_2 + a_3 + \cdots.$$

Of course, this notation does not mean that we add together all the infinitely many terms of the sequence $\{a_n\}$. It is just another way of saying that $\lim_{n \uparrow \infty} S_n = S$. We call the indicated sum

$$\sum_{k=1}^{\infty} a_k = a_1 + a_2 + a_3 + \cdots$$

an **infinite series.** The numbers $a_1, a_2, a_3, \ldots$ are its **terms,** and the sequence $\{S_n\}$, where $S_n = \sum\limits_{k=1}^{n} a_k$, is the sequence of **partial sums** of the series. If the sequence $\{S_n\}$ converges, then the series **converges;** otherwise the series is **divergent.** The limit S of S_n (if a limit exists) is called the **sum** of the series. Notice that when we work with an infinite series $\sum\limits_{k=1}^{\infty} a_k$ we are dealing with *two* sequences, the sequence $\{a_n\}$ of *terms* of the series and the sequence $\{S_n\}$ of *partial sums.* You must keep the distinction between these two sequences clearly in mind.

Example 114-2.   Find the sum of the infinite series $\sum\limits_{k=1}^{\infty} \dfrac{1}{k(k+1)}$.

Solution.   The sequence of terms of this series is $\left\{\dfrac{1}{k(k+1)}\right\}$, and in Example 114-1 we found that the corresponding sequence of partial sums is $\left\{\dfrac{n}{n+1}\right\}$. Since $\lim\limits_{n\uparrow\infty} \dfrac{n}{n+1} = 1$, our given series converges, and its sum is 1. Thus we have established the equation

$$(114\text{-}4) \qquad \sum_{k=1}^{\infty} \frac{1}{k(k+1)} = \frac{1}{1\cdot 2} + \frac{1}{2\cdot 3} + \frac{1}{3\cdot 4} + \cdots = 1.$$

We are now going to investigate the convergence of a very important infinite series. Suppose that x is some real number, and consider the **geometric series**

$$(114\text{-}5) \qquad \sum_{k=0}^{\infty} x^k = 1 + x + x^2 + x^3 + \cdots.$$

The sequence of terms of this series is the *geometric progression* $\{x^k\}$. Our index of summation starts at 0 here, so we find it convenient to think of 1 as being the 0th term of the sequence $\{x^k\}$, x as being the first term, and so on. On the other hand, we find that it makes our formulas a little simpler if we label the terms in our sequence $\{S_n\}$ of partial sums so that $S_1 = 1$, $S_2 = 1 + x$, and in general

$$S_n = \sum_{k=0}^{n-1} x^k = 1 + x + x^2 + \cdots + x^{n-1}.$$

In this form it is not clear what the limit of S_n is (or even that S_n has a limit). However, you may remember that there is a simple formula for the partial sums of the terms of a geometric progression. To obtain this formula, we write

$$S_n - xS_n = (1 + x + \cdots + x^{n-1}) - (x + x^2 + \cdots + x^n) = 1 - x^n.$$

Then we solve this equation for S_n and find (if $x \neq 1$) that

$$S_n = \frac{1 - x^n}{1 - x} = \frac{1}{1 - x} - \frac{1}{1 - x} \cdot x^n.$$

Since the expression $\dfrac{1}{1 - x}$ is independent of n, the last equation tells us that

$$\lim_{n \uparrow \infty} S_n = \frac{1}{1 - x} - \frac{1}{1 - x} \lim_{n \uparrow \infty} x^n,$$

if $\lim_{n \uparrow \infty} x^n$ exists. The existence of this limit depends on our original choice of x. If $|x| < 1$, then $\lim_{n \uparrow \infty} x^n = 0$ (see Problem 113-12 for a way to prove this statement), and so $\lim_{n \uparrow \infty} S_n = \dfrac{1}{1 - x}$. If $|x| > 1$, or if $x = -1$, then $\lim_{n \uparrow \infty} x^n$ does not exist and hence $\{S_n\}$ is divergent. If $x = 1$, we must use a different formula for S_n; in this case, $S_n = n$, and so again the sequence $\{S_n\}$ is divergent. We can sum up the results of our study of geometric series as follows: *The geometric series* $\sum_{k=1}^{\infty} x^k$ *converges if, and only if, $|x| < 1$, and then we have*

(114-6) $$\sum_{k=1}^{\infty} x^k = \frac{1}{1 - x}, \qquad |x| < 1.$$

Example 114-3. Find the sum of the series $\sum_{k=0}^{\infty} \left(\dfrac{1}{10}\right)^k$.

Solution. We obtain the sum of this geometric series by replacing x with $\frac{1}{10}$ in Equation 114-6:

$$\sum_{k=0}^{\infty} \left(\frac{1}{10}\right)^k = \frac{1}{1 - \dfrac{1}{10}} = \frac{10}{9}.$$

Although infinite series are not sums of numbers in the usual sense, they do have some of the properties of ordinary sums. For example, if the sequences of partial sums of the series $\sum_{k=1}^{\infty} a_k$ and $\sum_{k=1}^{\infty} b_k$ are $\{A_n\}$ and $\{B_n\}$, and if c and d are any two real numbers, then it is clear that the sequence of partial sums of the series $\sum_{k=1}^{\infty} (ca_k + db_k)$ is $\{cA_n + dB_n\}$. According to Theorem 113-1, if the sequences $\{A_n\}$ and $\{B_n\}$ converge, so does the sequence $\{cA_n + dB_n\}$, and its limit is the corresponding combination of their limits. In the language of series: *If* $\sum_{k=1}^{\infty} a_k$

and $\displaystyle\sum_{k=1}^{\infty} b_k$ *are convergent series, and if c and d are any two real numbers, then the*

series $\displaystyle\sum_{k=1}^{\infty} (ca_k + db_k)$ *converges, and*

(114-7) $$\sum_{k=1}^{\infty}(ca_k + db_k) = c\sum_{k=1}^{\infty} a_k + d\sum_{k=1}^{\infty} b_k.$$

Equation 114-7 suggests that the summation symbol $\displaystyle\sum_{k=1}^{\infty}$ and the integration symbol $\displaystyle\int_{1}^{\infty}$ behave in much the same manner. In Problem 114-11 we ask you to show that convergence or divergence of the infinite series $\displaystyle\sum_{k=1}^{\infty} a_k$ is equivalent to convergence or divergence of the improper integral $\displaystyle\int_{1}^{\infty} f(x)\,dx$, where $f(x) = a_k$ for $x \in [k, k+1)$, $k = 1, 2, 3, \ldots$. Corresponding to Equation 110-1 for integrals we have the equation

(114-8) $$\sum_{k=1}^{\infty} a_k = \sum_{k=1}^{h} a_k + \sum_{k=h+1}^{\infty} a_k,$$

where h is any positive integer.

Let us illustrate our remarks about sequences and infinite series by considering the decimal notation that we use to represent real numbers. An unending decimal representation of a real number a determines a sequence of which the number a is the limit. For example, the decimal 1.111 ... represents the number that is the limit of the sequence $\{1, 1.1, 1.11, 1.111, \ldots\}$. We can regard the terms of this sequence as the partial sums of the infinite series

$$1 + .1 + .01 + .001 + .0001 + \cdots = \sum_{k=0}^{\infty} \left(\frac{1}{10}\right)^k,$$

and then the limit of the sequence is the sum of the series. In Example 114-3, we found that the sum of this geometric series is $\frac{10}{9}$. Thus the unending decimal 1.111 ... represents the number $\frac{10}{9}$.

Example 114-4. Show that 2.999 ... $= 3$.

Solution. The unending decimal 2.999 ... represents the sum of the series $2 + .9 + .09 + .009 + \cdots = 2 + \frac{9}{10} + 9(\frac{1}{10})^2 + 9(\frac{1}{10})^3 + \cdots$.
According to Equations 114-7 and 114-8, this series can be written

$$2 + \tfrac{9}{10}[1 + (\tfrac{1}{10}) + (\tfrac{1}{10})^2 + \cdots].$$

The series in brackets is the geometric series whose sum we have found to be $\frac{10}{9}$. Thus the decimal 2.999 ... represents the number

$$2 + (\tfrac{9}{10})(\tfrac{10}{9}) = 2 + 1 = 3,$$

as was to be shown.

Suppose we have an infinite series $\sum_{k=1}^{\infty} a_k$ and the corresponding sequence of partial sums $\{S_n\}$. In Problem 113-11 we saw that if this sequence is convergent, then $\lim_{n \uparrow \infty} S_n = \lim_{n \uparrow \infty} S_{n-1}$. According to Equation 114-2, $a_n = S_n - S_{n-1}$, and so

$$\lim_{n \uparrow \infty} a_n = \lim_{n \uparrow \infty} S_n - \lim_{n \uparrow \infty} S_{n-1} = 0.$$

We have therefore proved the following simple, but important, theorem.

Theorem 114-1. *If the series $\sum_{k=1}^{\infty} a_k$ converges, then $\lim_{n \uparrow \infty} a_n = 0$. In other words, if a_n does not approach zero, then the series diverges.*

Example 114-5. Test the series

$$1 - \frac{3}{4} + \frac{4}{6} - \frac{5}{8} + \frac{6}{10} - \cdots + (-1)^{n+1}\left(\frac{n+1}{2n}\right) + \cdots$$

for convergence.

Solution. The terms of this series are the terms of the sequence $\left\{\dfrac{n+1}{2n}\right\}$ alternately prefaced by plus and minus signs. Since $\lim_{n \uparrow \infty} \dfrac{n+1}{2n} = \frac{1}{2}$, you can see that a term with a large index is close to either $\frac{1}{2}$ or $-\frac{1}{2}$, so a_n does not approach 0. Thus Theorem 114-1 tells us that the series is divergent.

One of the most common mistakes that students studying infinite series make is to read Theorem 114-1 backwards. The theorem says that *if* a series converges, then its terms approach 0. It does *not* say that if its terms approach 0, then a series converges. For example, consider the series $\sum_{k=1}^{\infty} \ln\left(\dfrac{k+1}{k}\right)$. For this series,

$$\lim_{n \uparrow \infty} a_n = \lim_{n \uparrow \infty} \ln\left(\frac{n+1}{n}\right) = \ln 1 = 0.$$

On the other hand,

$$S_n = \sum_{k=1}^{n} \ln\left(\frac{k+1}{k}\right) = \sum_{k=1}^{n} [\ln (k+1) - \ln k]$$

$$= [\ln 2 - \ln 1] + [\ln 3 - \ln 2] + \cdots + [\ln (n+1) - \ln n]$$

$$= \ln (n+1).$$

Since $\lim_{n \uparrow \infty} S_n = \lim_{n \uparrow \infty} \ln (n+1)$ does not exist, we see that the series $\sum_{k=1}^{\infty} \ln\left(\dfrac{k+1}{k}\right)$ is divergent, even though its terms approach 0.

PROBLEMS 114

1. Find the fifth partial sum S_5 of each of the following sequences. Can you find a formula for S_n? How can you tell, without computing S_n, that $\lim_{n \uparrow \infty} S_n$ does not exist in these examples?

(a) $\{n\}$ (b) $\{(-1)^{n+1}\}$ (c) $\{(n+1)! - n!\}$

(d) $\{\sinh n\}$ (e) $\{(-1)^{n+1} - 1\}$ (f) $\{(-1)^{n+1}n\}$

2. If we have a given sequence $\{a_k\}$, we can find its sequence of partial sums. Conversely, suppose we have a given sequence $\{S_n\}$. Show that we can find a sequence $\{a_k\}$ of which the given sequence is the sequence of partial sums. Find a formula for a_k for the following choices of S_n. Does your formula give you a_1?

(a) $n/(n+1)$ (b) $(-1)^n$ (c) n (d) 1 (e) $1 + (-1)^n$ (f) $[\![\frac{1}{2}n]\!]$

3. (a) What is the sum of the infinite series $\sum_{k=1}^{\infty} \int_k^{k+1} e^{-x} \, dx$?

(b) Does the infinite series $\sum_{k=1}^{\infty} \int_k^{k+1} e^{-x^2} \, dx$ converge?

4. Find the sum of each of the following infinite series. (Watch the lower limit of the index of summation.)

(a) $\sum_{k=1}^{\infty} 3^{-k}$ (b) $\sum_{k=4}^{\infty} (-\frac{5}{8})^k$ (c) $\sum_{k=0}^{\infty} [2(\frac{4}{5})^k + 3(\frac{1}{4})^k]$

(d) $\sum_{k=1}^{\infty} 4(\frac{2}{3})^{2k}$ (e) $\sum_{k=1}^{\infty} \sin^{2k} \theta$ (f) $\sum_{k=0}^{\infty} \tanh^{2k} x$

5. Show that if h is any positive integer and x is a number in the interval $(-1, 1)$, then

$$\sum_{k=h}^{\infty} x^k = \frac{x^h}{1 - x}.$$

6. Show that the following series diverge.

(a) $\sum_{k=1}^{\infty} \frac{k!}{100^k}$ (b) $\sum_{k=1}^{\infty} \frac{(-1)^k(k^2 + k)}{4k^2 + 5k - 1}$ (c) $\sum_{k=1}^{\infty} \frac{\ln(k + e^k)}{k + \ln k}$ (d) $\sum_{k=1}^{\infty} \sin k$

7. Find the sum of the series

$$\frac{3}{4} + \frac{5}{36} + \frac{7}{144} + \cdots + \frac{2k + 1}{k^2(k + 1)^2} + \cdots.$$

(Notice that $a_k = 1/k^2 - 1/(k + 1)^2$.)

8. Show that if $\sum_{k=1}^{\infty} a_k$ converges, then $\sum_{k=1}^{\infty} \cos a_k$ diverges.

9. Find an expression for the nth partial sum of the series

$$\ln 2 + \ln \frac{3}{4} + \ln \frac{8}{9} + \cdots + \ln\left(1 - \frac{1}{n^2}\right) + \cdots.$$

What is the sum of this series?

10. If the series $\sum\limits_{k=1}^{\infty} (a_k + b_k)$ converges, does it necessarily follow that the series $a_1 + b_1 + a_2 + b_2 + a_3 + b_3 + \cdots$ converges? (Examine the situation when $a_k = 1$ and $b_k = -1$ for all k.)

11. Let $\{a_k\}$ be a given sequence and define the function f by means of the equations $f(x) = a_k$ if $x \in [k, k+1)$, $k = 1, 2, 3, \ldots$.

(a) Sketch the graph of the equation $y = f(x)$ if $a_k = \dfrac{1}{k}$.

(b) Show that if the integral $\displaystyle\int_1^{\infty} f(x)\, dx$ converges, then the series $\sum\limits_{k=1}^{\infty} a_k$ converges.

(c) Show that if the series $\sum\limits_{k=1}^{\infty} a_k$ converges, then the integral $\displaystyle\int_1^{\infty} f(x)\, dx$ converges.

115 COMPARISON TESTS

When we examine an infinite series $\sum\limits_{k=1}^{\infty} a_k$, three questions naturally arise:

(i) Does the series converge?

(ii) If it does converge, what is its sum?

(iii) For a given index n, how well does the partial sum S_n approximate the sum S?

For the geometric series $\sum\limits_{k=0}^{\infty} x^k$, we can answer all these questions completely. We know that this series converges if $|x| < 1$; we know that if it converges, then its sum is $S = \dfrac{1}{1-x}$; and finally, since the formula for the nth partial sum is $S_n = \dfrac{1-x^n}{1-x}$, we know that $S - S_n = \dfrac{x^n}{1-x}$. For most other series, however, we cannot answer all three questions so completely. Our attention will mainly be devoted to finding the answer to the first question. For certain kinds of series, we will develop some tools that will help us answer the other two questions as well.

The convergence tests for infinite series that we develop in this section are completely parallel to the convergence tests for improper integrals that we have already met in Section 111. In fact, because of the relationship between series and improper integrals that we have pointed out, these convergence tests for series are easy consequences of the convergence tests for integrals. Nevertheless, we will give their proofs in terms of series to fix the concepts and notation of infinite series more firmly in your mind.

The convergence tests of this section apply only to series whose terms are non-negative; we will take up other types of series later. If the terms of the series $\sum\limits_{k=1}^{\infty} a_k$ are all non-negative numbers, then the sequence $\{S_n\}$ of partial sums is a non-decreasing sequence. This sequence will converge if it is bounded (Theorem 113-3), and it will diverge if it is unbounded. Therefore, we ·have the following theorem.

Theorem 115-1.   *An infinite series of non-negative terms converges if, and only if, its sequence of partial sums is a bounded sequence.*

Example 115-1.   Test the following series for convergence

(115-1) $1 + \frac{1}{2} + \frac{1}{4} + \frac{1}{4} + \frac{1}{8} + \frac{1}{8} + \frac{1}{8} + \frac{1}{8} + \frac{1}{16} + \cdots,$

where there are eight consecutive $\frac{1}{16}$'s, then sixteen consecutive $\frac{1}{32}$'s, and so on.

Solution.   We will show that the sequence $\{S_n\}$ of partial sums of this series is unbounded. For let us just consider those terms whose indices are powers of 2, such as S_1, S_2, S_4, S_8, and so on. We have $S_1 = 1 = \frac{2}{2}$, $S_2 = \frac{3}{2}$, $S_4 = \frac{4}{2}$, $S_8 = \frac{5}{2}$, and it is not hard to see that, in general, $S_{2^r} = \dfrac{r+2}{2}$. Since the sequence $\{S_n\}$ contains each of these numbers, for $r = 1, 2, 3, \ldots$, it is clear that $\{S_n\}$ is unbounded, and our given series diverges.

Now we take up the **comparison test** for the convergence of series of non-negative terms.

Theorem 115-2.   *Suppose that $0 \le a_k \le b_k$ for each positive integer k. If the series $\sum\limits_{k=1}^{\infty} b_k$ converges, then the series $\sum\limits_{k=1}^{\infty} a_k$ converges. This conclusion also implies that if the series $\sum\limits_{k=1}^{\infty} a_k$ diverges, then the series $\sum\limits_{k=1}^{\infty} b_k$ diverges. We say that the series $\sum\limits_{k=1}^{\infty} b_k$ **dominates** the series $\sum\limits_{k=1}^{\infty} a_k$.*

Proof.   By hypothesis, the series of non-negative terms $\sum\limits_{k=1}^{\infty} b_k$ is convergent and therefore, according to Theorem 115-1, its sequence $\left\{ \sum\limits_{k=1}^{n} b_k \right\}$ of partial sums is a bounded sequence. Now since $a_k \le b_k$, we see that for each positive integer n, $\sum\limits_{k=1}^{n} a_k \le \sum\limits_{k=1}^{n} b_k$. Hence it is clear that boundedness of the sequence $\left\{ \sum\limits_{k=1}^{n} b_k \right\}$ implies that the sequence $\left\{ \sum\limits_{k=1}^{n} a_k \right\}$ of partial sums of the series $\sum\limits_{k=1}^{\infty} a_k$ is also bounded. Then Theorem 115-1 tells us that the series $\sum\limits_{k=1}^{\infty} a_k$ converges, and our proof is complete.

Example 115-2.   Test the following series, known as the **harmonic series**, for convergence.

(115-2) $\sum\limits_{k=1}^{\infty} \dfrac{1}{k} = 1 + \dfrac{1}{2} + \dfrac{1}{3} + \dfrac{1}{4} + \cdots.$

Solution.   We will compare this series with Series 115-1 of the preceding example. To make this comparison, we write Series 115-1 on one line and Series 115-2 below it:

$$1 + \tfrac{1}{2} + \tfrac{1}{4} + \tfrac{1}{4} + \tfrac{1}{8} + \tfrac{1}{8} + \tfrac{1}{8} + \tfrac{1}{8} + \tfrac{1}{16} + \cdots,$$
$$1 + \tfrac{1}{2} + \tfrac{1}{3} + \tfrac{1}{4} + \tfrac{1}{5} + \tfrac{1}{6} + \tfrac{1}{7} + \tfrac{1}{8} + \tfrac{1}{9} + \cdots.$$

Now it is clear that the second series dominates the first. But we found in Example 115-1 that the first series is divergent, and therefore the comparison test tells us the second series is divergent also.

Example 115-3. Show that the series

$$\text{(115-3)} \qquad \sum_{k=1}^{\infty} \frac{1}{k^2} = 1 + \frac{1}{2^2} + \frac{1}{3^2} + \frac{1}{4^2} + \cdots$$

is convergent. (This series, like the harmonic series is frequently used as a comparison series, so you should remember this example.)

Solution. Series 115-3 converges if, and only if, the series

$$\frac{1}{2^2} + \frac{1}{3^2} + \frac{1}{4^2} + \cdots$$

that we obtain by dropping the first term converges. This series is dominated by the series

$$\frac{1}{1 \cdot 2} + \frac{1}{2 \cdot 3} + \frac{1}{3 \cdot 4} + \cdots,$$

which (see Example 114-2) converges and has 1 as its sum. Thus we see from Theorem 115-2 that Series 115-3 is convergent. Furthermore, since the sum of our comparison series is 1, it is clear that the sum of Series 115-3 is a number between 1 and 2. After this course you may study Fourier Series, and then you will learn that the sum of Series 115-3 is $\frac{1}{6}\pi^2$.

In the last example, we used the obvious fact that if one convergent series of non-negative terms dominates another, then its sum will be larger than the sum of the other series (unless the two series are identical). We can sometimes use this fact, as in the next example, to get an idea of how well partial sums approximate the sum of a series.

Example 115-4. Estimate how well the sum of the first six terms approximates the sum of the series $\sum_{k=0}^{\infty} \frac{1}{k!} = 1 + \frac{1}{1!} + \frac{1}{2!} + \frac{1}{3!} + \cdots$.

Solution. The sum of our given series is the sum of the first six terms plus the "remainder after six terms"

$$\text{(115-4)} \qquad \sum_{k=6}^{\infty} \frac{1}{k!} = \frac{1}{6!} + \frac{1}{7!} + \frac{1}{8!} + \cdots.$$

The remainder Series 115-4 is dominated by the series

$$\frac{1}{6!} + \frac{1}{6!7} + \frac{1}{6!7^2} + \frac{1}{6!7^3} + \cdots = \frac{1}{6!}\left[1 + \left(\frac{1}{7}\right) + \left(\frac{1}{7}\right)^2 + \cdots \right].$$

The series in the brackets is a geometric series whose sum is $\dfrac{1}{1-\frac{1}{7}} = \dfrac{7}{6}$, so the remainder series converges, and its sum is less than the number $\dfrac{1}{6!} \cdot \dfrac{7}{6} \approx .0016$.

The following "limit comparison test" is a simple consequence of Theorem 115-2. It doesn't do anything this previous comparison test cannot do, but it is often much easier to apply to particular series.

Theorem 115-3. *Let $\displaystyle\sum_{k=1}^{\infty} a_k$ and $\displaystyle\sum_{k=1}^{\infty} b_k$ be series of positive terms. If $\displaystyle\lim_{k \uparrow \infty} \frac{a_k}{b_k} = c$, where $c > 0$, then the series $\displaystyle\sum_{k=1}^{\infty} a_k$ converges if, and only if, the series $\displaystyle\sum_{k=1}^{\infty} b_k$ converges. If $\displaystyle\lim_{k \uparrow \infty} \frac{a_k}{b_k} = 0$, and if $\displaystyle\sum_{k=1}^{\infty} b_k$ converges, then the series $\displaystyle\sum_{k=1}^{\infty} a_k$ converges.*

*(Notice that in the second case—when the limit of the ratio $\dfrac{a_k}{b_k}$ is 0—that divergence of the series $\displaystyle\sum_{k=1}^{\infty} b_k$ does **not** imply that the series $\displaystyle\sum_{k=1}^{\infty} a_k$ diverges.)*

Proof. We will write out the proof for the case in which $\displaystyle\lim_{k \uparrow \infty} \frac{a_k}{b_k}$ is positive. If this limit is 0, the proof is practically the same, and we leave it for you in the problems. Since $\displaystyle\lim_{k \uparrow \infty} \frac{a_k}{b_k} = c$, we know that to the neighborhood $N_{\frac{1}{2}c} c = (\frac{1}{2}c, \frac{3}{2}c)$ there corresponds an index K such that for $k > K$, we have $\dfrac{a_k}{b_k} \in (\frac{1}{2}c, \frac{3}{2}c)$; that is, $\frac{1}{2}c < \dfrac{a_k}{b_k} < \frac{3}{2}c$. Thus $\frac{1}{2}cb_k < a_k < \frac{3}{2}cb_k$, and so the series $\displaystyle\sum_{k=K+1}^{\infty} a_k$ dominates the series $\displaystyle\sum_{k=K+1}^{\infty} \frac{1}{2}cb_k$ and is dominated by the series $\displaystyle\sum_{k=K+1}^{\infty} \frac{3}{2}cb_k$. Therefore, if the series $\displaystyle\sum_{k=1}^{\infty} b_k$ converges, then the series $\displaystyle\sum_{k=K+1}^{\infty} \frac{3}{2}cb_k$ converges, and so the series $\displaystyle\sum_{k=1}^{\infty} a_k$ converges. On the other hand, if the series $\displaystyle\sum_{k=1}^{\infty} b_k$ diverges, the series $\displaystyle\sum_{k=K+1}^{\infty} \frac{1}{2}cb_k$ diverges, and so the series $\displaystyle\sum_{k=1}^{\infty} a_k$ diverges.

Example 115-5. Test the series $\displaystyle\sum_{k=0}^{\infty} \frac{1}{5 \cdot 2^k + 3 \sin k}$ for convergence.

Solution. We will compare this series with the convergent geometric series $\displaystyle\sum_{k=0}^{\infty} \frac{1}{2^k}$ by investigating the limit of the ratio

$$\frac{\dfrac{1}{2^k}}{\dfrac{1}{5 \cdot 2^k + 3 \sin k}} = \frac{5 \cdot 2^k + 3 \sin k}{2^k} = 5 + \frac{3 \sin k}{2^k}.$$

Since $\lim_{k \uparrow \infty} \left(5 + \dfrac{3 \sin k}{2^k} \right) = 5$, Theorem 115-3 tells us that our given series converges.

Example 115-6. Test the series $\displaystyle\sum_{k=1}^{\infty} \dfrac{\ln k}{k^3}$ for convergence.

Solution. Let $b_k = \dfrac{1}{k^2}$ and $a_k = \dfrac{\ln k}{k^3}$. With the aid of l'Hospital's Rule, we find

that $\lim_{k \uparrow \infty} \dfrac{a_k}{b_k} = 0$, and since the series $\displaystyle\sum_{k=1}^{\infty} \dfrac{1}{k^2}$ converges (Example 115-3), Theorem 115-3 tells us that our given series converges also.

PROBLEMS 115

1. Use a comparison test to test the following series for convergence.

(a) $\displaystyle\sum_{k=1}^{\infty} \dfrac{1}{2k^2 - k}$
(b) $\displaystyle\sum_{k=1}^{\infty} \dfrac{1}{k^k}$
(c) $\displaystyle\sum_{k=5}^{\infty} \dfrac{1}{2^k - k^2}$
(d) $\displaystyle\sum_{k=1}^{\infty} \operatorname{sech} k$

(e) $\displaystyle\sum_{k=0}^{\infty} \operatorname{Arcsin} 2^{-k}$
(f) $\displaystyle\sum_{k=2}^{\infty} \dfrac{1}{\ln k}$
(g) $\displaystyle\sum_{k=0}^{\infty} \dfrac{1}{\llbracket e^k \rrbracket}$
(h) $\displaystyle\sum_{k=1}^{\infty} \dfrac{k^3}{3^k}$

2. In Example 115-3, we saw that when $p = 2$, the series $\displaystyle\sum_{k=1}^{\infty} \dfrac{1}{k^p}$ converges. Use this result to show that when $p > 2$ the series also converges. Show that the series diverges if $p < 1$.

3. Show that the series $\displaystyle\sum_{k=r}^{\infty} \dfrac{a_n k^n + a_{n-1} k^{n-1} + \cdots + a_0}{b_m k^m + b_{m-1} k^{m-1} + \cdots + b_0}$, where $a_n b_m \neq 0$ and m and n are positive integers, converges if $m \geq n + 2$ and diverges if $m \leq n + 1$.

4. Test the following series for convergence.

(a) $\displaystyle\sum_{k=1}^{\infty} \sin \dfrac{1}{k}$
(b) $\displaystyle\sum_{k=1}^{\infty} \sin \dfrac{1}{k^2}$
(c) $\displaystyle\sum_{k=1}^{\infty} \left(\dfrac{\pi}{2} - \operatorname{Arctan} k \right)$

(d) $\displaystyle\sum_{k=1}^{\infty} \left(\dfrac{\pi}{2} - \operatorname{Arctan} k^2 \right)$
(e) $\displaystyle\sum_{k=0}^{\infty} e^k \sin^2 2^{-k}$
(f) $\displaystyle\sum_{k=0}^{\infty} 2^{-k} \sin^2 e^k$

5. Show that for $k \geq 4$, $\dfrac{3^k}{k!} \leq \dfrac{3}{2} \cdot \left(\dfrac{3}{4}\right)^k$. Use this result to find a bound on the error that we incur when we use the first six terms of the series $\displaystyle\sum_{k=0}^{\infty} \dfrac{3^k}{k!}$ to approximate its sum.

6. Show that $\displaystyle\sum_{k=r}^{\infty} \dfrac{1}{k^2} < \dfrac{1}{r - 1}$ if r is an integer greater than 1.

7. If $\{S_n\}$ is the sequence of partial sums of the harmonic series, we have seen that $\lim_{n \uparrow \infty} S_n = \infty$. Thus if we add together sufficiently many terms of the harmonic series, our sum will exceed 1,000,000. From our work in this section, find how many terms would be "sufficiently many."

8. Prove Theorem 115-3 for the case in which $\lim\limits_{k \uparrow \infty} \dfrac{a_k}{b_k} = 0$.

9. Prove that a series of positive numbers $\sum\limits_{k=1}^{\infty} a_k$ converges if, and only if, the series $\sum\limits_{k=1}^{\infty} \ln(1 + a_k)$ converges.

10. Suppose f is a function such that $f(x) \geq 0$ if $x > 0$, $f(0) = 0$, and $f'(0) \neq 0$. Show that the series $\sum\limits_{k=1}^{\infty} f\!\left(\dfrac{1}{k}\right)$ diverges.

116 ALTERNATING SERIES

Many convergence tests, such as the comparison tests of the last section, do not apply directly to a series $\sum\limits_{k=1}^{\infty} a_k$ that has both positive and negative terms. However, the comparison tests do apply to the series $\sum\limits_{k=1}^{\infty} |a_k|$ that we get when we replace each term with its absolute value, and if this series converges, then the following theorem tells us that our original series converges. We discussed the analogous result for improper integrals in Section 111.

Theorem 116-1. *If the series $\sum\limits_{k=1}^{\infty} |a_k|$ converges, then the series $\sum\limits_{k=1}^{\infty} a_k$ converges. (If $\sum\limits_{k=1}^{\infty} |a_k|$ converges, we say that the series $\sum\limits_{k=1}^{\infty} a_k$ **converges absolutely**.)*

Proof. For each index k,

$$0 \leq \tfrac{1}{2}(|a_k| + a_k) \leq |a_k| \quad \text{and} \quad 0 \leq \tfrac{1}{2}(|a_k| - a_k) \leq |a_k|,$$

and hence the comparison test tells us that the series $\sum\limits_{k=1}^{\infty} \tfrac{1}{2}(|a_k| + a_k)$ and $\sum\limits_{k=1}^{\infty} \tfrac{1}{2}(|a_k| - a_k)$ converge. Now in Equation 114-7 we replace c with 1, d with -1, a_k with $\tfrac{1}{2}(|a_k| + a_k)$, and b_k with $\tfrac{1}{2}(|a_k| - a_k)$, and we see that

$$\sum_{k=1}^{\infty} [\tfrac{1}{2}(|a_k| + a_k) - \tfrac{1}{2}(|a_k| - a_k)] = \sum_{k=1}^{\infty} a_k$$

converges.

Example 116-1. Show that the series $\sum\limits_{k=1}^{\infty} \dfrac{\sin k^2}{k^2}$ converges absolutely.

Solution. Since $\left| \dfrac{\sin k^2}{k^2} \right| \leq \dfrac{1}{k^2}$, and since (Example 115-3) the series $\sum\limits_{k=1}^{\infty} \dfrac{1}{k^2}$ converges, the comparison test tells us that the series $\sum\limits_{k=1}^{\infty} \left| \dfrac{\sin k^2}{k^2} \right|$ converges. Hence our given series converges absolutely.

The converse of Theorem 116-1 is *not* true; that is, just because a series

$\sum\limits_{k=1}^{\infty} a_k$ converges, it does not follow that the series of absolute values $\sum\limits_{k=1}^{\infty} |a_k|$ converges. For example, let us change the sign of every other term in Series 115-1 to obtain the series

$$(116\text{-}1) \qquad 1 - \tfrac{1}{2} + \tfrac{1}{4} - \tfrac{1}{4} + \tfrac{1}{8} - \tfrac{1}{8} + \tfrac{1}{8} - \tfrac{1}{8} + \tfrac{1}{16} - \cdots.$$

In Example 115-1 we showed that Series 115-1 is divergent, so Series 116-1 is *not* absolutely convergent. Nevertheless, it is convergent, as we will now see. To investigate the convergence of Series 116-1, we look at its sequence of partial sums and find that

$$S_1 = 1, \; S_2 = \tfrac{1}{2}, \; S_3 = \tfrac{3}{4}, \; S_4 = \tfrac{1}{2}, \; S_5 = \tfrac{5}{8}, \; S_6 = \tfrac{1}{2}, \; S_7 = \tfrac{5}{8}, \; S_8 = \tfrac{1}{2}, \; S_9 = \tfrac{7}{16},$$

and so on. We immediately observe that if n is an even index, then $S_n = \tfrac{1}{2}$. If n is an odd index, then $S_n = \tfrac{1}{2} + a_{n+1}$, where a_{n+1} is the $(n+1)$st term of Series 116-1. Thus the inequality

$$(116\text{-}2) \qquad\qquad |S_n - \tfrac{1}{2}| \leq |a_{n+1}|$$

holds for every choice of n, odd or even. Since $\lim\limits_{n \uparrow \infty} a_n = 0$, we conclude that $\lim\limits_{n \uparrow \infty} S_n = \tfrac{1}{2}$. Therefore, Series 116-1 converges, and its sum is $\tfrac{1}{2}$. A series which converges, but which does not converge absolutely, is said to be **conditionally convergent**; we have just shown that Series 116-1 is conditionally convergent.

The number $R_n = S - S_n$ is called the **remainder after n terms** of the series that has $\{S_n\}$ as its sequence of partial sums. It represents the error that one makes by taking the number S_n as an approximation of the sum S of the series (see Example 115-4). In the process of demonstrating the convergence of Series 116-1 we also found a bound on the remainder (Inequality 116-2), which is always a nice thing to know.

Series 116-1 is typical of the class of infinite series that we are now going to study. An **alternating series** is a series of the form

$$(116\text{-}3) \qquad \sum_{k=1}^{\infty} (-1)^{k+1} a_k = a_1 - a_2 + a_3 - a_4 + \cdots,$$

where each of the numbers $a_1, a_2, a_3, \ldots$ is positive. The most important theorem about alternating series is the following.

Theorem 116-2. *Let $\{a_k\}$ be a non-increasing sequence such that* $\lim\limits_{k \uparrow \infty} a_k = 0$. *Then Series 116-3 converges to a sum S, and for each positive integer n,* $|S - S_n| \leq a_{n+1}.$

Proof. As we did with our example of Series 116-1, we will look separately at the terms of the sequence $\{S_n\}$ of partial sums of Series 116-3 with even subscripts and those with odd subscripts. A typical term with an even subscript has the form

(116-4) $\begin{aligned} S_{2k} &= a_1 - a_2 + a_3 - a_4 + \cdots - a_{2k-2} + a_{2k-1} - a_{2k} \\ &= (a_1 - a_2) + (a_3 - a_4) + \cdots + (a_{2k-1} - a_{2k}) \\ &= a_1 - (a_2 - a_3) - (a_4 - a_5) - \cdots - (a_{2k-2} - a_{2k-1}) - a_{2k}. \end{aligned}$

We have inserted parentheses in this sum in two different ways to demonstrate two different things. Since $\{a_k\}$ is non-increasing, each of the expressions in parentheses is greater than or equal to 0. Thus, since $S_2 = (a_1 - a_2)$, $S_4 = (a_1 - a_2) + (a_3 - a_4)$, and so on, we see that the sequence $\{S_{2k}\}$ is non-decreasing. Our last expression for S_{2k} in Equation 116-4 tells us that S_{2k} is obtained by subtracting non-negative numbers from a_1. Therefore, $S_{2k} \le a_1$, and so $\{S_{2k}\}$ is bounded above. Thus the sequence $\{S_{2k}\}$ is bounded and non-decreasing and hence is convergent; let us denote its limit by S.

A typical term with an odd subscript looks like this:

$$S_{2k+1} = S_{2k} + a_{2k+1}.$$

Figure 116-1

We have just found that $\lim_{k \uparrow \infty} S_{2k} = S$, and since $\lim_{k \uparrow \infty} a_{2k+1} = 0$, we now see that $\lim_{k \uparrow \infty} S_{2k+1} = S$, also. It follows readily that $\lim_{n \uparrow \infty} S_n = S$, so Series 116-2 converges and its sum is S.

To see how well the terms of the sequence $\{S_n\}$ approximate its limit S, let us look more closely at the subsequence $\{S_{2k+1}\}$. The term that follows S_{2k+1} is S_{2k+3}, which we obtain by adding $(-a_{2k+2} + a_{2k+3})$ to S_{2k+1}. This number in parentheses is not positive, so we see that S_{2k+3} is not greater than S_{2k+1}. Thus the sequence $\{S_{2k+1}\}$ is non-increasing. We already know that the sequence $\{S_{2k}\}$ is non-decreasing, so the even partial sums of Series 116-3 approach the sum S from below, while the odd partial sums approach S from above, as indicated in Fig. 116-1. From the figure, it is apparent that the difference between any particular term S_n and the sum S cannot be greater than the difference between S_n and S_{n+1}; that is, $|S - S_n| \le |S_n - S_{n+1}|$. For example, we see that $|S - S_5| \le |S_5 - S_6|$. Since $|S_n - S_{n+1}| = a_{n+1}$, we have shown that $|S - S_n| \le a_{n+1}$. Thus the remainder after n terms is no larger than the first term that we do not use when we form the sum S_n, as our theorem asserts.

Example 116-2. Show that the series

(116-5) $1 - \frac{1}{2} + \frac{1}{3} - \frac{1}{4} + \frac{1}{5} - \cdots$

converges, and approximate its sum with an error of less than .1.

Solution. The absolute values of the terms of our given alternating series form the decreasing sequence $\left\{\dfrac{1}{k}\right\}$ whose limit is obviously 0. Thus the hypotheses of Theorem 116-2 are satisfied, and the series converges. According to the theorem, the remainder of such a convergent alternating series is less than the first unused term, so we make an error of less than .1 if we use the partial sum

$$1 - \tfrac{1}{2} + \tfrac{1}{3} - \tfrac{1}{4} + \tfrac{1}{5} - \tfrac{1}{6} + \tfrac{1}{7} - \tfrac{1}{8} + \tfrac{1}{9} = .648$$

to approximate the sum of the series. In Section 120 we will find that the sum is $\ln 2 = .693$, so the actual remainder is $.693 - .648 = .045$. This series converges "slowly;" we must use many terms to form a partial sum that gives a close approximation to the sum of the series.

In order to apply our alternating series test to a given series $\displaystyle\sum_{k=1}^{\infty} (-1)^{k+1} a_k$, we must show that each term of the sequence $\{a_k\}$ is not less than its successor; that is, we must show that $a_k \geq a_{k+1}$ for each index k. Sometimes it is more convenient to verify this inequality when it is written in one of the forms

$$a_k - a_{k+1} \geq 0 \quad \text{or} \quad \frac{a_{k+1}}{a_k} \leq 1.$$

We can even use calculus, as the following simple example shows.

Example 116-3. Test the series $\displaystyle\sum_{k=1}^{\infty} (-1)^{k+1} \frac{k}{1 + k^2}$ for convergence.

Solution. It is clear that $\displaystyle\lim_{k \uparrow \infty} \frac{k}{1 + k^2} = 0$, so it only remains for us to show that the sequence $\left\{\dfrac{k}{1 + k^2}\right\}$ is non-increasing. We observe that the terms of this sequence are the values at the positive integers of the function defined by the equation $f(x) = x/(1 + x^2)$. We can readily calculate $f'(x) = (1 - x^2)/(1 + x^2)$, and we see that $f'(x) < 0$ if $x > 1$. Hence f is decreasing in the interval $(1, \infty)$. It follows that $f(k + 1) < f(k)$ for each positive integer k, and so our sequence is non-increasing. Thus the hypotheses of Theorem 116-2 are satisfied, and therefore our series converges.

Although infinite series display many of the properties of ordinary sums, series and sums are not the same in all respects. Let us illustrate this statement by performing a few manipulations with Series 116-5. We have not yet shown that its sum is $\ln 2$, but we do know that the series converges, so let us denote its sum by S. Thus

$$(116\text{-}6) \qquad S = 1 - \tfrac{1}{2} + \tfrac{1}{3} - \tfrac{1}{4} + \tfrac{1}{5} - \tfrac{1}{6} + \tfrac{1}{7} - \tfrac{1}{8} + \cdots.$$

Hence

$$\tfrac{1}{2}S = \qquad \tfrac{1}{2} \qquad - \tfrac{1}{4} \qquad + \tfrac{1}{6} \qquad - \tfrac{1}{8} + \cdots,$$

and so when we add these two series, we obtain

(116-7) $$\tfrac{3}{2}S = 1 + \tfrac{1}{3} - \tfrac{1}{2} + \tfrac{1}{5} + \tfrac{1}{7} - \tfrac{1}{4} + \cdots.$$

If you write out this addition for many terms, you will readily convince yourself that the series on the right-hand side of Equation 116-7 contains the same terms as the series on the right-hand side of Equation 116-6. Since the value of an ordinary sum is independent of the order in which its terms are written, we are naturally tempted to conclude that these series also have the same sum, and thus that $\tfrac{3}{2}S = S$. It would therefore follow that $S = 0$. But you can easily check (Theorem 116-2) that S must be a number between $\tfrac{1}{2}$ and 1, so we must have gone wrong somewhere. We erred when we tried to conclude that just because the series in Equations 116-6 and 116-7 contain the same terms, then they have the same sum. It can be shown that if two series have the same terms, and if one of the series converges absolutely, then the other series also converges absolutely, and the two sums are the same. However, in the case of conditionally convergent series (such as the series in Equations 116-6 and 116-7) the sums of two series containing the same terms (but in different orders) need not be equal.

PROBLEMS 116

1. Test each of the following series for absolute convergence.

(a) $\displaystyle\sum_{k=1}^{\infty} \frac{\sin e^k}{e^k}$ (b) $\displaystyle\sum_{k=1}^{\infty} \frac{\sin k^e}{k^e}$ (c) $\displaystyle\sum_{k=1}^{\infty} \sin (-e)^{-k}$ (d) $\displaystyle\sum_{k=1}^{\infty} \sin^k (-e)$

2. Show that the geometric series $\displaystyle\sum_{k=0}^{\infty} x^k$ does not converge conditionally for any number x.

3. Test each of the following series for absolute convergence and for convergence.

(a) $\displaystyle\sum_{k=2}^{\infty} \frac{(-1)^k}{\ln k}$ (b) $\displaystyle\sum_{k=1}^{\infty} \frac{(-1)^{k+1}}{\sqrt{k}}$ (c) $\displaystyle\sum_{k=1}^{\infty} (-1)^{k+1} \ln\left(1 + \frac{1}{k}\right)$ (d) $\displaystyle\sum_{k=1}^{\infty} \frac{(-1)^{k(k+1)/2}}{2k + 1}$

4. Theorem 116-2 states that the absolute value of the error we incur if we approximate the sum of the series $1 - \tfrac{2}{3} + (\tfrac{2}{3})^2 - (\tfrac{2}{3})^3 + \cdots$ by taking the sum of the first n terms is no larger than $(\tfrac{2}{3})^n$. What is the actual absolute value of the error?

5. Approximate the sum of the series with an error whose absolute value is no more than indicated.

(a) $\dfrac{1}{3 \cdot 2!} - \dfrac{1}{5 \cdot 3!} + \dfrac{1}{7 \cdot 4!} - \dfrac{1}{9 \cdot 5!} + \cdots,\ |E| \leq .001$

(b) $1 - \dfrac{1}{2! \, 2^2} + \dfrac{1}{4! \, 2^4} - \dfrac{1}{6! \, 2^6} + \cdots, \; |E| \leq .00005$

(c) $1 - \dfrac{1}{3 \cdot 3^3} + \dfrac{1}{5 \cdot 3^5} - \dfrac{1}{7 \cdot 3^7} + \cdots, \; |E| \leq .00005$

6. The following series satisfy only part of the hypotheses of Theorem 116-2; which part? Do they converge?

(a) $\displaystyle\sum_{k=0}^{\infty} (-1)^{k+1} \dfrac{k}{3k-1}$

(b) $\displaystyle\sum_{k=1}^{\infty} (-1)^{k+1} \dfrac{1 + \cos k\pi}{k}$

7. The graph of a certain function f is the polygonal line that successively joins the points $(0,0)$, $(1,1)$, $(2,0)$, $(3, -\frac{1}{3})$, $(4,0)$, $(5, \frac{1}{5})$, $(6,0)$, $(7, -\frac{1}{7})$, and so on. Evaluate the integral $\displaystyle\int_0^{\infty} f(x)\, dx$ with an error of no more than $\frac{1}{10}$.

8. Show that even though both of the series $\displaystyle\sum_{k=1}^{\infty} a_k$ and $\displaystyle\sum_{k=1}^{\infty} b_k$ converge, it may be possible that the series $\displaystyle\sum_{k=1}^{\infty} a_k b_k$ diverges. Show that if both series converge, at least one converging absolutely, then the series $\displaystyle\sum_{k=1}^{\infty} a_k b_k$ converges absolutely.

9. Show that if f is continuous and non-increasing in the interval $(1, \infty)$, and if $\displaystyle\lim_{x \uparrow \infty} f(x) = 0$, then the integral $\displaystyle\int_1^{\infty} (-1)^{[x]} f(x)\, dx$ converges.

10. Suppose that $\{a_k\}$ is a non-increasing sequence such that $\displaystyle\lim_{k \uparrow \infty} a_k = 0$. Show that the series

$$a_1 + a_2 - 2a_3 + a_4 + a_5 - 2a_6 + a_7 + a_8 - 2a_9 + \cdots$$

converges.

| | 7 THE INTEGRAL TEST

We have pointed out that if we are given an infinite series $\displaystyle\sum_{k=1}^{\infty} a_k$, we can find a function f such that the integral $\displaystyle\int_1^{\infty} f(x)\, dx$ converges if, and only if, the given series converges. In this section we will investigate a case where we go in the opposite direction; that is, we will start with a given function, rather than a given series.

Suppose f is a non-increasing function that does not take negative values in the interval $[1, \infty]$, and consider the infinite series

(117-1) $\qquad\qquad \displaystyle\sum_{k=1}^{\infty} a_k = a_1 + a_2 + a_3 + \cdots$

whose terms are given by the equations

$$a_k = f(k), \quad k = 1, 2, 3, \ldots.$$

Thus for a given positive integer n, the nth partial sum of our series has the form

$$S_n = \sum_{k=1}^{n} f(k) = f(1) + f(2) + \cdots + f(n).$$

Now let us write the integral $\int_1^n f(x)\,dx$ as a sum,

$$\int_1^n f(x)\,dx = \int_1^2 f(x)\,dx + \int_2^3 f(x)\,dx + \cdots + \int_{n-1}^n f(x)\,dx = \sum_{k=1}^{n-1} \int_k^{k+1} f(x)\,dx,$$

and take a close look at a typical term $\int_k^{k+1} f(x)\,dx$. Since f is non-increasing, we see that

$$f(k+1) \leq f(x) \leq f(k) \text{ for } x \in [k, k+1].$$

If we integrate from k to $k+1$, these inequalities tell us that

(117-2) $$f(k+1) \leq \int_k^{k+1} f(x)\,dx \leq f(k),$$

and by adding these bounds on the terms of the sum $\sum_{k=1}^{n-1} \int_k^{k+1} f(x)\,dx$, we obtain a bound on the sum itself. Since the sum is the number $\int_1^n f(x)\,dx$, we therefore have

$$\sum_{k=1}^{n-1} f(k+1) \leq \int_1^n f(x)\,dx \leq \sum_{k=1}^{n-1} f(k).$$

In these inequalities, the sum on the left is

$$\sum_{k=1}^{n-1} f(k+1) = f(2) + f(3) + \cdots + f(n) = S_n - a_1,$$

and the sum on the right is $S_n - a_n$, a number that is not greater than S_n. Thus $S_n - a_1 \leq \int_1^n f(x)\,dx \leq S_n$; that is,

(117-3) $$\int_1^n f(x)\,dx \leq S_n \leq a_1 + \int_1^n f(x)\,dx.$$

A geometric interpretation of the argument we used to deduce these inequalities can be based on Fig. 117-1 (for $n = 5$). That figure shows the graph of a

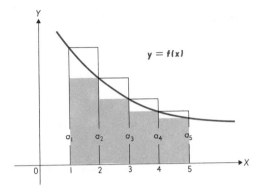

Figure 117-1

function f satisfying our given conditions. The sum of the areas of the shaded "interior" rectangular regions is $a_2 + a_3 + a_4 + a_5 = S_5 - a_1$. The sum of the areas of the "exterior" rectangular regions bounded in black is S_4. Then from the geometric interpretation of the integral,

$$S_5 - a_1 \le \int_1^5 f(x)\, dx \le S_4.$$

Since $S_5 \ge S_4$, these inequalities remain valid if S_4 is replaced by S_5. When we make this replacement and rearrange, we obtain Inequalities 117-3 with $n = 5$.

By hypothesis, the terms of Series 117-1 are non-negative, so we know that it converges if, and only if, its sequence $\{S_n\}$ of partial sums is bounded. From Inequalities 117-3, it is clear that this sequence is bounded if, and only if, the integral $\int_1^\infty f(x)\, dx$ is convergent, and hence we have the following theorem, the **integral test** for the convergence of an infinite series.

Theorem 117-1.   *An infinite series whose terms are the values at the positive integers of a non-increasing function f that does not take negative values in the interval $[1, \infty]$ converges if, and only if, the improper integral $\int_1^\infty f(x)\, dx$ converges.*

Example 117-1.   Use the integral test to examine the convergence of the series

$$\sum_{k=1}^\infty \frac{1}{1 + k^2}.$$

Solution.   According to Theorem 117-1, the given series converges if, and only if, the improper integral $\int_1^\infty \frac{dx}{1 + x^2}$ converges. Therefore, we investigate the limit of the proper integrals of the form

$$\int_1^R \frac{dx}{1+x^2} = \mathrm{Tan}^{-1} x \Big|_1^R = \mathrm{Tan}^{-1} R - \frac{\pi}{4}.$$

Since $\lim_{R \uparrow \infty} \mathrm{Tan}^{-1} R = \frac{\pi}{2}$, we see that the integral $\int_1^\infty \frac{dx}{1+x^2}$ converges, and so our given series converges.

Example 117-2. For what choices of the exponent p is the *p*-series $\sum_{k=1}^\infty \frac{1}{k^p}$ convergent?

Solution. The series obviously diverges if $p \le 0$; if $p > 0$, the integral test says that the *p*-series will converge if, and only if, the improper integral $\int_1^\infty x^{-p} dx$ _converges. We found in Example 110-2 that the improper integral converges if $p > 1$ and diverges if $p \le 1$. Thus

$$\sum_{k=1}^\infty \frac{1}{k^p} \begin{cases} \text{converges if } p > 1. \\ \text{diverges if } p \le 1. \end{cases}$$

If Series 117-1 converges, we may take the limit of each term in Inequalities 117-3 and thus gain an estimate of the sum S of the series:

$$(117\text{-}4) \qquad \int_1^\infty f(x)\, dx \le S \le a_1 + \int_1^\infty f(x)\, dx.$$

We can improve on this estimate by means of the following argument. If m is a given positive integer, the remainder after m terms of Series 117-1 is the number $S - S_m = a_{m+1} + a_{m+2} + \cdots$. This number is the sum of what is left of Series 117-1 after an initial segment has been deleted, so essentially the same argument that led to Inequalities 117-4 gives us the inequalities

$$\int_{m+1}^\infty f(x)\, dx \le S - S_m \le a_{m+1} + \int_{m+1}^\infty f(x)\, dx.$$

When we write these inequalities in the form

$$(117\text{-}5) \qquad 0 \le S - \left(S_m + \int_{m+1}^\infty f(x)\, dx \right) \le a_{m+1},$$

we see how the number $S_m + \int_{m+1}^\infty f(x)\, dx$ approximates the sum S of our series.

Example 117-3. How good is our approximation of the sum of the series $\sum\limits_{k=3}^{\infty} \dfrac{1}{k^2 - 4}$ if we compute the sum of the first twelve terms and then integrate to estimate the remainder?

Solution. Since the index of summation starts at 3 in this example, the twelfth term is the one whose index is 14. Thus we choose $m = 14$, and Inequalities 117-5 tell us that the number

$$\frac{1}{5} + \frac{1}{12} + \cdots + \frac{1}{192} + \int_{15}^{\infty} \frac{dx}{x^2 - 1} \approx .5157 + .0347 = .5504$$

approximates the sum of our series with an error that lies between 0 and $\frac{1}{221}$.

Theorem 117-1 says that the sequence $\{S_n\}$ of partial sums of Series 117-1 and the sequence $\left\{\int_{1}^{n} f(x)\, dx\right\}$ of integrals of f either both converge or both diverge. Of course, if they both converge, we know that the sequence of differences $\{d_n\}$, where $d_n = S_n - \int_{1}^{n} f(x)\, dx$, converges. But the sequence of differences even converges when the series and the sequence of integrals diverge. We first notice that we can write Inequalities 117-3 in the form $0 \le d_n \le a_1$. Thus $\{d_n\}$ is a bounded sequence; we will show that it is also monotone, and then we will know that it converges. By definition,

$$d_n - d_{n+1} = S_n - \int_{1}^{n} f(x)\, dx - S_{n+1} + \int_{1}^{n+1} f(x)\, dx = \int_{n}^{n+1} f(x)\, dx - a_{n+1}.$$

Since $a_{n+1} = f(n + 1)$, this equation and the first of Inequalities 117-2 tells us that $d_n - d_{n+1} \ge 0$; in other words, $\{d_n\}$ is a non-increasing sequence.

Example 117-4. Discuss the sequence $\left\{1 + \frac{1}{2} + \cdots + \dfrac{1}{n} - \ln n\right\}$.

Solution. We obtain this sequence by setting $f(x) = \dfrac{1}{x}$ and calculating the sequences of differences between the partial sums of the series $1 + \frac{1}{2} + \frac{1}{3} + \cdots$ and the members of the sequence $\left\{\int_{1}^{n} \dfrac{dx}{x}\right\}$. Both the series and the improper integral $\int_{1}^{\infty} \dfrac{dx}{x}$ diverge, but we just saw that the sequence of differences converges, nevertheless. The limit of this sequence, the number $\lim\limits_{n \uparrow \infty} \left(1 + \frac{1}{2} + \cdots + \dfrac{1}{n} - \ln n\right)$, is called **Euler's constant**; its value is .5772156 .... To 3 decimal places, $d_5 = .574$.

Not only can we use our knowledge of improper integrals to test the convergence of infinite series, but we can use our knowledge of series to examine the convergence of improper integrals, as the following example illustrates.

Example 117-5. Discuss the convergence of the improper integral $\int_0^\infty \dfrac{\sin x}{x}\,dx.$

Solution. In Problem 111-4 we asked you to use integration by parts to show that this integral converges; now we will use a different technique. If we break up the positive X-axis into the intervals $[0, \pi]$, $[\pi, 2\pi]$, $[2\pi, 3\pi]$, and so on, then our integral converges if, and only if, the following series converges:

$$(117\text{-}6) \qquad \int_0^\pi \frac{\sin x}{x}\,dx + \int_\pi^{2\pi} \frac{\sin x}{x}\,dx + \int_{2\pi}^{3\pi} \frac{\sin x}{x}\,dx + \cdots.$$

The kth term of this series is given by the formula

$$a_k = \int_{(k-1)\pi}^{k\pi} \frac{\sin x}{x}\,dx.$$

Our series is an alternating series since, for x in the interval $((k-1)\pi, k\pi)$, $\sin x$ is positive if k is odd and negative if k is even. In either case,

$$\frac{|\sin x|}{k\pi} \le \frac{|\sin x|}{x} \le \frac{|\sin x|}{(k-1)\pi},$$

and so

$$(117\text{-}7) \qquad \int_{(k-1)\pi}^{k\pi} \frac{|\sin x|}{k\pi}\,dx \le \int_{(k-1)\pi}^{k\pi} \left|\frac{\sin x}{x}\right|\,dx \le \int_{(k-1)\pi}^{k\pi} \frac{|\sin x|}{(k-1)\pi}\,dx.$$

Now we observe that

$$\int_{(k-1)\pi}^{k\pi} |\sin x|\,dx = \int_0^\pi \sin x\,dx = 2, \text{ and } |a_k| = \int_{(k-1)\pi}^{k\pi} \left|\frac{\sin x}{x}\right|\,dx.$$

Therefore, Inequalities 117-7 can be written as

$$(117\text{-}8) \qquad \frac{2}{k\pi} \le |a_k| \le \frac{2}{(k-1)\pi}.$$

From these inequalities we see that $\lim_{k \uparrow \infty} a_k = 0$. Furthermore, if we replace k with $k+1$, we have $\dfrac{2}{(k+1)\pi} \le |a_{k+1}| \le \dfrac{2}{k\pi}$, and hence $|a_{k+1}| \le |a_k|$. Thus Series 117-6 is an alternating series whose terms decrease in absolute value. According to the alternating series test, this series converges, and so we see that the integral

$$\int_0^\infty \frac{\sin x}{x}\, dx \text{ converges. The integral } \int_0^\infty \left|\frac{\sin x}{x}\right| dx \text{ converges if, and only if, Series}$$

117-6 converges absolutely. But Inequalities 117-8 say that the series $\sum_{k=1}^\infty |a_k|$ domi-

nates the divergent series $\sum_{k=1}^\infty \frac{2}{k\pi}$, so $\sum_{k=1}^\infty |a_k|$ diverges; hence the integral $\int_0^\infty \left|\frac{\sin x}{x}\right| dx$

diverges. Therefore, our given improper integral is conditionally convergent.

PROBLEMS 117

1. Use the integral test to test the following series for convergence.

(a) $\sum_{k=1}^\infty k^{1492} e^{-k}$ (b) $\sum_{k=1}^\infty \coth k$ (c) $\sum_{k=1}^\infty \frac{1}{k\sqrt{k^2+3}}$ (d) $\sum_{k=1}^\infty \left(\frac{\pi}{2} - \text{Arctan } k\right)$

2. Test the following series for convergence.

(a) $\sum_{k=1}^\infty \frac{1}{\sqrt{k(k+1)}}$ (b) $\sum_{k=3}^\infty \frac{\cos k + e^{-k}}{k^3 - 2k + 4}$ (c) $\sum_{k=1}^\infty \frac{\text{Arctan } k}{\sqrt{k^2+1}}$ (d) $\sum_{k=1}^\infty \frac{1}{k^{1/2} + (\frac{1}{2})^k}$

3. Find an example of a function that takes non-negative values in the interval $[1, \infty]$ and is such that $\sum_{k=1}^\infty f(k)$ converges but $\int_1^\infty f(x)\, dx$ diverges. Can you find an example of another such function for which the integral converges but the series does not?

4. Show that the series $\sum_{k=2}^\infty \frac{1}{k(\ln k)^p}$ converges if $p > 1$ and diverges if $p \leq 1$.

5. Let $\zeta(p)$ be the sum of the p-series (Example 117-2) for $p > 1$.

(a) Use Equation 117-4 to show that $1 \leq \zeta(p) \leq \frac{p}{p-1}$.

(b) Show that for each positive integer m,

$$\zeta(p) = \frac{1}{1^p} + \cdots + \frac{1}{m^p} + \frac{1}{(p-1)(m+1)^{p-1}} + E_m, \text{ where } 0 \leq E_m \leq \frac{1}{(m+1)^p}.$$

6. Estimate the sum of the series $\sum_{k=1}^\infty \frac{1}{1+k^2}$ with an error of no more than .01.

7. Let r be a number between 0 and 1. Use the integral test to show that the geometric series $\sum_{k=0}^\infty r^k$ converges. Use Inequalities 117-4 to show that $1 - r \leq \ln\frac{1}{r} \leq \frac{1-r}{r}$.

8. Suppose that f is continuous and non-decreasing in the interval $(0, 1]$ and does not take negative values. Show that $\lim_{n \uparrow \infty} \left[f(1) + \cdots + f\left(\frac{1}{n}\right) - \int_{1/n}^1 x^{-2}f(x)\, dx\right]$ exists.

9. Show that if $\lim_{k \uparrow \infty} ka_k = L$, then the series $\sum_{k=1}^\infty a_k$ is divergent unless $L = 0$. Give an

example of a divergent series $\sum\limits_{k=1}^{\infty} a_k$ such that $\lim\limits_{k\uparrow\infty} ka_k = 0$, and of a convergent series $\sum\limits_{k=1}^{\infty} b_k$ such that $\lim\limits_{k\uparrow\infty} kb_k = 0$.

10. Let g be a function that is continuous and non-increasing in an interval $[a, \infty]$ and is such that $\lim\limits_{x\uparrow\infty} g(x) = 0$. Use the technique of Example 117-5 to show that the integral $\int_a^\infty g(x) \sin x \, dx$ converges, and show that this integral converges absolutely if, and only if, the integral $\int_a^\infty g(x) \, dx$ converges.

118 THE RATIO AND ROOT TESTS

The tests we will develop in this section are applied to determine divergence or absolute convergence, so in addition to a given series

$$(118\text{-}1) \qquad \sum_{k=1}^{\infty} a_k = a_1 + a_2 + a_3 + \cdots,$$

we consider the series

$$(118\text{-}2) \qquad \sum_{k=1}^{\infty} |a_k| = |a_1| + |a_2| + |a_3| + \cdots.$$

Because we will be dividing by the terms of our series, we will assume that none of them is 0; therefore, all the terms of Series 118-2 are positive.

Let us suppose that, after a certain index, the ratio of any term of Series 118-2 to the preceding term is less than or equal to a number q which itself is less than 1. For example, if we take the ratio of any term beyond the fifth to the preceding term of the series $\sum\limits_{k=1}^{\infty} \dfrac{3^k}{k!}$, we obtain a number that is not greater than $\frac{1}{2}$, and $\frac{1}{2}$, in turn, is less than 1. Thus we are assuming that there is some index such that for each larger index k we have

$$(118\text{-}3) \qquad \frac{|a_{k+1}|}{|a_k|} \le q < 1.$$

Since $q = \dfrac{q^{k+1}}{q^k}$, the first of Inequalities 118-3 can be written as $\dfrac{|a_{k+1}|}{|a_k|} \le \dfrac{q^{k+1}}{q^k}$ or $\dfrac{|a_{k+1}|}{q^{k+1}} \le \dfrac{|a_k|}{q^k}$. Thus, after a certain term, the sequence $\left\{\dfrac{|a_k|}{q^k}\right\}$ of positive terms is non-increasing, and so it has a limit. The terms of this sequence are ratios of corresponding terms of our series $\sum\limits_{k=1}^{\infty} |a_k|$ and the convergent (because $0 < q < 1$) geometric series $\sum\limits_{k=1}^{\infty} q^k$. Therefore, Theorem 115-3 tells us that Series 118-2 converges.

To use the test we developed in the preceding paragraph to show that a series converges, we must show that the ratios of the absolute values of successive terms are ultimately less than or equal to a number q which itself is actually less than 1. The analogous test for divergence does not require us to be so careful. Suppose there is an index such that for each larger index k, we have

(118-4)
$$\frac{|a_{k+1}|}{|a_k|} \geq 1.$$

Then from some term onward, the sequence of positive terms $\{|a_k|\}$ is non-decreasing and hence cannot have 0 as a limit. Therefore, according to Theorem 114-1, Series 118-1 diverges. We summarize our results as a theorem.

Theorem 118-1.   *If after some term in the infinite series* $\sum_{k=1}^{\infty} a_k$ *we have* $\dfrac{|a_{k+1}|}{|a_k|} \leq q < 1$ *for each index k, then the series is absolutely convergent. If after some term we have* $\dfrac{|a_{k+1}|}{|a_k|} \geq 1$ *for each index k, the series diverges.*

Example 118-1.   For what choices of x does the series

(118-5)
$$\sum_{k=0}^{\infty} [2 + (-1)^k] x^k = 3 + x + 3x^2 + x^3 + 3x^4 + \cdots$$

converge, and for what choices does it diverge?

Solution.   For each non-zero number x, the sequence of ratios of the absolute values of successive terms of our given series is

$$\{ \tfrac{1}{3} |x|, \, 3 |x|, \, \tfrac{1}{3} |x|, \, 3 |x|, \ldots \}$$

No term of this sequence is greater than $3 |x|$, so this number can serve as the number q of Theorem 118-1 if it is less than 1. Thus if $|x| < \tfrac{1}{3}$, our series converges. For example, the series $3 + \dfrac{1}{4} + \dfrac{3}{4^2} + \dfrac{1}{4^3} + \dfrac{3}{4^4} + \cdots$ converges; it is the series we get when we replace x with $\tfrac{1}{4}$ in Series 118-5, and $\tfrac{1}{4} < \tfrac{1}{3}$.

No term of our sequence of ratios is less than $\tfrac{1}{3} |x|$, and this number will be greater than or equal to 1 if $|x| \geq 3$. Therefore, according to the second part of Theorem 118-1, our series diverges if $|x| \geq 3$.

In summary, our theorem tells us that the given series diverges if $x \leq -3$, converges if x is a number in the interval $(-\tfrac{1}{3}, \tfrac{1}{3})$, and diverges if $x \geq 3$. If $x \in (-3, -\tfrac{1}{3}] \cup [\tfrac{1}{3}, 3)$, Theorem 118-1 does not apply, and we must use other tests. We will complete our answer to the question asked here in Example 118-3.

In order to apply Theorem 118-1, we must show that the appropriate one of

Inequalities 118-3 or 118-4 holds for each integer k that is larger than some particular integer K. Thus we must really verify infinitely many inequalities. One method of showing that these inequalities hold is to calculate the limit of the quotient $\dfrac{|a_{k+1}|}{|a_k|}$, if this limit exists. Let us suppose that

$$\lim_{k \uparrow \infty} \frac{|a_{k+1}|}{|a_k|} = L.$$

Thus if $N_p L$ is any neighborhood of L, there is an index K beyond which $\dfrac{|a_{k+1}|}{|a_k|} \in N_p L$; that is, if $k > K$, then

(118-6) $$L - p < \frac{|a_{k+1}|}{|a_k|} < L + p.$$

If L is a number that is less than 1, we can choose our positive number p so small that $L + p$ is also less than 1. Then $L + p$ will serve as the number q of Theorem 118-1, and hence our series converges absolutely. If L is greater than 1, we can choose the positive number p so small that $L - p \geq 1$; hence the first of Inequalities 118-6 implies that Inequality 118-4 holds, so our series diverges. If $L = 1$, we do not have enough information to tell whether our series converges or diverges, as the example of the p-series $\sum_{k=1}^{\infty} k^{-p}$ shows. Here the ratio $\dfrac{|a_{k+1}|}{|a_k|}$ is $\dfrac{k^p}{(k+1)^p} = \left(\dfrac{k}{k+1}\right)^p$, and its limit is 1, regardless of the choice of p. But we know that the p-series converges if $p > 1$ and diverges if $p \leq 1$, so we see that there are both convergent and divergent series for which $\lim_{k \uparrow \infty} \dfrac{|a_{k+1}|}{|a_k|} = 1$. Thus we have the following theorem, the **ratio test.**

Theorem 118-2. *Suppose that* $\lim_{k \uparrow \infty} \dfrac{|a_{k+1}|}{|a_k|} = L$. *Then*

(i) *if* $L < 1$, *the series* $\sum_{k=1}^{\infty} a_k$ *converges absolutely,*

(ii) *if* $L > 1$, *the series* $\sum_{k=1}^{\infty} a_k$ *diverges, and*

(iii) *if* $L = 1$, *we need further information to determine whether or not the series converges.*

Example 118-2. Test the series $\sum_{k=1}^{\infty} \dfrac{10^{2k}}{k!}$ for convergence.

Solution. Here

$$\frac{|a_{k+1}|}{|a_k|} = \frac{10^{2k+2}}{(k+1)!} \cdot \frac{k!}{10^{2k}} = \frac{100}{k+1},$$

so

$$\lim_{k \uparrow \infty} \frac{|a_{k+1}|}{|a_k|} = \lim_{k \uparrow \infty} \frac{100}{k+1} = 0.$$

Certainly this limit, $L = 0$, is less than 1, so the ratio test tells us that the series converges.

Because they are closely related, students often confuse the ratio test with the limit comparison test (Theorem 115-3). To apply Theorem 115-3, we take the limit of the ratios of the terms of a given series to corresponding terms of some comparison series. The ratios we compute when we apply Theorem 118-2 are of successive terms of the same series.

The basic technique that we have used so far in this section to test a given series for convergence is to compare it with a geometric series. There are many other applications and refinements of this idea; let us mention one that we will use when we study power series in the next section.

With our given Series 118-1 we can associate the sequence

$$\{|a_k|^{1/k}\} = \{|a_1|, |a_2|^{1/2}, |a_3|^{1/3}, \ldots\}.$$

Suppose there is a number q and an integer K such that for each index k that is larger than K we have

(118-7) $$|a_k|^{1/k} \leq q < 1.$$

These inequalities tell us two things: (1) that the series $\sum_{k=K+1}^{\infty} |a_k|$ is dominated by the geometric series $\sum_{k=K+1}^{\infty} q^k$, and (2) that this geometric series converges. It follows that Series 118-1 converges absolutely. On the other hand, suppose that for infinitely many indices we have

(118-8) $$|a_k|^{1/k} \geq 1.$$

Then the sequence $\{a_k\}$ cannot have a limit of 0, and so Series 118-1 diverges.

To give us a criterion for determining which (if either) of Inequalities 118-7 or 118-8 holds, we now introduce the concept of the upper limit of a sequence.

Definition 118-1. *A number L is called the **upper limit** of a sequence $\{r_k\}$, and we write $\overline{\lim}_{k \uparrow \infty} r_k = L$, if for every $N_p L$:*
   (i) there are infinitely many terms of the sequence in $N_p L$, and
   (ii) there is an integer K such that $r_k < L + p$ for each $k > K$.
In other words, infinitely many terms of the sequence $\{r_{K+1}, r_{K+2}, \ldots\}$ are greater than $L - p$, and all are less than $L + p$.

If the sequence $\{r_k\}$ has a limit L, then to every $N_p L$ there corresponds an integer K such that all terms of the sequence $\{r_{K+1}, r_{K+2}, \ldots\}$ belong to $N_p L$, and hence statements (i) and (ii) of Definition 118-1 are satisfied. Thus, if a sequence has a limit, then that number is also its upper limit. But a sequence can have an upper limit without having a limit. The sequence $\{(-1)^k\}$ is an example; it does not have a limit, but its upper limit is 1. With the aid of the Completeness Property 2-1, we can show that a sequence has an upper limit if, and only if, it is bounded above. If we write $\overline{\lim\limits_{k \uparrow \infty}} \, r_k = \infty$ when $\{r_k\}$ is not bounded above, then the equation

$\overline{\lim\limits_{k \uparrow \infty}} \, r_k = L$ has a meaning for every sequence $\{r_k\}$, bounded or not.

Now we can prove another convergence theorem, called the **root test.**

Theorem 118-3. *Suppose that* $\overline{\lim\limits_{k \uparrow \infty}} \, |a_k|^{1/k} = L$. *Then*

(i) *if* $L < 1$, *the series* $\sum\limits_{k=1}^{\infty} a_k$ *converges absolutely,*

(ii) *if* $L > 1$ *or if* L *is the symbol* ∞, *the series* $\sum\limits_{k=1}^{\infty} a_k$ *diverges, and*

(iii) *if* $L = 1$, *we need further information to determine whether or not the series converges.*

Proof. Suppose first that L is a number. The equation $\overline{\lim\limits_{k \uparrow \infty}} \, |a_k|^{1/k} = L$ means that to each neighborhood $N_p L$ there corresponds an integer K such that for each index $k > K$ we have $|a_k|^{1/k} < L + p$, and there are infinitely many terms of the sequence such that $|a_k|^{1/k} > L - p$. If $L < 1$, we can choose the positive number p so small that $L + p < 1$; this number $L + p$ will therefore serve as the number q of Inequalities 118-7, and so our series converges. If $L > 1$, we can choose the positive number p so small that $L - p \geq 1$; therefore Inequality 118-8 holds and our series diverges.

If $\overline{\lim\limits_{k \uparrow \infty}} \, |a_k|^{1/k} = \infty$, the terms of our series are unbounded, so it diverges. We will leave to you the problem of finding examples of convergent and divergent series for which $L = 1$, thus showing that in this case we have insufficient information from which to conclude convergence or divergence.

Example 118-3. Apply the root test to the series of Example 118-1.

Solution. For convenience of notation, let us simply discard the first term of Series 118-5; thus for a given number x our sequence $\{|a_k|^{1/k}\}$ is

$$\{|x|, \, 3^{1/2} |x|, \, |x|, \, 3^{1/4} |x|, \, |x|, \, 3^{1/6} |x|, \, |x|, \ldots\}$$

Since $\lim\limits_{n \uparrow \infty} 3^{1/2n} = 1$, we see that $\lim\limits_{k \uparrow \infty} |a_k|^{1/k} = |x|$. Therefore, $\overline{\lim\limits_{k \uparrow \infty}} \, |a_k|^{1/k} = |x|$, so Theorem 118-3 tells us that our series converges if $|x| < 1$ and diverges if $|x| > 1$.

This result, of course, does not conflict with the result of Example 118-1; it is simply more complete. Now we know that our series diverges if $x < -1$, converges if $x \in (-1, 1)$, and diverges if $x > 1$. Neither test tells us what happens if x is equal to 1 or -1. When you replace x in Series 118-5 with either 1 or -1, you can easily see that you have a divergent series. Thus the complete answer to the question raised in Example 118-1 is that Series 118-5 converges if $|x| < 1$ and diverges otherwise.

P R O B L E M S   1 1 8

1. Test the following series for convergence.

(a) $\displaystyle\sum_{k=1}^{\infty} \frac{k^2}{2^k}$ (b) $\displaystyle\sum_{k=2}^{\infty} \frac{k + (-1)^k}{3^k}$ (c) $\displaystyle\sum_{k=1}^{\infty} \frac{\exp \displaystyle\int_0^k \sin x^2 \, dx}{k!}$ (d) $\displaystyle\sum_{k=1}^{\infty} \frac{(2^k)!}{2^{k!}}$

(e) $\displaystyle\frac{1}{3} + \frac{1 \cdot 3}{3 \cdot 6} + \frac{1 \cdot 3 \cdot 5}{3 \cdot 6 \cdot 9} + \cdots$ (f) $1 + \displaystyle\frac{2!}{1 \cdot 3} + \frac{3!}{1 \cdot 3 \cdot 5} + \frac{4!}{1 \cdot 3 \cdot 5 \cdot 7} + \cdots$

(g) $\displaystyle\sum_{k=1}^{\infty} \frac{(k!)^2}{(2k)!}$ (h) $\displaystyle\sum_{k=1}^{\infty} \frac{k!}{k^k}$

2. The ratios of successive terms of the harmonic series $\displaystyle\sum_{k=1}^{\infty} \frac{1}{k}$ form the sequence $\left\{\dfrac{k}{k+1}\right\}$. Each term of this sequence is less than 1, yet the harmonic series diverges. Does this fact contradict Theorem 118-1?

3. Apply the root test to the following series.

(a) $\displaystyle\sum_{k=2}^{\infty} \frac{1}{(\ln k)^k}$ (b) $\displaystyle\sum_{k=1}^{\infty} \frac{1}{k^k}$ (c) $\frac{1}{2} + (\frac{1}{3})^2 + (\frac{1}{2})^3 + (\frac{1}{3})^4 + (\frac{1}{2})^5 + (\frac{1}{3})^6 + \cdots$

(d) $\displaystyle\sum_{k=1}^{\infty} e^{\sin k}$ (e) $\displaystyle\sum_{k=2}^{\infty} \frac{1}{(\ln k)^{\ln k}}$ (f) $\displaystyle\sum_{k=0}^{\infty} \exp \int_k^0 \tanh^4 x \, dx$

4. Use the ratio test to determine x so that the following series are convergent.

(a) $\displaystyle\sum_{k=1}^{\infty} kx^k$ (b) $\displaystyle\sum_{k=1}^{\infty} \frac{e^{kx}}{k}$ (c) $\displaystyle\sum_{k=0}^{\infty} \sin^k x$

(d) $\displaystyle\sum_{k=1}^{\infty} \frac{k^2}{x^k}$ (e) $\displaystyle\sum_{k=0}^{\infty} \frac{(2x)^k}{(x^2 + 1)^k}$ (f) $\displaystyle\sum_{k=1}^{\infty} k^3 x^{3k}$

5. Is the ratio test applicable to the series $\dfrac{1}{2} + \dfrac{1 \cdot 3}{2 \cdot 4} + \dfrac{1 \cdot 3 \cdot 5}{2 \cdot 4 \cdot 6} + \cdots$? Does the series converge?

6. Suppose that the ratio test or the root test shows that the series $\displaystyle\sum_{k=1}^{\infty} a_k$ converges. Show that then $\displaystyle\sum_{k=1}^{\infty} k a_k$ also converges. Is $\displaystyle\sum_{k=1}^{\infty} k^2 a_k$ convergent?

7. Let $\sum_{k=1}^{\infty} a_k$ be a convergent series of positive terms and suppose that $\dfrac{a_{k+1}}{a_k} \leq q < 1$ for all $k \geq m$. Show that $0 \leq R_m \leq \dfrac{a_{m+1}}{1-q}$. Find an upper bound for the error you incur when you use the first five terms of the series $\sum_{k=1}^{\infty} \dfrac{2^k}{k!}$ to approximate its sum.

8. Find a convergent series $\sum_{k=1}^{\infty} a_k$ of positive terms and a divergent series $\sum_{k=1}^{\infty} b_k$ of positive terms such that $\varlimsup_{k \uparrow \infty} a_k^{1/k} = 1$ and $\varlimsup_{k \uparrow \infty} b_k^{1/k} = 1$.

9. Show that $\varlimsup_{k \uparrow \infty} (-1)^k = 1$.

10. Make up several examples of series to which Theorem 118-1 applies but Theorem 118-2 does not. Find examples of series to which Theorem 118-3 applies but Theorem 118-2 does not. Can you find a series to which Theorem 118-2 applies but Theorem 118-3 does not?

11. (a) Show that if $\varlimsup_{k \uparrow \infty} \dfrac{|a_{k+1}|}{|a_k|} < 1$, the series $\sum_{k=1}^{\infty} a_k$ converges absolutely.

(b) Show that if $\varlimsup_{k \uparrow \infty} \left(-\dfrac{|a_{k+1}|}{|a_k|} \right) < -1$, the series $\sum_{k=1}^{\infty} a_k$ diverges.

12. Give a definition for the *lower limit* of a sequence. Give an example of a sequence for which the lower limit exists, but which does not have a limit. Prove that a sequence has a limit if, and only if, its upper limit and its lower limit are the same number.

119 POWER SERIES

Suppose we select a sequence $\{c_k\}$ of numbers and a number a. Then for each number x we can form the **power series** in $(x - a)$

$$(119\text{-}1) \qquad \sum_{k=0}^{\infty} c_k(x - a)^k = c_0 + c_1(x - a) + c_2(x - a)^2 + \cdots .$$

The terms of the sequence $\{c_k\}$ are called the **coefficients** of the series. The series

$$(119\text{-}2) \qquad \sum_{k=0}^{\infty} \dfrac{(x - 3)^k}{k!} \quad \text{and} \quad \sum_{k=0}^{\infty} (-1)^k x^k$$

are examples of power series. In the first of these examples, $a = 3$, $c_0 = \dfrac{1}{0!} = \dfrac{1}{1} = 1$, $c_1 = 1$, $c_2 = \dfrac{1}{2!}$, and so on; and in the second example, $a = 0$, $c_0 = (-1)^0 = 1$, $c_1 = -1$, $c_2 = 1$, and so on. Power series play a large role in certain branches of mathematical analysis, and they are widely used in applied mathematics. We will see why they are important as we study the next few sections.

We can use any number x when we form a power series, and we naturally want to know what numbers yield convergent series. For example, if we replace x with 4 in the first of Series 119-2, we obtain the convergent series $\sum_{k=0}^{\infty} \dfrac{1}{k!}$, while substituting 1 for x in the second series gives us the divergent series $\sum_{k=0}^{\infty} (-1)^k$. We observe that when we replace x with a in Series 119-1, we obtain the convergent series $c_0 + 0 + 0 + \cdots$, so every power series converges for at least this one choice of x. But suppose $x \neq a$; does our series converge or diverge? The answer to this question is furnished by the root test (Theorem 118-3). To apply that test, we must calculate $L = \varlimsup_{k \uparrow \infty} |c_k(x - a)^k|^{1/k}$. We first observe that $|c_k(x-a)^k|^{1/k} = |c_k|^{1/k} |x - a|$, and it is easy to see that $\varlimsup_{k \uparrow \infty} (|c_k|^{1/k} |x - a|) = \left(\varlimsup_{k \uparrow \infty} |c_k|^{1/k} \right) |x - a|$. Therefore we have

$$L = \left(\varlimsup_{k \uparrow \infty} |c_k|^{1/k} \right) |x - a|.$$

Now we consider the three possibilities, (1) $\varlimsup_{k \uparrow \infty} |c_k|^{1/k} = 0$, (2) $\varlimsup_{k \uparrow \infty} |c_k|^{1/k} = C$, where C is a positive number, and (3) $\varlimsup_{k \uparrow \infty} |c_k|^{1/k} = \infty$. In the first case, $L = 0$; this number is less than 1, so our series converges absolutely, regardless of the choice of x. In the third case, $L = \infty$, and our series diverges, again regardless of the choice of x (different from a). In the second case, $L = C|x - a|$. According to Theorem 118-3, our series converges absolutely if this number is less than 1 and diverges if this number is greater than 1. Thus our series converges absolutely if $|x - a| < \dfrac{1}{C}$ and diverges if $|x - a| > \dfrac{1}{C}$. The inequality $|x - a| < \dfrac{1}{C}$ says that $x \in N_{1/C}a$. We call the number $\dfrac{1}{C}$ the **radius of convergence** of our power series, and we denote it by r. Our series converges absolutely at each point of the open interval $(a - r, a + r)$, the **interval of convergence** of the series, and diverges for each number outside the closed interval $[a - r, a + r]$. The root test does not tell what happens at the endpoints $a - r$ and $a + r$; some series converge at both endpoints, some at only one endpoint, and some at neither endpoint. In case (3), in which our series converges only when $x = a$, we say that the series has the radius of convergence 0. In case (1), in which our series converges for all choices of x, the interval of convergence is the interval $(-\infty, \infty)$. We summarize our results as a theorem.

Theorem 119-1. *For a power series $\sum_{k=0}^{\infty} c_k(x - a)^k$, one of the following statements is true:*
   (i) *The series converges only for the "trivial choice" $x = a$.*
   (ii) *The series converges absolutely for every number x.*

(iii) *There is a positive number r such that the series converges absolutely for every number x in the open interval $(a - r, a + r)$ and diverges for every number x outside the closed interval $[a - r, a + r]$.*

While, theoretically, we can always use the root test to find the interval of convergence of a given power series (as we did in Ex   'e 118-3), in practice it is usually easier to use the ratio test.

Example 119-1. Find the interval of convergence of the power series $\sum_{k=0}^{\infty} \dfrac{x^k}{k!}$.

Solution. The ratios of the absolute values of successive terms of our series have the form

$$\frac{|x|^{k+1}}{(k+1)!} \cdot \frac{k!}{|x|^k} = \frac{k!}{(k+1)!} \frac{|x|^{k+1}}{|x|^k} = \frac{1}{k+1} |x| .$$

No matter what number x is, $\lim\limits_{k \uparrow \infty} \dfrac{1}{k+1} |x| = 0$, and since this number is less than 1, Theorem 118-2 tells us that our series converges. Thus the interval of convergence of the given series is $(-\infty, \infty)$.

The example we just worked has a byproduct that will serve us in Section 121, so let us list it here. We have just shown that if x is any number, then the series $\sum_{k=0}^{\infty} \dfrac{x^k}{k!}$ converges. Hence its sequence of terms has the limit 0. Therefore, we see that *for each number x,*

(119-3) $$\lim_{k \uparrow \infty} \frac{x^k}{k!} = 0.$$

Example 119-2. Discuss the convergence of the power series $\sum_{k=1}^{\infty} \dfrac{(-1)^k 2^k (x-5)^{2k}}{k^2}$.

Solution. We first find the limit of the ratios of the absolute values of successive terms. Here $|a_k| = \dfrac{2^k (x-5)^{2k}}{k^2}$, so

$$\lim_{k \uparrow \infty} \frac{|a_{k+1}|}{|a_k|} = \lim_{k \uparrow \infty} \frac{2^{k+1}(x-5)^{2k+2}}{(k+1)^2} \cdot \frac{k^2}{2^k (x-5)^{2k}}$$

$$= \lim_{k \uparrow \infty} 2(x-5)^2 \left(\frac{k}{k+1}\right)^2 = 2(x-5)^2.$$

Our series will converge if the number $2(x-5)^2$ is less than 1, and it will diverge if $2(x-5)^2 > 1$. The inequality $2(x-5)^2 < 1$ is equivalent to the inequality

$|x - 5| < \dfrac{1}{\sqrt{2}}$. Thus the radius of convergence of our series is the number $\dfrac{1}{\sqrt{2}}$;

its interval of convergence is the interval $\left(5 - \dfrac{1}{\sqrt{2}}, 5 + \dfrac{1}{\sqrt{2}}\right)$. If we replace x

with $5 - \dfrac{1}{\sqrt{2}}$ or with $5 + \dfrac{1}{\sqrt{2}}$, we get the series $\displaystyle\sum_{k=1}^{\infty} \dfrac{(-1)^k}{k^2}$, which is convergent.

Therefore, our given series converges for x in the closed interval

$$\left[5 - \frac{1}{\sqrt{2}}, 5 + \frac{1}{\sqrt{2}}\right],$$

and it diverges for x outside this interval.

We close this section with a few remarks about the algebra of power series. We define the sum (and similarly the difference) of two power series $\displaystyle\sum_{k=0}^{\infty} c_k(x - a)^k$

and $\displaystyle\sum_{k=0}^{\infty} d_k(x - a)^k$ by means of the equation

$$(119\text{-}4) \quad \sum_{k=0}^{\infty} c_k(x - a)^k + \sum_{k=0}^{\infty} d_k(x - a)^k = \sum_{k=0}^{\infty}(c_k + d_k)(x - a)^k.$$

Thus the sum of two power series is again a power series, and Equation 114-7 tells us that if x is any number for which the summand series converge, then the sum series converges. Therefore, the radius of convergence of the sum series is at least as large as the smaller of the radii of convergence of the summand series.

The product of two power series is also a power series, and again we define its coefficients in the "natural way," although here the "natural way" is not quite so obvious as it was in the case of the sum. The term that contains $(x - a)^k$ in the

product of the series $\displaystyle\sum_{k=0}^{\infty} c_k(x - a)^k$ and $\displaystyle\sum_{k=0}^{\infty} d_k(x - a)^k$ is the sum of the products $c_0 \cdot d_k(x - a)^k$, $c_1(x - a) \cdot d_{k-1}(x - a)^{k-1}$, $c_2(x - a)^2 \cdot d_{k-2}(x - a)^{k-2}$, and so on; that is,

$$(c_0 d_k + c_1 d_{k-1} + c_2 d_{k-2} + \cdots + c_k d_0)(x - a)^k = \left(\sum_{r=0}^{k} c_r d_{k-r}\right)(x - a)^k.$$

Thus we define the product of two power series by means of the equation

$$(119\text{-}5) \quad \left(\sum_{k=0}^{\infty} c_k(x - a)^k\right)\left(\sum_{k=0}^{\infty} d_k(x - a)^k\right) = \sum_{k=0}^{\infty}\left(\sum_{r=0}^{k} c_r d_{k-r}\right)(x - a)^k.$$

We won't prove it, but it can be shown that the radius of convergence of the product series is at least as large as the smaller of the radii of convergence of the factor series.

Rather than use Equation 119-5, which is sometimes rather complicated to apply, we frequently find it easier to find an initial segment of a product series in the following way. To obtain the initial segment that ends with the term containing $(x - a)^k$, we multiply the initial segments of the factor series that end with the terms containing $(x - a)^k$ and then discard all terms that contain $(x - a)$ to a power larger than k.

Example 119-3. Discuss the product of the power series $\sum\limits_{k=0}^{\infty} x^k$ and $\sum\limits_{k=1}^{\infty} kx^{k-1}$.

Solution. As we just said, perhaps the easiest way to find a given initial segment of the product is by straightforward algebra, rather than relying on Formula 119-5. Thus suppose we want to find the initial segment of the product series that ends with the term containing x^3. Then we multiply initial segments of the factor series as shown:

$$\begin{array}{r} 1 + x + x^2 + x^3 \\ 1 + 2x + 3x^2 + 4x^3 \\ \hline 1 + 3x + 6x^2 + 10x^3 + 9x^4 + 7x^5 + 4x^6. \end{array}$$

Now we discard the terms that contain x to a power higher than 3, and we obtain the desired initial segment of the product:

$$1 + 3x + 6x^2 + 10x^3.$$

If we want to use Equation 119-5, our first task is to write the power series $\sum\limits_{k=1}^{\infty} kx^{k-1}$ in "standard form;" that is, as $\sum\limits_{k=0}^{\infty} d_k x^k$. You can readily check that $\sum\limits_{k=1}^{\infty} kx^{k-1} = \sum\limits_{k=0}^{\infty} (k + 1)x^k$; now we are ready to apply Equation 119-5 with $c_k = 1$ for all k, and $d_k = k + 1$. Therefore,

$$\sum_{r=0}^{k} c_r d_{k-r} = \sum_{r=0}^{k} 1 \cdot (k - r + 1) = (k + 1) + k + (k - 1) + \cdots + 1.$$

Here we have the sum of the first $k + 1$ positive integers, an arithmetic progression whose sum, you may recall, is $\frac{1}{2}(k + 1)(k + 2)$. It therefore follows that

$$\sum_{k=0}^{\infty} x^k \sum_{k=0}^{\infty} (k + 1)x^k = \sum_{k=0}^{\infty} \tfrac{1}{2}(k + 1)(k + 2)x^k.$$

You will observe that the initial segment that contains the first four terms of this series agrees with the result we obtained in the preceding paragraph.

We will not discuss quotients of power series other than to say that here again we proceed "naturally." Once more, to find the initial segment of the quotient series that ends with the term containing $(x - a)^k$ we divide corresponding initial segments of the divisor and dividend series and discard all terms of the resulting quotient that contain $(x - a)$ to a power larger than k. There are some complications in the theory of division; for example, we require that the first coefficient of the divisor series be different from 0, and the radius of convergence of the quotient series may be less than the radius of convergence of either the divisor or the dividend.

PROBLEMS 119

1. Find the radius of convergence, the interval of convergence, and the set of points for which the following power series converge.

(a) $\displaystyle\sum_{k=0}^{\infty} \frac{x^k}{2^k}$

(b) $\displaystyle\sum_{k=1}^{\infty} k(x - 2)^k$

(c) $\displaystyle\sum_{k=0}^{\infty} \frac{(-1)^k}{3^k + k} (x + 1)^k$

(d) $\displaystyle\sum_{k=1}^{\infty} \frac{k^5}{5^k} (x - 5)^k$

(e) $\displaystyle\sum_{k=1}^{\infty} \frac{(x - 4)^k}{\sqrt{3k}}$

(f) $\displaystyle\sum_{k=1}^{\infty} \frac{x^k}{k(k + 1)}$

(g) $\displaystyle\sum_{k=0}^{\infty} e^{\sin k} x^k$

(h) $\displaystyle\sum_{k=1}^{\infty} 2^{\ln k} x^k$

2. Find the interval of convergence of each of the following power series.

(a) $\displaystyle\sum_{k=0}^{\infty} \frac{(x - 2)^k}{2^k \sqrt{k + 1}}$

(b) $\displaystyle\sum_{k=1}^{\infty} (\text{Arctan } k)(x - 2)^k$

(c) $\displaystyle\sum_{k=1}^{\infty} (\text{csch } k) x^k$

(d) $\displaystyle\sum_{k=1}^{\infty} \frac{k^k}{k!} x^k$

(e) $\displaystyle\sum_{k=1}^{\infty} \frac{(-1)^k 5 \cdot 6 \ldots (k + 4)}{k!} x^{2k}$

(f) $\displaystyle\sum_{k=0}^{\infty} \frac{(x - 2)^{4k}}{2^k}$

(g) $\displaystyle\sum_{k=0}^{\infty} \frac{(-1)^k}{2^{2k+12} k! (k + 12)!} x^{2k+12}$

(h) $\displaystyle\sum_{k=1}^{\infty} [3^k + (-3)^k](x + 1)^{3k-2}$

3. Find the set of points for which the power series $\displaystyle\sum_{k=1}^{\infty} \frac{x^k}{k^p}$ converges for various choices of p.

4. Show that if $\displaystyle\lim_{k \uparrow \infty} \frac{|c_{k+1}|}{|c_k|} = L > 0$, then the radius of convergence of the power series $\displaystyle\sum_{k=0}^{\infty} c_k(x - a)^k$ is $\dfrac{1}{L}$. What if $L = 0$?

5. If $|t| < 1$, we know that the sum of the geometric series $\displaystyle\sum_{k=0}^{\infty} t^k$ is $\dfrac{1}{1 - t}$. Use this fact to find the sums of the following power series.

(a) $\displaystyle\sum_{k=0}^{\infty} (-x)^k$

(b) $\displaystyle\sum_{k=0}^{\infty} x^{2k}$

(c) $\displaystyle\sum_{k=0}^{\infty} 3(x + 1)^k$

(d) $\displaystyle\sum_{k=0}^{\infty} \left(\sin k \frac{\pi}{2}\right) x^k$

6. Replace t in the equation $\dfrac{1}{1 - t} = \displaystyle\sum_{k=0}^{\infty} t^k$ with x, $-x$, and x^2 to obtain power series whose sums are $\dfrac{1}{1 - x}$, $\dfrac{1}{1 + x}$, and $\dfrac{1}{1 - x^2}$. Show that the third series is the product of the other two.

7. (a) Divide the "power series" 1 by the "power series" $2 - x$ to obtain a power series whose sum is $\dfrac{1}{2 - x}$.

(b) Multiply this series by a series in powers of x whose sum is $\dfrac{1}{1 - x}$ to obtain a series whose sum is $\dfrac{1}{(1 - x)(2 - x)}$.

(c) Achieve the same result by writing $\dfrac{1}{(1 - x)(2 - x)}$ in the form $\dfrac{A}{1 - x} + \dfrac{B}{2 - x}$ and then adding two power series that have these numbers as sums.

8. (a) Find two power series such that the radius of convergence of their sum is greater than the radius of convergence of either summand.

(b) Find two power series such that the radius of convergence of their product is greater than the radius of convergence of either factor.

(c) Find two power series such that the radius of convergence of the quotient of the first by the second is less than the radius of convergence of either the divisor or the dividend.

9. Use Equation 119-5 to show that $\displaystyle\sum_{k=0}^{\infty} \frac{x^k}{k!} \sum_{k=0}^{\infty} \frac{(-x)^k}{k!} = 1$.

10. Suppose that $\displaystyle\sum_{k=0}^{\infty} c_k(x - a)^k$ and $\displaystyle\sum_{k=0}^{\infty} d_k(x - a)^k$ are two power series such that for each k, $|c_k| \le |d_k|$. Show that the radius of convergence of the first series is at least as large as the radius of convergence of the second.

11. Show that the series $\displaystyle\sum_{k=1}^{\infty} kc_k(x - a)^{k-1}$ and $\displaystyle\sum_{k=0}^{\infty} \frac{c_k}{k + 1} (x - a)^{k+1}$ have the same radius of convergence as the series $\displaystyle\sum_{k=0}^{\infty} c_k(x - a)^k$. (You may use the fact that if $\lim\limits_{k \uparrow \infty} p_k = P$, where $P > 0$, then $\varlimsup\limits_{k \uparrow \infty} p_k q_k = P \varlimsup\limits_{k \uparrow \infty} q_k$.)

120 FUNCTIONS DEFINED BY POWER SERIES

Let us agree not to bother with power series that converge at only one point. Then the interval of convergence of a power series

$$(120\text{-}1) \qquad \sum_{k=0}^{\infty} c_k(x - a)^k$$

is either the infinite interval $(-\infty, \infty)$ or else it is a finite interval $(a - r, a + r)$. In the latter case we may also have to adjoin one or both of the endpoints $a - r$ or $a + r$ to obtain the set of points for which the series is convergent. Let us denote by I the *interval of convergence* of our series and by D the *set of points for which the series converges*. These two sets of points may coincide, and at worst D can be obtained from I by adjoining two more points. So the difference between the two sets is small. Nevertheless, in the statements of the various theorems that follow, it is necessary to distinguish between the sets D ánd I, even though it looks as if we are splitting hairs.

Corresponding to each number $x \in D$ we obtain a number, the sum of the Series 120-1. Thus our power series defines a function; we will call it f. The domain of f is the convergence set D, and the values of f are the sums of the series. So we have

(120-2)
$$f(x) = \sum_{k=0}^{\infty} c_k(x - a)^k.$$

Among the functions whose values can be expressed as sums of power series are most of the important functions of mathematics. For example, the trigonometric, logarithmic, and exponential functions belong to this class, as we shall see. Therefore, this class of functions has been studied extensively. We now state three important theorems that apply to functions of this class. Proofs of these theorems are best left to a course in advanced calculus, where more mathematical machinery is available.

Our first theorem tells us that functions defined by power series are continuous.

Theorem 120-1. *The function f defined by the equation $f(x) = \sum_{k=0}^{\infty} c_k(x - a)^k$ is continuous at each point of the convergence set D of the defining infinite series. That is, if b is any point of the convergence set, then*

(120-3)
$$\lim_{x \to b} f(x) = f(b) = \sum_{k=0}^{\infty} c_k(b - a)^k.$$

If b is an endpoint of the interval of convergence, this limit is a limit from the right or from the left.

We will give an application of this theorem after we have stated the theorems about differentiation and integration of series.

If $f(x)$ were an ordinary sum of terms of the form $c_k(x - a)^k$, we could find its derivative by differentiating each term in the sum and then adding; that is, it is immaterial whether we add and then differentiate or differentiate and then add. But $f(x)$ is *not* an ordinary sum; it is the "sum" of an infinite series. On the face of it, therefore, it is not obvious that we can obtain derivatives or integrals of $f(x)$ by differentiating or integrating each term of the series that defines f and then calculating the sum of the resulting series. Such "term-by-term" differentiation or integration is not always possible in the case of functions defined by some kinds of infinite series. When a function is defined by a *power series*, however, we may differentiate or integrate "under the summation sign" according to the following theorems.

Theorem 120-2. *The function f defined by the equation $f(x) = \sum\limits_{k=0}^{\infty} c_k(x - a)^k$ is differentiable at every point of the interval of convergence I of the defining series, and at each point x of I we have*

(120-4) $$f'(x) = \sum_{k=1}^{\infty} kc_k(x - a)^{k-1}.$$

In Problem 119-11 we asked you to show that the interval of convergence of the series in Equation 120-4 is the interval of convergence of the original series.

Theorem 120-3. *If x is any point of the convergence set D of the infinite series of Equation 120-2, then*

(120-5) $$\int_a^x f(t)\, dt = \sum_{k=0}^{\infty} \frac{c_k(x - a)^{k+1}}{k + 1}.$$

In Problem 119-11 we asked you to show that the interval of convergence of the series in Equation 120-5 is the interval of convergence of the original series.

To give you an idea of how these theorems can be used, and to help fix them in your mind, we will apply them to some specific series. Right now the only power series whose sum we know is the geometric series. Thus

(120-6) $$\frac{1}{1 - x} = \sum_{k=0}^{\infty} x^k,$$

where $D = I = (-1, 1)$. According to Equation 120-5, if x is any point of the interval $(-1, 1)$, then

$$\int_0^x \frac{dt}{1 - t} = \sum_{k=0}^{\infty} \frac{x^{k+1}}{k + 1} = x + \frac{x^2}{2} + \frac{x^3}{3} + \cdots.$$

But we know that

$$\int_0^x \frac{dt}{1 - t} = -\ln(1 - t)\Big|_0^x = -\ln(1 - x),$$

so we have the following equation, valid for $x \in (-1, 1)$;

(120-7) $$-\ln(1 - x) = x + \frac{x^2}{2} + \frac{x^3}{3} + \frac{x^4}{4} + \cdots.$$

Thus, for example, if we set $x = \frac{1}{2}$, and recall that $-\ln \frac{1}{2} = \ln 2$, we see that

$$\ln 2 = \tfrac{1}{2} + \tfrac{1}{8} + \tfrac{1}{24} + \tfrac{1}{64} + \cdots.$$

The sum of the first four terms of this series is .68, which is a close approximation of the value ln 2 = .69. Of course, the more terms we add, the more nearly we will approximate ln 2, and *we can approximate* ln 2 *with any degree of accuracy we wish simply by adding together enough terms.* In practice, we would probably use a machine to help us with the computation.

We are only sure that Equation 120-7 is valid when $|x| < 1$, but it is not hard to develop a series that will give us the logarithm of any positive number. In Equation 120-7 we replace x with $-x$ and obtain the equation

$$(120\text{-}8) \qquad -\ln(1+x) = -x + \frac{x^2}{2} - \frac{x^3}{3} + \frac{x^4}{4} + \cdots.$$

Then we subtract the corresponding sides of Equations 120-7 and 120-8:

$$\ln(1+x) - \ln(1-x) = 2\left(x + \frac{x^3}{3} + \frac{x^5}{5} + \cdots\right).$$

Thus, since $\ln(1+x) - \ln(1-x) = \ln\dfrac{1+x}{1-x}$, we have

$$(120\text{-}9) \qquad \ln\frac{1+x}{1-x} = 2\left(x + \frac{x^3}{3} + \frac{x^5}{5} + \cdots\right).$$

Now we have a series that will give us the logarithm of any positive number. For if N is any positive number and we solve the equation $\dfrac{1+x}{1-x} = N$ for x, we find that $x = \dfrac{N-1}{N+1}$, and therefore $|x| < 1$. Thus we may replace x in Equation 120-9 with the number $\dfrac{N-1}{N+1}$ and we will obtain a convergent series whose sum is ln N:

$$(120\text{-}10) \quad \ln N = 2\left[\left(\frac{N-1}{N+1}\right) + \frac{1}{3}\left(\frac{N-1}{N+1}\right)^3 + \frac{1}{5}\left(\frac{N-1}{N+1}\right)^5 + \cdots\right].$$

Now let us look more closely at the series in Equation 120-7. We know that $(-1, 1)$ is the interval of convergence of this series, and when we substitute the endpoints -1 and 1, we find that its convergence set is the half-open interval $[-1, 1)$. According to Theorem 120-3, Equation 120-7 gives us the sum of our series if x belongs to the open interval $(-1, 1)$; that is, if the series defines a function f whose domain is the interval $[-1, 1)$, then for each $x \in (-1, 1)$ we have $f(x) = -\ln(1-x)$. To find the number $f(-1)$, the sum of our series when x is replaced by -1, we turn to Theorem 120-1. Equation 120-3 tells us that $f(-1) = \lim\limits_{x\downarrow-1} f(x) = \lim\limits_{x\downarrow-1} -\ln(1-x) = -\ln 2$. Since $f(-1) = -1 + \frac{1}{2} - \frac{1}{3} + \frac{1}{4} - \cdots$, we have the interesting equation

(120-11) $\ln 2 = 1 - \frac{1}{2} + \frac{1}{3} - \frac{1}{4} + \frac{1}{5} - \cdots$

that we mentioned in Example 116-2.

Now let us take up an application of Theorem 120-2.

Example 120-1.   Find a power series in x whose sum is $\dfrac{1}{(1 - x)^2}$.

Solution.   Equation 120-6 shows us a power series in x whose sum is $\dfrac{1}{1 - x}$. According to Theorem 120-2, the derivative of this sum is the sum of the series of derivatives of the terms of our original geometric series. Thus, since $D_x\left(\dfrac{1}{1 - x}\right) = \dfrac{1}{(1 - x)^2}$, we have

$$\frac{1}{(1 - x)^2} = \sum_{k=0}^{\infty} kx^{k-1} = 1 + 2x + 3x^3 + 4x^3 + \cdots,$$

and this equation is valid if $|x| < 1$.

P R O B L E M S   1 2 0

1. The equation $f(x) = \displaystyle\sum_{k=1}^{\infty} \frac{x^k}{k^2}$ defines a function f.
  (a) What is the domain of f?
  (b) Calculate $f(-\frac{1}{2})$ with an error of less than .01.
  (c) Show that f is an increasing function.
  (d) Find $\displaystyle\lim_{x \to 0} f(x)$.
  (e) Show that the range of f is a subset of the interval $(-1, 2)$.

2. The equation $f(x) = \displaystyle\sum_{k=0}^{\infty} \frac{x^{2k+1}}{(2k + 1)!}$ defines a function f.
  (a) Find the domain of f.
  (b) Find the range of f.
  (c) Show that f is an odd function.
  (d) Show that f is increasing.
  (e) Show that $y = f(x)$ satisfies the differential equation $y'' - y = 0$.
  (f) Compare $f'(x)$ and $\displaystyle\int_0^x f(t)\, dt$.

3. Use a power series to find an approximation to $\ln N$ and check your result with Table II.
  (a) $N = .9$ (b) $N = 1.1$ (c) $N = 5$ (d) $N = .3$

4. Equation 120-11 gives us one infinite series whose sum is ln 2, and we can obtain two others by replacing x with $\frac{1}{2}$ in Equation 120-7 and N with 2 in Equation 120-10. Which of these three series is "best."

5. Let $g(x) = 1 - \frac{1}{2}x^3 + \frac{1}{4}x^6 - \frac{1}{8}x^9 + \cdots$.

(a) Find a two-place decimal approximation to $\int_{-1/2}^{1/2} g(x)\,dx$.

(b) Find a two-place decimal approximation to $g'(\frac{1}{2})$.

6. Use the equation developed in Example 120-1 to find the sum of the series $\sum_{k=1}^{\infty} \frac{k}{2^k}$.

Can you find the sum of the series $\sum_{k=0}^{\infty} \frac{1}{(k+1)2^k}$?

7. In Example 120-1 we differentiated a series whose sum is $\frac{1}{1-x}$ to find a series whose sum is $\frac{1}{(1-x)^2}$. Show that we get the same result by squaring our original series.

8. Find a power series in t of which $\frac{1}{1-t^2}$ is the sum. Now integrate from 0 to x and obtain Equation 120-9.

9. If we replace x with $-t^2$, Equation 120-6 becomes $\frac{1}{1+t^2} = \sum_{k=0}^{\infty} (-1)^k t^{2k}$.

(a) Use this equation and Theorem 120-3 to show that

$$\text{Arctan } x = \sum_{k=0}^{\infty} \frac{(-1)^k x^{2k-1}}{2k+1} \quad \text{if } |x| < 1.$$

(b) Use the result of Part (a) and Theorem 120-1 to show that

$$\frac{\pi}{4} = 1 - \frac{1}{3} + \frac{1}{5} - \frac{1}{7} + \cdots.$$

(c) Use power series to show that $\int_0^x \text{Arctan } t\,dt = x \text{ Arctan } x - \frac{1}{2}\ln(1+x^2)$.

10. What is the domain of the function f that is defined by the equation $f(x) = \sum_{k=1}^{\infty} \frac{\sin k^2 x}{k^2}$? Can we find $f'(x)$ by term-by-term differentiation?

121 TAYLOR'S SERIES

A power series $\sum_{k=0}^{\infty} c_k(x-a)^k$ determines a function f whose domain is the set of points for which the series converges, and whose values are the sums of the series; that is,

(121-1) $f(x) = c_0 + c_1(x-a) + c_2(x-a)^2 + \cdots.$

Thus we see, for example, that $f(a) = c_0$. We will now show how to express the derivatives of f at a in terms of the other coefficients of our series.

According to Theorem 120-2, the derivative $f'(x)$ is the sum of the series that results from differentiating the given series term-by-term; that is,

$$f'(x) = c_1 + 2c_2(x - a) + 3c_3(x - a)^2 + \cdots.$$

We may apply Theorem 120-2 again and again to obtain the equations

$$f''(x) = 2c_2 + 2 \cdot 3c_3(x - a) + 3 \cdot 4c_4(x - a)^2 + \cdots,$$
$$f'''(x) = 2 \cdot 3c_3 + 2 \cdot 3 \cdot 4c_4(x - a) + 3 \cdot 4 \cdot 5c_5(x - a)^2 + \cdots,$$

and so on. You can easily convince yourself that in general

$$(121\text{-}2) \qquad f^{(k)}(x) = k!\, c_k + (k + 1)!\, c_{k+1}(x - a) + \cdots,$$

for $k = 0, 1, 2, \ldots$ (We will agree that $f^{(0)}(x) = f(x)$, and that $0! = 1$.) When we replace x with a in Equation 121-2, we obtain the following formula for the derivatives of f at a in terms of the coefficients of our given series:

$$(121\text{-}3) \qquad f^{(k)}(a) = k!\, c_k, \quad k = 0, 1, 2, 3, \ldots.$$

Example 121-1.   Let $f(x) = \dfrac{1}{1 - x^2}$. Find $f^{(14)}(0)$.

Solution.   We will find a power series of which our given $f(x)$ is the sum, and then we will use Equation 121-3. If we simply divide 1 by $1 - x^2$, or replace x with x^2 in Equation 120-6, we find that

$$\frac{1}{1 - x^2} = 1 + x^2 + x^4 + x^6 + \cdots.$$

Here $a = 0$ and it is clear that $c_{14} = 1$, and so Equation 121-3 shows us that $f^{(14)}(0) = 14!$. You might try to calculate this number by starting with the given quotient and differentiating fourteen times.

Suppose the sum $f(x)$ in Equation 121-1 is the number 0 for each x in some neighborhood $N_p a$. Then all the derivatives of f at a are 0, and hence Equation 121-3 tells us that all the coefficients of our power series are 0. Thus the only power series in $(x - a)$ whose sum is 0 in some neighborhood of a is the one with zero coefficients. This result leads to the following theorem.

Theorem 121-1. *If* $\displaystyle\sum_{k=0}^{\infty} a_k(x - a)^k = \sum_{k=0}^{\infty} b_k(x - a)^k$ *for each number x in some* *neighborhood $N_p a$, then $a_k = b_k$ for each integer $k = 0, 1, 2, \ldots$. Thus one equation between power series is equivalent to infinitely many equations between their coefficients.*

Proof. To prove this theorem, we simply note that the equation

$$\sum_{k=0}^{\infty} a_k(x - a)^k = \sum_{k=0}^{\infty} b_k(x - a)^k$$

implies that

$$\sum_{k=0}^{\infty} (a_k - b_k)(x - a)^k = 0,$$

and we have just seen that if the sum of a power series in $(x - a)$ is 0 in a neighborhood of a, then all its coefficients must be 0. Therefore, $a_0 - b_0 = 0$, $a_1 - b_1 = 0$, and so on, as the theorem claims.

If we start with a power series $\sum_{k=0}^{\infty} c_k(x - a)^k$, Equation 121-1 defines a function f that has derivatives of all orders in the interval of convergence of the series. This interval is a neighborhood $N_r a$. Now let us proceed in the opposite direction. Suppose we start with a function f that has derivatives of all orders in a neighborhood of a point a and see if we can find a power series in $(x - a)$ of which $f(x)$ is the sum. From what we have said in the preceding paragraphs, we see that the coefficients of such a power series (if there is one) must be the numbers given by Equation 121-3. That is, we must have $c_k = \dfrac{f^{(k)}(a)}{k!}$. So let us form the power series in $(x - a)$ that has these numbers as coefficients,

$$(121\text{-}4) \quad \sum_{k=0}^{\infty} \frac{f^{(k)}(a)}{k!}(x - a)^k = f(a) + f'(a)(x - a) + \frac{f''(a)}{2!}(x - a)^2 + \cdots,$$

and see whether or not it converges to $f(x)$ at each point x of a neighborhood of a. Series 121-4 is called **Taylor's Series** for $f(x)$ about the point a. We can form Taylor's Series for any function that has derivatives of all orders at a, and it turns out that for many of the familiar functions of mathematics Taylor's Series converges to the value of the function at each point x in some neighborhood of a.

Example 121-2. Find Taylor's Series for e^x about the origin.

Solution. Here $f(x) = e^x$ and $a = 0$. Since $f(x)$ and all its derivatives equal e^x, we have $f(0) = f'(0) = f''(0) = \cdots = 1$. Thus in this case, $f^{(k)}(a) = 1$ for each index k, and so Taylor's Series for e^x about the origin is

$$\sum_{k=0}^{\infty} \frac{x^k}{k!} = 1 + x + \frac{x^2}{2!} + \frac{x^3}{3!} + \cdots.$$

The ratio test shows (Example 119-1) that this series converges for every number x.

We have just seen that Taylor's Series for e^x about the origin converges. Now we want to go one step farther and show that its sum is e^x. To find out whether or not Taylor's Series for $f(x)$ converges to $f(x)$, we use Taylor's Formula. Thus if x is a point of a neighborhood $N_r a$ in which f has derivatives of all orders, and if n is any positive integer, we can replace b with x in Equation 112-3 and write it as

$$(121\text{-}5) \quad f(x) = f(a) + f'(a)(x - a) + \cdots + \frac{f^{(n)}(a)}{n!}(x - a)^n + R_n(x)$$

$$= S_n(x) + R_n(x),$$

where $S_n(x)$ is the nth partial sum of Taylor's Series, and the remainder $R_n(x)$ is given by the formula

$$(121\text{-}6) \qquad R_n(x) = \frac{f^{(n+1)}(m)}{(n+1)!}(x - a)^{n+1},$$

in which m is some number between a and x. Since $S_n(x) = f(x) - R_n(x)$, we see that $\lim_{n \uparrow \infty} S_n(x) = f(x)$ if, and only if, $\lim_{n \uparrow \infty} R_n(x) = 0$. Thus *Taylor's Series for $f(x)$ has $f(x)$ as its sum if, and only if,* $\lim_{n \uparrow \infty} R_n(x) = 0$.

Example 121-3. Show that for each real number x, Taylor's Series for e^x about the origin converges to e^x.

Solution. Here for each positive integer n we have $R_n(x) = \dfrac{e^m x^{n+1}}{(n+1)!}$, where m is a number such that $|m| \leq |x|$. Therefore,

$$|R_n(x)| \leq \frac{e^{|x|} |x|^{n+1}}{(n+1)!}.$$

Equation 119-3 says that, for every number x, $\lim_{k \uparrow \infty} \dfrac{x^k}{k!} = 0$, from which it follows that $\lim_{n \uparrow \infty} \dfrac{e^{|x|} |x|^{n+1}}{(n+1)!} = e^{|x|} \lim_{n \uparrow \infty} \dfrac{|x|^{n+1}}{(n+1)!} = e^{|x|} \cdot 0 = 0$. Thus $\lim_{n \uparrow \infty} R_n(x) = 0$, and we have derived the important equation

$$(121\text{-}7) \qquad e^x = \sum_{k=0}^{\infty} \frac{x^k}{k!} = 1 + x + \frac{x^2}{2!} + \frac{x^3}{3!} + \cdots, \, x \in (-\infty, \infty).$$

Example 121-4. Find Taylor's Series for $\cos x$ about an arbitrary point a; show that it converges to $\cos x$ for each $x \in (-\infty, \infty)$, and use the result to calculate $\cos 3$.

Solution. Here we have $f(x) = \cos x$; we know that f has derivatives of all orders at each point of the interval $(-\infty, \infty)$, and $f(a) = \cos a$, $f'(a) = -\sin a$, $f''(a) = -\cos a$, $f'''(a) = \sin a$, and so on. Depending on n, the derivative $f^{(n+1)}(m)$ will be one of the numbers $\cos m$, $\sin m$, $-\cos m$, or $-\sin m$. In any event, $|f^{(n+1)}(m)| \leq 1$, and so $|R_n(x)| \leq \dfrac{|x - a|^{n+1}}{(n + 1)!}$. Now we let $|x - a|$ play the role of x in the equation $\lim\limits_{k \uparrow \infty} \dfrac{x^k}{k!} = 0$, and we see that $\lim\limits_{n \uparrow \infty} R_n(x) = 0$. Thus we have shown that Taylor's Series for $\cos x$ has $\cos x$ as its sum for each $x \in (-\infty, \infty)$; that is,

$$(121\text{-}8) \quad \cos x = \cos a - \sin a(x - a) - \cos a\, \frac{(x - a)^2}{2!} + \sin a\, \frac{(x - a)^3}{3!} + \cdots.$$

To use this formula to find $\cos 3$, we must choose a "suitable" number a. This choice is governed by two considerations:

(i) We must be able to find $f(a), f'(a)$, and so on; in this case we must know what the numbers $\cos a$ and $\sin a$ are.

(ii) The number a should be close to 3 so that when we set $x = 3$ in Formula 121-8, the number $(x - a)$ will be small and we can use a reasonably short initial segment of our series to approximate its sum. These considerations suggest that we take $a = \pi$. Then

$$\cos 3 = -1 + \frac{(\pi - 3)^2}{2!} - \frac{(\pi - 3)^4}{4!} + \frac{(\pi - 3)^6}{6!} - \cdots.$$

This series is an alternating series, so the error that we make by taking the sum of the first three terms as an approximation of $\cos 3$ is less than the fourth term. It is not hard to show that the fourth term is less than .0000001. Then we find that the sum of the first three terms gives us $\cos 3 = -.989992$ with 6-place accuracy. If we set $a = 0$ in Equation 121-8, we obtain the equation

$$(121\text{-}9) \qquad\qquad \cos x = 1 - \frac{x^2}{2!} + \frac{x^4}{4!} - \frac{x^6}{6!} + \cdots.$$

We get a series whose sum is $\cos 3$ by putting $x = 3$ in this series, but to be sure of an error of less than .0000001 (according to our rule for alternating series) we would have to take the sum of the first nine terms. Equation 121-9 would be more suitable for calculating a number such as $\cos .1$.

PROBLEMS 121

1. Use some of the series we worked with in the last section to find $f^{(9)}(0)$.

(a) $f(x) = \dfrac{1}{(1 - x)^2}$ (b) $f(x) = \ln(1 + x)$

(c) $f(x) = \text{Arctan } x$ (d) $f(x) = \text{Arctan } x^2$

2. Find Taylor's Series for $\sin x$ about 0. Show that this series converges to $\sin x$ for each $x \in (-\infty, \infty)$. Use this series to compute $\sin .1$ and $\sin 1$, and compare your results with tabulated values. If $f(x) = \sin 3x$, find $f^{(7)}(0)$.

3. Find Taylor's Series for e^x about an arbitrary point a in two ways: (1) by using Equation 121-4, and (2) by replacing x with $x - a$ in Equation 121-7.

4. Find Taylor's Series for e^{-x} about the origin by replacing x with $-x$ in Equation 121-7, and use the resulting series to find Taylor's Series for $\sinh x$ and $\cosh x$ about 0. Now use Equation 121-4 to get the same result.

5. Let a be an arbitrary positive number and find Taylor's Series for $\ln x$ about a. What is the radius of convergence of this series? Can you show directly that for each $x \in (0, 2a)$, $\lim\limits_{n \uparrow \infty} R_n(x) = 0$? In Equation 120-8, replace x with $\dfrac{x - a}{a}$ to show that the series we have just calculated does have $\ln x$ as its sum.

6. See how many terms you can find of Taylor's Series for $\tan x$ about the origin.

7. Show that for an arbitrary real number a, $\cos x = \sum\limits_{k=0}^{\infty} \dfrac{\cos (a + \frac{1}{2}k\pi)}{k!} (x - a)^k$ and $\sin x = \sum\limits_{k=0}^{\infty} \dfrac{\sin (a + \frac{1}{2}k\pi)}{k!} (x - a)^k$ for each $x \in (-\infty, \infty)$.

8. Let x and y be any given numbers. Find Taylor's Series for $f(x) = \sin (x + y)$ about 0 to show that

$$\sin (x + y) = \sin y + (\cos y)x - (\sin y)\frac{x^2}{2!} - (\cos y)\frac{x^3}{3!} + \cdots.$$

Now group the terms that contain $\sin y$ and those that contain $\cos y$, recognize series you have already found whose sums are $\cos x$ and $\sin x$, and so find the addition formula for $\sin (x + y)$.

9. Prove the following theorem. If a function f has derivatives of all orders at each point of a neighborhood $N_r a$, and if there is a number B such that for each positive integer n the values of the function $f^{(n)}$ are bounded by the number B^n throughout $N_r a$, then Taylor's Series for $f(x)$ converges to $f(x)$ for each $x \in N_r a$.

10. Suppose Taylor's Series for $f(x)$ and $g(x)$ about the point a converge to $f(x)$ and $g(x)$ in some neighborhood of a. Multiply these series, using Equation 119-5, to find Taylor's Series for the product $p(x) = f(x)g(x)$. From this result, show that for each positive integer k,

$$p^{(k)}(a) = \sum\limits_{r=0}^{k} \frac{k!}{r! \, (k - r)!} f^{(r)}(a) g^{(r)}(a).$$

122 FINDING TAYLOR'S SERIES. THE BINOMIAL SERIES

The straightforward way to find Taylor's Series for $f(x)$ about a point a is to calculate $f(a), f'(a), f''(a)$, and so on, and then substitute these numbers in Formula 121-4. Even if the resulting series converges, we must still investigate the remainder

$R_n(x)$ to see if the sum of the series is $f(x)$ As we saw in some of the problems at the end of the last section, however, it is often easier to find a desired Taylor's Series by "operating on"—with calculus or algebra—some series we already know, such as the series for e^x, $\dfrac{1}{1-x}$, and $\cos x$.

Example 122-1.   Find Taylor's Series for $\sin x$ about 0.

Solution.   Equation 121-9 gives us Taylor's Series for $\cos x$ about 0, and we may differentiate both sides of this equation and then multiply by -1 to see that

(122-1) $$\sin x = x - \frac{x^3}{3!} + \frac{x^5}{5!} - \frac{x^7}{7!} + \cdots .$$

Example 122-2.   Find Taylor's Series for $\tan x$ about 0.

Solution.   When you worked Problem 121-6, you found that, after the first few, a straightforward calculation of the derivatives of $\tan x$ becomes quite complicated. We can ease the difficulties somewhat by observing that the trigonometric identity $\sec^2 x = 1 + \tan^2 x$ tells us that $f(x) = \tan x$ satisfies the differential equation $f'(x) = 1 + f(x)^2$. From this equation, we successively find that $f''(x) = 2f(x)f'(x)$, $f'''(x) = 2f(x)f''(x) + 2f'(x)^2$, and so on. We have $f(0) = \tan 0 = 0$, so $f'(0) = 1 + 0 = 1$, $f''(0) = 2f(0)f'(0) = 0$, $f'''(0) = 2f(0)f''(0) + 2f'(0)^2 = 2$, and it is clear how to continue step-by-step to find $f^{(4)}(0)$, $f^{(5)}(0)$, and so on. Now we may substitute in Equation 121-4 and we find that the first few terms of Taylor's series for $\tan x$ are $0 + x + 0 \cdot x^2 + \dfrac{2}{3!}x^3 + \cdots = x + \dfrac{x^3}{3} + \cdots$.

 We can even do away with differentiation altogether if we regard $\tan x$ as $\dfrac{\sin x}{\cos x}$ and divide the series for $\sin x$ by the series for $\cos x$. Thus

$$\tan x = \frac{x - \dfrac{x^3}{3!} + \dfrac{x^5}{5!} - \cdots}{1 - \dfrac{x^2}{2!} + \dfrac{x^4}{4!} - \cdots}$$

and we see, for example, that the initial segment $c_0 + c_1 x + c_2 x^2 + c_3 x^3 + c_4 x^4 + c_5 x^5$ of the series for $\tan x$ is the corresponding initial segment of the quotient that we obtain by dividing the polynomial $x - \dfrac{x^3}{3!} + \dfrac{x^5}{5!}$ by the polynomial $1 - \dfrac{x^2}{2!} + \dfrac{x^4}{4!}$. When we perform this division, we find that

$$\tan x = x + \frac{x^3}{3} + \frac{2x^5}{15} + \cdots .$$

 In elementary algebra we learned the Binomial Theorem, which is a rule for writing a power of a sum as a sum of powers. Thus we can use the Binomial

Theorem to write the expression $(1 + x)^p$ as a sum of powers of x. In our elementary work, we had to assume that the exponent p is a positive integer, but even when p is not a positive integer we can still formally apply the rules of the Binomial Theorem to the expression $(1 + x)^p$. In that case, however, the rules generate an infinite series rather than a finite sum. If we assume that the sum of this **binomial series** is really $(1 + x)^p$, we have the equation

$$(122\text{-}2) \quad (1 + x)^p = 1 + px + \frac{p(p - 1)}{2!} x^2 + \cdots$$

$$+ \frac{p(p - 1) \cdots (p - k + 1)}{k!} x^k + \cdots.$$

This equation says that the infinite series is Taylor's Series for $(1 + x)^p$ about 0, so to justify our use of the equals sign it might seem natural to calculate the remainder $R_n(x)$ and show that it approaches 0. If you try this straightforward assault on the problem, you will see how difficult it is, and you will then appreciate why we take what appears to be a roundabout approach.

We can write the series on the right-hand side of Equation 122-2 as $\sum_{k=0}^{\infty} c_k x^k$, in which the coefficients satisfy the recursion formulas

$$(122\text{-}3) \quad c_0 = 1 \quad \text{and} \quad c_{k+1} = \frac{p - k}{k + 1} c_k, \quad k = 0, 1, 2, \ldots.$$

Thus we see that

$$\frac{|c_{k+1} x^{k+1}|}{|c_k x^k|} = \frac{|p - k|}{k + 1} |x|.$$

Since p is independent of k, we have $\lim_{k \uparrow \infty} \dfrac{|p - k|}{k + 1} = 1$, and hence the limit of the ratios of consecutive terms of our series is $|x|$. Thus the ratio test tells us that the series converges when $|x| < 1$ and diverges when $|x| > 1$; the interval of convergence of the binomial series is $(-1, 1)$.

We have found the interval of convergence of the binomial series, but we have not yet shown that its sum is $(1 + x)^p$. So let us temporarily denote the sum by $f(x)$; that is,

$$(122\text{-}4) \qquad f(x) = \sum_{k=0}^{\infty} c_k x^k, \quad x \in (-1, 1).$$

To show that $f(x) = (1 + x)^p$, we will show that the quotient $\dfrac{f(x)}{(1 + x)^p}$ is the number 1 for each $x \in (-1, 1)$. As the first step in this direction, we will show that the derivative of this quotient is 0, which will tell us that the quotient is independent of

x. Since the derivative of $\dfrac{f(x)}{(1+x)^p}$ is

$$\frac{(1+x)^p f'(x) - p(1+x)^{p-1}f(x)}{(1+x)^{2p}} = \frac{(1+x)f'(x) - pf(x)}{(1+x)^{p+1}},$$

we see that if it is to be 0, we must have

(122-5) $\qquad\qquad (1+x)f'(x) = pf(x),$

so let us verify this equation. From Equation 122-4, we see that

(122-6) $\quad f'(x) = \displaystyle\sum_{k=0}^{\infty} kc_k x^{k-1} = 0 \cdot c_0 + 1 \cdot c_1 + 2 \cdot c_2 x + 3 \cdot c_3 x^2 + \cdots .$

You will notice that we can also write this series as $\displaystyle\sum_{k=0}^{\infty}(k+1)c_{k+1}x^k$, and so

(122-7) $\qquad\qquad f'(x) = \displaystyle\sum_{k=0}^{\infty}(k+1)c_{k+1}x^k.$

The left-hand side of Equation 122-5 is $f'(x) + xf'(x)$; we use Equation 122-7 to express $f'(x)$ as a series, and we find a series for $xf'(x)$ by multiplying both sides of Equation 122-6 by x. Now we add these series and obtain the equation

$$(1+x)f'(x) = \sum_{k=0}^{\infty}[(k+1)c_{k+1} + kc_k]x^k.$$

For each index k, Equation 122-3 tells us that $(k+1)c_{k+1} + kc_k = pc_k$. Thus

$$(1+x)f'(x) = \sum_{k=0}^{\infty} pc_k x^k = p\sum_{k=0}^{\infty} c_k x^k = pf(x),$$

and hence Equation 122-5 is verified. Since the derivative of $\dfrac{f(x)}{(1+x)^p}$ is 0 at each point of the interval $(-1, 1)$, it follows that the value of this quotient at any point x of the interval is the same as its value at 0; that is, $\dfrac{f(x)}{(1+x)^p} = \dfrac{f(0)}{(1+0)^p} = f(0)$. But Equations 122-7 and 122-4 tell us that $f(0) = c_0 = 1$, and so we have finally shown that $\dfrac{f(x)}{(1+x)^p} = 1$. Therefore, we see that the Binomial Theorem, Equation 122-2, is valid for any real number p, as long as x is in the interval $(-1, 1)$. Of course, if p is a positive integer, Equation 122-2 is valid for every number x.

Example 122-3.   Find an infinite series of which the integral $\int_0^1 \sqrt{1-x^2}\,dx$ is the sum.

Solution.   We first use the Binomial Theorem to write

(122-8) $\sqrt{1-x^2} = (1-x^2)^{1/2} = 1 - \tfrac{1}{2}x^2 - \tfrac{1}{8}x^4 - \tfrac{1}{16}x^6 - \tfrac{5}{128}x^8 - \cdots.$

Then we integrate term-by-term:

$$\int_0^1 \sqrt{1-x^2}\,dx = 1 - \frac{1}{2\cdot 3} - \frac{1}{8\cdot 5} - \frac{1}{16\cdot 7} - \frac{5}{128\cdot 9} - \cdots.$$

We know that $\int_0^1 \sqrt{1-x^2}\,dx = \dfrac{\pi}{4}$, so if we like, we can use our series to calculate π.

Example 122-4.   Find an approximation to the circumference C of an ellipse.

Solution.   An ellipse with major and minor diameters of lengths $2a$ and $2b$ is the graph of the parametric equations

$$x = a\cos t \text{ and } y = b\sin t,\ t \in [0, 2\pi].$$

Thus (see Equation 71-9)

$$C = \int_0^{2\pi} \sqrt{a^2\sin^2 t + b^2\cos^2 t}\,dt$$

$$= a\int_0^{2\pi} \sqrt{1 - e^2\cos^2 t}\,dt,$$

where $e = \dfrac{\sqrt{a^2-b^2}}{a}$ is the eccentricity of the ellipse. Now we replace x with $e\cos t$ in Equation 122-8, and we have

$$C = a\int_0^{2\pi}\left(1 - \frac{e^2}{2}\cos^2 t - \frac{e^4}{8}\cos^4 t + \cdots\right)dt.$$

Even though the series in parentheses is not a power series, it is a fact that term-by-term integration is also permissible in this case. We use the first two terms to give us the following approximation of the circumference of the ellipse:

$$C \approx a\left[t - \frac{e^2}{2}\left(\frac{t}{2} + \frac{\sin 2t}{4}\right)\right]\Big|_0^{2\pi} = 2\pi a\left(1 - \frac{e^2}{4}\right).$$

PROBLEMS 122

1. Multiply or divide series you know to find Taylor's Series about 0 for the following.

(a) $e^x \sin x$ (b) $e^x \cos x$ (c) $\sec x$ (d) e^{-x} (e) $\dfrac{e^x}{1+x}$ (f) $e^x \sec x$

2. Use the identity $\sin^2 x = \frac{1}{2}(1 - \cos 2x)$ to find Taylor's Series for $\sin^2 x$ about 0. Differentiate the result to find Taylor's Series for $\sin 2x$ about 0. How else could you find this series?

3. Use the binomial series to compute the following numbers.

(a) $\sqrt{1.02}$ (b) $\sqrt{3.92}$ (c) $\sqrt[3]{.98}$ (d) $\sqrt[5]{30}$ (e) $10^{-2/3}$ (f) $\sqrt[4]{17}$

4. Use series and term-by-term integration to evaluate the following integrals.

(a) $\displaystyle\int_0^1 \cos \sqrt{x}\, dx$ (b) $\displaystyle\int_0^{.5} x \ln(1+x)\, dx$ (c) $\displaystyle\int_0^{.4} x\sqrt{1-x^3}\, dx$ (d) $\displaystyle\int_0^{.1} (1+x^2)^{.9}\, dx$

5. Expand $(1 - t^2)^{-1/2}$ by the binomial formula and integrate from 0 to x term-by-term to obtain a series of powers of x whose sum is Arcsin x. Can you find a series whose sum is Arccos x?

6. Find the area of the region $\{(x, y) \mid 1 \leq x \leq 2, y \geq 0, xy = \sin x\}$.

7. Find the first five terms of Taylor's Series about the origin for $f(x)$ if you know that $y = f(x)$ satisfies the differential equation $y'' + y = 0$ and the initial conditions $y = 1$ and $y' = -1$ when $x = 0$.

8. The **error function** erf is defined by the equation $\text{erf } x = \dfrac{2}{\sqrt{\pi}} \displaystyle\int_0^x e^{-t^2}\, dt$. Find Taylors' Series for erf x about the origin.

9. Show that if $p \leq -1$ the binomial series diverges when x is a number such that $|x| = 1$.

10. In Example 109-5 we found that if $f(x) = e^{-1/x^2}$ when $x \neq 0$ and $f(0) = 0$, then $f'(0) = 0$. Can you show that $f''(0) = 0$? By continuing the argument, one can show that $f^{(k)}(0) = 0$ for each positive integer k. What is Taylor's Series for $f(x)$ about the origin? Does it have $f(x)$ as its sum?

REVIEW PROBLEMS—CHAPTER FOURTEEN

You can use these problems to test yourself on the material of this chapter.

1. The terms of a certain sequence $\{a_n\}$ are given by the following rule. The first term is 1 and each of the other terms is the square of one-half of its predecessor. Express a_n in terms of n. What is $\lim_{n \uparrow \infty} a_n$?

2. Find a formula for the nth partial sum S_n of the infinite series $\displaystyle\sum_{k=1}^{\infty} \ln\left(\dfrac{\text{Arctan}(k+1)}{\text{Arctan } k}\right)$. What is the sum of this series?

3. Test the following series for convergence.

(a) $\displaystyle\sum_{k=1}^{\infty} \dfrac{1}{2^{\ln k}}$ (b) $\displaystyle\sum_{k=1}^{\infty} \dfrac{\sin \frac{1}{3}k\pi}{k}$

4. Evaluate the following integrals.

(a) $\displaystyle\int_0^\infty e^{-[x]}\,dx$ (b) $\displaystyle\int_0^\infty (-1)^{[x]}e^{-x}\,dx$ (c) $\displaystyle\int_1^\infty \frac{e^x}{[x]!}\,dx$

5. Find the set of points for which the power series $\displaystyle\sum_{k=1}^\infty (\sin k)\, x^k$ converges.

6. Show that we can use the Binomial Theorem to expand $(a + b)^p$, where p is any real number, if $|b| < |a|$.

7. Let $\{p_k\}$ be the sequence of prime numbers; that is, $p_1 = 2$, $p_2 = 3$, $p_3 = 5$, and so on. Find a function f such that for each positive integer k, $f^{(k)}(3) = p_k$. It can be shown that $\displaystyle\lim_{k \uparrow \infty} \frac{p_{k+1}}{(k + 1)p_k} = 0$; what does this equation tell you about the domain of your function?

8. Show that if a series of positive terms $\displaystyle\sum_{k=1}^\infty a_k$ converges, then the series $\displaystyle\sum_{k=1}^\infty a_k^2$ converges. Does it necessarily follow that $\displaystyle\sum_{k=1}^\infty \sqrt{a_k}$ converges? What if we delete the word "positive" in the first sentence?

9. Suppose that $f(x) = 1 + c_1 x + c_2 x^2 + c_3 x^3 + \cdots$ and that $f'(x) = f(x)$. Show that for each positive integer k, $c_k = \dfrac{1}{k!}$.

10. Let f be a function such that $f(0) = 0$ and $f'(0)$ exists. Show that if a series of positive terms $\displaystyle\sum_{k=1}^\infty a_k$ converges, then the series $\displaystyle\sum_{k=1}^\infty f(a_k)$ converges absolutely.

APPENDIX

A. TRIGONOMETRIC FORMULAS

The following trigonometric identities are valid for any numbers t, u, and v for which the functions involved are defined.

$$\csc t = \frac{1}{\sin t} \qquad \tan t = \frac{\sin t}{\cos t} \qquad \tan^2 t + 1 = \sec^2 t$$

$$\text{(A-1)} \qquad \sec t = \frac{1}{\cos t} \qquad \cot t = \frac{\cos t}{\sin t} \qquad \cot^2 t + 1 = \csc^2 t$$

$$\cot t = \frac{1}{\tan t} \qquad \sin^2 t + \cos^2 t = 1$$

$$\sin (u \pm v) = \sin u \cos v \pm \cos u \sin v$$

$$\text{(A-2)} \qquad \cos (u \pm v) = \cos u \cos v \mp \sin u \sin v$$

$$\tan (u \pm v) = \frac{\tan u \pm \tan v}{1 \mp \tan u \tan v}$$

743

$$\sin(-t) = -\sin t$$

(A-3) $$\cos(-t) = \quad \cos t$$

$$\tan(-t) = -\tan t$$

$$\sin 2t = 2 \sin t \cos t$$

(A-4) $$\cos 2t = \cos^2 t - \sin^2 t = 1 - 2\sin^2 t = 2\cos^2 t - 1$$

$$\tan 2t = \frac{2 \tan t}{1 - \tan^2 t}$$

(A-5) $$\sin^2 t = \tfrac{1}{2}(1 - \cos 2t)$$

$$\cos^2 t = \tfrac{1}{2}(1 + \cos 2t)$$

The length s of the arc of a circle of radius r that is intercepted by a central angle that measures t radians is given by the formula

$$s = rt.$$

The area of the sector that this angle cuts from the interior of this circle is given by the formula

$$K = \tfrac{1}{2}rs = \tfrac{1}{2}r^2 t.$$

If an angle measures A degrees and t radians, then

$$\frac{A}{180} = \frac{t}{\pi}.$$

The following brief table of values of the trigonometric functions is often useful; you should know it by heart.

t	$\cos t$	$\sin t$	$\tan t$
0	1	0	0
$\pi/6$	$\sqrt{3}/2$	$\tfrac{1}{2}$	$1/\sqrt{3}$
$\pi/4$	$\sqrt{2}/2$	$\sqrt{2}/2$	1
$\pi/3$	$\tfrac{1}{2}$	$\sqrt{3}/2$	$\sqrt{3}$
$\pi/2$	0	1	—
$2\pi/3$	$-\tfrac{1}{2}$	$\sqrt{3}/2$	$-\sqrt{3}$
$3\pi/4$	$-\sqrt{2}/2$	$\sqrt{2}/2$	-1
$5\pi/6$	$-\sqrt{3}/2$	$\tfrac{1}{2}$	$-1/\sqrt{3}$
π	-1	0	0

B. TABLES

TABLE I   *Trigonometric Functions*

t	$\sin t$	$\cos t$	$\tan t$	$\cot t$	$\sec t$	$\csc t$
0.0	.0000	1.0000	.0000	. . . . .	1.000	. . . . .
0.1	.0998	.9950	.1003	9.967	1.005	10.02
0.2	.1987	.9801	.2027	4.933	1.020	5.033
0.3	.2955	.9553	.3093	3.233	1.047	3.384
0.4	.3894	.9211	.4228	2.365	1.086	2.568
0.5	.4794	.8776	.5463	1.830	1.139	2.086
0.6	.5646	.8253	.6841	1.462	1.212	1.771
0.7	.6442	.7648	.8423	1.187	1.307	1.552
0.8	.7174	.6967	1.030	.9712	1.435	1.394
0.9	.7833	.6216	1.260	.7936	1.609	1.277
1.0	.8415	.5403	1.557	.6421	1.851	1.188
1.1	.8912	.4536	1.965	.5090	2.205	1.122
1.2	.9320	.3624	2.572	.3888	2.760	1.073
1.3	.9636	.2675	3.602	.2776	3.738	1.038
1.4	.9854	.1700	5.798	.1725	5.883	1.015
1.5	.9975	.0707	14.101	.0709	14.137	1.003
1.6	.9996	$-.0292$	-34.233	$-.0292$	-34.25	1.000

TABLE II   *Natural Logarithms*

x	$\ln x$	x	$\ln x$	x	$\ln x$	x	$\ln x$	x	$\ln x$
0.0	. . . . .	2.0	0.6931	4.0	1.3863	6.0	1.7918	8.0	2.0794
0.1	-2.303	2.1	0.7419	4.1	1.4110	6.1	1.8083	8.1	2.0919
0.2	-1.609	2.2	0.7885	4.2	1.4351	6.2	1.8245	8.2	2.1041
0.3	-1.204	2.3	0.8329	4.3	1.4586	6.3	1.8406	8.3	2.1163
0.4	$-.916$	2.4	0.8755	4.4	1.4816	6.4	1.8563	8.4	2.1282
0.5	$-.693$	2.5	0.9163	4.5	1.5041	6.5	1.8718	8.5	2.1401
0.6	$-.511$	2.6	0.9555	4.6	1.5261	6.6	1.8871	8.6	2.1518
0.7	$-.357$	2.7	0.9933	4.7	1.5476	6.7	1.9021	8.7	2.1633
0.8	$-.223$	2.8	1.0296	4.8	1.5686	6.8	1.9169	8.8	2.1748
0.9	$-.105$	2.9	1.0647	4.9	1.5892	6.9	1.9315	8.9	2.1861
1.0	0.0000	3.0	1.0986	5.0	1.6094	7.0	1.9459	9.0	2.1972
1.1	0.0953	3.1	1.1314	5.1	1.6292	7.1	1.9601	9.1	2.2083
1.2	0.1823	3.2	1.1632	5.2	1.6487	7.2	1.9741	9.2	2.2192
1.3	0.2624	3.3	1.1939	5.3	1.6677	7.3	1.9879	9.3	2.2300
1.4	0.3365	3.4	1.2238	5.4	1.6864	7.4	2.0015	9.4	2.2407
1.5	0.4055	3.5	1.2528	5.5	1.7047	7.5	2.0149	9.5	2.2513
1.6	0.4700	3.6	1.2809	5.6	1.7228	7.6	2.0282	9.6	2.2618
1.7	0.5306	3.7	1.3083	5.7	1.7405	7.7	2.0412	9.7	2.2721
1.8	0.5878	3.8	1.3350	5.8	1.7579	7.8	2.0541	9.8	2.2824
1.9	0.6419	3.9	1.3610	5.9	1.7750	7.9	2.0669	9.9	2.2925
								10.0	2.3026

TABLE III   *Exponential and Hyperbolic Functions*

x	e^x	e^{-x}	$\sinh x$	$\cosh x$	$\tanh x$
0.0	1.0000	1.0000	0.0000	1.0000	0.0000
0.1	1.1052	.9048	.1002	1.0050	.0997
0.2	1.2214	.8187	.2013	1.0201	.1974
0.3	1.3499	.7408	.3045	1.0453	.2913
0.4	1.4918	.6703	.4108	1.0811	.3799
0.5	1.6487	.6065	.5211	1.1276	.4621
0.6	1.8221	.5488	.6367	1.1855	.5370
0.7	2.0138	.4966	.7586	1.2552	.6044
0.8	2.2255	.4493	.8881	1.3374	.6640
0.9	2.4596	.4066	1.0265	1.4331	.7163
1.0	2.7183	.3679	1.1752	1.5431	.7616
1.1	3.0042	.3329	1.3356	1.6685	.8005
1.2	3.3201	.3012	1.5095	1.8107	.8337
1.3	3.6693	.2725	1.6984	1.9709	.8617
1.4	4.0552	.2466	1.9043	2.1509	.8854
1.5	4.4817	.2231	2.1293	2.3524	.9051
1.6	4.9530	.2019	2.3756	2.5775	.9217
1.7	5.4739	.1827	2.6456	2.8283	.9354
1.8	6.0496	.1653	2.9422	3.1075	.9468
1.9	6.6859	.1496	3.2682	3.4177	.9562
2.0	7.3891	.1353	3.6269	3.7622	.9640
2.1	8.1662	.1225	4.0219	4.1443	.9705
2.2	9.0250	.1108	4.4571	4.5679	.9757
2.3	9.9742	.1003	4.9370	5.0372	.9801
2.4	11.023	.0907	5.4662	5.5569	.9837
2.5	12.182	.0821	6.0502	6.1323	.9866
2.6	13.464	.0743	6.6947	6.7690	.9890
2.7	14.880	.0672	7.4063	7.4735	.9910
2.8	16.445	.0608	8.1919	8.2527	.9926
2.9	18.174	.0550	9.0596	9.1146	.9940
3.0	20.086	.0498	10.018	10.068	.9951

TABLE IV   *Differentiation Formulas*

IV-1 $D_x u^r = r u^{r-1} D_x u$

IV-2 $D_x |u| = u |u|^{-1} D_x u$

IV-3 $D_x \sin u = \cos u\, D_x u$

IV-4 $D_x \cos u = -\sin u\, D_x u$

IV-5 $D_x \tan u = \sec^2 u\, D_x u$

IV-6 $D_x \cot u = -\csc^2 u\, D_x u$

IV-7 $D_x \sec u = \sec u \tan u\, D_x u$

IV-8 $D_x \csc u = -\csc u \cot u\, D_x u$

IV-9 $D_x e^u = e^u\, D_x u$

IV-10 $D_x \ln |u| = u^{-1} D_x u$

IV-11 $D_x a^u = a^u \ln a\, D_x u$

IV-12 $D_x \log_b |u| = u^{-1} \log_b e\, D_x u$

IV-13 $D_x \operatorname{Arcsin} u = \dfrac{1}{\sqrt{1 - u^2}} D_x u$

IV-14 $D_x \operatorname{Arccos} u = -\dfrac{1}{\sqrt{1 - u^2}} D_x u$

IV-15 $D_x \operatorname{Arctan} u = (1 + u^2)^{-1} D_x u$

IV-16 $D_x \cosh u = \sinh u\, D_x u$

IV-17 $D_x \sinh u = \cosh u\, D_x u$

IV-18 $D_x \tanh u = \operatorname{sech}^2 u\, D_x u$

IV-19 $D_x \coth u = -\operatorname{csch}^2 u\, D_x u$

IV-20 $D_x \operatorname{sech} u = -\operatorname{sech} u \tanh u\, D_x u$

IV-21 $D_x \operatorname{csch} u = -\operatorname{csch} u \coth u\, D_x u$

IV-22 $D_x \sinh^{-1} u = \dfrac{1}{\sqrt{u^2 + 1}} D_x u$

IV-23 $D_x \operatorname{Cosh}^{-1} u = \dfrac{1}{\sqrt{u^2 - 1}} D_x u$

IV-24 $D_x \tanh^{-1} u = \dfrac{1}{1 - u^2} D_x u$

IV-25 $D_x \coth^{-1} u = \dfrac{-1}{u^2 - 1} D_x u$

IV-26 $D_x \operatorname{Sech}^{-1} u = \dfrac{-1}{u \sqrt{1 - u^2}} D_x u$

IV-27 $D_x \operatorname{csch}^{-1} u = \dfrac{-1}{u \sqrt{1 + u^2}} D_x u$

IV-28 $D_x \displaystyle\int_c^u f(t)\, dt = f(u) D_x u$, (if f continuous)

TABLE V   *Basic Integration Formulas*

(Note: The number a is assumed to be positive in the following 25 basic formulas.)

V-1 $\int u^r \, du = \dfrac{u^{r+1}}{r+1}$ $(r \neq -1)$

V-2 $\int \cos u \, du = \sin u$

V-3 $\int \sin u \, du = -\cos u$

V-4 $\int \sec^2 u \, du = \tan u$

V-5 $\int \csc^2 u \, du = -\cot u$

V-6 $\int \sec u \tan u \, du = \sec u$

V-7 $\int \csc u \cot u \, du = -\csc u$

V-8 $\int e^u \, du = e^u$

V-9 $\int \dfrac{du}{u} = \ln |u|$

V-10 $\int a^u \, du = a^u / \ln a$

V-11 $\int \ln |u| \, du = u(\ln |u| - 1)$

V-12 $\int \dfrac{du}{\sqrt{a^2 - u^2}} = \operatorname{Arcsin}\left(\dfrac{u}{a}\right)$

V-13 $\int \dfrac{du}{a^2 + u^2} = \dfrac{1}{a} \operatorname{Arctan}\left(\dfrac{u}{a}\right)$

V-14 $\int \sinh u \, du = \cosh u$

V-15 $\int \cosh u \, du = \sinh u$

V-16 $\int \operatorname{sech}^2 u \, du = \tanh u$

V-17 $\int \operatorname{csch}^2 u \, du = -\coth u$

V-18 $\int \operatorname{sech} u \tanh u \, du = -\operatorname{sech} u$

V-19 $\int \operatorname{csch} u \coth u \, du = -\operatorname{csch} u$

V-20 $\int \dfrac{du}{\sqrt{u^2 + a^2}} = \sinh^{-1}\left(\dfrac{u}{a}\right) = \ln\left(\dfrac{u + \sqrt{u^2 + a^2}}{a}\right)$

V-21 $\int \dfrac{du}{\sqrt{u^2 - a^2}} = \operatorname{Cosh}^{-1}\left(\dfrac{u}{a}\right) = \ln\left(\dfrac{u + \sqrt{u^2 - a^2}}{a}\right)$

V-22 $\int \dfrac{du}{a^2 - u^2} = \dfrac{1}{a}\tanh^{-1}\left(\dfrac{u}{a}\right) = \dfrac{1}{2a}\ln\left(\dfrac{a + u}{a - u}\right), (u^2 < a^2)$

V-23 $\int \dfrac{du}{u^2 - a^2} = -\dfrac{1}{a}\coth^{-1}\left(\dfrac{u}{a}\right) = -\dfrac{1}{2a}\ln\left(\dfrac{u + a}{u - a}\right), (u^2 > a^2)$

V-24 $\int \dfrac{du}{u\sqrt{a^2 - u^2}} = -\dfrac{1}{a}\operatorname{Sech}^{-1}\left(\dfrac{u}{a}\right) = -\dfrac{1}{a}\ln\left(\dfrac{a + \sqrt{a^2 - u^2}}{u}\right), 0 < u < a$

V-25 $\int \dfrac{du}{u\sqrt{a^2 + u^2}} = -\dfrac{1}{a}\operatorname{csch}^{-1}\left(\dfrac{|u|}{a}\right) = -\dfrac{1}{a}\ln\left(\dfrac{a + \sqrt{a^2 + u^2}}{|u|}\right)$

Additional Integration Formulas

V-26 $\int \dfrac{u \, du}{au + b} = \dfrac{u}{a} - \dfrac{b}{a^2}\ln |au + b|$

V-27 $\int \dfrac{u \, du}{(au + b)^2} = \dfrac{b}{a^2(au + b)} + \dfrac{1}{a^2}\ln |au + b|$

V-28 $\int \dfrac{du}{u(au + b)} = \dfrac{1}{b}\ln \left|\dfrac{u}{au + b}\right|$

TABLE V   *Additional Integration Formulas (continued)*

V-29 $\displaystyle\int \frac{du}{u(au+b)^2} = \frac{1}{b(au+b)} + \frac{1}{b^2}\ln\left|\frac{u}{au+b}\right|$

V-30 $\displaystyle\int \sqrt{a^2-u^2}\,du = \frac{u}{2}\sqrt{a^2-u^2} + \frac{a^2}{2}\operatorname{Arcsin}\frac{u}{a}$

V-31 $\displaystyle\int \sqrt{u^2\pm a^2}\,du = \frac{u}{2}\sqrt{u^2\pm a^2} \pm \frac{a^2}{2}\ln\left|u+\sqrt{u^2\pm a^2}\right|$

V-32 $\displaystyle\int u^2\sqrt{a^2-u^2}\,du = -\frac{1}{4}u(a^2-u^2)^{3/2} + \frac{a^2u}{8}\sqrt{a^2-u^2} + \frac{a^4}{8}\operatorname{Arcsin}\frac{u}{a}$

V-33 $\displaystyle\int \tan u\,du = \ln|\sec u|$

V-34 $\displaystyle\int \cot u\,du = \ln|\sin u|$

V-35 $\displaystyle\int \sec u\,du = \ln|\sec u + \tan u|$

V-36 $\displaystyle\int \csc u\,du = \ln|\csc u - \cot u|$

V-37 $\displaystyle\int \sec^3 u\,du = \tfrac{1}{2}(\tan u \sec u + \ln|\sec u + \tan u|)$

V-38 $\displaystyle\int e^{au}\sin bu\,du = \frac{e^{au}(a\sin bu - b\cos bu)}{a^2+b^2}$

V-39 $\displaystyle\int e^{au}\cos bu\,du = \frac{e^{au}(b\sin bu + a\cos bu)}{a^2+b^2}$

V-40 $\displaystyle\int u^n \ln u\,du = u^{n+1}\left[\frac{\ln u}{n+1} - \frac{1}{(n+1)^2}\right]$

V-41 $\displaystyle\int \sin^n u\,du = \frac{-\sin^{n-1}u\cos u}{n} + \frac{n-1}{n}\int \sin^{n-2}u\,du$

V-42 $\displaystyle\int \cos^n u\,du = \frac{\cos^{n-1}u\sin u}{n} + \frac{n-1}{n}\int \cos^{n-2}u\,du$

V-43 $\displaystyle\int \tan^n u\,du = \frac{\tan^{n-1}u}{n-1} - \int \tan^{n-2}u\,du$

V-44 $\displaystyle\int u^n e^{au}\,du = \frac{u^n e^{au}}{a} - \frac{n}{a}\int u^{n-1}e^{au}\,du$

V-45 $\displaystyle\int u^n \sin au\,du = \frac{-u^n}{a}\cos au + \frac{n}{a}\int u^{n-1}\cos au\,du$

V-46 $\displaystyle\int u^n \cos au\,du = \frac{u^n}{a}\sin au - \frac{n}{a}\int u^{n-1}\sin au\,du$

V-47 $\displaystyle\int \frac{du}{au^2+bu+c} = \frac{2}{\sqrt{4ac-b^2}}\operatorname{Tan^{-1}}\left(\frac{2au+b}{\sqrt{4ac-b^2}}\right), \qquad (b^2 < 4ac)$

V-48 $\displaystyle\int \frac{u\,du}{au^2+bu+c} = \frac{1}{2a}\ln|au^2+bu+c| - \frac{b}{a\sqrt{4ac-b^2}}\operatorname{Tan^{-1}}\left(\frac{2au+b}{\sqrt{4ac-b^2}}\right), \qquad (b^2 < 4ac)$

V-49 $\displaystyle\int \frac{du}{(au^2+bu+c)^r} = \frac{2au+b}{(r-1)(4ac-b^2)(au^2+bu+c)^{r-1}} + \frac{2(2r-3)a}{(r-1)(4ac-b^2)}\int \frac{du}{(au^2+bu+c)^{r-1}}$

V-50 $\displaystyle\int \frac{u\,du}{(au^2+bu+c)^r} = \frac{-(2c+bu)}{(r-1)(4ac-b^2)(au^2+bu+c)^{r-1}} - \frac{b(2r-3)}{(r-1)(4ac-b^2)}\int \frac{du}{(au^2+bu+c)^{r-1}}$

V-51 $\displaystyle\int f^{-1}(u)\,du = uf^{-1}(u) - \int_c^{f^{-1}(u)} f(t)\,dt, \quad (c \text{ arbitrary})$

C. SELECTED ANSWERS

Because of space limitations, certain formulas in these answers have been broken in unnatural places as they were carried from line to line.

PROBLEMS 1. *Page 5*

1. (a) $\frac{7}{3}$; (c) -2. **2.** $\{-1, 0, 1, 2\}$, no, no.
3. (a) and (c). **4.** (a) $x = 4$ or $x = -4$;
(c) $x \geq 0$. **5.** (a) $-4 \leq x \leq 4$; (c) This statement is true for every number. **6.** $|a| < |b|$.
7. (a) $x > y + 3$; (c) $|x - 3| < \frac{1}{2}$. **9.** (a)
$x = 3.141$, $y = 3.142$. **14.** (a) $x > \frac{1}{4}$; (c)
$\frac{1}{3} < x < 1$; (e) $-3 < x < 3$.

PROBLEMS 2. *Page 11*

2. $[a, b] = [-\infty, \infty]$. **4.** (a) $(-\infty, -3)$
$\cup (3, \infty)$; (c) $[-5, -1]$; (e) $(\frac{1}{2}, 2)$; (g) $(0, 1) \cup$
$(2, \infty)$; (i) $[0, \infty]$. **7.** (d) $A \neq B$; (e) $\{0, 1\} \subseteq B$;
(g) $[-\infty, \infty]$; (h) $I \cap B = \{0, -1, 1\}$, $I \cap A =$
$\emptyset$. **9.** (a) $[4, 6]$; (b) $(a + b - p - q, a + b +$
$p + q)$; (c) $(-\infty, \infty)$; (e) no; (f) yes. **11.** (a)
$[-1, 2]$; (c) $[-\infty, \infty]$; (e) $[0, \sin 1]$; (g)
$[\sqrt{2}/2, \infty]$. **12.** (a) intersection $\{3\}$, union
$(-\infty, \infty)$.

PROBLEMS 3. *Page 18*

1. (a) $\sqrt{29}$; (c) 5; (e) 1; (g) $\sqrt{2} \log 2$.
2. (a) $2 |t|$; (c) $|\sec t|$; (e) $\sqrt{2} |\log |\tan t||$.
3. (a) II; (c) IV. **4.** $\sqrt{2}$. **6.** 8. **7.** $(-7, 2)$ and
$(-7, 6)$, $(1, 2)$ and $(1, 6)$, $(-5, 4)$ and $(-1, 4)$.
8. (a) $(2, 7)$; (c) $\left(\dfrac{x_1 + x_2}{2}, \dfrac{y_1 + y_2}{2}\right)$. **10.** $(4, 0)$.
11. $x + y = 1$. **12.** (a) not collinear. **13.** $(-\infty,$
$-2) \cup (6, \infty)$. **14.** $(-2, 2)$, $(4, 6)$, $(0, -4)$.
15. (a) 1; (c) 4.

PROBLEMS 4. *Page 24*

2. (a) $(x - 1)^2 + (y + 2)^2 > 9$; (c)
$xy < 0$; (e) $4 < x^2 + y^2 < 9$. **5.** (a) $(x + 1)^2 +$
$(y + 3)^2 = 4$; (c) $3x^2 + 3y^2 - 4x + 14y + 15$
$= 0$; (e) $x = \pi$. **6.** (a) $\{(0, 0), (1, 1)\}$; (c)
$\{(k\pi, 0) \mid k$ an integer$\}$; (e) $\{(1, 1), (-\frac{1}{2}, \frac{1}{4})\}$.
9. The fourteenth.

PROBLEMS 5. *Page 30*

1. (a) Domain $= \{1, 2, \ldots\}$, Range $=$
$\{2, 3, \ldots\}$, $f(n) = n + 1$; (c) Domain $= (0, \infty)$,
Range $= [2, \infty]$, $h(x) = x + \dfrac{1}{x}$; (e) Domain $=$
$\{n \mid n$ a prime number$\}$, Range $= \{0, 6\}$,

$q(x) = \frac{3}{20}(x - 3)(10 - 3x)(x - 7 - |x - 7|)$.
2. (a) $(0, \infty)$; (c) $(-\infty, 1)$; (e) $(-\infty, -1) \cup$
$(1, \infty)$; (g) $(-\infty, 0) \cup [1, \infty]$. **4.** (a) 2; (c) 37;
(e) $\frac{17}{16}$; (g) 4; (i) $(\log 2)^2 + 1$; (k) $\sec^2 1$. **5.** (e) is
true for every constant function. **7.** Domain $=$
$\{1, \ldots, 14\}$, Range $= \{0, 1, 2\}$, 1. **8.** No.
9. Yes. **10.** Domain $= [-3, 0]$, Range $= [0, 6]$,
-8. **11.** The characteristic. **13.** $-5[\![-x]\!]$.

14. $2x^2 + \dfrac{100}{x}$. **15.** $22x^2$. **16.** $c = .1\pi r^2 (1 +$

$.1\sqrt{1 + 81r^{-6}})$.

PROBLEMS 6. *Page 36*

1. (a) .84; (c) .07. **2.** (a) F; (c) T; (e) F.
3. (a) $\sqrt{2}/2$; (c) 1; (e) $\frac{1}{2}$. **5.** (a), (c), (f). **7.** (a)
$\{\frac{1}{2}\pi + 2n\pi \mid n$ an integer$\}$; (c) $\{\frac{1}{2}n\pi \mid n$ an
integer$\}$; (d) $\emptyset$. **8.** (c) is a function, (a), (b),
and (d) are not. **10.** (a) $\sqrt{2}$; (c) $\sqrt{2}$; (e) 1.
12. (a) 1; (c) $-\cos 4t$; (e) $-\cot 2t$; (g) 1.

13. $\frac{5}{2}$ radians, $\dfrac{450}{\pi}$ degrees. **14.** $\frac{42}{5}\pi$ inches.

PROBLEMS 7. *Page 42*

3. $(-a, b)$. **5.** $\log y = x$. **7.** (a) $y =$
$x^2 + 1$; (c) $y = x$. **10.** (a) the integers;
(c) $[0, 1)$; (e) $(-1, 3)$. **11.** (a) T; (b) T; (c) F.

PROBLEMS 8. *Page 48*

1. (a) $f(x) = 3x - 2$; (c) $f(x) =$
$\frac{1}{3}\pi(1 - x)$. **2.** (a) $[-3, 1]$; (c) $\{2\}$; (e) $[5, \frac{17}{3}]$;
(g) $\{-3, -2\}$. **3.** (a) $f(x) = mx$; (c) $f(x) =$
$x + b$; (e) $f(x) = \frac{1}{4}x + \frac{5}{4}$; (g) $f(x) = b$,
where $b \geq 0$ or $f(x) = mx$, where $m \geq 0$.
4. $\{(-1, 1)\}$. **5.** (a) $f(x) = 2x - 3$ or $f(x) =$
$3 - 2x$; (c) $f(x) = x$; (e) $f(x) = x + 1$ or
$f(x) = 4 - x$. **6.** 80 calories. **7.** $f(x) = 3x + 2$.

PROBLEMS 9. *Page 53*

1. (a) 3 and -1; (c) 2 and $\frac{7}{2}$; (e) $-\frac{1}{2}$
and $-\frac{1}{4}$. **3.** (a) $y = 4x - 1$, $[-1, 3]$; (c) $y =$
$\frac{22}{7}x + (\pi - \frac{22}{7})$, $[\pi - \frac{22}{7}, \pi]$. **4.** Negative.
5. (a) 1; (c) 0. **6.** (a) $y = x + 1$; (c) $y = 1$.
7. $3x + 5y - 7 = 0$, $5x - 3y + 11 = 0$.
8. No. **9.** $x + \sqrt{3}y = 4$.

10. (a) not collinear. **12.** $\dfrac{x}{7} + \dfrac{y}{11} = 1$. **13.** $(3, 1)$

and $(-27, 41)$. **15.** P_2 is the point $\left(-\dfrac{a}{b}\,y_1,\right.$ $\left.b-y_1\right)$ and P_3 is (x_1, y_1). **16.** 5.

PROBLEMS 10. *Page 62*

2. (a) 4; (c) 0; (e) $\frac{1}{6}$; (g) 1. **4.** (a) 1, 0, $-$; (c) $-4, 0, -$; (e) 0, 0, 0. **6.** (a) $\{-\frac{3}{2}, -1, 0, \frac{1}{2}, 1\}$; (c) no limit, value 0; (e) $\{0\}$, $\{0, 1\}$. **7.** (a) $[0, 6)$, $(0, 4)$; (c) 2; (d) yes. **11.** (a) limit does not exist. **12.** (a) $(r - 3, -3)$, $\{0\}$, $(r - 3, 3) \cup \{0\}$; (b) -3, 0, does not exist. **14.** Hint: If $\lim_{x \to a} f(x) = A$, then there is an $N_r^* a$ such that

$$f(N_r^* a) \subseteq N_A A.$$

PROBLEMS 11. *Page 68*

2. (a) -2. **3.** (a) 0. **10.** s is continuous at every point of its domain. **12.** The statement is certainly true if A is not an integer.

REVIEW PROBLEMS, CHAPTER ONE.
Page 70

1. Yes, no, no, yes. **4.** (b) and (d). **5.** See Fig. I-1. **8.** (5, 2). **9.** (c) $f(x) = 1 - |1 + 2[\![\frac{1}{2}x]\!] - x|$. **12.** $x = 12 \sin 6\pi t$, $x = 12(\sin 6\pi t + 1 - \cos 6\pi t)$. **13.** (a) $\{k\pi \mid k \text{ an integer}\}$; (c) 0. **16.** (a) 0; (c) -2.

PROBLEMS 12. *Page 77*

1. (a) -2; (c) $\frac{1}{2}$; (e) $-\frac{17}{4}$. **2.** The constant function with value 0. **3.** $x = k\pi$, where k is an integer. **4.** (a) The union of the intervals of the form $((2k - 1)\pi, 2k\pi)$; (c) $\varnothing$. **5.** (a) $\frac{1}{2}$; (c) 2. **8.** (a) 4.074; (c) .4974. **9.** $\{0, 1, 2, 3\}$. **10.** If $x \in (0, 1), g'(x) = -x/\sqrt{1 - x^2}$; if $x \in (-1, 0)$, $g'(x) = x/\sqrt{1 - x^2}$. **11.** (a) 0, 9, -6; (c) $f'(x) = 3[\![x]\!]$. **12.** $-1, -1, 1$. **13.** $f'(x) = (x - 2)/\sqrt{21 + 4x - x^2}$. **14.** $f'(x) = \dfrac{1}{[\![x]\!] + 1} - \dfrac{1}{[\![x]\!]}$.

PROBLEMS 13. *Page 85*

1. (a) 2; (c) $-2(x + 1)^{-2}$; (e) $3x^2 - 7$. **2.** $f'(x) = m$; $f'(x) = 0$. **3.** (a) $x^{-1/2}$; (c) $-\frac{1}{2}(x + 1)^{-3/2}$; (e) $1 + x^{-2}$. **4.** (a) 4; (c) 2; (e) 0. **7.** $f'(0) = 1$. **8.** (a) 0; (c) 0. **10.** $g'(x) = f'(x) + 2x$. **11.** (a) .43, .043, .0043, 4.3; (b) 100/43; (c) $10^{x+2}/43$. **13.** $f'(a) \le g'(a)$.

PROBLEMS 14. *Page 88*

1. (a) $6x + 2$ and $6x + 2$; (c) $-x^{-2}$ and 1. **2.** (a) positive; (c) negative. **3.** (a) 6 and 12 ft/sec; (c) $2 + \sqrt{2}/2$ and $4 + 1/2\sqrt{2}$ ft/sec.

4. Velocities are approximately 1, .88, and .54. **5.** $v \approx .15$ cm/sec. **6.** $D_r A = 2\pi r$. **7.** $-10,800$ π in/min. **8.** (a) $-3, 0, \frac{3}{4}$; (b) to left, stopped, to right. **9.** It is 0. **11.** $D_x y D_y x = 1$.

PROBLEMS 15. *Page 93*

1. (a) $7x^6$; (c) $\frac{1}{6}t^{-4/5}$; (e) $\frac{1}{8}x^{-7/8}$. **2.** (a) $x - 3y = -2, 3x + y = 4$; (c) $3x - y = 2$, $x + 3y = 4$. **3.** Not necessarily. **6.** (a) (0, 0) and $(\frac{2}{3}, \frac{4}{9})$, $(\frac{2}{3}, \frac{8}{27})$; (c) $(2^{-4/3}, 2^{2/3})$, $(2^{-4/3}, 2^{-2/3})$. **9.** $D_x y D_y x = 1$. **11.** $-\frac{5}{16}\sqrt{41}$. **12.** $\frac{1}{3}$. **16.** $|rar + 1/r\,a^{r-2}|$.

PROBLEMS 16. *Page 97*

1. (a) $-21x^{-9/2}$; (c) $10/3x^{1/3}$; (f) $-4[\![x]\!]/5x^{9/5}$. **2.** (a) $x - 3y = -8$; (c) $5x - 3y = -7$. **5.** $v/2x$. **6.** $4\pi g(t)^2 g'(t)$. **7.** $2\pi g(t)g'(t)$. **10.** $D_x f(3x + 4) = 3f'(3x + 4)$, $D_x f(x + 4) = f'(x + 4)$. **12.** $D_y x = D_u x D_y u$ and $D_x u = D_x v D_v u$. **14.** $\left\{k\dfrac{\pi}{2}\,\Big|\, k \text{ an integer}\right\}$.

PROBLEMS 17. *Page 102*

1. (a) $(2x)^{-1/2} - 2^{1/2}$; (c) $(2x)^{-1/2} - (2x)^{-3/2}$; (e) $2x$; (g) $1/\sqrt{4x(1 + x)^3}$; (i) $3(x - 1)^3(x + 2)^4(x - 3)^5(5x^2 - 6x - 7)$; (k) $(x^2 + 1)(3 - x^{-2})$; (m) $16(16 - x^2)^{-3/2}$. **2.** (a) $36\frac{1}{4}$; (c) -5; (e) $-\frac{2}{5}$, (g) $\frac{24}{5}$. **3.** (a) (4, 1); (c) $(\frac{1}{16}, \frac{7}{2})$. **5.** (a) $(3t^2 + t - 1)/2t^{3/2}$; (c) $(5t^2 + 3t + 1)/2\sqrt{t}$.

PROBLEMS 18. *Page 108*

1. (a)$(\cos x)/2\sqrt{\sin x} - (\cos \sqrt{x})/2\sqrt{x}$; (c) 2 sec $2x$ tan $2x - 2$ sec x tan x; (e) $-2 \sin 2x + (\cos 2) \sin x$; (g) $(x \cos x - \sin x)x^{-2}$; (i) $-2x \sin (2 \cos^2 x^2) \sin 2x^2$; (k) $-\dfrac{\cot x}{|\cot x|}$ csc^2 x. **3.** (a) $y = x$, $y = -x$; (c) $y = 1$, $x = \frac{1}{2}\pi$. **4.** (a)$\left(\dfrac{2\pi}{3}, \dfrac{\sqrt{3}}{2}\right)$. **8.** $v = Ab \cos (bt + c)$. **10.** $4\pi\sqrt{3}$ units per min.

PROBLEMS 19. *Page 115*

1. (a) $[0, 1]$; (c) $[0, 1]$; (e) $[\cos 1, 1]$. **2.** (a) See Example 11-4; (b) Theorem 19-1; (c) no; (d) no; (e) no. **3.** $f(x) = \sin 10x$. **4.** $f(x) = [\![x]\!]$. **5.** No, yes. **6.** (a) $\frac{1}{2}\pi$; (c) $\frac{1}{2}$; (e) $\frac{5}{3}$. **7.** $g(x) = f(x) + C$, where (a) $C = -\frac{1}{2}$, (b) $C = 4$; (c) $C = -1$; (d) $C = 1$; (e) $C = -1$. **8.** $f'(x) = g'(x)$. **9.** Yes. **11.** (a)$f(x) = 3 \cdot 10^{-x}$; (b) $f(x) \ge 3 \cdot 10^{-x}$. **12.** Conclusion holds in (d), not in (a), (b), (c).

PROBLEMS 20. *Page 119*

1. (a) $4(1 + x)^{-3}$; (c) $2 \cos 2x$; (e) $2x/|x|$.
2. (a) $-\sqrt{3}\pi^2/162$; (c) .104. **5.** (b) $a = 5$, $b = -2$. **7.** $k = 1$ or -1. **12.** k an integer.
13. (a) $ry'' y'^{r-1}$; (c) $y'' \sec y' \tan y'$. **14.** There is a number C such that $y' = (C - x)^{-1}$. We don't yet have the background to find y.

PROBLEMS 21. *Page 125*

1. (a) increasing in $[-\infty, 1]$ and $[3, \infty]$; (c) increasing in $(-1, 5]$; (e) increasing in $[-1, 1]$; (g) increasing in $\left[0, \dfrac{\pi}{4}\right]$, $\left[\dfrac{\pi}{2}, \dfrac{3\pi}{4}\right]$, $\left[\pi, \dfrac{5\pi}{4}\right]$, $\left[\dfrac{3\pi}{2}, \dfrac{7\pi}{2}\right]$; (i) increasing in $\left[0, \dfrac{\pi}{3}\right]$ and $\left[\dfrac{4\pi}{3}, 2\pi\right]$. **2.** (a) concave up in $\left[-\dfrac{2}{3}, \infty\right]$ concave up in $(-\infty, \infty)$; concave up in intervals of the form $\left[k\pi, \dfrac{2k + 1}{2}\pi\right]$; concave down in $[-2, -\tfrac{2}{3}]$; concave up in intervals of the form $[(2k - 1)\pi, 2k\pi]$.

REVIEW PROBLEMS, CHAPTER TWO.
Page 126

1. $f'(\pi) = -1, f'(1776) = 1, f''(x) = 0$, points of the form k^2 and $k^2 + k + \tfrac{1}{4}$ are not in the domain of f' or f''. **2.** The two numbers in (b) are the same. **3.** (a) -7; (c) -1; (e) -2; (g) $(-1, 3)$; (i) 1; (k) 1. **4.** $(1.38)4^x$. **5.** No. **7.** $f'([a, b]) = [f'(a), f'(b)]$. **10.** $P'(r)$.

PROBLEMS 22. *Page 136*

1. (a) $y = -\tfrac{5}{2}, -2, -\tfrac{5}{2}, \tfrac{5}{2}, 2, \tfrac{5}{2}; y' = \tfrac{3}{4}$, $0, -3, -3, 0, \tfrac{3}{4}; y'' = -\tfrac{1}{4}, -2, -16, 16, 2, \tfrac{1}{4}$; (b) concave up when $x \in (0, \infty)$; (c) maximum point $(-1, -2)$, minimum point $(1, 2)$. **3.** Maximum point $(1, 0)$, minimum points when $x = \tfrac{1}{4}(1 \pm \sqrt{105})$; concave down when $x \in (-1, 2)$. **4.** (a) Minimum points $(-1, 0)$ and $(1, 0)$; maximum point $(0, 1)$; (c) minimum point $(\tfrac{1}{2}, -\tfrac{1}{3})$; (e) minimum points of the form $\left(\dfrac{2k + 1}{2}\pi, 0\right)$, maximum points of the form $(k\pi, 1)$; (g) minimum points $(0, 0)$ and $(\tfrac{1}{2}\pi, 0)$, X-coordinate of a maximum point satisfies the equation $x = \cot x$. **10.** (a) X-coordinates of the form $x = \dfrac{2k + 1}{2}\pi$; (c) X-coordinates of the form $(2k + 1)\pi$ and $(2k + \tfrac{3}{2})\pi$. **11.** (a) $[2, \tfrac{10}{3}]$. **12.** $[-\sqrt{5}, \sqrt{5}]$.

PROBLEMS 23. *Page 142*

1. (a) $\sqrt{50}$ by $\sqrt{50}$ by $\sqrt{50}$. **2.** $\theta \approx 1.3$ radians. **3.** 16 cu in. **7.** $\sqrt{6}$ yds wide, $2\sqrt{6}$ yds high. **8.** 60°. **9.** 6 in by 9 in. **10.** r. **11.** Walk to a point three-quarters of a mile from the intersection of the paved roads. **12.** Where the perpendicular bisector of AB intersects the far shore. **14.** $8(\sqrt[3]{9} + 1)^{3/2}$.

PROBLEMS 24. *Page 148*

1. (a) $v = -31, r = 31, a = 192$; (c) $v = -2, r = 2, a = 6$. **3.** (a) 256 ft; (b) 400 ft; (c) 160 ft/sec. **4.** (a) 100 mi; (b) $400\sqrt{3}$ mi/min; (c) $\tfrac{1}{3}\pi$ min; (d) $400\sqrt{3}$ mi/min. **5.** 1; 0; $-\tfrac{16}{9}$ for $t > 0$. **6.** $2/\pi$ in/sec. **7.** $1/\pi$ in/sec. **8.** 60 cu in/min, $\tfrac{1}{3}$ in/min. **9.** $\tfrac{24}{5}$ ft/sec. **10.** 800 ft/sec, 400 ft/sec. **11.** $8\tfrac{1}{3}$ ft/sec, $3\tfrac{1}{3}$ ft/sec. **12.** $\tfrac{13}{12}$ ft/sec. **13.** No, $D_t s = gT$.

PROBLEMS 25. *Page 156*

1. (a) 5.1; (c) $\tfrac{81}{40}$; (e) $\tfrac{191}{768}$; (g) $\tfrac{80}{243}$. **2.** $A_1 = 2\pi a(b - a)$, $A = \pi(b^2 - a^2)$, 5% error. **3.** .7033. **4.** $V \approx 2\pi hrt$. **5.** $V \approx 4\pi r^2 t$. **6.** (a) 1.04; (c) $-.515$; (e) 1.722; (g) 0, 1.896, -1.896. **7.** 3.14 ft. **10.** $x_1 = [(n - 1)x_0^n + a]/nx_0^{n-1}$. **11.** Approximately (.59, .35).

PROBLEMS 26. *Page 161*

1. (a) $(1 + y^2 + y^4)^{-1}$; (c) $(20 - 3x^2)/3y^2$; (e) $(2y - y^3)/(3xy^2 - 2x + 2y)$; (g) $y/x - (x + y)^2$; (i) $x(y^2 - 1)/y(1 - x^2)$. **2.** (a) $-\tfrac{1}{2}$; (c) $-b^2x_0/a^2y_0$. **4.** $my_0(x - x_0) + nx_0(y - y_0) = 0$. **5.** $2x + y = 12$ and $14x + y = 60$. **7.** (a) $-y^{-3}$; (c) $-4a^2y^{-3}$.

REVIEW PROBLEMS, CHAPTER THREE.
Page 162

2. Not according to our definition of minimum point. **3.** .37 seconds after the initial instant. **4.** $t = \sqrt{(2k - 1)\pi}$. **5.** $b^2 \leq 3ac$. **6.** $10\sqrt{5}$. **7.** $(\tfrac{3}{5}, \tfrac{4}{5})$. **8.** $-\tfrac{5}{2}$. **10.** $(1, 1)$. **11.** $\sqrt[3]{3}$. **12.** 12 by 12 by 24. **13.** $\tfrac{1}{3}K$. **14.** $\dfrac{K}{R^2 - 1}$ (if $R > 1$).

PROBLEMS 27. *Page 168*

1. (a) $(x - 3)^2 + (y + 2)^2 = 25$; (c) $x^2 + y^2 = 2(x \cos 2 - y \sin 2)$. **2.** (a) $(2, -1)$, 3; (c) $(\tfrac{1}{2}, 0)$, 1. **3.** (a) $(x - \tfrac{1}{2})^2 + (y - \tfrac{1}{2})^2 = \tfrac{1}{2}$; (c) either $(x - 4)^2 + y^2 = 17$ or $(x + 4)^2 +$

$y^2 = 17$; (e) $x^2 + y^2 + 2(\sqrt{2} - 2)(x + y) = 4\sqrt{2} - 6$. **4.** (a) $(-7, 4)$, $(-3, -2)$; (c) $([a - 2], [b + 3])$, $([a + 2], [b - 3])$. **5.** (a) $m = 3$, (b) $(h, k) = (-1, 2)$, $\bar{x} = 3\bar{y}$, $\bar{y} = 2\bar{x}$. **6.** $\bar{y} = y$, $\bar{x} = x - \frac{1}{2}\pi$. **7.** (a) $x^2 + y^2 - 10y + 16 = 0$, translate origin to $(0, 5)$; (b) if $r = 1$, path is the X-axis, otherwise path is a circle whose center is a point of the Y-axis. **8.** $a^2 + b^2 > 4c$. A circular disk or the empty set. **11.** (a) $x = \frac{9}{5}$; (b) $5\bar{x}^2 + 5\bar{y}^2 + 18\bar{x} - 24\bar{y} = 0$.

PROBLEMS 28. *Page 175*

1. (a) $\dfrac{x^2}{9} + \dfrac{y^2}{4} = 1$; (c) $\dfrac{x^2}{16} + \dfrac{y^2}{12} = 1$; (e) $\dfrac{x^2}{9} + \dfrac{y^2}{25} = 1$. **2.** Place tacks on the line through the center of the paper and parallel to the 11-inch edge at points $\sqrt{195}/4 \approx 7/2$ inches from the center. String should be approximately 18 inches long. **3.** (a) $(-3, -2)$ and $(5, -2)$. **4.** (a) tangent $2x + 3y = 12$, normal $3x - 2y = 5$. **9.** Slope is $-c/a$. **11.** (a) curve is a circle and the given points are endpoints of a diameter; (b) curve is an ellipse and given points are two of the vertices.

PROBLEMS 29. *Page 182*

1. (a) foci $(-\sqrt{5}, 0)$, $(\sqrt{5}, 0)$, vertices $(-2, 0)$, $(2, 0)$, asymptotes $y = \frac{1}{2}x$, $y = -\frac{1}{2}x$; (c) foci $(0, \sqrt{5})$, $(0, -\sqrt{5})$, vertices $(0, 1)$, $(0, -1)$, asymptotes $y = \frac{1}{2}x$, $y = -\frac{1}{2}x$; (e) foci $(-6, 2)$, $(4, 2)$, vertices $(-5, 2)$, $(3, 2)$, asymptotes $3x + 4y = 5$, $4y = 3x + 11$. **2.** (a) $5x^2 - 4y^2 = 20$; (c) $4x^2 - y^2 = 3$. **3.** (a) $7y^2 - 4x^2 = 28$. **4.** No, no. **5.** (a) tangent $y = 2x - 4$, normal $x + 2y = 7$. **8.** The union of an ellipse and a hyperbola. **9.** Slope is $\dfrac{c}{a}$. **10.** A hyperbola.

PROBLEMS 30. *Page 187*

1. (a) $(2, 0)$, $x = -2$; (c) $(1, -2)$, $y = 0$. **2.** (a) $y^2 = 12x$; (c) $(x - 1)^2 = -20(y + 3)$. **6.** (b) 12, 12, 20, 2. **7.** Slopes are 1 and -1, tangents meet at right angles. **8.** $(x - \frac{5}{2}c)^2 + y^2 = \frac{25}{4}c^2$. **9.** $\dfrac{x^2}{8} + \dfrac{y^2}{4} = 1$. **10.** $y^2 = 4(c - a)(x - a)$. **11.** $y^2 = 4(c - a) \times (x - a)$, where $c^2 = a^2 - b^2$.

PROBLEMS 31. *Page 195*

1. $e = \dfrac{c}{b}$, $y = \pm\dfrac{b^2}{c}$. **2.** (a) $3x^2 - y^2 +$

$20x + 12 = 0$; (c) $3x^2 + 4y^2 - 20x + 12 = 0$; (e) $y^2 + 2x = 3$; (g) $9x^2 + 8y^2 - 18x - 40y + 41 = 0$. **3.** (a) $e = \frac{1}{2}$, $x = \pm 4$; (c) $e = \sqrt{3}$, $x = \pm 2/\sqrt{3}$; (e) $e = \sqrt{3}$, $x = -1 \pm 2/\sqrt{3}$. **4.** (a) An ellipse with eccentricity near 0 is relatively circular, an ellipse with eccentricity near 1 is relatively flat or narrow; (b) a hyperbola with eccentricity near 1 is relatively narrow, a hyperbola with a large eccentricity is relatively open or wide. **5.** $y^2 - x^2 \pm 6x + 9 = 0$. **6.** $2^{-1/2}$. **7.** $x + y + 2 = 0$. **8.** $2^{-1/2}$. **9.** $\sqrt{2} - 1$.

REVIEW PROBLEMS, CHAPTER FOUR.
Page 196

1. $\dfrac{x^2}{8} + \dfrac{y^2}{4} = 1$, $e = 2^{-1/2}$. **3.** $y' = -e$. **4.** $(d_2 - d_1)/(d_2 + d_1)$. **5.** P is a point of the parabola $y = 4x^2$. **9.** Ellipse if a, b, and $\dfrac{c^2}{a} + \dfrac{d^2}{b} - e$ have the same sign, hyperbola if $ab\left(\dfrac{c^2}{a} + \dfrac{d^2}{b} - e\right)^2 < 0$, parabola if $a = 0$ and $bc \neq 0$ or $b = 0$ and $ad \neq 0$.

PROBLEMS 32. *Page 204*

1. (a) 4, 6, 8, 10; (c) $-\frac{7}{5}, \frac{1}{5}, \frac{9}{5}, \frac{17}{5}$. **2.** Actual areas: (a) 64; (c) 306; (e) 8π. **4.** Actual areas: (a) 9; (c) .7; (e) π. **5.** (a) $[-1, 1]$; (c) $\{-1, -\frac{1}{2}, 0, \frac{1}{2}, 1\}$. **6.** (a) $\frac{1}{2}(2 + \sqrt{2} + \sqrt{3})$; (c) $F(100) - F(0)$. **7.** 29. **8.** 164.

PROBLEMS 33. *Page 211*

1. (a) 2; (c) 4; (e) 9; (g) $2 + \frac{1}{2}\pi$; (i) $20 + 2\pi$; (k) $\frac{3}{2}$. **2.** $\frac{17}{4}$. **5.** 1. **8.** $S(1) = \{0, 1\}$; if $u \in (0, \frac{1}{2}]$, $S(u) = [0, u]$. **11.** $S(2) = \{0, 2, 4\}$; if $u \in (0, 1]$, $S(u) = (1 - u, 1 + 2u]$.

PROBLEMS 34. *Page 220*

1. (a) does not exist; (c) does not exist; (f) 4; (h) 1. **3.** 0. **4.** π, $m = \pm\sqrt{16 - \pi^2}$. **5.** $m = \dfrac{d + c}{2}$, $f(m) = m\left(\dfrac{d + c}{2}\right) + b$. **6.** 0. **7.** 0. **9.** (a) no; (b) yes; (c) no. **13.** $7 - \sqrt{2} - \sqrt{3}$

PROBLEMS 35. *Page 225*

2. (a) 24; (c) 24; (e) $-\frac{26}{3}$; (g) $\frac{3}{5}$. **4.** (a) $\frac{64}{3}$, (c) $-\frac{125}{6}$; (e) -6; (g) -2; (i) $8a^4$. **8.** (a) $\frac{1295}{4}$; (c) 15; (e) $\frac{17}{4}$. **11.** (a) $\frac{16}{3}$.

PROBLEMS 36. *Page 233*

2. (a) 6.25; (c) 1.82. **3.** (a) 2.004; (c) .78; (e) 1.8538. **5.** .0789, .3965. **6.** No. **8.** Tangent Rule gives .3966, Trapezoidal Rule gives .3961. **9.** (a) 3.00; (b) 3.08; (c) 3.18. **10.** No.

PROBLEMS 37. *Page 238*

1. (a) 64; (c) $\frac{1}{4}$; (e) 2. **2.** (a) $-\frac{7}{15}$; (c) $\frac{32}{3}$; (e) 16. **3.** (a) 16; (c) $2\sqrt{2}/3$. **4.** (a) $\frac{7}{3}$; (c) -2; (e) $\frac{3}{2}$; (g) $\frac{53}{6} - 2\sqrt{3}$. **6.** (a) $\frac{256}{3}$; (c) $\frac{8a^5}{5}$. **7.** $f(m) = 6$, $m = \frac{4}{3} + \frac{2}{\sqrt{3}}$. **8.** $x = 2$. **9.** No. **10.** (a) $3 - 2\sqrt{2}$; (c) 1.

PROBLEMS 38. *Page 243*

1. (a) 3; (c) .9597; (e) 0. **2.** (a) $2 - \sqrt{2}$; (c) 0; (e) 0; (g) 8. **3.** (a) 4; (c) 4. **4.** $\frac{1}{6}\pi$. **5.** 2.36. **7.** (a) $\frac{1}{8}$; (c) $\frac{1}{4}$.

PROBLEMS 39. *Page 251*

1. $\frac{9}{2}$. **2.** $7\sqrt{2}/3$. **3.** (a) 4; (c) $\frac{1}{2}$; (e) 2. **4.** (a) 9; (c) 18; (e) $\frac{16}{3}$. **8.** $\int_a^b |f(x)|\, dx$. **9.** $\frac{1}{2} - \frac{1}{n+2}$, $\frac{1}{2}$. **10.** (a) -4. **11.** $|m| = .95$.

PROBLEMS 40. *Page 257*

1. $4\pi ab^2/3$. **2.** (a) $128\pi/7$; (c) $\pi a^3/15$. **3.** $\pi/2$. **4.** (a) $96\pi/5$; (c) $64\pi/7$. **5.** $2n$, $2/n$. **7.** (a) $125\pi/12$; (c) $3456\pi/35$. **8.** $\pi^2/2$. **9.** $2\pi^2 a^2 b$. **10.** $4\pi ab(b^2 - a^2 + a\sqrt{a^2 + b^2})/3\sqrt{a^2 + b^2}$ if $a < b$. **12.** (a) $\pi/2$; (c) 4π.

PROBLEMS 41. *Page 261*

1. 10. **2.** $4\pi r^3/3k$. **3.** $20\sqrt{15}\pi$. **4.** $4\pi abc/3$. **5.** $256\sqrt{3}/5$. **6.** 32/3. **7.** π. **8.** $16ab^2/3$. **9.** $\frac{1}{3}$. **10.** $16r^3/3$.

PROBLEMS 42. *Page 266*

1. 50 in-lbs. **2.** $\frac{200}{3}$ ft-lbs. **3.** 112,500 ft-lbs. **4.** 250π ft-lbs. **5.** 875π ft-lbs. **6.** $\frac{745}{3} \cdot 10^7$ ft-lbs. **7.** $6.9\pi \cdot 10^4$ ft-lbs. **8.** 54,000 ft-lbs. **9.** $16 \cdot 10^6$ mi-lbs. **10.** 5000 mi-lbs.

REVIEW PROBLEMS, CHAPTER FIVE.
Page 267

1. (a) $\frac{1}{2}x^2 - \frac{1}{3}t$; (c) $-\frac{8 + 2\sqrt{3}}{3}$.

2. (a) $p = q = -1$; (c) $p = q = -1$. **4.** (a) $\frac{8}{3}$, (c) $24\pi/5$. **5.** About 12. **6.** 2750 ft-lbs. **10.** (c) 5.

PROBLEMS 43. *Page 274*

2. (a) 0; (b) maximum when $x = \pi$, minimum when $x = 0$; (d) concave up in $(-\frac{1}{2}\pi, \frac{1}{2}\pi)$, and so on. **3.** Maximum when $x = \frac{1}{2}\pi$, minimum when $x = \frac{3}{2}\pi$. **4.** Domain $[-3, 3]$, range $[0, \frac{9}{2}\pi]$. **6.** (a) $5^x + x^5$; (c) $-(1 + x^2)^{-1}$. **7.** (a) $2x^5$; (c) $f(-x)$. **8.** (d) $S(x) = \pi$. **10.** Maximum when $x = 0$, minimum when $x = 1$. **13.** $F(x) = G(x)$.

PROBLEMS 44. *Page 279*

4. (a) $-.6144$; (c) .05. **7.** (a) $[1 - (\ln x)^{-1/2}]/2x$; (c) $\cot x - x^{-1} \cos \ln x$; (e) $\sec x$. **8.** $G(2) = .4$, $G(\frac{1}{2}) = .15$. **9.** $\frac{1}{8} \ln 2$. **10.** (a) $\ln \frac{1}{2}x$; (c) $\ln (x - 1)$. **12.** (a) $\ln \frac{10}{7}$.

PROBLEMS 45. *Page 285*

1. (a) $f^{-1}(x) = (x + 1)^{1/3}$; (c) $f^{-1}(x) = f(x)$. **2.** (a) Domain of f^{-1} is $(-\infty, \infty)$; (c) does not have inverse. **3.** $I = (0, 2)$, $f(x) = [\![x]\!](3 - 2x) + x$. **4.** (a) $y = \sqrt[3]{x} + 1$. **6.** $b^2 - 3ac < 0$.

PROBLEMS 46. *Page 291*

1. (a) e; (c) $\frac{1}{25}$. **2.** (a) 10.4986; (c) .0659. **4.** (a) maximum when $x = 2$, minimum when $x = 0$. **5.** (a) $2xe^{x^2} - 2e^{2x}$; (c) $e^x \exp (e^x)$; (e) 0. **6.** .57. **8.** (b) $m = \frac{1}{2}$ or $m = -2$. **9.** $\frac{1}{4}\pi$. **11.** 1350, 23 years. **12.** (a) 13 exp $(x^2/2)$.

PROBLEMS 47. *Page 294*

3. (a) xe^x; (c) $xe^x(1 + x)^{-2}$. **4.** (a) $\int xe^x\, dx = e^x(x - 1)$; (c) $\int xe^x(1 + x)^{-2}\, dx = e^x(1 + x)^{-1}$. **5.** (a) $\ln 2$; (c) $\frac{1}{3}e^3 + 2e - e^{-1}$; (e) 3; (g) $4 \ln 2 + \frac{1}{3}$; (i) $\frac{3}{2} \ln 2 - \frac{1}{2}$. **6.** $\int \ln ax\, dx = x \ln ax - x$. **7.** $\frac{1}{2}\pi(e - e^{-1})$. **9.** (a) 4.87. **10.** -48. **11.** e^{-1}.

PROBLEMS 48. *Page 300*

1. (a) $2(\ln 3)3^{2x-1}$; (c) $x^\pi \pi^x(\pi x^{-1} + \ln \pi)$; (e) $2^{5x^2}(\ln 2)10x - 100x^3$; (g) $\frac{1}{2\sqrt{x}}(\ln x + 2)$.

3. $\pi^e \approx 22.5$, $e^\pi \approx 23.1$. **5.** $e^{-1/e}$. **6.** (a) e^π; (c) $(\pi^e - 1)/e \ln \pi$; (e) $8/\ln 9$; (g) $10e$. **7.** 4. **8.** 4. **9.** (a) $3/\ln 4$. **11.** $-\ln 3/x(\ln x)^2$.

PROBLEMS 49. *Page 305*

1. (a) $\frac{1}{3}\pi$; (c) $\frac{1}{2}\pi$; (e) .2. **3.** (a) x; (c) $\mathrm{Sin}^{-1} x$. **4.** (a) positive, (c) positive; (e) negative

5. (a) $\frac{1}{2}\pi - 1$; (c) $\frac{\pi}{12} + \frac{\sqrt{3}}{2} - 1$. **7.** $2^{-1/2}$.

10. $\left(\sqrt{\dfrac{\sqrt{5}-1}{2}}, \mathrm{Sin}^{-1}\dfrac{\sqrt{5}-1}{2} \right)$.

PROBLEMS 50. *Page 309*

1. (a) $2x/(1 + x^4) - 2(\mathrm{Arctan}\ x)/$ $(1 + x^2)$; (c) $-(e^{-2x} - 1)^{-1/2}$; (e) $-1/\sqrt{1 - x^2}$ $\mathrm{Cos}^{-1} x$; (g) $-1 + x/\sqrt{1 - x^2}$. **2.** (a) $-\sqrt{\dfrac{1 - y^2}{1 - x^2}}$; (c) $-\dfrac{1 + y^2}{\sqrt{1 - x^2}}$. **3.** (a) $(\cos x)/|\cos x|$; (c) $(\sin x)/|\sin x|$. **4.** (a) yes; (c) yes. **5.** $D_x y = -\dfrac{\sin x}{|\sin x|} - \dfrac{\cos x}{|\cos x|}$. **6.** $\mathrm{Arctan}\ x^{-1} = \dfrac{x}{|x|}\dfrac{\pi}{2} - \mathrm{Arctan}\ x$. **7.** 12 ft. **8.** $h/\sqrt{2}$. **9.** 1. **12.** (b) $5\pi^3/4$.

PROBLEMS 51. *Page 313*

1. Approximately 63.2. **2.** $10\pi/9$. **3.** (a) $\pi/3$; (c) $7\pi/6\sqrt{3}$; (e) .23. **4.** (a) $\frac{1}{2}\pi - 2x$. **6.** $\pi^2/4$. **7.** $4\pi - 3\sqrt{3}$. **10.** $V \approx \pi^2/4$.

PROBLEMS 52. *Page 319*

3. (a) $e^x \sinh e^x - e^{\cosh x} \sinh x$; (c) $\tanh x - \coth x$; (e) $\sinh x \cos (\cosh x) + \cosh x \sin (\sinh x)$. **4.** (c) $\frac{1}{4}\pi(2 + \sinh 2)$. **9.** (b) no; (c) $\int \operatorname{sech} x\ dx = 2\ \mathrm{Tan}^{-1} e^x$, $\int \operatorname{sech} x\ dx = \mathrm{Tan}^{-1} (\sinh x)$.

PROBLEMS 53. *Page 323*

5. 1. **6.** (a) $-\csc x$; (c) $-\operatorname{csch} x$; (e) y only defined when x is an integral multiple of 2π. **7.** (a) .9; (c) .5; (e) $\ln 3$; (g) .0933.

REVIEW PROBLEMS, CHAPTER SIX.
Page 324

1. (a) $a^2 x^{a^2-1} + 2xa^{x^2} \ln a + 2^{a^x} (\ln 2)$ $(\ln a)$; (c) $4xe^{x^4}$. **4.** $x = 1$ is the only solution. **5.** Maximum points $(e^{-1/2}, \frac{1}{2}e^{-1})$ and $(-e^{-1/2}, \frac{1}{2}e^{-1})$, concave up in $(-e^{-3/2}, 0)$ and $(0, e^{-3/2})$.

6. $(99e^{101} - 100e^{100} + e)/(e - 1)$. **9.** (a) $\dfrac{\pi}{3}$; (c) $\frac{1}{6}(e^{-3} + 3e - 4)$. **10.** (c) $F'(1) = 1$, $F'(3) = 3$; (d) no; (e) yes. **11.** (b) $\sec x$.

PROBLEMS 54. *Page 330*

1. (a) $\frac{1}{6}$; (c) -1, **3.** (a) $e^{x+2} + \dfrac{xe^{x+3}}{e+3}$.

5. (a) $-\dfrac{1}{4(3x - 4)} + \dfrac{1}{16} \ln \left| \dfrac{x}{3x - 4} \right|$; (c) $-\dfrac{x}{4}(5 - x^2)^{3/2} + \dfrac{5x}{8}(5 - x^2)^{1/2} + \frac{25}{8}$ $\mathrm{Arcsin}\ \dfrac{x}{\sqrt{5}}$; (e) $\frac{1}{6}x^5(\ln x - \frac{1}{6})$. **6.** (a) $\dfrac{7 \cdot 5 \cdot 3 \cdot 1}{8 \cdot 6 \cdot 4 \cdot 2}$ $\dfrac{\pi}{2}$; (c) $9e - 24$. **7.** (a) $\dfrac{8 + 3\pi}{256}$; (c) $1 + \dfrac{\pi}{2}$. **8.** $\ln \frac{4}{3}$. **9.** $\pi(\ln \frac{8}{5} - \frac{3}{10})$. **10.** No.

PROBLEMS 55. *Page 335*

1. (a) $\sqrt{3}/4$; (c) $\frac{1}{3}(2\sqrt{2} - 1)$; (e) $2e(e - 1)$; (g) $-\frac{2}{3}(5^{3/2} - 3^{3/2})$. **2.** $\frac{1}{2} \ln 2$. **3.** (a) $\frac{34}{3}$; (c) $\ln \frac{13}{5}$; (e) $\frac{1}{6}$. **4.** $\frac{1}{24}\pi$. **5.** (a) $e^7 - e^2$; (c) $-\dfrac{2}{\pi}$. **6.** $\frac{32}{3}$. **9.** 4. **10.** $\frac{8}{3}\pi$. **11.** $\frac{1}{5}\pi$.

PROBLEMS 56. *Page 339*

1. (a) e^{x^3}; (c) $-\frac{1}{3} \cos x^3$; (e) $\frac{1}{6}$ Arctan $\dfrac{3x}{2}$; (g) $\frac{1}{4}(\ln x)^4$; (i) $\ln |\sec x|$. **2.** (a) $u = e^x$, $\int f(u)\ du$; (c) $u = \sqrt{x}$; $2\int f(u)\ du$; (e) $u = x^r$, $\dfrac{1}{r} \int f(u)\ du$; (g) $u = mx + b$, $\dfrac{1}{m} \int f(u)\ du$. **3.** (a) $\exp (\sin x)$; (c) $\frac{1}{2} \tan (2x + 3)$; (e) $\frac{2}{3}\sqrt{x^3 - 5}$; (g) $\sec e^x$. **4.** (a) $\frac{1}{3} \sec^3 x$; (c) $\ln (\sec 2x + \tan 2x)^{3/2} \sec^2 x$; (e) $e^x - \ln (1 + e^x)$. **5.** (a) $\frac{1}{3}$ $\mathrm{Arctan}\ \dfrac{x + 2}{3}$; (c) $\frac{1}{2} \mathrm{Arcsin}\ (x - 1)$. **6.** $\tan x + \frac{2}{3} \tan^3 x + \frac{1}{5} \tan^5 x$.

PROBLEMS 57. *Page 345*

1. (a) $-x - \cot x$; (c) $\frac{1}{3} \sin^3 x - \frac{1}{5}$ $\sin^5 x$; (e) $-\frac{2}{3}(\cos x)^{3/2}$. **2.** (a) $\dfrac{3x}{8} - \dfrac{\sin 2x}{4} + \dfrac{\sin 4x}{32}$; (c) $\dfrac{x}{16} - \dfrac{\sin x}{64} + \dfrac{\sin^3 2x}{48}$. **4.** (a) $\frac{1}{4} \sec^4 x$; (c) $\ln |\sec x + \tan x| - \sin x$. **6.** (a) $-\sqrt{x^2 + 25}/25x$; (c) $-\sqrt{9 - x^2}/9x$. **7.** (a) $\dfrac{8}{3}$; (c) $\dfrac{10\sqrt{2}}{3}$. **8.** $\dfrac{\pi + 4}{8}$. **9.** $\frac{1}{2}\pi$.

PROBLEMS 58. *Page 351*

1. (a) $x^2 - x + 1 - \dfrac{1}{x + 1}$; (c) $\dfrac{2}{x + 2} + \dfrac{3}{x - 2}$; (e) $\dfrac{5x + 2}{x^2 + 4}$. **2.** (a) $\dfrac{x^3}{3} - \dfrac{x^2}{2} + x - $

$\ln |x + 1|$; (c) $\ln (x + 2)^2 + \ln |x - 2|^3$;
(e) $\frac{5}{2} \ln (x^2 + 4) + \text{Tan}^{-1} \frac{x}{2}$. **3.** (a) $\ln [x^2(x + 2)^4$
$\times |x+1|^{-3}]$; (c) $\frac{x^2}{2} - 2x + \frac{1}{x + 1} + 3\ln|x + 1|$;
(e) $\ln |x| - \frac{2}{x} - \frac{1}{2x^2}$; (g) $\frac{t^2}{2} - 2t + \frac{4}{t} +$
$\ln (t^2 + 2t)^2$. **6.** (a) $\ln [(x + 1)^2\sqrt{x^2 + x + 1}]$
$- \sqrt{3} \text{ Tan}^{-1} \frac{2x + 1}{\sqrt{3}}$; (c) $\ln |x - 1| + \text{Arctan}$
x; (e) $\ln\sqrt{\dfrac{z - 1}{z + 1}} - \text{Tan}^{-1} z$. **7.** (a) $\ln (\frac{4}{3})^4 - \frac{3}{2}$;
(c) $\frac{1}{3}\left(\ln 2 + \frac{\pi}{3}\right)$; (e) $\ln [\frac{1}{5}\frac{2}{2}(\frac{2}{1}\frac{0}{3})^{3/2}]$. **9.** (a)
$-2/(\tan \frac{1}{2}x + 1)$; (c) $\frac{1}{2} \text{ Tan}^{-1} \left(\dfrac{5 \tan \frac{1}{2}x + 3}{4}\right)$

PROBLEMS 59. *Page 357*

1. (a) $\sin x - x \cos x$; (c) $\frac{1}{2}xe^{2x} - \frac{1}{4}e^{2x}$;
(e) $\frac{x^6}{6} \ln x - \frac{x^6}{36}$; (g) $x \text{ Sin}^{-1} x + \sqrt{1 - x^2}$;
(i) $\dfrac{(x + 25)^{101}(101x - 25)}{101 \cdot 102}$. **2.** (a) $\frac{32}{15}$; (c) $\frac{\pi}{2} - 1$;
(e) $2(\ln 2 - 1)^2$. **3.** (a) $x^2 \sin x + 2x \cos x - 2$
$\sin x$; (c) $\frac{1}{4}(x^4 -1) \text{ Tan}^{-1} x - \frac{x^3}{12} + \frac{x}{4}$; (e) $\pi - 2$.
6. (a) $\frac{1}{2}x^2 \sin x^2 + \frac{1}{2} \cos x^2$. **8.** $\frac{4}{15}\pi$. **9.** (c) $\frac{4}{5} \cdot \frac{2}{3}$
and $\frac{5}{6} \cdot \frac{3}{4} \cdot \frac{1}{2} \cdot \frac{1}{2}\pi$.

PROBLEMS 60. *Page 364*

1. (a) $y = \frac{1}{2}(3 - \cos x^2)$; (c) $\cos x +$
$\sin y = 1$. **2.** (a) $\sin \ln x + 2$; (c) $\sqrt{x^2 + 8}$.
3. (a) $y = 2x + 3 - 3 \sin x - 2 \cos x$.
4. (a) 2.89. **6.** $x^2 + y^2 = 13$. **7.** $y = c$
$\exp \left(-\int_a^x p(t)dt\right) + \int_a^x q(u) \exp \left(-\int_u^x p(t)dt\right)du$.
8. (a) $y = 4x^2 + 4$; (b) $y = 4 \cdot 2^x$; (c) $y = 4 \cdot 2^{x^2}$.
9. $16(1 + \sqrt{3})$. **10.** No. **11.** $v_{100} \approx 4000$ ft/sec;
$s_{100} \approx 130,000$ ft; rocket reaches a height of
about 360,000 ft.

PROBLEMS 61. *Page 369*

1. (a) $-3x^{-4} - 3^{-x} \ln 3$; (c) $\dfrac{x}{|x|} \dfrac{1}{1 + x^2}$.
2. (a) $(4x^2 - 2)e^{-x^2}$; (b) 0. **3.** (a) and (b).
6. (a) $\dfrac{1}{2(x + 1)}$; (c) x; (d) $1/3x |x|$. **7.** (a) $-4y^{-3}$;
(c) $(2xy + 2y \cos y + y^2 \sin y)(x + \cos y)^{-3}$.
8. 0. **10.** $y = r - \ln |1 + as - sx|$.

REVIEW PROBLEMS, CHAPTER SEVEN.
Page 370

1. (a) $\frac{1}{3}e^{x^3}$; (b) $\frac{1}{2}(x^2 - 1)e^{x^2}$; (c) $\frac{1}{6}x^3 +$
$\frac{1}{8}x^2 + \frac{1}{8}x - \frac{63}{16} \ln |2x - 1|$; (d) $\frac{1}{8} \ln \dfrac{(x - 2)^2}{x^2 + 2x + 4}$
$+ \dfrac{5}{4\sqrt{3}} \text{ Tan}^{-1} \dfrac{x + 1}{\sqrt{3}}$; (e) $\frac{2}{9}(x^3 + 1)^{3/2}$;
(f) $\frac{1}{15}(x^2 - 1)^{3/2}(3x^2 + 2)$; (g) $\frac{1}{4}x^2 + \frac{1}{8} \sin 2x^2$;
(h) $x^2 \sin x + 2x \cos x - 2 \sin x$. **2.** $\ln\left(1 + \dfrac{2}{\sqrt{3}}\right)$.
3. (a) 1; (b) $\frac{1}{2}\pi$; (c) $\dfrac{\sqrt{2}}{4} \ln (3 + 2\sqrt{2})$; (d) $1 +$
$\sin 1 - \sin 2 + \frac{1}{2} \sin 4 - \frac{1}{2} \sin 6 + \frac{1}{3} \sin 9$.
6. $\int \text{Sin}^{-1} x \, dx = x \text{ Sin}^{-1} x + \sqrt{1 - x^2}$.
7. Strictly speaking, we must stay in the interval
$(-\infty, 0)$.

PROBLEMS 62. *Page 378*

1. (a) $(2\sqrt{3}, 2)$; (c) $(3\sqrt{2}, -3\sqrt{2})$;
(e) $(0, 90)$. **2.** (a) $(4, 180°)$; (c) $(12, 120°)$;
(e) $(270, 270°)$. **3.** No. **4.** (a) $x^2 + y^2 = 2x$;
(c) $y = 5x$. **7.** No. **8.** $r(\sin \theta - 2 \cos \theta) = 2$.
9. Symmetric with respect to (a) pole; (c) line
containing pole and perpendicular to polar
axis; (e) line containing polar axis. **11.** (a)
$(2, 30°)$ and seven other points; (c) $(0, 0)$,
$(1, \frac{1}{4}\pi)$, $(1, \frac{3}{4}\pi)$.

PROBLEMS 63. *Page 385*

1. 6. **2.** $r \cos (\theta - 27°) = 3$. **3.** $r =$
$2\sqrt{2} \cos (\theta - 135°)$. **5.** (a) Hyperbola, vertices
$(2, \frac{1}{2}\pi)$ and $(-8, \frac{3}{2}\pi)$, foci $(0, 0)$ and $(10, \frac{1}{2}\pi)$;
(c) Parabola, vertex $(2, \frac{1}{2}\pi)$, focus $(0, 0)$;
(e) Parabola, vertex $(\frac{1}{2}, \frac{1}{2}\pi)$, focus $(0, 0)$.
6. (a) Hyperbola; (b) Parabola; (c) Ellipse.
8. $x^2(1 - e^2) + y^2 - 2pe^2x - e^2p^2 = 0$.
9. Practically a circle of radius 5.

PROBLEMS 64. *Page 390*

1. $\psi \approx 81°$. **2.** (a) Undefined; (c) $-1/\sqrt{3}$.
3. (a) $\theta = \frac{1}{4}\pi, \theta = -\frac{1}{4}\pi$; (c) Same as (a).
4. (a) -2; (c) $\sqrt{\pi} + 2\pi$. **6.** $(4, \pi)$, $(1, \frac{1}{3}\pi)$,
$(1, -\frac{1}{3}\pi)$. **7.** $(3, \frac{3}{2}\pi)$. **8.** $\frac{1}{2}\pi$. **10.** No. **13.** (a) $30°$,
$30°, 90°$.

PROBLEMS 65. *Page 395*

1. $\dfrac{\pi}{2}$. **2.** (a) $\dfrac{4\pi^3}{3}$; (b) $\frac{1}{4}(e^{4\pi} - 1)$; (c) $\dfrac{\pi}{2} +$
$\dfrac{\sinh 4\pi}{8}$. **3.** 25π. **4.** $\frac{1}{32}\pi$. **6.** 3π. **7.** 11π. **8.** 8 sq.
units. **9.** π. **11.** $\dfrac{32}{3}$. **12.** $\dfrac{8\pi}{3}$.

PROBLEMS 66. *Page 400*

2. (a) $(2 - \sqrt{3}, 2\sqrt{3} + 1)$; (c) $(1 - 2\sqrt{3}, -2 - \sqrt{3})$; (e) $(2, -4)$; (g) $(-2, 4)$. **3.** (a) $(\frac{1}{2}, \frac{1}{2}\sqrt{3})$; (c) $\left(\dfrac{1 - \sqrt{3}}{2}, \dfrac{1 + \sqrt{3}}{2}\right)$. **4.** $\theta \approx .64$. **5.** $-m$. **6.** (a) $(\bar{x} - \bar{y})^{1/2} + (\bar{x} + \bar{y})^{1/2} = 2^{1/4}$, parabola; (c) $[\![\sqrt{2}\bar{x}]\!] = 0$. **7.** (a) 6; (c) $4\sqrt{2}$.

8. $\dfrac{3\sqrt{2}}{4}$. **9.** $\bar{x} = (x - h)\cos\alpha + (y - k)\sin\alpha$, $\bar{y} = -(x - h)\sin\alpha + (y - k)\cos\alpha$. **10.** $\bar{y} = 8\bar{x}^3$. **11.** No.

PROBLEMS 67. *Page 407*

1. (a) $3\bar{x}^2 - \bar{y}^2$; (c) $5\bar{x}^2$. **2.** (a) $4\bar{x}^2 - \bar{y}^2 = 4$; (c) $4\bar{x}^2 - \bar{y}^2 = 4$. **3.** (a) $4\bar{\bar{x}}^2 + \bar{\bar{y}}^2 = 16$; (c) $\bar{\bar{y}}^2 = 4\bar{\bar{x}}$. **5.** $3x^2 - 2xy + 3y^2 = 8$, $\bar{x}^2 + 2\bar{y}^2 = 4$. **6.** $\bar{y}^2 = -2\bar{x}$, $x^2 - 2xy + y^2 - 4x - 4y = 0$. **7.** Ellipse. **8.** Hyperbola. **9.** (a) Parabola; (c) Hyperbola. **10.** $A = C, B = 0$.

PROBLEMS 68. *Page 413*

1. (a) $(1, 2)$; (c) $(1, 3)$. **2.** (a) $0, 2\sqrt{5}$. **3.** (a) $\sqrt{|A|^2 + |B|^2}$; (c) $\sqrt{9|A|^2 + 16|B|^2}$; (e) $\sqrt{2}|A||B|$. **4.** (a) AC; (c) BA. **5.** $A - B$. **6.** 0. **7.** (a) $t = 2$; (b) No solution. **8.** $t = \frac{1}{2}$, no. **10.** $\left(1 + \dfrac{1}{\sqrt{5}}, 1 - \dfrac{2}{\sqrt{5}}\right)$ or $\left(1 - \dfrac{1}{\sqrt{5}}, 1 + \dfrac{2}{\sqrt{5}}\right)$. **11.** (a) $a \geqslant 0$; (c) $A = rB$, where $r \geqslant 0$. **12.** A perpendicular to B.

PROBLEMS 69. *Page 418*

1. (a) $3i + 4j$, 5; (c) $-5j$, 5. **2.** (a) $(4, -6)$; (c) $(6, -2)$; (e) $(16, -3)$. **3.** $\left(\dfrac{x_1 + x_2}{2}, \dfrac{y_1 + y_2}{2}\right)$. **4.** (a) $(4, 3)$; (c) $(19, 23)$. **5.** $45°, 45°, 90°$. **7.** $2x + 3y = 0$, $\dfrac{1}{\sqrt{13}}(-3i + 2j)$. **10.** $a = -\dfrac{1}{10}, b = -\dfrac{7}{\sqrt{10}}$. **12.** (a) The line $3x + 4y = 12$; (c) The circle $(x + 3)^2 + (y + 4)^2 = 144$.

PROBLEMS 70. *Page 425*

1. (a) Semi-circle; (c) Line segment; (e) Branch of a hyperbola. **5.** (a) $x = 1 - t$, $y = 10 - 3t$; (c) $x = 5$, $y = t$. **6.** (a) $x = t^2$, $y = t^3$; $x = t^{2/3}$, $y = t$; (c) $x = \sec t$, $y = \tan t$; $x = \coth t$, $y = \operatorname{csch} t$. **7.** (a) $R =$

$(3t + 2)i + (3 - t)j$; (c) $R = (t - 1)i + (3t + 1)j$. **8.** $m = -\frac{5}{3}, b = -\frac{2}{3}$. **12.** M, N, and $B - C$ all parallel. **13.** $M = bi - aj$, $B = -\dfrac{c}{a^2 + b^2}(ai + bj)$.

PROBLEMS 71. *Page 433*

1. (a) $i + j$; (c) $\sin 2(-i + j)$. **2.** $i - j$, $m = -e^{-2}$. **3.** (a) $\frac{3}{5}i + \frac{4}{5}j$; (c) $\dfrac{ei + j}{\sqrt{1 + e^2}}$. **5.** $R = (t + 1)ei + tj$. **7.** $8a$. **8.** $\frac{1}{2}\sqrt{5} + \frac{1}{4}\ln(2 + \sqrt{5})$. **9.** 6. **10.** $6a$. **11.** $\frac{61}{7}$. **12.** $\frac{56}{27}$. **13.** $\frac{17}{12}$.

PROBLEMS 72. *Page 443*

2. (a) 2; (c) $2^{-1/2}$. **3.** (a) 2; (c) 0. **4.** Radius of curvature a minimum when $x = \pm 45^{-1/4}$, minimum curvature (0) at $(0, 0)$. **6.** $y' \approx 0$. **7.** (a) bj, maximum speed a, minimum speed b; (c) $A = -R$. **9.** (a) $\dfrac{\sqrt{10}}{30}$ and $\dfrac{\sqrt{10}}{10}$; (b) 16, 0. **10.** (a) $V = 8\pi i$, $A = -8\pi^2 j$.

PROBLEMS 73. *Page 448*

3. (a) $\frac{49}{4}\pi$. **4.** $2\pi b\left[b + \dfrac{a^2}{\sqrt{a^2 - b^2}} \operatorname{Arcsin} \dfrac{\sqrt{a^2 - b^2}}{a}\right]$ if $a > b$, $2\pi b\left[b + \dfrac{a^2}{\sqrt{b^2 - a^2}} \ln\left(\dfrac{b + \sqrt{b^2 - a^2}}{a}\right)\right]$ if $a < b$. **5.** $\dfrac{2\sqrt{2}\pi}{5}(1 - 2e^{-\pi})$. **6.** (a) $\frac{208}{3}\pi$; (c) $\frac{1}{2}\pi(2 + \sinh 2)$. **7.** $\pi\left[\dfrac{1928\sqrt{10}}{81} + \dfrac{8}{243}\ln(3 + \sqrt{10})\right]$. **8.** $\frac{13}{3}\pi$. **9.** $\frac{64}{3}\pi a^2$. **11.** $4\pi a^2$.

REVIEW PROBLEMS, CHAPTER 8.
Page 450

1. $Q(r, \pi - \theta)$, $R(-r, \theta)$, $S(r, -\theta)$. **2.** $r = \dfrac{4}{1 - \cos(\theta - \frac{1}{4}\pi)}$. **4.** $r = 2\sqrt{2}e^\theta$. **5.** Any integral multiple of $\frac{1}{2}\pi$. **6.** $(4\sqrt{2} + 3\sqrt{3})x - (3\sqrt{2} - 4\sqrt{3})y = 7\sqrt{2} - \sqrt{3}$. **7.** $\dfrac{A \cdot B}{|B|^2}$. **9.** $R = F'(a)t + F(a)$. **10.** (a) $\dfrac{\sqrt{5}}{2} + \frac{1}{4}\ln(2 + \sqrt{5})$; (b) $2(1 + 4t^2)^{-3/2}$; (c) $4\pi a^2$.

PROBLEMS 74. *Page 456*

1. (a) $\{(x, y, z) \mid x \geqslant 0, y \geqslant 0, z \geqslant 0\}$;
(b) Four of the eight "octants" into which the coordinate planes partition three-space; (c) $\{(x, y, z) \mid z \in [2, 3)\}$; (d) The spherical ball of radius 4 whose center is the point $(2, -1, 0)$; (e) A plane parallel to the Z-axis and making angles of $45°$ with the X- and Y-axes; (f) A circular cylinder parallel to the Z-axis. **2.** (a) $(i, j, A), (j, k, A), (A, C, B)$; (e) $|B - D| = 4$, $|B| = 3$, $|D| = 5$; (f) $a = \sin 1 + \cos 1$, $b = 1 + \frac{1}{3}(\sin 1 + \cos 1)$, $c = 2(\cos 1 - \sin 1)$. **3.** (a) $12i + 9j + 6k$; (b) $(3, 5, -1)$; (c) $3\sqrt{29}$; (d) $(23, 20, 9)$; (e) The sphere whose center is the midpoint of PQ and whose diameter is $\overline{PQ}$. **4.** $c = 3$, no, no. **6.** 3. **7.** $A + B$ and $\frac{1}{2}(A + B)$. **9.** $|A + X| \leq |A| + |X|$, equality when $X = \dfrac{xA}{|A|}$.

PROBLEMS 75. *Page 463*

2. (a) $-\frac{4}{9}$; (b) $\sqrt{65}/9$; (c) 1; (d) yes; (e) $65^{-1/2}(2i - 5j - 6k)$; (f) $11i + 8j - 3k$; (g) $\frac{1}{2}\sqrt{3}$. **3.** (c) $(A \cdot C)B - (B \cdot C)A$. **4.** $x = -4$, no, $x = 16$, $y = 12$. **5.** (b) If $|A| = |B|$; (c) $-6^{-1/2}$. **6.** 11. **7.** $\sin (\gamma - \beta)i + \sin (\alpha - \gamma)j + \sin (\beta - \alpha)k$.

PROBLEMS 76. *Page 467*

1. (a) $\frac{1}{3}(2i + j - 2k)$; (c) $3^{-1/2}(i + j + k)$. **2.** (a) $2x - 3y + z + 1 = 0$; (c) $x = 0$. **3.** A set of parallel planes. **4.** $2x - 4y + 5z + 3 = 0$. **5.** $2x - 3z + 7 = 0$. **6.** $i - j - k$. **7.** $3x + 4y - z - 16 = 0$. **8.** $\sqrt{21}/6$. **9.** 3. **10.** $(-2, -2, -2)$. **11.** $x - 7y + 5\sqrt{2}z = 0$ or $x - 7y - 5\sqrt{2}z = 0$. **12.** $6x - 14y - 6z - 15 = 0$.

PROBLEMS 77. *Page 472*

2. (a) $9(x^2 + y^2) = 4(3 - z)^2$, $4(x^2 + z^2) = 9(2 - y)^2$; (c) $y^2 + z^2 = x^2$, $z^2 = x^2 + y^2$; (e) $x^2 + z^2 = \cos^2 \pi y$, $\pi^2(x^2 + y^2) = (\text{Arccos } z)^2$. **4.** Ellipse rotated about a line parallel to the Z-axis. **5.** $(x^2 + y^2 + z^2 - r^2 - b^2)^2 = 4b^2(r^2 - x^2)$. **6.** $4(x^2 + y^2 + z^2) = (x^2 + y^2 + z^2 + 2x)^2$. **7.** A parabolic cylinder. **8.** $5\pi(20 + 9 \ln 2)/2$.

PROBLEMS 78. *Page 476*

2. (a) Parabola, $(0, 0, 0)$; (b) Two lines intersecting in $(0, 0, 0)$; (c) Parabola, $(0, 3, -1)$;

(d) Hyperbola, $(0, 3, -1)$ and $(0, -3, -1)$; (e) Parabola, $(4, 0, 4)$. **3.** (a) $x^2 - 2y^2 + 3z^2 = 2$, hyperboloid of one sheet; (c) $12x^2 + 5y^2 - 27z^2 = 5$, hyperboloid of one sheet. **4.** (a) $(1, -1, 0)$, 2. **5.** (a) $x + 2y + 2z = 9$. **7.** (a) $8y = x^2 + z^2$; (c) $4x^2 + 4z^2 + 3y^2 - 20y + 12 = 0$. **8.** (a) $5x^2 + 5z^2 = 2y$.

PROBLEMS 79. *Page 481*

1. (a) $3^{-1/2}(-i + j + k)$, $3^{1/2}(e^\pi - 1)$; (c) $\dfrac{2}{\sqrt{9\pi^2 + 100}}(-\frac{3}{2}\pi i + 3j + 4k)$, $\dfrac{\pi\sqrt{9\pi^2 + 25}}{2}$ + $\dfrac{25}{6} \ln \left(\dfrac{3\pi + \sqrt{9\pi^2 + 25}}{5}\right)$. **2.** $\frac{1}{4}\pi$.

3. $26^{-1/2}(i + 3j + 4k)$. **4.** $R = ti + \sin tj + \cos tk$. **5.** $\frac{14}{3}$. **6.** $\left(\dfrac{1}{\sqrt{2}} - \dfrac{\pi\sqrt{2}}{8}, \dfrac{1}{\sqrt{2}} + \dfrac{\pi\sqrt{2}}{8}, \dfrac{\pi}{8}\right)$.

7. One arc is a translation of the other. **8.** -2.
9. $T = 2^{-1/2}(\tanh ti + j + \text{sech } tk)$, $N = \text{sech } ti - \tanh tj$, $B = 2^{-1/2}(-\tanh ti + j - \text{sech } tk)$. **10.** (a) $F(t) \times F''(t)$; (c) $\dfrac{F(t) \cdot F'(t)}{|F(t)|}$.

11. $\frac{1}{2}$. **12.** It is a plane curve. **13.** $\sqrt{\kappa^2 + \tau^2}$.
14. $\kappa_T B - \kappa^2 T + (D_s \kappa)N$. **15.** (a) $-\kappa\tau$;
(c) $-\kappa^2$; (e) $\kappa^2\tau$.

PROBLEMS 80. *Page 485*

1. (a) $R = (3t + 2)i - 2tj + (7t + 3)k$;
(c) $R = (2t + 1)i + (5t + 2)j + (t + 3)k$.
3. (a) $R = (3t + 2)i + (2t - 1)j + (3 - t)k$.
4. (a) $R = (2t - 2)i + (t + 1)j + (2t + 2)k$.
5. No. **6.** $R = (1 - 2t)i - tj + (t + 3)k$.
7. The segment joining the terminal points of A and B. **9.** $R = (t - 1)i - (7t - 2)j - (11t - 1)k$. **10.** Yes. **11.** (a) $-1/\sqrt{11}, 3/\sqrt{11}, 1/\sqrt{11}$ and $7/\sqrt{59}, -3/\sqrt{59}, 1/\sqrt{59}$; (b) Yes, at $(-1, 8, 3)$. **12.** $\pi/3$. **13.** $R = F'(a)(t - a) + F(a)$.

PROBLEMS 81. *Page 491*

1. (a) $(2\sqrt{2}, 30°, 135°)$; (c) $(\pi\sqrt{2}, \pi, 3\pi/4)$.
2. (a) $\sqrt{r_1^2 + r_2^2 - 2r_1r_2 \cos (\theta_1 - \theta_2) + (z_1 - z_2)^2}$;
(b) $\sqrt{\rho_1^2 + \rho_2^2 - 2\rho_1\rho_2 \sin \phi_1 \sin \phi_2 \cos (\theta_1 - \theta_2) + \cos \phi_1 \cos \phi_2}$.
6. (a) $r^2 = z$; (b) $3r \cos \theta + 4r \sin \theta + z = 6$; (c) $\rho = 4 \cos \phi$; (d) $\rho = 2 \sin \phi$. **8.** (a) $\frac{5}{2} \ln 3$.
9. $\rho = 2$, $\theta = t$, $\phi = \pi/3$, $L = 2\pi\sqrt{3}$.
10. $\frac{1}{2}\pi\sqrt{1 + k^2}$.

REVIEW PROBLEMS, CHAPTER NINE.
Page 492

1. $Q(3, 4, -3)$, $R(-7, 4, 5)$, $S(-1, 0, 1)$,
$T(-4, -3, 5)$. **2.** $(4, -5, 7)$. **3.** $\frac{4}{7}$. **5.** $\frac{x}{a} + \frac{y}{b} + \frac{z}{c} = 1$. **6.** $x + y - 2z = 1$. **8.** $(10, 18, 17)$.
9. $R = F'(a)t + F(a)$, $F'(a) \cdot R = F'(a) \cdot F(a)$.
10. $(a, \theta, a \cot \phi)$. **11.** $\dfrac{|d - e|}{\sqrt{a^2 + b^2 + c^2}}$.

PROBLEMS 82. *Page 499*

1. (a) $(2, -1)$; (c) $(0, 1)$; (e) $(\frac{3}{4}, \frac{4}{5})$.
2. (a) $(1, 2, -1)$; (c) $(2, 0, 1)$; (e) $(1, -1, 0, 2)$.
3. $x = \dfrac{ud - vb}{ad - bc}$, $y = \dfrac{av - uc}{ad - bc}$. **4.** (a) $(0, 0, 0)$.
6. $80°$, $85°$, $15°$. **8.** (a) $\{(x, y) \mid x \in [-1, 0),\ y \in [2, 3)\}$; (c) $(\frac{1}{10}, 100)$.

PROBLEMS 83. *Page 505*

1. (a) $(2, 1)$; (c) $(-1, 1)$; (e) $(4, 3)$.
2. (a) $(1, -1, 1)$; (c) $(0, 0, 0)$; (e) $(2, 0, -1, 1)$.
3. (a) $(5t, 3t, -7t)$. **4.** Yes. **5.** (a) $(7t, 1 + 3t, -1 - 5t)$; (c) No solution. **6.** 374, no. **8.** (a) $(x, 7x - 6, 11x - 10)$; (c) No solution.
11. $f(x) = \frac{2}{3}x^3 - \frac{1}{2}x^2 + x - \frac{1}{6}$.

PROBLEMS 84. *Page 513*

1. (a) $(-8, -2, -5)$; (c) 1. **2.** (a) $\begin{pmatrix} 2 \\ -2 \end{pmatrix}$; (b) $\begin{bmatrix} 13 & 0 \\ 2 & 0 \end{bmatrix}$. **3.** (a) 10; (c) 70. **4.** (a) $(1, -2)$; (b) $(1/\sqrt{5}, -2\sqrt{5})$, 2; (c) $(-3/\sqrt{35}, -5/\sqrt{35}, 1/\sqrt{35})$. **6.** (b) Zero matrix. **8.** (a) $3^9 S$.

PROBLEMS 85. *Page 520*

2. (a), (c), and (f) are true.
3. (a) $\begin{bmatrix} \frac{3}{2} & 0 & 0 \\ 0 & -1 & 0 \\ 0 & 0 & \frac{5}{3} \end{bmatrix}$; (c) $\begin{bmatrix} -5 & -1 & 6 \\ 1 & 0 & -1 \\ 9 & 2 & -10 \end{bmatrix}$;
(e) $\begin{bmatrix} 9 & -2 & 0 & 0 \\ -4 & 1 & 0 & 0 \\ 0 & 0 & -3 & 1 \\ 0 & 0 & -8 & 3 \end{bmatrix}$. **4.** $x = -5u - v + 6w$, $y = u - w$, $z = 9u + 2v - 10w$.
5. (a) $A^{-1} = \dfrac{1}{ad - bc} \begin{bmatrix} d & -b \\ -c & a \end{bmatrix}$. **6.** (a) $\begin{bmatrix} \frac{1}{2} & \frac{1}{2} & -\frac{1}{2} \\ -\frac{1}{10} & -\frac{3}{10} & \frac{1}{2} \\ -\frac{3}{10} & \frac{1}{10} & \frac{1}{2} \end{bmatrix}$; (c) $\begin{bmatrix} \frac{2}{7} & \frac{3}{7} & -\frac{4}{7} \\ \frac{1}{7} & -\frac{2}{7} & \frac{5}{7} \\ -\frac{3}{7} & -\frac{1}{7} & \frac{6}{7} \end{bmatrix}$.
8. $C = A^{-1}B$. **9.** Yes.

PROBLEMS 86. *Page 526*

1. (a) -2; (c) 0. **4.** (a) -7; (c) 0; (e) -24.
6. Yes. **7.** $x = 1$ or $x = 6$. **8.** $k = 2$ or $k = 7$.
11. (d) $\begin{bmatrix} 0 & 1 \\ -1 & 0 \end{bmatrix}$.

PROBLEMS 87. *Page 531*

7. No. **8.** v, x, and y must be 0; u, w, and z must be either $+1$ or -1.

PROBLEMS 88. *Page 536*

1. (a) $\lambda^2 - 4\lambda + 3 = 0$; (b) 3, 1; (c) $(1, 1)$ and $(-1, 1)$; (d) $\begin{bmatrix} 1/\sqrt{2} & -1/\sqrt{2} \\ 1/\sqrt{2} & 1/\sqrt{2} \end{bmatrix}$.
3. (a) $\begin{bmatrix} 5 & 0 \\ 0 & 3 \end{bmatrix}$; (c) $\begin{bmatrix} 1 & 0 \\ 0 & -1 \end{bmatrix}$;
(e) $\begin{bmatrix} \sqrt{13} & 0 \\ 0 & -\sqrt{13} \end{bmatrix}$. **5.** (a) $\lambda^3 - 5\lambda^2 + 6\lambda = 0$;
(b) 3, 2, 0; (c) $(1, 1, 1)$, $(0, 1, -1)$, $(2, -1, -1)$;
(d) $\begin{bmatrix} 1/\sqrt{3} & 0 & 2/\sqrt{6} \\ 1/\sqrt{3} & 1/\sqrt{2} & -1/\sqrt{6} \\ 1/\sqrt{3} & -1/\sqrt{2} & -1/\sqrt{6} \end{bmatrix}$.
7. (a) $\begin{bmatrix} 2 & 0 & 0 \\ 0 & 1 & 0 \\ 0 & 0 & -2 \end{bmatrix}$; (c) $\begin{bmatrix} 3 & 0 & 0 \\ 0 & 1 & 0 \\ 0 & 0 & 1 \end{bmatrix}$;
(e) $\begin{bmatrix} 6 & 0 & 0 \\ 0 & 3 & 0 \\ 0 & 0 & 2 \end{bmatrix}$.
8. It must be a scalar multiple of I. **10.** (a) Characteristic values i and $-i$, vectors $(1, i)$ and $(1, -i)$; (c) Characteristic values 0, $3i$, and $-3i$, vectors $(2, -1, 2)$, $(1 - 3i, 4, 1 + 3i)$ and $(1 + 3i, 4, 1 - 3i)$.

PROBLEMS 89. *Page 541*

3. $30°$. **5.** $R = \begin{bmatrix} 0 & 1 & 0 \\ 0 & 0 & -1 \\ 1 & 0 & 0 \end{bmatrix}$, no. **6.** (a) $(-6, 3, 9)$; (c) $\bar{x} + 2\bar{y} - 11\bar{z} = 1$; (e) $2\bar{x} - 2\bar{y} - \bar{z} = 0$. **7.** $(1, 1, 0)$. **8.** Rn. **10.** $\bar{v} = v + a$, $\bar{v} = Rv + a$, $\bar{v} = R(v + a)$.

PROBLEMS 90. *Page 548*

1. (a) $3\bar{x}^2 + \bar{y}^2 = 1$;
(b) $\begin{bmatrix} 1/\sqrt{2} & 1/\sqrt{2} \\ -1/\sqrt{2} & 1/\sqrt{2} \end{bmatrix}$; (c) $45°$. **3.** (a) $5\bar{x}^2 + 3\bar{y}^2 = 3$; (c) $\bar{x}^2 - \bar{y}^2 = 1$; (e) $\bar{x}^2 = 1$. **4.** (a) $3\bar{x}^2 + 2\bar{y}^2 = 1$;

(b) $\begin{bmatrix} 1/\sqrt{3} & 1/\sqrt{3} & 1/\sqrt{3} \\ 0 & 1/\sqrt{2} & -1/\sqrt{2} \\ 2/\sqrt{6} & -1/\sqrt{6} & -1/\sqrt{6} \end{bmatrix}$. **6.** (a) $5\bar{x}^2 +$

$3\bar{y}^2 + 2\bar{z}^2 = 2$; (c) $\bar{x} - \bar{z}^2 = \sqrt{2}$; (e) $\bar{x}^2 + \dfrac{\bar{y}^2}{2} + \dfrac{\bar{z}^2}{3} = 1$. **9.** The surface is a sphere. **10.** A cylinder.

REVIEW PROBLEMS, CHAPTER 10.
Page 548

1. 4 nickels, 3 dimes, and 3 quarters or 1 nickel, 7 dimes, and 2 quarters. **2.** The line with parametric equations $x = -3t + 2$, $y = t, z = -2t + 2$. **5.** $b = c$ or $b = -c$ and $a = d$. **7.** $\bar{z}^2 + \frac{1}{4}\bar{x}^2 - \bar{y}^2 = 0$. **8.** A circular cone. **9.** (a) $\begin{bmatrix} 10 & 6 \\ 5 & 5 \end{bmatrix}$; (b) $\begin{bmatrix} 2 & 1 & 1 \\ -2 & 2 & 4 \end{bmatrix}$; (c) [32].

PROBLEMS 91. *Page 554*

1. (a) $f(x, y, z) = xy^2z^3$; (b) no; (c) no, yes; (e) $(xyz)^6$; (f) $\lim_{h\to 0} q(h) = 12$. **2.** (a) $4\ln 3$; (c) 12; (e) 0. **3.** (a) Domain R^2, range $[0, \infty]$, continuous everywhere; (c) Domain R^3, range is the set of integers, continuous except on the set $\{(x, y) \mid$ one of the numbers x or y is an integer$\}$. **4.** (a) Domain $\{(x, y, z) \mid x \geqslant y, z > 0\}$, range is R^1; (c) Domain is all of R^3 except for a certain family of concentric spheres, range is R^1. **5.** $f(x, y) = y/x$. **6.** Range is the set $\{-1, 0, 1\}$. **7.** $R = L/25r^2$. **8.** The planes $y = x$, $z = x$, and $z = y$. **9.** (a) The plane $2x - 3y + 4z = 7$; (b) The line $x = mt + b$, where $b = -i - j - k$. **10.** $f(x, y, z) = f(y, z, x)$.

PROBLEMS 92. *Page 559*

1. (a) $6e^{-2}$; (c) not defined; (e) 6; (g) $-\frac{2}{3}$; (i) -1. **3.** All negative. **5.** Positive Y-axis. **9.** (a) x; (c) $\sin(x^2 - y^2)$. **10.** $4(ac - b^2)$. **11.** True for some functions, false for others. **12.** $1/20$ lb., -2 cm³. **13.** $f_1(0, 0) = f_2(0, 0) = 0$.

PROBLEMS 93. *Page 566*

2. $D_x w = y^x x^{y^x}\left(\ln x \ln y + \dfrac{1}{x}\right)$, $D_y w = y^x x^{y^x} \cdot \dfrac{x}{y} \ln x$. **3.** $38e^{15}$. **4.** (a) $D_u f(x, y) = f_1(x, y)D_u x + f_2(x, y)D_u y$; (c) $D_t F(p, q, r) = F_1(p)D_t p + F_2(p)D_t q + F_3(p)D_t r$. **5.** 0. **8.** They make an angle of 135° with the positive X-axis. **11.** (c) $D_x u = g_2(u, v)/J(u, v)$ and $D_x v = -g_1(u, v)/J(u, v)$.

PROBLEMS 94. *Page 571*

1. (a) $(3, -2)$; (c) $(-\frac{1}{2}\log_2 3 \log_2 e, \frac{1}{2}\log_2 e)$. **2.** (b) $(f_1(g, h), f_2(g, h))$; (d) $(x_1(f), x_2(f), x_3(f))$. **5.** (a) $2x$; (c) $-4|x|^2 \sin|x|^4 x$.

PROBLEMS 95. *Page 576*

1. (a) $-\frac{6}{5}$; (c) 0; (e) $\frac{4}{5}$ or $-\frac{4}{5}$. **2.** (a) ascending at 33 meters per meter; (b) neither ascending nor descending; (c) northeast; (d) northwest or southeast. **3.** (a) k; (c) $(i + k)/\sqrt{2}$. **4.** a. **5.** $2e^{-14}\sqrt{14}$. **8.** $(6, \frac{1}{3})$.

PROBLEMS 96. *Page 580*

2. (a) $2i - 3j + 4k$; (c) $i + 2j$. **3.** (a) $7x - 11y + z + 9 = 0$; (c) $z = 0$. **4.** $(-1, 3, -15)$. **5.** $M = 7i + 4j + 10k$, $B = i - 2j + k$. **6.** $(2, 2, 0)$ and $(-2, -2, 0)$. **7.** **7.** **8.** $3i + 2j - 3k$.

PROBLEMS 97. *Page 585*

1. (a) $(1, 2, 2)$. **2.** (a) $(8, 12, -64)$. **3.** (a) $(-1, 3, 10)$. **5.** $1/\sqrt{2}$. **7.** $1/\sqrt{3}$. **9.** $2x + y + 2z = 6$. **11.** $\frac{1}{27}$ and 0. **13.** 2 feet by 2 feet by 5 feet.

REVIEW PROBLEMS, CHAPTER 11.
Page 586

3. 3. **5.** 114, 57, 0. **6.** There is a number c such that $g(x) = f(x) + c$. **8.** (a) The ellipsoidal region $\frac{1}{9}x^2 + y^2 + \frac{1}{36}z^2 \leqslant 1$; (b) $[-\pi/6, \pi/2]$; (d) $x + 3y - z = 6$; (e) $-14\sqrt{3}/27$. **10.** (a) 0; (b) $w_{xx} + w_{yy} + w_{zz}$; (c) 0; (d) $\begin{bmatrix} w_{xx} & w_{xy} \\ w_{yx} & w_{yy} \end{bmatrix}$.

PROBLEMS 98. *Page 594*

1. (a) 6; (c) 6. **2.** Yes. **3.** (a) 4; (c) π; (e) 4. **4.** (a) $\frac{16}{3}$; (c) $12\ln 2 - 4$. **6.** Only (c). **7.** Yes.

PROBLEMS 99. *Page 602*

1. (a) $\frac{2}{3}$; (c) $(e^2 - 1)\sin 1 + \sin e^2$. **2.** (a) $\frac{7}{6}$; (c) $\frac{1}{2}$. **3.** (a) $\frac{64}{3}$; (c) $\frac{1}{4}e^4 - \frac{1}{3}e^3 + \frac{1}{12}$; (e) $\frac{3}{2}e^4 - \frac{25}{6}$. **4.** (a) π; (c) πc. **5.** (a) 16; (c) $\frac{1}{8}$. **7.** 0. **8.** (a) 18; (c) $\pi/12$; (e) $\frac{1}{2}\ln 3$; (g) $1/4 \ln 3$. **9.** (a) $\frac{1}{4}(e^{16} - 1)$; (c) $e - 1$. **10.** $\int_0^a \int_a^b f(x, y) \, dx\,dy + \int_a^b \int_y^b f(x, y)dx \, dy$. **11.** $e^{2\pi} - \frac{1}{2}e^{\pi} + \frac{1}{2}e^{\pi/2}$. **12.** Positive, positive.

PROBLEMS 100. *Page 608*

1. (a) $\frac{9}{2}$; (c) $\frac{15}{2}$ − ln 256; (e) 1. **2.** 20.
3. $abc/6$. **4.** (a) $\frac{1}{2}$; (c) $\frac{52}{3}$. **6.** $\frac{4}{3}$. **7.** $\frac{8}{15}$. **8.** 15π.
9. $\frac{1}{2}\pi$.

PROBLEMS 101. *Page 615*

1. (a) $\left(\dfrac{4a}{3\pi}, \dfrac{4a}{3\pi}\right)$; (c) $(\frac{8}{5}, \frac{3}{4})$; (e) $\left(\dfrac{a+c}{3}, \dfrac{b}{3}\right)$;
(g) $(\frac{9}{20}, \frac{9}{20})$. **2.** $\left(1, \dfrac{\pi}{8}\right)$. **5.** (a) $-5\pi a^3$; (c) $-\dfrac{80}{3}$.
6. (a) $\frac{1}{4}ab^3$, $\frac{1}{4}a^3b$, $\frac{1}{4}ab(a^2 + b^2)$; (c) $\frac{1}{3}$, $\frac{1}{3}$, $\frac{2}{3}$.
7. (b) $I_L = I_Y + h^2A$; (c) $I_L = I_Y - h^2A$.
8. (a) $\frac{1}{4}\pi a^3b$; (b) $\frac{1}{4}\pi ab^3$, $\frac{1}{4}\pi ab(a^2 + b^2)$; (c) $\frac{1}{4}\pi a^4$;
(d) $\pi ab(\frac{5}{4}a^2 - b^2)$; (e) $\pi a^3b(\frac{1}{4} + a^2c^{-2})$. **9.** $I_0 = 10\pi$, $I_L = 9\pi$. **10.** No.

PROBLEMS 102. *Page 620*

1. (a)π; (c) $\frac{2}{3}\pi$. **3.** (a) $\frac{2}{3}\pi a^3$; (c) $\frac{5}{3}\pi$.
5. (a) $\frac{1}{4}\pi(1 - e^{-4})$; (c) $\frac{1}{4}\pi(1 - \cos 18)$.
6. (a) $\frac{4}{3}\pi a^3(8 - 3\sqrt{3})$. **7.** (a) $\frac{1}{4}a^3s$; (b) $\dfrac{4a^2}{3s}$
$\sin\dfrac{s}{2a}$; (c) $\dfrac{a^4}{16}\left(\dfrac{2s}{a} - \sin\dfrac{2s}{a}\right)$. **9.** (a) $(-\frac{5}{6}a, 0)$;
(c) $\left(\dfrac{512}{105\pi}, \dfrac{512}{105\pi}\right)$. **10.** (a) $\bar{x} = 4b/3\pi$; (b) $2b/\pi$;
(c) Yes, yes.

PROBLEMS 103. *Page 627*

1. (a) $-e(\ln 2)^2$; (c) $\frac{544}{3}$. **2.** (a) $8 - \frac{4}{3}\pi$;
(c) $256 - \frac{1}{3}\pi(36 - 8\sqrt{2} - 24\sqrt{3})$. **3.** (a) 36;
(c) $\frac{1}{15}$. **5.** $\frac{1}{3}abc(a^2 + c^2)$. **6.** $(\frac{1}{4}a, \frac{1}{4}b, \frac{1}{4}c)$.
7. $(0, \frac{3}{7}, \frac{2}{7})$. **8.** $\frac{1}{30}$. **9.** $I_Z + a^2 + b^2$, $I_Z - a^2 - b^2$.

PROBLEMS 104. *Page 632*

4. (a) $\frac{1}{2}V(a^2 + b^2)$; (c) Vc^2, $\frac{1}{3}\pi Lch(6c^2 + L^2)$. **5.** $\frac{8}{15}\pi(b^5 - a^5)$. **6.** $2\pi\left(\dfrac{64}{15} - \dfrac{11\sqrt{3}}{5}\right)$,
$(0, 0, \frac{21}{296}(8 + 3\sqrt{3}))$. **7.** $\frac{1}{10}\pi a^4h$, $\frac{1}{4}h$. **8.** $\bar{z} = \frac{3}{16}(b^4 - a^4)/(b^3 - a^3)$.

PROBLEMS 105. *Page 638*

1. (a) $\frac{7}{4}$; (c) $8/3\pi + \frac{1}{2}$; (e) $\frac{3}{2}$. **2.** 10. **3.**
(a) $\frac{2}{3}ab(a - b)$. **8.** 2, no. **10.** $a = \frac{1}{3}$.

PROBLEMS 106. *Page 644*

4. $-\pi(a + b)$. **5.** (a) $xe^{xy} - 1$; (c)
$3xy^2 + 2x - 14$.

PROBLEMS 107. *Page 649*

1. (a) $3x^3y^2 + xy^{-1}$, yes; (c) No. **5.** (a)
$y = (1 - x)e^{-x}$; (c) $y = \tan x^2$. **5.** No.

REVIEW PROBLEMS, CHAPTER 12.
Page 650

1. (a) 0, $\frac{31}{2}$; (c) $-7(1 + \frac{1}{4}i)$, $\frac{35}{3}$. **2.** (a)
13π; (b) $\frac{27}{2}(4\pi - 7)$; (c) $-\frac{9}{2}\pi$. **5.** $\displaystyle\int_0^1\int_{\text{Arcsin}\,y}^{\pi-\text{Arcsin}\,y}$
$f(x, y)\,dx\,dy$. **7.** $\frac{3}{16}\pi^2$. **10.** $\sqrt{2}a^4/3$.

PROBLEMS 108. *Page 657*

1. (a) Arccot $\frac{1}{4}$; (c) $\frac{1}{4}\pi$. **2.** (a) 3; (c)
$1/2\pi$; (e) 2. **3.** (a) $\frac{1}{2}$; (c) 0. **4.** (a) $\frac{1}{2}$. **5.** (a) 1;
(c) e. **7.** (a) $\frac{5}{3}$; (c) $\frac{1}{2}$. **8.** 0. **9.** 3a units to the left
of A. **10.** Et/L. **11.** $\dfrac{\sin f(a)}{f(a)}$ if $f(a) \neq 0$, 1 if
$f(a) = 0$.

PROBLEMS 109. *Page 663*

1. (a) ∞; (c) $\frac{3}{7}$; (e) 1. **2.** About -16.
3. (a) 0; (c) 0; (e) $\frac{1}{2}$. **4.** (a) 0; (c) $\frac{1}{2}$. **5.** (a) 0;
(c) ∞. **6.** (a) 1; (c) 1. **7.** r. **9.** 0.

PROBLEMS 110. *Page 668*

1. (a) 1; (c) $1/2e^{25}$; (e) Divergent.
2. (a) Convergent; (c) Divergent. **3.** (a) $\frac{3}{2}$;
(c) $\frac{1}{2}\pi$; (e) Divergent. **4.** (a) Divergent; (c) π.
5. (a) No. **6.** (c) $\frac{1}{2}$. **7.** 1. **9.** 42.24 × 10⁹ ft. lbs.

PROBLEMS 111. *Page 674*

1. (a) Convergent; (c) Divergent; (e)
Convergent; (g) Convergent. **2.** (a) Divergent;
(c) Convergent; (e) Divergent. **3.** (a) Convergent; (c) Divergent. **6.** (a) $2\pi a^2$; (c) $\pi/8$.
9. No.

PROBLEMS 112. *Page 679*

1. (a) .27; (c) .2. **2.** (a) $b - \frac{1}{2}b^2 + \frac{1}{3}b^3 - \frac{1}{4}b^4 + \frac{1}{5}b^5$; (c) $\frac{1}{2} - \frac{1}{4}b + \frac{1}{48}b^3$. **4.** $(x - 1)^4 + 4(x - 1)^3 + 9(x - 1)^2 + 10(x - 1) + 6$.
5. .00034. **6.** 1.462. **8.** $m = \frac{9}{16}$ or $-\frac{9}{16}$.
11. $f(x) - g(x)$ is a polynomial of degree at
most $n - 1$.

REVIEW PROBLEMS, CHAPTER 13.
Page 681

2. No. **3.** (a) 1; (b) 3; (c) 1; (d) 1.
5. j. **6.** ln 4.5. **8.** (a) Divergent; (b) Divergent;
(c) Convergent. **9.** (a) Convergent; (b) Divergent; (c) Divergent; (d) Divergent; (e) Divergent; (f) Divergent. **10.** $m = 1 - (1 - x)^{1/(n+2)}$.

PROBLEMS 113. *Page 689*

1. (a) Divergent, $[-1, 1]$; (c) Converges to 0, $[0, \frac{2}{3}]$; (e) Converges to 0 (it is hard to show that the limit is 0), $[0, \frac{1}{2}]$; (g) Converges to 0, $[\frac{1}{4} \sin 4, \sin 1]$; (i) Converges to $\frac{1}{2}\sqrt{\pi}$, $\left[\int_0^1 e^{-x^2}\, dx, \frac{1}{2}\sqrt{\pi}\right]$. **2.** (a) $c_n = 5n!$; (c) $c_n = 6$ if $n > 5$. **3.** (a) $2^n - 1$; (c) $n^2 - 1$. **4.** (a) $\frac{1}{2}(3^{n-1} + 1)$. **6.** (a) 9; (c) 12. **7.** $\frac{n}{2} \sin \frac{2\pi}{n}$, π. **8.** $a_n = \frac{1}{2}(n + 1)/n$. **11.** The positive integers, the integers greater than h.

PROBLEMS 114. *Page 696*

1. (a) $n(n + 1)/2$; (c) $(n + 1)! - 1$; (e) $-2[\![\frac{1}{2}n]\!]$. **2.** (a) $a_k = 1/k(k + 1)$; (c) $a_k = 1$; (e) $a_1 = 0$, $a_k = 2(-1)^k$. **3.** (a) e^{-1}; (b) Yes. **4.** (a) $\frac{1}{2}$; (c) 14; (e) $\sec^2 0$. **7.** 1. **9.** $S_n = \ln (1 + 1/n)$, $S = 0$.

PROBLEMS 115. *Page 701*

1. (a) Convergent; (c) Convergent; (e) Convergent; (g) Convergent. **4.** (a) Divergent; (c) Divergent; (e) Convergent. **5.** $\frac{243}{32}$. **7.** $4^{1,000,000}$ will be more than sufficient.

PROBLEMS 116. *Page 706*

1. (a) Convergent; (c) Convergent. **3.** (a) Conditionally convergent; (c) Conditionally convergent. **4.** (a) $\frac{3}{5}(\frac{3}{5})^n$. **5.** (a) .139; (c) .3217. **6.** (a) Divergent. **7.** .83.

PROBLEMS 117. *Page 713*

1. (a) Convergent; (c) Convergent. **2.** (a) Divergent; (c) Divergent. **3.** $f(x) = |\sin \pi x|$, $f(x) = [\![\cos \pi x]\!]$. **6.** 1.10. **9.** $\sum_{k=2}^{\infty} \frac{1}{k \ln k}$, $\sum_{k=1}^{\infty} k^{-2}$.

PROBLEMS 118. *Page 719*

1. (a) Convergent; (c) Convergent; (e) Convergent; (g) Convergent. **3.** (a) Convergent; (c) Convergent; (e) Convergent. **4.** (a) $x \in (-1, 1)$; (c) $x \neq \frac{1}{2}(2n - 1)\pi$; (e) $|x| \neq 1$. **5.** No, no. **6.** Yes. **10.** It is proved in more

advanced courses that whenever Theorem 118-2 applies, so does Theorem 118-3.

PROBLEMS 119. *Page 725*

1. (a) 2, $(-2, 2)$, $(-2, 2)$; (c) 3, $(-4, 2)$, $(-4, 2)$; (e) 1, $(3, 5)$, $[3, 5)$; (g) 1, $(-1, 1)$, $(-1, 1)$. **2.** (a) $(0, 4)$; (c) $(-e, e)$; (e) $(-1, 1)$; (g) $(-\infty, \infty)$. **3.** $p \leq 0$, $x \in (-1, 1)$; $0 < p \leq 1$, $x \in [-1, 1)$; $p > 1$, $x \in [-1, 1]$.

5. (a) $1/(1 + x)$; (c) $-3/x$. **8.** (a) $\sum_{k=0}^{\infty} x^k$ and $\sum_{k=0}^{\infty} -x^k$; (b) $1 + 2x + 2x^2 + 2x^3 + \cdots$ and $1 - 2x + 2x^2 - 2x^3 + \cdots$; (c) 1 and $1 - x$.

PROBLEMS 120. *Page 730*

1. (a) $[-1, 1]$; (b) $-\frac{65}{144}$; (d) 0. **2.** (a) $(-\infty, \infty)$; (b) $(-\infty, \infty)$; (f) $f'(x) = 1 + \int_0^x f(t)\, dt$. **5.** (a) .13; (b) .33. **6.** 8, $\ln 4$. **10.** R^1, no.

PROBLEMS 121. *Page 735*

1. (a) 10!; (c) 8!. **2.** $-3^7/7!$.

PROBLEMS 122. *Page 741*

1. (a) $x + x^2 + \frac{1}{3}x^3 - \frac{1}{30}x^5 + \cdots$; (c) $1 + \frac{1}{2}x^2 + \frac{5}{4}x^4 + \frac{61}{720}x^6 + \cdots$. **3.** (a) 1.01; (c) .99; (e) .22. **4.** (a) .764; (c) .079. **5.** $x + \frac{1}{2}\frac{x^3}{3} + \frac{1 \cdot 3}{2 \cdot 4}\frac{x^5}{5} + \cdots$. **6.** .659. **7.** $1 - x + \frac{x^2}{2!} - \frac{x^3}{3!} + \cdots$.

REVIEW PROBLEMS, CHAPTER 14.
Page 741

1. $a_n = 2^{(2-2^n)}$, $\lim_{n \uparrow \infty} a_n = 0$. **2.** $\ln \frac{1}{2}\pi$. **3.** (a) Divergent; (b) Conditionally convergent. **4.** (a) $\frac{e}{e - 1}$; (b) $\frac{e - 1}{e + 1} = \tanh \frac{1}{2}$; (c) $(e + 1)(e^e - 1)$. **5.** $(-1, 1)$. **7.** $f(x) = \sum_{k=1}^{\infty} \frac{p_k}{k!}(x - 3)^k$, domain is R^1.

D. INDEX OF SYMBOLS

INDEX